cook
STEP BY STEP

cook
STEP BY STEP

LONDON, NEW YORK, MELBOURNE, MUNICH, AND DELHI

Editor Lucy Bannell
Project Editor Sarah Ruddick
Managing Editor Dawn Henderson
Managing Art Editors Christine Keilty, Marianne Markham
Senior Jacket Creative Nicola Powling
Senior Presentations Creative Caroline de Souza
Category Publisher Mary-Clare Jerram
Art Director Peter Luff
Production Editor Maria Elia
Production Controller Alice Holloway
Creative Technical Support Sonia Charbonnier

DK INDIA
Designer Devika Dwarkadas
Senior Editors Rukmini Kumar Chawla, Saloni Talwar
Design Manager Romi Chakraborty
DTP Designers Dheeraj Arora, Manish Chandra,
Nand Kishore, Arjinder Singh, Jagtar Singh, Pushpak Tyagi
DTP Manager Sunil Sharma
Production Manager Pankaj Sharma

First published in Great Britain in 2010
by Dorling Kindersley Limited
80 Strand, London WC2R 0RL
Penguin Group (UK)

This edition produced for The Book People Ltd, Hall Wood Avenue,
Haydock, St Helens, WA11 9UL

A CIP catalogue record for this book is available
from the British Library

ISBN 978-1-4053-6196-5

Colour reproduction by Media Development Printing, UK
Printed and bound in China by Toppan

Discover more at www.dk.com

Contents

Introduction

We used to learn to cook by peering over our mother's shoulder as she chopped and sautéed onions, browned meat, added her favourite seasonings, and fried, simmered, or roasted her way to a delicious family meal. We marvelled at her impressive "special occasion" cakes and puddings, and vowed to make them just as well when we grew up.

These days, this time-honoured way of learning how to feed ourselves good food is disappearing. Many of our mothers were not taught to cook themselves, so could not pass on their knowledge to us. This book will bridge that gap: The step-by-step images will lead you through every aspect of making a meal, from something as basic as how to chop an onion, to showing you when a custard is thick enough, to what a caramel should look like in the saucepan.

Whether you have never picked up a wooden spoon before or are already an experienced cook, these recipes will work for you and your family and will enable you to improve your skills. Reassuringly, they give you exact timings for every stage of making a dish, making it almost impossible for you to go wrong.

In this book, you'll find more than 300 delicious recipes, from time-honoured classics such as roast beef and Yorkshire pudding or lemon meringue pie, to the mouthwatering modern treats of sushi, crisp salmon with coriander pesto, or homemade pasta. Before you know it you'll be producing baguettes to beat any you can buy, or turning out irresistible chocolate-orange truffle cake.

There is something for everyone in this book, whether you prefer not to eat meat, have only minutes each day to cook, love to entertain with flair, or simply need to feed a growing family. Many of the recipes suggest simple ways to vary a dish, serving as starting points for your own imagination as your cooking confidence grows.

You'll find a recipe for every occasion here, too. A summer party will be a huge hit when you serve a whole poached salmon with watercress sauce, while friends will clamour for an invite to supper when they know you'll serve an exotic and delicious Moroccan chicken tagine followed by a cinnamon-orange crème brûlée.

Your cooking education starts here. Enjoy the journey!

Crostini p32
 PREP 15-20 MINS
 COOK 5-10 MINS

Tapenade p33
 PREP 30-35 MINS
COOK 10-15 MINS

Cheddar and courgette soufflés p60
 PREP 30-35 MINS
 COOK 25-30 MINS

Leeks vinaigrette p50
 PREP 15-20 MINS
COOK 15-25 MINS

Herb and flower garden salad p82
 PREP 15-20 MINS
 COOK NONE

Borscht p63
 PREP 50-55 MINS
COOK 1-1¼ HOURS

Basque hot pepper omelette p54
 PREP 20-25 MINS
 COOK 15-25 MINS

Roman herb and garlic artichokes p52
 PREP 25-30 MINS
 COOK 25-45 MINS

Pear, fennel, and walnut salad p109

PREP 30-35 MINS   **COOK** NONE

Stuffed vine leaves p68

PREP 40-45 MINS   **COOK** 45-60 MINS

Tabbouleh with cacik p108

PREP 35-40 MINS   **COOK** NONE

MORE VEGETARIAN STARTERS:

Stuffed mushrooms with herbs p36

Genoese minestrone with red pesto p46

Marinated goat's cheese salad p83

Roast pepper and artichoke salad p88

Greek salad p90

Tortilla bean salad p106

Spinach gnocchi in tomato cream p356

Gado gado p98

PREP 35-45 MINS   **COOK** 20-25 MINS

Warm salad of wild mushrooms p91

PREP 25-30 MINS   **COOK** 8-10 MINS

Cod and mussel chowder p44

PREP 45-50 MINS COOK 55-60 MINS

Herbed salmon cakes p70

PREP 35-40 MINS COOK 15-20 MINS

Asian noodle salad p112

PREP 30-35 MINS COOK 6-9 MINS

Grilled pepper-stuffed mussels p229

PREP 25-30 MINS COOK 1-2 MINS

Tuna Niçoise salad p84

PREP 25-30 MINS COOK 20-25 MINS

Saltimbocca of salmon p260

PREP 20-25 MINS COOK 1-2 MINS

Clear soup with sea bass p34

PREP 30-35 MINS COOK 25 MINS

Scallops with lemon-herb potatoes p370

PREP 45-50 MINS COOK 20 MINS

Blini with smoked salmon p66

PREP 25-30 MINS COOK 8-16 MINS

Tuna and bacon kebabs p265

PREP 20-25 MINS COOK 10-12 MINS

Nori-maki sushi p78

PREP 50-60 MINS COOK 12 MINS

Mussels with saffron cream sauce p41

PREP 25-30 MINS COOK 10-12 MINS

Spiced seafood salad p94

PREP 30-40 MINS COOK 12-15 MINS

MORE FISH STARTERS:

Tropical prawn kebabs p58

PREP 20-25 MINS COOK 4-6 MINS

Smoked trout mousse p37

PREP 20-25 MINS COOK NONE

Chicken liver and apple pâté p51

PREP
30-35 MINS
COOK
12-15 MINS

Chicken and cheese quesadillas p72

PREP
35-40 MINS
COOK
3-6 MINS

Chicken Pojarski p300

PREP
35-40 MINS
COOK
40-50 MINS

Tex-Mex chicken p259

PREP
20-25 MINS
COOK
NONE

Sauté of chicken with mussels p286

PREP
30-35 MINS
COOK
40-50 MINS

Thai skewered chicken p62

PREP
20-30 MINS
COOK
6-8 MINS

Devilled drumsticks p241

PREP
20-25 MINS
COOK
35-40 MINS

Chicken mousse with Madeira sauce p42

PREP
25-35 MINS

COOK
20-30 MINS

Cobb salad p119

PREP
20-25 MINS

COOK
5 MINS

Japanese one-pot
yosenabe p218

PREP
40-50 MINS

COOK
5-7 MINS

Pinwheel chicken with
goat's cheese p230

PREP
30-40 MINS

COOK
15-20 MINS

Lacquered chicken
salad p105

PREP
25-30 MINS

COOK
10-15 MINS

MORE POULTRY STARTERS:

Festive wild rice salad p104

Indonesian chicken satay p247

Grilled chicken thighs in yoghurt p270

Cold chicken and ham pie p340

Lemongrass chicken p76

PREP
45-55 MINS

COOK
10 MINS

Waldorf chicken
salad p111

PREP
25-30 MINS

COOK
25-35 MINS

Gratin of chicory and ham p48

PREP 15-20 MINS   COOK 1-1¼ HOURS

Steak salad with red onions p114

PREP 20-30 MINS   COOK 6-12 MINS

Vietnamese spring rolls p56

PREP 50-60 MINS   COOK 25 MINS

Spinach-stuffed veal p362

PREP 45-50 MINS   COOK 30-40 MINS

Home-made straw and hay pasta p374

PREP 55-60 MINS   COOK 10 MINS

Country terrine p366

PREP 35-40 MINS   COOK 1¼-1½ HOURS

Beef carpaccio p77

PREP 20-25 MINS   COOK NONE

Szechuan sweet and sour spare ribs p40

PREP 15-20 MINS   COOK 1½ HOURS

Spiced lamb pies p360

PREP 40-45 MINS   COOK 20-25 MINS

Cabbage with chestnut and pork p350

Turkish lamb kebabs p234

Avocado, grapefruit, and Parma ham p97

PREP 35-40 MINS | COOK 50-60 MINS

PREP 30-35 MINS | COOK 10-15 MINS

PREP 25-30 MINS | COOK NONE

Beef noodle soup p38

PREP 1½ HOURS | COOK 4-5 HOURS

Quiche Lorraine p372

PREP 45-50 MINS | COOK 30-35 MINS

MORE MEAT STARTERS:

Parma ham pizzas p74

Red cabbage and bacon salad p100

Salade Lyonnaise p110

Ham with prunes in a wine sauce p364

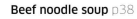

Stir-fried Thai vegetables p140

PREP 30-35 MINS COOK 15-20 MINS

Tempura p128

PREP 45-50 MINS COOK 3-5 MINS

Vegetable couscous p154

PREP 35-40 MINS COOK 30-35 MINS

Aubergine cannelloni p144

PREP 40-45 MINS COOK 50-60 MINS

Potato and blue cheese filo pie p162

PREP 35-40 MINS COOK 45-55 MINS

Herbed aioli platter p126

PREP 50-60 MINS COOK 65-70 MINS

Summer frittata with ratatouille p133

PREP 20-25 MINS COOK 20-25 MINS

Buddha's delight p134

PREP 40-50 MINS COOK 15-20 MINS

Roast pepper lasagne p143

PREP 1½ HOURS COOK 35-45 MINS

Mixed vegetable curry p148

PREP 45-50 MINS COOK 25-35 MINS

Three-cheese Swiss chard crêpes p130

PREP 1 HOUR COOK 20-25 MINS

Stuffed veggies with walnut sauce p156

PREP 40-45 MINS COOK 15-20 MINS

Mexican cheese-stuffed peppers p138

PREP 30-35 MINS COOK 45-50 MINS

Baked polenta with wild mushrooms p152

PREP 40-45 MINS COOK 20-25 MINS

MORE VEGETARIAN MAINS:

Fisherman's pie p348
  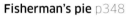
PREP 35-45 MINS **COOK** 20-30 MINS

Oriental halibut en papillote p236

PREP 15-20 MINS **COOK** 10-12 MINS

Five-spice fillet of salmon p254

PREP 30-35 MINS **COOK** 20-25 MINS

Perfect fish and chips p336

PREP 45-50 MINS **COOK** 20-25 MINS

Sole bonne femme p376

PREP 30-35 MINS **COOK** 25-30 MINS

Monkfish Americaine p302

PREP 45-50 MINS **COOK** 35-40 MINS

Roast monkfish with two sauces p294

PREP 25-30 MINS **COOK** 12-15 MINS

Spicy, saucy fish p266

PREP 30-35 MINS **COOK** 30-35 MINS

Sautéed trout with hazelnuts p271

PREP 20-25 MINS COOK 10-15 MINS

Crisp salmon with coriander pesto p235

PREP 5-10 MINS COOK 10-15 MINS

Seafood and tomato cioppino p180

PREP 45-50 MINS COOK 20-25 MINS

MORE FISH MAINS:

Monkfish and white wine stew p176

Fish plaits with warm vinaigrette p244

Pan-fried mackerel in rolled oats p258

Roast sea bass with herb butter p276

Poached salmon, watercress sauce p310

Bouillabaisse p318

Trout with orange-mustard glaze p322

Prawn risotto p363

PREP 15-20 MINS COOK 25-30 MINS

Griddled tuna steaks with salsa p250

PREP 25-30 MINS COOK 5-7 MINS

Duck with turnips and apricots p196

 **PREP** 35-40 MINS **COOK** 1½-2 HOURS

Chinese roast duck p296

 PREP 45 MINS **COOK** 1¾-2 HOURS

Chicken pot pies with herb crust p214

 PREP 25-35 MINS **COOK** 22-25 MINS

Coq au vin p278

 PREP 30 MINS **COOK** 1½-1¾ HOURS

Chicken en cocotte with parmesan p344

 PREP 15-20 MINS **COOK** 45-55 MINS

Southern fried chicken p248

 PREP 10-15 MINS **COOK** 20-30 MINS

Szechuan pepper chicken p282

PREP 20-25 MINS
COOK 40-50 MINS

Turkey mole p190

PREP 45-50 MINS
COOK 1¼-1¾ HOURS

Indonesian fried rice p334

PREP 40-45 MINS
COOK 10-15 MINS

Very garlicky sautéed chicken p324

PREP 15-20 MINS
COOK 1-1¼ HOURS

Sweet-sour duck with cherries p284

PREP 30-35 MINS
COOK 1¼-1½ HOURS

MORE POULTRY MAINS:

Oriental stir-fried chicken p242

PREP 15-20 MINS
COOK 10-12 MINS

Poussins with mushroom sauce p320

PREP 30-40 MINS
COOK 35-40 MINS

Rack of lamb coated with parsley p280

PREP 35-40 MINS COOK 25-30 MINS

Malaysian fried rice noodles p256

PREP 30-40 MINS COOK 8-12 MINS

Lamb shanks in red wine p222

PREP 45-50 MINS COOK 2½-2¾ HOURS

Provençal daube of beef p210

PREP 45-50 MINS COOK 3½-4 HOURS

Hungarian beef goulash p187

PREP 25-30 MINS COOK 2½-3 HOURS

Lamb dhansak p202

PREP 40-45 MINS COOK 1½-1¾ HOURS

Minute steak marchand du vin p268

PREP 15-20 MINS COOK 40-50 MINS

Milanese veal escalopes p232

PREP 20-25 MINS COOK 4-12 MINS

Pork and ginger sukiyaki p252

 PREP 15-20 MINS **COOK** 15-20 MINS

Leg of lamb with roasted garlic p308

PREP 15-20 MINS **COOK** 1¼-2 HOURS

Steak and wild mushroom pie p368

 PREP 50-55 MINS **COOK** 2½-3 HOURS

Beef rendang p312

PREP 40-50 MINS **COOK** 3½-4 HOURS

Steak au poivre p238

 PREP 25-30 MINS **COOK** 10-15 MINS

Mexican barbecued pork with salsa p240

 PREP 35-40 MINS **COOK** 40-50 MINS

Roast leg of pork with orange p301

 PREP 20-25 MINS **COOK** 3½-4 HOURS

MORE MEAT MAINS:

Raspberry soufflés, kirsch custard p504

PREP 20-25 MINS

COOK 10-12 MINS

Chocolate soufflés p523

PREP 20-25 MINS
COOK 15-18 MINS

Caramelized mango tartlets p488

PREP 40-45 MINS
COOK 20-25 MINS

Baked peaches with Amaretti p498

PREP 15-20 MINS

COOK 1-1¼ HOURS

Cherry clafoutis p458

PREP 20-25 MINS
COOK 30-35 MINS

Crêpes Suzette p508

PREP 40-50 MINS
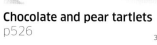
COOK 45-60 MINS

Chocolate and pear tartlets p526

PREP 30-35 MINS

COOK 25-30 MINS

Mincemeat tart with whisky butter p448

PREP 40-45 MINS

COOK 40-45 MINS

Grand Marnier soufflé p518

PREP
30-35 MINS
COOK
20-25 MINS

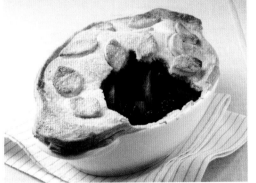

Blackberry and apple pie p418
PREP
35-40 MINS
COOK
50-60 MINS

Flaky pear tartlets p449

PREP
35-40 MINS
COOK
30-40 MINS

Baked Alaska p536

PREP
45-50 MINS
COOK
30-40 MINS

Filo apricot turnovers p440
PREP
35-40 MINS
COOK
12-15 MINS

Tarte tatin p442

PREP
45-50 MINS
COOK
20-25 MINS

Apple and almond galettes p510

PREP
25-30 MINS
COOK
20-30 MINS

MORE HOT DESSERTS:

Pear pie with walnut pastry p424

Bavarian plum tart p428

Peach pie p434

Cherry strudel p444

Gratin of fresh berries with sabayon p505

Tiramisu p481

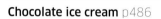
PREP
35-40 MINS
COOK
30-40 MINS

Chocolate decadence p506

PREP
30-40 MINS
COOK
20 MINS

Chocolate ice cream p486

PREP
15-20 MINS
COOK
10-15 MINS

Tri-chocolate terrine p520

PREP
35-40 MINS
COOK
20-25 MINS

Creamy rice pudding with peaches p492

PREP
15-20 MINS

COOK
3 HRS

Apricot and hazelnut ice cream p500

PREP
35-40 MINS

COOK
25-30 MINS

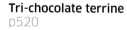

Pavlova with tropical fruit p482

PREP 25-30 MINS | COOK 2-2½ HOURS

Poires belle Hélène p517

PREP 30-35 MINS | COOK 25-35 MINS

Mango sorbet p522

PREP 25-30 MINS | COOK 2-3 MINS

Profiteroles with ice cream p499

PREP 25-30 MINS | COOK 25-30 MINS

Ginger cheesecake p493

PREP 40-45 MINS | COOK 50-60 MINS

Orange and cinnamon crème brulée p480

PREP 15-20 MINS | COOK 30-35 MINS

MORE COLD DESSERTS:

Multi-grain breakfast bread p388

PREP 45-50 MINS COOK 40-45 MINS

Dinner rolls p396

PREP 45-55 MINS COOK 15-18 MINS

Onion and walnut crown p398

PREP 40-45 MINS COOK 45-50 MINS

Sourdough bread p384

PREP 45-50 MINS COOK 40-45 MINS

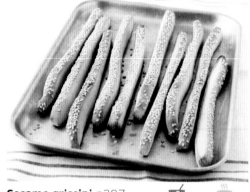

Sesame grissini p387

PREP 40-45 MINS COOK 15-18 MINS

Split-top white bread p380

PREP 40-50 MINS COOK 35-40 MINS

Cornbread p386

PREP 15-20 MINS COOK 20-25 MINS

Focaccia with rosemary p392

PREP 30-35 MINS COOK 15-20 MINS

Seeded rye bread p394

PREP 35-40 MINS COOK 50-55 MINS

Marbled chocolate cheesecake p472

PREP
35-40 MINS

COOK
50-60 MINS

Lemon-blueberry muffins p466

PREP
20-25 MINS

COOK
15-20 MINS

Apple cake p464

PREP
20-25 MINS

COOK
1¼-1½ HRS

Chocolate bread p414

PREP
35-40 MINS

COOK
45-50 MINS

Buttermilk scones p403

PREP
15-20 MINS

COOK
12-15 MINS

MORE BAKING:

Small brioches p410

PREP
45-50 MINS

COOK
15-20 MINS

Rich chocolate cake p468

PREP
15 MINS

COOK
30-35 MINS

Starters and light bites

Tempting small plates for appetizers and snacks

Crostini

AN UNLIMITED VARIETY OF TOPPINGS can be invented for these. Authentic crostini call for Italian peasant-style bread, but use any crusty loaf with a chewy crumb. An assertive, fragrant, preferably unrefined olive oil is the best choice, to stand up to the strong flavours of the topping.

SERVES	PREP	COOK
SERVES 8	15-20 MINS	5-10 MINS

Ingredients

750g (1lb 10oz) ripe tomatoes

small bunch of basil

4 garlic cloves, finely chopped

salt and pepper

4 tbsp extra virgin olive oil

150g (5½oz) Italian or Greek black olives, stoned and chopped

4 canned anchovy fillets, chopped

1 small loaf Italian peasant-style bread

PREPARE THE TOPPING

1 **Cut the cores** from the tomatoes and score an "x" on their bases with a small knife. Immerse in a pan of boiling water until the skin starts to split, 8–15 seconds, depending on ripeness. Plunge into a bowl of cold water, then peel off the skins. Halve, squeeze out the seeds, then coarsely chop.

2 **Strip the basil leaves** from the stalks, reserving 8 sprigs for garnish, and coarsely chop. Mix the tomatoes, garlic, and basil in a bowl. Stir in a little salt and pepper with the olive oil. Cover and let stand at room temperature for 30–60 minutes.

3 **Stir in the olives** and anchovies and taste for seasoning. You probably won't need any salt, as the anchovies and olives are salty enough, but the topping should have a strong flavour, so season well with pepper.

MAKE THE CROSTINI

4 **Preheat the oven** to 200°C (400°F/ Gas 6). Cut the bread into 8 x 1cm (½in) thick slices. Spread out the slices on a baking sheet and toast in the oven for 5–10 minutes, until lightly browned, turning once.

5 **Spoon the topping** on to the toasted bread, spreading it roughly. Garnish each with a basil sprig. Arrange the crostini on a platter and serve warm or at room temperature.

Tapenade

THIS PROVENÇAL SAUCE combines all the flavours of the Mediterranean: black olives, anchovies, garlic, capers and olive oil. It can be made up to 1 week ahead. Pour a thin layer of olive oil over the top so all the surface is protected from the air and keep it, tightly covered, in the refrigerator.

SERVES	**PREP**	**COOK**
SERVES 6-8	30-35 MINS	10-15 MINS

lemon juice, to taste

black pepper, to taste

Ingredients

FOR THE TAPENADE

6 slices of white bread, crusts cut off

4 garlic cloves, peeled

200g (7oz) oil-cured black olives, stoned

30g (1 oz) capers, drained

6 canned anchovy fillets

125ml (4fl oz) olive oil

FOR THE CRUDITÉS

1 red pepper

1 green pepper

1 bunch of spring onions, trimmed

1 cucumber

1 baguette

1 bunch of radishes, trimmed

250g (9oz) cherry tomatoes

MAKE THE TAPENADE

1 **Tear the bread** into pieces, place in a bowl and cover with cold water. Leave to soak for 5 minutes, then squeeze dry and put into a food processor.

2 **Add the garlic,** olives, capers, and anchovies and chop coarsely. With the blades turning, gradually add the oil. Add lemon juice and pepper to taste and work until the texture is as you prefer; it can be either a coarse or rough paste. Transfer to a bowl, cover, and set aside.

PREPARE THE CRUDITÉS AND TOASTS

3 **With a small knife,** cut around the core of the peppers, twist them and pull them out. Halve each pepper lengthways, scrape out the seeds and the white ribs. Slice each half lengthways into strips.

4 **Cut the spring onions** into 5cm (2in) pieces, including some green tops. Trim the ends from the cucumber, peel, cut in half lengthways, and scoop out the seeds with a teaspoon. Cut each half into 2-3 strips lengthways, then across into 5cm (2in) pieces.

5 **Preheat the oven** to 190°C (375°F/Gas 5). Cut the baguette into 5mm (¼in) slices on the diagonal. Set the slices on a baking sheet and bake for 10-15 minutes, until crisp.

6 **Set the tapenade** in the centre of a platter, or serve smaller bowls to each guest. Arrange the crudités, with the radishes and cherry tomatoes, around the tapenade and serve the toasted bread separately.

Clear soup with sea bass

THIS HEARTY SOUP is served in the winter in Japan. White radish, or daikon, gives a crisp bite and a pleasantly hot flavour to the broth. Almost every Japanese meal includes a soup, ranging from a classic, light miso to a thick broth that is a satisfying meal in itself. This clear soup, which is based on the fish- and seaweed-flavoured stock, dashi, should be served piping hot.

SERVES	PREP	COOK
SERVES 4	30–35 MINS	25 MINS

Ingredients

FOR THE STOCK

10cm (4in) piece of dried kelp

5g (¼oz) dried bonito flakes

1 tsp Japanese soy sauce, or to taste

FOR THE SOUP

½ small carrot, cut into 8 slices

salt

2.5cm (1in) piece daikon, cut into 8 wedges

1 sea bass (about 375g/13oz), cleaned

1 tbsp Japanese rice wine

1 tbsp cornflour

zest of 1 lemon

125g (4½oz) spinach, or 1 small bunch watercress

PREPARE THE SOUP STOCK

1 **Put 1 litre (1¾ pints) cold water** in a large saucepan and add the dried kelp. Bring to a boil over high heat, then immediately remove and discard the kelp. Remove the pan from the heat. If the kelp is allowed to boil, the stock will be bitter and cloudy.

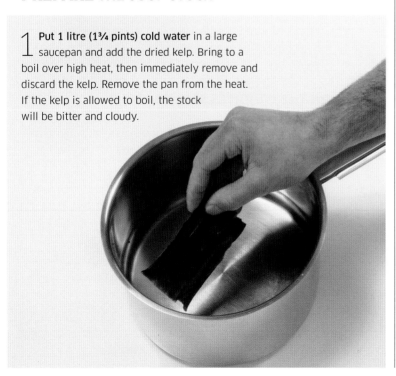

2 **Sprinkle the dried bonito flakes** evenly over the surface of the kelp-infused water.

3 **Let the stock stand** until the flakes settle to the bottom. It should take 3–5 minutes, depending on how thick and dry the flakes are. Line a sieve with damp muslin (the damp cloth will not shed fibres). Strain the stock through the muslin.

PREPARE THE VEGETABLES

4 **Half-fill a saucepan with water** and bring to the boil. Add the carrot slices and a pinch of salt and simmer for 3-5 minutes, until tender. Drain and set aside. Repeat with the daikon wedges, simmering for 8-10 minutes until just tender. Drain and set aside.

PREPARE THE FISH AND LEMON ZEST

5 **Cut the sea bass** across into 4 steaks, discarding both the head and tail (unfortunately, bass is no good for making fish stock, so there's nothing you can do with these trimmings). Toss the fish with the rice wine. Put the cornflour on a plate and press both sides of each sea bass steak into it, shaking off any excess. Make sure all the cut surfaces of the fish are finely and evenly covered with the flour.

6 **Bring a wide saucepan of water** to the boil. Drop in the sea bass steaks and bring back to a gentle simmer. Do not allow the water to heat any further than a very slow bubble, or the fish steaks may break up, or overcook and turn to mush. Cook for 2-3 minutes, until just firm, then drain the fish and set aside.

7 **With a vegetable peeler,** pare 2-3 strips of zest from the lemon, being sure to leave behind any bitter white pith. (If you pick up any pith by mistake, put the strip of zest on a flat work surface and remove it with a very sharp knife.) Cut the zest into 12 very thin strips. These are known as julienne. Meanwhile, trim and discard any tough stalks from the spinach and wash the leaves thoroughly. Bring a pan of water to the boil, add the spinach and simmer for 3 minutes, or until tender. Drain, rinse with cold water to cool the spinach rapidly, then gently squeeze with your fist to remove the excess water. Chop, divide into 4 small, neat piles and keep warm until serving.

FINISH THE SOUP

8 **Bring the soup stock to a very gentle boil** with the soy sauce. Taste, adding more soy sauce if you like. Arrange the fish, carrots, and daikon in 4 warmed soup bowls. Carefully ladle in the boiling soup and sprinkle each bowl with 3 strips of lemon zest. Decorate each with a bundle of spinach, or with a sprig of watercress, if you prefer.

Stuffed mushrooms with herbs

LIFE ISN'T TOO SHORT to stuff a mushroom! In fact these are hard to beat when they are filled with wild mushrooms and walnuts, then perfumed with garlic and plenty of herbs. They can be made up to 4 hours ahead and kept in the refrigerator.

SERVES	PREP	COOK
SERVES 4	25–30 MINS	15–20 MINS

Ingredients

12 large cap mushrooms, total weight about 500g (1lb 2oz)

90g (3oz) fresh wild mushrooms, or 20g (¾oz) dried wild mushrooms

12-14 tarragon sprigs, leaves chopped, plus a few sprigs for garnish

10-12 chervil sprigs, leaves chopped, plus a few sprigs for garnish

7-10 thyme sprigs, leaves chopped, plus a few sprigs for garnish

3-4 tbsp grated Parmesan cheese

4 tbsp olive oil

3 garlic cloves, finely chopped

juice of ½ lemon

salt and pepper

90ml (3fl oz) double cream

100g (3½oz) walnuts, coarsely chopped

PREPARE THE MUSHROOMS AND STUFFING

1 **Pull out the stalks** from the large mushrooms, leaving the caps whole for stuffing. Wipe the caps with damp kitchen paper and trim the separated stalks. Wipe the fresh wild mushrooms and trim the stalks. If using dried mushrooms, soak them in hot water until plump, about 30 minutes. Drain them and cut into pieces.

2 **Finely chop the wild mushrooms** and the large mushroom stalks with a sharp knife, or chop in a food processor, taking care to retain their texture and not to overwork them to a purée. Combine a quarter of the chopped herbs with the Parmesan and set aside.

3 **Heat half the oil** in a frying pan. Add the chopped mushrooms and garlic with the lemon juice and salt and pepper. Cook, stirring, for 3–5 minutes, or until all the liquid has evaporated. Stir in the cream and cook for 1-2 minutes, until slightly thickened. Add the walnuts and herbs and stir to mix. Remove from the heat and taste for seasoning.

STUFF AND BAKE THE MUSHROOMS

4 **Preheat the oven** to 180°C (350°F/Gas 4). Lightly oil a baking dish. Season the mushroom caps and spoon 1-2 spoonfuls stuffing into each, mounding it well. Set in the baking dish.

5 **Sprinkle about 1 tsp Parmesan** and herb topping on each mushroom along with the remaining oil. Bake for 15-20 minutes, or until the mushrooms are tender when pierced with a knife and the filling is very hot. Serve garnished with the reserved herbs.

Smoked trout mousse

A REFRESHING START to any meal, lifted with pungent horseradish and fragrant dill and lightened with yogurt. If you use a mould made from aluminium or tin, do not store in the refrigerator for more than 4 hours, or it will taint the flavour.

SERVES	PREP	COOK
SERVES 8-10	20-25 MINS PLUS CHILLING	NONE

Ingredients

2 eggs, hard-boiled

small bunch of dill

2 smoked trout, total weight about 750g (1lb 10oz)

1 tbsp powdered gelatine

3 small spring onions, finely sliced

125ml (4fl oz) mayonnaise

125ml (4fl oz) plain yogurt

60g (2oz) grated fresh horseradish, or to taste

juice of 1 lemon

salt and pepper

175ml (6fl oz) double cream

bunch of watercress, to serve

PREPARE THE INGREDIENTS

1 **Coarsely chop the eggs.** Strip the dill fronds from the stalks and finely chop them. Peel the skin from the smoked trout with a sharp knife, then carefully lift the fish from the bones. Discard the heads, bones, and skin and gently flake the flesh, removing any remaining small bones.

2 **Sprinkle the gelatine** evenly over 4 tbsp cold water in a small bowl and let it stand for about 5 minutes, until the granules become spongy. Brush a 1.2 litre (2 pint) terrine mould with oil.

MAKE THE MOUSSE

3 **Put the eggs**, trout, dill, spring onions, mayonnaise, and yogurt in a bowl. Add the horseradish, lemon juice, salt, and pepper and stir. Taste; it should be well seasoned.

4 **Whip the cream** for 3-5 minutes, until soft peaks form. Melt the gelatine in a small saucepan placed over low heat. Add it to the trout mixture and mix thoroughly. At once, fold in the cream, working quickly. Spoon into the mould and smooth the top. Cover with a lid, or with clingfilm, and chill in the refrigerator for 3-4 hours, until set.

UNMOULD THE MOUSSE

5 **Run a small knife** around the edges of the mould. Dip the base in a bowl of warm water for a few seconds to loosen the mousse, then wipe the base dry.

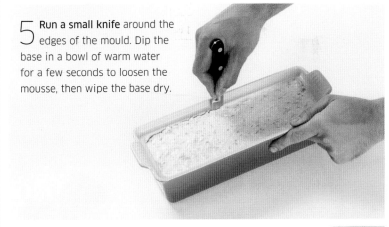

6 **Set a platter** on top of the mould and invert to unmould the mousse. Cut the mousse into 2cm (¾in) slices and set a slice on each plate. Decorate each serving with 1-2 sprigs of watercress.

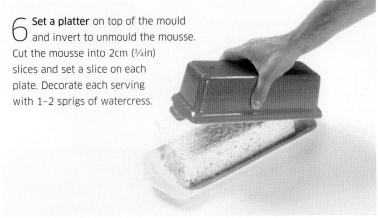

Beef noodle soup (pho)

FRAGRANT WITH SPICES, this Vietnamese soup takes time to simmer, but gives a rich, meat-laden broth that is a meal in itself. It should be quite hot with chillies, so use as many as you dare here, and deseed them or not, depending on the strength of heat you prefer (if you leave in the seeds, the dish will be much hotter).

SERVES	PREP	COOK
SERVES 4	1½ HRS	4-5 HRS

Ingredients

FOR THE SOUP STOCK

1.4kg (3lb) oxtail, cut into pieces

1kg (2¼lb) beef bones, cut into pieces

1 large onion, halved

5cm (2in) piece of fresh root ginger, thickly sliced

3 shallots

4 star anise

10cm (4in) cinnamon stick

3 whole cloves

FOR THE RICE STICKS AND TOPPINGS

250g (9oz) 5mm (¼in) dried rice sticks

2 spring onions, trimmed

250g (9oz) beef fillet

4 tbsp fish sauce

125g (4½oz) beansprouts

4 coriander sprigs

1 hot red chilli, deseeded and thinly sliced, or to taste

1 lime, cut into wedges

MAKE THE SOUP STOCK

1 Put the oxtail and beef bones in a large saucepan. Add water to cover, bring to a boil and simmer for 10 minutes. Drain in a colander and rinse with cold water. Rinse the pan then return the oxtail and bones. Add 3 litres (5¼ pints) of water, cover, and bring slowly to a boil.

2 Meanwhile, heat the grill. Put the onion halves and ginger pieces on the grill rack. Add the unpeeled shallots. Grill 7.5cm (3in) from the heat for 3-5 minutes, until well browned, then turn and brown the other sides for another 3-5 minutes. Add them to the saucepan with the star anise, cinnamon stick, and cloves.

3 Cover and simmer over low heat for 3-4 hours, until the oxtail pieces are tender. While it cooks, add more water, if needed, to keep the bones covered, and occasionally skim the fat from the surface. Remove the oxtail pieces from the stock and set aside. When cool enough to handle, remove the meat from the oxtail bones with your fingers and reserve.

4 Return the oxtail bones to the stock, and continue simmering for another hour. Line a colander with a piece of dampened muslin large enough to hang generously over the side. Strain the stock through this into a large, clean saucepan. Discard the bones, spices, and vegetables. Skim off all the fat and taste for seasoning. You should have 2 litres (3½ pints).

PREPARE THE RICE STICKS AND TOPPINGS

5 **Put the rice sticks** in a bowl and cover with warm water. Let soak for 20 minutes, until soft, or according to packet directions. Cut the spring onions into diagonal slices. Cut the beef across the grain into very thin slices. Arrange the slices on a tray, cover them tightly and refrigerate.

ASSEMBLE THE SOUP

6 **Add the oxtail meat** and fish sauce to the soup stock and bring to a boil. Remove the beef from the refrigerator.

7 **Half-fill a large pan with water** and bring to a boil. Drain the rice sticks, add them to the boiling water and stir to help prevent them sticking together. Return the water to a boil, then drain thoroughly in a colander, shaking to remove as much water as possible. Divide the rice sticks equally between 4 large, warmed soup bowls and top with the beansprouts, raw beef slices, and spring onions.

8 **Carefully ladle some of the boiling soup stock** and shredded oxtail meat evenly into each bowl. Serve at once, while still very hot, decorated with a few coriander sprigs. Allow each guest to add slices of chilli and squeeze over lime juice to taste. Urge them not to be too timid: this soup is supposed to be devilishly hot.

Szechuan sweet and sour spare ribs

SERVE WITH BOILED OR FRIED RICE to make this recipe into a main course for 4. These ribs are first browned in chilli-flavoured oil, then very slowly simmered until completely tender, and finally coated in a delectable sauce.

SERVES SERVES 6	**PREP** 15–20 MINS	**COOK** 1½ HRS

Ingredients

4 tbsp dark soy sauce

4 tbsp cider vinegar

3 tbsp honey

1 tbsp sesame oil

1 tsp chilli paste

4 tbsp dry sherry

4 tbsp vegetable oil

1 dried red chilli

1.4kg (3lb) spare ribs

PREPARE THE SAUCE AND BROWN THE RIBS

1 **In a small bowl,** whisk together the soy sauce, cider vinegar, honey, sesame oil, chilli paste, and sherry. Cover tightly with cling film and set this sweet and sour sauce aside.

2 **Heat the vegetable oil** in a wok, add the chilli and cook for 1 minute until dark brown. Add 3–4 ribs and stir over high heat for 2–3 minutes, until browned on all sides. Transfer to a plate. Working in batches, brown the remaining ribs in the same way. Pour off all but 2 tbsp oil from the wok.

SIMMER THE SPARE RIBS

3 **Return the ribs** to the wok, pour in enough water to completely cover and bring to a boil. Reduce the heat and cover the wok. Simmer, for about 1 hour, stirring occasionally. The ribs are cooked when the meat shrinks slightly on the bone and feels tender to the tip of a knife.

4 **Remove the chilli** and discard. Pour the sauce into the wok and stir thoroughly to mix. Simmer, stirring occasionally, for 25–30 minutes, until the liquid is reduced to a thick brown sauce and the ribs are glazed. If necessary, remove the ribs and reduce the sauce further by boiling fast. Serve the ribs on a warmed plate, coated with the sauce.

Mussels with saffron-cream sauce

FROM THE SHORES OF BRITTANY comes this interesting dish. The mussel juices add rich flavour to the cooking liquid. Make sure you steam the mussels briefly, just until the shells pop open, so they remain juicy and sumptuous.

SERVES	**PREP**	**COOK**
SERVES 4-6	25-30 MINS	10-12 MINS

Ingredients

3kg (6½lb) mussels

3 shallots, very finely chopped

250ml (9fl oz) dry white wine

1 bouquet garni, made with 5-6 parsley stalks, 2-3 thyme sprigs, and 1 bay leaf

large pinch of saffron

salt and pepper

125ml (4fl oz) double cream

leaves from 5-7 parsley sprigs, finely chopped

PREPARE THE MUSSELS

1 **Clean the mussels:** scrub each thoroughly under cold running water with a small stiff brush, then scrape with a knife to remove any barnacles.

2 **Discard any damaged mussels** that have cracked or broken shells and any that do not close when tapped lightly on the work surface. Detach and discard any weeds or 'beards' from each mussel.

COOK THE MUSSELS

3 **Put the shallots,** wine, bouquet garni, saffron, and plenty of pepper in a casserole which has a lid. Bring to a boil and simmer for 2 minutes. Add the mussels, cover and cook over high heat, stirring occasionally, for 5-7 minutes. Discard any mussels that have not opened. With a slotted spoon, transfer the mussels to a large, warmed bowl.

4 **Cover tightly with foil** and keep in a warm place while making the sauce. You must work quickly now, so the mussels remain as plump and moist as possible and lose none of their fresh-cooked savour.

MAKE THE SAUCE

5 **Discard the bouquet garni** and bring the cooking liquid to a boil. Simmer until reduced by half. Pour in the cream, stirring, and bring back to the boil. Simmer until slightly thickened, stirring; it should take 2-3 minutes. Lift out the spoon and run your finger across; it should leave a clear trail. Stir in the parsley and season to taste. Remove the foil and spoon the saffron-cream sauce over the mussels.

Chicken mousse with Madeira sauce

THIS SMOOTH, CREAMY MOUSSE wrapped in fine slices of courgette makes an excellent hot first course. If you would like to serve it as a light main dish instead, add some delicious saffron rice (p262) as an accompaniment.

SERVES SERVES 4	**PREP** 25-35 MINS	**COOK** 20-30 MINS

Ingredients

500g (1lb 2oz) skinless, boneless chicken breasts

2 egg whites

salt and pepper

pinch of ground nutmeg

175ml (6fl oz) double cream

2 courgettes, trimmed

butter, for the ramekins

FOR THE BUTTER SAUCE

125g (4½oz) butter

2 garlic cloves, finely chopped

2 shallots, finely chopped

4 tbsp Madeira

1 tbsp double cream

MAKE THE CHICKEN MOUSSE

1 **Cut the chicken** into chunks and work it through the fine blade of a food mincer, or process in a food processor until not too fine. It should remain a coarsely minced mixture.

2 **Whisk the egg whites** until frothy. With a wooden spoon, gradually add them to the chicken, beating until smooth and firm after each addition. Season with salt, pepper, and nutmeg.

3 **Beat in the cream**, a little at a time. Chill the mixture for about 15 minutes, or until firm. It should hold its shape. To test for seasoning, fry a little piece in a frying pan and taste. Adjust the seasoning if necessary.

PREPARE THE COURGETTES

4 **Cut the courgettes** into very thin slices. Bring a saucepan of salted water to the boil. Add the courgettes and simmer for 1-2 minutes, until softened. Drain in a colander, rinse under cold water to stop the cooking, then drain thoroughly on kitchen paper.

PREPARE THE RAMEKINS

5 **Using a ramekin as a guide**, cut out 6 circles of baking parchment. Butter 6 ramekins. Lay a parchment paper circle in the base of each and brush it, too, with butter. Be sure to cover all the paper, to prevent the courgette slices from sticking. Meanwhile, preheat the oven to 180°C (350°F/Gas 4).

ASSEMBLE AND COOK THE MOUSSE

6 **Line the bottoms and sides** of the ramekins with overlapping slices of courgettes.

7 **Spoon the chicken mousse** mixture in, smoothing the top, then put in a baking dish. Pour in boiling water to come more than halfway up the sides.

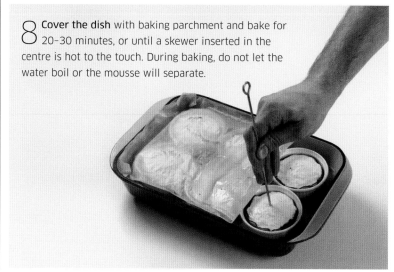

8 **Cover the dish** with baking parchment and bake for 20-30 minutes, or until a skewer inserted in the centre is hot to the touch. During baking, do not let the water boil or the mousse will separate.

MAKE THE SAUCE AND FINISH THE DISH

9 Heat about 30g (1oz) of the butter in a small saucepan, add the garlic and shallots and cook, stirring, for 2–3 minutes. Make sure the garlic does not brown too much, or the sauce will taste bitter. Add the Madeira and bring to a boil, stirring to dissolve the pan juices, for 2–3 minutes, or until it has reduced to a syrupy glaze. Add the cream and boil again until reduced to a glaze. Remove from the heat and add the remaining butter, a few pieces at a time, whisking constantly and moving the pan on and off the heat. The butter should thicken the sauce creamily without melting to oil. Make sure the sauce does not become too hot, or it will separate.

10 Run a fine, sharp knife around the edge of each ramekin. Unmould the chicken mousses on to warm plates, carefully rearranging any slices of courgette which have become displaced. Spoon the warm Madeira sauce around each mousse.

 VARIATION: Cold chicken mousse with tomato and mint coulis

Served at room temperature with a vibrant red sauce.

1 Prepare and cook the mousse as directed in the main recipe. Leave it to cool to room temperature.

2 Omit the butter sauce and make a tomato coulis instead: skin, seed and roughly chop 250g (8oz) fresh tomatoes; purée in a food processor until very smooth. With the motor running, gradually add 1 tbsp olive oil to make an emulsion. Season to taste.

3 Run a fine-bladed knife around the edge of each ramekin, then unmould the mousses on to individual plates. Spoon around the tomato coulis and sprinkle evenly with chopped fresh mint.

Cod and mussel chowder

A HEARTY DISH laden with chunks of cod and potatoes, with mussels to add colour and flavour. The recipe can be made up to and including step 7 and kept, tightly covered, in the refrigerator. Finish the chowder just before serving.

SERVES	PREP	COOK
SERVES 8	45–50 MINS	55–60 MINS

Ingredients

3 potatoes, total weight about 500g (1lb 2oz)

1kg (2¼lb) skinned cod fillets

1kg (2¼lb) mussels

1.5 litres (2¾ pints) fish stock

2 bay leaves

125ml (4fl oz) white wine

175g (6oz) streaky bacon rashers, diced

2 onions, finely chopped

2 celery sticks, peeled and finely chopped

1 carrot, finely chopped

2 tsp dried thyme

60g (2oz) plain flour

250ml (9fl oz) double cream

salt and pepper

leaves from 5–7 dill sprigs, finely chopped

PREPARE THE INGREDIENTS

1 Peel and dice the potatoes into 1cm (½in) cubes and put in a bowl of cold water so they do not discolour. Rinse the cod fillets and pat dry with kitchen paper. Cut into 2.5cm (1in) cubes. Prepare the mussels (see p41).

2 Put the fish stock and bay leaves into a large saucepan and pour in the wine. Bring to the boil and simmer for 10 minutes, until very hot and all the flavours have combined.

3 Put the bacon in a casserole dish and cook, stirring occasionally, for 3–5 minutes, until crisp and the fat is rendered. Add the onions, celery, carrot, and thyme. Cook, stirring, for 5–7 minutes, until soft but not brown.

MAKE THE CHOWDER

4 Sprinkle the flour over the casserole and cook, stirring, for a minute.

5 Add the hot stock mixture and bring to a boil, stirring until the liquid thickens slightly.

6 Drain the potatoes and add them to the casserole. Simmer, stirring occasionally, until the potatoes are very tender, about 40 minutes.

7 Remove the casserole from the heat. With a fork, crush about a third of the potatoes against the side of the casserole, then stir to combine.

FINISH THE CHOWDER

8 Return the casserole to the heat and tip in the mussels. Simmer for 1–2 minutes until the shells start to open. Stir in the cod and simmer until the fish just flakes easily, 2–3 minutes more. Do not continue to cook, or the fish will start to break apart. Pour in the cream and bring just to a boil. Taste for seasoning, adding salt and pepper to taste.

9 Discard the bay leaves and any mussels that have not opened, and warn your guests to do the same, should they come across any firmly shut shellfish. Ladle the chowder into warmed soup bowls and sprinkle each with dill. Serve very hot. The traditional New England accompaniment to this chowder is oyster crackers, crumbled into the bowls by each diner, to taste.

 VARIATION: Manhattan chowder

This adds tomatoes for a colourful finish.

1 Peel, seed, and coarsely chop 1.2kg (2¾lb) tomatoes, or use 2 x 400g (14oz) cans tomatoes. If tomatoes are not ripe and in season, canned are usually the better choice. Finely chop 4 garlic cloves.

2 Make the chowder as directed, using double the amount of wine, 1 tbsp dried thyme, and half the plain flour. Add the garlic and 1–2 tbsp tomato puree with the onion, celery, and carrots.

3 Add the tomatoes with the potatoes; do not crush any of the potatoes. Omit the double cream. Sprinkle with chopped thyme and serve with crusty wholewheat bread.

Genoese minestrone with red pesto

A PURÉE OF TOMATO, GARLIC, AND BASIL is stirred in at the finish here to give a burst of fresh flavour. A hearty soup full of beans and pasta, this recipe makes a perfect starter for the colder months; follow it with a lighter main course. Both the soup and the pesto can be made 1 day ahead and refrigerated separately; reheat the soup before adding the sauce.

SERVES
SERVES 6

PREP
45–50 MINS

COOK
2½ HRS

Ingredients

FOR THE MINESTRONE

175g (6oz) dried red kidney beans

175g (6oz) dried cannellini beans

salt and pepper

125g (4½oz) elbow macaroni

175g (6oz) French beans

3 carrots, total weight about 250g (9oz)

3 potatoes, total weight about 375g (13oz)

1 courgette

175g (6oz) shelled fresh peas or defrosted frozen peas

125g (4½oz) Parmesan cheese, grated

FOR THE TOMATO PESTO

large bunch of basil

2 tomatoes, peeled, deseeded, and chopped

4 garlic cloves, peeled

1 tsp salt

pepper

175ml (6fl oz) olive oil

PREPARE THE DRIED BEANS AND MACARONI

1 **Put the kidney and cannellini beans** in separate bowls. Add water to cover generously and leave to soak overnight. Drain, rinse with cold water, and drain again. Put the beans in separate saucepans, and add water to cover generously.

2 **Bring to a boil** and boil for 10 minutes. Reduce the heat to a simmer. Cook for about 1½ hours, seasoning with salt and pepper halfway through cooking, until tender but still slightly firm when gently squeezed. Drain thoroughly.

3 **Fill a medium saucepan** with water, bring to a boil and add salt. Add the macaroni and cook, stirring occasionally, for 5–7 minutes, until just tender. Drain and rinse with hot water, then set aside.

MAKE THE SOUP

4 **Break the ends from the French beans** and cut them into 1cm (½in) pieces. Peel the carrots and potatoes; trim the ends from the courgette. Dice the carrots, potatoes, and courgette.

5 **Put the cooked, dried beans** in a large saucepan and add the French beans, carrots, potatoes, courgette, peas, and a little salt and pepper. Add 2 litres (3½ pints) of water and bring to a boil, then reduce the heat and simmer for 1 hour, until the vegetables are very tender.

6 **Strip the leaves** from the basil stalks, reserving 6 sprigs. Put the basil, tomatoes, garlic, salt, and a little pepper in a food processor or blender and purée until smooth.

7 **With the blades turning**, gradually add the oil. Scrape down the sides of the processor bowl from time to time during the process with a rubber spatula. Taste the sauce for seasoning.

8 **Add the macaroni** to the soup and taste again for seasoning. Gently reheat to boiling, but do not cook further or the pasta and vegetables will overcook, rather than staying firm and vibrant. Remove from the heat, and stir in the tomato pesto. Ladle the soup into warmed bowls, top each serving with basil leaves, and serve the Parmesan separately.

 VARIATION: Soupe au pistou, croûtes gratinées

With a few changes, Genoese minestrone becomes the famous French soup, pistou. It's hardly surprising, as the Italian town that gives its name to the main minestrone recipe here is very close to the French border.

1 Cook the dried beans and macaroni, and make the vegetable soup as directed, omitting the fresh or frozen peas. Make the tomato pesto sauce as directed, then set aside.

2 Preheat the oven to 180°C (350°F/Gas 4). Make toasted cheese croûtes: cut 1 small loaf of French bread (weighing about 175g/6oz) into 24 slices, each 2cm (¾inch) thick.

3 Spread the slices on a baking sheet. Brush each lightly with olive oil and sprinkle evenly with 60g (2oz) finely grated Parmesan cheese. Bake for about 5 minutes.

4 Stir the pesto sauce into the hot soup, ladle into warmed bowls, and float a croûte on each serving. Pass the remaining croûtes separately. Omit the grated Parmesan for sprinkling.

Gratin of chicory and ham

A SIMPLE DISH from Belgium, home of chicory. Make sure you remove the bitter core at the bottom of each head of chicory as you trim it, to allow it to cook more evenly. This is a great starter or side dish for a party, as it can be assembled up to the end of step 6 the day before, then covered tightly and refrigerated. Bring the gratin to room temperature before sprinkling it with Gruyère cheese and baking.

SERVES
SERVES 4

PREP
15–20 MINS

COOK
1–1¼ HRS

Ingredients

8 heads of chicory, trimmed

1 tsp granulated sugar

salt and pepper

500ml (16fl oz) milk

1 slice of onion

1 bay leaf

6 peppercorns

30g (1oz) plain flour

60g (2oz) butter

ground nutmeg

45g (1½oz) Gruyère cheese

8 thin slices of cooked ham

BRAISE THE CHICORY

1 **Preheat the oven** to 180°C (350°F/Gas 4). Brush a flan dish with butter. Arrange the chicory evenly spaced apart in the dish and sprinkle with the sugar, salt, and pepper. Butter a piece of foil and press it, butter-side down, on top. Bake, turning once or twice, for 45–55 minutes, until brown and slightly caramelized. The chicory should be tender right to the centre when pierced with a knife. Transfer the chicory to a plate and let cool slightly. Wipe the flan dish.

MAKE THE BÉCHAMEL SAUCE

2 **Scald the milk** in a saucepan with the onion slice, bay leaf, and peppercorns (you should be able to hear the milk begin to sizzle at the sides of the pan, but it should not come to the boil). Cover the pan and set it aside in a warm place off the heat for 10 minutes, for the milk to infuse with all the other flavours. Melt the butter in another saucepan over medium heat. Whisk in the flour and cook for 30-60 seconds, whisking all the time, until foaming.

3 **Remove the pan from the heat,** then strain in the hot milk and whisk. Return to the heat, whisking constantly to avoid lumps, until the sauce boils and begins to thicken. Season with salt, pepper, and a pinch of nutmeg (or to taste), and simmer the sauce for 2 minutes more, to cook out the raw taste of the flour, stirring to spread the heat and ensure the sauce does not catch on the bottom of the saucepan.

ASSEMBLE AND BAKE THE GRATIN

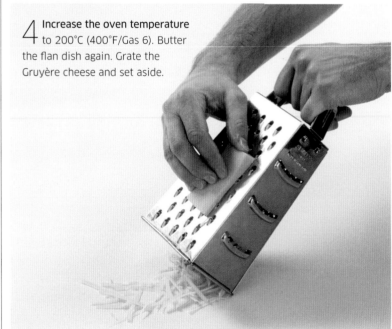

4 **Increase the oven temperature** to 200°C (400°F/Gas 6). Butter the flan dish again. Grate the Gruyère cheese and set aside.

5 **Lay a slice of ham** on a work surface. Set a head of chicory on top and roll the ham slice round to form a neat cylinder. Repeat with the remaining ham and chicory, arranging the cylinders neatly in the dish, seam-side down, to keep them intact.

6 **Ladle the béchamel sauce** evenly over the chicory and ham cylinders.

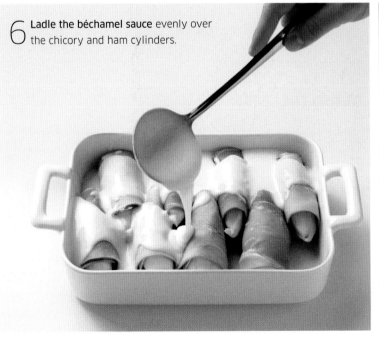

7 **Sprinkle with the cheese.** Bake for 20–25 minutes, until bubbling and browned. Serve hot from the dish.

Leeks vinaigrette

COMPLETELY DELICIOUS; so much more than the sum of its parts. This simple, elegant dish should be prepared with the freshest leeks you can find. They can be left to marinate in the vinaigrette, covered and refrigerated, for up to 1 day. Let them come to room temperature before sprinkling with the egg and parsley. Substitute baby leeks if you prefer; use the same weight, but do not tie them together in step 2 of the recipe, and simmer them for only 5 minutes, or until just tender to the tip of a knife.

SERVES
SERVES 4-6

PREP
15-20 MINS
PLUS MARINATING

COOK
15-25 MINS

Ingredients

6 leeks, total weight about 1kg (2¼lb)

salt and pepper

3 tbsp white wine vinegar

1 tsp Dijon mustard

175ml (6fl oz) flavourless vegetable oil

2 shallots, finely chopped

1 egg

leaves from 5-7 parsley sprigs, finely chopped

COOK THE LEEKS

1 **Trim the leeks,** discarding the roots and tough green tops. Slit lengthways, leaving the leeks attached at the root end. Wash thoroughly, fanning the leeks out under cold, running water.

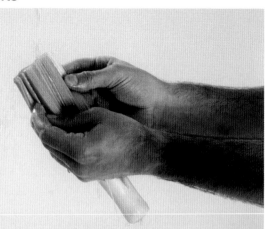

2 **Divide the leeks** into 2 bundles, then tie them together at each end with kitchen string. Fill a wide shallow pan with salted water, and bring to a boil. Add the leeks, and simmer for about 10 minutes, or until just tender.

MAKE THE VINAIGRETTE

3 **Whisk together the vinegar,** mustard, salt, and pepper. Gradually whisk in the oil, so the vinaigrette emulsifies and thickens slightly. Whisk in the shallots; taste for seasoning.

DRESS THE LEEKS

4 **Test whether the leeks are tender** by piercing with the tip of a small knife. Drain in a colander, remove the strings, pat dry with kitchen paper, and cut on the diagonal into 7.5cm (3in) lengths.

5 **Lay the leeks** in a dish and pour over the vinaigrette. Cover and refrigerate for 1 hour, then bring to room temperature. Meanwhile, hard-boil and shell the egg.

FINISH THE SALAD

6 **Divide the leeks** between plates. Cut the egg in half, and separate yolk from white. Chop the white. Work the yolk through a sieve with a spoon. Sprinkle the leeks with parsley, egg whites, and yolks.

Chicken liver and apple pâté

TOPPED WITH GOLDEN SLICES of caramelized apple, these individual pâtés make an elegant first course. The smooth richness of the chicken livers is pleasantly contrasted with the sweet apples. A touch of Calvados is added and then flamed for a greater depth of flavour.

SERVES	PREP	COOK
SERVES 6	30-35 MINS	12-15 MINS

Ingredients

3 dessert apples

250g (9oz) butter

salt and pepper

500g (1lb 2oz) chicken livers, trimmed

4 shallots, finely diced

2 garlic cloves, finely chopped

4 tbsp Calvados or cognac

2 tbsp caster sugar

6 slices wholemeal bread

6 mint sprigs, to serve (optional)

PREPARE THE APPLES

1 **Core, peel, and dice** 2 of the apples. Melt 2 tbsp butter in a frying pan. Add the diced apples, salt and pepper. Sauté, stirring frequently, for 5-7 minutes, until tender. Transfer to a bowl with a slotted spoon.

PREPARE THE LIVERS

2 **Melt another 2 tbsp butter** in the frying pan. Add the chicken livers and season. Fry, stirring, for 2-3 minutes, until brown on the outside. Tip in the shallots and garlic. Cooking, stirring, for 1-2 minutes, until the shallots are slightly softened. Remove a liver from the frying pan, then slice into it. It should still be pink in the centre.

3 **Increase the heat** to medium-high. Pour the Calvados into the pan and bring to a boil. Stand back and hold a lighted match to the pan's side to set the alcohol alight. Baste the chicken livers for 20-30 seconds, until the flames subside. Let the livers cool.

MAKE THE PÂTÉ

4 **Purée the chicken liver mixture** in a food processor until almost smooth. Wipe out the frying pan. With an electric mixer, cream 150g (5oz) butter until soft. Add the livers with the diced and sautéed apples. Mix and season.

5 **Spoon into six ramekins,** filling them at least three-quarters full. Smooth the tops with the back of a spoon dipped in hot water so it does not stick to the pâté. Cover and chill for 2-3 hours, until firm.

PREPARE THE GARNISH AND SERVE

6 **Core the remaining apple** and slice into 6. Melt the remaining butter in the frying pan. Add the apple and sprinkle with half the sugar. Turn and sprinkle with the remaining sugar. Fry for 2-3 minutes each side, until caramelized. Meanwhile, toast the slices of bread. Set a caramelized apple slice and a mint sprig, if liked, on top of each pâté and serve with the toast.

Roman herb and garlic artichokes

YOUNG GLOBE ARTICHOKES with tender stalks are best for this delicious appetizer. Serve warm or at room temperature. If you can only find the older vegetables, you will have to trim away the more fibrous green parts. When choosing artichokes, check the cut stalks: buy only those that are moist, not dry, as they will be the freshest.

SERVES
SERVES 6

PREP
25–30 MINS

COOK
25–45 MINS

Ingredients

6 young globe artichokes

2 lemons, halved, plus 1 for garnish

6 garlic cloves, finely chopped

leaves from 1 small bunch of flat-leaf parsley, finely chopped

leaves from 8–10 mint sprigs, finely chopped, plus more for decoration

salt and pepper

125ml (4fl oz) olive oil

PREPARE THE ARTICHOKES

1 **Trim** the tough end of an artichoke stalk, leaving about 4cm (1½in) of stalk. Snap off the large bottom leaves with your fingers. Continue to remove the leaves, tearing off about three-quarters of each leaf so the edible white part remains attached to the artichoke heart.

3 **Peel the stalk** of the artichoke, cutting away the tough, fibrous exterior. Trim the green parts of the base to remove any tough, fibrous leaves.

2 **Continue** until you reach the cone of soft, small leaves in the centre. Trim the cone of leaves with a sharp knife. Rub the cut edges of the artichoke with a lemon half to prevent discolouration.

4 **Scoop out** the hairy choke with a teaspoon and squeeze lemon juice into the hollowed-out centre. Rub the juice thoroughly around the inside with your finger. Prepare the remaining artichokes in the same way.

STUFF AND COOK THE ARTICHOKES

5 **Combine the garlic,** parsley, mint, and a little salt in a bowl. Put 2–3 spoonfuls of the garlic-herb stuffing in the centre of an artichoke and press it down well against the bottom and sides so that they are as full as possible and the stuffing will not fall out when the artichokes are cooked upside-down. Stuff the remaining artichokes, keeping back 2–3 tbsp of the stuffing to sprinkle on top.

6 **Set the artichokes,** tops down and stalks up, in a single, tight layer in a large pan. They should be packed tightly enough so they do not topple over during cooking. Sprinkle the remaining stuffing over and pour on the oil. Sprinkle with salt and pepper and add enough water to come halfway up the sides, not including the stalks.

7 **Bring to a boil,** then cover the pan and simmer for 25–45 minutes, until tender. Add more water if necessary, so the artichokes are always half covered. To test if the artichokes are cooked, pierce them with the point of a knife; they should be tender.

8 **Transfer the artichokes** to a large, warmed serving dish with a slotted spoon, arranging them in a single layer, still with their stalks upwards. Try to make sure you take as little as possible of the cooking liquid from the pan. Boil the cooking liquid until it is strongly flavoured and reduced to about 250ml (8fl oz).

9 **Squeeze the juice** from the remaining lemon half, discarding any seeds, then add this to the cooking liquid to lift all the flavours. Taste for seasoning, adding more salt, pepper, or lemon if you think it needs it. Pour the cooking liquid over the artichokes and let cool to room temperature. Slice the lemon for garnish.

10 **Serve the artichokes warm** or at room temperature, decorated with lemon wedges and mint sprigs. They are delicious at either temperature, which makes them a very forgiving dish. If necessary, you can prepare the artichokes up to 1 day ahead, cover, and refrigerate. Let them come to room temperature before serving.

Basque hot pepper omelette

LIKE A SPANISH TORTILLA, this omelette is browned on both sides. Use this recipe as a template for whatever varieties of sweet peppers and chillies you prefer, or can find. It's even better if you can use a good selection of shapes, colours, and levels of heat.

SERVES	PREP	COOK
SERVES 2	20–25 MINS	15–25 MINS

Ingredients

250g (9oz) tomatoes

60g (2oz) butter

1 onion, thinly sliced

1 red pepper, thinly sliced

1–2 small hot red chillies, deseeded and finely chopped

2 garlic cloves, finely chopped

salt and pepper

leaves from small bunch of parsley, finely chopped

5 eggs

PREPARE THE FILLING

1 **Cut the cores** from the tomatoes, and score an "x" on their bases. Immerse in boiling water for 8–15 seconds, or until the skin starts to split. Plunge into cold water, peel, halve, squeeze out the seeds, and coarsely chop.

2 **Melt half the butter** in a frying pan, add the onion, pepper, and chillies, and cook for 5–8 minutes, or until softened. Add the tomatoes, garlic, salt, and pepper, and cook for 5–10 minutes, until thick. Stir in the parsley.

COOK THE OMELETTE

3 **Crack the eggs** into a bowl, season, and beat until thoroughly mixed. Melt the remaining butter in an omelette or frying pan. When it stops foaming and starts to brown, pour in the eggs. Stir briskly with the flat of a fork for 8–10 seconds, until the eggs start to thicken.

4 **Quickly but carefully,** use a fork to pull the cooked egg mixture from the sides of the pan to the centre, so the uncooked egg flows to the sides. Continue until the eggs are partly set, about 30 seconds.

5 **Stir the filling** into the eggs until well mixed. Reduce the heat and cook undisturbed for 2–3 minutes, until the omelette is set on top and browned underneath.

6 **Remove the pan** from the heat. Working quickly, place a large plate, that is bigger in diameter than the pan, over the omelette, and, holding both plate and pan firmly, invert to turn out the omelette on to the plate. Carefully slide it back into the pan, and brown the other side for only 30–60 seconds, or until the egg is cooked (lift an edge carefully with a palette knife to check). Alternatively, make the omelette entirely in a flameproof frying pan and don't invert the omelette to cook the other side; instead, preheat the grill and, at the end of step 5, slide the frying pan under the grill until the top is browned and the egg just cooked.

7 **Slide the omelette** on to a warmed serving plate. Cut it into wedges and serve hot, or at room temperature, with a crisp green salad, if you like. Once you have mastered making a Spanish-type omelette such as this, you can ring the changes as you please. There are one or two basic rules, however: if adding a watery vegetable, or a mushroom, these should be first sautéed until all their moisture has been drawn out and has evaporated from the pan, otherwise the omelette will be sloppy and the flavour diluted. When adding cheese, sprinkle it over at the last minute and flash the frying pan under the grill so it melts on top of the omelette (be sure to use a flameproof frying pan in this instance).

 VARIATION: Country omelette

With potatoes, onion, and bacon, this is typical fare in French cafés.

1 Omit the garlic, red pepper, chillies, and tomatoes. Slice the onion and chop the parsley as directed in the main recipe, reserving a few small parsley sprigs for decoration.

2 Take 250g (9oz) of streaky bacon rashers. Cut them across into strips. Peel 500g (1lb 2oz) potatoes and square off the sides. Cut them into 1cm (½in) cubes, stacking them up first for ease. Heat the bacon in a large frying pan and cook over medium heat, stirring occasionally, for 5 minutes, or until the fat has rendered. Remove all but 2 tbsp of the bacon fat.

3 Stir the onions and potatoes into the remaining fat in the frying pan. Cook, stirring occasionally, for 20 minutes, or until the onion and potatoes are tender and golden. Season to taste with salt and pepper. Cook the omelette as directed in the main recipe, adding the potato mixture in place of the tomato and pepper filling. Serve hot or at room temperature, cut into wedges, and decorate with the reserved parsley sprigs.

Vietnamese spring rolls

THESE ARE WRAPPED IN SOFT RICE PAPER, unlike the crisp, fried version, and are served with a sweet and spicy dipping sauce. The rolls are light and very adaptable; you can use almost any meat or fish you wish in place of the prawns and pork.

SERVES SERVES 4	**PREP** 50-60 MINS	**COOK** 25 MINS

Ingredients

FOR THE DIPPING SAUCE

2 garlic cloves, finely chopped

1 small hot red chilli, finely chopped

2 tbsp sugar

4 tbsp rice vinegar

4 tbsp fish sauce

2 tbsp lime juice

FOR THE SPRING ROLLS

250g (9oz) boneless loin of pork

8 raw, unpeeled prawns, total weight 125g (4½oz)

1 large carrot, in julienne strips

1 tsp sugar

60g (2oz) dried thin rice noodles

8 small lettuce leaves, plus more to serve

75g (2½oz) beansprouts

12-15 mint sprigs

15-20 coriander sprigs

8 round sheets of rice paper, 21cm (8½in) in diameter

MAKE THE DIPPING SAUCE

1 In a small bowl, combine the garlic, chilli, sugar, rice vinegar, fish sauce, and 4 tbsp water. Pour in the lime juice and whisk well until thoroughly mixed. Set aside for the flavours to meld together.

PREPARE THE FILLING

2 Half-fill 2 pans with water and bring to a boil. Add the pork to 1 pan and simmer for 15-20 minutes, just until tender. Drain the pork, rinse with cold water and drain again. Cut it across the grain into 3 mm (⅛in) slices.

3 Add the prawns to the other pan and simmer for 1-2 minutes, until pink. Drain, rinse with cold water and drain again. Peel off the shells. Cut each lengthways in half. Using the tip of a knife, remove the dark intestinal vein.

4 In a bowl, toss the carrot with the sugar and set aside. Bring a large pan of water to a boil. Add the noodles and cook for 1-2 minutes, until tender but still slightly chewy. Drain and cut into 7.5cm (3in) lengths.

5 Wash the lettuce leaves. Dry, then tear large leaves into 2-3 pieces. Pick over the beansprouts, discarding any that are discoloured. Strip the mint and coriander leaves from the stalks, reserving a few sprigs for garnish.

ASSEMBLE THE SPRING ROLLS

6 Pour about 1cm (½in) of hot water into a shallow dish. Work with 1 sheet of rice paper at a time and keep the remaining sheets wrapped. Dip 1 sheet of rice paper into the water for 20-25 seconds, to soften. Remove and spread it out on a dry tea towel.

7 Place a lettuce leaf on the rice paper. Top with one-eighth of the noodles, carrot, pork, beansprouts, and mint and coriander leaves. Roll up the paper, halfway, into a cylinder. Fold both ends over the filling.

8 **Place a few more coriander leaves** on top, then 2 prawn halves. Continue rolling the paper into a cylinder and press the end lightly to seal. Place the roll, prawn-side up, on a tray or plate and cover with a dampened tea towel to keep the roll moist. Repeat with the remaining rice papers and filling. Serve with small bowls of dipping sauce, and sprinkled with the reserved herbs.

 VARIATION: Vegetarian spring rolls

Mushrooms and onions replace the meat in this version.

1 Omit the pork, prawns, and dipping sauce. Soak 8 Chinese black mushrooms in about 175ml (6fl oz) boiling water for 15 minutes, until plump and soft. Prepare the noodles and carrots as directed. Drain the mushrooms, reserving 120ml (4fl oz) liquid. Cut off the mushroom stalks and slice the caps. Thinly slice 1 onion.

2 Heat a wok over medium-high heat and drizzle in 1 tbsp oil. When hot, add the onion and cook, stirring, for 2 minutes, until softened. Add the mushrooms and reserved liquid. Cover and cook for 4 minutes, until the mushrooms are tender. Uncover and cook until the liquid is evaporated. Stir in 1 tsp soy sauce, 1 tsp sugar, and salt to taste. Leave to cool. Assemble the spring rolls as directed, using all the carrots and replacing the prawns with the mushrooms.

3 Make a hoisin dipping sauce: finely chop 1 garlic clove. In a small pan, heat 2 tsp oil, add the garlic and cook until fragrant. Stir in 120ml (4fl oz) hoisin sauce, 3 tbsp water, 1 tbsp light soy sauce and a pinch of crushed dried chilli. Let cool. Pour into 4 bowls and sprinkle with 2 tbsp chopped peanuts. Serve the rolls and sauce with a salad of carrot julienne, lettuce and herbs.

Tropical prawn kebabs

SERVED WITH A PEANUT SAUCE, these make a great starter for a summer meal. They can be cooked on a barbecue or grilled indoors if the weather is bad; either method will give a fabulous result. Try serving them with Chilli-Cucumber Salad (see p95) and boiled rice to turn them into a more substantial main course dish.

SERVES	PREP	COOK
SERVES 8	20–25 MINS	4–6 MINS

Ingredients

For the kebabs

125ml (4fl oz) vegetable oil, more for grill rack

6 tbsp lime juice (about 2 limes)

1cm (½in) piece of fresh root ginger, peeled and finely chopped

2 large garlic cloves, finely chopped

½ tsp granulated sugar, or to taste

½ tsp chilli powder

leaves from a small bunch of coriander, chopped

1 tbsp soy sauce

salt and pepper

32 large raw prawns, total weight about 750g (1lb 10oz)

For the peanut sauce

60ml (2fl oz) vegetable oil

1 small onion, finely chopped

2 large garlic cloves, finely chopped

½ tsp crushed chillies

juice of ½ lime

2 tsp soy sauce

5 tbsp crunchy peanut butter

1 tsp soft brown sugar

250ml (9fl oz) coconut milk

MARINATE THE PRAWNS

2 Soak 8 bamboo skewers in water for 30 minutes, then thread 4 prawns on to each skewer and lay them in a shallow dish. (If using metal skewers, marinate the prawns before putting them on the skewers.)

1 Whisk together the oil, lime juice, ginger, and garlic. Add the sugar, chilli powder, chopped coriander, soy sauce, and salt and pepper to taste; stir well to mix.

3 Pour the marinade over the prawns. Cover and refrigerate for 1–2 hours, turning occasionally.

MAKE THE PEANUT SAUCE

4 Heat the oil in a small saucepan. Add the onion and cook, stirring, for 2–3 minutes, until lightly browned. Add the garlic and chillies and cook until the onion is golden, but do not let the garlic brown or it will be bitter.

5 Add the lime juice and soy sauce to the onion mixture; stir to combine. Remove from the heat and stir in the peanut butter and brown sugar. Let cool to room temperature.

6 Whisk the coconut milk in its tin until smooth, then measure the amount needed and pour it into the peanut sauce. Stir until the sauce is evenly mixed. Season to taste and let stand.

7 Heat the grill and brush the grill rack with oil. Transfer the kebabs from the dish to the rack. Brush the kebabs with marinade. Grill them 5–7.5 cm (2–3in) from the heat for 2–3 minutes, until they turn pink. Brush with marinade once or twice during grilling. Turn and brush again with marinade. Continue grilling until the prawns are pink on the other side, 2–3 minutes longer.

8 Set the kebabs on warmed plates, adding a small bowl of peanut sauce. Lime wedges are a great addition – a squeeze of lime juice really lifts the flavours of this dish.

Cheddar and courgette soufflés

USE MATURE OR MILD CHEDDAR according to your taste. The courgette mixture can be prepared up to 3 hours ahead to the end of step 6. Whisk the egg whites and finish the recipe just before baking. If you would prefer to make a large soufflé instead of individual dishes, use a 2 litre (3½ pint) dish and cook the whole mixture for 25–30 minutes.

SERVES	PREP	COOK
SERVES 6	30–35 MINS	25–30 MINS

Ingredients

60g (2oz) unsalted butter, plus more for the dishes

2 shallots, finely chopped

500g (1lb 2oz) courgettes, trimmed and coarsely grated

salt and pepper

175ml (6fl oz) milk

20g (¾oz) plain flour

125ml (4fl oz) double cream

pinch of ground nutmeg

4 eggs, separated, plus 2 egg whites

90g (3oz) Cheddar cheese, coarsely grated

PREPARE THE COURGETTES

1 **Melt half the butter** in the frying pan. Stir in the shallots and cook over a medium heat for about 2 minutes, until soft. Add the courgettes, season, and cook, stirring, for 3–5 minutes, until just tender. Transfer to a sieve set over a bowl and allow the liquid to drain thoroughly.

MAKE THE SAUCE

2 **Scald the milk** in a small saucepan. Melt the remaining butter in a medium saucepan. Over the heat add the flour all at once and cook, whisking briskly, until the mixture starts to foam, 30–60 seconds.

3 **Remove the pan** from the heat then slowly pour in the hot milk, whisking all the time, and continue to whisk until well mixed. Return to the heat, whisking constantly to prevent lumps.

4 **When the sauce boils** and thickens, pour in the cream and whisk until thoroughly combined. Season to taste with salt, pepper, and nutmeg. Simmer for 2 minutes longer.

MAKE THE SOUFFLÉ

5 Whisk the egg yolks into the hot sauce, one at a time, whisking well after each addition. Return the pan to the heat. Bring the mixture back to a boil, whisking constantly, and simmer for 1 minute longer to ensure the egg yolks are fully cooked.

6 Remove the pan from the heat and stir in the Cheddar and courgettes. Taste for seasoning; it should be highly seasoned. Preheat the oven to 190°C (375°F/Gas 5). Melt a little butter and use it to grease 6 x 350ml (12fl oz) capacity ramekins. Reheat the courgette mixture until hot.

FINISH THE SOUFFLÉ

7 Beat all the egg whites with a pinch of salt in a metal bowl for 3-5 minutes, until stiff peaks form. Do not overbeat or they will become grainy. Add about a quarter to the warm sauce and gently stir.

8 Add the lightened sauce to the remaining egg whites in the bowl. Fold the mixture together until the egg whites are thoroughly incorporated. Spoon into the prepared dishes. Bake until puffed and brown, 10-15 minutes. The centre should remain quite soft.

9 Serve immediately: the soufflés will lose much of their volume within minutes as they cool. Instruct your diners to plunge small spoons straight into the centre of the dish.

 VARIATION: Onion and sage soufflé

A classic combination; try this for a satisfying and unusual vegetarian Sunday lunch, alongside the more conventional pairing of roast pork or chicken for the meat eaters.

1 Omit the courgettes, shallots, and Cheddar. Thinly slice 8 onions. Melt 45g (1½oz) butter in a saucepan. Add the onions with salt and pepper, press a piece of buttered foil on top, and cover. Cook very gently for 15-20 minutes, until the onions are very soft but not brown. Stir occasionally so the onions cook evenly and do not catch on the base of the pan. Uncover and cook, stirring, until any liquid has evaporated.

2 Meanwhile, strip the leaves from 5-7 sprigs of fresh sage and chop them as finely as possible. Don't be tempted to add more herbs here, though it may not look like very much, as sage has a very strong taste and even a little bit too much could easily overpower the subtle balance of the flavourings in this dish.

3 Make the white cream sauce as directed. Add the onions and sage to the sauce and stir well to mix evenly. Finish and bake the soufflé as directed, using a 2 litre (3½ pint) dish and allowing 25-30 minutes for this larger soufflé to bake through fully. Make sure the centre remains quite soft; soufflés should not be solid in the middle: rather unctuous and melting is the ideal texture here.

Thai skewered chicken

COCONUT MILK AND FISH SAUCE flavour this popular street food snack threaded on to bamboo skewers. The sauce can be prepared 1 day ahead and the chicken can be marinated up to 12 hours in advance. Keep both, covered, in the refrigerator and grill the chicken just before serving.

SERVES	PREP	COOK
SERVES 4	20–30 MINS PLUS MARINATING	6–8 MINS

Ingredients

6 large boneless chicken thighs, total weight about 1kg (2¼lb)

FOR THE MARINADE

2 garlic cloves, chopped

150ml (5fl oz) canned coconut milk

2 tsp ground coriander

1 tsp ground cumin

1 tsp ground turmeric

FOR THE SAUCE

leaves from 8–10 coriander sprigs, chopped, plus a few more for garnish

juice of 1 lemon

3 tbsp light brown sugar

2 tbsp fish sauce

3 tbsp light soy sauce

½ tsp crushed chillies

PREPARE AND MARINATE THE CHICKEN

1 **Cut each thigh** into 6 even chunks, discarding any sinew. Combine all the marinade ingredients in a large bowl and mix. Add the chicken and toss to coat. Cover and refrigerate for at least 2 and up to 12 hours.

MAKE THE SAUCE

2 **In a small bowl,** combine all the sauce ingredients and stir until mixed. Cover the bowl and refrigerate for the flavours to combine, but remember to bring it to room temperature before serving.

SKEWER AND COOK THE CHICKEN

3 **Put 12 bamboo skewers** in water to soak for 30 minutes, so they do not burn during grilling. Heat the grill and lightly oil the grill rack. Thread the chicken chunks on to the skewers, dividing them equally.

4 **Arrange the skewers,** skin-side up, on the oiled rack. Grill about 7.5 cm (3in) from the heat for 4–5 minutes, until speckled with brown. Turn the skewers and continue grilling for 2–3 minutes longer, until the chicken is no longer pink in the centre. (Grill in batches if necessary to avoid crowding.)

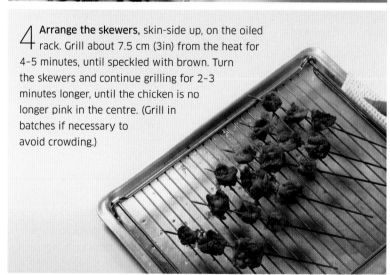

5 **Arrange the chicken skewers** on a warmed serving platter, decorate with the reserved coriander leaves and serve with the sauce. Serve with Cucumber-chilli salad (see p95) for a burst of refreshing heat.

Borscht

THE CLASSIC SOUP of Eastern Europe. During a spell of cold weather, there is little that can be more cheering on the dinner table than a bowl of this startlingly bright, deep pink broth with its hearty and warming flavours.

SERVES	PREP	COOK
SERVES 8–10	50–55 MINS	1–1¼ HRS

Ingredients

6 raw beetroot

60g (2oz) butter

2 small carrots, chopped

2 small onions, chopped

1 small white cabbage, cored and shredded

2 x 400g (14oz) cans chopped tomatoes

2 litres (3½ pints) chicken stock or water, plus more if needed

salt and pepper

1 tsp sugar, or to taste

leaves from 3–4 dill sprigs, finely chopped

leaves from 3–4 parsley sprigs, finely chopped

juice of 1 lemon

2–3 tbsp red wine vinegar

125ml (4fl oz) soured cream

PREPARE THE BEETROOT

1 **Trim and wash the beetroot.** Never peel beetroot before cooking because they 'bleed'. Bring to a boil in a pan of salted water. Cook for about 30 minutes, until tender when tested with the tip of a knife.

2 **Drain the beetroot.** When cool enough to handle, peel off the skin and grate the flesh on to a plate, using the coarse side of a box grater. (You may want to wear kitchen gloves for this, to avoid staining your fingers with beetroot juice.)

MAKE THE BORSCHT

3 **Melt the butter** in a large saucepan. Add the carrots and onions and cook, stirring, for 3–5 minutes, until soft but not brown. Add the cabbage, beetroot, tomatoes, stock, salt, pepper, and sugar to taste, and bring to a boil. Simmer for 45–60 minutes. Taste for seasoning and add more stock if the soup is too thick.

4 **Just before serving,** stir in the herbs, lemon juice, and red wine vinegar, and taste for seasoning. Pour the soup into warmed bowls and top each with a spoonful of the soured cream.

Cheese gougères with salmon

TRADITIONAL IN BURGUNDY, so a glass of white Burgundy is the perfect accompaniment! Here, smoked salmon and spinach gives the puffs a luxurious edge. You will need to make a choux pastry, which is a useful skill. Don't be put off; it's easy as long as you follow the steps carefully. You'll find that, once mastered, you will make choux pastry often for both sweet and savoury dishes.

SERVES	PREP	COOK
SERVES 8	40-45 MINS	30-35 MINS

Ingredients

FOR THE CHOUX PASTRY

75g (2½oz) unsalted butter cut into small pieces, plus more for the baking sheets

1¼ tsp salt

150g (5½oz) plain flour, sifted

5-6 eggs

125g (4½oz) Gruyère cheese, grated

FOR THE FILLING

1kg (2¼lb) fresh spinach

30g (1oz) butter

1 onion, finely chopped

4 garlic cloves, finely chopped

1 pinch of ground nutmeg

salt and pepper

250g (9oz) cream cheese

175g (6oz) smoked salmon, sliced into strips

4 tbsp milk

MAKE THE CHOUX PASTRY

1 **Butter 2 baking sheets** and preheat the oven to 190°C (375°F/Gas 5). Melt the butter in a saucepan with 250ml (8fl oz) water and ¾ tsp salt. Bring just to a boil. Remove from the heat and vigorously beat in the flour all at once, until the mixture is smooth and pulls away from the pan.

2 **Return the pan to the stove** and beat over a very low heat to dry out the dough, about 30 seconds. Remove from the heat. Add 4 of the eggs, one at a time, beating well after each. Beat the fifth egg; add it gradually until the choux is shiny and soft. Lift some of the mixture on a wooden spoon held over the saucepan; it should fall off by a count of three.

3 **Add half the Gruyère** to the mixture and stir it into the choux until thoroughly mixed.

4 **Using 2 spoons,** drop eight 6cm (2½in) mounds of dough on to the baking sheets, leaving room for the dough to puff as it bakes.

GLAZE AND BAKE THE CHOUX PASTRY

5 Lightly beat the remaining egg with the remaining ½ tsp salt. Brush some glaze over each of the choux puffs. Sprinkle the remaining cheese over the puffs. Bake in the oven for 30-35 minutes, until firm and brown.

6 With a palette knife, carefully remove the cheese puffs from the baking sheets and transfer them to a wire rack. Using a serrated knife, slice the top off each puff and leave them to cool for 5-10 minutes.

MAKE THE FILLING AND FILL THE PUFFS

7 Discard the tough ribs and stalks from the spinach, then wash the leaves thoroughly. Bring a large saucepan of salted water to a boil. Add the spinach and simmer for 1-2 minutes, until tender. Drain the spinach, rinse with cold water and drain again. Squeeze the cooked spinach in your fists to remove excess water, then finely chop.

8 Melt the butter in a frying pan. Add the onion and cook for 3-5 minutes, until soft but not brown. Add the garlic and nutmeg, salt and pepper to taste, and the spinach. Continue cooking, stirring occasionally, for about 5 minutes longer, until any remaining liquid has evaporated. Make sure that the garlic is not browning; if it does, its slightly bitter taste will then spoil the flavour of the dish.

9 Add the cream cheese to the spinach and stir until it has melted and the mixture is thoroughly and evenly combined. Remove the frying pan from the heat. Add the smoked salmon and pour in the milk. Stir thoroughly, heat for 1-2 minutes until piping hot, then taste the sauce for seasoning.

10 Mound 2-3 spoonfuls of the filling in each cheese puff, making sure to distribute it evenly between the portions. Rest the lid against the side of each filled puff and serve at once, before the choux pastry absorbs the liquid and becomes soft.

Blini with smoked salmon

BLINI ARE RUSSIAN PANCAKES, with a lightness and nutty flavour from buckwheat flour. Soured cream is the mandatory and delicious traditional accompaniment, but you can add melted butter, too, if you like, for an even richer version.

SERVES	PREP	COOK
SERVES 8	25–30 MINS	8–16 MINS

Ingredients

FOR THE BLINI

250ml (8fl oz) milk, plus more if needed

1½ tsp dried yeast or 9g (⅓oz) fresh yeast

60g (2oz) plain flour

100g (3½oz) buckwheat flour

½ tsp salt

2 eggs

60g (2oz) butter, plus more if needed

2 tbsp soured cream

FOR THE CONDIMENTS

2–3 tbsp capers, drained

1 small red onion, very finely diced

8 radishes, thinly sliced

175g (6oz) sliced smoked salmon

175ml (6fl oz) soured cream, to serve

125g (4½oz) butter, to serve (optional)

MAKE THE BLINI BATTER

1 **Pour three-quarters of the milk** into a saucepan and bring just to a boil over a medium heat. Let the milk cool to lukewarm. Meanwhile, sprinkle or crumble the yeast over 4 tbsp lukewarm water in a small bowl and let stand until dissolved, about 5 minutes.

2 **Sift the flours** and salt into a large bowl. Using your fingers, make a well in the centre. Add the yeast mixture and the lukewarm milk to the well. Stir the mixture with a wooden spoon, gradually drawing the flour into the centre, then beat to make a smooth batter, about 2 minutes.

3 **Dampen a tea towel** and cover the bowl. Transfer to a warm place and let the batter rise for 2–3 hours, until it is light and full of bubbles.

PREPARE THE CONDIMENTS

4 **Coarsely chop the drained capers** if they are large. Transfer them to a small serving bowl. Put the onion and radish in separate serving bowls. Cover all the bowls. Arrange the slices of smoked salmon on a serving plate and cover. Keep everything in the refrigerator until ready to serve.

COOK THE BLINI

5 **Preheat the oven** to low for keeping the blini warm. Separate the eggs. Melt half the butter in a small saucepan and cool slightly. Pour the remaining milk into the risen batter and stir until mixed. Stir in the egg yolks, melted butter, and soured cream. Add more milk if necessary so the consistency is that of double cream.

6 **Put the egg whites** into a metal bowl and beat until stiff peaks form. Add about one-quarter to the blini batter and gently stir until thoroughly mixed together. Pour the batter and egg-white mixture into the metal bowl with the remaining beaten egg whites. Fold together gently until everything is thoroughly blended.

7 **Heat half the remaining butter** in a frying pan. Ladle in the batter to make 7.5cm (3in) rounds, being sure not to overcrowd the pan. Cook for 1–2 minutes, until the undersides are lightly browned and the tops are bubbling. Turn them over and brown the other side. Transfer to a heatproof plate, overlapping them so they remain moist, and keep warm in the oven while you make the rest, adding more butter to the pan as needed.

8 **Melt the butter for serving**, if using. Arrange the blini on a serving plate with the capers, onions, radishes, and smoked salmon. Serve a bowl of soured cream separately and a bowl of melted butter if you like.

VARIATION: Blini with red and black caviar

Choose lumpfish or beluga caviar, depending on your budget.

1 Make the blini batter as directed in the main recipe. Omit the capers, red onion, radishes, and smoked salmon accompaniments for this version of the dish.

2 Hard-boil 2 eggs and leave to cool. Peel the eggs then separate the yolks and whites; finely chop them both. Trim 2 spring onions and cut the green tops into thin diagonal slices.

3 Finish the batter and cook the blini as directed. Serve them with 30g (1oz) each red and black caviar (or more to taste), egg yolks and whites, spring onion slices, and a spoonful of soured cream.

Stuffed vine leaves (dolmades)

FROM GREECE, this is one of the great first courses. If you find fresh vine leaves, they must be steamed or blanched before use. More likely you will find them, year round, either canned, vacuum-packed, or bottled in brine. All work well here.

SERVES SERVES 8	**PREP** 40–45 MINS PLUS MARINATING	**COOK** 45–60 MINS

Ingredients

60g (2oz) pine nuts

200g (7oz) long-grain rice

175ml (6fl oz) olive oil

2 onions, diced

45g (1½oz) sultanas

1 bunch of dill, leaves coarsely chopped, plus a few sprigs to serve

1 small bunch of mint, leaves coarsely chopped, plus a few sprigs to serve

juice of 2 lemons

salt and pepper

40 vine leaves packed in brine, plus more if needed

750ml (1¼ pints) chicken stock or water, plus more if needed

MAKE THE STUFFING

1 **Preheat the oven** to 190°C (375°F/Gas 5). Toast the pine nuts on a baking sheet for 5–8 minutes, until lightly browned, stirring occasionally. Take care not to let them burn.

2 **Bring a saucepan** of salted water to a boil. Add the rice and bring back to a boil. Simmer for 10–12 minutes, until just tender. Stir occasionally to prevent the rice from sticking. Drain the rice in a sieve, rinse with cold water to wash away the starch and drain again thoroughly.

3 **Heat one-third of the oil** in a large saucepan. Add the onions and cook for 3–5 minutes, until soft but not brown. Stir in the rice, toasted pine nuts, sultanas, herbs, and a quarter of the lemon juice. Season and taste; it should be highly seasoned at this stage as the flavours will mellow during cooking.

STUFF THE VINE LEAVES

4 **Bring a saucepan** of water to a boil. Put the vine leaves in a large bowl and cover them generously with the boiling water. Separate them with a wooden spoon, so they do not stick together. Let the leaves stand for about 15 minutes, or according to the package directions, to rinse off most of the brine in which they were packed. Stir occasionally, to make sure they are not sticking together. Drain in a colander, rinse under cold running water, then drain again thoroughly.

5 **Gently place the vine leaves** in layers between sheets of kitchen paper and pat gently to dry. Spread about 8 over the bottom of a sauté pan.

6 **Spread 1 vine leaf** flat on a work surface, vein-side up, stem end towards you. Put 1–2 spoonfuls of the rice stuffing in the centre.

7 **Fold the sides** and stem end over the stuffing. Starting at the stem end, roll up the leaf away from you into a neat cylinder. Repeat with the remaining leaves and stuffing.

8 Pack the stuffed leaves tightly, in a single layer, in the sauté pan and pour over the stock. Add half the remaining oil and half the remaining lemon juice. Cover with a heatproof plate to weigh the leaves down for even cooking. Bring to a boil on top of the stove, then cover the pan with its lid and simmer over low heat, 45–60 minutes. Check every now and then to make sure the pan does not dry out, adding a splash of water if it looks as though it might.

9 Pierce the leaves with a skewer or sharp knife; they should be very tender and offer no resistance. Let them cool in the pan, then transfer to a non-metallic dish with a slotted spoon. Spoon over any remaining cooking liquid, cover and marinate in the refrigerator for at least 12 hours so the flavours can mellow.

10 Set the stuffed vine leaves on a serving platter, bring to room temperature, and spoon over the remaining olive oil and lemon juice cooking liquid. Garnish with the reserved dill and mint sprigs. Let your guests help themselves.

 VARIATION: Lamb and rice stuffed vine leaves

Minced lamb adds substance and a simple yogurt and mint sauce piquancy to this recipe.

1 Omit the pine nuts, fresh dill, and sultanas from the stuffing. Cook 150g (5½oz) rice as directed. Sauté the chopped onions in 4 tbsp olive oil. Add 375g (13oz) minced lamb to the softened onions and cook, stirring, for 5–7 minutes, until it loses its pink colour.

2 Chop the leaves from a large bunch of mint. Stir the rice, mint, juice of ½ lemon, ½ tsp ground cinnamon, a pinch of ground nutmeg, salt, and pepper into the lamb mixture.

3 Stuff the vine leaves as directed. Cook, using water instead of chicken stock. Serve warm, with a plain yogurt and chopped mint sauce. Garnish with fresh mint, if you like.

Herbed salmon cakes

THIS IS AN EXCELLENT WAY to use up leftover cooked fish. A tangy sweetcorn relish is the perfect foil to the richness of the salmon. This recipe does not include mashed potato; instead, breadcrumbs bring the mixture together and make the cakes a light and airy start to any meal. Vary the herbs, to taste.

SERVES
SERVES 8

PREP
35–40 MINS

COOK
15–20 MINS

Ingredients

FOR THE RELISH

500g (1lb 2oz) canned or frozen sweetcorn, drained

1 onion, finely chopped

1 celery stick, peeled and thinly sliced

1 green pepper, diced

125ml (4fl oz) olive oil

1 tbsp caster sugar

1 tsp mustard powder

salt and pepper

75ml (2½fl oz) red wine vinegar

FOR THE SALMON CAKES

butter, for the baking dish and foil

2 lemons

1kg (2¼lb) salmon fillet

175ml (6fl oz) fish stock or water, plus more if needed

4 slices of white bread

leaves from a small bunch of parsley, chopped

leaves from a small bunch of dill, chopped

4 tbsp mayonnaise

salt and pepper

2 eggs

4 tbsp vegetable oil

MAKE THE RELISH AND SALMON CAKE MIXTURE

1 **Put the sweetcorn,** onion, celery, and pepper in a large bowl and mix thoroughly. Take a look at the mixture and decide whether you would like more of any of the vegetables, to taste.

2 **Put the oil,** sugar, and mustard powder in a medium bowl with salt and pepper. Pour in the vinegar. Whisk together and pour this over the vegetables. Toss to mix thoroughly and season to taste. Cover and let stand at room temperature for 2–4 hours, to let the flavours combine and mellow and the dressing infuse the vegetables.

3 **Preheat the oven** to 180°C (350°F/Gas 4) and butter a baking dish. Squeeze the juice from 1 lemon. Remove the skin from the salmon, then rinse in cold water and pat dry. Arrange in a single layer in the dish. Sprinkle with the lemon juice, salt, and pepper. Add enough stock or water to half cover. Brush a little butter over a piece of foil and use to cover the salmon. Seal the foil to the sides of the baking dish. Poach in the heated oven for 15–20 minutes.

4 **Meanwhile,** trim and discard the crusts from the bread. Put the slices in a food processor and pulse-blend until they form even-sized crumbs.

5 **Test if the salmon is cooked**: it should just flake easily when pierced with a fork. Remove from the oven; reduce the oven temperature to its lowest setting. Drain the salmon and flake with 2 forks. Pick over with your fingers, making sure there are no small bones. Transfer the flaked salmon to a large bowl.

6 **Add the breadcrumbs,** herbs, and mayonnaise, and season. Stir gently but thoroughly. Lightly beat the eggs. Add them to the salmon mixture and stir to combine. To test for seasoning, heat 1 tbsp oil in a frying pan and fry a little piece of the mixture until brown on both sides. Taste, then adjust the seasoning of the remaining mixture if necessary.

SHAPE AND COOK THE SALMON CAKES

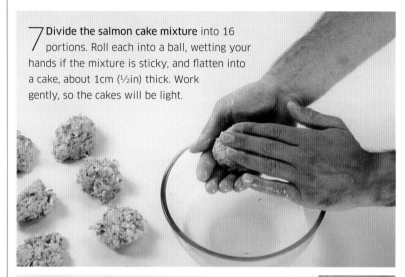

7 **Divide the salmon cake mixture** into 16 portions. Roll each into a ball, wetting your hands if the mixture is sticky, and flatten into a cake, about 1cm (½in) thick. Work gently, so the cakes will be light.

8 **Heat the remaining oil** in a frying pan. Add a batch of salmon cakes to fill the pan without overcrowding. Fry over medium-high heat for 3–4 minutes, until golden. Carefully turn over each cake with a palette knife and brown the other side.

9 **Line a heatproof plate** with kitchen paper and transfer the cooked salmon cakes to the plate to drain off any excess oil. Pat the tops of the cakes with kitchen paper, too, so each remains as light and grease-free as possible. Keep warm in the oven while cooking the remaining cakes. Work as quickly as possible as you finish frying the cakes, so the delicate insides of the cooked cakes do not dry out, or the cakes become tough on the outside, before you're ready to eat. Make sure your oven is on its lowest possible setting, as fierce heat at this stage will spoil the cakes. Cut the second lemon into wedges for serving.

10 **Stir the sweetcorn relish** to evenly amalgamate all the flavours and distribute the dressing, then divide it between 8 warmed plates and serve 2 salmon cakes on each, with a lemon wedge. Alternatively, serve all the salmon cakes together on a warmed platter, and the sweetcorn relish and lemon wedges in bowls on the side, and allow your diners to help themselves to everything.

 VARIATION:
Maryland crab cakes

Fresh or canned crab work equally well in this recipe.

1 Prepare the sweetcorn relish as directed, replacing the green pepper with a red pepper.

2 Omit the salmon fillets. Pick over 1kg (2¼lb) crab meat with your fingers, discarding any cartilage or shell. Work carefully, as any hard matter in the crab mixture will spoil the dish. Prepare the crab mixture as for the salmon cakes. Divide into 16 portions. Shape the crab cakes about 1cm (½inch) thick. Fry them as directed.

3 Serve 2 crab cakes per person with the sweetcorn relish. Decorate with dill sprigs, if you like.

Chicken and cheese quesadillas

A GREAT WAY to use up cooked chicken. Mild Cheddar would make a good substitute for the traditional American Monterey Jack cheese. Don't use a strongly flavoured mature cheese, as it will upset the delicate balance of this dish.

SERVES	PREP	COOK
SERVES 8	35-40 MINS	3-6 MINS

Ingredients

FOR THE QUESADILLAS

500g (1lb 2oz) tomatoes, peeled, deseeded and chopped

2 onions, diced

salt and pepper

3 hot green chillies

4 tbsp vegetable oil, plus more if needed

4 garlic cloves, finely chopped

125ml (4fl oz) chicken stock or water

375g (13oz) cooked boneless chicken, shredded

12 flour tortillas, each about 15cm (6in) in diameter

250g (9oz) Monterey Jack cheese, grated

FOR THE GUACAMOLE

leaves from 5-7 coriander sprigs, finely chopped

1 small ripe tomato, peeled, deseeded and finely chopped

1 small onion, chopped

1 garlic clove, chopped

1 ripe avocado

2-3 drops Tabasco sauce

juice of ½ lime

COOK THE QUESADILLAS

6 **Heat the oven** to its lowest setting. Heat the remaining oil in a frying pan and add 1 tortilla. Sprinkle with about 2 tbsp grated cheese, leaving a 1cm (½in) border. Put about 2 spoonfuls of the chicken mixture on top and cook until the cheese begins to melt.

7 **Using a palette knife,** fold the quesadilla over in half to enclose the filling. Cook for 1-2 minutes, until the tortilla is crispy and golden brown.

MAKE THE GUACAMOLE AND FILLING

1 **Combine the tomatoes** with one-quarter of the chopped onion. Season to taste and set aside. Slice the stalks from 2 of the chillies; remove the cores and seeds with a teaspoon or by tapping against the work surface. Cut into thin rings and set aside. Core, seed, and dice the remaining chilli.

2 **Heat 3 tbsp of the oil** in a frying pan. Add the remaining chopped onion, garlic, and diced chilli and cook for 2-3 minutes, until the onions are soft but not brown. Add the stock and simmer for 5-7 minutes, until almost all the liquid has evaporated. Stir in the chicken and cook for 1-2 minutes. Season to taste. Transfer to a bowl and wipe the frying pan.

3 **Place the coriander,** tomato, onion, and garlic for the guacamole in a bowl and toss to combine all the flavours. It's fine to do this ahead of time, as the ingredients will only enhance each other.

4 **Cut lengthwise around the avocado.** Twist to separate each half, remove the stone and scrape the flesh into the bowl. Mash with the other ingredients. Add a pinch of salt and a few drops of Tabasco.

5 **Add the lime juice** and stir well to mix. Taste for seasoning. Cover and refrigerate until serving to allow the flavours to combine and the seasonings to infuse throughout.

8 **Turn the quesadilla** over and cook until crispy. Transfer to a heatproof plate and keep warm in the oven while cooking the remaining quesadillas, adding oil to the pan as necessary. Halve the quesadillas and serve 3 halves on each plate with the guacamole, tomato-onion garnish, and chilli rings.

 VARIATION: Pork quesadillas

Cubes of pork add body to the filling and again, this is an excellent way to use up cooked pork.

1 Prepare the filling ingredients, but omit the chicken and instead cut 500g (1lb 2oz) cooked, boneless pork into 2.5cm (1in) cubes. Use only 2 hot chillies and dice both of them. Use 60g (2oz) mild Cheddar cheese instead of Monterey Jack. Chop the leaves from 5-7 coriander sprigs quite finely and set aside.

2 Sauté all the chopped onion with the garlic and diced chillies, then add the pork and cook until browned, 3-5 minutes longer. Omit the chicken stock or water and stir in the chopped tomatoes. Continue cooking until the filling is slightly thickened, 5-7 minutes. Taste for seasoning and add salt and pepper and necessary; let cool slightly.

3 Omit the guacamole. Cook the quesadillas as directed, sprinkling each with 1-2 tsp Cheddar cheese and a pinch of chopped coriander before adding the pork filling and folding over the quesadillas. Cut into halves and serve decorated with finely sliced red onion rings and more coriander sprigs.

Parma ham pizzas

A WELCOME OPENING to any meal and enjoyed by children and adults alike. Vary the toppings as you prefer, adding sliced salami, grated Parmesan cheese, anchovies, olives, artichokes, chillies, or peppers, to taste. The dough and tomato sauce can be made up to 12 hours ahead, covered and kept refrigerated until needed.

SERVES	PREP	COOK
SERVES 8	15–20 MINS	5–10 MINS

Ingredients

FOR THE DOUGH

1½ tsp dried yeast or 9g (⅓oz) fresh yeast

375g (13oz) strong flour, plus more if needed

salt and pepper

2 tbsp olive oil, plus more for the bowl

FOR THE TOPPING

1–2 tbsp olive oil

1 small onion, diced

1 garlic clove, finely chopped

625g (1lb 6oz) tomatoes, peeled, deseeded, and chopped

1½ tbsp tomato purée

pinch of sugar

90g (3oz) Parma ham slices, cut into strips

small bunch of basil

375g (13oz) mozzarella cheese, thinly sliced

MAKE THE DOUGH

1 **Sprinkle or crumble the yeast** over 2–3 tbsp of lukewarm water in a small bowl; let stand for 5 minutes until completely dissolved and well blended. Make sure no crumbs of yeast remains on the side of the bowl, it should all be well mixed into the water. Sift the flour into a large bowl with 1 tsp salt, lifting the sieve high in the air to aerate the flour as it floats down, then add ½ tsp pepper.

2 **Make a well in the centre** of the flour and add the yeast mixture, making sure you leave none behind, 250ml (9fl oz) lukewarm water, and the oil. Work the ingredients together well with your hands, drawing in the dry ingredients from the centre until you reach the outside and all the flour is mixed into the wet ingredients.

3 **When the ingredients are combined,** continue to mix well with your hands, ensuring that there are no lumps in the mixture and that the crumbs of dough start to come together to form a ball. Empty the dough out of the bowl on to a lightly floured work surface, for kneading.

KNEAD THE DOUGH

4 **Draw in the flour** with a pastry scraper, if liked, or your hands, and work it into the other ingredients with your fingertips to form a smooth ball of dough.

5 **Peel back the dough** in one piece, then shape it into a loose ball and turn it 90 degrees. Continue kneading the dough by pushing it away from you and gathering it up into a ball, for 5–8 minutes, until it is smooth and very elastic.

6 **Lightly oil a large bowl.** Transfer the dough to the bowl, cover with cling film and let rise in a warm place for about 1 hour, until doubled in bulk. Alternatively, leave the dough to rise overnight in the refrigerator.

PREPARE THE TOPPING

7 Heat the olive oil in a small saucepan and sauté the onion and garlic for 1-2 minutes, until soft but not brown. Stir in the tomatoes, tomato purée, salt, pepper, and a pinch of sugar. Cook, stirring occasionally, for 7-10 minutes, until thick.

ASSEMBLE AND BAKE THE PIZZAS

8 Preheat the oven to 230°C (450°F/Gas 8) and place a baking sheet near the bottom. Generously sprinkle another baking sheet with flour. Knead the dough lightly to knock out the air and cut into 8 equal pieces. Lightly flour a work surface and shape 4 pieces of dough into balls.

9 Roll each ball into a 15cm (6in) round with a rolling pin, then transfer to the floured baking sheet. Fold over about 1cm (½inch) of the edge of each round with your fingertips to form a shallow rim, if you would like a deeper filling. Leave it flat if you prefer a thinner pizza.

10 Spoon half the tomato sauce on to the pizzas and arrange half the Parma ham on top. Place 2 basil leaves on each pizza and cover with half the slices of mozzarella cheese. Let stand in a warm place for 10-15 minutes, until the dough has puffed up.

11 Carefully transfer the pizzas on to the heated baking sheet and bake until the topping is lightly browned and the dough is crisp, 10-12 minutes. Shape, top, and bake the remaining 4 pizzas. Garnish with basil sprigs and serve at once.

Lemongrass chicken

A DELICIOUS WARM Southeast Asian salad. Chillies can vary wildly in strength, so choose ones as mild or as fiery as you dare! You may wish to wear kitchen gloves when slicing them, to protect your fingers from picking up their hot juices.

SERVES	PREP	COOK
SERVES 4	45-55 MINS PLUS MARINATING	10 MINS

Ingredients

FOR THE STIR-FRY

8 large skinless boneless chicken thighs, total weight about 1.15kg (2½lb)

2 stalks lemongrass, peeled and finely chopped

2 garlic cloves, finely chopped

3 tbsp fish sauce, more if needed

¼ tsp freshly ground black pepper

2 tbsp oil

2 red chillies, thinly sliced

1 tsp sugar

3 spring onions, thinly sliced

30g (1oz) roasted unsalted peanuts

FOR THE SALAD

1 small cucumber

leaves from ½ head of round lettuce

125g (4½oz) beansprouts

leaves from 1 small bunch basil, preferably Asian

PREPARE AND MARINADE THE CHICKEN

1 **Cut the chicken** into 2.5cm (1in) cubes. For the marinade, combine the lemongrass, garlic, 2 tbsp of the fish sauce, and the pepper in a large bowl and stir until well mixed. Add the chicken and toss until well coated. Cover the bowl tightly and refrigerate for at least 1 or up to 24 hours.

MAKE THE SALAD

2 **Trim the cucumber.** With a vegetable peeler, remove strips of its skin to create a striped effect. Slice in half lengthways, then slice each half finely. Arrange the lettuce, beansprouts, half the basil and the cucumber in piles on a plate. Cover tightly and chill.

MAKE THE STIR-FRY

3 **Heat a wok** over high heat until hot. Drizzle in the oil to coat the bottom and sides. Continue heating until the oil is hot. Add the chicken and marinade; stir-fry, stirring and tossing frequently, for 8-10 minutes, until the chicken is no longer pink.

4 **Add the remaining fish sauce,** the chillies, sugar, and spring onions. Stir-fry for about 1 minute. Add the remaining basil and toss quickly to mix. Taste for seasoning, adding more fish sauce, if necessary.

5 **Serve the chicken** with the salad. Invite each guest to make a bed of salad and top with chicken and a few peanuts.

Beef carpaccio

HERE, LEAN BEEF FILLET is semi-frozen so it is easy to cut into paper-thin slices, so thin, it's said, that light will shine through them. The success of the dish will depend on using the very best quality lean beef, so make friends with a butcher you can trust and don't rely on supermarket pre-wrapped meat for this recipe.

SERVES	PREP	COOK
SERVES 4	20–25 MINS PLUS FREEZING	NONE

Ingredients

500g (1lb 2oz) beef fillet

8 canned anchovy fillets

45g (1½oz) drained capers

125g (4½oz) rocket

125g (4½oz) Parmesan cheese

1 small onion, very finely diced

2 lemons

125ml (4fl oz) extra virgin olive oil, or to taste

freshly ground black pepper

PREPARE THE BEEF AND GARNISHES

1 **Wrap the beef fillet** tightly in aluminium foil. Twist the ends of the foil to seal well and form a cracker shape, then freeze for 2½–3 hours, until firm but not frozen solid.

2 **Meanwhile,** drain the anchovies and spread them out on kitchen paper. If the capers are large, coarsely chop them. Wash the rocket then dry the leaves very well with a tea towel and strip out and discard any tough stalks. Set aside.

ASSEMBLE THE CARPACCIO

3 **Take the beef** from the freezer and unwrap it. If the meat is too hard to cut, let it thaw slightly at room temperature. Using a very sharp knife, cut paper-thin slices from the fillet. Slice as much of the meat as you can; there will be a little left at the end.

4 **As you slice** the beef, arrange it, overlapping, on 4 plates. Shave over the Parmesan, using a vegetable peeler. Divide the anchovies, chopped onion, and capers between the plates. Squeeze the juice from the lemons and spoon over the beef. Sprinkle with the olive oil. Arrange the rocket on top. Serve at room temperature. Pass the pepper mill separately.

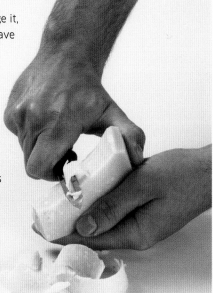

Nori-maki sushi

THE JAPANESE TERM 'SUSHI' covers a wide assortment of vinegared rice dishes. In *nori-maki*, a bamboo mat is used to roll sheets of roasted seaweed (*nori*), around a filling. Needless to say, the fish must be absolutely fresh.

SERVES	PREP	COOK
SERVES 12	50-60 MINS	12 MINS

Ingredients

FOR THE RICE

500g (1lb 2oz) short-grain white rice

75ml (2½fl oz) rice vinegar

2 tbsp caster sugar, more if needed

1 tsp salt, more if needed

FOR THE ROLLS

4 tsp wasabi powder

20cm (8in) piece of cucumber

125g (4½oz) fresh raw tuna, well chilled

6 sheets of *nori* (roasted seaweed)

TO SERVE

pink pickled ginger

Japanese soy sauce

PREPARE THE RICE

1 **Put the rice** in a bowl, cover with water, and stir until the water turns milky. Drain. Repeat until the water is fairly clear. Drain in a sieve, then put it in a saucepan. Add 600ml (1 pint) water, cover, and bring to a boil.

2 **Reduce the heat** to low and simmer until the water is absorbed and the rice is tender, about 12 minutes. Remove from the heat and let the rice stand, without lifting the lid, for about 30 minutes.

3 **Meanwhile,** in a small saucepan, combine the rice vinegar, sugar, and salt. Bring to a boil, stirring until the sugar dissolves. Let cool. Turn the hot rice into a bowl. Dampen a spatula with water. Drizzle the vinegar and sugar mixture evenly over the rice and mix together gently but thoroughly.

4 **Quickly cool the rice** to room temperature by fanning it while tossing with the spatula. Taste and add more vinegar, sugar, or salt if needed, then cover the bowl with a dampened tea towel.

PREPARE THE FILLING

5 **Put the wasabi powder** in a small bowl. Mix in 1 tbsp water to make a thick paste. Halve the cucumber lengthways and scoop out the seeds. Set one half cut-side down; cut it lengthways into 6 strips, then trim to the width of the roasted seaweed sheets. Reserve the other cucumber half for the decoration, if you like. Rinse the tuna and pat dry with kitchen paper. Cut it into 1cm (½in) slices, then into 1cm (½in) strips.

ASSEMBLE THE ROLLS

6 **Cut each sheet of seaweed** across in half with scissors. Lay one piece, smooth-side down, on a bamboo mat. Moisten your fingers, then spread about 90g (3oz) of the cooked rice in an even 5mm (¼in) layer on the seaweed, leaving a 1cm (½in) strip uncovered at the end furthest from you. Spread a thin line of wasabi lengthways along the centre of the rice. Arrange one of the cucumber strips lengthways over the wasabi paste.

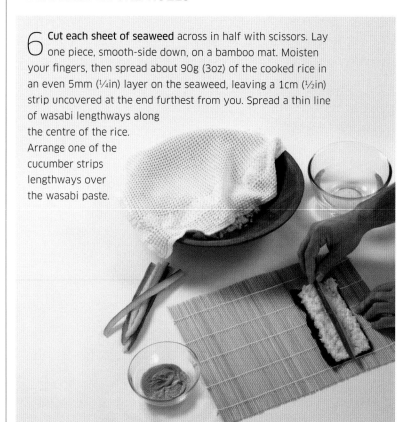

7 **Make 6 cucumber rolls:** Starting from the edge closest to you, lift the mat and seaweed securely together and roll away from you over the filling. Press down firmly and roll up the seaweed, lifting the mat at the same time.

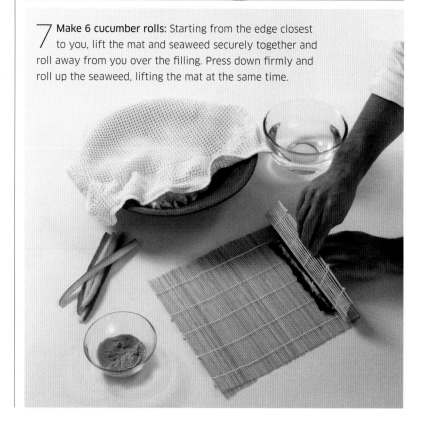

8 **Once you have reached** the exposed end of the seaweed, moisten it lightly with wet fingertips to seal the roll. Wrap and press the mat around the roll to shape a smooth, tight cylinder. Unroll the mat and transfer the cucumber roll to the chopping board. Repeat to make 5 more cucumber rolls.

9 **Make 6 tuna sushi rolls** in the same way as the cucumber rolls, piecing the tuna strips together as necessary to cover the full length of the seaweed and rice.

CUT AND SERVE

10 **Moisten a sharp knife** with a damp tea towel. Cut 1 cucumber roll into 3 equal pieces, wiping the knife clean between cuts with the damp towel. Cut each small piece of cucumber roll crosswise in half. Repeat with the remaining rolls.

11 **Cut each tuna roll** crosswise into 8 equal pieces, again wiping the knife with the damp cloth between cuts. This will help each cut be sharp and clean, to keep each roll looking pristine on its cut edges.

12 **Divide the pieces of tuna** and cucumber *nori-maki* among 12 individual serving plates, or on a large platter for the whole table of diners, setting them neatest side up.

13 **Decorate each plate** with pickled ginger, if you like, or leave it in a big pile on the table for your guests to serve themselves. Serve with Japanese soy sauce, decanted into small bowls, for dipping, and make sure you have supplied chopsticks on the table.

Salads

Fresh and light, or hearty
and filling; on the side,
or a meal in itself

Herb and flower garden salad

FEEL FREE TO TRY A NUT OIL, or a favourite vinegar, until you achieve your perfect vinaigrette. A sprinkling of edible flowers, or just their petals (make sure they are unsprayed), makes a beautiful finishing touch. Serve this during high summer.

SERVES	PREP	COOK
SERVES 8	15–30 MINS	NONE

Ingredients

FOR THE SALAD

2 heads of chicory

leaves from 1 small head of frisée

leaves from 1 head of radicchio

125g (4½oz) lamb's lettuce

125g (4½oz) rocket

1 small bunch of chives, with flowers if possible

leaves from 5–7 basil sprigs

leaves from 5–7 tarragon sprigs

1 package of edible flowers (optional)

FOR THE VINAIGRETTE

4 tbsp red wine vinegar

salt and pepper

2 tsp Dijon mustard (optional)

175ml (6fl oz) extra-virgin olive oil

PREPARE THE GREENS

1 **Using a small knife,** cut out and discard the core from the base of each head of chicory. Discard any withered leaves, and cut into 1cm (½in) diagonal slices. Put in a large bowl with the frisée, radicchio, lamb's lettuce, and rocket.

PREPARE THE HERBS AND DRESSING

2 **If the chives have flowers,** cut them 5cm (2in) below the flowers, and set aside. Snip the remaining chives into 2.5cm (1in) lengths. Add the chives, basil, and tarragon to the salad leaves.

3 **In a small bowl,** whisk the vinegar with the salt, pepper, and mustard, if using. Gradually whisk in the oil in a steady steam, until it emulsifies and thickens slightly. Taste for seasoning.

FINISH THE SALAD

4 **Briskly whisk the vinaigrette,** and pour it over the salad. Gently toss, until the greens are evenly coated. Taste the leaves, to be sure the seasoning is well-balanced.

5 **Carefully arrange any chive flowers** and other edible flowers or petals on top of the salad. Serve immediately, while the leaves and flowers are still fresh and vibrant.

Marinated goat's cheese salad

A GLASS JAR of little goat's cheeses, herbs, and chillies in golden oil is an eye-catcher in any kitchen. The goat's cheese should be firm but not dry. You'll need to begin marinading it 1 week in advance of serving, for the best flavour.

SERVES
SERVES 8

PREP
20-25 MINS
PLUS MARINATING

COOK
5-8 MINS

Ingredients

8 slices of wholemeal bread

FOR THE MARINATED GOAT'S CHEESES

4 small round goat's cheeses, each weighing about 60-90g (2-3oz) each, or 1 goat cheese log, weighing about 320g (11oz)

2 bay leaves

2-3 thyme sprigs

2-3 rosemary sprigs

2-3 oregano sprigs

2 tsp black peppercorns

2 small dried red chillies

500ml (16fl oz) olive oil, plus more if needed

FOR THE VINAIGRETTE

2 tbsp red wine vinegar

1 tsp Dijon mustard

salt and pepper

leaves from 5-7 thyme sprigs

FOR THE SALAD

2 heads chicory, leaves separated

1 oak leaf lettuce, leaves separated

MARINATE THE CHEESES

1 **Put the cheeses** in a large glass jar with the bay leaves, thyme, rosemary, oregano, peppercorns, and chillies. Add enough oil to cover generously. Cover and leave at least 1 week before using. Alternatively, if using a goat's cheese log, put it in a non-metallic bowl with the other ingredients, cover with clingfilm and marinate for 1-3 days.

MAKE THE VINAIGRETTE

2 **Remove the cheeses** from the marinade with a slotted spoon, draining off excess oil. Strain the oil. You will need 90ml (3fl oz) for the vinaigrette and a little more for the bread.

3 **Whisk the vinegar in the bowl** with the mustard, salt, and pepper. Gradually whisk in the reserved oil so the vinaigrette emulsifies and thickens slightly. Stir in half the thyme and taste for seasoning.

MAKE THE GOAT'S CHEESE TOASTS

4 **Preheat the oven** to 200°C (400°F/Gas 6). Cut each goat cheese in half horizontally. If using a goat cheese log, cut it into 8 equal slices. With a pastry cutter, cut out a round from each slice of bread.

5 **Set the bread rounds** on a baking sheet and brush with a little of the strained olive oil. Bake for 3-5 minutes, until lightly toasted. Heat the grill. Put a piece of cheese on top of each toasted bread round. Grill for 2-3 minutes, until bubbling and golden.

6 **Arrange the salad leaves** on individual plates and drizzle with the vinaigrette. Place the cheese toasts on top and sprinkle with thyme.

Tuna Niçoise salad

MADE WITH CANNED TUNA ORIGINALLY, these days using the fresh fish is far more popular. This salad is from Nice in southern France, home town of the great French chef, Escoffier, who wrote various recipes for it. The dressing can be made up to 1 week ahead and stored in a sealed jar in the refrigerator; do not add the garlic and herbs until just before using.

SERVES SERVES 6	
PREP 25–30 MINS PLUS MARINATING	
COOK 20–25 MINS	

Ingredients

FOR THE SALAD

1kg (2¼lb) potatoes

1kg (2¼lb) fresh tuna steaks

salt and pepper

375g (13oz) French beans

6 eggs

500g (1lb 2oz) tomatoes

10 anchovy fillets

125g (4½oz) black olives

FOR THE HERB VINAIGRETTE

125ml (4fl oz) red wine vinegar

2 tsp Dijon mustard

3 garlic cloves, finely chopped

375ml (12fl oz) olive oil

leaves from 7–10 thyme sprigs

leaves from 1 bunch of chervil, chopped

COOK THE POTATOES AND MAKE THE DRESSING

1 **Peel the potatoes** and, if large, cut each into 2–4 pieces. Put them in a large saucepan of cold, salted water, cover, and bring to a boil. Simmer just until tender when pierced with the tip of a knife, 15–20 minutes.

2 **Meanwhile,** make the vinaigrette. In a bowl, whisk the vinegar with the mustard, garlic, salt, and pepper. Slowly whisk in the olive oil so the dressing emulsifies and thickens slightly. Add the herbs, whisk well, and taste for seasoning.

3 **Drain the potatoes,** rinse with warm water and drain again thoroughly. Cut into chunks and put them in a large bowl. Briskly whisk the vinaigrette then spoon 75ml (2½fl oz) of it over the warm potatoes, stir, and allow to cool.

PREPARE THE TUNA

4 **Cut the tuna** into 2.5cm (1in) cubes and transfer to a shallow, non-metallic dish. Briskly whisk the herb vinaigrette dressing and pour over 75ml (2½fl oz) . Cover and refrigerate, turning occasionally, for 1 hour.

PREPARE THE SALAD

5 **Top and tail the beans.** Bring a saucepan of salted water to a boil, add the beans and cook for 5–7 minutes, until tender but still firm, then drain. Put the beans in a bowl. Whisk the remaining vinaigrette and add 3 tbsp of it to the beans. Toss them to coat.

6 **Put the eggs** in a saucepan of cold water, bring to a boil, and simmer for 10 minutes. Plunge into a bowl of cold water to cool, then shell and cut each into quarters.

PREPARE THE TOMATOES

7 **Bring a small saucepan** of water to a boil. Cut the cores from the tomatoes and score an 'X' on the base of each with a small knife.

8 **Immerse the tomatoes** in the boiling water until the skins start to split, 8–15 seconds, depending on their ripeness. Transfer them at once to a bowl of cold water.

9 **When the tomatoes** are cool, peel off the skins. Cut each tomato in half, then slice each half into 4 wedges.

ASSEMBLE THE SALAD AND **COOK** THE TUNA

10 **Drain the anchovies.** Arrange the potatoes, beans, egg, and tomato attractively on a large platter, or on individual plates if you prefer. Briskly whisk the remaining dressing and spoon most of it evenly over everything, making sure all the elements on the plate are well moistened. Do not dress the salad too far in advance or the vinegar will start to break down the tomatoes and make them mushy in texture.

11 **Heat the grill** and oil the grill rack. Put the tuna on the rack, reserving the marinade, and season the fish well. Grill the tuna about 7.5cm (3in) from the heat for about 2 minutes. Turn, baste with some of the reserved marinade and grill until lightly brown on the outside but still slightly rare in the centre, about 2 minutes longer. It is very important to retain a juicy pink centre to each tuna piece, so do not overcook or the fish will be dry and mealy in texture.

12 **Arrange the grilled tuna,** olives, and anchovy fillets attractively on top of the salad platter or the individual plates. Pour over any remaining vinaigrette and serve immediately, while the fish is still warm and all the elements of the salad remain sprightly and crisp.

Creamy coleslaw

THIS SALAD MAKES A GENEROUS QUANTITY for a party, or the recipe can easily be halved. This version of the old favourite is pepped up with caraway seeds, soured cream and mustard powder. You can make the coleslaw 2 days in advance and keep it, covered, in the refrigerator. You'll find that a generous bowlful of this on any buffet table will disappear far more quickly than you expected.

SERVES SERVES 8-10	**PREP** 15-20 MINS PLUS CHILLING	**COOK** NONE

Ingredients

FOR THE SALAD

500g (1lb 2oz) carrots

1 white cabbage, weighing about 1.4kg (3lb)

1 onion, finely diced

FOR THE SOURED CREAM DRESSING

2 tbsp sugar

salt and pepper

250ml (8fl oz) soured cream

175ml (6fl oz) cider vinegar

2 tsp mustard powder

2 tsp caraway seeds

250ml (8fl oz) mayonnaise

PREPARE THE SALAD INGREDIENTS

1 **Trim and peel the carrots.** Using the coarse side of a grater, grate them all. Leave them in a bowl of iced water for half an hour; you wil find the carrot strips will crisp up. Drain them very well, then wrap in a clean tea towel and shake to remove all the excess water.

2 **Trim the cabbage** and discard any wilted leaves. Cut it into quarters then cut out and discard the core. Shred the leaves into a large bowl using a mandoline, discarding any thick ribs. Alternatively, shred the cabbage in a food processor, using the slicing blade.

MAKE THE DRESSING

3 **Put the sugar,** salt, pepper, soured cream, and cider vinegar in a bowl. Add the mustard powder and caraway seeds. Add the mayonnaise and whisk to combine. Taste for seasoning.

4 **Put the onion,** carrot, and cabbage in a bowl, and pour the dressing over. Stir until coated. Cover and refrigerate, so the flavours mellow, for at least 4 hours. Taste for seasoning.

FINISH THE SALAD

5 **Remove the coleslaw** from the refrigerator, and stir it once more to redistribute the dressing (you may find it has sunk to the bottom of the bowl in the refrigerator). Serve chilled.

Caesar salad

THE SUCCESS OF THIS CLASSIC DISH depends on crisp cos lettuce and the best quality Parmesan cheese, while the anchovies in the dressing are essential. The garlic croutons can be made 1 day in advance and stored in an airtight container.

| **SERVES**
SERVES 6-8 | **PREP**
20-25 MINS | **COOK**
2-3 MINS |

Ingredients

FOR THE GARLIC CROUTONS

½ a day-old baguette

4 tbsp olive oil

3 garlic cloves, peeled

FOR THE DRESSING

6 anchovy fillets

3 garlic cloves, finely chopped

1 tbsp Dijon mustard

pepper

juice of 1 lemon

175ml (6fl oz) olive oil

FOR THE SALAD

1 cos lettuce, weighing about 1kg (2¼lb), leaves torn into pieces

1 egg

125g (4½oz) Parmesan cheese, freshly grated

MAKE THE GARLIC CROUTONS

1 **Cut the baguette** into 1cm (½in) slices, then into cubes. Heat the oil in a large frying pan. Add the garlic and bread and fry, stirring constantly, for 2–3 minutes, until golden. Tip the croutons on to kitchen paper to drain of any excess oil. Discard the garlic.

MAKE THE DRESSING

2 **Put the anchovy fillets** into a large salad bowl and crush them with a table fork. Add the garlic, mustard, pepper, and lemon juice and stir.

3 Gradually whisk in the oil so the dressing emulsifies and thickens slightly, and taste for seasoning.

MAKE THE SALAD

4 **Add the lettuce** to the dressing and toss until well coated. Crack the egg into a small bowl, beat it with a fork, then add it to the leaves and dressing and toss together.

5 **Add half the croutons** and two-thirds of the Parmesan and toss again. Taste a piece of lettuce for seasoning, adding salt only if necessary; the cheese and anchovies are already salty. Serve the salad directly from the bowl and pass the remaining Parmesan and croutons separately.

Roast pepper and artichoke salad

ARTICHOKE HEARTS and roasted red peppers are delicious with the crunch of pine nuts. The blue cheese wafers here add a wonderful piquancy and, once tasted, will become a favourite accompaniment to all sorts of dishes.

SERVES	**PREP**	**COOK**
SERVES 8	40-45 MINS PLUS FREEZING	25-35 MINS

Ingredients

FOR THE CHEESE WAFERS

125g (4½oz) Stilton, Danish blue, or Roquefort cheese, chilled

125g (4½oz) Cambozola or Bavarian blue cheese, chilled

125g (4½oz) butter, at room temperature

175g (6oz) plain flour

FOR THE DRESSING

4 tbsp balsamic vinegar

2 tbsp Dijon mustard

salt and pepper

175ml (6fl oz) olive oil

FOR THE SALAD

3 red peppers

60g (2oz) pine nuts

leaves from 1 head of lollo rosso

leaves from 1 round lettuce

250g (9oz) spinach leaves

180g (6oz) jar artichoke heart in oil, drained

MAKE THE CHEESE WAFER DOUGH

1 **Cut the cheeses** into chunks, discarding the rind, and allow to come to room temperature. Beat the butter in a bowl until softened, then add the blue cheese.

2 **Beat the chunks of cheese** into the butter with the wooden spoon, until they are evenly blended in and the mixture is creamy and smooth.

3 **Add the flour** and stir with a wooden spoon just until the dough comes together into a ball.

ROLL AND FREEZE THE CHEESE WAFER DOUGH

4 **Set** a 30x30cm (12x12in) piece of baking parchment on a work surface. Transfer the dough to the paper and spread it as evenly as possible along the length.

5 **Roll the paper** tightly around the dough, shaping it into a cylinder 4cm (1½in) in diameter. Twist the ends of the paper to seal. Put the dough in the freezer for 1-2 hours, until firm.

MAKE THE DRESSING

6 **Whisk the balsamic vinegar,** mustard, and salt and pepper together in a small bowl. Gradually whisk in the oil so the vinaigrette emulsifies and thickens slightly.

ROAST THE PEPPERS

7 **Heat the grill** and set the red peppers on the rack. Grill about 10cm (4in) from the heat, turning, for about 10–12 minutes, until black and blistered all over. Put them in a plastic food bag, seal, and leave until cool enough to handle.

8 **Peel off the skin,** then halve each pepper and cut out and discard the core, white pith that runs along the ribs, and seeds. Cut the flesh into even strips.

TOAST THE PINE NUTS

9 **Put the pine nuts** into a dry frying pan and place over a medium heat, shaking and watching constantly, until golden and toasted but not burned. Remove to a plate and set aside. Do not leave the pine nuts in the pan to cool, as they will continue to cook and may scorch. Any burning of the pine nuts will mar their flavour.

BAKE THE CHEESE WAFERS

10 **Preheat the oven** to 180°C (350°F/Gas 4). Cut 6 slices, each about 5mm (¼inch) thick, from the cheese wafer dough, using a thin-bladed knife dipped in hot water. Space out on a baking sheet. Re-wrap and return the remaining dough to the freezer.

11 **Bake the wafers** for 6–8 minutes, until lacy and golden brown. Allow to cool slightly, then carefully transfer to a wire rack lined with kitchen paper. Allow the baking sheet to cool, slice more of the dough, and continue baking the cheese wafers.

ASSEMBLE AND SERVE THE SALAD

12 **Put all the leaves** in a large salad bowl and add the peppers. Toss with the vinaigrette and sprinkle with pine nuts. Top with the artichoke hearts, arrange a few wafers on top and serve the rest alongside.

Greek salad

A CLASSIC, DEEPLY REFRESHING combination that needs very ripe, flavourful tomatoes. Make sure you use very tasty, pungent black olives, and an aromatic, strong extra-virgin olive oil for the dressing, for the best results.

SERVES	PREP	COOK
SERVES 6-8	25-30 MINS PLUS STANDING	NONE

Ingredients

FOR THE HERB VINAIGRETTE

3 tbsp red wine vinegar

salt and pepper

125ml (4fl oz) extra-virgin olive oil

leaves from 3-5 mint sprigs, finely chopped

leaves from 3-5 oregano sprigs, finely chopped

leaves from 7-10 parsley sprigs, finely chopped

FOR THE SALAD

2 small cucumbers

1kg (2¼lb) tomatoes

1 red onion

2 green peppers, cored, deseeded, and diced

125g (4½oz) Kalamata or other Greek olives

175g (6oz) feta cheese, cubed

MAKE THE HERB VINAIGRETTE

1 Whisk together the vinegar, salt, and pepper. Gradually whisk in the oil so the vinaigrette emulsifies and thickens slightly. Add the herbs, then whisk again and taste for seasoning.

PREPARE THE CUCUMBER

2 Peel the cucumbers and cut each in half lengthways. Scoop out the seeds with a teaspoon. Discard the seeds.

3 Cut them lengthways into 2-3 strips, then into 1cm (½in) slices.

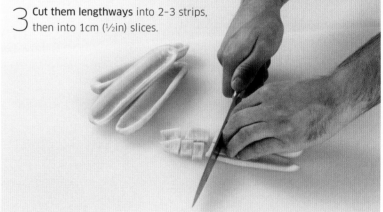

PREPARE THE OTHER VEGETABLES

4 With the tip of a small knife, core the tomatoes. Cut each one into 8 wedges, then cut each wedge in half. Peel and trim the red onion and cut into very thin rings. Gently separate the concentric circles within each ring with your fingers.

ASSEMBLE THE SALAD

5 Put the cucumbers, tomatoes, onion rings, and peppers in a large bowl. Briskly whisk the dressing, pour it over and toss thoroughly. Add the olives and feta and gently toss again. Taste for seasoning. In Greece, olives would be left whole, but you may prefer to stone them. Allow the flavours to mellow for about 30 minutes before serving.

Warm salad of wild mushrooms

WILD MUSHROOMS ARE A TRUE DELICACY
calling for the simplest preparation. To make
expensive wild mushrooms go further, you can
replace half of the amount with field mushrooms
for this salad.

SERVES	PREP	COOK
SERVES 4	25–30 MINS	8–10 MINS

Ingredients

FOR THE VINAIGRETTE

2 tbsp red wine vinegar

½ tsp Dijon mustard

salt and pepper

3 tbsp vegetable oil

3 tbsp walnut oil

FOR THE SALAD

375g (13oz) mixed wild mushrooms,
such as chanterelles, oyster mushrooms,
and ceps

30–45 g (1–1½oz) butter

2 shallots, finely diced

leaves from 1 small head of frisée

leaves from 1 small head of radicchio

75g (2½oz) rocket

leaves from 1 small bunch of
parsley, chopped

MAKE THE VINAIGRETTE

1 **In a bowl,** whisk together the vinegar, mustard, and salt and pepper.
Gradually whisk in the vegetable and walnut oils so the vinaigrette
emulsifies and thickens slightly. Taste for seasoning.

PREPARE THE MUSHROOMS

2 **Wipe the wild mushrooms** with damp kitchen
paper. Trim the stalks
and remove woody
portions.

3 **Place the mushrooms** on
a chopping board and cut
them into medium pieces.

COOK THE MUSHROOMS AND FINISH THE SALAD

4 **Heat the butter** in a frying pan until foaming. Add the shallots and cook,
stirring occasionally, for 2–3 minutes, until soft. Add the mushrooms and
salt and pepper. Cook, stirring, for 5–7 minutes, until the mushrooms are
tender and all the liquid has evaporated. Stir in the parsley and taste for
seasoning, adjusting if necessary.

5 **Briskly whisk the vinaigrette** to re-emulsify it, then pour it over the
salad leaves in a bowl and toss them well until all are coated. Taste for
seasoning. Divide the salad leaves between 4 plates and spoon over the
mushrooms from the pan. Serve at once while the salad remains crisp and
the mushrooms are still warm from the stove.

Prawn, courgette, and saffron salad

SHELLFISH AND SAFFRON have an extraordinary affinity, which is celebrated in this dish. In fact, so successful has the combination always been that a very similar recipe to this was recorded 600 years ago in Italy.

SERVES SERVES 6

PREP 30-35 MINS PLUS MARINATING

COOK 6-10 MINS

Ingredients

1 large pinch of saffron threads	salt and pepper
3 lemons	250ml (9fl oz) olive oil
6 garlic cloves, coarsely chopped	4 tbsp capers, drained
4 tbsp white wine vinegar	500g (1lb 2oz) courgettes, halved and sliced
	18 raw, unpeeled jumbo prawns

MAKE THE MARINADE AND **MARINATE** THE COURGETTES

1 **Put the saffron** in a bowl and pour over 2 tbsp hot water. Leave for 5 minutes. Squeeze in the juice from 2 of the lemons and add the garlic, vinegar, salt, pepper, olive oil, and capers. Stir, lightly crushing the capers to extract their flavour. Put the courgettes into a shallow non-metallic dish and spoon over two-thirds of the marinade. Toss, cover and refrigerate for 3-4 hours. Cut the remaining lemons into wedges and set aside for serving.

PREPARE AND **MARINATE** THE PRAWNS

3 **Pull out and discard** the dark intestinal vein running along the back of each prawn. Rinse the prawns under cold, running water then place on kitchen paper and pat dry.

2 **Hold each prawn,** underside-up, on a chopping board. Leaving the tail end intact, cut each in half to open in a butterfly shape.

4 **Put the prawns** into another non-metallic dish, spoon the remaining marinade over and toss to coat. Cover and refrigerate for 3-4 hours.

COOK THE COURGETTES AND PRAWNS

5 **Heat a frying pan,** then add the courgettes along with all their marinade. Simmer, stirring, for 3–5 minutes, just until the slices are tender but still retain a little bite. Meanwhile, heat the grill and oil the grill rack. Take each prawn from the marinade and set it, cut-side up, on the rack. Brush each with a little marinade and spoon over the capers, retaining some marinade to brush over the prawns while grilling.

6 **Grill the prawns** about 5cm (2in) from the heat for 3–4 minutes, until pink and sizzling fiercely, brushing with the reserved marinade once or twice during cooking to keep them as moist and juicy as possible. Do not overcook the prawns, or they will be tough. You will find that they cook in very little time. Slice the remaining lemon into thin wedges.

7 **Pile the warm courgettes** into the centre of 6 warmed plates, moistening them with some of the marinade, and spread them out to make an attractive bed. Arrange the hot, butterflied prawns on top and serve with the lemon wedges.

 VARIATION: Marinated prawn and mushroom salad

A simple antipasto

1 Prepare the marinade as directed, omitting the saffron. Butterfly and devein the unpeeled prawns as directed. Marinate the butterflied prawns as directed, using one-third of the marinade.

2 Omit the courgettes. Wipe the caps of 375g (13oz) button or field mushrooms, trim the stalks, and cut any large mushrooms into quarters. Bring a small pan of salted water to a boil, add the mushrooms and simmer for 5–7 minutes. Drain very well, then add the mushrooms to the remaining marinade, stir, cover, and refrigerate for 3–4 hours.

3 Using a slotted spoon, divide the mushrooms among 6 plates, discarding the marinade. Grill the prawns as directed, add to the plates and serve immediately.

Spiced seafood salad

THIS TANGY THAI DISH is light and refreshing, just perfect for summer. When served immediately, the flavour is delicate; if left overnight, it becomes a little more pungent. Choose the version that suits your palate best.

| **SERVES** SERVES 4 | **PREP** 30-40 MINS | **COOK** 12-15 MINS |

Ingredients

FOR THE SALAD

250g (9oz) small squid, cleaned

250g (9oz) large scallops, trimmed

salt

250g (9oz) boneless white fish steak or fillet

250g (9oz) raw, shelled large prawns

small lettuce leaves, to serve

FOR THE DRESSING

4 kaffir lime leaves, or finely grated zest of 1 lime

2 garlic cloves, finely chopped

1 green chilli, finely chopped

1 stalk lemongrass, peeled, crushed, and thinly sliced

juice of 3 large limes, plus more if needed

4 tbsp fish sauce, plus more if needed

2 tbsp sugar

PREPARE THE SEAFOOD

1 **Cut the squid bodies** into 1cm (½in) wide rings. Cut the tentacles into 2-3 pieces if large. Cut the scallops horizontally into 2 rounds. Line a tray with kitchen paper. Fill a large saucepan with 5cm (2in) of water, add a pinch of salt and bring to a boil. Reduce the heat, add the squid and simmer for about 2 minutes, until opaque and starting to curl. Remove and drain on the kitchen paper. Repeat with the white fish.

2 **Add the prawns** to the simmering water and cook for 1-2 minutes, or just until they turn pink. Remove and drain on the kitchen paper. Repeat with the scallop slices.

MAKE THE DRESSING AND ASSEMBLE THE SALAD

3 **Cut out any hard central veins** from the lime leaves, if necessary. Very finely dice the leaves. Put the lime leaves, garlic, chilli, lemongrass, lime juice, fish sauce, and sugar in a small bowl. Stir until the sugar dissolves.

4 **Put the squid, scallops, and prawns** in a large bowl. Pour the dressing over the seafood. Toss the mixture to coat. Remove any skin from the white fish then add it, tossing gently to break into large pieces. Taste for seasoning, adding more lime juice or fish sauce if necessary.

5 **Arrange a bed of lettuce leaves** on individual plates, then mound a pile of the dressed seafood on top.

Cucumber-chilli salad

DELICIOUS WITH GRILLED OR BARBECUED DISHES. The longer it's left to marinate, the spicier it will be, but even if you like a milder dish, do give it at least 1 hour to allow the flavours to meld. This is an incredibly useful recipe to have in your repertoire, and you may well find yourself making it all the time to accompany rich meat dishes.

SERVES	PREP	COOK
SERVES 4	15–20 MINS	NONE

Ingredients

125g (4½oz) caster sugar, or to taste

½ tsp salt, or to taste

125ml (4fl oz) rice vinegar, or to taste

1 cucumber

1 hot red chilli

MAKE THE MARINADE AND PREPARE THE CUCUMBER

1 Pour 125ml (4fl oz) water into a small pan and tip in the sugar and salt. Place over a medium heat and stir until the sugar dissolves, then bring to a boil. Remove from the heat, stir in the vinegar and let cool.

2 Peel and trim the cucumber. Cut it lengthways in half, and scoop out the seeds with a teaspoon. Cut the halves across into thin slices.

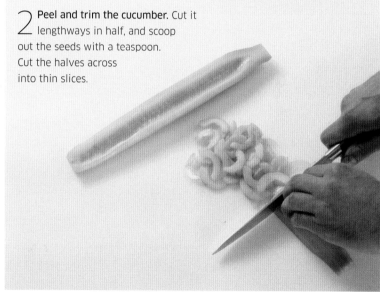

PREPARE THE CHILLI

3 Wearing rubber gloves, cut the chilli lengthways in half, discarding the core. Scrape out the seeds and cut away the fleshy white ribs from each chilli half. Cut each half lengthways into very thin strips

MAKE AND MARINATE THE SALAD

4 Combine the cucumber, chilli, and vinegar mixture in a bowl. Cover and marinate in the refrigerator for at least 1 and up to 4 hours. Taste just before serving, adding more salt, sugar, or vinegar to taste.

Melon and mint salad

THE SWEETLY KITSCH PRESENTATION used here will add fun to any summer meal. This refreshing salad, with its sweet and savoury dressing, is ideal to accompany cold meats on a picnic. It can be made up to 6 hours ahead and kept, covered and without the dressing, in the refrigerator.

SERVES SERVES 6	**PREP** 15-20 MINS, PLUS CHILLING	**COOK** NONE

Ingredients

FOR THE SALAD

2 small orange- or yellow-fleshed melons, such as cantaloupe, total weight about 1.4kg (3lb)

1 medium green-fleshed melon, such as honeydew, weighing about 1.4kg (3lb)

375g (13oz) cherry tomatoes

1 bunch of mint

FOR THE DRESSING

75ml (2½fl oz) port

juice of 2 lemons

2 tbsp honey

salt and pepper

PREPARE THE MELONS

1 **Halve the melons,** scoop out the seeds with a spoon and discard.

2 **Using a melon baller,** cut balls from the flesh of each melon into a large bowl.

PREPARE THE SALAD INGREDIENTS

3 **Remove the stalks** from the cherry tomatoes. Immerse in a saucepan of boiling water very briefly, just until the skins start to split, then plunge into a bowl of cold water. When cold, peel off the skins. Add the tomatoes to the melon.

4 **Strip the mint leaves** from the stalks, reserving some sprigs for garnish. Pile the mint leaves on a board and coarsely chop. Add the mint to the melon and tomatoes.

MAKE THE DRESSING AND DRESS THE SALAD

5 **Put the port** in a bowl. Add the lemon juice, honey, salt, and pepper and whisk. Taste for seasoning. Pour the dressing over the melon, tomatoes, and mint. Stir gently, and taste for seasoning, adding more of any of the dressing ingredients if you like. Cover the bowl and refrigerate, so the flavours mellow, about 1 hour. Serve in melon shells for extra kitsch value, or in pretty bowls, decorated with the reserved mint sprigs.

Avocado, grapefruit, and Parma ham

GREAT FLAVOUR AND TEXTURE contrasts, with the sweet and silky Parma ham against the bitter rocket and sharp grapefruit. As ever when using avocado, be sure it is completely covered with citrus juice – in this case, grapefruit – to prevent any unattractive discolouration.

SERVES
SERVES 4

PREP
25–30 MINS

COOK
NONE

Ingredients

FOR THE POPPY-SEED VINAIGRETTE

½ small onion

3 tbsp red wine vinegar

1 tbsp honey

½ tsp mustard powder

¼ tsp ground ginger

salt and pepper

150ml (5fl oz) vegetable oil

1 tbsp poppy seeds

FOR THE SALAD

4 grapefruit

125g (4½oz) Parma ham

2 avocados

175g (6oz) rocket leaves

MAKE THE VINAIGRETTE

1 **Grate the onion** into a bowl, add the vinegar, honey, mustard powder, ginger, salt, and pepper and whisk. Gradually whisk in the oil so the vinaigrette emulsifies and thickens slightly. Stir in the poppy seeds and taste for seasoning.

PREPARE THE GRAPEFRUIT

2 **With a vegetable peeler,** peel half of the zest from 1 grapefruit, leaving behind the white pith. Cut into very fine julienne strips. Half-fill a small saucepan with water and bring to a boil. Add the grapefruit julienne, simmer 2 minutes, drain and set aside.

3 **Slice off the top and base of the grapefruits.** Cut away the zest, pith and skin, following the curve of the fruit. Holding each grapefruit over a bowl, cut out the segments, cutting down between the membranes. Release the segments into the bowl. Discard any seeds, cover, and refrigerate.

PREPARE THE SALAD INGREDIENTS

4 **Cut the Parma ham** into 2.5cm (1in) strips, cutting off and discarding any fat from the slices. Cut lengthways around each avocado, through to the stone. Twist and pull the halves apart. With a chopping movement, embed the blade of a knife into the stone, lift it free, and discard.

5 **Peel the avocados** and slice lengthways. Brush the slices on all surfaces with grapefruit juice so they do not discolour. Be sure to be punctilious about this, to avoid any of your diners receiving an ugly, browning slice.

ASSEMBLE THE SALAD

6 **Briskly whisk the dressing.** Toss the rocket with one-third of it, taste for seasoning, then divide between 4 plates. Arrange the grapefruit, Parma ham, and avocado on top. Spoon over the remaining vinaigrette and sprinkle with grapefruit julienne.

Gado-gado

THE PEANUT SAUCE can be made spicy or sweet, as you prefer. Feel free to use this recipe as a blueprint, adding whatever fresh vegetables are in season. This is a version to make in winter, using the produce of the cooler months. The vegetables can be blanched and the peanut sauce made 1 day ahead and kept, covered, in the refrigerator.

SERVES	**PREP**	**COOK**
SERVES 8	35-45 MINS	20-25 MINS

Ingredients

FOR THE SALAD

florets from 1 small cauliflower

salt and pepper

500g (1lb 2oz) carrots, cut into 5cm (2in) batons

375g (13oz) beansprouts

300g (10oz) tofu

500g (1lb 2oz) cucumbers, cut into 5cm (2in) batons

3 eggs

1 tbsp vegetable oil

FOR THE PEANUT SAUCE

125ml (4fl oz) vegetable oil

250g (9oz) unsalted peanuts

1 onion, finely chopped

3 garlic cloves, finely chopped

½ tsp crushed chillies

1 tbsp soy sauce

juice of 1 lime

2 tsp brown sugar

200ml (7fl oz) canned coconut milk

PREPARE THE VEGETABLES AND TOFU

1 **Cut any large cauliflower** florets in half. Bring a large saucepan of salted water to a boil. Add the florets and boil for 5-7 minutes, just until tender. Drain.

2 **Put the carrots** in a saucepan of cold, salted water. Bring to a boil and simmer for 3-5 minutes, just until tender. Drain.

3 **Put the beansprouts** in a bowl. Cover with boiling water and let stand, 1 minute. Drain. Drain the tofu then cut into 1cm (½in) cubes.

MAKE THE OMELETTE

4 **Beat the eggs** and seaon to taste. Heat the oil in a frying pan. Pour in the eggs, tilting to make an even layer. Cook over medium heat for 2 minutes, until the edge is slightly crispy and pulls away from the side.

5 **Turn and cook** for about 30 seconds, until firm. Slide on to a chopping board, let it cool slightly, then roll it up loosely and cut across the width into curled strips.

MAKE THE PEANUT SAUCE

6 **Heat half the oil** in a frying pan. Add the peanuts and cook, stirring, for 3-5 minutes, until brown. Transfer to a food processor and pulse-chop until slightly chunky.

7 **Heat the remaining oil** in the frying pan and cook the onion, stirring, for 2-3 minutes, until lightly brown. Add the garlic and chillies, and cook until golden. Add the soy sauce and lime juice. Remove from the heat. Stir in the brown sugar and ground peanuts.

8 **Gradually add the coconut milk** to the peanut sauce, and stir until smooth and creamy. Season to taste. Arrange the bean sprouts on a serving platter, or on individual plates, and top with the carrots, cucumbers, tofu cubes, and cauliflower. Garnish with the omelette curls and serve the peanut sauce in a small bowl on the side.

🍲 VARIATION: Bird's nest salad with peanut sauce

Crunchy red cabbage and French beans add brilliant colour to this version of Gado-gado.

1 Omit the cauliflower, carrots, cucumbers, omelette, and tofu. Peel 500g (1lb 2oz) potatoes, cut them into even-sized chunks and add to a pan of well-salted water. Cover, and bring to a boil. Simmer for about 15 minutes until tender, drain, then cut into 1cm (1/2in) cubes. Make the peanut sauce as directed in the main recipe.

2 Trim 375g (13oz) French beans and cut them into 2.5cm (1in) slices. Cook in boiling water for 5 minutes, or until just tender, then drain very well. Trim half a head of red cabbage, cut it in half and remove the core from each piece. Set the cabbage halves cut side down on a board and finely shred. Discard any thick ribs.

3 Cook the cabbage in boiling, salted water, for 1 minute only. Drain and toss, while still hot, with 4 tbsp red wine vinegar. Prepare the beansprouts as directed in the main recipe, then divide them evenly among 8 plates. Top with the red cabbage. Arrange the French beans in the centre, then pile the potatoes on top. Add a spoonful of the peanut sauce to the potatoes, and provide the rest on the side.

Red cabbage and bacon salad

A HEARTY FIRST COURSE for winter, or a tasty lunch for 4. The contrasts in taste, texture, and colour are wonderful, especially with the addition here of crumbled, creamy blue Roquefort cheese. Just eating this salad will make you feel healthy and more invigorated.

SERVES	PREP	COOK
SERVES 6	20-25 MINS PLUS MARINATING	5 MINS

Ingredients

FOR THE VINAIGRETTE

4 tbsp red wine vinegar, plus more if needed

1 tbsp Dijon mustard

salt and freshly ground black pepper

175ml (6fl oz) olive oil

FOR THE SALAD

½ head red cabbage (about 750g/1lb 10oz), cored and finely shredded

4 tbsp red wine vinegar

250g (9oz) lardons or thick streaky bacon rashers

leaves from 1 small cos lettuce, chopped

90g (3oz) Roquefort cheese, crumbled

PREPARE THE VINAIGRETTE

1 **Combine the vinegar,** mustard, and a pinch of salt. Grind in the pepper. Gradually whisk in the oil so the vinaigrette emulsifies and thickens. Taste for seasoning.

PREPARE THE CABBAGE

2 **Transfer the shredded cabbage** to a large bowl. Boil the vinegar in a small saucepan, then pour over the cabbage and toss. Pour 2 litres (3½ pints) boiling water over and let stand for 3-4 minutes, until slightly softened. Drain thoroughly, then return it to the large bowl.

3 **Toss the cabbage** with enough vinaigrette to moisten it well. Taste for seasoning, adding more vinegar if necessary. Cover and marinate for 1-2 hours.

PREPARE THE SALAD

4 **If using bacon rashers,** cut into strips about 10 minutes before serving. Fry the lardons or bacon strips in a frying pan, stirring occasionally, for 3-5 minutes, or until crisp and the fat is rendered. Spoon the hot bacon and its pan juices over the cabbage, reserving some bacon pieces for garnish. Toss them together.

5 **Arrange a bed of lettuce** on each of 6 plates. Spoon the remaining dressing over the lettuce. Mound the red cabbage and bacon mixture over the top. Top the salads with the crumbled blue cheese and reserved bacon and serve at once.

Celeriac rémoulade with carrot salad

YOU'LL FIND THIS UNPRETENTIOUS autumn dish on the menu of every French bistro. Both salads can be prepared and tossed in their dressings up to 1 day ahead. Store them, covered, in the refrigerator. The flavours will mellow and deepen. Try chopped walnuts or apple, or even some toasted sesame seeds, in place of the raisins in the carrot salad.

SERVES	PREP	COOK
SERVES 6	25–30 MINS PLUS CHILLING	1–2 MINS

Ingredients

FOR THE CARROT SALAD

3 tbsp cider vinegar

1 tsp sugar

salt and pepper

75ml (2½fl oz) light olive oil

500g (1lb 2oz) carrots, coarsely grated

90g (3oz) raisins

FOR THE CELERIAC SALAD

1 celeriac, weighing about 750g (1lb 10oz)

175ml (6fl oz) mayonnaise

2 tbsp Dijon mustard, or to taste

MAKE THE CARROT SALAD AND DRESSING

1 Whisk the vinegar with the sugar, salt, and pepper. Gradually whisk in the oil, so the vinaigrette emulsifies and thickens slightly. Taste for seasoning. Add the carrots to the dressing, then the raisins. Toss everything together, and taste for seasoning. Cover and refrigerate for at least 1 hour.

PREPARE THE CELERIAC

2 Place the celeriac on a chopping board, and slice away all the thick, knobbly peel. Cut into thin slices, then into fine, even strips.

3 Put the celeriac strips in a saucepan of cold, salted water, and bring to a boil. Simmer for 1–2 minutes, until tender, but still retaining bite, then drain.

DRESS THE SALAD

4 Mix the mayonnaise, salt, pepper, and 2 tbsp mustard in a bowl. Taste, adding more mustard if you like. Add the celeriac, toss, then taste for seasoning. Cover, and refrigerate for at least 1 hour. Arrange the celeriac and carrot salads in individual bowls.

Spring rice salad

ASPARAGUS AND SMOKED SALMON make a perfect marriage with the sweet, aniseed taste of a tarragon dressing in this recipe. If you make this in April, when the asparagus is young and the stalks slender, they will not need to be peeled before cooking. The rice salad can be made 1 day in advance and kept, covered, in the refrigerator, but make sure it is brought to room temperature - and the rice fluffed up with a fork - before serving.

SERVES	**PREP**	**COOK**
SERVES 4-6	20-25 MINS, PLUS CHILLING	15-20 MINS

Ingredients

FOR THE SALAD

salt and pepper

1 lemon

200g (7oz) long-grain rice

250g (9oz) asparagus

3 celery sticks

250g (9oz) sliced smoked salmon

FOR THE DRESSING

3 tbsp tarragon vinegar

2 tsp Dijon mustard

175ml (6fl oz) flavourless vegetable oil

COOK THE RICE AND MAKE THE VINAIGRETTE

1 Bring a large saucepan of salted water to a rolling boil. Squeeze the juice from half the lemon into the water, then add the lemon half as well to flavour the water. Add the rice, stir and bring back to a fast boil. Simmer just until tender, stirring occasionally to separate the grains and ensure they do not stick to the base of the pan. It should take about 10-12 minutes. Taste a grain to make sure it is tender before removing from the heat. There should be no hard core in the centre.

2 Meanwhile, make the vinaigrette. Put the vinegar, salt, and pepper in a small bowl. Add the mustard and whisk together well. Gradually whisk in the oil in a thin stream so the vinaigrette emulsifies and thickens slightly. Taste for seasoning and set aside. You can make this dressing in advance and keep it, in a sealed jar in the refrigerator, for up to 1 week. Shake the jar well before using to re-emulsify the vinaigrette..

3 Drain the rice, discard the lemon half, then place in a sieve and rinse with cold water to wash away the starch and drain again thoroughly. Repeat a couple of times more. This rinsing process is very important for rice that is to be served cold, as too much starch will make the grains stick together in clumps, which are unpleasant to eat. You are aiming for fluffy clouds of rice. Transfer to a large bowl. Squeeze and reserve the juice from the remaining lemon half.

PREPARE THE ASPARAGUS

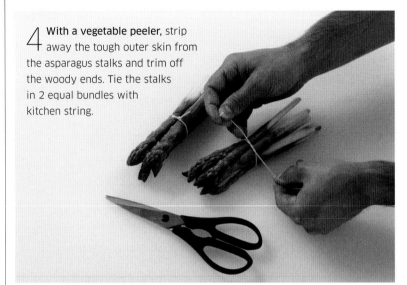

4 With a vegetable peeler, strip away the tough outer skin from the asparagus stalks and trim off the woody ends. Tie the stalks in 2 equal bundles with kitchen string.

5 Bring a large saucepan of salted water to a boil, add the asparagus and simmer for 5-7 minutes, just until tender when pierced with the tip of a small knife.

6 Drain the asparagus and discard the strings. Trim off and reserve about 5cm (2in) of the asparagus tips. Cut the stalks into 1cm (½in) pieces.

ASSEMBLE THE SALAD

7 Peel the strings from the celery sticks with a vegetable peeler, then dice each stick quite finely. Cut the smoked salmon slices into even 1cm (½in) strips.

8 Briskly whisk the vinaigrette to re-emulsify it, and pour it over the rice, reserving 1-2 tbsp. Stir the rice well to distribute the dressing evenly, and fluff it up with a fork to separate the grains. Add the asparagus, celery, smoked salmon, and reserved lemon juice.

9 Toss all the ingredients together and taste for seasoning. Cover and refrigerate for at least 1 hour to allow the flavours to mingle together. Before serving, let the rice salad come to room temperature. Brush the asparagus tips with the reserved dressing and arrange on top of the rice salad. Serve in bowls.

 VARIATION: Rice salad with smoked trout and peas

Vivid green peas and red tomatoes add colour.

1 Omit the smoked salmon and asparagus. Cook the rice and make the vinaigrette as directed. Simmer 125g (4½oz) shelled, fresh green peas or frozen peas for 3-5 minutes, just until tender. Drain.

2 Using a small knife, peel the skin from 2 smoked trout (weighing 250g/9oz each), lift off the fillets, discarding the bones, and flake the flesh, checking for any remaining small bones as you do so.

3 Cut 375g (13oz) cherry tomatoes in half. Assemble the salad as directed and taste for seasoning. Transfer to a broad, shallow serving bowl and arrange the tomatoes on top.

Festive wild rice salad

THIS TASTES EVEN BETTER after standing for a few hours, so it is an ideal buffet party dish for Christmas time. You can prepare the wild rice salad 1 day ahead and keep it, covered, in the refrigerator. Let it come to room temperature before adding the smoked turkey and serving.

SERVES SERVES 8	**PREP** 30-35 MINS PLUS STANDING	**COOK** ¾-1¼ HRS

Ingredients

FOR THE SALAD

salt and pepper

375g (13oz) wild rice

60g (2oz) pecans

375g (13oz) sliced smoked turkey breast

FOR THE CRANBERRY DRESSING

175g (6oz) fresh cranberries

50g (1¾oz) sugar

1 orange

4 tbsp cider vinegar

2 shallots, very finely chopped

125ml (4fl oz) flavourless vegetable oil

PREPARE THE RICE, CRANBERRIES, AND PECANS

1 Put 1.5 litres (2¾ pints) water in a large saucepan with 1 tsp salt and bring to a boil. Stir in the rice, cover, and simmer for about 1 hour, or until tender. Drain, cool, then tip into a large bowl.

2 Preheat the oven to 190°C (375°F/Gas 5). Spread the cranberries in a baking dish, sprinkle with sugar and bake in the heated oven for 10-15 minutes, until they start to pop. Let cool in the dish.

3 Spread the pecans on a baking sheet and bake for 5-8 minutes, stirring occasionally, until toasted, then coarsely chop.

PREPARE THE ORANGE JULIENNE

4 With a vegetable peeler, peel the zest from the orange, leaving behind the pith. Cut the zest into very fine julienne strips.

5 Bring a small saucepan of water to a boil and add the orange julienne. Simmer for 2 minutes, then drain and finely chop. Set aside. Squeeze the juice from the orange into a bowl.

PREPARE THE DRESSING AND **ASSEMBLE** THE SALAD

6 Add the vinegar, shallots, salt, and pepper to the orange juice. Gradually whisk in the oil so the dressing emulsifies and thickens slightly. Taste for seasoning. Add the cranberries, leaving their juice behind, and stir.

7 If necessary, remove the skin from the smoked turkey breast. Add the pecans, orange zest, and two-thirds of the dressing to the rice. Toss and let stand for 1 hour, for the flavours to combine. Taste for seasoning. To serve, transfer the rice salad to a platter, arrange the turkey on top and spoon over the remaining cranberry dressing.

Lacquered chicken salad

FRESH ROOT GINGER gives an Asian sparkle to this salad. When buying fresh root ginger, choose firm hands with no wrinkles and check that the broken part of the root is moist, to get the freshest specimens. If you can't find the rice wine for the marinade, use sherry instead.

SERVES	PREP	COOK
SERVES 4	25–30 MINS PLUS MARINATING	10–15 MINS

Ingredients

FOR THE SALAD

4 boneless, skinless chicken breasts, total weight about 750g (1lb 10oz)

leaves from 1 cos lettuce, shredded

125g (4½oz) bean sprouts

90g (3oz) baby sweetcorn, halved lengthways

FOR THE MARINADE AND DRESSING

1cm (½in) piece of fresh root ginger, peeled and finely chopped

1 garlic clove, finely chopped

45g (1½oz) soft brown sugar

2 tbsp Dijon mustard

3 tbsp rice wine

3 tbsp sesame oil

salt and pepper

4 tbsp soy sauce

125ml (4fl oz) vegetable oil

MARINADE THE CHICKEN

1 **Lightly score** the top of each chicken breast and set them in a shallow, non-metallic dish.

2 **Combine the ginger,** garlic, soft brown sugar, mustard, 1 tbsp each of the rice wine and sesame oil, and pepper in a bowl. Pour in the soy sauce and stir. Remove and reserve 4 tbsp, then pour the rest of the marinade over the chicken, cover, and refrigerate for 1–2 hours, turning 3–4 times.

PREPARE THE DRESSING AND BEANSPROUTS

3 **Add the remaining rice wine** and sesame oil to the reserved marinade and mix. Gradually whisk in the vegetable oil, so the dressing emulsifies and thickens slightly. Taste for seasoning and set aside, or refrigerate, tightly sealed, for up to 12 hours. Put the bean sprouts in a bowl. Cover generously with boiling water and let stand for 1 minute. Drain, rinse with cold, running water, and drain again.

GRILL THE CHICKEN AND FINISH THE SALAD

4 **Heat the grill** and oil the grill rack. Put the chicken on the rack and brush with the marinade. Grill about 7.5cm (3in) from the heat, brushing often with marinade, for 5–7 minutes, until well browned.

5 **Turn the breasts** over. Brush them with more marinade. Grill for a further 5–7 minutes, until they are well browned, glossy, and tender. Put them on a chopping board and cut diagonally into slices.

6 **Add the bean sprouts** and sweetcorn to the lettuce. Briskly whisk the dressing again and pour it over the salad. Toss and taste for seasoning. Arrange the salad attractively on a serving plate, top with the chicken, and serve while still hot.

Tortilla bean salad

A RIOT OF COLOUR with a vibrant chilli dressing. This is a Tex-Mex style of food, and best suited to the hot months of the year. You could also use black beans, for an even more dramatic-looking bowlful. Don't be too timid with the chillies, as beans can take a lot of seasoning and will soak up much of the heat. Wearing rubber gloves to prepare the chillies will protect your hands.

SERVES	PREP	COOK
SERVES 6-8	25-30 MINS PLUS CHILLING	1-1½ HRS

Ingredients

FOR THE CHILLI VINAIGRETTE

1 small bunch of coriander

125ml (4fl oz) cider vinegar

½ tsp ground cumin

3 green chillies

125ml (4fl oz) flavourless oil, plus more for tortillas and baking sheet

FOR THE SALAD

4 cobs of fresh sweetcorn, or 300g (10oz) canned, drained, or defrosted sweetcorn kernels, rinsed

1 red pepper

1 green pepper

1 yellow pepper

750g (1lb 10oz) tomatoes

2 x 400g (14oz) cans red kidney beans, rinsed

salt and pepper

6 corn tortillas

¼ tsp cayenne pepper

MAKE THE CHILLI VINAIGRETTE

1 **Strip the coriander leaves** from the stalks and finely chop them. Whisk together the vinegar, cumin, salt, and pepper.

2 **Cut the chillies** in half lengthways, discarding the cores. Scrape out the seeds and cut away the fleshy white ribs. Cut into fine dice. Add the chillies to the whisked dressing ingredients.

3 **Gradually whisk in the oil** so the vinaigrette emulsifies and thickens slightly. Stir in the coriander, reserving a little for garnish; taste for seasoning.

PREPARE THE VEGETABLES AND TOSS THE SALAD

4 **If using** fresh sweetcorn cobs, remove the husks and silks. Bring a large saucepan of water to a boil, add the sweetcorn, and cook at a lively bubble for 5-7 minutes.

5 **Lift one of the sweetcorn cobs** from the pan: it is cooked if the kernels pop out easily when tested with the point of a knife. Drain, let cool a little, and cut off the kernels. Core and seed all the peppers, and dice.

6 **Core the tomatoes** and score an "X" on the base of each. Immerse in boiling water until the skins start to split. Plunge them into cold water. Peel the tomatoes, then cut in half; squeeze out the seeds, and coarsely chop.

7 **In a large bowl,** combine the kidney beans, sweetcorn, tomatoes, peppers, and chilli vinaigrette. Gently toss the salad and taste for seasoning. Cover and refrigerate for at least 1 hour.

GRILL THE TORTILLAS AND FINISH THE SALAD

8 **Just before serving,** heat the grill and oil a baking sheet. Brush the tortillas with oil and season with salt and cayenne pepper, then slice them into triangles.

9 **Spread the tortilla triangles** on the baking sheet. Grill, 10cm (4in) from the heat, for 4-6 minutes, until golden brown and crisp, stirring occasionally so they colour evenly.

10 **Divide the salad** among 6-8 deep plates and top with the tortilla triangles. Sprinkle the reserved chopped coriander over the top, if you like. Serve chilled or at room temperature.

 VARIATION: Red bean, sweetcorn, and onion salad

With cheesy tortilla triangles.

1 Omit the peppers from the salad. Prepare the sweetcorn, tomatoes, and the chilli vinaigrette dressing as directed in the main recipe. Dice 1 large, sweet red onion. Trim and thinly slice 2 spring onions, including some of their aromatic green tops.

2 Assemble the salad as directed, cover and refrigerate for at least 1 hour. Meanwhile, heat the grill. Grate 90g (3oz) mild Cheddar cheese. Arrange 6 corn tortillas on a baking sheet. Brush them with 1 tbsp oil and grill for 2-3 minutes, until crisp.

3 Sprinkle the tortillas with the cheese, cayenne pepper, and salt and grill for 1-2 minutes, until the cheese has melted. Watch carefully so they do not scorch and blacken, as this will make them bitter. Cut each tortilla into 6 triangles. Spoon the salad on to a large serving plate and garnish with coriander leaves, if you like. Serve the crispy tortilla triangles separately.

Tabbouleh with cacik

WARMED PITTA BREAD makes a fitting and delicious accompaniment to these "mezze" salads. Mezze are little dishes of vegetables, salads, olives, and such like that are the standard opening for a meal all over the Middle East.

SERVES SERVES 6-8	**PREP** 35-40 MINS PLUS CHILLING	**COOK** NONE

Ingredients

200g (7oz) bulghur wheat

2 small cucumbers, seeded and diced

salt and pepper

500g (1lb 2oz) tomatoes, peeled, deseeded and chopped

3 spring onions, chopped

leaves from 1 bunch of parsley, chopped

juice of 3 lemons

125ml (4fl oz) olive oil

leaves from 2 bunches of mint, chopped

3 garlic cloves, finely chopped

½ tsp ground coriander

¼ tsp ground cumin

500ml (16fl oz) plain yogurt

TO SERVE

125g (4½oz) black olives

6-8 pitta breads

PREPARE THE SALAD AND CACIK INGREDIENTS

1 **Put the bulghur** in a large bowl and pour over enough cold water to cover generously. Let soak for 30 minutes, then drain through a sieve and squeeze out any remaining water with your fist.

2 **Put the cucumber** in a colander, sprinkle with salt and stir to mix. Leave it for 15-20 minutes, to draw out the bitter juices, then rinse under cold, running water. Let drain.

MAKE THE TABBOULEH AND CACIK

3 **For the tabbouleh,** in a large bowl, combine the bulghur, tomatoes, spring onions, parsley, lemon juice, olive oil, two-thirds of the mint, and plenty of salt and pepper. Mix and taste for seasoning then cover and chill in the refrigerator for at least 2 hours.

4 **Make the cacik:** put the cucumbers in a bowl and add the garlic, remaining mint, ground coriander, ground cumin, salt, and pepper. Pour in the yogurt. Stir to combine and taste for seasoning. Chill in the refrigerator, to allow the flavours to blend, for at least 2 hours.

5 **Warm the pitta breads** in a low oven for 3-5 minutes, then remove and cut into strips. Take the salads from the refrigerator and allow to come to room temperature, then arrange them in separate bowls with the warm pitta bread fingers alongside.

Pear, fennel, and walnut salad

GORGONZOLA DRESSING CONTRASTS well with the sweet pears and aniseed flavor of the fennel. This salad really needs to be assembled right at the last minute, to retain the freshness and vibrancy of the pears and walnuts.

SERVES SERVES 6	**PREP** 30-35 MINS	**COOK** NONE

3 ripe pears	
1 lemon	

Ingredients

FOR THE SALAD

60g (2oz) walnut pieces

1 large fennel bulb

FOR THE DRESSING

125g (4½oz) Gorgonzola cheese

4 tbsp red wine vinegar

salt and pepper

75ml (2½fl oz) olive oil

TOAST THE WALNUTS AND MAKE THE DRESSING

1 **Preheat the oven** to 180°C (350°F/Gas 4). Spread the walnuts on a baking sheet and toast them in the heated oven for 5–8 minutes until crisp, stirring occasionally so they toast evenly.

2 **Cut the rind** from the Gorgonzola and crumble with your fingers or crush with the tines of a fork. Put two-thirds into a bowl, add the red wine vinegar, salt and pepper, and whisk together.

3 **Gradually whisk in the oil** so the dressing emulsifies and thickens slightly. Stir in the remaining cheese so a few larger pieces are left intact, and taste for seasoning. Cover and chill in the refrigerator.

PREPARE THE FENNEL

4 **Trim the stalks**, root end, and any tough outer pieces from the fennel. Reserve any fronds for decoration. Cut the fennel bulb in half lengthways.

5 **Set each fennel** half flat-side down on the chopping board and slice it lengthways.

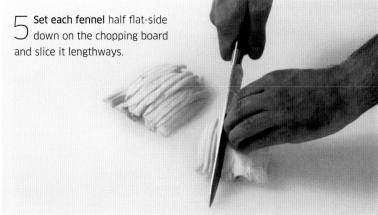

PREPARE THE PEARS

6 **Peel the pears,** halve lengthways, and remove the core. Set each half cut-side down and cut lengthways into thin slices. Cut the lemon in half and squeeze lemon juice over the pear slices, tossing to coat.

7 **On individual plates,** arrange the pear and fennel slices and spoon on the Gorgonzola dressing. Scatter some toasted walnuts over each serving and decorate with fennel fronds

Salade Lyonnaise

A DRESSING OF RED WINE VINEGAR and bacon enlivens this warm spinach salad. It is a favourite in Lyon, which claims to be the gastronomic capital of France. For a more substantial dish, top with a warm poached egg, breaking the yolk into the dressing as you eat.

SERVES	PREP	COOK
SERVES 6	30–35 MINS	20–25 MINS

Ingredients

FOR THE CROUTES

½ baguette

3 tbsp olive oil

1 garlic clove

FOR THE SALAD

2 eggs

500g (1lb 2oz) fresh spinach

250g (9oz) lardons or streaky bacon rashers, chopped

75ml (2½fl oz) red wine vinegar

MAKE THE CROUTES

1 **Preheat the oven** to 200°C (400°F/Gas 6). Cut the baguette into 5mm (¼in) slices. Brush both sides of each slice with oil and set on the baking sheet. Bake for 7–10 minutes, until toasted and golden brown, turning once.

2 **Cut the garlic clove** in half. Rub one side of each slice of bread with the cut side of the garlic. Set the croutes aside.

PREPARE THE SALAD INGREDIENTS

3 **Hard-boil and shell** the eggs. Tear the spinach leaves into large pieces and put in a bowl. Separate the egg yolks from the whites by gently pulling the whites apart. Chop the whites. Put the yolks in a sieve set over a bowl; work them through with the back of a metal spoon.

DRESS THE SALAD

4 **Heat a frying pan,** add the bacon and cook, stirring, for 3–5 minutes, until it is crisp and the fat is rendered. Add to the spinach and toss vigorously for 30 seconds, until the spinach is slightly wilted.

5 **Pour the vinegar** into the frying pan. Bring it to a boil, stirring, and boil it for about 1 minute, until reduced by one-third. Pour over the spinach and bacon and toss together well.

6 **Pile the salad** on to 6 individual plates. Sprinkle each serving evenly with the chopped egg white and sieved yolk, and serve at once, with a pile of the croutes on the side.

Waldorf chicken salad

A CONTEMPORARY TAKE ON A CLASSIC, with yogurt in the dressing for lightness. This salad is a great way to use up leftover roast chicken, which saves poaching the chicken breasts. The recipe can be made up to 6 hours ahead and kept, covered, in the refrigerator. Be sure to bring it back up to room temperature before serving.

SERVES	PREP	COOK
SERVES 6	25–30 MINS PLUS CHILLING	25–35 MINS

Ingredients

FOR THE POACHING LIQUID

4 celery sticks, with leaves if possible

1 onion, peeled and quartered

1 carrot, peeled and quartered

10–12 black peppercorns

1 bouquet garni, made with 5–6 parsley stalks, 2–3 thyme sprigs, and 1 bay leaf

FOR THE SALAD

4 skinless, boneless chicken breasts, total weight about 750g (1lb 10oz)

125g (4½oz) walnut pieces

500g (1lb 2oz) tart, crisp apples

juice of 1 lemon

175ml (6fl oz) plain yogurt

175ml (6fl oz) mayonnaise

salt and pepper

POACH THE CHICKEN

1 **Trim the tops** and leaves from the celery (reserve the sticks), and put the trimmings in a wide, shallow pan with the onion, carrot, peppercorns, bouquet garni, and salt. Bring to a boil and simmer for 10–15 minutes. Add the chicken and simmer for a further 10–12 minutes, turning once, until the juices run clear when the meat is pierced at its thickest point.

2 **Remove from the heat,** and cool the chicken in the poaching liquid for 10–15 minutes, then put on kitchen paper to drain. With your fingers, pull the chicken into slivers about 5cm (2in) long. The meat will be juicier than if you were to cut it.

PREPARE THE SALAD

3 **Preheat the oven** to 180°C (350°F/Gas 4). Spread the walnut pieces on a baking sheet and bake for 5–8 minutes, until crisp, stirring occasionally so that they toast evenly. Peel and slice the celery sticks.

4 **Cut the top** and bottom ends from the apples, halve, core, then dice the flesh. Put in a large bowl, pour over the lemon juice, and toss to coat. Add the chicken, celery, yogurt, mayonnaise, and two-thirds of the walnuts, to the apple. Season and stir until combined. Taste for seasoning, cover, and chill for 1 hour. Coarsely chop the remaining walnuts. Spoon the salad into individual bowls, and sprinkle with the reserved walnuts.

Asian noodle salad

A FANTASTIC SPICY DRESSING really lifts this dish. Use this recipe as a blueprint: omit the prawns and add tofu if you have vegetarian guests, or replace the prawns with cooked chicken, pork, ham, or spicy Chinese sausage to ring the changes. This is a very convenient dish, as the flavours only benefit from getting to know each other in the refrigerator for up to 1 day.

SERVES	PREP	COOK
SERVES 6	30–35 MINS PLUS MARINATING	6–9 MINS

Ingredients

FOR THE DRESSING	FOR THE SALAD
2cm (¾in) piece of fresh root ginger	250g (9oz) thin egg noodles
2 fresh green chillies	175g (6oz) mangetout
2 garlic cloves	4 spring onions
2 tsp sugar	75g (2½oz) roasted unsalted peanuts
salt and pepper	1 small bunch of coriander
4 tbsp rice wine vinegar	375g (13oz) cooked, peeled prawns

125ml (4fl oz) soy sauce

4 tbsp flavourless oil

2 tbsp sesame oil

MAKE THE DRESSING AND **COOK** THE NOODLES

1 With a small knife, peel the skin from the root ginger. Slice the ginger, cutting across the fibrous grain. Crush each slice with the flat of the knife, then finely chop the slices.

2 Core, seed, and dice the chillies. Set the flat side of a knife on top of each garlic clove and strike it with your fist. Discard the skin and finely chop the garlic. Put the crushed ginger, chillies, garlic, sugar, pepper, and vinegar in a bowl. Pour in the soy sauce. Gradually whisk in the oils so the sauce emulsifies and thickens slightly. Taste for seasoning.

3 Fill a large pan with water, bring to a boil and add salt. Add the noodles and simmer for 4–6 minutes, or according to package directions, just until they are tender but still chewy. Stir them occasionally to prevent sticking.

4 Drain the noodles in the colander, rinse with hot water, and drain again thoroughly.

DRESS THE NOODLES AND PREPARE THE SALAD INGREDIENTS

5 Transfer the noodles to a large bowl. Briskly whisk the dressing, pour it over the warm noodles and toss until well coated. Set aside for at least 1 hour to marinate and allow the flavour to mellow.

6 Trim the stem end from each mangetout, then pull the string from the edge of the pods. Trim the other end. Cook in boiling salted water for 2–3 minutes, until tender but still crisp. Drain, rinse with cold water and drain again. Cut each diagonally into 2–3 slices.

7 Trim the spring onions and cut into thin diagonal slices, including some of the green tops. Coarsely chop the peanuts. Strip the coriander leaves from the stalks, pile the leaves on a chopping board and chop them coarsely.

8 Add the mangetout, spring onions, two-thirds of both the chopped peanuts and coriander, and all of the prawns to the noodles. Toss thoroughly. Taste for seasoning. It may be unnecessary to add salt because soy sauce is salty. Mound the salad on to a serving plate and top with the remaining chopped peanuts and coriander.

 VARIATION: Thai noodle salad

A great way to use up leftover pork.

1 Make the dressing: omit the ginger and rice wine vinegar. Chop the garlic and fresh chillies. Coarsely chop 1 stalk of lemongrass and squeeze the juice from 1 lime. Whisk together the soy sauce, lime juice, garlic, chillies, lemongrass, sugar, and pepper. Gradually whisk in the oils. Taste for seasoning.

2 Cook and drain the noodles as directed and toss them in the dressing. Omit the prawns and mangetout. Cut 250g (9oz) cooked pork into thin strips. Chop the peanuts and coriander. Coarsely chop 7–10 basil sprigs. Drain a 250g (9oz) can of sliced water chestnuts.

3 Toss the noodles and dressing with the pork, water chestnuts, spring onions, all the chopped peanuts, and the herbs. Cover, and let stand, at least 1 hour. Divide among 6 plates. Garnish each serving with a basil sprig, if you like.

Steak salad with red onions

INSPIRED BY THE STEAK SANDWICH! Thick wedges of crusty French baguette would be fabulous alongside. Even the most ardent salad-dodgers will adore this hearty dish. The steak is marinated for the best flavour before grilling.

SERVES	**PREP**	**COOK**
SERVES 4	20-30 MINS PLUS MARINATING	6-12 MINS

Ingredients

625g (1lb 6oz) rump steak

250ml (9fl oz) vegetable oil

3 tbsp Worcestershire sauce

dash of Tabasco sauce, or to taste

salt and pepper

2 garlic cloves, chopped

500g (1lb 2oz) red onions, in 1cm (½in) slices

90g (3oz) mushrooms, trimmed and thinly sliced

1 lollo rosso lettuce

PREPARE THE MARINADE AND STEAK

1 **Trim the meat** of fat and sinew. With the point of a knife, lightly score both sides in a lattice pattern and lay it in a shallow, non-metallic dish.

2 **In a bowl,** whisk together the oil, Worcestershire sauce, Tabasco sauce, salt, and pepper. Set aside 125ml (4fl oz). Stir the garlic into the remaining dressing and pour over the steak. Cover, and leave to marinate in the refrigerator, turning several times, for at least 3 or up to 12 hours for maximum flavour and tenderness.

PREPARE THE VEGETABLES

3 **Insert a cocktail stick** into the side of each onion slice to hold it together during cooking. Toss the mushrooms very well with half the reserved dressing, being sure to coat them entirely.

4 **Twist off and discard** the root end from the lettuce. Immerse the leaves in plenty of cold water for 15-30 minutes, then dry thoroughly. Coarsely shred the leaves and put them in a large bowl.

GRILL THE STEAK AND ONIONS

5 **Heat the grill.** Lay the steak on the grill rack. Set the onion slices around it and brush with the marinade. Grill 7.5cm (3in) from the heat, allowing 3-4 minutes for rare, 5-6 minutes for medium, then turn and repeat.

6 **Press the steak** with a finger to test: it will feel quite spongy if rare; it will resist slightly if medium. Divide the lettuce and mushrooms evenly among 4 plates.

ASSEMBLE THE SALAD

7 **Cut the steak** into thin diagonal slices and arrange on the lettuce and mushrooms. Take the cocktail sticks from the onion slices, separate the rings, and arrange some over each serving.

German potato salad

THE PIQUANT CARAWAY DRESSING makes this salad great with cooked meats. It is inspired by recipes that came from the Black Forest in Germany, where few dishes are complete without ham, or sausage, or both!

SERVES	PREP	COOK
SERVES 6–8	25–30 MINS PLUS CHILLING	15–20 MINS

Ingredients

FOR THE SALAD

1.4kg (3lb) red-skinned new potatoes

salt and pepper

150g (5½oz) thinly sliced smoked ham

leaves from 7–10 parsley sprigs, chopped

FOR THE DRESSING

1 small red onion, very finely chopped

3 tbsp red wine vinegar

3 tbsp soured cream

2 tbsp hot mustard

2 tsp caraway seeds

250ml (9fl oz) flavourless vegetable oil

COOK THE POTATOES

1 **Scrub the potatoes** under cold, running water but do not peel. Cut any larger potatoes into 2–4 pieces. Put in a large saucepan with plenty of cold, salted water, cover, and bring to a boil. Simmer for 15–20 minutes, just until tender, then drain.

MAKE THE DRESSING AND DRESS THE POTATOES

2 **Put the onion** in a bowl with the vinegar, soured cream, mustard, salt, and pepper. Sprinkle in the caraway seeds. Whisk together just until mixed, then gradually whisk in the oil so the dressing emulsifies and thickens slightly. Taste for seasoning and set aside.

3 **While still warm, cut the potatoes** into 1cm (½in) slices. Transfer to a large bowl. Briskly whisk the dressing, then pour it over the warm potatoes. Stir gently to thoroughly coat and leave to cool.

4 **Trim the fat** from the ham, then cut into 1cm (½in) strips. Add the ham to the potatoes. Sprinkle three-quarters of the parsley over the top. Stir, taste for seasoning, cover, and refrigerate for at least 1 hour.

5 **Transfer the salad** to a large platter or into individual plates or shallow bowls, and sprinkle evenly with the remaining chopped parsley. Serve at room temperature.

Pasta and mussel salad

THE SPIRAL FUSILLI PASTA absorbs this gorgeous, tart dressing wonderfully, though hollow shells or macaroni would be good too. The pasta perfectly complements the texture of the mussels. This can be made 1 day ahead, covered, and refrigerated.

SERVES SERVES 4-6	**PREP** 30-35 MINS	**COOK** 8-10 MINS

Ingredients

FOR THE HERB DRESSING

4 shallots

3 garlic cloves

1 bunch of tarragon

1 bunch of parsley

2 lemons

salt and pepper

175ml (6fl oz) olive oil

FOR THE SALAD

1kg (2¼lb) mussels

175ml (6fl oz) dry white wine

250g (9oz) fusilli pasta spirals

3 spring onions, trimmed and sliced

MAKE THE HERB VINAIGRETTE

1 **Peel and finely dice** the shallots. Finely chop the garlic. Strip the tarragon and parsley leaves from the stalks, and finely chop.

2 **Squeeze the juice** from each of the lemons; there should be about 75ml (2½fl oz) juice. If you first roll the lemons on a hard surface, you will be able to extract more juice.

3 **Whisk together the lemon juice,** half the shallots, the garlic, salt, and pepper. Gradually whisk in the oil, so the dressing emulsifies and thickens slightly. Whisk in the herbs. Taste for seasoning and set aside.

PREPARE AND COOK THE MUSSELS

4 **Scrape each mussel** with a small knife to remove any barnacles, then detach and discard any weed or 'beard'. Scrub under cold, running water; discard any with broken shells or those that do not close when tapped.

5 **Put the wine,** remaining shallots, and plenty of pepper, in a large saucepan. Bring to a boil and simmer for 2 minutes. Add the mussels, cover, and cook over high heat for 4-5 minutes, stirring occasionally, just until the mussels open.

6 **Transfer the mussels** to a large bowl, discarding the cooking liquid. Leave until they are cool enough to handle. Discard any that have not opened at this point.

7 **With your fingers,** remove the mussels from their shells, reserving 4-6 mussels in their shells. Pull off and discard the rubbery ring from around each shelled mussel, and put them in a large bowl.

DRESS THE MUSSELS AND COOK THE PASTA

8 **Briskly whisk** the herb vinaigrette, and pour it over the mussels.

9 **Stir gently,** so all the mussels are well coated with dressing. Cover and refrigerate, while cooking the pasta.

10 **Fill a large pan** with water, bring to a boil, and add ½ tsp salt. Add the pasta, and simmer for 8-10 minutes, until tender but still chewy, or according to package directions. Stir occasionally to keep from sticking. Drain, rinse with cold water, and drain again.

11 **Tip the pasta** into the bowl of mussels and dressing. Sprinkle the spring onions over the pasta, add salt and pepper, toss well, and taste for seasoning. Arrange on 4–6 plates. Garnish each serving with a reserved mussel in its shell, adding a lemon slice and tarragon sprig, if you like.

 VARIATION: Pasta and scallop salad

One for when you're feeling flush!

1 Omit the mussels and wine. Chop the garlic, 2 shallots, the tarragon, and parsley, as directed. Snip 1 bunch of chives. Make the dressing as directed, using half the chopped garlic, 1 lemon, and 125ml (4fl oz) olive oil. Whisk in the herbs with 3 tbsp double cream, and taste for seasoning.

2 Prepare 500g (1lb 2oz) scallops in place of the mussels, and cut large scallops into 2 rounds. Heat 1 tbsp olive oil in a frying pan. Add the scallops with the remaining garlic, and sprinkle with salt and pepper. Sauté, turning once, for 1–2 minutes each side, until brown and slightly crisp.

3 Cook 250g (9oz) spinach pasta and slice the spring onions as directed. Drain the pasta. Toss with the spring onions, scallops and dressing. Taste for seasoning and serve at room temperature.

Warm salmon and orange salad

A RICH DISH, with cream and Grand Marnier dressing. The velvety bed of lamb's lettuce adds a touch of astringency to cut through the dressing, while segments of refreshing orange and toasted hazelnuts give great bursts of flavour and texture contrasts to this exciting salad. If you don't have any sherry vinegar in the cupboard, use white wine vinegar instead.

SERVES SERVES 6	**PREP** 35–40 MINS	**COOK** 6–12 MINS

Ingredients

FOR THE DRESSING

4 oranges

60g (2oz) skinned hazelnuts

salt and pepper

2 tbsp sherry vinegar

1 tbsp Grand Marnier

2 tbsp double cream

125ml (4fl oz) hazelnut oil

FOR THE SALAD

500g (1lb 2oz) salmon fillet

1 tbsp vegetable oil

250g (9oz) lamb's lettuce

MAKE THE DRESSING

1 **Preheat the oven** to 180°C (350°F/Gas 4). Peel and segment the oranges, squeezing the leftover orange membranes over a bowl to catch the remaining juice. Cover and refrigerate. Spread the hazelnuts on a baking sheet and toast for 5–10 minutes, until lightly browned, stirring occasionally. Let cool, then chop the nuts coarsely.

2 **Put 3 tbsp of the orange juice** in a bowl (reserve the rest) and add salt, pepper, vinegar, Grand Marnier, and cream. Stir, then gradually whisk in all but 2 tbsp of the hazelnut oil, so the dressing emulsifies and thickens slightly. Add the hazelnuts, stir, and taste for seasoning.

PREPARE THE SALMON

3 **With a filleting knife,** trim off any cartilage from the salmon. If necessary, pull out any pin bones with tweezers.

4 **Holding the fish steady** with one hand, tail facing away from you and working towards it, use a filleting knife to cut 12 even slices, each about 5mm (¼in) thick. Leave any skin behind.

COOK THE SALMON

5 **Sprinkle the salmon** with salt and pepper. Heat the vegetable oil in a frying pan. Cook the salmon for 1–2 minutes each side, until lightly browned. Brush with 2 tbsp orange juice and the remaining hazelnut oil.

6 **Toss the lamb's lettuce** with half the dressing and the orange segments and arrange on 6 plates with 2 warm salmon slices. Sprinkle over the remaining dressing.

Cobb salad

A CALIFORNIAN CLASSIC. A wonderful main course salad that will satisfy with the smooth textures of avocado and Roquefort cheese against crispy bacon bits, mild chicken, and crunchy cos lettuce leaves. Tarragon vinaigrette brings the whole dish together.

SERVES
SERVES 4-6

PREP
20-25 MINS

COOK
5 MINS

Ingredients

FOR THE SALAD

1.8kg (4lb) whole cooked chicken or 500g (1lb 2oz) cooked skinless, boneless chicken

6 unsmoked back bacon rashers, sliced

2 avocados

juice of 1 lemon

1 shallot, finely chopped

500g (1lb 2lb) large cos lettuce or Little Gem lettuces, leaves sliced into strips

2 large tomatoes, cored and sliced

90g (3oz) Roquefort or other blue cheese, crumbled

FOR THE VINAIGRETTE

4 tbsp red wine vinegar

2 tsp Dijon mustard

½ tsp salt

¼ tsp pepper

175ml (6fl oz) vegetable oil

leaves from 3 tarragon sprigs, finely chopped

PREPARE THE CHICKEN

1 If using a whole cooked chicken, remove the meat from the bones, discarding all skin and any gristle, and cut into thin slices.

MAKE THE VINAIGRETTE

2 Put the vinegar, mustard, salt, and pepper in a small bowl and whisk. Add the oil in a steady stream, whisking constantly. The dressing will emulsify and thicken slightly.

3 Stir the tarragon in to the dressing and taste for seasoning.

COOK THE BACON

4 In a small frying pan, cook the bacon strips until golden and crispy, and the fat has rendered. Remove with a slotted spoon and drain on kitchen paper to blot off any excess fat.

PREPARE THE AVOCADO

5 Cut lengthways around the avocados, remove the stone, peel, and thinly slice. Toss the slices gently with lemon juice to prevent discolouration.

ASSEMBLE THE SALAD

6 Toss the chicken, shallot, and lettuce with a little dressing. Arrange in bowls with all the other ingredients, drizzling with more vinaigrette.

Meat-free

A rich variety of recipes for vegetarians and vegetable lovers

Greek-style vegetables

THE FLAVOURS WILL MELLOW in the refrigerator if you make these up to 2 days in advance. This piquant dish is great on the side of a rich main course, or as an appetizer. Adapt it to include other vegetables to take the recipe through the seasons.

SERVES	PREP	COOK
SERVES 6-8	25-30 MINS	25-30 MINS

Ingredients

FOR THE SPICE BAGS AND COOKING LIQUID

15g (½oz) coriander seeds

1 tbsp black peppercorns

4 bay leaves

5-7 thyme sprigs

3-4 parsley sprigs

2 tbsp tomato purée

750ml (1¼ pints) vegetable stock or water, plus more if needed

juice of 1 lemon

4 tbsp dry white wine

FOR THE VEGETABLES

24 baby onions

4 tbsp vegetable oil

4 tbsp olive oil

500g (1lb 2oz) button mushrooms, trimmed

400g (14oz) can tomatoes

salt and pepper

500g (1lb 2oz) fennel bulbs, sliced

45g (1½ oz) raisins

PREPARE THE INGREDIENTS

1 **Combine** the coriander seeds, black peppercorns, bay leaves, thyme and parsley sprigs. Halve the spice mixture and tie each portion up in a small piece of muslin.

2 **Make the cooking liquid:** whisk the tomato purée, half the vegetable stock or water, the lemon juice, and white wine in a bowl.

3 **Put the baby onions** in a bowl, cover with hot water, and let stand for 2 minutes. Drain and peel, leaving a little of the root attached.

COOK THE ONIONS AND MUSHROOMS

4 **Heat half the vegetable oil** and half the olive oil in a sauté pan. Add half the baby onions and sauté for about 3 minutes, until lightly browned. Add the mushrooms, a spice bag, and the tomatoes.

5 **Pour in half the cooking liquid;** there should be enough almost to cover the vegetables. Add salt. Bring to a fast boil over high heat. Stir occasionally, adding a little stock or water as the liquid evaporates. Cook for 25-30 minutes, until tender to the tip of a knife.

COOK THE ONIONS AND FENNEL

6 **Heat the remaining oils** in another sauté pan and sauté the remaining onions until lightly browned. Put in the second spice bag, remaining cooking liquid and salt. Add the fennel and bring to a fast boil over high heat.

7 **Continue boiling,** for 10-12 minutes, then add the raisins and stir. Cook for 15-20 minutes, until tender when pierced with a knife. Remove the spice bags from both mixtures and taste for seasoning.

Mixed pickled vegetables

THIS ASSORTMENT OF FRESH VEGETABLES tossed in a golden turmeric sauce is often served as part of a Malaysian meal. It will enliven any stir-fry, curry, or Asian noodle dish, adding crunch and a pleasing sweet-sour flavour.

SERVES	PREP	COOK
SERVES 8-10	1½-2½ HRS	10 MINS

Ingredients

FOR THE VEGETABLES

1 cucumber

3 large carrots

florets from ½ small cauliflower

30 French beans, trimmed

250g (9oz) wedge of green cabbage, cored and finely shredded

45g (1½oz) roasted unsalted peanuts

FOR THE PICKLING SAUCE

6 unsalted roasted macadamia nuts

2 garlic cloves, finely chopped

6 shallots, diced

4cm (1½in) piece of fresh galangal or root ginger, finely chopped

1½ tsp ground turmeric

2 hot red chillies, finely chopped

4 tbsp oil

100g (3½oz) sugar

1 tsp salt

125 ml (4fl oz) rice vinegar

PREPARE AND BLANCH THE VEGETABLES

1 **Peel the cucumber** and cut in half lengthways, and scoop out the seeds. Cut lengthways into 5mm (¼in) strips, then into 5cm (2in) sticks. Cut the carrots into sticks as well. Cut any large cauliflower florets in half.

2 **Fill a wok** 5cm (2in) deep with water and bring to a boil. Add the carrots, cauliflower, and beans. Simmer for 2-3 minutes, until tender but still crisp, then add the cucumber and cabbage for 1 minute. Drain well.

MAKE THE PICKLING SAUCE

3 **Finely chop** the macadamia nuts. (Asians use native kemiri nuts, often called candlenuts. Macadamias have a similar rich flavour and texture.)

4 **Pound the nuts,** garlic, shallots, galangal, turmeric, and chillies in a mortar and pestle, adding one ingredient at a time and pounding well after each addition. Alternatively, work the ingredients to a paste in a food processor.

PICKLE THE VEGETABLES

5 **Heat a wok** over medium heat until hot. Drizzle in the oil to coat the sides and bottom. When the oil is hot, add the chilli-nut paste and stir for 3-5 minutes, until slightly thickened and the spices are fragrant.

6 **Stir in the sugar,** salt, and vinegar; bring to a boil. Remove the wok from the heat and add the vegetables, tossing to coat. Transfer to a bowl, and cover. Let stand, about 1 hour at room temperature or at least 2 hours in the refrigerator. Coarsely chop the peanuts and sprinkle on top.

Tomato tagliatelle with artichokes

THIS FLAVOURFUL PASTA can be made, dried, and stored, loosely wrapped, in the refrigerator for up to 48 hours. Use a good extra virgin olive oil so the flavour of the finished dish is intense. Walnuts complement the artichokes in the sauce perfectly in this recipe.

SERVES
SERVES 4-6

PREP
50-60 MINS
PLUS DRYING

COOK
3-4 MINS

Ingredients

FOR THE PASTA DOUGH

300g (10oz) strong plain flour, plus more if needed

3 eggs

1 tbsp vegetable oil

1 tsp salt

2½ tbsp tomato purée

FOR THE SAUCE

6 large canned or frozen artichoke hearts

5 tbsp extra virgin olive oil

2 shallots, finely chopped

4 garlic cloves, finely chopped

3 tbsp dry white wine

salt and pepper

leaves from 1 small bunch of parsley, chopped

45g (1½oz) walnut halves, roughly chopped

30g (1oz) grated Parmesan cheese

MAKE THE PASTA

1 **Sift the flour** on to a work surface. With your fingers, make a well in the centre.

2 **Add the eggs,** oil, salt, and tomato purée. Gradually mix in the flour to make a firm dough and press into a ball. Knead for 5–10 minutes, until elastic.

3 **Cut the dough** into 3 or 4 pieces and roll through a pasta machine, ending at the second narrowest setting and the wider of the machine's cutters. Toss the tagliatelle gently with a little flour, coil in bundles and leave for 1–2 hours on a floured tea towel.

MAKE THE SAUCE

4 **Thickly slice** the artichoke hearts. Heat the olive oil in a frying pan. Add the shallots and garlic and sauté gently for about 1 minute, until soft but not brown. Add the artichokes and white wine and simmer for 2–3 minutes. Season to taste. Stir only very gently, to avoid breaking up the artichokes.

COOK THE PASTA AND FINISH THE DISH

5 **Fill a large pan** with water, bring to the boil and add 1 tbsp salt. Add the tagliatelle and simmer for 2-3 minutes, until tender but still chewy, stirring to prevent sticking. Drain and add the tagliatelle to the pan of artichoke mixture and toss over moderate heat until the pasta is hot and evenly coated with olive oil.

6 **Pile the pasta** on to a warmed serving dish and sprinkle evenly with the parsley and walnuts. Finish by sprinkling with most of the Parmesan cheese, offering the remainder on the side.

 VARIATION: Tomato tagliatelle with Jerusalem artichokes and walnuts

A delicious, wintry alternative for an underused vegetable.

1 Make the tagliatelle as directed.

2 Replace the artichoke hearts with 500g (1lb 2oz) Jerusalem artichokes. Peel and simmer for 15-20 minutes, until tender.

3 Drain the Jerusalem artichokes, slice, and simmer in wine as directed for artichoke hearts. Finish the dish as directed.

Herbed aioli platter

A SPECTACULAR DISH, popular with everyone, and known as "le grand aioli" in France. In Marseille, this recipe is traditionally served on Ash Wednesday. For those who eat fish, add squid or salt cod, if you like. Because this dish relies on the quality of the vegetables, choose only the freshest and perkiest you can find, substituting any of the vegetables listed here with those that look at their peak. Be careful not to boil the eggs for too long; they are best just slightly moist inside, and will be spoiled if their yolks are ringed with grey.

SERVES	PREP	COOK
SERVES 8	50-60 MINS	65-70 MINS

Ingredients

FOR THE EGGS AND VEGETABLES

8 eggs

8 globe artichokes

1 lemon

500g (1lb 2oz) baby carrots

4 fennel bulbs

500g (1lb 2oz) new potatoes

500g (1lb 2oz) asparagus

FOR THE HERBED AIOLI

2 garlic cloves, or to taste

salt and pepper

5-7 tarragon and parsley sprigs

1 large egg yolk

1 tsp Dijon mustard

275ml (9fl oz) extra virgin olive oil

275ml (9fl oz) vegetable oil

lemon juice, to taste

COOK THE EGGS AND MAKE THE HERBED AIOLI

1 **Put all the eggs** in a pan of cold water, bring to a boil and simmer for 8 minutes. Drain, plunge into cold water to stop the cooking, then peel. Set aside in cold water.

2 **Crush the garlic** with 1 tsp salt in a pestle and mortar, then strip the herb leaves from the stalks and crush them, too, in the mortar. It doesn't matter if the paste is not completely smooth, but the herbs should have broken down a little. Mix the egg yolk and mustard in a small bowl.

3 **Very slowly trickle the oils** into the egg yolk, whisking constantly, until the mixture emulsifies, then whisk in the remaining oils in a slow but steady stream until you have a glossy, wobbly mayonnaise. Stir in the garlic and herbs and season with lemon juice, salt, and pepper, to taste. Cover and set aside until serving, or refrigerate for up to 1 day.

PREPARE THE ARTICHOKES

4 **Prepare the artichoke hearts** as directed on page 52. Cut them into quarters, rubbing with lemon juice to prevent discolouration.

5 **Bring a saucepan of water** to the boil, add salt, then the artichokes and weigh them down with a heatproof plate. Simmer for about 15-20 minutes, until tender.

6 **Drain and allow to cool,** then scoop out the hairy chokes from each artichoke.

7 **Trim any green tops** from the baby carrots, leaving about 5mm (¼in) of green. Scrape the carrots to remove the thin skin. Put them in a saucepan of cold water, add salt, and bring to a boil. Simmer until just tender, 8–10 minutes, then drain.

PREPARE THE REMAINING VEGETABLES

8 **Trim the tops and bases of the fennel bulbs** to remove stalks and any dry ends. Discard any tough outer pieces. Cut each bulb lengthways into quarters. Bring a saucepan of water to a boil, add salt, then the fennel, and simmer until just tender, 12–15 minutes. Drain.

9 **Scrub the potatoes** and cut larger ones in half, so they are all about the same size. Put in a saucepan of cold water, add salt, and bring to a boil. Simmer until they are just tender, 12–15 minutes. Drain.

10 **With a vegetable peeler,** strip away the tough skin at the bottom of each asparagus stalk. Trim off any woody ends. With kitchen string, tie into bundles of 5–7 spears. Bring a shallow pan of water to a boil, add salt, then the asparagus and simmer for 5–6 minutes, until just tender. Drain.

11 **Drain and dry the hard-boiled eggs** and cut them in half. Arrange the vegetables on a large serving platter with the eggs. Serve at room temperature with the bowl of aioli.

Tempura

DELICIOUS JAPANESE FRITTERS with a lively dipping sauce. Tempura was actually introduced to Japan by Portuguese missionaries as a way to cook fish. Today, an authentic version is mainly based on vegetables. Meat and fish may be added and fried in the same way, for carnivores. Each piece of tempura must be dry and crisp, so ensure the oil is at the correct temperature before adding the vegetables (it's best to use a thermometer).

SERVES
SERVES 6-8

PREP
45-50
MINUTES

COOK
3-5 MINUTES

Ingredients

FOR THE VEGETABLES

1 head of broccoli

2 courgettes

125g (4½oz) mangetout

8 spring onions

2 sweet potatoes, total weight about 300g (10oz)

250g (9oz) shiitake mushrooms

125g (4½oz) canned water chestnuts

vegetable oil, for deep-frying

60g (2oz) plain flour, for dredging

FOR THE DIPPING SAUCE

60g (2oz) piece of daikon (white radish)

2.5cm (1in) fresh root ginger

125ml (4fl oz) sake

125ml (4fl oz) light soy sauce

FOR THE BATTER

2 eggs

300g (10oz) plain flour

PREPARE THE VEGETABLES

1 **Cut the broccoli florets** from the main stalk (discard the thick stalk). Cut any large florets in half straight through their stems. Trim the courgettes and cut them diagonally into 5mm (¼in) even slices. Trim the tops and tails from the mangetout and pull away any tough strings you find from the edges of the pods.

2 **Trim the spring onions** and cut each into 7.5cm (3in) lengths, discarding any thin, dark green ends or any discoloured outer leaves. Peel the sweet potatoes, making sure to remove all the "eyes", halve them lengthways then cut horizontally into 5mm (¼in) thick slices. Make sure the sweet potato slices are no thicker than this, or they may not cook through in the deep-fryer.

3 **Wipe the shiitakes** with damp kitchen paper, then trim off and discard any woody stalks. Cut any large mushrooms in half vertically, straight through the stalk. Drain and rinse the water chestnuts and slice them into thick discs.

MAKE THE DIPPING SAUCE AND BATTER

4 **Peel and grate the daikon.** Peel and slice the ginger, then crush each slice with the flat of a knife and very finely chop it.

5 **Mix the sake** and soy sauce together. Add the daikon and ginger and set aside.

6 **Lightly beat the eggs** in a large bowl and stir in 600ml (1 pint) cold water.

7 **Sift the** flour. Add it to the egg mixture and lightly whisk just until combined. The consistency should be slightly lumpy.

COAT AND FRY THE VEGETABLES

8 **Heat the oil** in a deep-fat fryer until it is hot enough to brown a cube of fresh bread in 40 seconds. If using a deep-fat thermometer, it should register 190°C (375°F). Heat the oven to very low, to keep the vegetables warm.

9 **Pour the batter** into a large, shallow dish. Put the flour for dredging in another shallow dish. Toss the broccoli florets in the flour to coat each evenly and lightly.

10 **Dip the vegetable pieces** in the batter so they are completely coated. Lift out the florets with a fork and drain off any excess batter. Lower the pieces gently into the hot oil. Do not crowd the pan; instead cook in small batches.

11 **Deep-fry until crisp** (it should take 3–5 minutes), turning once during cooking. With a slotted spoon, transfer the broccoli to a baking sheet lined with several layers of kitchen paper. Keep warm in the oven.

12 **Cook the other vegetables** in the same way, flouring them, then coating with batter, deep-frying, and transferring to the lined baking sheet to keep warm. Arrange the deep-fried vegetables on a serving platter. Warm the sauce in a saucepan just until hot, and taste for seasoning. Serve it in small bowls alongside the tempura.

Three-cheese Swiss chard crêpes

A VIVACIOUSLY FLAVOURED DISH for a cold day, indulgently filled with Gruyère, feta, and goat's cheese. Make sure your crêpes are as thin and lacy as possible, so that the dish isn't heavy. Most greens can be substituted for the Swiss chard in the recipe: try spinach, or even pak choi, if you prefer.

SERVES	PREP	COOK
SERVES 6	1 HR PLUS STANDING	20-25 MINS

Ingredients

FOR THE BATTER

125g (4½oz) plain flour

½ tsp salt

3 eggs

250ml (9fl oz) milk

3-4 tbsp vegetable oil

FOR THE FILLING

750g (1lb 10oz) Swiss chard

30g (1oz) butter

2 garlic cloves, finely chopped

3 shallots, finely chopped

90g (3oz) soft goat's cheese

125g (4½oz) feta cheese

salt and pepper

ground nutmeg

FOR THE CREAM SAUCE

250ml (9fl oz) milk

30g (1oz) butter

2 tbsp plain flour

125ml (4fl oz) double cream

ground nutmeg

30g (1oz) Gruyère cheese, coarsely grated

MAKE THE CRÊPES

1 Sift the flour and salt into a bowl, and make a well in the centre. Pour the eggs into the well, and whisk until just mixed. Add half the milk and whisk, drawing in the flour to make a paste. Stir in half of the remaining milk. Cover and let stand for 30–60 minutes. Stir in the remaining milk until the batter is the consistency of thin cream.

2 Heat about 1 tbsp oil in a pan until very hot; pour off the excess. Pour in a small ladle of batter, rotating and shaking the pan to coat the bottom evenly. Fry quickly for 1-2 minutes, until set on top and brown underneath. Loosen the crêpe, then flip it over with a palette knife, and cook for 30-60 seconds, until brown on the other side.

3 Transfer the crêpe to a plate. Continue making crêpes, adding oil to the pan as necessary, until all the batter is used, to make a total of 12. Pile them on the plate so that they stay moist and warm.

PREPARE THE SWISS CHARD

4 Trim the root from the Swiss chard, and discard any tough stalks and leaves. Thoroughly wash the stalks and leaves. Cut off the green leaves around the stalks. Using a vegetable peeler, remove any strings from the outer sides of the stalks, and set aside.

5 Cut the stalks into 1cm (½in) slices. Bring a large pan of water to a boil, add salt and the leaves, and simmer for 2-3 minutes, until tender. Drain, then chop.

MAKE THE FILLING

6 Heat the butter in a large frying pan. Add the garlic and shallots, and cook until soft but not brown. Add the chard stalks; sauté for 3-5 minutes, stirring, until just tender. Add the chard leaves; sauté for 2-3 minutes, stirring, until all moisture has evaporated. Remove the pan from the heat.

7 Crumble the goat's cheese into the chard mixture, then crumble in the feta. Season to taste with salt, pepper, and a pinch of nutmeg. Stir to mix, then set aside.

FILL AND BAKE THE CREPES

8 Preheat the oven to 180°C (350°F/Gas 4). Butter a shallow baking dish. To make the cream sauce: scald the milk in a saucepan. Melt the butter in another saucepan, over medium heat. Whisk in the flour, and cook for 30-60 seconds, until foaming.

9 Remove from the heat and let cool slightly, then whisk in the hot milk. Return to the heat and cook, whisking, until it boils and thickens. Whisk in the cream. Season with salt, pepper, and a pinch of nutmeg, and simmer for 2 minutes. Remove from the heat, cover, and keep warm.

10 Put 2 spoonfuls of filling on to one half of the paler side of a crêpe. Fold the crêpe in half, then in half again, to form a triangle. Arrange in the dish, then continue. Spoon over the sauce. Sprinkle with the Gruyère. Bake for 20-25 minutes, until bubbling and brown. Serve hot from the dish.

 VARIATION: Crêpes with wild mushrooms and herbs

Juicy and delicious.

1 Make the crêpes as directed. Wipe 250g (9oz) fresh shiitake mushrooms with a damp paper towel, trim the stalks, and halve any large mushrooms. Cut into 1cm (½in) slices. Clean 250g (9oz) button mushrooms, trim the stalks even with the caps, then slice.

2 Melt the butter, add the garlic, shallots, and shiitake and button mushrooms, and sauté for about 5 minutes, until the liquid has evaporated, stirring constantly. Set aside a few mushrooms for garnish. Chop the leaves from several sprigs of parsley, tarragon, and chives.

3 Make the white sauce as directed, saving the cream to add later, then stir in the herbs. Mix half the sauce with the mushrooms, put in each crêpe, fold in 2 sides, and roll up into cylinders. Arrange in the baking dish. Add the cream to the remaining herb sauce, and pour it over. Bake as directed, sprinkling with the reserved mushrooms just before serving.

Fusilli with pesto

PESTO SAUCE IS A REAL TREAT to have on hand and this is how to make it for yourself, to serve as an appetizer. It's so much better than the pesto you can buy that it's almost like a different sauce. Make it in a pestle and mortar, if you prefer, though you will need strong arms and a little more patience.

SERVES	PREP	COOK
SERVES 6-8	10-15 MINS	8-10 MINS

Ingredients

60g (2oz) basil

6 garlic cloves, peeled

45g (1½oz) pine nuts

125g (4½oz) grated Parmesan cheese

175ml (6fl oz) olive oil

salt and pepper

500g (1lb 2oz) fusilli pasta

cherry tomatoes, to serve (optional)

MAKE THE PESTO

1 **Strip the leaves** from the basil and put in a food processor with the garlic, pine nuts, Parmesan, and about 3 tbsp of the olive oil.

2 **Purée until smooth,** scraping down the sides of the bowl as necessary. With the blade turning, slowly pour in the remaining oil through the feed tube, until the pesto emulsifies. Season to taste.

COOK THE PASTA

3 **Fill a large pan** with cold water, bring it to the boil and add 1 tbsp salt. Add the pasta and simmer for 8-10 minutes, until tender but still chewy, or according to packet instructions, stirring occasionally to prevent the pasta spirals from sticking together. Drain the pasta thoroughly in a colander, shaking to remove any excess water.

FINISH THE DISH

4 **Put the pesto sauce** in a mixing bowl and tip in the pasta. Toss with 2 spoons or large forks until the pasta is evenly coated with pesto. Pile on to plates and decorate with a few cherry tomatoes, if you like, or more basil sprigs. Serve hot or warm.

Summer frittata with ratatouille

WHILE THE EGGS COOK slowly in this Italian-style omelette, you can sit back and enjoy a glass of wine. Use any vegetables you have to hand to make the filling, which can be prepared up to 24 hours ahead and kept, tightly covered, in the refrigerator. Cook the frittata just before serving.

SERVES	**PREP**	**COOK**
SERVES 3-4	20-25 MINS	20-25 MINS

Ingredients

6 eggs

salt and pepper

15–30g (½–1oz) butter

FOR THE FILLING

1 small aubergine

1 courgette

4 tbsp olive oil, plus more if needed

1 green pepper, sliced into strips

1 onion, thinly sliced

250g (9oz) tomatoes, peeled, deseeded and chopped, or 1 x 200g (7oz) can chopped tomatoes

2 garlic cloves, finely chopped

leaves from 5-7 thyme sprigs, plus a few sprigs to decorate

½ tsp ground coriander

1 large bouquet garni (10-12 parsley stalks, 4-5 thyme sprigs and 2 bay leaves)

PREPARE THE RATATOUILLE

1 **Trim the aubergine** and cut into 1cm (½in) chunks. Cut the courgette into 1cm (½in) slices. Put the aubergine and courgette on a tray and sprinkle generously with salt. Leave for 30 minutes, then place in a colander, rinse and pat dry with kitchen paper.

2 **Heat about half the oil** in a frying pan. Add the aubergine to the pan and stir-fry for 3-5 minutes, until browned. Transfer to a bowl with a slotted spoon. Repeat with the courgette slices.

3 **Add the green pepper** to the pan with a little more oil and stir-fry until limp; remove to the bowl. Heat about 1 tbsp more oil in the pan, add the onion and sauté for 2-3 minutes, until lightly browned.

4 **Return the aubergine,** courgette, and pepper to the pan and add the tomatoes, garlic, salt, pepper, thyme, coriander, and the bouquet garni. Stir until mixed. Cover and cook for 10–15 minutes, until tender. Remove and discard the bouquet garni. Let cool.

COOK THE FRITTATA

5 **Whisk the eggs** in a bowl until completely mixed. Stir in the ratatouille mixture and season with salt and pepper.

6 **Wipe the frying pan;** melt the butter over medium heat until foaming, then add the egg mixture. Reduce the heat, cover and cook very gently for 20-25 minutes, until the centre is set and the base is cooked and lightly browned when you lift the edge.

7 **Invert the frittata** onto a large warmed plate and decorate with the reserved thyme sprigs. Cut the frittata into wedges for serving.

Buddha's delight

A VISIT TO AN ASIAN STORE will be required for the ingredients, but it's worth it. Chinese vegetarian cooking originated in Buddhist monastery kitchens. The monks abstain from meat so protein-packed tofu is used in this typical dish.

SERVES	PREP	COOK
SERVES 4	40-50 MINS PLUS SOAKING	15-20 MINS

Ingredients

30g (1oz) dried Chinese black mushrooms	250g (9oz) lotus root
	2 tbsp lemon juice
45g (1½oz) dried tiger lily buds	6 large fresh water chestnuts
15g (½oz) dried tree ears	3 tbsp rice wine, plus more if needed
50g (1¾oz) cellophane noodles	3 tbsp light soy sauce, plus more if needed
175g (6oz) baby sweetcorn	2 tsp dark sesame oil
	2 tbsp cornflour
250g (9oz) mangetout	250g (9oz) firm tofu
	4 tbsp groundnut oil
	3 garlic cloves, finely chopped

PREPARE THE VEGETABLES

1 **Put the black mushrooms,** tiger lily buds, and tree ears in separate bowls. Add enough warm water to each bowl to cover, and let soak, about 30 minutes. Put the cellophane noodles in a bowl and cover with warm water. Let soak until soft, about 30 minutes.

2 **Trim the baby sweetcorn** and cut each diagonally in half. Trim the end from each mangetout and pull the string from down the side of the pod. Repeat at the other end, pulling the string from the other side.

3 **With a cleaver,** scrape the skin from the lotus root and slice across into 1cm (½in) rounds. Put the lotus root and the lemon juice in a bowl of cold water to prevent discolouration.

PREPARE THE REMAINING INGREDIENTS

4 **With a small knife,** cut the peel from the water chestnuts, dropping them into a bowl of cold water as you work. Remove them from the water, slice into rounds, then return the slices to the water.

5 **Drain the tiger lily buds** and tree ears and rinse well to remove any grit. Drain and squeeze dry. Cut off and discard the tough ends of the tiger lily buds and tree ears. If the tree ears are large, cut into 5cm (2in) pieces.

6 **Drain the cellophane noodles** in a colander, then cut into 12.5cm (5in) lengths. Drain the black mushrooms, reserving the liquid. Trim off the woody stalks, then slice the mushroom caps.

7 **Line a sieve** with kitchen paper and set it over a measuring jug. Strain 175ml (6fl oz) of the mushroom soaking liquid into the jug; the kitchen paper will remove any grit. Discard the remainder.

8 **In a bowl,** combine the mushroom liquid, rice wine, soy sauce, sesame oil, and half the cornflour, and stir until the cornflour has dissolved into the liquid and it is smooth, with no lumps.

CUT AND FRY THE TOFU

9 **Set the tofu** on a chopping board and cut it diagonally twice from corner to corner to make 4 triangles. Cut each triangle in half to make 8 triangles. Pat each dry on kitchen paper.

10 **Put the remaining cornflour** on a plate. Dip the tofu into the cornflour, turning and patting the triangles lightly to coat them evenly. Heat a wok over high heat until very hot.

11 **Drizzle in the oil** to coat the bottom and sides. Heat until very hot, then add the tofu and fry for 6–8 minutes, until golden brown, turning. Transfer to a plate and keep warm. Reduce the heat to medium.

STIR-FRY THE VEGETABLES

12 **Drain the lotus root** and water chestnuts. Add them to the wok with the baby sweetcorn, and stir-fry for 3–4 minutes, until the lotus root begins to soften. Add the mangetout and garlic and stir-fry for about 1 minute longer, taking care the garlic doesn't burn.

13 **Add the tiger lily buds,** black mushrooms, and tree ears and stir-fry for about 1 minute. Stir the cornflour mixture again, then add it to the wok. Bring to a boil, stir-frying until the mixture thickens; it should take 1–2 minutes. Add the noodles and stir-fry until very hot. Taste for seasoning, adding more rice wine or soy sauce if needed.

14 **Transfer the vegetables** and noodles to a warmed serving dish or into individual bowls, and carefully arrange the fried tofu triangles on top of the crisp, aromatic vegetables.

Artichokes stuffed with olives

A WONDERFUL PROVENÇAL WAY to eat artichokes, simmered with white wine and served with a fantastic and tasty rich red pepper sauce. In France, this preparation of the vegetable is known as "à la barigoule".

SERVES	PREP	COOK
SERVES 4	50–55 MINS	40–45 MINS

Ingredients

FOR THE ARTICHOKES

4 globe artichokes, total weight about 1.4kg (3lb)

½ lemon

salt and pepper

250ml (9fl oz) white wine

FOR THE STUFFING

4 slices of white bread

45g (1½oz) butter

3 small onions, finely chopped

6 garlic cloves, finely chopped

250g (9oz) mushrooms, finely chopped

250g (9oz) Parma ham, cut into strips

2 anchovy fillets, finely chopped

175g (6oz) stoned black olives, finely chopped

leaves from 2–3 thyme sprigs

ground allspice

FOR THE RED PEPPER SAUCE

750g (1lb 10oz) red peppers

2 tbsp olive oil

400g (14oz) can chopped tomatoes

1 garlic clove, chopped

2 spring onions, chopped

leaves from 1 small bunch of basil, chopped, plus 4 sprigs for garnish

PREPARE THE ARTICHOKES

1 **Snap the stalk** from each artichoke so the fibres are pulled out with the stalk. Trim the base of each so they sit flat, and rub the cut surfaces with the lemon half to prevent discolouration. Trim the outer leaves with kitchen scissors to remove the pointed tips.

2 **Cut off** about 2cm (¾in) from the pointed top of each artichoke. Rub all cut surfaces with lemon. Fill a casserole with water, bring to a boil and add salt. Add the artichokes. Weigh them down with the heatproof plate to submerge. Simmer until almost tender and a leaf can be pulled out with a slight tug, 25–30 minutes.

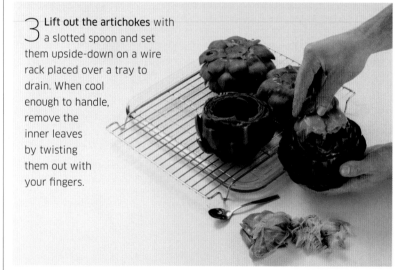

3 **Lift out the artichokes** with a slotted spoon and set them upside-down on a wire rack placed over a tray to drain. When cool enough to handle, remove the inner leaves by twisting them out with your fingers.

4 **With a teaspoon,** scoop out the hairy choke from each to make a neat cavity for the stuffing.

MAKE THE STUFFING

5 Trim and discard the crusts from the bread. Work the bread slices in a food processor to form crumbs. Melt the butter in the frying pan, add the onions and garlic, and cook, stirring, until soft but not brown.

6 Stir in the mushrooms, Parma ham, anchovies, and olives, then remove from the heat. Add the breadcrumbs, thyme, and a large pinch of allspice and mix thoroughly. Season to taste with pepper.

STUFF AND BAKE THE ARTICHOKES

7 Preheat the oven to 180°C (350°F/Gas 4). Fill the centre of each artichoke with stuffing. Tie a piece of kitchen string around each to hold the leaves together. Put the artichokes in a casserole and pour in the wine.

8 Put the casserole over high heat, bring to a boil and reduce by half; it should take about 5 minutes. Pour in enough water to half-cover the artichokes and add salt and pepper. Bring back to a boil and cover.

9 Transfer to the oven. Bake, basting occasionally with the wine and juices, until tender and a central leaf can be pulled out easily. It should take 40–50 minutes, depending on the size of the artichokes.

MAKE THE SAUCE

10 Heat the grill. Set the peppers on a rack about 10cm (4in) from the heat and grill, turning, until black and blistered. Seal in a plastic bag and let cool. Peel, then core and scrape out the seeds. Cut into chunks.

11 Heat the olive oil in a frying pan. Add the peppers, tomatoes, garlic, spring onions, and basil and cook, stirring occasionally, for 15–20 minutes, until thickened. Pour into a food processor and purée until still slightly chunky. Season to taste.

12 Discard the strings from the artichokes and put on individual plates. Spoon some sauce around the base of each, garnish with a basil sprig, if liked, and pass the remaining sauce separately.

Mexican cheese-stuffed peppers

POBLANO CHILLIES are traditionally used in this dish as they are large and mild; do use them if you can find them. Green peppers make an excellent substitution in this recipe, which is known in Mexico as "chiles rellenos".

SERVES	PREP	COOK
SERVES 4	30–35 MINS, PLUS STANDING	45–50 MINS

Ingredients

FOR THE PEPPERS

8 large green peppers

2 onions

2 tbsp vegetable oil, plus more for the dish

500g (1lb 2oz) mild Cheddar cheese

2 tsp dried oregano

salt and pepper

FOR THE TOMATO SALSA

leaves from 1 small bunch of coriander, finely chopped

500g (1lb 2oz) tomatoes, peeled, deseeded and finely chopped

2 garlic cloves, finely chopped

2 large onions, finely chopped

2 green chillies, deseeded and finely chopped

juice of 1 lemon

1 tsp Tabasco sauce

FOR THE CUSTARD

3 eggs

125ml (4fl oz) milk

½ tsp dried oregano

ROAST, PEEL, AND STUFF THE PEPPERS

1 **Heat the grill** and set the whole peppers on a rack about 10cm (4in) from the heat. Grill them, turning once or twice, for 10–12 minutes, until the skin is black and blistered. Wrap in plastic bags and let cool.

2 **Peel off the skin,** then rinse under cold running water and pat dry with kitchen paper. Cut out the core from the centre of each pepper, then scrape out and discard the seeds with a teaspoon.

3 **Chop the onions.** Heat the vegetable oil in a frying pan, add the onions and cook, stirring, until soft but not brown. Let cool. Grate the cheese and put it in a bowl. Add the oregano, salt, pepper, and onions and mix well. Taste for seasoning.

4 **Oil the baking dish.** Spoon the cheese-onion mixture into each pepper and put the peppers sideways in the dish. They should fit snugly.

MAKE THE SALSA

5 Set aside some coriander for serving. Mix the chopped tomatoes, garlic, onions, chillies, lemon juice, remaining coriander, and Tabasco and season to taste with salt. Let stand for at least 30 minutes.

BAKE THE PEPPERS

6 Heat the oven to 180°C (350°F/Gas 4). Make the custard: whisk together the eggs, milk, oregano, salt, and pepper. Pour it around the peppers and bake for 45-50 minutes.

7 Decorate the salsa by sprinkling evenly with the reserved coriander leaves, scatter a spoonful of it over each pepper and serve the rest in a bowl on the side.

VARIATION: Red peppers stuffed with sweetcorn

A really pretty dish.

1 Cook 2 corn cobs in a large pan of boiling water for 15-20 minutes, until the kernels pop out easily when tested with the point of a knife. Drain and cut the kernels from the cob. Or use a drained large can of sweetcorn.

2 Make the tomato salsa as directed in the main recipe. Peel, core, and deseed 8 red peppers as directed. Make the cheese filling as directed and stir in the sweetcorn.

3 Stuff the peppers and arrange them upright in individual baking dishes, 2 peppers to each dish. Pour in the custard and bake as directed.

Stir-fried Thai vegetables

ALMOST ANY CRISP VEGETABLE is excellent stir-fried; the textures stay firm and the colours vivid. There's only really one firm rule for a stir-fry: you have to be organised. All the component parts must be chopped and close to hand before you start, as the cooking must be done very quickly and at the last possible minute before serving.

SERVES
SERVES 4

PREP
30-35 MINS

COOK
15-20 MINS

Ingredients

300g (10oz) long-grain rice

salt

30g (1oz) dried oriental mushrooms, or other dried wild mushrooms

60g (2oz) skinned unsalted peanuts

175g (6oz) beansprouts

1 stalk lemongrass

3 tbsp fish sauce (*nam pla*)

2 tbsp oyster sauce

1 tsp cornflour

1 tsp sugar

3 tbsp vegetable oil

2 garlic cloves, finely chopped

2 dried red chillies

1 cauliflower, cut into florets

1 red pepper, cut into strips

500g (1lb 2oz) bok choi, trimmed and shredded

175g (6oz) mangetout, trimmed

leaves from 3-5 basil sprigs

BOIL THE RICE

1 **Cook the long-grain rice** in boiling salted water for 10–12 minutes, until barely tender. Drain in a colander, rinse with cold running water to wash away the starch, and let drain thoroughly. Meanwhile, prepare the vegetables. Butter a baking dish and enough foil to cover the dish.

PREPARE THE VEGETABLES

2 **Preheat the oven** to 190°C (375°F/Gas 5). Put the dried mushrooms in a bowl, pour over warm water to cover, and set aside to soften, about 30 minutes, then drain and slice.

3 **Scatter the peanuts** on a baking sheet and toast in the oven until brown, 5–7 minutes, then coarsely chop. Turn the oven to its lowest possible setting. Rinse the beansprouts in a colander. Trim the lemongrass. Slice the stalk lengthwise in half, then cut across to chop it.

4 **Spread the rice evenly** in the buttered baking dish, gently fluffing up the grains to separate them with a fork, and cover with the sheet of buttered foil. Keep the rice warm in the very low oven while you cook the stir-fry.

STIR-FRY THE VEGETABLES

5 **Put the fish sauce**, oyster sauce, cornflour, sugar, and lemongrass in a small bowl and whisk together.

6 **Heat the oil** in a wok. Add the garlic and chillies and stir-fry for 30 seconds, until fragrant. Add the cauliflower, red pepper, beansprouts, and bok choi and cook for 3 minutes, stirring constantly. Tip in the mushrooms and mangetout and stir-fry for 3 minutes more.

7 Add the basil leaves and fish sauce mixture to the vegetables and stir-fry for a final 2 minutes. Taste and season with more fish sauce, oyster sauce, and sugar, if needed. Remove the chillies and discard. Pile the rice on warmed plates. Spoon the vegetables and sauce over, and sprinkle with peanuts.

VARIATION: Chinese stir-fried vegetables

Best served with boiled Chinese noodles.

1 Prepare the mushrooms, bok choi, and beansprouts as directed in the main recipe; omit the cauliflower, mangetout, and red pepper. Omit the peanuts; toast 45g (1½ oz) flaked almonds in the oven for 3–5 minutes instead. You must be sure to watch very carefully, as flaked almonds can go from toasted to burned very quickly.

2 Cut the florets from 1 head of broccoli. Drain 60g (2oz) canned bamboo shoots and rinse 60g (2oz) baby sweetcorn. Slice the green parts only of 2 spring onions. Omit the fish sauce mixture. For the sauce, whisk together 3 tbsp rice wine, 2 tbsp soy sauce, 2 tsp sesame oil, 1 tsp cornflour, and a pinch of sugar.

3 Heat the oil in a wok, add the broccoli and bok choi and stir-fry for 2–3 minutes. Add the mushrooms and baby corn and stir-fry for 2 minutes more. Add the soy sauce mixture, bamboo shoots, beansprouts, and spring onions and cook, stirring, for 2 minutes. The sauce should thicken slightly. Continue to turn all the vegetables very well, so that everything is evenly cooked. Season with more rice wine, soy sauce, sesame oil, and sugar, if needed, and sprinkle with the toasted almonds.

Gratin dauphinois

WONDERFULLY RICH, and simply superb. Floury baking potatoes work best in this dish; look for the widely available Maris Piper or King Edward varieties. They are simmered in milk to keep them as sweet as possible before being cooked with double cream. If it is more convenient, you can assemble the gratin up to the point of baking, then keep it, covered, in the refrigerator for 1 day. Bake it just before serving.

SERVES	PREP	COOK
SERVES 6-8	30-40 MINS	20-25 MINS

Ingredients

750g (1lb 10oz) potatoes

600ml (1 pint) milk

freshly grated nutmeg

salt and pepper

300ml (10fl oz) double cream

1 garlic clove

45g (1½oz) Gruyère cheese, coarsely grated

PREPARE THE POTATOES

1 Peel the potatoes. With a mandolin or knife, cut them into 3mm (⅛in) slices. Cover the slices with a wet tea towel, so that they do not discolour. Do not soak them in water; this would remove the starch that gives the gratin its creamy consistency.

PRE-COOK THE POTATOES

2 Bring the milk to a boil in a saucepan, stirring occasionally so it does not burn. Season it with a little grated nutmeg, salt, and pepper. Add the potatoes and cook, stirring occasionally, for 10–15 minutes, until just tender.

3 Drain the potatoes in a colander. Discard the milk, or save it for another use, such as soup, if you like.

ASSEMBLE AND BAKE THE GRATIN

4 Return the potatoes to the saucepan, and pour in the cream. Bring to a boil and simmer, stirring occasionally, for 10–15 minutes, until very tender. Taste for seasoning. Preheat the oven to 190°C (375°F/Gas 5).

5 Peel the garlic clove, cut it in half, and use the cut side to rub the bottom and sides of a 1.5 litre (2¾ pint) baking dish. Brush the bottom and sides of the dish with melted butter.

6 Layer the potatoes and cream in the dish, then sprinkle with the cheese. Bake for 20–25 minutes, until golden brown. Test with a small knife; the blade should feel hot when withdrawn. Serve the gratin dauphinois hot, directly from the baking dish.

Roast pepper lasagne

THIS RECIPE IS EASILY DOUBLED or tripled, and freezes well. You can assemble the dish, cover, and refrigerate for up to 2 days before baking. If you are pushed for time, use shop-bought roasted peppers in jars instead of roasting your own.

SERVES	PREP	COOK
SERVES 8	1½ HRS	35-45 MINS

Ingredients

FOR THE TOMATO SAUCE

2 x 400g (14oz) cans tomatoes

6 garlic cloves, finely chopped

leaves from 1 bunch of basil, chopped

leaves from 7-10 oregano sprigs, chopped

leaves from 1 bunch of flat-leaf parsley, chopped

salt and pepper

FOR THE LASAGNE

4 red peppers

4 green peppers

2 tbsp olive oil

750g (1lb 10oz) mushrooms, thinly sliced

1kg (2¼lb) ricotta cheese

pinch of ground nutmeg

375g (13oz) lasagne

175g (6oz) freshly grated Parmesan cheese

MAKE THE SAUCE

1 **Put the tomatoes,** half the garlic, and two-thirds of the herbs in a shallow pan. Season. Cook over medium heat, stirring occasionally, for 25-35 minutes, until thickened. Ladle into a food processor, and purée until smooth.

PREPARE THE VEGETABLES AND PASTA

2 **Heat the grill.** Set the peppers on a rack 10cm (4in) from the heat and grill, turning, until blackened. Put in a plastic bag, seal, and cool. Peel off the skins. Halve the peppers, and scrape out the cores and seeds. Cut into 1cm (½in) strips.

3 **Heat the oil** in a frying pan. Add the mushrooms with the remaining garlic and cook, stirring, for 10-12 minutes, until the liquid evaporates. Put the ricotta, remaining herbs, nutmeg, salt, and pepper in a bowl. Stir until thoroughly combined.

4 **Fill a large pan** with water and bring to a boil. Add 1 tbsp salt, and the lasagne, a sheet at a time. Simmer for 8-10 minutes, or according to package directions, until tender. Drain thoroughly on a tea towel.

FINISH THE LASAGNE

5 **Heat the oven** to 180°C (350°F/Gas 4). Brush a baking dish with oil. Spread 3-4 tbsp of tomato sauce in the dish; cover with a layer of lasagne sheets, overlapping slightly.

6 **Spread on a quarter of the ricotta,** then a quarter of the mushrooms and peppers. Spoon over a fifth of the remaining tomato sauce, and Parmesan. Continue to make 4 layers, finishing with lasagne on top. Cover with the remaining sauce and Parmesan. Bake the lasagne for 35-45 minutes, until bubbling and golden brown.

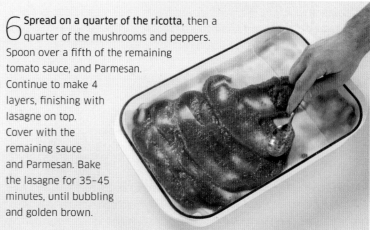

Aubergine cannelloni

CHOOSE BROAD AUBERGINES so you have big slices for filling with lots of luscious mozzarella and ricotta cheeses. These cannelloni can be baked up to 2 days ahead. Cover and chill, then reheat them in the oven for 20 minutes.

SERVES	PREP	COOK
SERVES 4-6	40-45 MINS PLUS STANDING	50-60 MINS

Ingredients

FOR THE AUBERGINES

4 aubergines, total weight about 1.4kg (3lb)

salt and pepper

4 tbsp olive oil

250g (9oz) mozzarella cheese

250g (9oz) ricotta cheese

leaves from 1 bunch of basil, plus a few sprigs for serving

30g (1oz) Parmesan cheese, grated

FOR THE SAUCE

75ml (2½fl oz) olive oil

3 onions, finely chopped

5 garlic cloves, finely chopped

90ml (3fl oz) tomato purée

1 bouquet garni

3 x 400g (14oz) cans chopped tomatoes

granulated sugar

PREPARE THE AUBERGINES

1 **Trim the aubergines** and cut them lengthways into 1cm (½in) slices. Lay on a non-metallic tray, in 1 layer, and sprinkle generously on both sides with salt. Leave 30 minutes. Preheat the oven to 190°C (375°F/Gas 5).

2 **Rinse the aubergine** slices with cold water and dry on kitchen paper. Lightly brush one side of each slice with olive oil and set oil-side down on baking sheets. Brush the tops with more oil.

3 **Bake the aubergine** slices in the oven, turning once, for about 20 minutes, until tender and lightly browned. Do not cook them for too long or they will be too soft to handle.

MAKE THE SAUCE

4 **Heat the oil** in a frying pan, add the onions, and cook over medium heat, stirring occasionally, for 3-4 minutes, until soft but not brown. Add the garlic, tomato purée, bouquet garni, tomatoes, a pinch of sugar, salt, and pepper. Cover and cook over very low heat, about 10 minutes.

5 **Uncover the frying pan** and continue cooking the tomato sauce, stirring occasionally, for about 15 minutes, until thick. Lift out and discard the bouquet garni. Taste for seasoning and adjust if necessary.

FILL THE CANNELLONI

6 **Spread one-third of the tomato sauce** in the bottom of a baking dish, about 23x32cm (9x13in). Cut the mozzarella into 1cm (½in) sticks.

7 **Spread a slice of aubergine** with 1 tbsp ricotta. Put a basil leaf at one end, set a mozzarella stick on top and sprinkle with pepper. Roll up the aubergine slice.

8 **Transfer the roll** to the baking dish and repeat with the remaining aubergine slices, ricotta, basil, and mozzarella cheese. Spoon over the remaining tomato sauce and sprinkle with Parmesan. Bake until very hot and bubbling, 20–25 minutes. Serve on warmed plates.

 VARIATION: Aubergine feuilles

Lots of layers of luscious vegetables and molten cheese make this dish into an impressively tall, stacked plate.

1 Trim the aubergines and cut them into 1cm (¹/₂in) rounds. There should be 36 rounds. Spread them on a large, non-metallic tray, sprinkle with salt and leave for 25 minutes, then rinse, dry and bake with olive oil as directed. Make the tomato sauce as directed, cooking 5 minutes longer to make it thicker. Let it cool to tepid. Cut 300g (10oz) mozzarella cheese into 24 slices, each about 5mm (¹/₄in) thick.

2 Stir the ricotta cheese into half the cooled tomato sauce and taste for seasoning. Pull the basil leaves from the stalks, saving 6 sprigs for garnish. Oil a baking sheet. Spread a large aubergine round with the tomato and cheese filling, top with a slice of mozzarella and 2 basil leaves, then add a smaller round of aubergine. Repeat the layers, finishing with an even smaller piece of aubergine.

3 Secure the "feuilles" with a cocktail stick so they hold together during cooking. Transfer to the baking sheet and continue with the remaining aubergine rounds and filling. Bake in the heated oven until very hot and the mozzarella has melted, about 12 minutes. Reheat the remaining tomato sauce and spoon it on to 6 warmed plates. Set the hot feuilles on top. Remove the cocktail sticks and decorate with sprigs of basil.

Courgette tian

TIAN IS THE PROVENÇAL NAME for a shallow earthenware dish, as well as for a vegetable mixture, held together with eggs and cooked rice. Try to use small courgettes for this recipe, as they tend to have a more concentrated flavour than the larger, more watery examples. Use this recipe as a blueprint for other vegetables; all are equally delicious and make a satisfying vegetarian dish. For carnivores, this is also an excellent side dish with roast lamb or chicken.

SERVES	PREP	COOK
SERVES 6	30-35 MINS	20-30 MINS

Ingredients

75ml (2½ fl oz) olive oil

1kg (2¼lb) courgettes, in 5mm (¼in) slices

salt and pepper

65g (2¼oz) long-grain rice

2 onions, thinly sliced

3 garlic cloves, finely chopped

leaves from 5-7 flat-leaf parsley sprigs, finely chopped

60g (2oz) Parmesan cheese, grated

3 eggs

PREPARE THE COURGETTES

1 Heat one-third of the oil in a large frying pan. Add the courgettes, salt, and pepper, and cook over medium heat, stirring occasionally, for 10-15 minutes, until tender and evenly browned. Spread the slices out over a large plate to cool.

PREPARE THE REMAINING INGREDIENTS

2 Bring a saucepan of salted water to a boil, add the rice, and bring back to a boil. Simmer for 10-12 minutes, until just tender, stirring once or twice to prevent the grains sticking to the bottom of the pan. Drain the rice in a colander, rinse with cold water to remove some of the starch, and drain again thoroughly. Let the rice cool for 8-10 minutes, then stir with a fork to separate the grains.

3 Heat half the remaining oil in the frying pan, add the onions and garlic, and cook over medium heat, stirring occasionally, for 3-5 minutes, until soft but not coloured.

ASSEMBLE AND BAKE THE TIAN

4 Preheat the oven to 180°C (350°F/Gas 4). Brush a 1.5 litre (2¾ pint) baking dish with oil. Coarsely chop the cooled courgettes.

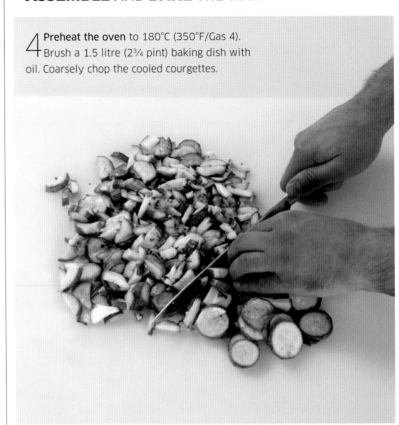

5 In a large bowl, combine the courgettes, onion mixture, parsley, rice, and Parmesan. Stir to mix, then taste for seasoning. Crack the eggs into a bowl and beat to mix. Stir them into the vegetable mixture with the wooden spoon.

6 **Spread the mixture** in the baking dish, and sprinkle with the remaining oil. Bake the tian in the heated oven for 10–15 minutes, until set. Increase the oven temperature to 200°C (400°F/Gas 6), and bake for 10–15 minutes longer, until brown. Serve hot, or at room temperature, from the baking dish.

 VARIATION: Spinach and mushroom tian

A tasty alternative.

1 Omit the courgettes, rice, and parsley. Trim the crusts from 2 slices of white bread, and work to fine crumbs in a food processor. Cook 1kg (2¼lb) spinach in a large saucepan of salted water for 1–2 minutes, until wilted. Drain, leave until cool enough to handle, then squeeze with your fist to remove any excess water. Chop coarsely. Wipe 375g (13oz) mushrooms, trim the stalks even to the caps (discard the base of the stalks), then thinly and evenly slice the caps.

2 Heat 2 tbsp olive oil in a large frying pan, and cook the onions and garlic as directed in the main recipe. Add the mushrooms and sauté for 5 minutes. Add the spinach, salt, and pepper, and cook, stirring occasionally, until all the liquid has been released and has then evaporated; it should take about 5 minutes. Make sure the pan is dry, or the tian will be soggy after baking. Let cool, then stir in the Parmesan. Taste for seasoning and adjust if necessary. Prepare a baking dish as directed.

3 Beat the eggs, then stir them evenly into the vegetable mixture. Spoon into the prepared baking dish, and sprinkle with the breadcrumbs and 2 tbsp olive oil. Bake as directed in the main recipe.

Mixed vegetable curry

TRY THIS WITH A RAITA of diced cucumber and plain yogurt, seasoned with salt and a pinch of cumin. There are a lot of spices used here, but each one is important for the total balance of the dish, and all are widely available. Replace some of the coconut milk in the curry with water for a lighter dish.

SERVES	PREP	COOK
SERVES 6-8	45-50 MINS	25-35 MINS

Ingredients

400g (14oz) basmati rice

salt

FOR THE SPICE MIXTURE

6 dried red chillies

12 cardamom pods

3 tbsp coriander seeds

1 tbsp cumin seeds

½ tsp mustard seeds

2 tsp each fenugreek seeds, ground turmeric, and ground ginger

FOR THE VEGETABLES

4 each onions, potatoes, and carrots

1 cauliflower

500g (1lb 2oz) French beans

75ml (2½ fl oz) vegetable oil

1 cinnamon stick

6 cloves

3 garlic cloves, finely chopped

4 large tomatoes, peeled and deseeded

250g (9oz) shelled fresh or defrosted frozen peas

2 x 400g (14oz) cans coconut milk

MAKE THE SPICE MIXTURE

1 Split the dried red chillies and discard the seeds. Crush the cardamom pods in a mortar and pestle and discard the pods, keeping the seeds in the mortar.

2 Put the chillies in a small frying pan with the coriander seeds and cumin seeds and toast over medium heat for about 2 minutes, stirring constantly to prevent burning, until browned and very fragrant. Set aside.

3 Put the toasted spices in the mortar with the cardamom and add the mustard seeds and fenugreek seeds. Crush to a fine powder. Add the turmeric and ginger, and stir well to mix.

PREPARE THE VEGETABLES

4 Dice the onions, then peel and cut each potato into 1cm (½in) dice. Put them in a bowl of water to prevent discolouration. Trim the florets from the cauliflower, then cut the florets into small pieces. Chop the carrots into 1cm (½in) slices, then trim the beans and cut into 5cm (2in) pieces.

MAKE THE CURRY

5 Heat the oil in the sauté pan, add the cinnamon stick and cloves, and cook for 30-60 seconds, until fragrant. Add the onions and garlic and sauté quickly, stirring to soften and cook evenly, until beginning to colour.

6 Add the spice mixture and cook over low heat, stirring constantly, for about 2-3 minutes. Drain the potatoes and add to the pan with the carrots, cauliflower, French beans, tomatoes, peas, and salt to taste. Sauté for 3-5 minutes, until thoroughly coated with spices.

7 Add the coconut milk and stir. Cover the pan and simmer for 15–20 minutes, until the vegetables are tender and the sauce is thick and rich. Remove and discard the cloves and cinnamon. Taste for seasoning.

COOK THE RICE

8 Put the rice in a large bowl, cover generously with cold water, and let soak for 2–3 minutes, stirring occasionally. Drain in a colander, rinse with cold water, and drain thoroughly.

9 Put the rice in a saucepan with 850ml (scant 1½ pints) water and a pinch of salt. Bring to a boil, then cover and simmer for 10–12 minutes, until just tender. Remove from heat and leave covered for at least 5 minutes, then gently stir the rice to fluff it. Serve the curry and rice hot on warmed plates.

 VARIATION: Winter vegetable curry

Use seasonal vegetables in the colder months.

1 Prepare the curry spice mixture, onions, garlic, potatoes, carrots, and cauliflower as directed; omit the green beans, tomatoes, and peas. Discard the seeds from 500g (1lb 2oz) pumpkin, cut into 7.5cm (3in) pieces and peel. Dice the flesh.

2 Trim, peel, and dice 3 turnips. Trim 250g (9oz) Brussels sprouts. Sauté the onions and garlic with the curry spice mixture. Add the prepared vegetables and continue with the curry as directed, simmering it for 15–20 minutes.

3 Spread the rice in a large, shallow serving bowl and add the vegetable curry. Serve hot.

Pumpkin stew

A HEARTY MEAL with an eye-popping presentation. Shown here ladled out into an individual serving bowl, the stew is best served inside a pumpkin. Take it to the table to make a real impact on your guests.

SERVES SERVES 8	PREP 50-60 MINS	COOK 2½-3 HOURS

Ingredients

1 pumpkin, weighing about 5kg (11lb)

1 celeriac, weighing about 750g (1lb 10oz)

juice of ½ lemon

4 tomatoes, total weight about 500g (1lb 2oz)

125g (4½oz) butter

3 leeks, cut into 2.5cm (1in) slices

2 garlic cloves, finely chopped

30g (1oz) plain flour

500ml (16fl oz) vegetable or chicken stock, plus more if needed

salt and pepper

cayenne

2 celery sticks, peeled, cut into 1cm (½in) slices

5 turnips, total weight about 500g (1lb 2oz), in 2.5cm (1in) dice

1 butternut squash, weighing about 750g (1lb 10oz), in 2cm (¾in) dice

1 courgette, in 2.5cm (1in) dice

leaves from 3-5 thyme sprigs

PREPARE THE PUMPKIN SHELL

1 **Preheat the oven** to 170°C (325°F/ Gas 3). Cut around the stalk end of the pumpkin at an angle and pull off the round "lid". Set the lid aside.

2 **Using your hands,** scoop out the seeds with all the fibrous threads and discard them. Put the pumpkin in a baking dish. Pour enough boiling water into the pumpkin to fill it. Replace the stalk end and bake for 1½-2 hours, until the flesh is just tender.

3 **Ladle out and discard** the cooking water. With a large spoon, scoop out the flesh, leaving the shell about 1cm (½in) thick. Set the shell aside. Cut the flesh into chunks and purée in a food processor until smooth.

PREPARE THE CELERIAC AND TOMATOES

4 Peel the celeriac with a sharp knife, being careful not to remove too much of the flesh with the skin. Take care, as the skin is tough and a slip of the knife could be painful. Cut the flesh into 2.5cm (1in) cubes. Put the cubes of celeriac in a large bowl of water along with the lemon juice, to prevent discolouration.

5 Cut the cores from the tomatoes and score an "x" on the base of each. Immerse them in boiling water until the skin starts to split, then plunge into a bowl of cold water. Peel off the skin. Cut in half and squeeze out the seeds, then cut each half into quarters. Alternatively, simply use 1 x 400g (14oz) can chopped tomatoes. If tomatoes are not beautifully ripe and in season, the latter is usually the best choice.

MAKE THE STEW

6 Heat the butter in a casserole, add the leeks and garlic and soften over low heat, stirring occasionally, for 3–5 minutes. Add the flour and cook, stirring, for 1–2 minutes, until foaming.

7 Stir in the stock and pumpkin purée. Drain the celeriac and add it to the pot with salt, pepper, and cayenne to taste. Bring to a boil and simmer gently for 20 minutes. Add the celery and turnips and simmer for 20 minutes longer, until beginning to soften.

8 Add the squash and courgette, tomatoes, and thyme and simmer for 10 minutes longer. Taste for seasoning and adjust if necessary. Set the pumpkin shell on a large, robust serving plate, and ladle in the steaming hot stew. Provide warmed bowls for your guests.

Baked polenta with wild mushrooms

YOU CAN PREPARE THIS A DAY AHEAD up to the end of step 5, and refrigerate, then bake on the day. It is a hugely tempting and comforting dish, with the slight sweetness of polenta and the melting, unctuous cheese and mushrooms. Make it on a cold winter's day to warm both bodies and souls.

SERVES
SERVES 6

PREP
40-45 MINS
PLUS CHILLING

COOK
20-25 MINS

Ingredients

FOR THE POLENTA

1 tbsp salt

375g (13oz) fine polenta

FOR THE WILD MUSHROOM STEW

250g (9oz) fresh wild mushrooms

375g (13oz) button mushrooms

3 tbsp olive oil

3 garlic cloves, finely chopped

leaves from 5-7 thyme or rosemary sprigs

125ml (4fl oz) dry white wine

250ml (9fl oz) vegetable stock or water

4 tbsp double cream

salt and pepper

250g (9oz) fontina cheese, sliced

MAKE THE POLENTA

1 **Sprinkle 2 baking sheets** with water. Bring 1.5 litres (2¾ pints) water to a boil in a saucepan and add the salt. Over medium heat, slowly whisk in the polenta in a thin, steady stream.

2 **Cook,** stirring, for 10-15 minutes, until thick enough to pull away from the pan. It should be soft and smooth. Spread on the baking sheets in a layer about 30cm (12in) square. Cool, then chill for 1 hour until very firm.

MAKE THE MUSHROOM STEW

3 **Wipe all the mushrooms** with damp kitchen paper and trim the stalks. Cut the wild mushrooms into slices and the common mushrooms into halves, or quarters if large.

4 **Heat the oil** in the frying pan. Add all the mushrooms, the garlic, and thyme or rosemary and cook, stirring, for 5-7 minutes, until the mushrooms are tender and the liquid has evaporated.

5 **Add the wine,** simmer for 2-3 minutes, then the stock and cook until reduced by half. Pour in the cream; cook until the liquid thickens. Season.

ASSEMBLE THE DISH

6 **Preheat the oven** to 220°C (425°F/ Gas 7). Brush a 23x33cm (9x13in) baking dish with oil. Cut the chilled polenta into 6 x 10cm (4in) squares; reserve the trimmings. Arrange half the squares in the dish in a single layer.

7 **Spoon half the mushroom stew** over, then half the fontina. Repeat with another layer of polenta and mushrooms. Top with the remaining fontina. Bake for 20-25 minutes, until the cheese has melted, and serve very hot.

Perfect pasta and cheese

GROWN-UP MACARONI CHEESE! The wild and domestic mushrooms in the pasta make this a sophisticated take on the old favourite, but use all button mushrooms if you want a more economical dish. A tomato salad is all you need on the side.

SERVES
SERVES 6

PREP
30-35 MINS

COOK
25-30 MINS

Ingredients

FOR THE PASTA

15g (½oz) butter

3 shallots, finely chopped

3 garlic cloves, finely chopped

125g (4½oz) mixed wild mushrooms, sliced

125g (4½oz) button mushrooms, sliced

salt and pepper

375g (13oz) penne pasta

FOR THE TOPPING AND CHEESE SAUCE

2 slices of white bread

1 small bunch of chives, snipped

250g (9oz) sharp Cheddar cheese, grated

1 litre (1¾ pints) milk

1 slice of onion

6 black peppercorns

1 bay leaf

30g (1oz) butter

2 tbsp plain flour

freshly grated nutmeg

PREPARE THE MUSHROOMS

1 **Melt the butter** in a sauté pan, add the shallots, and stir for 1 minute, until soft. Add the garlic, mushrooms, salt, and pepper. Cook, stirring, for 3-5 minutes, until the liquid has evaporated and the mushrooms are tender.

MAKE THE TOPPING

2 **Discard the crusts** from the bread, and break down to coarse crumbs in a food processor. Combine with a quarter of the chives, and 30g (1oz) of the cheese. Set aside.

MAKE THE SAUCE

3 **Scald the milk** in a saucepan with the onion slice, peppercorns, and bay leaf. Remove from the heat and leave for 10 minutes. Melt the butter in another pan, and whisk in the flour. Remove from the heat, and strain in two-thirds of the milk. Return to the heat, and whisk until it boils.

4 **Grate a little nutmeg** into the sauce, season well, and simmer for 2 minutes. Remove from the heat, and add the remaining cheese. Gradually whisk in the remaining milk. Taste for seasoning.

FINISH THE DISH

5 **Preheat the oven** to 180°C (350°F/Gas 4). Fill a large pan with water, bring to a boil, and add 1 tbsp salt. Add the pasta, and simmer for 5-7 minutes. Drain. Butter a 2 litre (3½ pint) dish. Mix the pasta with the sauce, mushrooms, and remaining chives. Spoon into the dish, and sprinkle over the topping. Bake for 25-30 minutes, until bubbling and golden.

Vegetable couscous

COUSCOUS LOOKS AND COOKS LIKE A GRAIN, though in fact it is made from a wheat-flour dough. It is a very popular dish in France, where Algerian and Moroccan immigrants have settled for a century, bringing their delicious food with them. This version is served in the Algerian style, with the broth separate from the fragrant vegetables and fluffy couscous. If you can find the Moorish spice blend *ras-el-hanout*, add a teaspoon of it to the broth at the same time as the ginger and turmeric. You'll need 16 bamboo skewers.

SERVES	PREP	COOK
SERVES 8	35-40 MINS PLUS MARINATING	30-35 MINS

Ingredients

FOR THE VEGETABLE BROTH

large pinch of saffron threads

2kg (4½lb) mixed vegetables: 2 leeks, 2 courgettes, 2 carrots, 2 turnips, 1 onion, 3 tomatoes

2 tbsp olive oil

2 litres (3½ pints) chicken stock

400g (14oz) can chickpeas

1 bouquet garni

1 tsp each ground ginger, turmeric, and paprika

salt and pepper

FOR THE VEGETABLE KEBABS

2 courgettes

2 red peppers

250g (9oz) mushrooms

5-6 small onions, total weight about 375g (13oz)

leaves from 1 small bunch of coriander, finely chopped

leaves from 4-6 thyme sprigs

125ml (4fl oz) olive oil

250g (9oz) cherry tomatoes

1 tsp ground cumin

FOR THE COUSCOUS

500g (1lb 2oz) couscous

45-60g (1½-2oz) butter

MAKE THE VEGETABLE BROTH

1 **Put the saffron** in a small bowl and pour over 3-4 tbsp hot water. Set aside to steep while you prepare the vegetables. Wash the leeks very well and cut them into strips. Cut the courgettes, carrots, and turnips into slices. Dice the onion.

2 **Peel, deseed, and coarsely chop** the tomatoes. Heat the oil in a large saucepan, add the onion and stir for 2-3 minutes, until they are soft but not brown. Add the tomatoes and cook for about 5 minutes, until the mixture has thickened.

3 **Add the chicken** stock, courgettes, carrots, turnips, leeks, chickpeas, and bouquet garni. Stir in the ginger, turmeric, paprika, saffron with its liquid, and salt and pepper.

4 **Bring to a boil** and simmer for 15-20 minutes until the vegetables are just tender to the point of a knife. Discard the bouquet garni, taste the broth for seasoning, and set aside.

MAKE THE KEBABS

5 **Trim the courgettes.** Cut each lengthways into quarters, then into chunky pieces. Cut the peppers into large squares. Cut the mushrooms in halves or quarters if large, or leave them whole if they are small.

6 **Cut the onions** into quarters, leaving on a little root to hold them together. Set aside 1-2 tbsp of the herbs; put the remainder in a small bowl, and mix in the olive oil.

7 **Put the mushrooms,** courgettes, red peppers, onions, and tomatoes in a large bowl. Pour the herb and olive oil mixture over the vegetables. Toss to coat, and leave to marinate for 1-2 hours at room temperature. Meanwhile, soak 16 bamboo skewers in water.

GRILL THE KEBABS AND **PREPARE** THE COUSCOUS

8 **Heat the grill.** Thread the vegetables on to the skewers. Scrape any herbs from the bowl and brush them on the kebabs. Set on the baking sheet, and grill about 7.5cm (3in) from the heat for about 5 minutes, until browned. Turn and grill on the other side for about 5 minutes longer, until browned and tender.

9 **While the kebabs are grilling,** prepare the couscous: put it in a large bowl and pour over 500ml (16fl oz) boiling water, stirring quickly with a fork. Let the couscous sit for about 5 minutes, until plump. The quantity of water required may vary with the type of couscous you use, so check the package directions.

10 **Add the butter,** salt, and pepper to the couscous. Stir and toss with the fork to fluff the grains and incorporate the butter. Taste for seasoning. Reheat the vegetable broth if necessary and transfer it to serving bowls. Pile the couscous on to warmed plates. Sprinkle the kebabs with salt, pepper, and cumin. Arrange the skewers on the couscous; serve with fiery *harissa* (Moroccan hot sauce), if liked.

Stuffed veggies with walnut sauce

TRY USING OTHER GRAINS such as buckwheat instead of bulghur wheat, if you prefer. The garlicky walnut sauce which forms the accompaniment here is a deliciously useful one to know, and can be used to go with any grilled or barbecued vegetables.

SERVES	PREP	COOK
SERVES 4	40–45 MINS PLUS STANDING	15–20 MINS

Ingredients

FOR THE VEGETABLES

4 large tomatoes

salt and pepper

4 red or Spanish onions

2 large courgettes

250g (9oz) bulghur wheat

3 tbsp olive oil, plus more for dish and foil

2 celery sticks, peeled and thinly sliced

4 garlic cloves, finely chopped

125g (4½oz) fresh shiitake or button mushrooms, chopped

leaves from 4–6 tarragon sprigs, chopped

leaves from 4–6 parsley sprigs, chopped

FOR THE WALNUT-GARLIC SAUCE

leaves from 4–6 parsley sprigs

4 garlic cloves, peeled

75g (2½oz) walnut halves

250ml (9fl oz) walnut oil

PREPARE THE VEGETABLES

1 **Core the tomatoes** and cut a slice from the top of each. Scoop out the seeds and flesh, leaving a 1cm (½in) wall of flesh. Scrape the seeds from the scooped-out flesh; reserve the flesh for the stuffing. Season the inside of the tomatoes and set them upside-down on kitchen paper for 30 minutes.

2 **Peel the onions.** Cut a flat slice from the top and a thin slice from the root end of each so it will sit flat. Put in a saucepan and cover with water. Add salt, put on the lid, and bring to a boil. Simmer for 10–15 minutes, until barely tender. Drain on kitchen paper. Hollow out the onions, leaving a 1cm (½in) wall, pushing out the core with your fingers. Reserve the cores for the stuffing.

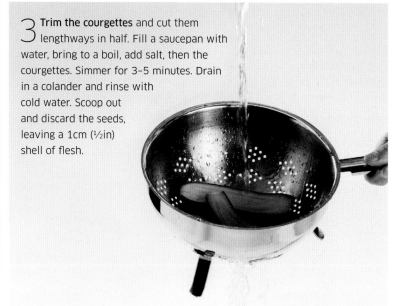

3 **Trim the courgettes** and cut them lengthways in half. Fill a saucepan with water, bring to a boil, add salt, then the courgettes. Simmer for 3–5 minutes. Drain in a colander and rinse with cold water. Scoop out and discard the seeds, leaving a 1cm (½in) shell of flesh.

MAKE THE STUFFING

4 **Put the bulghur** in a large bowl, pour on 750ml (1¼ pints) boiling water, cover and let stand for 30 minutes, until plump. Drain off any excess water. Chop the reserved onion cores and the tomato flesh.

5 **Heat the oil** in a frying pan. Add the celery, garlic, and chopped onion and cook, stirring, for 2–3 minutes, until soft but not brown. Add the mushrooms, season and cook for about 5 minutes, until the liquid has evaporated. Stir in the chopped tomato and cook until the liquid evaporates, about 2 minutes more. Add the chopped herbs and taste for seasoning. Mix the sautéed vegetables into the bulghur. Taste for seasoning.

STUFF AND BAKE THE VEGETABLES

6 **Preheat the oven** to 190°C (375°F/Gas 5). Oil a large baking dish. Spoon the stuffing into the onions, courgettes, and tomatoes. Spread the remaining stuffing over the bottom of the dish and arrange the vegetables on top. Cover with oiled foil, and bake for 15–20 minutes, until tender.

MAKE THE SAUCE

7 **Put the parsley,** garlic, walnuts, and 2 tbsp cold water in a food processor and purée to a paste. Season with salt and pepper. With the blade turning, gradually add the walnut oil. Taste for seasoning.

8 **Arrange a tomato,** an onion, and a courgette half, with extra stuffing from the baking dish, if you like, on 4 warmed plates. Serve the walnut-garlic sauce on the side.

 VARIATION: Vegetable trio with carrot-rice stuffing

Carrot makes a colourful addition here.

1 Prepare the vegetables as directed. Cook 250g (9oz) long-grain white rice in boiling salted water until barely tender; it should take 10–12 minutes, or according to the packet instructions. Drain in a colander and rinse with cold running water to remove some of the starch.

2 Peel and coarsely grate 2 carrots. Make the stuffing as directed, using the rice in place of the bulghur wheat and stirring in the grated carrot just before stuffing the vegetables.

3 Stuff and bake the vegetables as directed and serve with the walnut-garlic sauce. Decorate with sprigs of fresh tarragon.

Broccoli and mushroom quiche

LOOK FOR BROCCOLI with firm, juicy stalks that still seem moist, as it will be the freshest. When purple-sprouting broccoli is in season in early spring, use it here instead of the regular broccoli; it will be sweeter but with a more assertive flavour and a stronger colour. Try to choose mushrooms with good flavour; the large, flat-capped field or Portobello mushrooms are good, as well as being reasonably priced.

SERVES	**PREP**	**COOK**
SERVES 6-8	45–50 MINS PLUS STANDING	30–35 MINS

Ingredients

FOR THE PASTRY

200g (7oz) plain flour

1 egg yolk

½ tsp salt

100g (3½ oz) unsalted butter

FOR THE FILLING

1-2 heads of broccoli, total weight about 500g (1lb 2oz)

salt and pepper

30g (1oz) butter

175g (6oz) mushrooms, sliced

2 garlic cloves, finely chopped

ground nutmeg

FOR THE CUSTARD

3 eggs, plus 2 egg yolks

375ml (12fl oz) milk

250ml (9fl oz) double cream

60g (2oz) Parmesan cheese, grated

ground nutmeg

MAKE THE PASTRY

1 **Sift the flour** on to a work surface and make a well in the centre. Put the egg yolk, salt, and 3 tbsp water in the well. Wrap the butter in baking parchment and pound it with a rolling pin or meat mallet to soften it slightly, then add it to the well.

2 **With your fingers,** work the flour into the other ingredients until coarse crumbs form. Press the dough lightly into a ball. If it's too dry, sprinkle with a little more water.

3 **Lightly flour a work surface,** then knead the pastry for 1-2 minutes, or until it is very smooth and peels away from the work surface in one piece. Shape into a ball, wrap it tightly with cling film, and chill for about 30 minutes until firm.

LINE THE TIN

4 **Preheat the oven** to 220°C (425°F/Gas 7). Butter a 25cm (10in) fluted flan tin. Lightly flour a work surface and roll out the dough to a 30cm (12in) round. Drape over the tin. Gently lift the edge of the dough with one hand and press it well into the bottom edge of the tin.

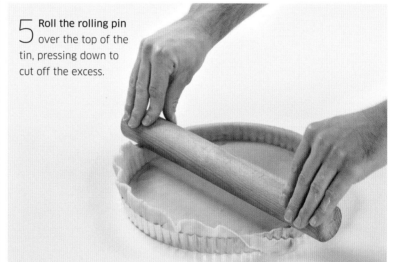

5 **Roll the rolling pin** over the top of the tin, pressing down to cut off the excess.

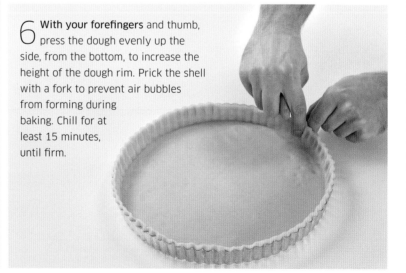

6 **With your forefingers** and thumb, press the dough evenly up the side, from the bottom, to increase the height of the dough rim. Prick the shell with a fork to prevent air bubbles from forming during baking. Chill for at least 15 minutes, until firm.

BLIND BAKE THE PASTRY

7 Line the pastry with a double thickness of foil, pressing it well into the bottom edges of the tin. If necessary, trim the foil so it stands about 4cm (1½in) above the sides of the tin. Spread an even layer of dried beans, baking beans, or raw rice on to the foil to weigh down the pastry, and stop it from rising while it is baking.

8 Bake the pastry dough shell until it is set and starting to turn golden brown; it should take about 15 minutes, but check after 12 by lifting up a corner of the foil and looking at the pastry underneath. When it is ready, remove the foil and all the beans or rice and reduce the oven temperature to 190°C (375°F/Gas 5). Continue baking the pastry shell until it is lightly browned all over. It should only take about 5 minutes, but check after 3 minutes, and turn the tin around if the pastry shell looks as though it is browning unevenly.

COOK THE BROCCOLI AND MUSHROOMS, AND ASSEMBLE THE QUICHE

9 Cut the florets from the broccoli stalk, then slice the stalk lengthwise into sticks. Half-fill a saucepan with water and bring to a boil. Add salt, then the broccoli. Cook until just tender; it should only take about 3–5 minutes. Drain.

10 Melt the butter in a frying pan, add the mushrooms and garlic and sauté until the mushrooms have first given out all their liquid, and then all that liquid has evaporated.

11 Whisk together the eggs, egg yolks, milk, cream, grated cheese, salt, pepper, and a pinch of nutmeg. Spread the mushrooms in the pastry shell. Arrange the broccoli on top. Ladle the cheese custard over to fill almost to the rim. Bake for 30–35 minutes, until browned and the custard has a slight wobble in the centre when shaken. Serve hot or at room temperature.

Polenta with vegetable stew

A WONDERFULLY SUBSTANTIAL meal. This is actually better if you make the vegetables the day before and refrigerate; the flavours will marry and the whole stew become far more succulent. Reheat just before serving. Creamy polenta is an ideal comfort food, and makes a great change from potatoes or rice as a filling side dish; add extra butter for a more indulgent treat. Once cooked, polenta can be flavoured with cheese and herbs – experiment to find your favourite combination.

SERVES	PREP	COOK
SERVES 6-8	40 MINS	50 MINS

Ingredients

FOR THE POLENTA

1 tbsp salt

450g (1lb) fine polenta

45g (1½oz) butter

FOR THE VEGETABLE STEW

2 aubergines

2 courgettes

salt and pepper

400g (14oz) can plum tomatoes

1 bunch of basil

4 tbsp olive oil, plus more if needed

3 onions, sliced

4 garlic cloves, finely chopped

1 red pepper, sliced

1 yellow pepper, sliced

1 green pepper, sliced

PREPARE THE POLENTA

1 Bring 2 litres (3½ pints) of water to a boil in a large, very heavy-based saucepan and add the salt. Over medium heat, slowly whisk in the polenta in a thin, steady stream, keeping a whirling eddy in the pan until all the grain has been added. Whisk constantly to avoid lumps; the polenta mixture should remain completely smooth throughout cooking.

2 Cook, stirring occasionally, until the polenta is thick enough to hold a shape and pulls away from the side of the pan; it should take 15-20 minutes. Make sure it does not threaten at any time to catch on the base of the pan, as the scorched taste will spoil the dish. Meanwhile, make the vegetable stew.

3 Taste the polenta; it should have no remaining taste of raw corn. If it does, continue to cook for 5 minutes more, than taste again. Cover, keep warm and set aside while you finish making the vegetable stew.

PREPARE THE AUBERGINES AND COURGETTES

4 **Trim the ends** from the aubergines and cut into 2.5cm (1in) chunks. Trim the courgettes, cut lengthways in half, then into 1cm (½in) slices.

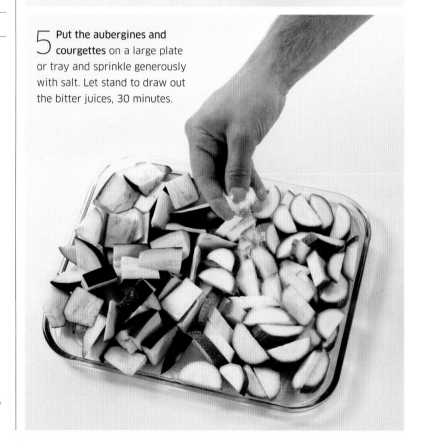

5 **Put the aubergines and courgettes** on a large plate or tray and sprinkle generously with salt. Let stand to draw out the bitter juices, 30 minutes.

6 Rinse the aubergines and courgettes with cold water and pat dry with kitchen paper.

COOK THE VEGETABLE STEW

7 Drain the canned tomatoes, reserving the juice, and chop. Strip the basil leaves from the stalks, reserving 6–8 sprigs for decoration, and coarsely chop.

8 Heat the olive oil in a sauté pan. Add the onions and garlic, and cook, stirring, for 3–5 minutes, until softened but not brown. Make sure that the garlic does not turn brown, as that will impair the flavour of the finished dish. Stir in the sliced peppers, then the aubergine chunks, and cook for 2–3 minutes longer, stirring constantly, until everything is just beginning to become tender.

9 Add the courgettes and continue cooking, stirring often, until all the vegetables are just tender to the point of a knife; it should take 7–10 minutes. Add more oil if the pan starts to dry out at any stage. Stir in the tomatoes with any of their juice, and add salt and pepper generously; the vegetables will be at their best if very well seasoned. Simmer, stirring occasionally, for 12–15 minutes, until the stew has thickened.

FINISH THE POLENTA

10 Beat the butter into the polenta until evenly mixed. Serve a golden pile of the polenta on warmed plates with the vegetable stew, and sprinkle with the reserved basil.

Potato and blue cheese filo pie

BASED ON THE GREEK SPINACH PIE, *spanokopita*, but with an indulgent twist to the filling. This is an excellent dish to make ahead for a mid-week meal as it can be prepared entirely, up to the point of baking, then wrapped tightly in clingfilm and refrigerated for 2 days. Bake it just before serving.

SERVES SERVES 6	**PREP** 35–40 MINS	**COOK** 45–55 MINS

Ingredients

1kg (2¼lb) potatoes, very thinly sliced

125g (4½oz) crumbly blue cheese

175g (6oz) butter

500g (1lb 2oz) package filo pastry

4 shallots, finely diced

leaves from 4–5 parsley sprigs, finely chopped

leaves from 4–5 tarragon sprigs, finely chopped

leaves from 4–5 chervil sprigs, finely chopped

salt and pepper

3–4 tbsp soured cream

PREPARE THE FILLING

1 **Bring a saucepan of water** to a boil, add the potatoes, and simmer for 5 minutes. Drain, and set aside to cool. Crumble the cheese.

CUT THE FILO

2 **Preheat the oven** to 180°C (350°F/ Gas 4). Melt the butter in a saucepan. Brush a 28cm (11in) springform tin with a little of the butter. Lay a damp tea towel on a work surface, and unroll the filo pastry sheets on to the towel.

3 **Using the tin** as a guide, cut through the pastry sheets to leave a 7.5cm (3in) border around the tin. Reserve the trimmings. Cover the sheets and the pastry trimmings with a second damp towel.

4 **Put a filo sheet** on a third damp tea towel and brush with butter, then press into the tin. Repeat with another sheet, putting it in the tin at a right angle to the first. Continue until half the filo is used.

5 **Arrange half the potatoes** in the tin, sprinkling with half the cheese, chopped shallots, herbs, salt, and pepper. Repeat, then pour over the soured cream.

6 **Cover the pie** with the remaining filo, buttering and layering as before. Cut a 7.5cm (3in) hole from the centre, so the filling shows through. Scrunch up and arrange the filo trimmings on top. Bake for 45–55 minutes, until golden brown. Serve in wedges, with salad leaves on the side.

Spaghetti primavera

THE YOUNGER THE VEGETABLES you can get your hands on, the better and sweeter this dish will be. Their beautiful pale greens and oranges epitomize the colours of spring. During the season, add asparagus tips, baby fennel bulbs, or tiny, new broad beans, as you prefer. This is a wonderfully light dish for the first of the warmer evenings.

SERVES	PREP	COOK
SERVES 4	45–50 MINS	10–12 MINS

Ingredients

2 courgettes, in 1cm (½in) dice

salt and pepper

2 carrots, in 1cm (½in) dice

210g (7½oz) shelled fresh peas

500g (1lb 2oz) spaghetti

45g (1½oz) butter

175ml (6fl oz) double cream

30g (1oz) grated Parmesan cheese

PREPARE THE VEGETABLES AND PASTA

1 **Bring a saucepan** of water to the boil. Add the courgettes and salt and cook for 2–3 minutes, until barely tender to the tip of a knife. Drain very well, then blot dry on kitchen paper. Set aside on fresh kitchen paper, to ensure the blanched courgettes are not at all soggy when added to the spaghetti sauce.

2 **Put the carrots** in a saucepan, cover with cold water, add salt and bring to the boil. Simmer for 5 minutes, or until just tender, then drain, rinse with cold water and set aside. Bring a clean saucepan of salted water to the boil. Add the peas and simmer for 3–8 minutes, depending on their size and age, until tender. Drain, rinse with cold water and set aside. It is necessary briefly to boil (or blanch) the vegetables separately, because each cooks at a different rate. In a dish such as this, which is all about showing off vegetables at the peak of their sweetness, each must be perfectly cooked.

3 **Fill a very large pan with water,** bring to the boil and add 1 tbsp salt. It may seem a lot, but the water in which you boil pasta must always be very salty. Add the spaghetti and simmer for 10–12 minutes, stirring to prevent sticking, until tender but still chewy. Drain it very well.

FINISH THE DISH

4 Meanwhile, heat the butter in a large saucepan, add the courgette and carrot dice, and the peas, and sauté for 1 minute.

5 Add the cream, stir well and bring to a simmer. Take the pan from the heat, add the spaghetti and toss well. Add the Parmesan and toss again. Serve on warmed plates, sprinkled with pepper.

Onion and Roquefort quiche

THE SECRET TO THIS DISH is that the onions should be cooked to a melting softness. Often, people are put off quiche because they are used to rubbery offerings. Success and true succulence come when the custard comes from the oven wobbly, not solid.

SERVES	PREP	COOK
SERVES 6-8	40-50 MINS PLUS CHILLING	30-35 MINS

Ingredients

FOR THE PASTRY

200g (7oz) plain flour, plus more to dust

1 egg yolk

½ tsp salt

100g (3½ oz) unsalted butter, plus more for the tin

FOR THE FILLING

2-3 thyme sprigs

500g (1lb 2oz) onions

30g (1oz) unsalted butter, plus more for foil

salt and pepper

1 egg

1 egg yolk

125ml (4fl oz) milk

1 pinch of ground nutmeg

4 tbsp double cream

175g (6oz) Roquefort cheese

MAKE THE PASTRY

1 **Sift the flour** on to a work surface and make a well in the centre. Put the egg yolk, salt, and 3 tbsp water in the well.

2 **Using a rolling pin,** pound the butter to soften it slightly, then add it to the well in the flour. Using your fingertips, work the ingredients in the well until thoroughly mixed.

3 **With your fingers,** work the flour into the other ingredients until coarse crumbs form. Press the dough into a ball.

4 **Lightly flour the work surface,** then blend the dough by pushing it away from you with the heel of your hand for 1-2 minutes, until it is very smooth and peels away from the work surface in 1 piece. Shape into a ball, wrap it tightly and chill for about 30 minutes, until firm.

LINE THE TIN

5 **Butter a 25cm (10in) flan tin.** Lightly flour a work surface. Roll out the chilled dough to a 30cm (12in) round. Roll up the dough around the rolling pin and drape it over the tin, so that it hangs over the edge.

6 **Gently lift** the dough and firmly press it into the tin. Roll the rolling pin over the top of the tin, pressing down to cut off the excess dough.

7 **With your forefingers** and thumb, press the dough evenly up the side, to increase the height of the dough rim. Prick the bottom lightly with a fork to prevent air bubbles. Chill again for at least 15 minutes, until firm.

BLIND BAKE THE PASTRY

8 **Preheat the** oven to 220°C (425°F/Gas 7). Line the pastry dough shell with foil, pressing it well into the bottom edge. Trim the foil if necessary so it stands about 4cm (1½in) above the edge of the tin.

9 **Half-fill the** foil with baking beans or raw rice to weigh down the dough. Bake the shell for about 15 minutes, until set and starting to brown.

10 **Remove the** foil and beans and reduce the oven temperature to 190°C (375°F/Gas 5). Continue baking for 5-8 minutes longer, until lightly browned. Remove from the oven.

PREPARE THE FILLING

11 **Strip the thyme leaves** from the stalks. Slice the onions. Melt the butter in a frying pan. Add the onions and thyme and season with salt and pepper. Butter a piece of foil, press it on top and cover with the lid. Cook very gently, stirring occasionally, for 20-30 minutes, until very soft but not brown.

12 **Meanwhile,** make the custard: put the egg, egg yolk, milk, salt, pepper, and a pinch of ground nutmeg into a bowl. Pour in the double cream. Whisk until thoroughly mixed.

13 Crumble the cheese into the onions; stir until melted. Let cool slightly. Using the back of a wooden spoon, spread the mixture evenly into the pastry shell. Place the tin on a baking sheet. Ladle the custard over the onion mixture to fill the shell almost to the rim, and gently mix in with a fork.

BAKE AND **SERVE** THE QUICHE

14 Bake in the hot oven for 30–35 minutes, just until lightly browned and a skewer inserted into the centre of the custard comes out clean. Watch it carefully through the oven door - but avoid opening the oven - and do not overcook, or the custard will become dry and rubbery. The custard should retain a slight wobble when the tin is gently shaken. Let cool slightly in the tin before unmoulding.

15 Remove the quiche from the tin and place on a serving plate. Serve warm or at room temperature, cut in wedges. (Never serve quiche cold from the refrigerator; the texture will be hard and unpleasant.) A refreshingly astringent salad of chicory, watercress, and tomatoes makes a delicious accompaniment, and cuts through the richness of the creamy blue cheese filling.

Aubergine Parmigiana

A WELL-LOVED CLASSIC dish, big, hearty, and immensely satisfying for even the keenest appetites. This dish is also a good way to introduce aubergines to people who haven't tried them before, as the immensely comforting layers of cheese, tomato sauce, and sweet vegetables is sure to win over even the most stubborn doubter.

SERVES	PREP	COOK
SERVES 8	45–50 MINS PLUS STANDING	40–50 MINS

Ingredients

FOR THE PARMIGIANA

4 aubergines

salt and pepper

175ml (6fl oz) olive oil

leaves from 1 bunch of basil, shredded

125g (4½oz) freshly grated Parmesan cheese

500g (1lb 2oz) mozzarella cheese, diced

FOR THE TOMATO SAUCE

2.5kg (5½lb) tomatoes

3 onions, finely chopped

5 garlic cloves, finely chopped

leaves from 5–7 oregano sprigs, coarsely chopped

3 tbsp tomato purée

1 pinch of sugar

1 bouquet garni, made with 5–6 parsley stalks, 2–3 thyme sprigs, and 1 bay leaf

PREPARE THE AUBERGINES AND SAUCE

1 **Trim the stalk ends** from each of the aubergines and cut them widthways into 1cm (½in) slices. Lay them in a shallow dish and sprinkle with salt. Let stand for 30 minutes to draw out the moisture and any bitter juices.

2 **Cut the cores** from the tomatoes and score an "X" on the base of each. Immerse in boiling water for 8–15 seconds, until the skins start to split, then plunge into cold water to stop the cooking. Peel off the skins, halve, squeeze out the seeds, then coarsely chop the flesh.

3 **Heat 3 tbsp of the oil** in a sauté pan, add the onions and cook over medium heat, stirring occasionally, for 3–4 minutes, until soft but not brown. Add the tomatoes, garlic, oregano, tomato purée, salt, pepper, sugar, and bouquet garni, then stir to combine.

4 **Cover the pan** and simmer over very low heat for 15 minutes. Uncover and continue cooking, stirring occasionally, until thick, about 15 minutes longer. Discard the bouquet garni and taste for seasoning.

5 **Rinse the aubergine slices** well in a colander under cold running water, to remove the salt. Dry the slices thoroughly on kitchen paper. Preheat the oven to 180°C (350°F/Gas 4).

ASSEMBLE AND BAKE THE PARMIGIANA

6 **Oil 2 baking sheets.** Lay the aubergine slices on the sheets and brush with oil. Bake just until tender, turning once and brushing again with oil. It should take 20–25 minutes in total.

7 **Spread about one-quarter of the tomato sauce** over the bottom of a baking dish. Arrange one-third of the aubergine slices on top of the sauce in rows, overlapping them slightly. Cover with about a third of the basil, a quarter of the Parmesan, and a quarter of the mozzarella.

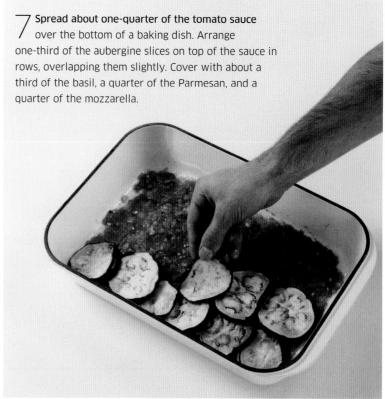

8 Repeat layering the sauce, aubergine, basil, Parmesan, and mozzarella to form 3 layers. Top with the remaining tomato sauce, mozzarella and Parmesan. Bake in the oven for 20–25 minutes, until bubbling and lightly browned on top. Leave to stand for 15 minutes, then serve.

VARIATION: Tian of Mediterranean vegetables

Named after the traditional Provençal earthenware dish.

1 Omit the tomato sauce and mozzarella. Trim and slice 6 small aubergines (total weight about 1kg/2¼lb) and 3 large courgettes (total weight about 750g/1lb 10oz). Salt the slices and rinse as directed in the main recipe. Thinly slice 6 large onions. Heat 2 tbsp olive oil in a large frying pan and add the onions, salt, and pepper. Cover with foil and cook over low heat, stirring occasionally, for 20 minutes, or until soft and just beginning to turn brown.

2 Peel, seed, and chop 1.5kg (3lb 3oz) of tomatoes. Strip the leaves from 1 bunch of thyme. Cook the tomatoes and three-quarters of the thyme leaves in the pan, uncovered, as directed; it should take about 10 minutes longer to become a thick sauce.

3 Brush eight 15cm (6in) gratin dishes with oil. Spread most of the tomato mixture in each dish, reserving about 120ml (4fl oz). Cover with the aubergines and courgettes, alternating in a spiral pattern. Sprinkle each dish with 1 tsp olive oil, the remaining thyme, salt, and pepper. Bake for about 15 minutes. Add a spoonful of the reserved tomato mixture to the centre of each dish. Sprinkle with another 1 tsp oil and 1 tbsp Parmesan cheese. Continue baking the tians for about 10 minutes, until they are completely tender when pierced with a knife.

Flemish vegetable tart

A QUICK BRIOCHE DOUGH makes a sumptuous crust for this unusual vegetable tart, which is really a hearty alternative to pizza. You can choose to cook the tart in a frying pan, if you like, for a more rustic effect. Don't be worried about making brioche: this version is very easy indeed, and has the advantage that it can be made the day ahead and refrigerated, wrapped in clingfilm, overnight.

SERVES SERVES 8	**PREP** 50-55 MINS PLUS RISING	**COOK** 40-45 MINS

Ingredients

FOR THE DOUGH

9g (⅓oz) fresh yeast, or 1½ tsp dried yeast

250g (9oz) strong plain flour, more if needed

1 tsp salt

3 eggs

125g (4½oz) unsalted butter, softened

FOR THE FILLING

500g (1lb 2oz) mushrooms

4 carrots

2 turnips

90g (3oz) unsalted butter

8-10 spring onions, finely sliced

salt and pepper

4 eggs

250ml (9fl oz) double cream

¼ tsp ground nutmeg

MAKE THE BRIOCHE DOUGH

1 **Crumble or sprinkle the yeast** over 2 tbsp lukewarm water in a small bowl and let stand for 5 minutes. Lightly oil a medium bowl. Sift the flour on to a work surface with the salt. Make a well in the centre and add the yeast and eggs.

2 **With your fingertips,** work the ingredients in the well until thoroughly mixed. Draw in the flour – using a pastry scraper if you like – and work into the other ingredients with your fingertips to form a smooth dough; add more flour if it is very sticky.

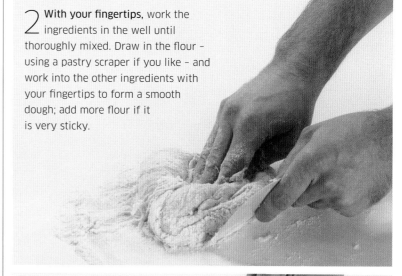

3 **Knead the dough** on a floured work surface, lifting it up and throwing it down until it is very elastic and resembles chamois leather; it will take about 10 minutes. Work in more flour as necessary, so that the dough is slightly sticky but peels easily from the work surface.

4 **Add the butter,** and pinch and squeeze to mix it into the dough, then knead for 3-5 minutes, until smooth again. Shape into a ball and put into the oiled bowl. Cover with clingfilm and refrigerate for about 1 hour. Or, if it's more convenient, leave to rise overnight in the refrigerator.

PREPARE THE VEGETABLES

5 **Wipe the mushrooms** clean with damp kitchen paper and trim the stalks level with the caps. Set each mushroom stalk-side down on a chopping board and cut into very thin strips.

6 **Peel and trim the carrots** and turnips, then cut them into very fine julienne strips. Melt the butter in a saucepan. Add the carrot strips and cook gently for about 5 minutes, stirring occasionally. Add the mushrooms and turnips and season with salt and pepper.

7 **Press a piece of buttered foil** over the vegetables. Cover with the lid of the pan and cook for about 10 minutes, until tender, stirring occasionally. The vegetables should gently steam without browning. Remove from the heat, add the spring onions and taste for seasoning.

LINE THE DISH

8 **Butter a 30cm (12in) flan dish.** Knead the brioche dough lightly to knock out the air. Lightly flour a work surface, then roll out the dough to a round 7.5cm (3in) larger than the dish. Roll the dough around the rolling pin and drape it over the dish.

9 **Gently lift the edges** of the dough with one hand and press it well into the bottom and edge of the flan dish with the other hand. Roll the rolling pin over the top of the dish, pressing down to cut off excess dough. With your forefinger and thumb, press the dough evenly up the side, from the bottom, to increase the height of the dough rim.

FILL AND BAKE THE TART

10 **Heat the oven** to 200°C (400°F/Gas 6). Spread the vegetable mixture evenly in the dough case. Whisk together the eggs, double cream, salt, pepper, and nutmeg until evenly mixed, then pour this custard over the vegetables in the flan dish.

11 **Fold the top edge of the dough rim** over the filling to form a border. Let rise in a warm place until puffed up; this will take 20–30 minutes, though it can take a little longer on a cool day. Bake until the brioche case is very brown and the custard set but retaining a slight wobble when tested with a knife; it will take 40–45 minutes. If the top gets too brown before the tart is ready, cover it with foil. Serve hot or at room temperature.

Three-pepper pizza with cheese

FOR A SPICY FLAVOUR HERE, the dough is made with black pepper. Choose peppers that are brightly coloured and firm, with no soft spots, and add finely sliced chillies instead of the cayenne, if you prefer (sprinkle the pizza with the chillies when it has just 5 minutes left to bake).

SERVES
SERVES 4-6

PREP
1¼ HRS
PLUS STANDING

COOK
20-25 MINS

Ingredients

FOR THE DOUGH

1½ tsp dried yeast, or 9g (⅓oz) fresh yeast

2 tbsp olive oil, plus more for the bowl

375g (13oz) strong plain flour, plus more if needed

½ tsp ground black pepper

salt

FOR THE TOPPING

4 tbsp olive oil

2 onions, thinly sliced

2 red peppers, cut into strips

1 green pepper, cut into strips

1 yellow pepper, cut into strips

3 garlic cloves, finely chopped

1 small bunch of any herb, such as rosemary, thyme, basil, or parsley, or a mixture, leaves finely chopped

cayenne, to taste

175g (6oz) mozzarella cheese

MAKE THE DOUGH

1 **Sprinkle or crumble the yeast** over 2-3 tbsp of lukewarm water, and let stand for about 5 minutes, until dissolved. Lightly oil a large bowl.

2 **Sift the flour** on to a work surface, then add the black pepper and ¼ tsp salt. Make a well in the centre and add the yeast mixture, 250ml (9fl oz) lukewarm water, and the 2 tbsp olive oil. Work the ingredients in the well with your fingertips until thoroughly mixed.

3 **Draw in the flour,** and work into the other ingredients with your fingertips to form a smooth dough; add more flour if the dough is very sticky. Knead until elastic, shape into a ball, and leave to rise for an hour.

PREPARE THE TOPPING

4 **Heat 1 tbsp of oil** in a frying pan, add the onions, and cook, stirring, for 2-3 minutes, until soft but not brown. Transfer to a bowl and set aside.

5 **Add the remaining oil** to the pan, then the peppers, garlic, and half the herbs. Season with salt and cayenne. Sauté, stirring, for 7-10 minutes, until softened but not brown. Taste for seasoning: it should be quite spicy. Let cool. Slice the mozzarella.

ASSEMBLE THE PIZZA

6 **Preheat the oven** to 230°C (450°F/Gas 8). Put a baking sheet near the bottom of the oven to heat. Generously flour a second baking sheet.

7 **Knead the dough** lightly to knock out the air, then shape into a ball. Lightly flour a work surface. Roll the dough into a round. Pull and slap it until the round is 1cm (½in) thick.

8 **Transfer the dough** round to the floured baking sheet, and press up the edge to form a shallow rim, if you like.

BAKE THE PIZZA

9 **Spread the onions,** and then the peppers, evenly on the pizza base, leaving a 2cm (¾in) border all around the edge, so it can become golden in the oven. Spoon any remaining oil from the frying pan over the peppers, and top them evenly with the slices of mozzarella. Let the assembled pizza stand in a warm place for 10-15 minutes, until the dough has puffed up well around the edges. Don't leave it for any longer, as it should be baked as soon as possible to retain maximum flavour.

10 **With a sharp, jerking movement,** slide the pizza on to the heated baking sheet at the bottom of the oven. (But don't be so exuberant that it splatters on the rear wall!) Bake the pizza until browned all over, and the cheese has melted into beautiful, tempting pools. It should take 20-25 minutes to cook, but it will depend on how fast your oven tends to be. Sprinkle the pizza evenly with the reserved herbs, and cut it into generous wedges to serve.

 ## VARIATION: Three-pepper calzone with cheese

The pizza recipe is made into a turnover; this will serve 4 people.

1 Make the pizza dough as directed. Prepare the topping as directed, and mix the onions and pepper strips together. Divide the dough into 4 equal pieces. Roll and pull each piece into a square about 1cm (½in) thick.

2 Spoon the pepper mixture onto a diagonal half of each square, leaving a 2.5cm (1in) border. Arrange the mozzarella slices on top. Moisten the edge of each square with water, and fold one corner over to meet the other, forming a triangle.

3 Pinch the edges together to seal. Put the triangles on the floured baking sheet and let rise (prove) for 30 minutes. Whisk 1 egg with ½ tsp salt, and brush over the calzone. Bake for 15-20 minutes, until golden brown. Brush each with a little olive oil, and serve.

One-pot dishes

All-in-one meals that almost cook themselves

Scallop and sweetcorn chowder

A LUXURIOUS AMERICAN CLASSIC. A wonderful dish for a special occasion that marries the sweetness of both the shellfish and sweetcorn with salty bacon. Oyster crackers, available from some specialist delicatessens, are the traditional accompaniment. If you can find them, allow diners to crumble them over their own bowl.

SERVES SERVES 6-8	**PREP** 25-30 MINS	**COOK** 15-20 MINS

Ingredients

4 cobs sweetcorn

750g (1lb 10oz) small scallops

250g (9oz) streaky bacon rashers, cut into strips

2 onions, thinly sliced

500g (1lb 2oz) new potatoes

1 bay leaf

salt and pepper

750ml (1¼ pints) fish stock

250ml (9fl oz) single cream

500ml (16fl oz) milk

paprika

PREPARE THE CHOWDER INGREDIENTS

1 **Hold each sweetcorn cob** vertically on a chopping board and cut from the tip down to remove the kernels. Put them in a small bowl. Working over the bowl, with the back of the knife, scrape the pulp and milk from each cob.

2 **If necessary,** discard the tough, crescent-shaped membrane at the side of each scallop. Make sure there is no black intestinal vein running around the edge of the shellfish. If you find one, peel it off and discard.

COOK THE CHOWDER BASE

3 **Heat a large saucepan,** add the bacon and fry for 3–5 minutes, stirring until the fat has rendered. With a slotted spoon, transfer the bacon to a plate lined with kitchen paper.

4 **Reduce the heat,** then add the onions and cook, stirring frequently, for 3–5 minutes, until soft and translucent. With a slotted spoon, transfer the onions to the lined plate. Discard any remaining fat from the pan.

FINISH THE CHOWDER

5 **Add the potatoes** to the pan with the bay leaf, salt, and pepper. Pour in the stock. Bring to a boil and simmer gently for 7–10 minutes, until the potatoes are slightly soft when pierced with the tip of a knife.

6 **Return most of the bacon and onions** to the pan with the sweetcorn kernels and pulp, cream, and milk. Bring to a boil and simmer for 7–10 minutes, until the potatoes are tender. Add the scallops. Bring back to a simmer, then discard the bay leaf, ladle into warmed bowls, and sprinkle with paprika and the reserved onion and bacon.

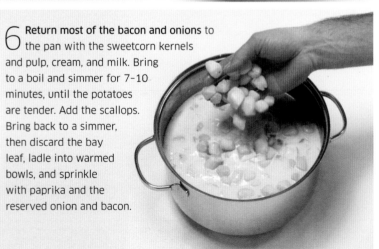

Hunter's chicken

THE ITALIAN WAY to cook a bird after a shoot. In Italy, the dish is called *alla cacciatora*, meaning "hunter's style". Add sage instead of rosemary, if you prefer. The slight bitterness of braised escarole makes a flavoursome accompaniment and must be made just before serving. The chicken can be made 2 days ahead and refrigerated in the sauce.

SERVES	PREP	COOK
SERVES 4	20-25 MINS	45-60 MINS

Ingredients

salt and freshly ground black pepper

1.5kg (3lb 3oz) chicken, jointed into 8 pieces

4 tbsp olive oil

1 onion, diced

4 garlic cloves, finely chopped

1 rosemary sprig

1 bay leaf

4 tbsp dry white wine

125ml (4fl oz) chicken stock, plus more if needed

1 head of escarole, weighing about 750g (1lb 10oz)

COOK THE CHICKEN

1 **Season the chicken** all over. Heat half the oil in a sauté pan over medium heat. Add the thighs and drumsticks, skin side down, and sauté for about 5 minutes, until they begin to brown. Add the breast pieces, and cook gently for 10-15 minutes, until very brown. Turn and brown the other side.

2 **Add the onion** and half the garlic, letting them fall to the bottom of the pan. Continue cooking gently until they are soft and golden brown, about 10 minutes. Add the rosemary, bay leaf, wine, stock, salt, and pepper and stir. Cover and simmer until tender, 15-20 minutes.

SAUTÉ THE ESCAROLE

3 **Meanwhile,** trim the root end of the escarole. Discard any tough, green outer leaves, then wash well. Cut into 8 wedges through the core. Heat the remaining oil in a frying pan. Add the rest of the garlic with the escarole, 4 tbsp water, salt and pepper. Bring to a boil, then cover and simmer gently for 10-20 minutes, turning occasionally. Test the escarole is tender by piercing near the core with a knife. The liquid should have evaporated so the leaves are lightly glazed with oil.

4 **Remove the chicken pieces** from the pan and arrange on warmed individual plates. Discard the bay leaf and rosemary from the sauce, and taste for seasoning; adjust if necessary.

5 **Arrange the escarole** next to the chicken, tucking large leaves under small ones to make neat packages. Spoon the sauce over the chicken and serve with crusty bread.

Monkfish and white wine stew

THE DELICATE FLAVOUR of monkfish here is highlighted by white wine, and the sauce is given a velvety consistency with the addition of a kneaded butter and flour paste, known as beurre manié. Make the stew up to the end of step 4 a day ahead.

SERVES	PREP	COOK
SERVES 6	45–50 MINS	25–30 MINS

Ingredients

FOR THE STEW

750g (1lb 10oz) skinned monkfish fillets

salt and pepper

2 leeks

500g (1lb 2oz) small courgettes

75g (2½oz) butter, at room temperature

2 shallots, diced

2 garlic cloves, finely chopped

250g (9oz) mushrooms, trimmed and quartered

leaves from 3–5 thyme sprigs

1 bay leaf

250ml (9fl oz) dry white wine

500ml (16fl oz) fish stock

3 tbsp flour

leaves from 1 small bunch of parsley, chopped

FOR THE CROUTES (optional)

6 slices of white bread

45g (1½oz) butter

3 tbsp vegetable oil

PREPARE THE FISH AND VEGETABLES

1 **If necessary,** cut away the thin membrane that covers the monkfish. Rinse and pat dry with kitchen paper. Holding each fillet steady, cut into 1cm (½in) diagonal slices. Season with salt and pepper.

2 **Trim the leeks.** Slit them lengthways, then cut diagonally into 1cm (½in) pieces. Wash the leeks thoroughly under cold running water to remove any remaining grit or soil. Drain well.

3 **Trim the courgettes** and cut them into 5cm (2in) pieces. Cut each piece lengthways into quarters.

SIMMER THE BROTH AND MAKE THE CROUTES

4 **Melt 30g (1oz) of butter,** and sauté the shallots, garlic, and leeks for 3–5 minutes. Add the mushrooms, thyme, bay, wine, and stock, cover and simmer for 10–15 minutes. Add the courgettes and cook for 8–10 minutes..

5 **Cut the crusts** from the bread, then cut into triangles. Melt the butter and oil in a frying pan. Add the bread in batches and fry for 1 minute on each side, until golden. Drain on kitchen paper.

COOK THE FISH AND THICKEN THE STEW

6 **Add the monkfish** to the broth with water, if necessary, so that the fish is barely covered, and stir very gently to combine. Too vigorous stirring may make the fish fall apart.

7 **Cover the pan,** bring back to a boil, and simmer for 3–5 minutes, until the fish is tender when tested with a fork.

8 **Fork together the remaining butter** with the flour to form a smooth paste. Add to the broth, stir to combine and simmer for 2 minutes.

9 **Discard the bay leaf,** stir in half the parsley and taste for seasoning. Serve in a warmed tureen, sprinkled with the remaining parsley, and serve with the croutes, if you like.

 VARIATION: Monkfish and red wine stew

Wonderfully unusual and full-flavoured

1 Omit the garlic, leeks, parsley, thyme, courgettes and white wine. Prepare the monkfish, shallots, and mushrooms as directed. Make the croutes as directed. Cook the shallots in butter for 1 minute, until soft. Add 500ml (16fl oz) red wine and simmer until reduced by half.

2 Meanwhile, peel 250g (9oz) pickling onions. Melt 30g (1oz) butter in a frying pan, add the onions and cook for 5-8 minutes, until golden. Add the mushrooms and cook for 3-5 minutes, until the liquid evaporates and the mushrooms are tender.

3 Add 500ml (16fl oz) fish stock and 1 bay leaf to the red wine. Add the monkfish and cover. Simmer for 3-5 minutes, until tender. Stir in the onions and mushrooms and thicken the stew as directed. Serve on warmed plates.

Paella

A DISH TO FEED A CROWD, so invite family and friends. This Spanish recipe of saffron-flavoured rice with chicken, prawns, mussels and chorizo is named after the paellera in which it is traditionally cooked. Of course, most kitchens won't have one of those in the cupboard, so just use your broadest frying pan. It is important that the ingredients are not piled up too deeply in the pan; they should form a relatively shallow layer for the best results.

SERVES
SERVES 8-10

PREP
1 HOUR

COOK
40-45 MINS

Ingredients

2 large pinches of saffron threads

500g (1lb 2oz) raw, unpeeled jumbo prawns

1kg (2¼lb) mussels

750g (1lb 10oz) chicken thighs, on the bone if preferred, diced

salt and pepper

4 tbsp olive oil

250g (9oz) chorizo sausage, in 1cm (½in) slices

2 large onions, diced

2 red peppers, sliced

750g (1lb 10oz) paella or other short-grain rice

3 garlic cloves, finely chopped

2 x 400g cans chopped tomatoes

375g (13oz) French beans, in 1cm (½in) slices

1-2 tbsp chopped parsley

PREPARE THE INGREDIENTS

1 **Put 3-4 tbsp boiling water** in a small bowl and sprinkle in the saffron threads. Leave to soak for at least 15 minutes; the saffron will give up its beautiful yellow-orange colour and subtle aromas during this time, meaning it will flavour the stew more highly later.

2 **Leaving the prawns in their shells,** pull off and discard the legs. Twist each prawn tail and pull it off very gently to remove the dark intestinal vein (this is attached to the tail and should emerge from along the back of the prawns). Rinse them as swiftly as possible under running water and dry very well; never leave prawns sitting in water as they will soak it up, adversely affecting their texture.

3 **Scrub the mussels** under cold running water with a small stiff brush. Scrape the shells with an old, blunt knife to remove any barnacles. Pull off and discard any weeds or 'beards' from the shells. Discard any mussels that have broken shells or that do not close when tapped on the side of the kitchen sink.

COOK THE PAELLA

4 **Season the chicken.** Heat the oil in a 30-35cm (12-14in) paella pan and sauté the chicken, turning, for 10-12 minutes, until brown. Transfer to a plate. Add the chorizo to the pan and sauté for 1-2 minutes on each side, until browned. Transfer to the plate with a slotted spoon.

5 **Add the onion** and red pepper to the pan; cook for 5-7 minutes, stirring occasionally, until soft. Stir in the rice and cook for 2-3 minutes, until the grains absorb the oil and all the other flavours.

6 **Stir in 1.5 litres (2¾ pints) water,** the garlic, the saffron with its soaking liquid, and plenty of salt, and pepper. Push the chicken pieces down into the rice. Scatter the chorizo slices over, followed by the tomatoes, beans, prawns and mussels. Bring to a boil.

7 Simmer, uncovered, for 25-30 minutes, until all the liquid has evaporated and the rice is tender but slightly chewy. Do not stir, or the rice will become sticky. If the rice is undercooked, add a little more water and simmer a few minutes longer. Remove from the heat and discard any mussels that have not opened. Cover with a tea towel and let stand for 5 minutes. Sprinkle with parsley and serve.

 VARIATION: Seafood paella

Squid replaces the chicken in this version.

1 Omit the French beans and chicken. Prepare the saffron, onions, garlic, tomatoes, and chorizo as directed in the main recipe, substituting green peppers for red and using the same weight of clams in place of the mussels. Cut the prawns in half to open in a butterfly shape. Remove the dark intestinal vein.

2 Rinse 375g (13oz) cleaned squid and drain it well. Cut the tentacles from the bodies and cut them into 2-3 pieces if large, or leave whole if small. Cut the body into 1cm (½in) rings.

3 Cook the chorizo, onions, peppers, and rice as directed. Pour in the water, arrange the chorizo over the rice, followed by the prawns, tomatoes, squid, 125g (4½oz) shelled fresh or defrosted peas, and finally the clams. Cook and serve as directed.

Seafood and tomato cioppino

A HEARTY DISH created by Italian immigrants to San Francisco in the 19th century. Make sure you cook this fragrant dish with care, as the crabs, mussels, and scallops will toughen if overcooked.

SERVES	**PREP**	**COOK**
SERVES 4	45-50 MINS	20-25 MINS

Ingredients

4 tbsp olive oil

2 large onions, diced

1 tbsp tomato purée

3 x 400g (14oz) tins chopped Italian plum tomatoes

3 garlic cloves, finely chopped

pinch of cayenne pepper

salt and pepper

1 bouquet garni, made with 5-6 parsley stalks, 2-3 thyme sprigs, and 1 bay leaf

500ml (16fl oz) dry white wine

2 whole cooked crabs, total weight about 1.4kg (3lb)

750g (1lb 10oz) mussels

500g (1lb 2oz) skinned white fish fillets

250g (9oz) small scallops

leaves from a small bunch of parsley, finely chopped

MAKE THE TOMATO BROTH

1 **Heat the oil** in a saucepan, add the onions and cook for 3-5 minutes, until soft and translucent. Add the tomato purée, tomatoes, garlic, cayenne, salt, pepper, and bouquet garni.

2 **Pour in the white wine.** Cover the pan and simmer gently, stirring occasionally, for about 20 minutes. The sauce should thicken slightly and release its aromas.

PREPARE THE CRABS

3 **Set the crabs,** back down, on a chopping board. Twist off the legs and reserve. Holding the crab body steady, twist off the claws at the bottom joint.

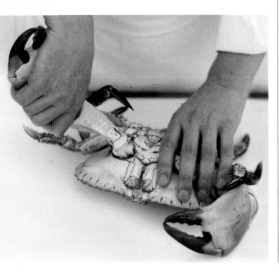

4 **Using crab crackers,** or the back of a heavy knife, crack the claws, leaving them whole and taking care not to crush the meat. If the legs are large, crack them also; discard them, or use to make stock if they are small.

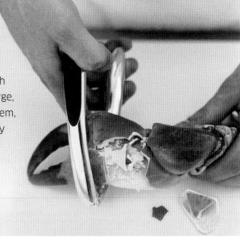

5 **Open the body:** with your fingers, lift off and discard the "apron" flap from the centre of the shell. With your thumbs, push along the perforation to crack the central section of the shell under the tail and prise it apart.

6 **Gently pull the body** from the shell. Scrape out any soft brown meat from the shell and reserve in a bowl. Pull off and discard the soft gills from the body. Crack the body in half. Pick out the meat from the body with the end of a teaspoon. Add to the crab meat in the bowl and reserve.

PREPARE THE REMAINING FISH

7 Scrub the mussels thoroughly under cold running water with a small stiff brush. Discard any with broken shells or that do not close when tapped against the side of the kitchen sink. Scrape with an old, blunt knife to remove any barnacles. Pull off and discard any weeds or 'beards' from the shells with your fingers.

8 Rinse the fish fillets under cold running water and dry. Set on a chopping board and cut into chunky 5cm (2in) pieces. If necessary, discard the tough crescent-shaped membrane at the side of each scallop (though these are usually trimmed off before the scallops are sold). Make sure the scallops have no black or brownish intestinal vein running around the edge; if they do, pull it off and discard.

COOK THE CIOPPINO

9 Discard the bouquet garni from the broth. Taste; it should be peppery. Pack the fish into the bottom of a casserole in an even layer, then the scallops. Arrange the crab meat, legs, and claws, and the mussels on top.

10 Ladle the hot tomato broth over the seafood and add water, if necessary, so the seafood is just covered. Cover the casserole with the lid and bring to a boil. Simmer for 3–5 minutes, until the mussels have opened and the white fish flakes easily with a fork.

11 Discard any mussels that have not opened. Taste for seasoning. Serve the cioppino in warmed bowls, with a crab claw in each bowl. Sprinkle with the parsley. Serve immediately, with slices of sourdough bread.

Chicken paprika with dumplings

GOOD-QUALITY HUNGARIAN PAPRIKA is the key to this dish. Caraway seed dumplings are delicious with the chicken, as well as being an aid to the digestion. Steamed, crisp green beans or sugarsnap peas would provide the ideal crunch and freshness alongside. The chicken paprika can be prepared 1 day ahead and kept, covered, in the refrigerator; add the soured cream and make the dumplings just before serving. As this dish is already so highly seasoned and flavoured, use water instead of chicken stock if you prefer.

SERVES SERVES 4-6	**PREP** 40-45 MINS	**COOK** 35-40 MINS

Ingredients

FOR THE DUMPLINGS

100g (3½oz) plain flour

¼ tsp baking powder

½ tsp salt

2 tsp caraway seeds

2 eggs

FOR THE CHICKEN

1.6kg (3½lb) chicken, jointed into 8 pieces

salt and pepper

2 tbsp vegetable oil
1 large onion, diced
2 garlic cloves, finely chopped
2 tbsp paprika, plus more to taste
1 tbsp plain flour
400g (14oz) can chopped tomatoes
500ml (16fl oz) chicken stock, plus more if needed
125ml (4fl oz) soured cream

PREPARE THE DUMPLINGS

1 **Sift the flour,** baking powder, and salt together into a large bowl, lifting the sieve high above the bowl in order to aerate the flour particles as they float down. Mix in the fragrant caraway seeds well, so they are distributed evenly through the flour and the dumplings will each receive their portion. Make a well in the centre.

2 **In a small bowl,** whisk the eggs together until broken down. Add them to the well with about 120ml (4fl oz) water. Gradually draw in the flour to the wet ingredients from the inside out, and stir until it is all combined. Add more water if it is dry; the dough should be moist but not soft or sticky. Cover and refrigerate.

COOK THE CHICKEN PAPRIKA

3 **Preheat the oven** to 180°C (350°F/Gas 4). Season the chicken pieces. Heat the oil in the casserole on top of the stove. Working in batches, if necessary, add the chicken to the casserole, skin-side down, and brown well for about 5 minutes.

4 **Turn the chicken** and brown the other side. Transfer to a plate and set aside. Add the onion to the casserole and cook over medium heat, stirring occasionally, for 2-3 minutes, until soft. Add the garlic and continue cooking for 3-5 minutes longer.

5 **Stir in the paprika.** Cook very gently, stirring occasionally, for about 5 minutes. Stir in the flour, then add the tomatoes, stock, salt and pepper; bring to a boil. Return the chicken, cover and cook in the heated oven for 35-40 minutes, until the chicken is tender.

COOK THE DUMPLINGS

6 Fill a shallow saucepan with salted water and bring to a boil. Take 2 small spoons, dip them first in the boiling water, then use them to shape the dumpling dough into 2cm (¾in) balls; drop the balls into the boiling water. Cook the dumplings in batches so the saucepan is not crowded.

7 Cover the pan, and simmer for 7–10 minutes, until the dumplings are firm and cooked in the centre. Using a slotted spoon, transfer the dumplings to a plate lined with kitchen paper.

FINISH AND SERVE THE CHICKEN PAPRIKA

8 Transfer the chicken pieces to a platter and keep warm. Stir the soured cream into the sauce and taste for seasoning. Add the dumplings to the casserole and turn each to coat in sauce. Cover and cook very gently for about 2 minutes.

9 Divide the chicken evenly among warmed plates; cover with the paprika sauce and add the dumplings, making sure all your diners receive the same number.

Chicken and beer stew

THE DARKER THE BEER, the richer this dish will be. Mashed potatoes would be good on the side and, naturally, you can guess what is the best drink to serve. If prepared up to the end of step 8 and refrigerated overnight, not only will the flavours blend together more harmoniously, but it will be easier to skim all the fat from the top of the dish. Bring to room temperature and reheat on top of the stove before serving.

SERVES	PREP	COOK
SERVES 4-6	25-30 MINS	50-55 MINS

Ingredients

1 chicken, weighing about 1.6kg (3½lb)	500g (1lb 2oz) mushrooms, quartered
salt and pepper	1 bouquet garni, made with 5-6 parsley stalks, 2-3 thyme sprigs and 1 bay leaf
30g (1oz) butter	2 tsp juniper berries, gently crushed
2 tbsp vegetable oil	750ml (1¼ pints) beer
750g (1lb 10oz) onions, thinly sliced	4 tbsp double cream
30g (1oz) plain flour	leaves from 1 small bunch of parsley, finely chopped
3-4 tbsp Cognac	

JOINT THE CHICKEN

1 **With a sharp knife,** cut down between one leg joint and the body. Twist the leg sharply outwards to break the joint, then cut through it and pull the leg from the body. Repeat for the other leg.

2 **Slit closely** along both sides of the breastbone to loosen the meat, then split the breastbone. Turn the bird over on to its breast and cut along one side of the backbone. The bird is now divided in half.

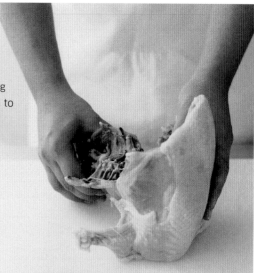

3 **Cut the backbone** and rib bones in one piece from the breast half where they are still attached, leaving the wing joints attached to the breast.

4 **Cut each breast** in half diagonally so a portion of breast meat is included with the wing. Cut each leg in half through the joint between thigh and drumstick. Cut off any sharp bones.

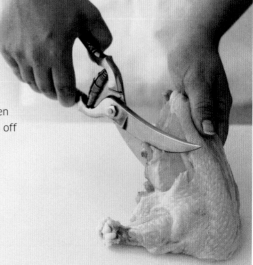

COOK THE STEW

5 **Season the chicken** pieces. Heat the butter and oil in a casserole until foaming, and add the chicken, skin-side down. Brown them well for about 5 minutes. Turn and brown the other side. Transfer the chicken to a plate.

6 **Add the onions** and cook, stirring occasionally, for 10-15 minutes, until soft and well browned. Sprinkle with the flour and cook, stirring, for 1-2 minutes, until the flour is just lightly browned. Return the chicken to the pan in a single layer.

7 **Add the Cognac.** Standing well back, set the alcohol alight with a lighted match. Baste the chicken with the Cognac until the flames subside; it should take 20-30 seconds.

8 **Add the mushrooms,** bouquet garni, and crushed juniper berries. Pour in the beer, bring to a boil, cover and simmer for 40-50 minutes, until the chicken is tender when pierced and the juices run clear.

9 **Discard the bouquet garni** and skim off excess fat from the surface with a large metal spoon. Stir in the cream and bring back just to a boil. Taste for seasoning and adjust if needed, then sprinkle with the parsley.

 ## VARIATION: Chicken with Cognac

This version increases the amount of Cognac and replaces the beer with chicken stock.

1 Omit the mushrooms, onions, beer, juniper berries, cream, and parsley. Joint the chicken as directed in the main recipe. Put 500g (1lb 2oz) pickling onions in a bowl, cover them with boiling water and let stand for 2 minutes. Remove and peel off the skins.

2 Brown the chicken as directed; set aside. Add the onions to the casserole and cook, stirring, for 5-7 minutes, until golden brown. Transfer to a bowl. Sprinkle the flour into the casserole and cook for 1-2 minutes, stirring to amalgamate the flour with all the juices in the casserole and to 'cook out' the flour's raw taste. Return the chicken to the pot and increase the heat to medium-high, continuing to stir so the flour does not scorch.

3 Add 250ml (9fl oz) Cognac and bring to a boil. Set alight, standing well back, and baste as directed until the flames subside. Add 250ml (9fl oz) chicken stock, the onions, bouquet garni, salt, and pepper and cook as directed. Discard the bouquet garni and taste for seasoning.

Rabbit Provençal

A WONDERFUL DISH, with tomatoes baked slowly in the oven. Herbes de Provence is one of the few dried herbs that it is still worth buying: the mixture includes wild thyme, savory, and fennel, and is wonderfully aromatic. As with all dried herbs, make sure to use them quickly or they lose their aroma.

SERVES	PREP	COOK
SERVES 4	35-40 MINS	3-3½ HOURS

Ingredients

FOR THE RABBIT

1 rabbit, weighing about 1.4kg (3lb), cut into 8 pieces

2 shallots, chopped

250ml (8fl oz) dry white wine

4 tbsp olive oil

2 tbsp herbes de Provence

1 tbsp plain flour

250ml (8fl oz) chicken stock

5-7 thyme sprigs

FOR THE TOMATOES

1 tbsp olive oil

6 plum tomatoes, total weight about 500g (1lb 2oz)

salt and pepper

MARINATE THE RABBIT

1 **In a shallow, non-metallic dish** wide enough to hold the rabbit pieces in 1 layer, combine the rabbit, shallots, white wine, half the oil, and the herbes de Provence.

2 **Add the rabbit** and turn until coated. Cover and refrigerate for 2-3 hours, to marinate. Meanwhile, bake the tomatoes.

BAKE THE TOMATOES

3 **Preheat the oven** to 130°C (250°F/Gas ½). Brush a grill rack with oil. Core the tomatoes and cut each lengthways into 3 slices. Put them in a bowl with the oil, salt and pepper, and toss to coat.

4 **Arrange the tomato slices** on the grill rack and bake for 2–2½ hours, until slightly shrivelled. Transfer to a plate and increase the oven temperature to 190°C (375°F/Gas 5).

FINISH THE DISH

5 **Take the rabbit** from the marinade; reserve the marinade. Season the rabbit with salt and pepper. Heat half the remaining oil in a casserole. Add half the rabbit and cook for 5 minutes, until browned. Transfer to a plate, add the remaining oil, and brown the remaining rabbit.

6 **Return all the rabbit** and sprinkle with the flour. Cook for 2-3 minutes, then stir in the marinade and stock. Cover and bake for 50-55 minutes, stirring occasionally, until very tender. Return the tomatoes to the oven for the last 10 minutes, to heat through. Strip the thyme leaves from the stems. Serve the rabbit and tomatoes sprinkled with the thyme.

Hungarian beef goulash

TRUE HUNGARIAN PAPRIKA, aromatic and piquant, makes a great difference to this recipe. Find it in specialist food shops. If you have no luck, you may want to add more paprika to the goulash, to taste, in step 2. You can make this dish up to 2 days ahead, cover, and refrigerate.

SERVES	**PREP**	**COOK**
SERVES 4	25–30 MINS	2½–3 HOURS

Ingredients

FOR THE GOULASH

1 tbsp vegetable oil

60g (2oz) smoked bacon, diced

6 onions, total weight about 750g (1lb 10oz), chopped

2 tbsp paprika

750g (1lb 10oz) braising steak, cut into 4cm (1½in) cubes

2 garlic cloves, finely chopped

½ tsp caraway seeds

2 tomatoes, cored, seeded and chopped

2 green peppers, sliced

salt and pepper

125ml (4fl oz) soured cream (optional)

FOR THE DUMPLINGS

1 egg

45g (1½oz) plain flour

COOK THE GOULASH

1 **Heat the oil** in a casserole, add the bacon and cook, stirring, for 3–5 minutes, until it is lightly browned and the fat has rendered. Stir in the onions. Cut a piece of foil to fit the casserole, then cover the mixture and add the lid. Cook over low heat, stirring occasionally, for 20–25 minutes until the onions are soft and translucent.

2 **Preheat the oven** to 180°C (350°F/ Gas 4). Stir the paprika into the onions and bacon and cook for 2 minutes longer; don't let the paprika scorch. Add the steak, garlic, caraway seeds, and 500ml (16fl oz) water and stir. Bring to a boil, stirring, then cover and cook in the oven until the beef is almost tender, 1–1½hours.

FINISH THE GOULASH

3 **Stir the tomatoes and peppers** into the goulash. Season to taste. Cover and cook for 30–45 minutes longer, until the meat is very soft and the stew rich and thick. Taste for seasoning.

MAKE AND COOK THE DUMPLINGS

4 **Lightly beat the egg** in a small bowl. Put the flour and a pinch of salt in another bowl, then stir in the egg.

5 **Transfer the goulash** to the top of the stove and heat to boiling. Using 2 teaspoons, drop spoonfuls of the dumpling mixture into the goulash and simmer for 5–7 minutes, until cooked through.

6 **Ladle the goulash and dumplings** into warmed soup bowls. Top each serving with a spoon of soured cream, if you like.

Poule au pot

A COMPLETE MEAL: you'll find this classic French dish becomes a real favourite. Mastering this recipe will also add to your repertoire the piquant sauce *gribiche*, which is a wonderful accompaniment here but also works marvels with fish and seafood, or even with offal.

SERVES SERVES 4-6	**PREP** 1 HR	**COOK** 1¼-1½ HRS

Ingredients

FOR THE POULE AU POT

1 large chicken, weighing about 2kg (4½lb)

salt and pepper

1 onion

1 clove

1 bouquet garni, made with 5-6 parsley stalks, 2-3 thyme sprigs, and 1 bay leaf

4 litres (7 pints) chicken stock, plus more if needed

1kg (2¼lb) leeks

375g (13oz) carrots

375g (13oz) turnips

60g (2oz) vermicelli

FOR THE SAUCE GRIBICHE

2 eggs

juice of ½ lemon

1 tsp Dijon mustard

2 tbsp dry white wine

250ml (9fl oz) vegetable oil

1 tbsp drained capers, finely chopped

3 gherkins, finely chopped

leaves from 5-7 parsley sprigs, finely chopped

1 small bunch of chives, finely snipped

COOK THE CHICKEN

1 **Truss the chicken,** and season. Trim the root and stalk from the onion, peel and stud it with the clove. Put the chicken in a casserole. Add the bouquet garni and onion; pour in enough stock to cover the chicken by about three-quarters. Bring to a boil, cover and simmer for 45 minutes.

2 **Trim the leeks,** discarding the roots and tough green tops. Slit them lengthways, wash thoroughly under cold water, and cut into 7.5cm (3in) lengths. Put them on a large piece of muslin, gather up the edges, and tie securely with string to make a bundle.

3 **Trim the carrots** and cut into 7.5cm (3in) lengths. Tie them in a piece of muslin as for the leeks. Peel the turnips and cut into 2.5cm (1in) cubes. Tie them in muslin in the same way as the leeks and carrots.

4 **Add the vegetable bundles** to the chicken with more stock, so they are covered. Cover and simmer for 25-30 minutes longer, until the chicken and vegetables are cooked.

MAKE THE SAUCE GRIBICHE

5 **Boil the eggs** for 10 minutes. Drain, cool, and shell them. Separate the yolks from the whites by gently pulling them apart. Cut the whites into strips and finely chop.

6 **Put the yolks** in a small sieve set over a bowl and work them through, using the back of a spoon. Scrape away the yolk clinging to the bottom of the sieve.

7 **Add the lemon juice** to the egg yolks with the mustard, salt, pepper, and white wine; whisk until combined. Gradually pour in the oil, whisking constantly. It will emulsify and thicken slightly. Add the chopped egg whites, capers, gherkins, and herbs; whisk together to combine. Taste for seasoning.

FINISH THE DISH

8 **Transfer the chicken** to a board, and remove the trussing string. Carve the chicken: cut down between one leg and the body. Turn the bird on its side, and cut around the oyster meat so it remains attached to the thigh. Twist the leg sharply to break the joint, then cut through and pull the leg from the body.

9 **Halve the leg** by cutting through the joint, using the line of fat on the underside as a guide. Repeat for the other leg. Cut horizontally above one wing joint, through to the breastbone, so you will be able to carve whole slices from the breast. Cut off the wing. Repeat with the other wing.

10 **Carve the breasts** in slices parallel to the ribcage. Put all the chicken pieces on a heatproof plate, cover with foil, and keep warm in a very low oven. Remove the vegetables from the broth with a slotted spoon and keep warm, still in their muslin.

11 **Strain the broth** into the saucepan, bring to a boil, and simmer for 10-20 minutes. With a large metal spoon, skim off as much fat as possible from the top, and taste for seasoning. Add the vermicelli to the boiling broth and simmer, just until tender. It will take 3-5 minutes, or according to package instructions.

12 **Meanwhile,** cut the string from the bundles of carrots, leeks, and turnips, unwrap them, and discard the muslin. Add to the chicken, gently mixing so everything is evenly spread, and continue to keep warm until ready to serve.

13 **Mix the chicken and vegetables** into the broth and remove from the heat. Stir very gently, then add to warmed bowls, making sure each diner gets a fairly even amount of chicken, vegetables, and vermicelli. Serve the *sauce gribiche* separately.

Turkey mole

A DELECTABLE BLEND of hot spices and dark chocolate combine in this famous Mexican dish. If you are unfamiliar with the recipe, it could seem a rather odd combination, but do try it because it is absolutely delicious and will soon become part of your regular repertoire. Don't let the rather long ingredients list put you off making this recipe; it is definitely worth the effort. Make sure you use the best quality dark chocolate.

SERVES	PREP	COOK
SERVES 8	45-50 MINS	1¼-1¾ HRS

Ingredients

FOR THE STEW

1.6kg (3½lb) boneless turkey thighs

salt and pepper

4 tbsp vegetable oil

1 celery stick, roughly chopped

2 onions, quartered

4 garlic cloves, peeled

1 tsp black peppercorns

1 carrot, roughly chopped

FOR THE MOLE MIXTURE

45g (1½oz) 70 per cent cocoa solids chocolate

1 slice of stale white bread

1 stale corn tortilla

400g (14oz) can chopped tomatoes

175g (6oz) blanched almonds

75g (2½oz) raisins

30g (1oz) chilli powder

1 tsp each ground cloves, coriander, and cumin

¼ tsp ground aniseed

2 tsp ground cinnamon

30g (1oz) sesame seeds

COOK THE TURKEY

1 **Season the turkey.** Heat half the oil in the casserole. Add the turkey pieces, skin-side down. Brown the turkey well, turning occasionally, for 10-15 minutes.

2 **Add 1 litre (1¾ pints) water,** the celery, 4 onion quarters, 1 garlic clove, the peppercorns, and carrot. Bring to a boil, cover, and simmer until the turkey is very tender when pierced, 45-60 minutes.

PREPARE THE MOLE PURÉE

3 **Break the chocolate** into pieces. Tear the bread and tortilla into pieces. Put the tomatoes in a food processor with the remaining onion and garlic, bread, tortilla, almonds, raisins, chilli powder, cloves, coriander, cumin, aniseed, cinnamon, and half the sesame seeds. Work to a smooth purée.

ASSEMBLE THE MOLE

4 **Remove the casserole** from the heat, transfer the turkey to a plate and let cool slightly. Strain the cooking liquid into a bowl, discarding the vegetables. Remove the skin and any fat from the turkey and pull the meat into bite-sized pieces with your fingers.

5 **Heat the remaining oil** in the casserole. Add the mole purée and cook, stirring constantly with the wooden spoon for about 5 minutes, until thick and dark. Add the chocolate and cook, stirring, to melt, for about 5 minutes longer.

6 **Pour in the cooking liquid,** season with salt, and stir. Simmer for 25-30 minutes, until the sauce begins to thicken. Meanwhile, toast the remaining sesame seeds for 2-3 minutes in a dry frying pan until lightly browned. Return the turkey to the casserole and simmer for 10-15 minutes longer, until the sauce is thick enough to coat the back of a spoon. Taste for seasoning. Serve in warmed individual bowls with white rice. Sprinkle with the toasted sesame seeds.

VARIATION: Pork mole

Sweet pork and soured cream make a delectable version of the Mexican dish.

1 Omit the turkey, celery, carrots, and black peppercorns. Peel and quarter 1 onion. Peel 3 garlic cloves. Make the mole purée as directed in the main recipe. Cook the purée and chocolate, substituting 1 litre (1¾ pints) water for the turkey cooking liquid. Simmer until the sauce has thickened; this should take 25-30 minutes. It should be thick enough to coat the back of a spoon.

2 Trim the excess fat from 8 pork chops (weighing about 175g/6oz each) and season both sides of each. Heat 2 tbsp oil in a large frying pan and brown the chops well over high heat for 1-2 minutes on each side. Add the chops to the hot mole sauce, cover and cook very gently until completely tender when pierced with the tip of a knife; it will take 1-1¼ hours.

3 Toast the sesame seeds as directed. Taste the mole for seasoning and adjust if necessary. Divide the pork and sauce among 8 warmed plates, or serve on a large warmed platter, sprinkle with the toasted sesame seeds, and top each serving with 1 tbsp soured cream. Serve with plenty of fluffy white rice.

Poussins with plums and cabbage

THE UNDERLYING SWEETNESS OF PLUMS works wonders in this dish. The dish can be made 1 day ahead and kept, covered, in the refrigerator. Reheat the birds with the cabbage, add the remaining plums and thicken the sauce just before serving.

SERVES	PREP	COOK
SERVES 6	35–40 MINS	1¼–1½ HRS

Ingredients

6 poussins, each weighing about 500g (1lb 2oz)

salt and pepper

1 Savoy cabbage, weighing about 1.4kg (3lb), cored and coarsely shredded

1 onion

1 clove

2 tbsp vegetable oil

250g (9oz) streaky bacon rashers, sliced

750g (1lb 10oz) purple plums, halved and stoned

1 bouquet garni

250ml (9fl oz) dry white wine

500ml (16fl oz) chicken stock or water

2 tsp arrowroot

TRUSS THE BIRDS FOR EVEN COOKING

1 **Season the insides** of the poussins with salt and pepper. Hold one bird, breast-side down, on a work surface, tuck the neck skin under the bird, and cover with the wings.

2 **Turn the bird over** and pass a length of string under the tail end of the bird; tie a secure knot over the leg joints. Bring the strings along the sides of the body, between the breast and the legs, and loop them around the legs.

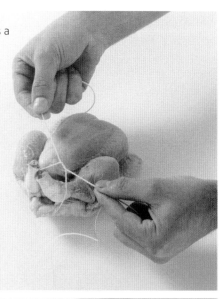

3 **Turn the bird over** so it is breast-side down again and tie the strings tightly under the body. Bring both ends of the string down between the sides of the body and the insides of the wings.

4 **Tie the wing bones** at the neck opening so they are tucked securely under the body. Repeat the process with the remaining poussins and set aside.

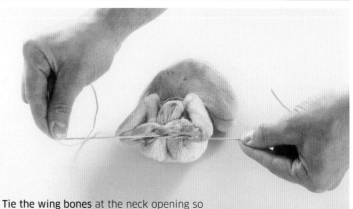

BLANCH THE CABBAGE

5 Fill a large pan with salted water and bring to a boil. Add the cabbage, return to a boil and simmer for 2 minutes until beginning to soften. Drain thoroughly in a colander.

ASSEMBLE AND BAKE THE DISH

6 Preheat the oven to 180°C (350°F/Gas 4). Peel the onion and stud it with the clove. Heat the oil in the casserole. Season the birds with salt and pepper. Brown them on all sides, turning, for 5–10 minutes. Transfer to a plate. Reduce the heat and let the casserole cool slightly.

7 Add the bacon and cook, stirring, for 3–5 minutes, until the fat has rendered. Spoon off all but 2 tbsp of fat. Stir in half the cabbage, and spread it evenly. Add the poussins and two-thirds of the plums.

8 Add the clove-studded onion and bouquet garni. Cover with the remaining cabbage and pour over the wine and stock. Cover and bake for 45–55 minutes, until the birds are cooked and the juices run clear when the thighs are pierced.

9 Discard the onion and bouquet garni. Transfer the birds to a chopping board; remove the strings. Taste the cabbage mixture for seasoning. With a slotted spoon, transfer the cabbage to a warmed large serving dish. Set the birds on top, cover with foil and keep warm.

FINISH THE DISH

10 Add the remaining plums to the cooking liquid and simmer for 5–8 minutes, until just tender. Lift them out with a slotted spoon and arrange them with the poussins and cabbage in the centre of the dish.

11 Boil the liquid until well-flavoured and reduced by about half; it should take 5–10 minutes. Stir the arrowroot and 1 tbsp water together to form a smooth paste with no lumps. Whisk enough of the paste into the liquid so it thickens to lightly coat the back of a spoon. Taste for seasoning, adjusting if necessary.

12 Spoon some sauce over each of the poussins, just to moisten the birds, and serve the rest separately in a warmed gravy boat for your diners to help themselves.

Chicken and prawn laksa

NOODLES AND TOFU add extra body to this aromatic recipe. For vegetarians, add more tofu and soaked dried oriental mushrooms and omit the meat and shellfish, or for more carnivorous souls add chunks of spicy sausage and pork.

SERVES	PREP	COOK
SERVES 6	35-40 MINS	30-35 MINS

Ingredients

750g (1lb 10oz) skinless, boneless chicken breasts

salt and pepper

500g (1lb 2oz) raw prawns

3 dried red chillies, or to taste

6 shallots, peeled and coarsely chopped

3 garlic cloves, peeled

1½ tsp ground turmeric

1 tbsp ground coriander

5cm (2in) piece of fresh root ginger, peeled, sliced, and crushed

250g (9oz) tofu

125g (4½oz) thin rice noodles

2 tbsp vegetable oil

250g (9oz) beansprouts

400ml (14fl oz) can coconut milk

1 small bunch of spring onions, thickly sliced

POACH THE CHICKEN

1 **Bring 750ml (1¼ pints) of water** to a boil in a saucepan and add the chicken breasts, salt, and pepper. Simmer for 12–15 minutes, or until tender when pierced at the thickest portion and the juices run clear.

2 **With a slotted spoon,** transfer the chicken to a chopping board. Reserve the poaching liquid.

3 **When the chicken is cool,** halve each breast lengthways, then cut across into 2.5cm (1in) pieces.

PREPARE THE OTHER INGREDIENTS

4 **Make a shallow cut** along the back of each prawn and remove and discard the dark intestinal vein that runs along its length with the tip of a sharp knife.

5 **Put the dried chillies** in a bowl and pour over hot water to cover. Soak for 5 minutes, then drain, cut in half, and scrape out and discard the seeds and white ribs.

6 **In a food processor,** combine the shallots, garlic, chillies, ground turmeric, coriander and ginger; work to a smooth paste. If the mixture is very thick, add 2-3 spoonfuls of the chicken poaching liquid.

7 **Drain the tofu** in a colander and discard the liquid. Cut it into 1cm (½in) cubes, being careful not to break up the pieces.

8 **Fill a large pan** with salted water and bring to a boil. Add the noodles and remove from the heat. Allow to soften for 3-5 minutes, until tender but still slightly chewy. Stir occasionally to prevent them sticking. Drain.

ASSEMBLE THE DISH

9 **Heat the oil** in a wok. Add the puréed ingredients, and cook gently, stirring constantly, for 1-2 minutes, or until you can clearly smell all the fragrant aromas. Add the chicken to the wok and continue cooking, stirring constantly, for 1-2 minutes longer, turning to make sure the chicken is coated all over in the aromatics. Stir in the reserved poaching liquid from the chicken and simmer until the sauce is rich and thickened. Expect it to take 20-25 minutes.

10 **Add the prawns** and simmer, stirring occasionally, just until they begin to lose their transparency and turn pink; it should only take 3-5 minutes and you should not cook them further or they will become tough. Add the tofu, beansprouts, and noodles. Pour in the coconut milk and stir. Simmer very gently for about 5 minutes, until the flavours combine. Stir in half the spring onions. Taste for seasoning, adding more salt and pepper if you think it necessary. Divide the laksa between 6 warmed bowls and sprinkle with the remaining spring onions.

Duck with turnips and apricots

WIDE NOODLES are the perfect accompaniment to this dish. Sweet Madeira wine adds a wonderful flavour and depth to the sauce. If you don't have any chicken stock to hand, you can use water here instead. It's a great recipe for entertaining, as it is rich enough to taste like a special treat, and it can be made 1 day ahead and kept, covered, in the refrigerator. Reheat it gently on top of the stove. You can, of course, ask your butcher to joint the bird for you, but it is easy to do yourself.

SERVES	PREP	COOK
SERVES 4	35–40 MINS	1½–2 HRS

Ingredients

1 duck, weighing about 1.8kg (4lb)	2 tbsp plain flour
12–16 pickling onions	175ml (6fl oz) dry white wine
500g (1lb 2oz) turnips	500ml (16fl oz) chicken stock, plus more if needed
salt and pepper	1 bouquet garni, made with 5–6 parsley stalks, 2–3 thyme sprigs and 1 bay leaf
1 tbsp vegetable oil	2 shallots, finely chopped
15g (½oz) butter	1 tsp granulated sugar
	175g (6oz) stoned dried apricots
	4 tbsp Madeira wine

JOINT THE DUCK

1 **Trim the excess fat** and skin from the duck. Using a thin, sharp knife, cut down between a leg and the body of the duck. Twist the leg sharply outwards to break the joint, cut through it, and cut the whole leg from the body. Repeat with the other leg.

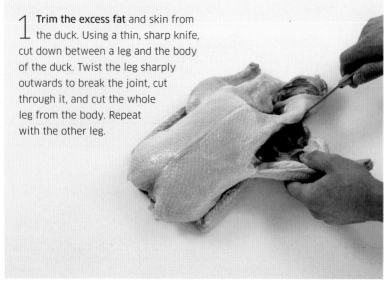

2 **Cut each leg in half** at the joint between the thigh and the drumstick, using the line of white fat on the underside as a guide.

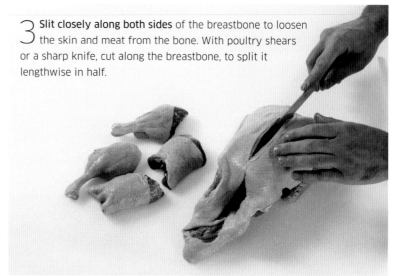

3 **Slit closely along both sides** of the breastbone to loosen the skin and meat from the bone. With poultry shears or a sharp knife, cut along the breastbone, to split it lengthwise in half.

4 **Turn the bird over,** and cut away the rib bones and backbone in one piece, from the breast, leaving the breast pieces with the wing joints attached. Discard the back and rib bones, or use them to make stock. Cut each breast piece diagonally in half, so a portion of breast meat is left with the wing joint. Cut off any sharp bones.

PREPARE THE VEGETABLES

5 **Put the pickling onions** in a bowl, cover with boiling water, and let stand for 2 minutes. Peel them, leaving a little of the root attached.

6 **Trim the ends** from the turnips, and peel them using a vegetable peeler. Cut small turnips into quarters, and larger ones into eighths. With a small knife, trim off the sharp edges, so they are rounded.

COOK THE STEW

7 **Preheat the oven** to 180°C (350°F/Gas 4). Season the duck. Heat the oil and butter in a casserole, and add the duck, skin-side down. Brown well over low heat for 20-25 minutes. Turn and brown the other side more quickly (for only about 5 minutes). Set aside.

8 **Transfer all but 2-3 tbsp fat** from the casserole to a frying pan. Return the casserole to the heat. Add the flour and cook, stirring constantly, for 1-2 minutes, until lightly browned but not burnt.

9 **Add the white wine,** stock, bouquet garni, salt, pepper, and shallots. Bring the mixture to a boil, and return the duck. Cover and cook in the oven for 40-45 minutes.

10 **Meanwhile,** heat the duck fat in the frying pan over a medium heat. Add the onions, turnips, sugar, salt and pepper, and cook, shaking the frying pan occasionally, for 5-7 minutes, until all the vegetables are evenly browned and beginning to become caramelized from the sugar. Make sure they do not scorch, as this may taint the flavour of the dish.

11 **Remove the stew** from the oven; add the onions, turnips, and apricots. Stir in more stock if the sauce is very thick and the ingredients are not covered (or add water to cover, if necessary). Cover with the lid and return to the oven for 20-25 minutes longer, until the duck and vegetables are tender.

12 **Skim off any fat** from the surface with a wide, shallow spoon. Stir in the Madeira, bring just to a boil on top of the stove, taste for seasoning, and adjust if needed. Serve on warmed individual plates, on a bed of wide noodles if you like.

Cassoulet

A QUICK VERSION OF DUCK CONFIT makes this complex but superb dish far more speedy to prepare than the traditional version. Save it for a very cold spell, when the warming, rich plateful of mixed meats and beans will be greeted by a welcoming and grateful chorus.

SERVES	**PREP**	**COOK**
SERVES 8	50–55 MINS PLUS MARINATING	1¾–2¼ HRS

Ingredients

FOR THE QUICK DUCK CONFIT

1 duck, weighing about 1.8kg (4lb), jointed into 8 pieces

1 tsp black peppercorns

3–5 thyme sprigs

3 bay leaves

3 tbsp sea salt flakes

1 tbsp vegetable oil

15g (½oz) butter

FOR THE CASSOULET

250g (9oz) streaky bacon rashers, cut into strips

750g (1lb 10oz) boneless lamb shoulder, in 5cm (2in) dice

375g (13oz) pork sausages

375g (13oz) onions, chopped

2 x 400g (14oz) cans chopped plum tomatoes

175ml (6fl oz) dry white wine

1.5 litres (2¾pints) chicken stock

4 garlic cloves, finely chopped

1 bouquet garni made with 5–6 parsley stalks, 3 thyme sprigs, and 1 bay leaf

1 tbsp tomato purée

salt and pepper

375g (13oz) garlic poaching sausages

4 x 400g (14oz) cans white beans

60g (2oz) dried breadcrumbs

MAKE THE CONFIT

1 **Remove the backbone** from the duck pieces, if necessary. Put the peppercorns in a plastic bag and crush with a rolling pin. Strip the thyme leaves from the stalks. Crush the bay leaves with your fingers. Combine the peppercorns, thyme, and bay in a bowl.

2 **Rub each piece of duck** with some sea salt and put the pieces into a non-metallic bowl. Sprinkle with the peppercorn mixture. Cover with clingfilm and refrigerate for 8–12 hours. Rinse the duck with cold water, then wipe with kitchen paper.

3 **Heat the oil** and butter in a casserole. Add the duck pieces, skin-side down, and brown well over low heat for 20–25 minutes, so the fat is thoroughly melted. Turn and brown the other side more quickly (only for about 5 minutes). Set aside. Spoon off and discard all but 2 tbsp of fat from the casserole.

COOK THE MEATS AND VEGETABLES

4 **Preheat the oven** to 190°C (375°F/Gas 5). Heat the casserole with the reserved duck fat, add the bacon and fry, stirring, for 3–5 minutes, until the fat is rendered. Transfer to a bowl with a slotted spoon.

5 **Season the lamb.** Add the lamb in batches to the casserole and cook over high heat, stirring, for 3–5 minutes, until evenly browned. Transfer to the bowl. Add the sausages to the casserole and brown all over. Transfer to a plate. Discard all but 2 tbsp fat. Add the onions and cook for 3–5 minutes, until soft.

6 **Return the lamb** to the casserole with the bacon and duck. Add the tomatoes, white wine, and two-thirds of the stock and stir to dissolve the pan juices. Stir in the garlic, bouquet garni, tomato purée, and salt and pepper. Bring to a boil on top of the stove, skimming occasionally. Cover and bake in the oven for 1–1¼ hours, until almost tender.

7 **Meanwhile,** put the poaching sausages into a pan with water to cover. Bring just to a boil. Simmer very gently for 20–25 minutes, until a skewer inserted in a sausage is warm to the touch. Do not boil or the sausages will burst. Drain, slit the skins with the knife, then peel and cut into 2cm (¾in) slices.

ASSEMBLE THE CASSOULET

8 **Drain the beans** in a colander. Rinse with cold water and drain again thoroughly. Add both kinds of sausage and the beans to the casserole. Stir and bring just to a boil on top of the stove. It should be very moist but not soupy. If necessary add more stock or water. Discard the bouquet garni and taste for seasoning.

9 **Sprinkle evenly with the breadcrumbs** and return the casserole to the oven. Bake, uncovered, for 20–25 minutes, until a beautifully crisp layer of golden crust forms on top of the cassoulet and the lamb beneath has become very tender.

10 **Serve the cassoulet** directly from the casserole, giving each diner a combination of lamb, duck, and sausages. Sprinkle with chopped parsley, if you like.

Italian beef braised in red wine

A FAVOURITE DISH in northern Italy. Barbera is the preferred wine, but substitute any good-quality dry red. When cooking with wine, it is very important to use a bottle you would also like to drink; you will taste a bad wine if you use it in a dish. Ovens did not find their way into many Italian kitchens until after World War II, so this dish was cooked on top of the stove, and you can do so too, if you prefer.

SERVES	**PREP**	**COOK**
SERVES 6	15–20 MINS	4–4½ HRS

Ingredients

1 rolled silverside of beef, weighing about 1.8kg (4lb)	1 small carrot, in 5mm (¼in) dice
	1 celery stick, peeled and diced
	500ml (16fl oz) dry red wine
2 tbsp olive oil	1 tbsp tomato purée
1 small onion, chopped	500ml (16fl oz) beef stock, plus more if needed
	2–3 thyme sprigs
	salt and pepper

ASSEMBLE THE DISH

1 **Preheat the oven** to 150°C (300°F/ Gas 2). With a sharp knife, trim any excess fat and sinew from the beef. Heat the oil in a casserole. Add the beef and brown well on all sides, turning. Transfer to a plate and set aside. Add the onion, carrot, and celery, and cook, stirring, for 3–5 minutes, until the vegetables are soft.

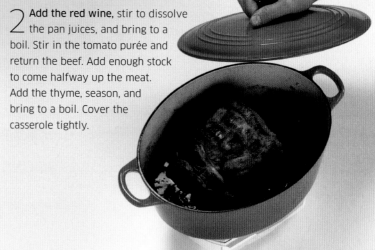

2 **Add the red wine,** stir to dissolve the pan juices, and bring to a boil. Stir in the tomato purée and return the beef. Add enough stock to come halfway up the meat. Add the thyme, season, and bring to a boil. Cover the casserole tightly.

BRAISE THE BEEF

3 **Cook in the oven** for 4–4½ hours, until the meat is very tender when pierced with a fork. Turn the meat 3–4 times during cooking, and add more stock if the casserole seems dry. Make sure the liquid remains at a simmer, not boiling, so the beef does not cook too quickly and become tough.

FINISH THE DISH

4 **Transfer the meat** to a chopping board and cover with foil to keep warm. Boil the liquid until thickened and reduced to about 250ml (9fl oz). Discard the thyme and taste the liquid for seasoning.

5 **Carve the meat** into neat slices on a chopping board. Arrange the beef slices on warmed plates. Spoon a little of the red wine sauce over, and serve the rest separately.

Lamb chops champvallon

DATING BACK to the reign of Louis XIV and attributed to one of his mistresses! Apparently, she created it in an attempt to stay in the king's good graces. The dish will certainly please your diners, with its succulent chops baked in the oven between layers of sliced potatoes and onions, which absorb all the delicious meaty flavours.

SERVES
SERVES 6

PREP
25–30 MINS

COOK
2–2¼ HOURS

Ingredients

6 lamb loin chops, each 2.5cm (1in) thick, total weight about 1kg (2¼lb), trimmed

salt and freshly ground black pepper

1 tbsp vegetable oil

500g (1lb 2oz) onions, thinly sliced

1.1kg (2½lb) baking potatoes

leaves from 1 small bunch of thyme, plus a few sprigs for garnish

3 garlic cloves, finely chopped

1 litre (1¾ pints) chicken or beef stock, plus more if needed

PREPARE THE INGREDIENTS

1 **Trim off** any excess fat from the lamb chops and season both sides. Heat the oil in a large frying pan, add the chops, and cook over high heat for 1–2 minutes each side, until well browned. Remove to a plate and set aside.

2 **Pour** off all but about 1 tbsp of fat from the pan. Add the onions and cook over medium heat, stirring, for 3–5 minutes, until soft and translucent. Remove the pan from the heat.

3 **Peel the potatoes** and cut into very thin slices. In a large bowl, gently stir the potato slices with the softened onions, thyme leaves, salt, and pepper.

ASSEMBLE AND BAKE THE DISH

4 **Preheat the oven** to 180°C (350°F/ Gas 4). Brush a 23x32cm (9x13in) baking dish with oil. Spread half the potato mixture in the dish and sprinkle with the garlic.

5 **Arrange the chops** on top. Cover with the remaining potato, arranging the slices neatly in rows. Pour over enough stock to come just to the top of the potatoes. Bake, uncovered, for 2 hours, or until the lamb and potatoes are tender when pierced.

6 **Divide the chops**, potatoes, and onions among 6 warmed plates and spoon over a little cooking liquid. Decorate with a sprig of thyme.

Lamb dhansak

FRESH MANGO RELISH is optional but it makes a colourful accompaniment to this curry. Traditionally, dhansak would be made with three different types of lentils and loads of vegetables. This version is simpler, but no less tasty for that. It can be made 2 days ahead and kept, covered, in the refrigerator.

SERVES	PREP	COOK
SERVES 6	40-45 MINS	1½-1¾ HRS

Ingredients

FOR THE CURRY

1 large aubergine

salt and pepper

2cm (¾in) piece of fresh root ginger

4 tbsp vegetable oil

750g (1lb 10oz) boned shoulder of lamb, cut into 2.5cm (1in) dice

1 large onion, finely chopped

5 garlic cloves, finely chopped

2 tsp each ground cumin, coriander, and turmeric

1 pinch of cayenne pepper

1 tbsp plain flour

175g (6oz) green lentils

1 small cauliflower, cut into florets

FOR THE MANGO RELISH

1 dried red chilli

1 large mango, weighing about 500g (1lb 2oz)

leaves from 7-10 coriander sprigs, finely chopped

5mm (¼in) piece of fresh root ginger, finely chopped

PREPARE THE AUBERGINE AND GINGER

1 **Trim the aubergine** and cut into 2.5cm (1in) chunks. Put them in a colander and sprinkle generously with salt. Let stand for about 30 minutes, to draw out some of the juices and soften slightly. Rinse under cold running water and drain well. Pat dry with kitchen paper.

2 **Using a small knife,** peel the skin from the fresh root ginger. Slice the ginger, cutting across the fibrous grain. Crush each slice with the flat of the knife, then finely chop the slices.

COOK THE CURRY

3 **Heat two-thirds of the oil** in a large casserole. Add some of the lamb and season. Cook over high heat for 3-5 minutes, stirring so the pieces brown evenly on all sides. Transfer to a bowl. Brown the rest of the lamb in the same way.

4 **Add the remaining oil** to the casserole, then add the aubergine and cook, stirring occasionally, for 5-7 minutes, until brown. With a slotted spoon, transfer to a separate bowl.

5 **Add the onion** to the casserole; cook, stirring occasionally, for 7-10 minutes, until golden brown. Stir in the garlic and ginger and cook for 2-3 minutes longer, until softened and fragrant.

6 **Stir in the ground cumin,** coriander, turmeric, and cayenne; cook, stirring constantly, for 1-2 minutes, until thoroughly combined. Return the lamb with any juices. Sprinkle with the flour and cook, stirring, for about 1 minute.

7 **Stir in 1 litre (1¾ pints) of water** and bring to a boil. Lower the heat, cover, and simmer gently, stirring occasionally, for 30 minutes. Stir in the lentils and cook for 15 minutes longer.

8 **Stir in the aubergine,** cauliflower, and 500ml (16fl oz) more water; continue simmering, stirring often, for 50-60 minutes, until completely tender. Add more water during cooking if the curry seems dry. Meanwhile, make the mango relish.

MAKE THE MANGO RELISH

9 **Put the dried chilli** in a small bowl and cover with hot water. Let soften for 5 minutes, then drain. Cut lengthways in half, discard the core, scrape out the seeds and chop very fine. Cut the mango lengthways into 3 pieces, slightly off-centre so the knife just misses the stone.

10 **With a small knife,** slash the cut side of the mango pieces in a lattice, at 5mm (¼in) intervals, just cutting through the flesh. Holding the mango flesh upwards, carefully push the peel with your thumbs to turn it inside out, opening out the cuts.

11 **Cut the cubes** of mango away from the skin into a bowl. In a small bowl, combine the mango, chilli, coriander, salt, pepper, and ginger, and stir until mixed. Taste for seasoning, cover and chill, 30 minutes. Serve with the curry.

VARIATION: Chicken dhansak

The same spices enhance chicken, chickpeas and vegetables.

1 Omit the lamb, cauliflower, and lentils. Prepare the aubergine as directed. Sprinkle 1 medium chicken, jointed into 8 pieces, with salt and pepper. Heat the oil in a large casserole, add the chicken, skin-side down, and brown well for 5–7 minutes, Turn and brown the other side, then transfer to a plate.

2 Brown the aubergine as directed. Drain a 400g (14oz) can of chickpeas. Cook the curry as directed, adding a 400g (14oz) can of chopped plum tomatoes and 1 litre (1¾ pints) water. Return the chicken to the casserole, cover and simmer for 20 minutes.

3 Add the aubergine and chickpeas, then continue cooking for 15–20 minutes, until the chicken is tender when pierced. Taste for seasoning and serve with cucumber raita and naan bread.

Brunswick stew

A COLONIAL AMERICAN DISH using lots of Southern ingredients – such as smoked bacon, beans, sweetcorn, and hot pepper – this was originally made with squirrel! Brunswick county in North Carolina and the county of the same name in Virginia both claim this famous recipe. It will freeze well for up to 3 months.

SERVES	PREP	COOK
SERVES 4-6	25-35 MINS	2-2½ HRS

Ingredients

1.5kg (3lb 3oz) chicken, jointed into 6 pieces

500g (1lb 2oz) smoked bacon hock

1 tbsp dark soft brown sugar

1 bouquet garni

1 onion, chopped

3 celery sticks, trimmed and thinly sliced

400g (14oz) can chopped tomatoes

200g (7oz) fresh, or thawed frozen, or canned sweetcorn

375g (13oz) potatoes

1 tsp dried chilli flakes

250g (9oz) shelled fresh or thawed frozen broad beans, peeled

salt and pepper

COOK THE CHICKEN AND HAM

1 **Put the chicken joints** in a casserole with the bacon hock and pour in enough water to cover. Add the sugar and bouquet garni. Bring to the boil and skim well with a slotted spoon.

2 **Cover and simmer** gently until the chicken joints are almost tender when pierced; it will take about 1 hour.

3 **Lift out the chicken** with a slotted spoon and reserve it. Remove the casserole from the heat and set aside.

FINISH THE STEW

4 **Bring the chicken liquid** in the casserole back to the boil. Add the onion, celery, and tomatoes and simmer, stirring often, for 20–30 minutes. Make sure the heat is very gentle; the liquid should be only barely bubbling. Add the sweetcorn and simmer for 10 minutes longer. Meanwhile, cut the potatoes into chunks and put them in a saucepan of salted water. Bring to the boil, cover and simmer for 15–20 minutes, until tender. Drain, then mash until very smooth (an old-fashioned potato ricer does the best job of getting potatoes really smooth).

5 **Stir the potatoes,** chilli flakes, and beans into the stew and season to taste, remembering that the heat of the chillies will mellow, if you are cooking this dish in advance. Return the chicken to the casserole and simmer, stirring often, until all the meats and vegetables are very tender, about 15 minutes longer.

6 **Lift out the bacon.** Using a fork and knife, pull the meat from the bones in large pieces, discarding the skin and fat. Shred the meat into chunky bits and stir it back into the stew. The sauce should be thick but, if it is too sticky (which it may be, depending on the potatoes you used), add a little more water to thin it out. Discard the bouquet garni and taste for seasoning.

 VARIATION: Chicken with kidney beans and garlic sausage

A colourful and spicier version.

1 Soak 500g (1lb 2oz) dried red kidney beans in enough cold water to cover them by 10cm (4in), leave overnight (or for at least 6 hours), then drain. Put the beans in a pot and add 1 onion stuck with a clove and a bouquet garni. Cover with fresh water and bring to a boil. Boil for at least 5 minutes, then reduce the heat and simmer for 25 minutes. Now add salt (adding salt before this will toughen the beans), and simmer for 45 minutes longer.

2 When the beans are ready, drain them into a colander, discarding the bouquet garni and the onion. Thickly slice a 375g (13oz) piece of garlic sausage, discarding the skin.

3 Prepare and cook the chicken as directed in the main recipe. Omit the broad beans and sweetcorn. Add the kidney beans to the casserole with the onion, tomatoes, and celery, and simmer until the beans are nearly tender. It should take about 30 minutes. Thicken the stew with the potatoes as directed in the main recipe, and add the sausage when you return the chicken to the stew.

Portuguese pork and clams

THIS COMBINATION of rich pork and salty clams – and indeed any pork with shellfish – has been enjoyed for centuries in Portugal and Spain. The dish really benefits from a squeeze of lemon at the end, so do encourage your diners to add some. You can make this dish to the end of step 4 up to 2 days in advance. Keep it, covered, in the refrigerator, then gently reheat the stew and cook the clams, following the instructions in step 5, just before serving.

SERVES	**PREP**	**COOK**
SERVES 6–8	30–35 MINS PLUS MARINATING	2–2½ HOURS

Ingredients

FOR THE MARINADE

2 garlic cloves, finely chopped

1 bay leaf, crumbled

1½ tbsp paprika

salt and pepper

3 tbsp olive oil

375ml (13fl oz) dry white wine, plus more if needed

FOR THE STEW

1.4kg (3lb) boned loin of pork, cut into 2.5cm (1in) cubes

1kg (2¼lb) clams, such as amandes

1 large onion, thinly sliced

2 garlic cloves, finely chopped

400g (14oz) can tomatoes

1 tbsp tomato purée

dash of Tabasco sauce, more to taste

1 lemon, cut into wedges, to serve

leaves from 1 bunch of parsley, chopped

MARINATE THE PORK

1 **Put the garlic,** bay leaf, paprika, plenty of black pepper, 1 tbsp oil, and the wine into a non-metallic bowl, then whisk to combine all the ingredients. Add the pork and mix well with its marinade. Cover and refrigerate for 24 hours, stirring occasionally so that all the cubes of pork come into contact equally with the marinade.

PREPARE THE CLAMS

2 **Scrub the clams** under cold running water with a stiff brush to remove any grit, sand, or seaweed, and discard any with broken shells, or that do not tightly close when tapped. As with any shellfish, if in any doubt about a clam, discard it. It's really not worth the risk of serving it up and poisoning your diners.

FINISH THE STEW

3 **Preheat the oven** to 180°C (350°F/Gas 4). Lift the meat from the marinade with a slotted spoon and pat dry with kitchen paper. Heat the remaining oil in a large casserole. Add the pork, in batches, and brown well on all sides. Transfer to a bowl.

4 **Reduce the heat** and add the onion and garlic. Cover and cook very gently for 20–25 minutes, until the onion is very soft and brown. Add the tomatoes, tomato purée, Tabasco, and pork. Pour in the marinade and stir. Cover and cook in the oven for 1½–1¾hours, until tender when pierced. Add more wine if the stew becomes dry.

5 **Arrange the clams** on top of the pork, cover with the lid, and cook in the oven for 15-20 minutes longer, until the clams open. Discard any clams that are still closed after cooking. Transfer to a warmed serving bowl. Sprinkle with chopped parsley. Serve the lemon wedges in a separate bowl.

 ## VARIATION: Chilean pork and beans

To save time, use canned kidney beans instead.

1 Omit the marinade and clams. Put 375g (13oz) dried red kidney beans in a bowl. Cover with water and let soak overnight. Drain and rinse. Put the beans in a saucepan, cover with fresh water, and boil for 10 minutes. Reduce the heat, cover, and simmer for 1 hour, or until almost tender but still slightly firm. Drain well.

2 Meanwhile, prepare the garlic and onion as directed. Core, seed and dice 1 hot green chilli and 2 green peppers. Peel 500g (1lb 2oz) each of yams and sweet potatoes, then cut them into 2.5cm (1in) cubes. Chop the leaves from a few sprigs each of parsley, coriander, and oregano. Brown the pork; cook the onions and garlic as directed. Return the pork to the pan. Add the tomatoes, tomato purée, herbs, and 500ml (16fl oz) water. Cover, and cook until the pork is just tender, 1¼-1½ hours. Add the vegetables, beans, and 750ml (1¼ pints) more water to cover.

3 Cook, stirring occasionally, until tender; this could take 40-45 minutes longer. Transfer the stew to the top of the stove, stir in 2 tbsp red wine vinegar, and simmer, uncovered, for 5 minutes. Taste for seasoning (you may want more herbs or seasoning, as beans need a lot) and serve in warmed bowls with rice or flour tortillas.

Navarin of lamb

THE BRIGHT FLAVOURS of young, melting lamb marry perfectly with vivid baby vegetables in this springtime stew. The secret is to cook the lamb until it is soft enough to fall from a fork, while only lightly cooking the vegetables.

SERVES	PREP	COOK
SERVES 6	45–50 MINS	2–2¼ HRS

Ingredients

500g (1lb 2oz) baby onions	1 bouquet garni made with 5–6 parsley stalks, 2–3 thyme sprigs, and 1 bay leaf
2 tbsp vegetable oil	500ml (16fl oz) chicken or lamb stock
750g (1lb 10oz) boneless lamb shoulder, in 2.5–4cm (1–1½in) dice	375g (13oz) tomatoes
	250g (9oz) baby carrots
salt and pepper	250g (9oz) turnips
2 tbsp plain flour	250g (9oz) French beans
1 tbsp tomato purée	750g (1lb 10oz) small new potatoes
2 garlic cloves, finely chopped	150g (5½oz) fresh or frozen peas (optional)
	leaves from 4–5 parsley sprigs, finely chopped

PREPARE THE ONIONS

1 **Put the baby onions** in a bowl, cover with boiling water, and let stand for 2 minutes. Drain, then peel. Heat the oil in a casserole. Add the onions and stir for 5–7 minutes, until golden. Remove and set aside.

SIMMER THE LAMB

2 **Season the lamb** with salt and pepper and add to the casserole, in batches if necessary. Cook over high heat, stirring occasionally, for 3–5 minutes until evenly browned. With a slotted spoon, transfer to a bowl.

3 **Return all the cooked lamb** to the pan, sprinkle with the flour, then stir to mix. Cook over medium heat, stirring occasionally, for 2–3 minutes, until the flour is browned.

4 **Let the casserole cool slightly**, then stir in the tomato purée, garlic, and bouquet garni. Pour in enough stock to just cover, stir, and bring to a boil. Cover with a lid and simmer for 1 hour.

PREPARE THE VEGETABLES

5 **Core the tomatoes** and score an "X" on the base of each. Immerse in boiling water until the skins start to split (8–15 seconds). Plunge at once into cold water. When cool, peel off the skins, cut in half, squeeze out the seeds, then coarsely chop.

6 **If the baby carrots have green tops**, trim them, leaving a little of the green, then scrape to remove the thin skin. Peel the turnips. Cut them into quarters or wedges, depending on their size, and trim off sharp edges with a small knife.

7 **Snap the ends off the beans** and cut into 2.5cm (1in) pieces. Peel the potatoes and put them into a bowl of cold water to prevent discolouration.

FINISH THE NAVARIN

8 With a slotted spoon, transfer the meat to a large bowl, then skim the fat from the sauce with a broad, shallow spoon. Strain the sauce back over the meat, then return both the meat and sauce to the casserole. Taste for seasoning, adjusting if necessary.

9 Drain the potatoes and add them to the casserole with the turnips, onions, tomatoes, and carrots. Pour in more stock to almost cover the meat and vegetables. Cover and simmer for 20-25 minutes, until the potatoes are tender to the point of a knife.

10 Add the peas, if using, and beans to the stew and simmer until they are just tender. Be sure not to cook the navarin for any longer than necessary to cook the vegetables through; they should retain their fresh crunch and bright colours. Taste for seasoning, and adjust if necessary. The sauce should be glossy and lightly thickened. Ladle the meat and vegetables on to warmed plates, moisten with the sauce, and sprinkle with parsley.

 VARIATION: Lamb ratatouille

Tasty Mediterranean vegetables add to the flavours.

1 Omit the baby onions, tomato purée, bouquet garni, carrots, turnips, French beans, potatoes, parsley, and peas. Brown the lamb as directed, using olive oil, then add the stock and simmer for 1¼ hours.

2 Trim 1 aubergine and cut into 2.5cm (1in) chunks. Put into a colander and sprinkle with salt. Let stand for 30 minutes. Meanwhile, chop 3 garlic cloves. Peel, seed, and chop 500g (1lb 2oz) tomatoes. Slice 1 green and 1 red pepper. Thinly slice 1 large onion. Rinse the aubergine chunks and pat dry.

3 Heat 3 tbsp olive oil in a frying pan. Add the onions and garlic and cook, stirring, for 3-5 minutes, until soft. Stir in the peppers and cook for 2-3 minutes. Add the aubergine and cook, stirring, until just tender (7-10 minutes). Add the tomatoes. Add the vegetables and 125ml (4½fl oz) chicken or lamb stock to the meat. Cook covered for 15 minutes, then cook uncovered for 20 minutes longer, until tender and well flavoured.

Provençal daube of beef

THE RICH, INTENSE AROMA of this dish is hard to beat. The beef is marinaded in all the aromas of the Mediterranean – oranges, red wine, and herbs – before being very slowly braised with lots of black olives. A truly delicious classic. You will need to start a day or two before your meal, to allow the beef a good long marinating time. If you can find salt pork, substitute it here for half the amount of bacon rashers in the recipe.

SERVES	**PREP**	**COOK**
SERVES 6-8	45-50 MINS PLUS MARINATING	3½-4 HRS

Ingredients

FOR THE MARINADE

1 orange

2 garlic cloves, finely chopped

500ml (16fl oz) red wine

2 bay leaves

3-4 sprigs each of rosemary, thyme, and parsley

10 peppercorns

2 tbsp olive oil

FOR THE STEW

1kg (2¼lb) braising steak, cut into 4cm (1½in) cubes

500g (1lb 2oz) piece of smoked streaky bacon, cut into 5mm (¼in) lardons

400g (14oz) can tomatoes

2 onions, sliced

2 carrots, sliced

175g (6oz) mushrooms, trimmed and sliced

200g (7oz) good-quality, stoned black olives

250ml (9fl oz) beef stock or water

salt and pepper

45g (1½oz) butter

3 tbsp plain flour

MARINATE THE BEEF

1 **Peel the zest** from the orange in wide strips. Combine the orange zest, garlic, red wine, bay leaves, rosemary, thyme, parsley, and peppercorns in a non-metallic bowl. Add the beef and mix well. Pour the olive oil on top. Cover tightly and refrigerate, turning occasionally, for 24-48 hours.

PREPARE THE BACON

2 **Put the bacon** in a saucepan of water, bring to a boil and blanch for 5 minutes. Drain in a colander and rinse with cold water. This removes excess salt from the large amount of bacon in the recipe.

COOK THE STEW

3 **Preheat the oven** to 150°C (300°F/Gas 2). Remove the beef pieces from the marinade, place on kitchen paper on a large plate and pat dry; set aside. Strain the marinade. Reserve the liquid and tie the flavouring ingredients in a piece of muslin.

4 **Spread the bacon** on the bottom of a casserole and cover with the beef. Layer the tomatoes and onions on top. Continue layering with the carrots, mushrooms, and olives. Pour in the strained marinade and stock and season with pepper. Add the bag of flavourings.

5 **Bring to a boil** on top of the stove, then cover the casserole, transfer to the heated oven, and cook for 3½-4 hours, stirring occasionally. The beef is ready when it is tender enough to crush in your fingers. Top up with more stock or water if it seems dry.

FINISH THE DISH

6 **Make a beurre manié** (kneaded butter): using a fork, crush the butter on a small plate until smooth, softened and easy to work. Work in the flour with the fork until the paste is smooth. This is an excellent technique to have in your repertoire, as the paste can be used to thicken any robust stew whose sauce is too thin for your taste (more delicate concoctions should not be thickened with it, though; reduce their sauces instead over a high heat).

7 **Transfer the casserole** to the top of the stove and scoop out the flavouring bag with a slotted spoon. Discard the flavouring bag. Add the beurre manié to the casserole in small pieces, stirring so each bit melts and thickens the sauce. Do not rush this process, as you want to cook out the taste of raw flour from the butter. Simmer for 2 minutes, then taste for seasoning. Serve in warmed dishes or bowls. Decorate with a few rosemary sprigs, if you like.

 VARIATION: Provençal lamb stew with green olives

Here, more traditional lamb replaces the beef.

1 Cut 1kg (2¼lb) boned lamb shoulder into large cubes, using a sharp knife. Marinate the lamb for 24-48 hours as directed in the main recipe.

2 Prepare the bacon and vegetables as directed, using green olives instead of black. Cook the stew as directed.

3 Make the beurre manié and finish the dish as directed, sprinkling a little chopped thyme on each serving, if you like. This stew can be made up to 2 days ahead and kept, covered, in the refrigerator. Bring to room temperature, then reheat on top of the stove until hot through and bubbling.

Beef with barley and mushrooms

BARLEY IS A TASTY GRAIN that used to be completely overlooked, unless one was making Scotch broth. Today it has made a well-deserved comeback, and is now a fashionable grain, adding body and earthy flavour to all sorts of dishes. For a treat, use wild mushrooms.

SERVES	PREP	COOK
SERVES 6–8	30–35 MINS	2¼–2½ HRS

Ingredients

3 tbsp vegetable oil

1.4kg (3lb) braising steak, in 5cm (2in) dice

625g (1¼lb) onions, thinly sliced

salt and pepper

1 bouquet garni, made with 5–6 parsley stalks, 2–3 thyme sprigs, and 1 bay leaf

1 litre (1¾ pints) beef stock, plus more if needed

375g (13oz) carrots, sliced

4 celery sticks, peeled and sliced

200g (7oz) pearl barley

500g (1lb 2oz) mushrooms, trimmed and sliced

leaves from 2–3 parsley sprigs, finely chopped (optional)

PREPARE THE INGREDIENTS

1 **Preheat the oven** to 180°C (350°F/Gas 4). Heat the oil in a casserole on top of the stove until hot. Add half the beef (it should sear when it hits the pan) and brown well. Transfer to a bowl. Brown the remaining beef in the same way.

2 **Add the onions** with a little salt and pepper. Cook over medium heat, stirring, for 5–7 minutes, until lightly browned. Return the beef, add the bouquet garni, salt, and pepper. Pour in the stock and stir.

COOK THE STEW

3 **Cover the casserole** and transfer to the heated oven. Cook, stirring occasionally, for about 1½ hours, then add the carrots, celery, and barley. Stir in more stock or water, if necessary, to keep the casserole moist.

4 **Cover and continue cooking** for 40–45 minutes longer, until the meat and vegetables are tender when pierced. The barley should be tender but still slightly chewy. About 10 minutes before the end of cooking, stir in the mushrooms.

5 **Discard the bouquet garni** and taste the stew for seasoning. Serve in warmed individual bowls, sprinkled with the parsley, if you like. Pass crusty bread alongside.

Spring veal blanquette

TO RETAIN THE WHITENESS of the rich sauce, be careful that nothing browns during the cooking of this classic French dish. Replace some of the total weight of meat with veal breast, for extra richness. Boiled white rice is the traditional accompaniment, though steamed new potatoes are also delicious.

SERVES	PREP	COOK
SERVES 6	45–50 MINS	1½–2¼ HRS

Ingredients

FOR THE VEAL

1.5kg (3lb 3oz) boned veal shoulder, in 5cm (2in) cubes

1 onion

1 clove

1 bouquet garni, made with 5–6 parsley stalks, 2–3 thyme sprigs and 1 bay leaf

salt and white pepper

1.5 litres (2¾ pints) chicken stock or water, plus more if needed

500g (1lb 2oz) pickling onions

1 large fennel bulb, thinly sliced, fronds reserved

500g (1lb 2oz) baby carrots, peeled

FOR THE SAUCE

45g (1½oz) butter

30g (1oz) plain flour

juice of ½ lemon

freshly grated nutmeg

2 egg yolks

125ml (4fl oz) double cream

SIMMER THE VEAL

1 **Put the diced veal** into a saucepan and cover with cold water. Bring to a boil, reduce the heat and simmer, skimming often, for 5 minutes. Drain the veal, rinse with cold water, and drain again. Trim the onion and peel it. Stud the onion with the clove.

2 **Transfer the veal** to a casserole. Add the clove-studded onion, bouquet garni, salt, and white pepper, and pour in the stock or water. Cover, bring to a boil and simmer very gently, skimming occasionally, until the meat is almost tender. Expect this to take up to 1 hour.

FINISH THE BLANQUETTE

3 **Put the pickling onions** in a bowl. Pour over hot water to cover and let stand for 2 minutes. Drain and peel. Discard the onion and the bouquet garni from the casserole. Add the pickling onions, fennel, and carrots, with more stock or water, if needed, so that everything is covered. Continue simmering for 20–30 minutes, until the veal and vegetables are tender.

MAKE THE SAUCE

4 **Remove the veal** and vegetables. Strain the liquid into a saucepan and simmer for 10–20 minutes, until well flavoured and reduced by about half. Melt the butter in the casserole. Whisk in the flour and cook for 30–60 seconds, until foaming. Cool slightly. Whisk in the cooking liquid and return to the heat, whisking constantly, for 3–5 minutes, until it boils and thickens. Simmer for 10–15 minutes, until it coats the back of a spoon.

5 **Return the veal and vegetables** to the sauce and season to taste with the lemon juice, salt, white pepper, and nutmeg. Gently heat the blanquette for 7–10 minutes longer, so the flavours blend. In a bowl, whisk together the egg yolks and cream, then whisk in a few spoonfuls of the hot sauce. Stir this mixture back into the stew and heat gently for 1–2 minutes, until the sauce thickens slightly. Serve immediately, sprinkled with fennel fronds.

Chicken pot pies with herb crust

A DELICIOUS RECIPE with a tasty scone topping. Best of all, no accompaniments are needed. The filling can be prepared 1 day ahead and kept, covered, in the refrigerator. Bring it to room temperature before topping and cooking. The scone dough should be made shortly before baking. You will need ovenproof individual casserole dishes.

SERVES
SERVES 4-6

PREP
25-35 MINS

COOK
22-25 MINS

Ingredients

FOR THE CHICKEN

1 litre (1¾ pints) chicken stock

3 carrots, sliced

750g (1lb 10oz) large potatoes, diced

3 celery sticks, thinly sliced

175g (6oz) peas

500g (1lb 2oz) cooked skinless, boneless chicken

60g (2oz) butter

1 onion, chopped

30g (1oz) flour

175ml (6fl oz) double cream

ground nutmeg

salt and pepper

leaves from 1 small bunch of parsley, chopped

1 egg

FOR THE TOPPING

250g (9oz) plain flour

1 tbsp baking powder

1 tsp salt

60g (2oz) butter

leaves from 1 small bunch of parsley, chopped

150ml (5fl oz) milk, more if needed

MAKE THE FILLING

1 **Heat the stock** to boiling in a large saucepan. Add the carrots, potatoes, and celery and simmer for 3 minutes. Add the peas and simmer for about 5 minutes until all the vegetables are tender.

2 **Drain the vegetables** in a colander, reserving the stock. Cut the chicken into slivers and put in a bowl. Add the vegetables.

3 **Melt the butter** in a small saucepan over moderate heat. Add the onion and cook for 3-5 minutes, until softened but not browned. Sprinkle the flour over the onions and cook, stirring, for 1-2 minutes.

4 **Stir in 500ml (16fl oz) stock and heat,** whisking, until the sauce comes to the boil and thickens. Simmer for 2 minutes, then add the cream and a pinch of nutmeg and taste for seasoning. Pour the sauce over the chicken and vegetables, add the parsley, and mix gently.

MAKE THE HERB SCONE TOPPING

5 **Sift the flour** into a large bowl with the baking powder and salt and make a well in the centre. Add the butter, cut into small pieces with two knives.

6 **Rub the mixture** with your fingertips until it forms fine crumbs, lifting and crumbling to aerate it. Add the parsley, make a well in the centre, add the milk and cut in quickly with a knife to form coarse crumbs. Add a little more milk if it seems dry.

7 **Mix the dough** with your fingers just until it comes together. Turn on to a floured surface and knead lightly for a few seconds until smooth. Pat the dough out to 1cm (½in) thick. Cut out rounds with a 8.5cm (3½in) pastry cutter or glass. Pat out the trimmings and cut additional rounds, for a total of 4-6.

ASSEMBLE AND BAKE THE PIES

8 Preheat the oven to 220°C (425°F/Gas 7). Divide the chicken filling evenly among 6 individual ovenproof dishes, making sure the vegetables are well distributed between them. Place a scone round on top of each pie (it's nice if the scone is positioned slightly off-centre, so you can see some of the creamy filling beneath). Lightly beat the egg with pinch of salt in a small bowl and brush the rounds with this glaze.

9 Bake the pies in the heated oven for 15 minutes. Reduce the heat to 180°C (350°F/Gas 4) and continue baking until the scone crust is golden brown and the filling is piping hot and bubbling. You need to cook at this lower temperature so that the filling heats through completely. It should take 7-10 minutes longer, but keep an eye on it. If the scone topping threatens to scorch, cover the pies loosely with a sheet of foil.

 VARIATION: Large chicken pot pie

The scone topping gives this pie a cheerful appearance.

1 Prepare the filling exactly as directed in the main recipe. Instead of baking in individual dishes, spoon the filling into a medium ovenproof dish, or a shallow soufflé dish, depending on preference.

2 Omit the chopped parsley from the scone dough and add chopped sage, thyme, or tarragon, as you prefer, instead. Cut the patted-out dough into 8 rounds, using a 6cm (2½in) pastry cutter.

3 Arrange the rounds evenly over the filling, then glaze the scones and bake the pie, allowing 15 minutes at 220°C (425°F/Gas 7) then 20-25 minutes at 180°C (350°F/Gas 4). The filling should be bubbling hot and give off delicious aromas.

Peppery Tuscan beef

ITALIAN CUISINE at its simple best. Chianti is the wine of Tuscany, but you can use any good-quality, full-bodied red wine. Here, sage-flavoured *fettunta* – rustic bread toasts – are served alongside. They must be made just before serving, but the beef itself will benefit from being prepared ahead and kept, covered, in the refrigerator; the flavours will mellow. Gently reheat it on top of the stove.

SERVES SERVES 6	**PREP** 35–40 MINS PLUS MARINATING	**COOK** 2–2½ HRS

Ingredients

5–6 sage sprigs

2 tbsp freshly ground black pepper

300ml (10fl oz) olive oil

1.4kg (3lb) braising steak, in 5cm (2in) dice

125g (4½oz) pancetta lardons

1 large onion, diced

6 garlic cloves

400g (14oz) can chopped tomatoes

2 bay leaves

250ml (9fl oz) beef stock, plus more if needed

500ml (16fl oz) red wine

salt

500g (1lb 2oz) loaf crusty Italian peasant-style bread

PREPARE THE SAGE OIL AND **MARINATE** THE BEEF

1 **Chop the leaves** from 2 of the sage sprigs, and put them in a small bowl. Don't be tempted to add more sage, as it is a strong flavour and can easily overpower a dish. In a large bowl, combine half the black pepper with all but 3 tbsp of the oil. Ladle one-quarter of this into the bowl with the chopped sage, and set it aside for the *fettunta*. This dish contains an awful lot of black pepper, but it is all necessary for the recipe. So don't be too timid and add less pepper, you will find it mellows and lends an incredible depth of flavour to the beef once marinated and braised.

2 **Add the beef** to the bowl with the black pepper and oil mixture. Stir until every piece of the beef is well coated, then cover tightly with clingfilm and refrigerate, stirring occasionally to redistribute the marinade, for 8–12 hours. Unfortunately, this step cannot be rushed, so make sure you can prepare the dish a day ahead; after all, it will only take about 5 minutes. The beef needs this long amount of marinating time in order to absorb all the pepper flavour. You will find the texture of the meat also becomes wonderfully tender during its bath in oil.

COOK THE STEW

3 **Chop the remaining** sage leaves. Remove the meat from the marinade with a slotted spoon, and transfer to a plate lined with kitchen paper. Pat dry. Heat half the remaining oil in a large pan over high heat, add half the meat and brown well on all sides for 3–5 minutes.

4 **Transfer the meat** to a bowl with a slotted spoon. Add the remaining oil to the pan, and brown the rest of the beef in the same way. Reduce the heat to medium, add the pancetta and cook, stirring occasionally, for 2–3 minutes, until the fat has rendered.

5 **Add the onion** and cook, stirring, for 3–5 minutes longer, until softened. Return the beef with 5 of the garlic cloves, finely chopped, the tomatoes, bay leaves, sage, remaining black pepper, stock, and wine. Bring to a boil, stirring. Cover, reduce the heat and simmer for 1¾–2 hours, until very tender, stirring occasionally.

6 **During cooking,** add more stock or water if the stew seems dry. The beef is ready when it is tender enough to crush in your fingers. Discard the bay and taste for seasoning. If the sauce is thin, increase the heat and boil, uncovered, until it has reduced and concentrated.

MAKE THE SAGE FETTUNTA

7 **Meanwhile,** heat the oven to 190°C (375°F/Gas 5). Cut the bread into fairly even 1cm (½in) slices. Cut any large slices in half. Set them on a baking sheet, spaced well apart so they do not steam rather than toast, and brush each generously, on both sides, with the sage-flavoured oil, then sprinkle the slices evenly with salt.

8 **Bake the bread** in the oven until toasted; it should take about 7–10 minutes. Turn it once during this time, so both sides become evenly golden brown. Cut the reserved garlic clove in half. Rub each bread slice all over with the cut side of the garlic clove, and transfer to a wire rack. You will find the toasted surface of the bread acts like a "grater" for the garlic, and that almost all of the clove disappears on to the bread. Discard any remaining garlic. Spoon the beef into a warmed serving dish. Serve the delicious, crispy *fettunta* alongside.

Japanese one-pot yosenabe

YOU WILL NEED A TABLETOP BURNER and a suitable pot that fits on top. An attractive flameproof casserole would serve perfectly. Food simmered at the table is common in northern Japan, and this recipe is simmered in the country's mother stock, called dashi. If you can't find Japanese rice wine, you can use dry sherry instead.

SERVES	PREP	COOK
SERVES 4	40–50 MINS PLUS STANDING	5–7 MINS

Ingredients

FOR THE DIPPING SAUCE

juice of 1 lemon

4 tbsp sweet Japanese rice wine

2.5cm (1in) piece of dried kelp

1 tsp dried bonito flakes

75ml (2½fl oz) Japanese soy sauce

FOR THE SOUP STOCK

10cm (4in) piece of dried kelp

1 tsp dried bonito flakes

2 tbsp Japanese soy sauce

2 tbsp sweet Japanese rice wine

salt

FOR THE POT

250g (9oz) fresh shirataki noodles or 60g (2oz) dried cellophane noodles

250g (9oz) firm tofu, in 2.5cm (1in) dice

1 large carrot, in 3mm (⅛in) slices

½ Chinese cabbage, sliced

4 spring onions, in 5cm (2in) pieces

4 fresh shiitake mushrooms, sliced

2 skinless boneless chicken breasts

8 clams, such as Venus

4 large oysters

MAKE THE DIPPING SAUCE AND SOUP STOCK

1 **For the dipping sauce,** combine the lemon juice, rice wine, dried kelp, bonito flakes and soy sauce in a bowl. Let stand at room temperature for at least 1 hour or up to 24 hours.

2 **For the stock,** pour 1 litre (1¾ pints) cold water into a large saucepan, and add the kelp. Bring to a boil, then immediately remove and discard the kelp. Remove the pan from the heat.

3 **Sprinkle the dried bonito flakes** evenly over the surface of the kelp-infused water. Let the stock stand for 3–5 minutes, until the flakes settle to the bottom (the time it takes will depend on the thickness and dryness of the flakes). Line a sieve with dampened muslin.

4 **Strain the stock** through the muslin into the pot in which you are serving the meal. Add the soy sauce and sweet rice wine. Stir and taste for seasoning, adding salt if necessary.

PREPARE THE INGREDIENTS

5 **Bring a large saucepan of water to a boil.** Add the shirataki noodles and boil for 1 minutes, until firm but still chewy, stirring occasionally. If using cellophane noodles, soak them in warm water for 30 minutes. Drain and cut into 12.5cm (5in) lengths.

6 **Arrange the tofu,** vegetables, and noodles on a large plate or tray. Cover tightly and chill. Slice the chicken breasts in half lengthways, then into 2.5cm (1in) pieces. Cover and chill.

PREPARE THE CLAMS AND OYSTERS

7 **Scrub and rinse the clams.** With a tea towel, grip a clam, keeping the hinge between your thumb and fingers. Press the cutting edge of an oyster knife between the halves opposite the hinge. Push in the knife and rotate the blade to pry the shell open. Cut the muscle from the top and bottom shells and discard the top shell.

8 **Scrub and rinse the oysters.** With a folded tea towel in one hand, grip an oyster. Holding the oyster knife in your other hand, insert the point of the blade next to the hinge of the shell. Twist to pry the shell open. Cut the top muscle of the oyster from the shell and discard the top shell.

9 **Using the blade** of the oyster knife, cut loose the muscle from the lower half of the shell. Repeat with the remaining oysters. Arrange the chicken in a bowl, and the clams and oysters on the half-shell on a serving platter.

FINISH THE DISH

10 **Line a sieve** with muslin. Strain the dipping sauce into a measuring jug and pour it into 4 small bowls, so each diner has their own. Set your chosen flameproof pot on a table-top burner. Pour in the stock and slowly bring it to a boil over medium heat.

11 **When the stock** is simmering, add the chicken and carrot. Cook until the chicken is firm and the carrot slices almost tender. It will only take 2–3 minutes.

12 **Add half the tofu**, vegetables, and noodles and cook until the vegetables are tender; again, it should take just 2–3 minutes. Add the oysters and clams, without their shells, and cook just until the edges of the oysters start to curl.

13 **Guests can help themselves**, using chopsticks to dip the ingredients into the sauce before eating. When the pot is empty, replenish it with the remaining ingredients and cook until tender. When these are finished, ladle the remaining broth into bowls and serve.

Boeuf à la Bourguignonne

FEW FRENCH DISHES are better known, and with good reason, than this classic from Burgundy. The secret of a successful pot roast – the technique used in this dish – is using well-aged beef, so find a good butcher. Try to use a hearty red wine, such as pinot noir, to add substance to the sauce. The dish can be made up to 3 days ahead and kept, covered, in the refrigerator. The flavour will improve.

SERVES SERVES 6-8	**PREP** 25-30 MINS	**COOK** 3½-4 HRS

Ingredients

1 onion

2 cloves

1 beef topside, weighing 1.4-1.6kg (3-3½lb)

3 tbsp olive oil

1 carrot, peeled and quartered

1 bouquet garni, made with 5-6 parsley stalks, 2-3 thyme sprigs, and 1 bay leaf

250ml (9fl oz) red wine

salt and pepper

250ml (9fl oz) beef stock, plus more if needed

16-20 pickling onions

250g (9oz) piece of smoked streaky bacon, cut into 5mm (¼in) lardons

250g (9oz) mushrooms, sliced

COOK THE POT ROAST

1 **Preheat the oven** to 160°C (325°F/Gas 3). Peel the onion and stud with the cloves. If necessary, roll the beef topside into a neat shape and, using string, tie at 2.5cm (1in) intervals to hold the shape.

2 **Heat 2 tbsp of the oil** in a casserole until very hot. Add the meat (it should sizzle) and brown it well on all sides. Remove the casserole from the heat, take out the meat and discard all but 2 tbsp of fat from the casserole.

3 **Replace the meat** in the casserole, and add the clove-studded onion, carrot, bouquet garni, red wine, salt (not too much, as the bacon will be salty), and pepper. Cover and cook in the oven for 30 minutes.

4 **Pour in the stock** and stir well. Cook for about 3 hours, turning the meat 3 or 4 times, and add more stock if too much liquid evaporates.

PREPARE THE GARNISH

5 Put the pickling onions in a bowl, pour over hot water to cover and let them stand for 2 minutes to help loosen the skins. Drain, and peel. Heat the remaining oil in a frying pan.

6 Add the bacon to the pan and fry for 3–5 minutes, until browned and the fat has rendered. Transfer to a bowl. Add the pickling onions to the pan and cook, stirring occasionally, for 3–5 minutes, until lightly browned. Add to the bacon using a slotted spoon.

7 Add the mushrooms to the frying pan and cook, stirring occasionally, for 2–3 minutes, until they are tender and their liquid has evaporated. Transfer them to the bowl containing the bacon and onions.

FINISH THE DISH

8 Remove the meat from the casserole. Strain the cooking liquid, discarding the flavourings. If the liquid is too thin, return it to the casserole and boil until reduced and slightly thickened. Return the meat to the casserole and add the bacon, pickling onions, and mushrooms. Cover and continue cooking for 30 minutes, or until very tender.

9 Transfer the meat to a chopping board. Skim off and discard any fat from the cooking liquid and taste it for seasoning. Remove and discard the strings from the beef, then cut into 12 thick slices.

10 Arrange the beef on warmed plates. Spoon the garnish and a little of the cooking liquid over and serve the remainder separately. Decorate each plate with fresh thyme sprigs, if you like.

Lamb shanks in red wine

PERFECT FOR A CHILLY DAY. You will need to start this dish at least 1 day ahead, so you have enough time to marinate the lamb. Shanks are cheap, so it's worth doubling this recipe and freezing some for another time. Defrost it in the refrigerator overnight, then reheat on top of the stove.

SERVES	PREP	COOK
SERVES 6	45–50 MINS PLUS MARINATING	2½–2¾ HRS

Ingredients

FOR THE MARINADE

2 tsp black peppercorns

2 tsp juniper berries

4 shallots, roughly chopped

2 garlic cloves, peeled

2 onions, quartered

2 carrots, roughly sliced

1 bouquet garni, made with 5–6 parsley stalks, 2–3 thyme sprigs, and 1 bay leaf

2 tbsp red wine vinegar

750ml (1¼ pints) dry red wine

FOR THE LAMB

6 lamb shanks, total weight about 1.8kg (4lb)

3 tbsp vegetable oil

30g (1oz) plain flour

750ml (1¼ pints) beef stock, plus more if needed

salt and pepper

30g (1oz) butter

1 celeriac, weighing about 500g (1lb 2oz), in 1cm (½in) dice

250g (9oz) mushrooms, quartered

3 tbsp redcurrant jelly

1 bunch of watercress, to garnish (optional)

MARINATE THE MEAT

1 **Combine the black peppercorns** and juniper berries in a plastic bag. Holding the end of the bag closed, crush them with a rolling pin. Alternatively, crush them in a mortar and pestle. They don't have to be finely ground, so a coarse texture is fine in this case.

2 **In a saucepan,** combine the peppercorns, juniper berries, shallots, garlic, onions, carrots, bouquet garni, and vinegar. Pour in the red wine, bring to a boil, and simmer for about 2 minutes so the flavours meld together. Transfer the marinade and vegetables to a shallow dish, so it loses its heat rapidly, and set aside to cool completely.

3 **Trim off and discard any excess fat** and sinew from the lamb shanks. Add the shanks to the dish, and stir to coat with the marinade. (First ensure that the marinade is cold, or the meat may turn sour.) Cover and refrigerate, turning occasionally to redistribute the marinade evenly around the shanks, for 1–2 days.

ASSEMBLE AND COOK THE STEW

4 **Preheat the oven** to 180°C (350°F/Gas 4). Put the lamb shanks on a plate lined with kitchen paper and pat dry. Reserve the bouquet garni. Drain the vegetables in a sieve set over a bowl. Reserve the vegetables and marinade separately. Heat half the oil in a casserole. Add three lamb shanks, and brown well on all sides over high heat for 3–5 minutes.

5 **Transfer the lamb** to a bowl. Heat the rest of the oil and brown the remaining shanks in the same way. Add the vegetables and cook, stirring frequently, for 5–7 minutes, until they start to brown. Sprinkle with the flour and cook, stirring, for 3–5 minutes more, until the flour has been absorbed and the vegetables are lightly browned.

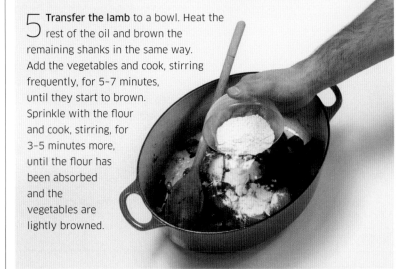

6 **Stir in the reserved marinade,** scraping the bottom of the pan to dissolve the pan juices. Add the lamb with any juices, the bouquet garni, stock, salt, and pepper. Cover and cook in the oven, turning occasionally, for 2–2¼ hours, until tender. If the sauce evaporates rapidly during cooking, add more stock.

COOK THE CELERIAC AND MUSHROOMS

7 Melt the butter in a frying pan, add the celeriac and season. Cook, stirring occasionally, for 8-10 minutes, until tender. Transfer to a bowl. Add the mushrooms to the pan. and cook for 3-5 minutes, until all the liquid has evaporated and they are tender. Add to the bowl with the celeriac.

8 Transfer the lamb shanks from the casserole to a plate, and keep warm. Ladle the sauce into a sieve set over a large pan, reserving some of the more attractive pieces of shallot and carrot. Press the remaining vegetables with a ladle to extract the juices.

FINISH THE SAUCE

9 Whisk the redcurrant jelly into the sauce with plenty of pepper. Bring back to a boil and simmer for 20-30 minutes, until reduced by half.

10 Add the mushrooms, celeriac, reserved carrot and shallot, and taste for seasoning. It should be fruity, but piquant with pepper. Return the lamb and heat for 5-10 minutes, until very hot. Return the lamb. Divide among warmed plates, and decorate with sprigs of watercress, if you like.

 VARIATION: Venison stew with pears

Wonderfully rich and sweet.

1 Omit the lamb shanks. Prepare the marinade as directed in the main recipe. Trim the fat and sinew from 1.6kg (3½lb) venison stew meat, and cut it into fairly even 4cm (1½in) cubes. Marinate the meat and vegetables as directed. Continue as directed, cooking the venison until tender; it should take 1¼-1½ hours.

2 Meanwhile, peel and core four firm ripe pears, and cut each half into thirds. Sprinkle with the juice of one lemon to prevent discolouration, and toss to coat. Remove the venison from the sauce and set it aside, keeping it warm. Strain the sauce into a saucepan, and whisk in the redcurrant jelly with plenty of pepper.

3 Add the pears, bring back to a boil, and simmer for 6-8 minutes, until tender. Remove the pears. Continue simmering the sauce for 5-10 minutes. until it has thickened slightly. Return the venison and pears and bring back just to a boil. Transfer to a warmed tureen.

French beef and herb potato pie

AN UPDATE OF A FRENCH CLASSIC. The recipe was originally designed as a way to use up the remains of a beef roast. If you would like to be thrifty and use leftover beef, add it to the gravy 10 minutes before the end of step 3, to heat through and absorb all the other flavours.

SERVES	PREP	COOK
SERVES 6	45–50 MINS	35–40 MINS

Ingredients

FOR THE BEEF

4 garlic cloves

75ml (2½fl oz) olive oil

1 large onion, diced

1kg (2¼lb) minced beef

salt and pepper

400g can chopped tomatoes

250ml (8fl oz) beef stock

125ml (4fl oz) dry white wine

FOR THE POTATOES

1kg (2¼lb) potatoes

1 bunch of basil

1 bunch of parsley

250ml (8fl oz) milk, plus more if needed

COOK THE MINCED BEEF

1 Remove the skins from the garlic cloves, and discard. Finely chop 2 of the cloves. Heat one-third of the oil in a sauté or frying pan. Add the onion and cook, stirring, until soft but not brown, 3–5 minutes.

2 Add the chopped garlic, minced beef, salt, pepper and tomatoes. Reduce the heat and cook very gently, stirring occasionally, for 10–12 minutes, until the meat is brown.

3 Stir in the stock and wine. Simmer over very low heat, stirring from time to time, for 25–30 minutes, until most of the liquid has evaporated but the meat is still very moist. Do not cook the meat too fast or it will be tough.

MAKE THE HERB MASHED POTATOES

4 Peel the potatoes and cut each into 2–3 pieces, depending on size. Put them in a saucepan with plenty of cold water and add salt. Cover and bring to a boil. Simmer for 15–20 minutes, until tender when pierced with a knife.

5 Meanwhile, strip the basil and parsley leaves from the stalks. Put the leaves and the 2 whole garlic cloves in a food processor. Work with the remaining oil to form a purée, scraping the side of the bowl occasionally.

6 Drain the potatoes, return them to the saucepan and mash. Add the herb purée. Scald the milk in another saucepan.

7 Gradually beat the milk into the potatoes over medium heat, and stir for 2–3 minutes, until the potatoes just hold a shape. Season to taste.

ASSEMBLE AND BAKE THE PIE

8 **Preheat the oven** to 190°C (375°F/Gas 5). Brush a large, shallow baking dish with oil. Taste the meat for seasoning, then spoon it, with any of its liquid, into the baking dish. Cover with an even layer of the herb potatoes and smooth the top with the back of a spoon, making sure the potatoes go right to the edges of the dish and no meat or sauce shows through.

9 **Make a scalloped pattern** on the herb potatoes with the tip of a dessert spoon or the tines of a fork. Dip the spoon or fork into a bowl of hot water set close to hand once or twice during the process, so the potato does not stick to it.

10 **Transfer the pie** to the heated oven and bake until the top is golden brown, the edges bubbling with gravy, and the tip of a skewer inserted in the centre for 30 seconds is hot to the touch when withdrawn; it should take 35–40 minutes. Cut the pie into 6 portions and transfer to warmed plates.

 ## VARIATION: Old Emily's Shepherd's Pie

Many of us were brought up on this!

1 Omit the beef, wine, garlic, basil, parsley, olive oil, and tomatoes. Cut 2 carrots into 5mm (¼in) cubes. Heat 1 tbsp vegetable oil in a large sauté or frying pan; sauté the carrots and onions until soft, 3–5 minutes; lower the heat to cool the pan.

2 Brown 1kg (2¼lb) minced lamb very gently. Add 250ml (8 floz) beef stock or water, with 1 sprig each thyme and rosemary; simmer as directed. Discard the herbs and taste for seasoning. Meanwhile, peel and cook 1kg (2¼lb) potatoes as directed. Drain, mash them and stir in 45g (1½oz) butter. Beat in the hot milk as directed. Season to taste.

3 Brush 6 heatproof bowls with melted butter and fill them with the lamb. Divide the mashed potatoes among the bowls and make a design on the top with a fork. Bake in the oven as directed until golden brown.

Home
from work

Simple but scintillating
dishes to make in a hurry

Sole fillets in wine vinegar

MARINATE THE NIGHT BEFORE you want to eat. This is an old Italian dish dating from before domestic kitchens had refrigeration, so pickling was a common method of preserving. If you would prefer a milder marinade, use just half the quantity of vinegar and an equal amount of white wine.

SERVES
SERVES 4-6

PREP
30-35 MINS
PLUS MARINATING

COOK
6-8 MINS

Ingredients

FOR THE SOLE

90ml (3fl oz) olive oil

1 large onion, thinly sliced

salt and pepper

250ml (9fl oz) red wine vinegar

45g (1½oz) raisins

500g (1lb 2oz) sole fillets

30g (1oz) plain flour

30g (1oz) pine nuts

FOR THE SALAD

juice of ½ orange

3 tbsp olive oil

250g (9oz) rocket

PREPARE THE MARINADE

1 **Heat a third of the oil** in a pan. Add the onion, salt, and pepper, cover, and cook for 15 minutes, until soft. Uncover, increase the heat, and cook until caramelized. Add the vinegar and raisins. Boil for 2 minutes. Set aside.

COOK THE FISH

2 **Rinse the sole** and pat dry. Cut the fillets across into 5cm (2in) pieces. Spread the flour on a large plate and season. Add some of the fish and turn to coat. Transfer to a second plate, and coat the remaining fish pieces.

3 **Heat the remaining oil** and add the sole. Cook over medium-high heat for 1-2 minutes, until browned. Turn and fry for 1-2 minutes, until the flesh just flakes when tested with a fork. Drain on kitchen paper and cool completely.

MARINATE THE FISH

4 **Spread the sole** in a baking dish, and cover with the vinegar mixture.

5 **Sprinkle with the pine nuts.** Cover tightly and leave to marinate in the refrigerator for 12 hours, or up to 24 hours. Remove it from the refrigerator 1 hour before serving.

PREPARE THE SALAD

6 **Pour the orange juice** into a bowl and season. Gradually whisk in the oil so the vinaigrette emulsifies and thickens slightly. Taste for seasoning. Add the rocket and toss. Serve with the sole and spoon on the marinade.

Grilled pepper-stuffed mussels

SO DELICIOUS that you'll want to make it everyday food. This light dish is perfect for a special romantic meal. To make it even quicker to prepare, use roast peppers from a jar rather than roasting them yourself, but be sure to drain them thoroughly.

SERVES	PREP	COOK
SERVES 4	25–30 MINUTES	1–2 MINUTES

Ingredients

1 small bunch of flat-leaf parsley

1 large red pepper

2 slices of white bread

2 garlic cloves, peeled

2 tbsp olive oil

salt and pepper

24 large mussels, total weight about 750g (1lb 10oz)

250ml (9fl oz) dry white wine

lemon wedges, to serve

MAKE THE TOPPING

1 **Reserving a few sprigs** for decoration, strip the parsley leaves from the stalks, keeping leaves and stalks separate.

2 **Heat the grill.** Set the pepper on a rack about 10cm (4in) from the heat and grill, turning, for 10–12 minutes, until black all over. Seal in a plastic bag and let cool, then peel, scrape out the seeds and ribs, and cut into strips.

3 **Trim and discard the crusts** from the bread. Cut the bread into cubes and work them in a food processor to form crumbs. Add the parsley leaves, garlic, oil, and red pepper. Work to a purée and season.

PREPARE THE MUSSELS

4 **Clean the mussels** (see p41). Discard any that have broken shells or do not close when tapped. Put the wine and parsley stalks in a saucepan. Bring to a boil and simmer for 2 minutes. Add the mussels.

5 **Cover and cook** over high heat, stirring once, for 2–3 minutes, until the mussels open. Transfer to a large bowl with a slotted spoon. Discard any that have not opened.

STUFF THE MUSSELS

6 **Heat the grill.** Remove the top shell from each mussel, and discard the rubbery ring surrounding the meat.

7 **Spoon a little topping** on to each mussel. Set the mussels in their bottom shells, in a baking dish. Grill for 1–2 minutes, until very hot and the topping is heated through. Serve with lemon wedges and parsley sprigs, if you like.

Pinwheel chicken with goat's cheese

THE PRETTY HERBAL GREEN FILLING makes a spiral pattern when sliced. You can make the chicken the night before, refrigerate, and reheat in simmering water for 10 minutes. This means you can have your beautifully presented dinner on the table in a flash – perfect for a mid-week supper for friends.

SERVES
SERVES 4

PREP
30-40 MINS

COOK
15-20 MINS

Ingredients

FOR THE CHICKEN

4 large skinless, boneless chicken breasts, total weight about 750g (1lb 10oz)

125g (4½oz) goat's cheese

2-3 tbsp single cream, if necessary

leaves from 1 small bunch of basil, finely chopped

leaves from 1 small bunch of parsley, finely chopped

leaves from 3 thyme sprigs

juice of ½ lemon

salt and pepper

FOR THE TOMATO BUTTER SAUCE

3 shallots, finely chopped

250ml (9fl oz) dry white wine

125g (4½oz) butter

1 tbsp tomato purée

PREPARE THE CHICKEN BREASTS

1 **Split each chicken breast** open by slicing three-quarters of the way through. Place it between 2 sheets of dampened baking parchment. Pound lightly with a rolling pin until the chicken is of an even thickness.

MAKE THE STUFFING

2 **Put the goat's cheese** in a bowl and mash with a fork (harder cheese may be crumbled by hand), discarding any rind. If the cheese is too dry, soften it with cream. Add the herbs and lemon and mix. Taste for seasoning.

STUFF THE CHICKEN

3 **Peel the top sheet** of baking parchment from each breast. With a palette knife, evenly spread a quarter of the herb and goat's cheese filling in the centre of each. Loosen the breast from the paper.

4 **Roll the chicken breast** up into a neat cylinder, beginning with a long side of the chicken.

5 **Fold in the ends** of the roll so the filling is sealed securely. Repeat with the remaining breasts.

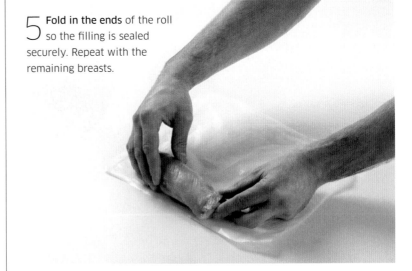

COOK THE CHICKEN

6 **Cut a piece of foil** to wrap generously around a rolled breast. Put it on the work surface, shiny-side down. Set the breast on the foil. Roll up the stuffed breast in the foil neatly and tightly, smoothing the foil to keep it taut. Twist the ends of the foil firmly to form a tight cylinder, sealing in the ends. Repeat the process for the remaining rolled breasts.

7 **Half fill a wide pan with water** and bring to the boil. With a slotted spoon, put the packages in the water and simmer until a skewer inserted in the centre is hot to the touch, about 15 minutes. Keep the chicken warm in its foil in the pan of hot (not boiling) water.

MAKE THE SAUCE

8 In a small saucepan, boil the shallots and wine with a small pinch each of salt and pepper until reduced to a syrupy glaze. Off the heat, whisk in the butter, a few small pieces at a time, whisking constantly and moving the pan on and off the heat. Do not boil; the butter should thicken the sauce creamily without melting to oil.

9 Whisk in the tomato purée and taste for seasoning. Butter sauces are delicate, and separate easily if overheated. To keep the sauce warm, set the saucepan in another pan of warm, not hot, water. Whisk occasionally but never leave for more than 30 minutes.

FINISH THE DISH

10 Remove the chicken rolls from the pan with a slotted spoon and carefully unwrap them on kitchen paper to absorb any water. Cut them into diagonal slices about 1cm (½in) thick. Spoon the sauce on to warmed individual plates, arrange the pinwheel slices on top and serve.

 VARIATION: Pinwheel chicken Italienne

With Parma ham and fontina cheese.

1 Prepare and pound the chicken breasts as directed in the main recipe. Trim 4 large, or 8 small, slices of Parma ham to the same size as the flattened breasts. Set the ham on the chicken evenly, so that each mouthful will contain the same amount of ham and chicken.

2 Cut a 125g (4½oz) piece of fontina cheese into thin slices, discarding the rind. Lay the cheese along one long side of each breast. Fontina melts beautifully, which is delicious, but does mean you will need to be punctilious about rolling the chicken so that there is a minimal chance of leaking. Roll up as directed in the main recipe, wrap in foil, and poach the breasts.

3 Prepare the butter sauce, omitting the tomato purée. For an attractive presentation, strain the sauce to separate the shallots, then garnish with the shallots and steamed, finely diced courgettes to add colour.

Milanese veal escalopes

A NORTHERN ITALIAN CLASSIC. It is very important, when frying this dish, that the escalopes have a lot of room in the frying pan. If they are too close together, they will steam instead of fry and you will not get the wonderfully crisp crust.

SERVES SERVES 6	**PREP** 20-25 MINS	**COOK** 4-12 MINS

Ingredients

FOR THE VEAL

6 veal escalopes, total weight about 375g (13oz)

30g (1oz) plain flour

salt and pepper

2 eggs

60g (2oz) dried breadcrumbs

FOR THE SAUTÉED PEPPERS

2 tbsp olive oil

1 garlic clove, finely chopped

1 small green pepper, sliced

1 small red pepper, sliced

leaves from 7-10 oregano sprigs, finely chopped, plus more to serve

60g (2oz) grated Parmesan cheese

30g (1oz) butter

2 tbsp olive oil, plus more if needed

1 lemon, sliced, to serve

PREPARE THE VEAL ESCALOPES

1 **If necessary,** flatten the veal: put 2 veal escalopes between 2 sheets of baking parchment. Lightly pound to 3mm (⅛in) thick with a rolling pin. Repeat with the remaining slices.

COAT THE VEAL

2 **Season the flour** with salt and pepper and sift it on to a sheet of baking parchment.

3 **Lightly beat the eggs** in a shallow dish. Mix the breadcrumbs and Parmesan together in a small bowl and spread on another sheet of baking parchment.

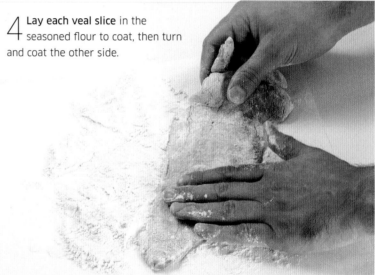

4 **Lay each veal slice** in the seasoned flour to coat, then turn and coat the other side.

5 **Using 2 forks,** dip each slice in the egg and coat it thoroughly on both sides. Finally, press the veal into the breadcrumb and cheese mixture and coat both sides evenly. Put each slice on a plate. Refrigerate, uncovered, while you sauté the peppers.

SAUTÉ THE PEPPERS

6 Heat the oil in a medium frying pan. Add the garlic, pepper, salt and pepper, and sauté, stirring occasionally, until softened, 7-10 minutes. Remove from the heat, add the oregano and taste for seasoning; keep warm while frying the escalopes.

FRY THE VEAL AND SERVE

7 Heat half the butter and 1 tbsp oil in a large frying pan, or divide the total amount of butter and oil between 2 frying pans. Add 2-3 escalopes to a pan and fry over medium-high heat until golden brown, 1-2 minutes. They should not touch or they will stick together. Reduce the heat if the crumbs threaten to scorch at any time.

8 Turn and continue cooking until brown and no longer pink in the centre. It should take about 1-2 minutes, but cut into an escalope with a sharp knife to check (served it with the other side uppermost). Transfer the cooked veal to a plate lined with kitchen paper to blot off the excess fat and keep warm. If you used just 1 pan, add the remaining butter and oil and make sure it gets hot before frying the remaining veal, adding more oil if necessary. Be sure not to add too much oil, as the escalopes should remain crisp and not soggy.

9 Transfer the escalopes to warmed individual plates and garnish each with a few lemon slices and a sprig of oregano. Spoon the pepper strips alongside. Encourage your diners to squeeze lemon liberally over the veal; the combination is quite wonderful.

Turkish lamb kebabs

SUCCULENT GRILLED cylinders, perfect on a bed of tabbouleh (p108). These whip up in no time for the evening meal, but can also be made in the morning and refrigerated for an even speedier supper, as their flavours will improve.

SERVES
SERVES 6

PREP
30-35 MINS

COOK
10-15 MINS

Ingredients

FOR THE YOGURT SAUCE

1 large cucumber

1 tsp salt

500ml (16fl oz) Greek yogurt

1 garlic clove, finely chopped

FOR THE KEBABS

1 large onion

1kg (2¼lb) minced lamb

2 tsp ground cumin

salt and pepper

3 garlic cloves, finely chopped

leaves from 3-5 mint sprigs, finely chopped, plus more leaves for garnish

leaves from 3-5 parsley sprigs, finely chopped

olive oil

MAKE THE SAUCE

1 **Wipe and trim** the cucumber. Grate it, with the skin, into a large bowl. Stir in the salt. Set a colander over a bowl. Transfer the grated cucumber to the colander and let drain for 10 minutes, to draw out excess moisture.

2 **Put the yogurt** in a large bowl. Remove more water from the cucumber by squeezing it in your hand. Add the cucumber to the yogurt. Stir in the garlic with salt to taste. Cover and chill.

PREPARE THE KEBABS

3 **Cut the onion** into chunks and put into a food processor. Blend until finely chopped, then stir it into the minced lamb in a large bowl. Mix in the cumin, salt and pepper, garlic, and herbs. To test for seasoning, fry a spoonful of meat in the small frying pan until browned on both sides. Taste, and add more salt and pepper to the raw mixture if necessary.

COOK THE KEBABS

4 **Heat the grill** and set the rack 5cm (2in) from the heat. Wet your hands to make the mixture easier to work, and divide the mixture into 12. Roll each into a cylinder 2.5cm (1in) in diameter.

5 **Brush 6 metal skewers** and the grill rack with olive oil. Thread the meat on to the skewers, pressing them well into shape, and place on the grill rack. Brush with oil and grill for 5-7 minutes, until brown and sputtering.

6 **Turn the skewers** and grill the other side. The meat should remain juicy in the centre. Serve on a bed of tabbouleh, with the reserved mint leaves and the yogurt sauce.

Crisp salmon with coriander pesto

CRISPY BUT LIGHTLY COOKED, this is a wonderful way to cook fillets of salmon and bass, or any other rich fish. It is always useful to have a jar of pesto in the refrigerator and this recipe will keep for 2 days, if the surface is covered with a thin layer of oil to keep it from the air. Surprisingly, this pesto will also freeze very successfully.

SERVES	PREP	COOK
SERVES 4	5–10 MINS	10–15 MINS

Ingredients

4 x 175g (6oz) salmon fillets, with skin

3 tbsp vegetable oil

1 lemon

2 tsp sea salt

coriander leaves, to serve

FOR THE PESTO

leaves from 1 large bunch of coriander

2–3 garlic cloves

2 tbsp pine nuts

75ml (2½fl oz) olive oil

30g (1oz) grated Parmesan cheese

salt and pepper

MAKE THE PESTO

1 **Put the coriander** in a food processor with the garlic, pine nuts, and 2 tbsp olive oil. Add the Parmesan. With the blade turning, slowly pour in the remaining oil in a steady stream. Continue working the pesto until it thickens and emulsifies. Season to taste, scrape into a bowl, and cover.

PREPARE THE SALMON

2 **If necessary,** pull out any bones from the salmon with tweezers. Cut off any fatty or bony edges and trim the fillets neatly. Rinse the salmon under cold water then pat dry with kitchen paper. Brush the skin side of each fillet with some vegetable oil.

COOK THE SALMON

3 **Heat the remaining oil** in a frying pan until hot. Add the salmon, skin side down.

4 **Cook over medium heat** until the skin is crispy. Then increase the heat to high, turn and brown the sides and top of each fillet very quickly. The top should remain slightly soft, showing it is rare. Slice the lemon into wedges. Serve the salmon on warmed plates, sprinkle with sea salt and spoon on some coriander pesto. Decorate with lemon wedges and coriander leaves.

Oriental halibut en papillote

EACH DINER OPENS A PAPER CASE and savours the aroma as it is freshly released, the dish having lost none of its delicious fragrance on the journey from the oven. Though the flavourings here are Chinese in origin, the method of cooking food in paper parcels is French. Noodles and stir-fried crisp vegetables would be excellent alongside.

SERVES SERVES 4	**PREP** 15–20 MINS	**COOK** 10–12 MINS

Ingredients

125g (4½oz) mangetout, trimmed	2 tbsp dry sherry
30g (1oz) black fermented Chinese beans, or 2 tbsp black bean sauce	½ tsp granulated sugar
	1 tbsp sesame oil
4 garlic cloves, finely chopped	2 tbsp vegetable oil
	1 egg
2.5cm (1in) piece fresh root ginger, finely chopped	½ tsp salt
	4 x 175g (6oz) skinned halibut fillets or steaks
3 tbsp light soy sauce	4 spring onions, thinly sliced

PREPARE THE MANGETOUT AND ORIENTAL SEASONING

1 Half-fill a saucepan with salted water and bring to the boil. Add the mangetout and simmer for 1–2 minutes. Drain. If you have found fermented black beans, rinse them with cold water and drain. Coarsely chop three-quarters of them.

2 **Combine** the garlic, ginger, whole and chopped black beans or black bean sauce, soy sauce, sherry, sugar, and sesame oil in a bowl. Stir well to mix, then set aside.

PREPARE THE PAPER CASES

3 Fold a sheet of baking parchment (about 30x34.5cm/12x15in) in half and draw a curve with a pencil to make a heart shape when unfolded. It should be large enough to leave a 7.5cm (3in) border around a fish fillet.

4 **Cut out the heart shape** with scissors. Repeat to make 4 paper hearts. Open each out and brush with the vegetable oil, leaving a border about 2.5cm (1in) wide at the edges.

5 **Put the egg** and salt in a small bowl and beat together. Brush this egg glaze evenly on the border of each of the paper hearts.

FILL THE PAPER CASES

6 **Preheat the oven** to 200°C (400°F/Gas 6). Rinse the fish fillets and pat dry with kitchen paper. Arrange a quarter of the mangetout on 1 side of each paper heart and set a halibut fillet on top.

7 **Spoon a quarter of the oriental seasoning** on top of each fillet and sprinkle with a quarter of the spring onions. Fold the paper over the fish and run your finger along the edge to stick the 2 sides of paper together. Make small pleats to seal the edges.

8 Twist the 'tails' of each paper case to seal them, so that the filling does not ooze out during baking. Lay the cases on a baking sheet and bake for 10–12 minutes, until puffed and brown. Transfer to warmed plates, allowing each guest to open their own aromatic fish package.

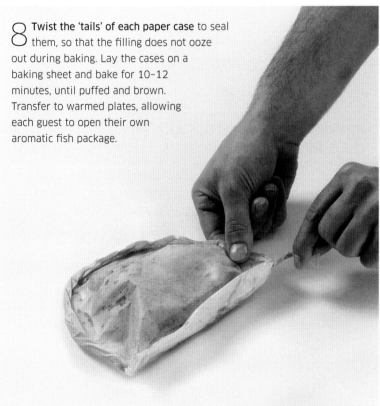

 VARIATION: Thai-style halibut en papillote

Beautifully piquant with chillies and lime.

1 Omit the mangetout and the oriental seasoning. Put 25g (1oz) dried Chinese black mushrooms in a bowl of warm water and soak for 30 minutes, until plump. Drain and slice if they are very large. Finely chop the fresh root ginger and 2 garlic cloves. Slice 2 spring onions. Very finely chop 1 green chilli, removing the seeds if you would prefer a milder dish (leave them in if you like a bit of heat). Strip the leaves from 5 basil sprigs. Peel and slice 1 lime. Squeeze the juice from a second lime.

2 Put the mushrooms, chopped garlic, 1 tbsp soy sauce, 1 tsp sugar, and 120ml (4fl oz) water in a small saucepan and boil for 5–7 minutes, until all the liquid has just evaporated. Make sure the pan does not boil dry, or the garlic will burn in the hot sugar. Stir in the ginger, chilli, basil leaves, 2 tsp fish sauce (*nam pla*; you'll find it is widely available in most supermarkets) and the lime juice.

3 Prepare the paper cases and fish as directed. Set the fish on the paper cases, evenly spoon over the mushroom mixture, then sprinkle with the spring onions. Put a lime slice on top of each pile and season well with pepper. Seal and pleat the paper cases and bake as directed. If you like, accompany each serving with a fine ribbon pasta, tossed with more shredded basil and diced mushrooms.

Steak au poivre

THE LONGER YOU CAN LEAVE THE STEAK to marinate in the peppercorns the better and more intense the flavour will be, so start it off before you leave home in the morning. Chips made at home are a thousand times better than any you can buy, especially when they are fried twice, as in this recipe. It really is worth having a go at making them for a treat, even if you don't deep-fry often.

SERVES
SERVES 4

PREP
25–30 MINS

COOK
10–15 MINS

Ingredients

1 sirloin steak, 5cm (2in) thick, weighing about 1kg (2¼lb)

3 tbsp black peppercorns

1kg (2¼lb) potatoes

1 tbsp vegetable oil, plus more for deep-frying

30g (1oz) butter

salt

FOR THE SAUCE

125ml (4fl oz) brandy

125ml (4fl oz) double cream

MARINATE THE STEAKS

1 **Trim any excess fat** and sinew from the steak. With a small knife, slash diagonally through the fat to the beef at 4cm (1½in) intervals. This will prevent the steak curling while cooking. Now slice the steak into 4 portions.

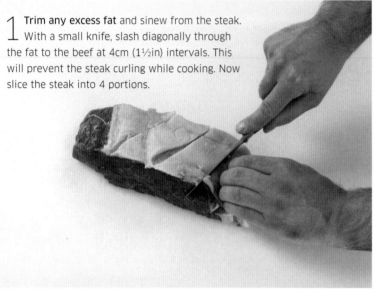

2 **Put the peppercorns** into a plastic bag and crush with a rolling pin.

3 **Put the steaks** into a shallow dish and press the crushed peppercorns on to both sides. Cover and leave to marinate. Meanwhile, prepare the potatoes.

PREPARE THE POTATOES AND FRY THEM FOR THE FIRST TIME

4 **Peel the potatoes**. Square off the sides of each and cut into 1cm (½in) sticks. Put them into a bowl of cold water to remove the starch, and leave to soak for 30 minutes.

5 **Heat the vegetable oil** in a deep-fat fryer to 180°C (350°F). To test the oil temperature without a thermometer, drop in a cube of bread: it should turn golden in 1 minute.

6 **Remove the potatoes** from the bowl of water, drain them in a colander, and dry on kitchen paper so that the oil does not splatter. Dip the frying basket into the hot oil to prevent the potatoes sticking. Lift the basket from the oil, put in a third of the potatoes, and carefully lower into the oil.

7 **Fry until tender** when pierced with the tip of a knife and just starting to brown; it should take 7–9 minutes. Remove the basket and let the potatoes drain over the fryer for 1–2 minutes. Transfer to a large plate. Repeat for the remaining potatoes.

COOK THE STEAKS, FINISH FRYING THE POTATOES

8 Reheat the oil in the deep-fat fryer to 190°C (375°F). If you don't have a thermometer, test with a cube of bread: it should turn golden in about 30 seconds.

9 Heat 1 tbsp vegetable oil with the butter in a large frying pan. For a mild flavour, scrape off and discard the pepper from the steaks; for a stronger flavour, leave it on. Season the steaks with salt. Put the steaks into the pan, and fry over high heat for 2–3 minutes, until brown.

10 Turn the steak and continue cooking until the second side is brown, 2–3 minutes for rare steak, or 4–6 minutes for medium steak, depending on thickness. To test if it is done, press the centre with your finger. If it feels spongy, it is rare; if firm, it is well done. Remove the steak from the pan and cover with foil. Pour off the fat and discard.

11 Return a third of the potatoes to the basket and lower it into the hot oil. Continue frying for 1–2 minutes, until crisp and golden brown. Drain on kitchen paper. Repeat with the remaining potatoes.

MAKE THE SAUCE

12 Return the cooked steaks to the frying pan. Pour in the brandy and bring it to a boil. Stand back and hold a lighted match to the side of the pan to light the brandy. Baste the steaks with the pan juices - using a long-handled spoon - until the flames subside. It should only take about 20–30 seconds.

13 Transfer the steaks to a carving board and cover with foil to keep warm and allow the meat to rest and become incredibly tender. Add the cream to the frying pan and simmer, stirring to dissolve the pan juices. Taste for seasoning, and adjust if necessary, though it is unlikely you will need any more pepper! Either leave the steaks whole, or carve into generous slices about 2.5cm (1in) thick.

14 Divide the steaks among 4 warmed plates and spoon a little of the sauce on top. Serve the rest on the side. Sprinkle the chips lightly with salt and pile them beside the steaks. Serve with a sprig of watercress, if you like.

Mexican barbecued pork with salsa

MARINATE THE PORK in the morning for your evening meal. The barbecue sauce will make it taste smoky, as if it was cooked outdoors, even in the kind of weather that would extinguish the flames!

SERVES	**PREP**	**COOK**
SERVES 6	35–40 MINS PLUS MARINATING	40–50 MINS

Ingredients

FOR THE SALSA

375g (13oz) tomatoes

1 large onion, diced

1 garlic clove, finely chopped

leaves from 3–4 coriander sprigs, finely chopped

1 green chilli, finely chopped

1 yellow or red pepper, diced

1 lemon

Tabasco sauce

salt

FOR THE BARBECUE SAUCE

3 tbsp vegetable oil

1 large onion, diced

3 garlic cloves, finely chopped

1 green chilli, finely chopped

1 tbsp coriander seeds

2 x 400g (14oz) cans chopped tomatoes

4 limes

4 tbsp red wine vinegar

125ml (4fl oz) black treacle

FOR THE PORK

1kg (2¼lb) boned loin of pork

3 ripe avocados

1 lemon

3 corn tortillas

75ml (2½fl oz) vegetable oil, plus more if needed

MAKE THE SALSA

1 **Cut the cores** from the tomatoes and score an "X" on the base of each. Immerse in boiling water for 8–15 seconds, then plunge into cold water. Peel off the skin, cut in half, squeeze out the seeds and chop the flesh.

2 **Combine** the onion, garlic, coriander leaves, chillies, tomatoes, and peppers in a large bowl. Squeeze the lemon and pour in the juice. Season to taste with Tabasco sauce and salt, then cover and refrigerate.

MAKE THE BARBECUE SAUCE

3 **Heat the oil** in a sauté pan, add the onion, garlic, and chilli, and sauté, stirring, for 3–4 minutes, until soft but not brown. Add the coriander seeds and tomatoes. Squeeze the limes and pour in the juice. Cook, stirring, for about 15 minutes, until reduced and thickened. Add the vinegar, bring to a boil and reduce until thickened again.

4 **Stir in** the treacle and simmer the mixture 1–2 minutes longer. Season with salt. Let the sauce cool slightly, then purée it in a food processor and allow to cool completely. Slice the pork, cover with barbecue sauce, cover and refrigerate for 2–8 hours.

GRILL THE PORK

5 **Heat the grill.** Slice the avocados and brush with lemon juice. Cut the tortillas into strips. Heat the oil in a frying pan, add the tortillas and fry, turning once, until crisp. Keep warm on kitchen paper.

6 **Brush the grill rack** with oil. Take the pork from the barbecue sauce with tongs, allowing excess sauce to drip off, and put on the rack. Cook about 5cm (2in) from the heat for 5–7 minutes, until slightly charred. Turn, brush with sauce, and cook until well browned and no longer pink inside. Put the pork on to warmed plates. Spoon on some of the salsa and add the tortilla strips and avocado.

Devilled drumsticks

THESE ARE ALSO EXCELLENT cooked on a barbecue. The drumsticks are served with a warm potato salad; when choosing potatoes for salad, go for a variety with a waxy texture that will hold their shape, such as Charlotte.

SERVES	PREP	COOK
SERVES 4	20-25 MINS	35-40 MINS

Ingredients

FOR THE DEVIL MIXTURE

125g (4½oz) butter

2 tbsp mango chutney

2 tbsp tomato purée or ketchup

2 tbsp Worcestershire sauce

1 tsp ground nutmeg

½ tsp anchovy paste

salt and pepper

cayenne pepper or Tabasco sauce

FOR THE POTATO SALAD

2 tbsp red wine vinegar

½ tsp Dijon mustard

90ml (3fl oz) vegetable oil

750g (1lb 10oz) baby potatoes

leaves from a few parsley sprigs, finely chopped

a few chives, snipped

FOR THE CHICKEN

8 chicken drumsticks

vegetable oil for grill rack

MAKE THE DEVIL MIXTURE

1 **Melt the butter** gently in a small saucepan. Chop any large pieces of fruit in the chutney. Put the chutney in a small bowl and add the remaining devil ingredients, with a pinch of cayenne pepper or dash of Tabasco sauce, and the melted butter. Mix well and taste for seasoning.

MAKE THE POTATO SALAD

2 **Whisk together** the vinegar, mustard, oil, and a pinch each of salt and pepper. Put the potatoes in a saucepan of salted water and bring to the boil. Cover and simmer for 15-20 minutes, or until tender.

3 **Drain thoroughly,** then halve and immediately transfer to a large bowl. While they are still warm, add the herbs and pour over the dressing; mix gently. Cover with foil and keep warm.

PREPARE AND GRILL THE CHICKEN

4 **Heat the grill.** Brush the rack in the grill pan with oil. Cut the skin from the chicken drumsticks and pull it off. Slash the meat diagonally several times with the point of a knife. Brush some of the devil mixture over each, working it well into the cuts.

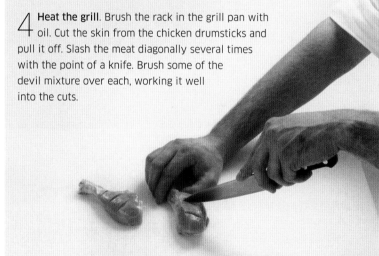

5 **Arrange the drumsticks** on the rack. Grill 7.5-10cm (3-4in) from the heat, turning once during cooking and basting frequently with the remaining devil mixture and any pan juices. Cook for 10-12 minutes on each side, until well browned and tender. Arrange the warm potato salad on plates, with the drumsticks alongside.

Oriental stir-fried chicken

THIS INVITES ENDLESS VARIATIONS, just always use fresh ingredients, finely cut. Make sure you prepare all the ingredients in advance, as the cooking time is swift and cannot be interrupted. For a properly "seasoned" wok, do not wash it after cooking. Instead, wipe it out with kitchen paper while still warm, then coat the inside surface with a thin layer of flavourless vegetable oil.

SERVES	PREP	COOK
SERVES 4	15–20 MINS PLUS MARINATING	10–12 MINS

Ingredients

FOR THE STIR-FRY

30g (1oz) dried Chinese black mushrooms or other dried wild mushrooms

45g (1½oz) flaked almonds

1 onion

4 celery sticks

500g (1lb 2oz) head of broccoli

2 skinless, boneless chicken breasts, total weight about 375g (13oz)

90ml (3fl oz) vegetable oil

1 tsp sesame oil

FOR THE MARINADE

4 tbsp soy sauce

4 tbsp rice wine or dry sherry

2 tsp cornflour

PREPARE THE VEGETABLES AND ALMONDS

1 Put the mushrooms in a bowl, cover with 250ml (9fl oz) warm water and allow to soften for 30 minutes.

2 Preheat the oven to 190°C (375°F/Gas 5). Spread the almonds evenly on a baking sheet and toast for 6–8 minutes, until lightly browned.

3 Cut the onion in half lengthways. Cut each half into 4–5 wedges. Trim the celery and cut across, on the diagonal, into 1cm (½in) thick slices. Cut the broccoli head into very small florets.

4 Drain the mushrooms, reserving the liquid. Trim off any woody stalks, then slice. Strain the liquid through a sieve lined with kitchen paper to remove any sand or grit.

MARINATE THE CHICKEN

5 Cut each chicken breast on the diagonal into very thin slices (try to get 10–15 from each breast). In a bowl, mix the soy sauce, rice wine, and cornflour, stirring until the cornflour dissolves. Add the chicken and stir to coat. Marinate for about 15 minutes.

COOK THE STIR-FRY

6 Heat half the oil in a wok. Add the onion and celery and stir and toss over high heat for 1–2 minutes, until beginning to soften. Add the broccoli and fry, stirring and tossing, for 2–3 minutes. Add the mushrooms and cook for 2 minutes more.

7 Remove the vegetables from the wok to a bowl and set aside in a warm place. Wipe the wok with kitchen paper. Add the remaining oil to the wok and heat it.

8 Drain the chicken, reserving the marinade. Add the chicken to the wok and cook over high heat, stirring and tossing, for 2–3 minutes, until opaque. Return the vegetables to the wok, adding 4 tbsp of the mushroom soaking liquid.

9 **Pour the marinade liquid** into the wok and cook, stirring, for 2 minutes. Sprinkle with sesame oil, stir and taste for seasoning. Sprinkle with the almonds and serve in individual bowls, with noodles if you like.

 VARIATION: Sweet and sour stir-fried chicken

Pineapple gives sweetness to this old-fashioned favourite.

1 Prepare the chicken breasts as directed in the main recipe. For the marinade, reduce the amount of rice wine to 1 tbsp, and add 1 tbsp wine vinegar and 1 tbsp caster sugar to give a sweet and sour flavour to the final stir-fry sauce.

2 Omit the broccoli and mushrooms from the recipe and replace them with 4 rings of canned pineapple in fruit juice (not syrup), cut into small pieces for even cooking. Add whatever other vegetables you would prefer; 1 red and 1 yellow pepper, sliced, and 120g (4oz) mangetout, halved widthways, would make good additions to the recipe.

3 Finish the stir-fry as directed, adding 4 tbsp pineapple juice from the can instead of the mushroom soaking liquid to increase the sweetness of the dish. Serve with plain boiled rice and sprinkle with sesame seeds, if liked.

Fish plaits with warm vinaigrette

THESE LOOK FANCY, but can be put together speedily for a special after-work dinner. Here, the fish have been carefully unplaited to serve in a casual style; however, the 3 different-coloured skins of the fish look beautiful kept together in their braids for a more formal occasion. The herb-dotted vinaigrette marries with the dish wonderfully, and the whole – steamed over an aromatic court bouillon – is light and immensely appetizing for even the most jaded palates.

SERVES	PREP	COOK
SERVES 6	35–40 MINS	8–10 MINS

Ingredients

FOR THE COURT BOUILLON

1 bouquet garni made with 5–6 parsley stalks, 2–3 thyme sprigs and 1 bay leaf

6 peppercorns

2 cloves

1 carrot, quartered

1 onion, quartered

FOR THE FISH

375g (13oz) red snapper fillets, with skin

375g (13oz) lemon sole fillets, with skin

375g (13oz) mackerel fillets, with skin

salt and pepper

FOR THE WARM VINAIGRETTE

125ml (4fl oz) red wine vinegar

2 tsp Dijon mustard

2 shallots, finely chopped

75ml (2½fl oz) olive oil

150ml (5fl oz) vegetable oil

leaves from 5–7 tarragon or thyme sprigs, finely chopped, plus more to garnish

leaves from 7–10 parsley or chervil sprigs, finely chopped, plus more to garnish

PREPARE THE COURT BOUILLON

1 **Combine** 1 litre (1¾ pints) water, the bouquet garni, peppercorns, cloves, carrot and onion in a pan over which you can fit a large steamer. Bring just to a boil and simmer for 20–30 minutes.

PREPARE THE FISH

2 **Rinse the fish** and pat dry with kitchen paper. Discard any bones and trim the fillets so they are roughly the same length. Cut each fillet into strips about 2cm (¾in) thick. You need 6 strips of each type of fish.

PLAIT AND STEAM THE FISH

3 **Take a strip each of** snapper, sole, and mackerel. Plait them together. Continue with the remaining fish. With a fish slice, transfer the plaits to the steamer and sprinkle with salt and pepper.

4 **Set the steamer over** the simmering court bouillon. Make sure there is at least 5cm (2in) of water underneath the steamer – if not, top up with boiling water.

5 **Cover and steam the fish** for 8–10 minutes, until it just flakes easily when tested with a fork.

MAKE THE VINAIGRETTE

6 **In a small saucepan,** whisk together the vinegar, mustard, and shallots. Add the olive oil, then the vegetable oil in a steady stream, whisking constantly so the vinaigrette emulsifies and thickens slightly. You may not need to add all the vegetable oil; stop when the consistency of the vinaigrette is as you would prefer. The shallots must be chopped very finely indeed, so they become an integral part of the vinaigrette, rather than intrusive lumps.

7 **Heat gently** until the vinaigrette is warm, whisking constantly. Remove from the heat and whisk in the herbs and salt and pepper to taste. Spoon the vinaigrette on to 6 warmed plates and put the fish plaits on top (unbraid them if you like, for a more casual presentation). Garnish with the reserved herb sprigs, which will serve as a vibrant and very green salad, and serve at once.

 VARIATION: Panache of steamed fish with warm sherry vinaigrette

A 'panache', or selection, of fish. French beans are a good accompaniment.

1 Make the court bouillon as directed. Rinse the fish fillets and pat dry. Cut into even diamonds. Steam as for the fish plaits, allowing 5–7 minutes, depending on thickness. You may have to steam in batches.

2 Meanwhile, prepare the warm vinaigrette as directed in the main recipe, substituting sherry vinegar for the red wine vinegar and walnut oil for the olive oil. Omit the herbs.

3 Arrange the fish on warmed plates, skin-side up. Spoon a little of the warm sherry vinaigrette over the fish and serve the remainder separately.

Russian beef sauté

BASED ON BEEF STROGANOFF. Fresh noodles are a good accompaniment. For a cheaper dish, substitute top sirloin for the fillet of beef; the slices are thinly enough cut that they shouldn't be tough. The mushrooms here are not strictly authentic, though they make a welcome addition. It is best to make this dish at the point of serving, as reheating may both curdle the cream and overcook the beef.

SERVES	PREP	COOK
SERVES 4	15-20 MINS	20-25 MINS

Ingredients

750g (1lb 10oz) fillet of beef

30g (1oz) butter, more if needed

2 tbsp vegetable oil

salt and pepper

2 onions, sliced

250g (9oz) mushrooms, sliced

1 tbsp plain flour

125ml (4fl oz) beef stock or water

2-3 tsp Dijon mustard

125ml (4fl oz) soured cream

leaves from 3-5 tarragon sprigs, chopped

PREPARE THE BEEF

1 **Trim the beef** of any fat or sinew. Cut the meat into 1cm (½in) slices. Cut each slice into 1cm (½in) strips, about 7.5cm (3in) long.

2 **Heat half the butter** and oil in a sauté pan, until starting to brown. Add half the beef, sprinkle with salt and pepper, and cook over very high heat, stirring, for 2-3 minutes, until well browned but still rare in the centre. Remove with a slotted spoon, and add more butter if the pan is dry. Brown the remaining beef in the same way.

BEGIN THE SAUTÉ

3 **Heat the remaining butter** and oil in the sauté pan, add the onions, separating the slices into rings, and sauté over medium heat for 5-7 minutes, until softened and browned, stirring occasionally. Transfer them to a bowl with the slotted spoon.

4 **Add the mushrooms** to the pan and sauté for 4-5 minutes, until all the moisture has evaporated. Stir in the flour, and cook for 1 minute. Pour in the stock and bring to a boil, stirring so the sauce thickens smoothly.

FINISH THE SAUTÉ

5 **Return the onions** to the pan, season, and simmer for 2 minutes. Stir in the mustard, and heat gently without boiling. If the mustard boils, the sauce will be bitter. Return the beef and its juices to the pan and heat through gently but thoroughly for 2-3 minutes. If the beef is overcooked, it will be tough.

6 **Stir in the soured cream,** and cook for about 1 minute longer. Taste for seasoning. Do not let the mixture get too hot or the soured cream may curdle. Serve immediately, with cooked fresh noodles. Sprinkle with the chopped tarragon.

Indonesian chicken satay

MARINATE THESE IN THE MORNING, for dinner. They are considered as street snacks in Indonesia, but make a wonderfully exotic main course with this spicy peanut sauce, a rice pilaf and a crisp salad; great to come home to after a hard day

SERVES	PREP	COOK
SERVES 6	15–20 MINS PLUS MARINATING	8–10 MINS

Ingredients

1.5kg (3lb 3oz) skinless, boneless chicken breasts

FOR THE MARINADE

3 shallots, finely chopped

2 garlic cloves, finely chopped

½ tsp chilli powder

2 tsp ground coriander

2 tsp ground ginger

3 tbsp soy sauce

2 tbsp distilled white vinegar

2 tbsp vegetable oil

FOR THE PEANUT SAUCE

1½ tbsp vegetable oil

175g (6oz) shelled, skinned raw peanuts

½ onion, sliced

1 garlic clove

½ tsp dried chilli flakes

2 tsp ground ginger

1 tsp brown sugar

1½ tbsp lemon juice

salt and pepper

PREPARE AND MARINATE THE CHICKEN

1 **Remove the tendon** from each chicken breast. Separate the fillet from each breast by lifting the end of the fillet, and pulling it towards you. With a sharp knife, cut each fillet in half lengthwise. Cut each breast into 7 thin strips on the diagonal, the same size as the strips of fillet.

2 **Put all the marinade ingredients** in a large bowl. Mix together with a metal spoon. Add the chicken strips, and mix until well coated with the marinade. Cover with clingfilm, and refrigerate for at least 3 hours or up to 12 hours.

MAKE THE PEANUT SAUCE

3 Soak 18 bamboo skewers in water for 30 minutes. Heat the oil in a pan. Add the peanuts and stir for 3–5 minutes, until brown. Transfer to a food processor. Add the onion, garlic, chilli, ginger, sugar, and lemon juice.

4 **Purée until very smooth,** scraping the bowl with the spatula as necessary. Blend in 375ml (12fl oz) hot water, adding enough to make a pourable sauce. Transfer to a saucepan, heat to boiling, and simmer for 2 minutes, stirring constantly. Season to taste. Remove from the heat and keep warm.

PREPARE AND COOK THE KEBABS

5 Heat the grill. Thread the chicken strips on to the skewers concertina fashion, using 3 strips per skewer, and twisting the strips slightly as you thread them. Brush the grill rack with oil. Arrange the chicken kebabs on the rack.

6 Grill the kebabs, about 5–7cm (2–3in) from the heat for 2–3 minutes, until browned. Turn and cook the other side. Arrange on plates with the warm peanut sauce. Accompany with a rice pilaf for a more substantial meal.

Southern fried chicken

SOAK THE CHICKEN the night before you want to eat this. An American favourite from the South, the chicken is soaked in milk to whiten the meat. The traditional accompaniment is mashed potatoes, enlivened if you like by a sprinkling of chopped herbs such as parsley or chives. The pan gravy served here may not be to everyone's tastes, though it is authentic; leave it out if it's not for you. The fried chicken is also delicious served cold on a picnic, with a potato salad and crisp green leaves.

SERVES	PREP	COOK
SERVES 4	10-15 MINS PLUS SOAKING	20-30 MINS

Ingredients

FOR THE CHICKEN

1.5kg (3lb 3oz) chicken, jointed into 8

500ml (16fl oz) milk, plus more if needed

250ml (8fl oz) vegetable oil for frying, plus more if needed

60g (2oz) plain flour

2 tsp pepper

1 lemon

FOR THE GRAVY (OPTIONAL)

2 tbsp flour

375ml (13fl oz) milk

salt and pepper

PREPARE THE CHICKEN

1 **Put the chicken** in a bowl and add enough milk to cover. Cover securely with clingfilm and refrigerate for 8–12 hours. With a slotted spoon, transfer the chicken joints to a dish. Discard the milk.

2 **Pour vegetable oil** into the frying pan to make a 2cm (¾in) deep layer. Heat over moderate heat until it measures 180°C (350°F) on a deep-fat thermometer. If you don't have one, drop in a cube of fresh bread: if it turns golden brown in 1 minute, the oil is ready.

3 **Mix the flour** and pepper in a shallow dish. Dip the chicken in the flour and pat off the excess with your hands to obtain an even coating.

FRY THE CHICKEN

4 **Gently add the chicken joints** to the pan, skin side down, taking care as the chicken may sputter. Fry for 3-5 minutes, until brown.

5 **Turn the chicken over** and reduce the heat to low.

6 **Continue frying** for 20-25 minutes, until the chicken is brown and tender when pierced. If some pieces cook before others, remove them, pat dry with kitchen paper, and keep warm, uncovered or the crisp coating will soften.

MAKE THE GRAVY (OPTIONAL)

7 **Discard all** but about 2 tbsp of the fat from the frying pan. You can strain it carefully and keep it, refrigerated, for frying chicken again, but it should not be used more than twice or the flavour will begin to taint and stale. Evenly sprinkle the flour into the remaining fat in the pan. Cook, stirring with a large metal spoon, until browned. It should take 2–3 minutes to cook out the taste of the raw flour. Do not skip or hurry this step, as the taste of uncooked flour will spoil the sauce.

8 **Whisk in the milk** and simmer until the gravy is thickened. It should only take about 2 minutes. Taste and season the gravy to taste (you may want to add pepper) and strain into a gravy boat.

9 **Cut the lemon** into wedges. Arrange the chicken on a serving dish with some lemon wedges, for your diners to squeeze over as they prefer. A squeeze of lemon really lifts this dish, cutting through the richness of the fried chicken. A few crisp green leaves are lovely on the side.

 VARIATION: Bacon-fried chicken

The flavour of the bacon is wonderful and the gravy spiked with a little Tabasco.

1 Soak the chicken in milk as directed in the main recipe. Omit the vegetable oil for frying and sauté 8–12 bacon rashers until crisp and brown and all the fat has been released into the pan. Remove the bacon, leaving its fat in the pan, drain the rashers on kitchen paper, and keep warm.

2 Flour the chicken as directed, then cook it in the bacon fat and drain on kitchen paper, blotting carefully to remove excess grease. Prepare the pan gravy, adding a dash of Tabasco sauce, to taste, when seasoning.

3 Crumble the bacon and sprinkle it over the chicken when serving. This version of fried chicken is especially delicious with the authentic addition of a pan of cornbread (p386).

Griddled tuna steaks with salsa

MARINATE AS YOU WALK IN THE DOOR for dinner later, after you've relaxed with a bath and a glass of wine. The tart, lemony marinade sets off the rich fish perfectly, while the crisp salsa is the perfect foil. Always be careful, when cooking tuna, to sear the outsides while keeping the centre of the fish moist and slightly rare. Tuna is not at all good dry and overcooked.

SERVES	PREP	COOK
SERVES 4	25–30 MINS PLUS MARINATING	5–7 MINS

Ingredients

FOR THE MARINADE

2–3 thyme sprigs

2 tbsp vegetable oil

½ lemon

FOR THE TUNA AND SALSA

4 x 250g (9oz) tuna steaks

salt and pepper

4 tomatoes

1 red pepper

1 onion

1 bunch of coriander

200g canned sweetcorn, drained

2 limes

3–4 tbsp vegetable oil

MARINATE THE TUNA

1 **Strip the thyme leaves** from the stalks, letting them fall into a shallow, non-metallic dish. Add the oil to the dish.

2 **Squeeze the juice** from the lemon half and add it to the thyme and oil in the dish.

3 **Rinse and pat dry the tuna** steaks. Season with salt and pepper, then put the tuna steaks in the marinade and turn to coat. Cover and refrigerate for 1 hour, turning occasionally. Meanwhile, make the salsa.

MAKE THE SALSA

4 **Cut the cores** from the tomatoes and score an "x" on the base of each. Immerse in a pan of boiling water until the skin starts to split, then plunge into cold water. Peel, cut in half and squeeze out the seeds. Coarsely chop the flesh.

5 **Core, deseed, and dice the pepper** and chop the onion. Strip the coriander leaves from the stalks and finely chop. Put the tomatoes, sweetcorn, coriander, onion, and pepper in a bowl. Squeeze 1 of the limes into the mixture and season. Leave to stand for the flavours to blend.

GRILL THE TUNA

6 Heat a griddle pan. Brush the griddle with oil, and add the tuna. While brushing each tuna steak with the marinade, cook for 2-3 minutes, without turning, until a steak comes away from the griddle without tearing. When you can lift off a steak, do so, and turn over each steak with tongs and brush with the remaining marinade. Griddle for 2-3 minutes more. The tuna should remain rare in the centre: flake with a knife, you should see a pinkish-red and translucent layer in the middle. Each steak should also feel slightly soft when gently pressed with the tongs. Be very careful not to overcook the fish.

7 Cut the remaining lime into wedges. Put the tuna - with its handsome griddle marks - on to 4 warmed plates. Serve the salsa in a bowl on the side, for everyone to help themselves. Arrange the lime wedges around and garnish with a few more coriander sprigs, if you like.

 VARIATION: Griddled swordfish with fennel and sun-dried tomatoes

Flavoured with aniseed liqueur.

1 Rinse and pat dry 4 x 250g (9oz) swordfish steaks. Marinate as directed. Omit the salsa. Slice 3 fennel bulbs. Melt 60g (2oz) butter in a saucepan, add the fennel, season and press a piece of buttered foil on top.

2 Cover and cook over low heat until very soft; it will take 40-45 minutes. Drain 60g (2oz) sun-dried tomatoes in oil and coarsely chop. Stir into the fennel with 1-2 tbsp aniseed-flavoured liqueur (such as Pernod). Cook for about 10 minutes, then season to taste.

3 Griddle the swordfish as directed and serve on warmed plates with the fennel mixture on the side.

Pork and ginger sukiyaki

MARINATE THE PORK soon after you walk in the door for dinner an hour or two later. If you can find the sweet Japanese rice wine, *mirin*, use it instead of the sweet sherry and sugar in this recipe, adding just 1 tbsp. You will find it in larger supermarkets and Asian stores. This is a great dish for a mid-week supper, as it's so quick to cook.

SERVES SERVES 6	**PREP** 15–20 MINS PLUS MARINATING	**COOK** 15–20 MINS

Ingredients

1kg (2¼lb) pork tenderloins

2.5cm (1in) piece fresh root ginger, coarsely chopped

125ml (4fl oz) saké

4 tbsp soy sauce

1 tbsp sweet sherry

1 tsp granulated sugar

60g (2oz) dried oriental mushrooms

10 spring onions

75ml (2½fl oz) vegetable oil, plus more if needed

cellophane noodles for serving (optional)

PREPARE AND **MARINATE** THE PORK

1 **Trim the pork tenderloins** of any fat and membrane. Cut diagonally across each to make thin, even slices. Combine the ginger, saké, soy sauce, sweet sherry, and sugar in a non-metallic bowl. Add the pork to the bowl and stir to coat. Cover and marinate for 1–2 hours in the refrigerator.

PREPARE THE REMAINING INGREDIENTS

2 **Put the mushrooms** in a bowl, and cover with warm water. Soak for about 30 minutes, until plump, then drain. Trim the spring onions, and cut diagonally into 4cm (1½in) pieces.

COOK THE SUKIYAKI

3 **Heat 1 tbsp oil** in a frying pan. Add the mushrooms and spring onions, and sauté over medium heat, stirring often, for 2–3 minutes, until they soften. Transfer to a large bowl. Drain the pork in a sieve, reserving the liquid.

4 **Heat another tablespoon of oil** in the pan. Add a quarter of the pork and sauté over very high heat, stirring constantly, for 2–3 minutes, until the meat is lightly coloured. Transfer to the bowl with the mushrooms and spring onions. Cook the remaining pork in batches, adding more oil as needed.

FINISH AND **SERVE** THE DISH

5 **Pour the reserved marinade** into the pan. Return the mushrooms, spring onions, and pork. Simmer for 1–2 minutes, until the meat is just heated through. Do not overcook, or the meat will be tough.

6 **Taste and season** with more sake, soy sauce, sherry, and sugar, if needed. Serve on warmed plates, with cellophane noodles, if you like.

Veal saltimbocca

SALTIMBOCCA literally means "jump into the mouth" in Italian. These take next to no time to prepare and, even better, can be prepared up to the end of step 2 before you leave for work in the morning. Layer them between sheets of baking parchment, cover tightly and refrigerate to cook quickly in the evening.

SERVES	**PREP**	**COOK**
SERVES 4	20–25 MINS	10–12 MINS

Ingredients

4 veal escalopes, total weight about 500g (1lb 2oz)

4 thin slices of Parma or cooked ham

12 sage leaves, plus more for garnish

60g (2oz) butter

75ml (2½fl oz) white wine

salt and pepper

PREPARE THE SALTIMBOCCA

1 **Put a veal** escalope between 2 sheets of baking parchment. Pound it to a thickness of about 3mm (⅛in), with a rolling pin. Peel the parchment away from the meat. Cut the veal into 3 pieces. Trim away any rind and excess fat from 1 of the Parma ham slices. Cut the slice into 3 pieces.

2 **Lay a sage leaf** on each escalope, and top with a piece of ham. Put a piece of baking parchment over the veal and ham, and pound gently to press the ham on to the meat. Peel off the parchment carefully, so the ham and sage adhere to the meat. Prepare the remaining escalopes in the same way.

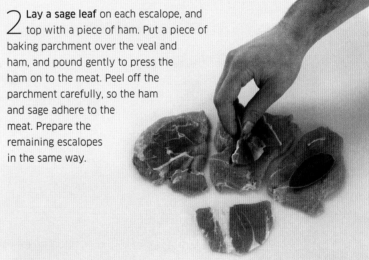

COOK THE SALTIMBOCCA

3 **Heat the butter** in a frying pan. Add a few of the saltimbocca to the pan, and brown over medium heat for about 2 minutes. Take care; veal escalopes cook very quickly, and will be tough if overcooked. Turn each saltimbocca and brown the other side for 1–2 minutes. As the saltimbocca are cooked, transfer them to a plate, and keep them warm.

4 **Add the wine** to the pan and heat to boiling, stirring to dissolve the pan juices. Season to taste. (You may not need salt because the Parma ham is quite salty.)

5 **Transfer the saltimbocca** to a warmed platter or individual plates, using a palette knife. Spoon the sauce around the veal, and garnish with a few chopped sage leaves, if you like.

Five-spice fillet of salmon

YOU CAN USE INDIAN SPICES, instead of Chinese five-spice, if you prefer, though the aroma and flavour of fennel is completely delicious. Try it even on a professed aniseed hater (without telling them). They will love it. This is a fabulous dish to make after a bad day at work; chopping is incredibly therapeutic, and preparing this meal is a great way to vent your frustrations.

SERVES	PREP	COOK
SERVES 4	30-35 MINS	20-25 MINS

Ingredients

FOR THE VEGETABLES AND FISH

375g (13oz) carrots

750g (1lb 10oz) courgettes

750g (1lb 10oz) leeks

60g (2oz) butter, plus more if needed

salt and pepper

4 x 175g (6oz) skinless salmon fillets

2 tbsp dry white wine

FOR THE SPICE MIXTURE

1 tbsp Chinese five-spice powder

1 tbsp ground fennel seed

1 pinch of cayenne pepper

PREPARE THE VEGETABLE JULIENNE

1 **Peel and trim the carrots.** Cut them into 7.5cm (3in) lengths and square off the sides. Cut each piece lengthways into fine slices. Stack the slices and cut lengthways into fine julienne.

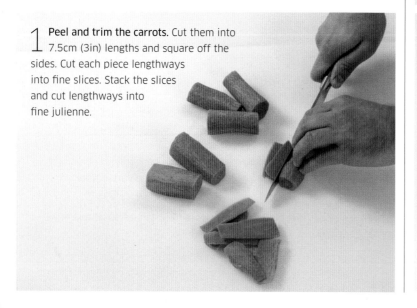

2 **Trim the courgettes** and cut them into 7.5cm (3in) lengths. Cut off the peel, including about 3mm (⅛in) of flesh.

3 **Cut the slices of peel** lengthwise into fine strips. Discard the interior pieces. Trim the leeks, discarding the roots and tough green tops. Cut into 7.5cm (3in) lengths, then cut lengthways in half. Fan each half slightly, and cut lengthways into thin julienne. Wash very thoroughly in a colander.

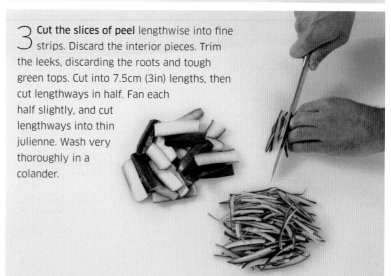

4 **Melt half the butter** in a sauté pan. Add the leeks, carrots, salt, and pepper. Press a piece of buttered foil on top, cover, and cook gently, stirring occasionally, for about 10 minutes. Add the courgette, cover with the foil, and cook until tender, stirring occasionally, for 8-10 minutes. Remove from the heat and transfer to a baking dish in an even layer.

PREPARE THE SALMON

5 Preheat the oven to 200°C (400°F/Gas 6). Rinse the salmon and dry with kitchen paper. Combine the five-spice powder, fennel, cayenne, and a pinch of salt. Sprinkle the spices on to a sheet of baking parchment. Coat the sides of each piece of salmon with the spice mixture, patting the fish gently with your hands so it is evenly coated.

COOK THE DISH

6 Heat the remaining butter in the sauté pan. Cook the salmon over high heat, turning once with a palette knife, for 1-2 minutes on each side. Transfer to a baking dish.

7 Sprinkle each piece of salmon with a little white wine. Bake the salmon and vegetables in the heated oven for 20-25 minutes. When done, the salmon flesh should just flake when tested with a fork.

8 Pile the vegetable julienne on warmed individual plates and set one piece of salmon on top of each. Decorate with lemon slices, if you like.

 VARIATION: Salmon fillets with mushroom and leek julienne

The spice coating is omitted here, to show off the pretty pink of the salmon flesh.

1 Omit the courgettes, carrots, and spice mixture. Cut the leeks as directed in the main recipe. Wipe 375g (13oz) mushrooms, trim the stalks even with the caps, and thinly slice the caps. Stack the slices on the chopping board and cut into very thin strips.

2 Cook the leeks as directed, add the mushrooms, and continue cooking, uncovered, until all the liquid has evaporated (the mushrooms will emit a lot of liquid, and then this has to be boiled off, or it will make the dish watery); it should take about 5-8 minutes longer.

3 Transfer the vegetables to individual baking dishes. Rinse the salmon as directed, season with salt and pepper and set 1 piece in each dish of vegetables. Sprinkle each piece of fish with a little white wine and bake as directed in the main recipe.

Malaysian fried rice noodles

ESPECIALLY POPULAR on the Malaysian island of Penang. Traditionally, this dish would be made with fresh rice noodles – do use them if you can find them in Asian stores – but the dried variety work just as well. If you need a meal really quickly in the evening, this is the one for you. You can speed it up even more if you chop all the ingredients in the morning and store them separately, tightly covered, in the refrigerator.

SERVES SERVES 4	**PREP** 30–40 MINS	**COOK** 8–12 MINS

Ingredients

250g (9oz) dried wide rice sticks

3 Chinese pork sausages, or 175g (6oz) smoked ham

250g (9oz) raw large prawns

3 eggs

4 tbsp oil

3 small onions, sliced into thin rings

3–4 red chillies, finely chopped

2 garlic cloves, finely chopped

125g (4½oz) beansprouts

3 tbsp light soy sauce, plus more if needed

4 tbsp chicken stock

2 spring onions, sliced diagonally

SOAK THE RICE STICKS

1 **Put the rice sticks in a bowl** and cover generously with warm water. Let soak until soft, about 30 minutes or according to packet instructions, stirring every so often, while you prepare the remaining ingredients. When the rice sticks have soaked for long enough, thoroughly drain them in a colander, shaking well, then fork them through to separate the strands and set aside.

PREPARE THE OTHER INGREDIENTS

2 **With a cleaver,** cut the Chinese sausages diagonally into thin slices. If using smoked ham instead, cut it into generous 2.5cm (1in) sticks. Devein the prawns: run a very sharp knife along the back of each prawn, then lift out and discard the dark intestinal vein with the tip of a knife. It is very important to do this each time you prepare prawns, as the vein can be gritty and unpleasant in the mouth. If you have had no time to do so beforehand, prepare the other ingredients now and place them separately in small bowls near to the stove top, as everything must be chopped and readily to hand once you start stir-frying. It is a rapid process and cannot be stopped and started. Bear this in mind every time you make a stir-fried dish, as a little preparation results in a very quick cooking time and a crisper, more satisfying meal.

MAKE THE STIR-FRY

3 **Beat the eggs** in a bowl. Heat a wok over medium heat until hot. Drizzle in 1 tbsp of the oil to coat the bottom and sides. When the oil is hot, pour in the eggs and stir at once until they are scrambled in small pieces; it will take just 1–2 minutes. Transfer to a bowl.

4 **Increase the heat** to medium-high and add the remaining oil. When hot, add the onions and stir-fry, tossing, for 3–4 minutes, until they start to brown. Add the chillies, garlic, and Chinese sausages and stir-fry until fragrant, about 30 seconds.

5 **Add the** prawns to the wok and stir-fry until they just turn pink, 1–1½ minutes. Increase the heat to high. Add the beansprouts, rice sticks, soy sauce, and chicken stock and stir-fry for 2–3 minutes, until the ingredients are just wilted.

6 **Add the eggs** to the other ingredients and stir for 1 minute, until thoroughly mixed and very hot. Taste and add more soy sauce, if necessary. Transfer to warmed plates and sprinkle with the spring onions. Serve at once.

Pan-fried mackerel in rolled oats

A TRADITIONAL SCOTTISH RECIPE. For true authenticity (and lots of added flavour), use lard or bacon drippings instead of oil. The accompanying mustard sauce is a very welcome and piquant contrast to the rich fish. These days, both mackerel and oats are classified as "super foods". Add the lemon wedges and hot, sinus-clearing mustard, and this dish is a true cold-weather winner.

SERVES	**PREP**	**COOK**
SERVES 6	15–20 MINS	8–12 MINS

Ingredients

FOR THE FISH

6 large mackerel fillets

salt and pepper

75ml (2½fl oz) vegetable oil, plus more if needed

wedges of lemon and watercress sprigs, to serve

TO COAT THE FISH

2 eggs

30g (1oz) plain flour

175g (6oz) rolled oats

FOR THE MUSTARD SAUCE

60g (2oz) butter

2 tbsp plain flour

juice of ½ lemon

1 tbsp Dijon mustard, or to taste

PREPARE THE MACKEREL AND COATING

1 **Rinse the mackerel** and pat dry. Beat the eggs in a dish. Sift the flour on to a sheet of baking parchment. With your fingers, combine the rolled oats, salt and pepper on a second sheet of baking parchment.

COAT THE FISH

2 **Turn each mackerel** fillet in the flour to coat evenly.

3 **Dip the mackerel** in the egg, then coat in oats. Set aside on a plate.

MAKE THE SAUCE

4 **Melt a third of the butter.** Add the flour and whisk to a paste until foaming. Whisk in 300ml (½ pint) boiling water. The sauce will thicken. Return to the heat and whisk for 1 minute. Remove from the heat, add the remaining butter, and whisk. Add the lemon juice and mustard and season.

FRY THE MACKEREL

5 **Line a baking sheet** with kitchen paper. Heat the oil in a large frying pan. Add half the fish and cook for 2–3 minutes on each side, until crisp and golden. Transfer to the baking sheet and keep warm while you cook the remaining fish. Serve with lemon wedges, watercress, and the sauce.

Tex-Mex chicken

A MEAL IN ITSELF. Tortilla chips are the best accompaniment. This is great to make on a warm summer evening after a hard day; the crisp, fresh flavours will lift the spirits wonderfully. It takes next to no time to whip up, especially as it contains cooked chicken, and is great for using up leftovers.

SERVES	PREP	COOK
SERVES 4-6	20-25 MINS	NONE

Ingredients

FOR THE DRESSING

4 tbsp red wine vinegar

2 tsp Dijon mustard

½ tsp salt

¼ tsp pepper

175ml (6fl oz) vegetable oil

leaves from 3 tarragon sprigs, finely chopped

FOR THE SALAD

500g (1lb 2oz) cooked skinless, boneless chicken, sliced

1 shallot, finely chopped

500g (1lb 2oz) large cos or Little Gem lettuce, sliced

2 large tomatoes, sliced

175g (6oz) drained canned sweetcorn

1 red pepper, cored, seeded, and diced

1-2 chillies, finely chopped, to taste

MAKE THE VINAIGRETTE AND DRESS THE SALAD

1 **Put the vinegar,** mustard, salt, and pepper in a small bowl and whisk. Add the oil in a thin stream, whisking constantly so the dressing emulsifies and thickens slightly.

2 **Stir the tarragon** into the dressing and taste for seasoning. Combine the chicken and shallot in a large bowl with 3-4 tbsp of the dressing. Put the lettuce in another large bowl. Add 3-4 tbsp of the dressing and toss.

ASSEMBLE THE SALAD

3 **Arrange the lettuce** on individual plates and mound the chicken on top. Arrange the tomatoes around the edges of the plates and spoon the sweetcorn on top.

4 **Scatter the red pepper** on top of the chicken and drizzle over the remaining vinaigrette. With a fork, sprinkle lightly with the chopped chilli and serve.

Saltimbocca of salmon

A VARIATION on the traditional veal dish (see p253), slices of salmon are marinated in olive oil and herbs (do so as you walk in the door), wrapped around succulent smoked salmon, and cooked to beautiful, toothsome bundles.

SERVES	PREP	COOK
SERVES 4-6	20-25 MINS PLUS MARINATING	1-2 MINS

Ingredients

FOR THE SALTIMBOCCA

1kg (2¼lb) fresh salmon fillet, with skin

5-7 basil sprigs

250g (9oz) sliced smoked salmon

45g (1½oz) butter

salt and pepper

FOR THE MARINADE

juice of ½ lemon

175ml (6fl oz) olive oil

3-4 thyme sprigs

2 bay leaves

FOR THE TOMATO-BASIL GARNISH

4 tomatoes, total weight about 625g (1lb 6oz)

small bunch of basil

2 tbsp olive oil

pinch of granulated sugar

PREPARE AND MARINATE THE SALMON

1 **Rinse the salmon** and pat dry with kitchen paper. If necessary, pull out any pin bones with tweezers. With the tail facing away from you and working towards it, use a filleting knife to cut 12 diagonal slices, as thin and even as possible. Leave the skin behind.

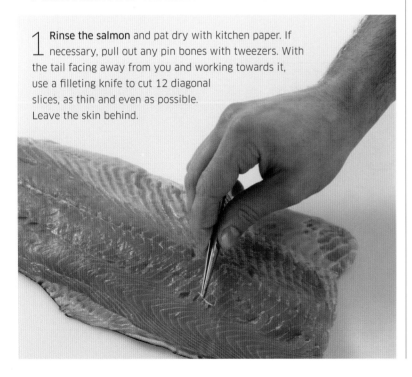

2 **Put the lemon juice** and oil in a shallow dish. Strip the thyme leaves from the stalks and add to the dish with pepper. Crush the bay leaves into the dish.

3 **Add the salmon slices,** cover and marinate in the refrigerator for 1 hour.

MAKE THE TOMATO-BASIL GARNISH

4 Cut the cores from the tomatoes. Cut an "x" in their bases. Immerse in boiling water for 8-15 seconds, until the skin starts to split, then plunge into cold water. Peel, cut in half and squeeze out the seeds, Chop the flesh.

5 Strip the basil leaves from their stalks and coarsely chop. Mix the tomatoes with the oil and basil and season, adding sugar to taste. Let stand to marinate at room temperature for 30-60 minutes.

ROLL AND COOK THE SALTIMBOCCA

6 Lift the salmon slices from the marinade and pat dry with kitchen paper. Strip the basil leaves from their stalks. Cut the smoked salmon slices into pieces the same size as the fresh salmon.

7 Arrange a piece of smoked salmon on top of each of the fresh salmon slices. placing it as centrally as possible so the flavours of fresh and smoked salmon are consistent throughout each bite. Put a basil leaf in the centre of each piece of smoked salmon. Roll up the saltimbocca as you would a Swiss roll, staring from the longest side and progressing carefully and gently, and secure shut with a cocktail stick.

8 Heat the butter in a frying pan and add a batch of the salmon saltimbocca, leaving space around each piece. Cook over high heat, turning, until lightly browned on all sides. It should take 1-2 minutes, but watch carefully; you must not overcook the salmon or it will lose its vibrant and tempting juiciness.

9 Remove from the pan and keep warm while you cook the remaining saltimbocca. Remove the cocktail sticks. Arrange the salmon rolls on warmed plates and serve with the tomato-basil garnish.

Curried chicken with saffron rice

AN UNUSUAL DRESSING thickened with cottage cheese and flavoured with chutney. Saffron rice provides a brilliant background. The curry dressing, saffron rice, tomatoes and vinaigrette can all be prepared 1 day ahead, and kept covered, separately, in the refrigerator, so the dish is very quick and easy to whip up in the evening.

SERVES	PREP	COOK
SERVES 4-6	25-35 MINS	20-30 MINS

	2 tsp apricot jam
	2 tbsp lemon juice
	250g (9oz) cottage cheese
	salt and pepper

Ingredients

FOR THE SAFFRON RICE

large pinch of saffron

300g (10oz) long-grain rice

3 celery sticks, thinly sliced

FOR THE CURRY DRESSING

90ml (3fl oz) vegetable oil

1 small onion, finely chopped

1 tbsp curry powder

4 tbsp tomato juice

4 tbsp red wine vinegar

FOR THE CHICKEN

1.8kg (4lb) whole cooked chicken

3 tbsp lemon juice

175ml (6fl oz) vegetable oil

500g (1lb 2oz) cherry tomatoes

½ tsp paprika

PREPARE THE SAFFRON RICE

1 **Put the saffron** and a pinch of salt in a large saucepan along with 600ml (1 pint) water. Bring to a boil and simmer for 2 minutes. Stir in the rice and bring back to a boil. Cover and simmer for 15-20 minutes, until tender. Let cool for 5-10 minutes, then taste for seasoning. Set aside.

MAKE THE CURRY DRESSING

2 **Heat 1 tbsp oil** in a small saucepan over moderate heat. Add the onion and sauté for about 2 minutes, until soft but not brown, stirring occasionally. Add the curry powder and cook gently for 2 minutes, stirring.

3 **Add the tomato juice** and vinegar and simmer until reduced by half. Stir in the jam. Let the mixture cool, then transfer to a food processor or blender. Blend until smooth. Add the lemon juice and cottage cheese and blend until smooth. With the blades turning, pour in the remaining oil. Taste for seasoning.

PREPARE THE CHICKEN

4 **Cut down** between the leg and body of the chicken. Twist the leg sharply outwards to break the joint, then cut through it and pull the leg from the body. Repeat for the other leg. Slit along one side of the breastbone. Using your fingers and a knife, loosen the breast meat and remove in one piece. Repeat on the other side.

5 **With your fingers**, pull away the wishbone and the meat adhering to it. Pull off any remaining meat from the chicken carcass. Pull off the skin from the breasts and discard it. Pull the meat into shreds with your fingers and pile on a dish.

6 **Using your fingers** and the point of the knife, tear and cut the meat from the leg bones. Trim away the tendons and discard the skin. Shred the meat with your fingers and add to the plate. There should be about 500g (1lb 2oz).

FINISH THE RICE

7 Stir the celery gently into the cooled saffron rice, to give it a nice crisp and varied texture. Transfer the rice to a bowl. Make a vinaigrette: put the lemon juice, salt, and pepper in a small bowl and whisk in the oil in a thin stream, so the dressing emulsifies and thickens slightly. Pour three-quarters of the vinaigrette on to the rice and toss together gently until it is evenly coated in the dressing.

8 Mix the cherry tomatoes gently with the remaining vinaigrette dressing. In another bowl, toss the chicken with half the curry dressing. Pile the saffron rice in the centre of a platter and arrange the chicken evenly on top. Sprinkle with paprika and garnish with cherry tomatoes to add a juicy fruitiness. Serve the remaining curry dressing alongside, for your diners to help themselves.

 VARIATION: Chicken with tarragon dressing and rice

A natural pairing.

1 Prepare the chicken as directed in the main recipe, cutting the chicken into slices rather than tearing it into shreds. Prepare the rice salad as directed, but omit the saffron.

2 Replace the curry dressing with this dressing: purée 250g (9oz) cottage cheese in a food processor or blender with 1 tbsp tarragon vinegar. Chop the leaves from 1 bunch of tarragon and stir it into the puréed cottage cheese. Season to taste.

3 Arrange the rice and chicken on individual plates and garnish with a few more tarragon sprigs.

Sautéed liver and onions

THIS DELICIOUS RECIPE is a classic Venetian dish. The onions can be cooked the night before if you want to get ahead, as it is important they are properly caramelized and that takes a little patience. However, it's easy enough to fry onions while you relax with a glass of wine, and talk to your family.

SERVES	PREP	COOK
SERVES 6	15-20 MINS	35-40 MINS

Ingredients

FOR THE LIVER AND ONIONS

90ml (3fl oz) olive oil

1kg (2¼lb) large onions, sliced

salt and pepper

750g (1lb 10oz) calf's liver

FOR THE MASHED POTATOES

635g (1lb 6oz) potatoes

4 tbsp milk

60g (2oz) butter

PREPARE THE ONIONS

1 **Heat two-thirds** of the oil in a frying pan. Add the onions with a little salt and pepper, and cover with foil. Cook over low heat, stirring occasionally, for 25-30 minutes, until very soft.

2 **Remove the foil** from the onions, increase the heat to medium-high, and cook, stirring constantly, for 5-7 minutes, until golden and caramelized but not burned. Transfer to a bowl with a slotted spoon, leaving any excess oil in the pan.

PREPARE THE MASHED POTATOES

3 **Meanwhile,** peel the potatoes and cut into pieces. Put in a saucepan of salted water, cover, and bring to a boil. Simmer for 15-20 minutes, until tender. Drain the potatoes thoroughly. Return them to the pan, and mash them with a potato masher.

4 **Heat the milk** in a small saucepan. Add the butter, salt, and pepper and beat until mixed. Gradually add the hot milk to the potatoes, beating until light and fluffy. Taste for seasoning and keep warm.

PREPARE THE LIVER

5 **Slice the liver** about 5mm (¼in) thick, and season. Add the remaining oil to the frying pan, and heat over high heat. Add half the liver and cook for 45-60 seconds on each side, just until browned. It should be pink in the centre. Transfer to a plate and keep warm. Cook the remaining liver.

6 **Return the onions** to the pan with all the liver and stir quickly over high heat for 30-60 seconds, until very hot. Season with salt and pepper. Serve at once, with the mashed potatoes.

Tuna and bacon kebabs

A TART MARINADE sets these off perfectly. This is about the quickest and freshest meal you can make when you get home from work, and is packed with the vitamins that will see you through tomorrow, with none of the heaviness and assorted nasties usually found in a ready-prepared bought dinner.

SERVES	PREP	COOK
SERVES 8	20-25 MINS PLUS MARINATING	10-12 MINS

Ingredients

FOR THE KEBABS

1.25kg (2¾lb) skinned tuna fillet or steak

500g (1lb 2oz) cherry tomatoes

500g (1lb 2oz) streaky bacon rashers

vegetable oil

salt and pepper

FOR THE MARINADE

juice of 2 limes

2 tbsp olive oil

Tabasco sauce

FOR THE SPINACH AND MANGO SALAD

1 ripe mango

juice of 1 lime

¼ tsp Dijon mustard

75ml (2½fl oz) vegetable oil

250g (9oz) baby spinach leaves

PREPARE AND MARINATE THE TUNA

1 **Rinse the tuna** and pat dry with kitchen paper. Cut into 4cm (1½in) cubes. To make the marinade, whisk the lime juice with the oil, a dash of Tabasco, and a little salt and pepper in a large non-metallic bowl.

2 **Add the tuna** and toss until the pieces are well coated in the marinade. Cover and marinate for 30-60 minutes, storing in the refrigerator if your kitchen is warm.

PREPARE THE SALAD AND DRESSING

3 **Peel the mango** and cut off the 'cheeks'. Cut each cheek into neat slices. In a small bowl, whisk the lime juice with the mustard, salt, and pepper. Gradually whisk in the oil so the dressing emulsifies. Taste for seasoning.

ASSEMBLE AND GRILL THE KEBABS

4 **Rinse and dry the cherry tomatoes.** Cut the bacon rashers in half; each piece should be 6cm (2½in) long. Heat the grill. Soak 8 bamboo skewers in a shallow bowl of water, or brush 8 long metal skewers with oil.

5 **Wrap a piece of bacon** around each cube of tuna. Thread the fish and tomatoes loosely on to the skewers.

6 **Set the kebabs** on the grill rack and grill about 7.5cm (3in) from the heat until the bacon is crisp. Turn and repeat. The fish should be rare within; do not overcook or it will be dry.

7 **Toss the spinach** with most of the dressing and put in a salad bowl. Arrange the mango on top and sprinkle with the remaining dressing. Serve with the tuna kebabs.

Spicy, saucy fish

DELICIOUS WITH POPPADUMS. Serve boiled, aromatic basmati rice on the side. If monkfish proves too expensive, this dish is equally wonderful with grey mullet, huss, or red snapper, all of which are reasonably priced. A satisfying meal for a cold winter's night.

SERVES	PREP	COOK
SERVES 6	30–35 MINS	30–35 MINS

Ingredients

FOR THE SPICY SAUCE

1 apple

30g (1oz) butter

1 onion, finely chopped

1 tsp ground cumin

1 tsp ground coriander

½ tsp ground ginger

½ tsp ground cloves

¼ tsp cayenne pepper or ½ tsp crushed chillies

1½ tbsp cornflour

200ml (7fl oz) coconut milk

150ml (¼ pint) fish stock

FOR THE FISH

1kg (2¼lb) skinned monkfish fillets

4 tbsp vegetable oil

2 onions, thinly sliced

2 tbsp paprika

300ml (½ pint) fish stock

2 x 400g cans tomatoes

6 garlic cloves, finely chopped

4 bay leaves

2 celery sticks, peeled and thinly sliced

2 carrots, thinly sliced

salt and pepper

MAKE THE SPICY SAUCE

1 **Peel and core** the apple, then cut into 1cm (½in) dice. Melt the butter in a saucepan. Add the onion and apple and cook for 3–5 minutes, until soft but not brown.

2 **Add the cumin,** coriander, ginger, cloves and cayenne. Cook, stirring, over low heat, for 2–3 minutes. Put the cornflour in a small bowl. Add 2–3 tbsp of the coconut milk and blend to a smooth paste.

3 **Add the remaining coconut milk** and the stock to the saucepan and bring to a boil. Stir in the cornflour paste; the sauce will thicken at once. Remove from the heat, season to taste and set aside.

PREPARE THE MONKFISH

4 **Cut the membrane** (if any) from the monkfish, then rinse the fish and pat dry with kitchen paper. Cut into 2.5cm (1in) cubes.

COOK THE FISH STEW

5 **Heat the oil** in a casserole. Add the onions and cook for 3–5 minutes, until soft but not brown. Add the paprika and cook for about 1 minute, stirring to combine evenly with the onions.

6 **Add the stock,** tomatoes, garlic, bay leaves, celery, and carrots. Season and bring to the boil. Reduce the heat and simmer until the liquid is reduced by a third; it should take 15–20 minutes.

7 **Add the spice sauce** and stir well, then bring back to a boil. Add the fish. Cover and simmer, stirring occasionally, for 12–15 minutes, until the fish flakes easily. Discard the bay leaves and taste for seasoning. Serve in warmed bowls.

VARIATION: Spicy fish with mixed peppers

There's an added crunch to this version.

1 Make the spicy sauce as directed in the main recipe, omitting the apple. Prepare the vegetables as directed, omitting the carrots and celery. The apple, carrots and celery, which sweeten the main recipe, are replaced in this version with peppers, whose sweetness is tempered with a very slight bitter tang.

2 Cut out the core from 1 green, 1 red, and 1 yellow pepper (or whatever mixture of colours and flavours you prefer), then halve the peppers and scrape out the seeds. Cut away the white ribs from the inside. Set each pepper half cut-side down on a chopping board and press with the heel of your hand to flatten it slightly. Slice it lengthways into even, medium strips. Omit the monkfish. Prepare the same weight of haddock fillets, cutting them into 2.5cm (1in) cubes.

3 Cook the stew as directed, adding the peppers along with the tomatoes (remember that it could take a few minutes more for the peppers to soften fully; check them before you put in the fish). Add the fish and simmer very gently as directed in the main recipe. Snip a few chives and sprinkle over the top to serve.

Minute steak marchand du vin

THIS RECIPE INCLUDES delicious, mild roasted shallots, and garlic. If you omit them, this simplest of dishes takes just 15-20 minutes to make from start to finish. Add the roast alliums on other occasions, when you have more time. The most important piece of equipment to make a good steak is a cast-iron frying or griddle pan, because it distributes the heat evenly, with no hot spots. Cook 1cm (½in) thick individual steaks, rather than a big piece, if you would prefer (don't pound these).

SERVES SERVES 4	**PREP** 15-20 MINS	**COOK** 40-50 MINS

Ingredients

1 large bulb of garlic

vegetable oil

salt and pepper

10 small shallots

750g (1lb 10oz) piece fillet of beef

250ml (9fl oz) red wine

leaves from 2-3 thyme sprigs

leaves from 1 small bunch of parsley, finely chopped

30g (1oz) butter

ROAST THE GARLIC AND SHALLOTS

1 **Preheat the oven** to 160°C (325°F/Gas 3). To separate the garlic cloves, crush the bulb, pushing down with the heels of your hands to exert pressure from the top. Break the separated garlic cloves apart, discarding the root, and remove any loose skin (or it could burn in the oven), but don't bother to peel them.

2 **Put the garlic cloves** in a small baking dish, add 1 tbsp oil, and sprinkle with salt and pepper. Stir until each garlic clove is evenly coated in oil and seasoning.

3 **Trim the roots,** and remove any papery or loose skin from the shallots, without peeling them. Put the shallots in a second baking dish, setting aside 2 to make the sauce later. Toss them with 2 tbsp oil, salt, and pepper, again ensuring they are evenly covered (any unoiled shallot or garlic skin is far more likely to scorch in the oven, which may risk tainting the flavour of the finished dish).

4 **Transfer the garlic** and shallots to the heated oven, placing them on a shelf towards the top. Roast the garlic for 30-35 minutes, and the shallots for 25-30 minutes, stirring occasionally, until both are sweet and tender. Finely chop the 2 reserved shallots for the sauce.

PREPARE AND FRY THE STEAKS

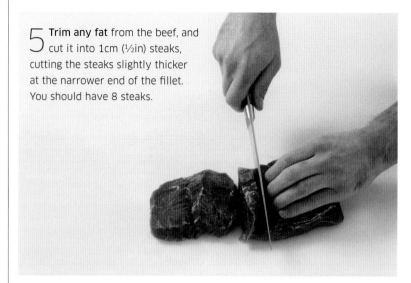

5 **Trim any fat** from the beef, and cut it into 1cm (½in) steaks, cutting the steaks slightly thicker at the narrower end of the fillet. You should have 8 steaks.

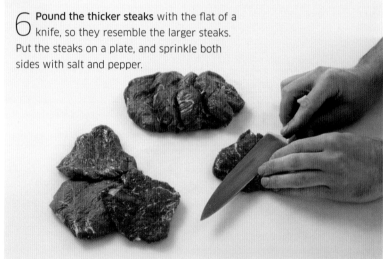

6 **Pound the thicker steaks** with the flat of a knife, so they resemble the larger steaks. Put the steaks on a plate, and sprinkle both sides with salt and pepper.

7 **Heat about 1 tbsp** oil in a heavy-based frying pan. Fry 4 steaks over moderately high heat for 1-2 minutes, until well browned. Turn and fry for 1-2 minutes more. The steaks are done when they yield if pressed with your finger. If firm, they are well done. Keep them warm while you fry the remaining steaks.

FINISH THE DISH

8 Add the chopped shallots to the pan and sauté, stirring for 1–2 minutes, until soft but not brown. Add the wine and thyme and bring to a boil, stirring to scrape up all the delicious savoury meat juices. Boil to slightly thicken and concentrate the flavour. It should take 3–5 minutes, and you must work quickly now as you should eat the steaks as soon as possible after cooking. Stir in most of the parsley and taste for seasoning. Add the butter and swirl the sauce, taking the pan on and off the heat, so that the butter thickens the sauce without melting into oil.

9 Sprinkle the steaks with the remaining parsley on individual plates. Arrange the garlic and shallots around the steaks for diners to peel themselves; their sweet, soft flesh is delicious when squashed on to pieces of crusty baguette and used as "butter". Serve with salad leaves and well-salted French fries, if you like.

 VARIATION: Minute steak Dijonnaise

A tangy sauce with white wine, tangy Dijon mustard, and cream.

1 Omit the roasted shallots and garlic. Put 20–24 pickling onions in a bowl, cover with hot water, and let stand for 2 minutes. Drain and peel with a small knife, leaving a little of the root to hold the onion together. Roast as for the shallots, sprinkling them with 1 tbsp sugar halfway through.

2 Chop 2 shallots. Prepare and fry the steaks as directed. Stir 250ml (9fl oz) dry white wine into the pan, and boil for 2–3 minutes, until reduced by half. Take the pan from the heat and stir in 1 tbsp Dijon mustard, and 2–3 tbsp double cream, omitting the butter. Taste for seasoning.

3 Put 1 or 2 steaks on each plate. Coat with the sauce, set the onions on the side, decorated with parsley sprigs, and serve with homemade game chips, if you like.

Grilled chicken thighs in yogurt

A MIDDLE EASTERN-STYLE DISH. Marinate the chicken in the morning for dinner. Yogurt plays two roles in this recipe: first it tenderizes the chicken; then it thickens and enriches the sauce. This can also be cooked on the barbecue. Serve it hot or at room temperature.

SERVES SERVES 4	**PREP** 20-25 MINS PLUS MARINATING	**COOK** 15-20 MINS

Ingredients

FOR THE CHICKEN

8 chicken thighs

250ml (9fl oz) plain yogurt

salt and pepper

vegetable oil for grill rack

FOR THE CORIANDER SAUCE

2 tbsp vegetable oil

1 onion, chopped

2 tbsp ground coriander

2 garlic cloves, finely chopped

250ml (9fl oz) plain yogurt

a few coriander sprigs

125ml (4fl oz) soured cream

PREPARE THE CHICKEN

1 **Put the chicken thighs** in a large bowl and pour over the plain yogurt. Season with salt and pepper to taste. Turn the thighs until well coated with yogurt, then cover the bowl tightly and refrigerate for 3-8 hours. Try not to leave it much longer, or it will have a woolly texture.

2 **Heat the grill**. Brush the grill rack with oil. Lift the chicken out of the bowl. Scrape off and discard the yogurt. Dry the chicken with kitchen paper, then arrange the thighs on the grill rack.

COOK THE CHICKEN

3 **Grill the chicken**, about 7.5cm (3in) from the heat, for 8-10 minutes, until very brown. Turn and continue grilling until the pieces are very brown and no pink juice runs out when they are pierced. It should take 7-10 minutes longer. Meanwhile, make the sauce.

MAKE THE CORIANDER SAUCE

4 **Heat the oil** in a saucepan and sauté the onion until soft and starting to brown. Add the ground coriander and garlic and continue cooking for 2-3 minutes, stirring constantly. Purée the onion mixture with the yogurt in a food processor. Add the coriander sprigs and process just until it is chopped.

5 **Return to the saucepan**. Pour in the soured cream, then season. Heat the sauce, stirring constantly. Taste for seasoning and keep warm. Do not let it boil or it will separate. Arrange 2 chicken thighs on each warmed plate and spoon the sauce around them.

Sautéed trout with hazelnuts

THE CRUNCHY TOPPING makes a delicious contrast to the soft-textured fish. This is about as quick as cooking gets, and produces a fresh, satisfying, and wholesome family dish. Serve with a rice pilaf (see p302) for a heartier meal. Mackerel would work equally well in this recipe, and is cheaper.

SERVES SERVES 4	**PREP** 20-25 MINS	**COOK** 10-15 MINS

Ingredients

4 x 300g (10oz) trout, cleaned and scaled

60g (2oz) hazelnuts

2 lemons

20-30g (¾-1oz) plain flour

salt and pepper

125g (4½oz) butter

leaves from 5-7 parsley sprigs, chopped

PREPARE THE TROUT

1 **Cut the fins** from the trout, and trim the tails. Rinse inside and out, and pat dry with kitchen paper.

2 **Preheat the oven** to 180°C (350°F/Gas 4). Spread the hazelnuts on a baking sheet, and toast them for 8-10 minutes, until browned. While still hot, rub in a tea towel to remove the skins. Set aside.

3 **Trim the ends** from one lemon, halve and cut into thin semi-circles. Peel the second lemon, being sure to remove all the white pith, and cut into thin rounds. Remove any pips.

COOK THE TROUT

4 **Put the flour** on a large plate and season. Coat each trout in flour, patting to coat evenly. Heat half the butter in a large frying pan, until foaming. Add two of the trout, and brown over medium heat for 2-3 minutes.

5 **Turn and continue cooking** over low heat for 3-5 minutes. When ready, the trout will be browned, and the flesh will flake easily when tested with a fork. Keep warm while you cook the remaining fish in the rest of the butter.

FINISH THE DISH

6 **Add the hazelnuts** to the pan, and sauté over medium heat for 3-4 minutes, until golden brown, stirring. Stir in most of the parsley. Serve the fish on warmed plates, and spoon over the hazelnuts. Decorate with the lemon semi-circles and rounds, and sprinkle with the remaining parsley.

Food to share

Something special for friends and family

Lamb korma

FRAGRANT AND LUXURIOUS. A korma is a mild Indian curry. The flavour will improve if the dish is made up to 3 days ahead and kept, covered, in the refrigerator. The sauce may thicken, so add water when reheating, if necessary.

SERVES	PREP	COOK
SERVES 4-6	25-30 MINS	2½-3 HRS

Ingredients

FOR THE SPICE MIXTURE

5 cardamom pods

1 cinnamon stick

2 dried red chillies, deseeded

5 cloves

7 black peppercorns

2 tsp ground cumin

1 tsp ground mace

1 tsp paprika

FOR THE KORMA

125ml (4fl oz) vegetable oil

6 onions, sliced

2.5cm (1in) piece fresh root ginger, finely chopped

2 garlic cloves, finely chopped

1.4kg (3lb) boned lamb shoulder, in 2.5cm (1in) dice

250ml (9fl oz) plain yogurt

250ml (9fl oz) double cream

salt

leaves from 3-5 coriander sprigs, chopped

PREPARE THE SPICE MIXTURE

1 **Crush the cardamom pods** with the flat of a small knife, and extract the seeds with the tip.

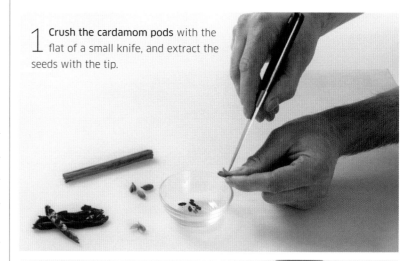

2 **Crush the cinnamon stick** with the end of a rolling pin. Put the chillies, cardamom seeds, cinnamon, cloves, and peppercorns in a mortar and crush them as finely as possible with the pestle. Stir in the cumin, mace, and paprika.

COOK THE KORMA

3 **Heat the oil** in a casserole. Add the onions and cook over low heat, stirring occasionally, for 20 minutes, until soft and golden brown. Stir in the ginger and garlic and cook for 2 minutes, until softened and fragrant.

4 **Add the spice mixture** and cook, stirring constantly, for 1-2 minutes, until thoroughly combined. Add the lamb and cook, stirring and tossing constantly, so it absorbs the flavour of the spices, for about 5 minutes.

5 **Add half the yogurt,** half the double cream, and a little salt, and bring almost to a boil. Reduce the heat, cover, and cook over very low heat for 2-2½ hours, until the meat is tender enough to crush with your finger. Stir occasionally. If the liquid evaporates too quickly, add a little water.

FINISH THE DISH

6 **Stir the remaining yogurt** and cream into the lamb. Taste for seasoning and heat until very hot. Transfer to warmed plates and sprinkle with coriander. Serve with rice.

Moroccan chicken tagine

ANY HEAVY CASSEROLE IS JUST AS GOOD if you don't have a tagine (an attractive North African earthenware vessel with a conical lid). If you don't want to joint the chicken yourself, simply buy it already jointed. Bear in mind that dark-meat chicken - such as leg or thigh pieces - take best to the long-cooking treatment they get in this recipe. Serve with couscous for true authenticity.

SERVES	PREP	COOK
SERVES 4	10–15 MINS	1½ HOURS

Ingredients

1.5kg (3lb 3oz) chicken	400g (14oz) can tomatoes
large pinch of saffron	2 tbsp honey
6 onions	2 tsp ground cinnamon
75g (2½oz) dried apricots	1 tsp ground ginger
	leaves from a few parsley sprigs, chopped
	salt and pepper
	125ml (4fl oz) olive oil

JOINT THE CHICKEN

1 **Cut down between the leg joint** and body on one side. Twist the bone sharply outwards to break the joint, then cut through it and pull the leg from the body. Repeat this procedure for the other leg.

2 **Slit the chicken closely** along both sides of the breastbone to loosen the meat, then split the breastbone with poultry shears.

3 **Turn the bird over** on to its breast and cut the rib bones and backbone from the breast in 1 piece, leaving the wing joints attached to the breast. The 2 breasts of the bird are now divided.

PREPARE THE INGREDIENTS

4 **Put the saffron** into a small bowl. Spoon over 3–4 tbsp boiling water. Set aside to soak. Thinly slice 4 of the onions and finely chop the remaining 2 onions. Cut the dried apricots into chunks using kitchen scissors or a knife.

COOK THE CHICKEN

5 **Preheat the oven** to 180°C (350°F/Gas 4). Put the chicken in a tagine or casserole. Cover with the sliced onions, then the tomatoes. Mix the chopped onions, saffron and its liquid, dried apricots, honey, cinnamon, ginger, parsley, salt, and pepper in a bowl. Add the oil. Spoon the mixture over the chicken.

6 **Cover and** bake in the heated oven for about 1½ hours, or until the chicken is tender when pierced. Taste for seasoning. Serve the chicken and sauce straight from the tagine or casserole on to warmed plates, on a bed of couscous if you like.

Sea bass with herb butter sauce

AN IMPRESSIVE DISH to share. A herb butter sauce is a useful thing to know how to cook, as it makes an unctuous, rich emulsion that is an excellent embellishment to quick-cooked fish fillets. This recipe will work equally well with whole salmon trout or sea bream, but either way is one to keep for an auspicious occasion. It is important to keep a close eye on the roasting fish, as it is all too easy to overcook, which will spoil the firm texture.

SERVES
SERVES 4

PREP
40-45 MINS

COOK
30-40 MINS

Ingredients

FOR THE HERB BUTTER SAUCE

1 bunch of watercress

8 spinach leaves

leaves from 10–12 parsley sprigs

leaves from 10–12 chervil sprigs

1 lemon

1 garlic clove, peeled

2 anchovy fillets

2 tsp capers, drained

1 small gherkin

75g (2½oz) butter

3 tbsp olive oil

1 tsp Dijon mustard

FOR THE FISH

1 whole sea bass, weighing about 2kg (4½lb), cleaned and scaled

3-5 thyme sprigs

30g (1oz) butter

125ml (4fl oz) dry white wine

salt and pepper

MAKE THE SAUCE

1 **Set aside** half the watercress to decorate the finished dish. Bring a saucepan of well-salted water to a boil. Add the watercress, spinach, parsley, and chervil, and simmer for just 1–2 minutes, until tender. Drain well in a colander.

2 **Rinse the greens** with cold water until cool enough to handle, and drain again thoroughly. Squeeze the leaves in your fist, to remove all the excess water.

3 **Cut the lemon** lengthways in half. Set one half, flat-side down, on a chopping board, cut it across into thin slices, and reserve them for cooking the fish (discard the end slices, which will mostly be white pith). Squeeze all the juice from the remaining lemon half.

4 **In a food processor,** work the garlic, anchovy fillets, capers, and gherkin until finely and evenly chopped, with no large lumps. Add the butter, piece by piece, and work the mixture to a smooth purée. Tip in the greens and work again, until finely chopped.

5 **With the blade** turning, slowly pour in the olive oil. Add the lemon juice, mustard, and salt and pepper, and work again briefly. Taste for seasoning, then transer to a serving dish and set aside.

ROAST THE SEA BASS

6 **Preheat the oven** to 190°C (375°F/Gas 5). Cut the fins from the sea bass with scissors. Rinse thoroughly inside and out with cold water, and pat dry with kitchen paper.

7 **Slash the fish** diagonally 3–4 times on each side. The slashes should be about 1cm (½in) deep for heat to penetrate. Set the sea bass in a roasting tin, and tuck a sprig of thyme and a slice of lemon, into each slash.

8 Dot with the butter, and sprinkle with white wine, salt, and pepper. Roast, basting occasionally, until it just flakes easily when tested with a fork, and is no longer translucent in the centre. It could take 30 minutes, but check it, so it does not overcook. Remove the head to serve, with the sauce.

VARIATION: Loire sea bass

Beurre blanc originated in Brittany, near the River Loire.

1 Omit the herb butter sauce. Roast 2 cleaned and scaled sea bass (each weighing about 1kg/2¼lb) as directed in the main recipe, replacing the thyme with an equal amount of tarragon. It will take 25–30 minutes, but check them often so that they do not overcook.

2 Meanwhile, dice 2 shallots. In a small heavy-based pan, combine 3 tbsp each of white wine vinegar and dry white wine with the shallots, then boil until reduced to about 1 tbsp. It will only take 3–5 minutes. Add 1 tbsp double cream, bring to a boil, and reduce the sauce again until only about 1 tbsp remains.

3 Cut 250g (9oz) cold butter into small, even pieces. Whisk the butter into the shallots, 1 piece at a time, waiting until the previous amount has melted before adding more. The sauce will emulsify and thicken slightly. Taste for seasoning. Cut each fish in half and remove the head and tail. Serve with the sauce on the side.

Coq au vin

THE FRENCH USE A BOILING FOWL or, best of all, the traditional cock bird. The more mature the chicken, the better the dish. The flavour will vary with the wine you use: a Rhône wine gives a rich dark sauce; a Loire wine a fruitier dish; a Burgundy makes a full-bodied sauce. You need to start the recipe 1 day ahead, to allow time for marinating.

SERVES	PREP	COOK
SERVES 4-6	30 MINS PLUS MARINATING	1½-1¾ HRS

Ingredients

FOR THE MARINADE

1 onion, thinly sliced

1 celery stick, thinly sliced

1 carrot, thinly sliced

1 garlic clove, peeled

6 black peppercorns

375ml (13fl oz) red wine

2 tbsp olive oil

FOR THE STEW

2kg (4½lb) chicken

1 tbsp vegetable oil

15g (½oz) butter

125g (4½oz) piece of bacon, diced

18–20 baby onions

250g (9oz) mushrooms, quartered

3 tbsp flour

500ml (16fl oz) chicken stock or water

1 garlic clove, finely chopped

2 shallots, finely chopped

1 bouquet garni

salt and pepper

JOINT AND MARINATE THE CHICKEN

1 Put the onion, celery, carrot, garlic clove, and peppercorns in a saucepan. Pour in the red wine and bring everything to a boil. Simmer for about 5 minutes, so all the flavours meld well together, then allow this marinade to cool completely. Putting it in a shallow dish with maximum surface area will mean the marinade cools far more rapidly.

2 Joint the chicken into eight pieces (see p184), or buy a pre-jointed chicken if you prefer. The chicken must be on the bone, and at least half of it should be dark meat, for the best results. Boneless white meat chicken pieces will disintegrate during cooking, and those that remain whole will become stringy, tough and dry, so save those chicken breasts for a more suitable, quick-cooked recipe. Put all the chicken pieces in a large bowl, pour over the cooled marinade, then spoon the olive oil over the top. Cover the bowl tightly with clingfilm and leave the chicken to marinate for 12-18 hours in the refrigerator, turning occasionally to redistribute the marinade and ensure all the pieces of chicken marinate evenly.

SAUTÉ THE CHICKEN

3 Remove the chicken pieces from the marinade, and pat them dry thoroughly with kitchen paper. Strain the marinade through the sieve over a bowl, and reserve both the liquid and the vegetables.

4 Heat the oil and butter in the casserole until foaming, add the bacon and fry until browned, and the fat has rendered. Remove the bacon with a slotted spoon.

5 Add the chicken to the casserole, skin side down, and cook for about 10 minutes, until well browned. Turn and brown the other side, then remove.

PREPARE THE GARNISH

6 **Put the baby onions** in a bowl, cover with hot water and leave for 2 minutes. Remove the onions and peel them. Add the baby onions to the casserole, and sauté lightly until browned. Lift out with a slotted spoon and reserve. Add the mushrooms and sauté for 2-3 minutes, until tender. Remove the mushrooms with the slotted spoon and reserve.

FINISH THE COOKING

7 **Discard all** but about 2 tbsp of fat from the casserole, and add the reserved vegetables from the marinade. Cook over very low heat for 5 minutes, until softened. Sprinkle the flour over the vegetables and cook, stirring, for 2-3 minutes, until lightly browned.

8 **Stir in the reserved marinade**, stock, garlic, shallots, bouquet garni, salt, and pepper. Heat until boiling, stirring well. Replace the chicken, cover and simmer over low heat for 45-60 minutes, until just tender.

9 **Transfer the chicken** to a plate and keep warm in a low oven while you finish the dish. Pour the sauce into a bowl and scoop out and reserve a few attractive pieces of carrot. Wipe out the casserole with kitchen paper and add the baby onions. Strain the sauce over them through a sieve, pressing down with a small ladle or spoon to extract the maximum flavour and liquid from the vegetables.

10 **Simmer over low heat** for 5-10 minutes, until the baby onions are almost tender. Add the mushrooms and reserved carrots and continue to simmer for 2-3 minutes longer, until the sauce is reduced, and lightly coats the back of a spoon. (Draw your finger down the back of the spoon; it should leave a clear trail through the sauce.) Taste for seasoning, and adjust it if necessary.

11 **Add the chicken pieces** and bacon to the sauce and reheat gently for 3-4 minutes. Spoon the chicken and sauce from the casserole on to warmed plates or shallow bowls. Serve with steamed baby potatoes, or potatoes fried in butter and oil for a richer accompaniment. Crusty bread on the side is great for soaking up the delicious wine sauce.

Rack of lamb with parsley crumb

THE BREADCRUMBS GIVE A CRISP FINISH to this dish. A rack of lamb is among the more expensive cuts, so be sure to cook it correctly. Medium is really the best way, to keep the meat wonderfully juicy and accentuate the deep, herby flavour. Look for a small joint with creamy fat and a good dark colour to the meat, and be sure that the butcher has trimmed off the chine bone (backbone) that keeps the rack together; it is almost impossible to do it at home without butchers' knives (and muscles).

SERVES SERVES 4	**PREP** 35–40 MINS	**COOK** 25–30 MINS

Ingredients

FOR THE LAMB

2 racks of lamb, weighing 750g–1kg (1lb 10oz–2¼lb) each, chine bones removed

2 garlic cloves

2 tbsp olive oil

4 slices white bread

45g (1½oz) butter

leaves from 1 small bunch of parsley, chopped

salt and pepper

FOR THE GRAVY

125ml (4fl oz) white wine

250ml (9fl oz) lamb, beef, or chicken stock

PREPARE THE RACKS OF LAMB

1 **Set a rack of lamb** on a chopping board, ribs upwards, and, with a sharp knife, cut out any sinew lying under the ribs. Turn the rack over. Cut away the small crescent of cartilage at one end.

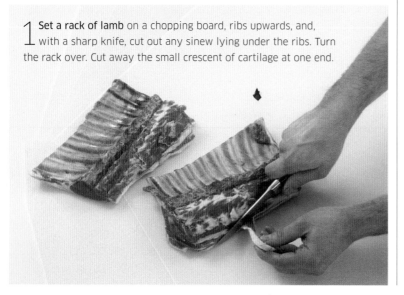

2 **Make a small incision** under the thin layer of skin covering the fat. Using your fingers, pull off the skin. If you can't get a good grip, use a clean tea towel to help. Score through the fat and meat down to the rib bones, about 5cm (2in) from the ends of the bones.

3 **Turn the rack over.** Place it over the edge of the board and score down to the bone, about 5cm (2in) from the ends of the bones.

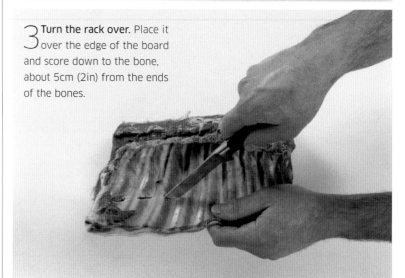

4 **Cut out the meat** between the bones, using the point of a knife. Scrape the bones clean. Be sure to scrape away all skin, or it will spoil the appearance of the roasted rack. Repeat for the second piece of meat.

ROAST THE LAMB

5 Preheat the oven to 230°C (450°F/Gas 8). Peel the garlic cloves with your fingers, then cut each into 4–5 thin slivers. Make several incisions in the lamb with the point of a knife, and push in the garlic.

6 Transfer the racks to a roasting tin, ribs downwards. Wrap the bones in foil to prevent them from burning. Spoon the oil over the lamb, and sprinkle with salt and pepper. Roast in the heated oven for 25–30 minutes, basting once or twice with the juices in the roasting tin. The meat will shrink away from the bones a little.

7 Test the lamb with a metal skewer: when inserted for 30 seconds, it will feel warm to the touch when withdrawn. A meat thermometer should register 60°C (140°F). This will give medium meat.

MAKE THE BREADCRUMB CRUST

8 Trim the crusts from the bread, and work the slices in a food processor to form crumbs. Melt the butter in a frying pan, add the breadcrumbs and cook, stirring, until just golden, 2–3 minutes. Stir in the parsley and season.

MAKE THE GRAVY

9 When the lamb is cooked to your taste, transfer the racks to a chopping board. Discard the foil used to cover the bones. Insulate the racks with more foil, and set aside to rest. This allows all the juices to flow back evenly through the meat, giving juicier lamb. Heat the grill.

10 Discard the fat from the roasting tin. Add the wine and boil until reduced by half, stirring to dissolve the roasting juices from the bottom of the tin. Add the stock, and boil for 5–7 minutes, until the gravy is well flavoured. Season to taste. Strain and keep warm until ready to serve. You can stir in 1–2 tsp cornflour, mixed with cold water until smooth, if you want a thicker gravy, though this thin sauce is more elegant.

FINISH THE DISH

11 Press the breadcrumbs on to the top surface of the lamb, and baste with the roasting juices. Grill, breadcrumb side up, until lightly browned. It should take 1–2 minutes, but watch that the breadcrumb coating does not scorch. Carve, and serve the gravy on the side.

Szechuan pepper chicken

A DISTANT COUSIN OF STEAK AU POIVRE (see p238) with aromatic, hot Szechuan pepper. This spice is a fabulous addition to your kitchen cupboard; its heat is not overpowering, but it does give a strangely pleasing tingling sensation to the mouth and lips. You'll find this recipe worryingly addictive...

SERVES	PREP	COOK
SERVES 4	20-25 MINS	40-50 MINS

1 tbsp vegetable oil

15g (½oz) butter

250ml (8fl oz) chicken stock

125ml (4fl oz) double cream

Ingredients

30g (1oz) Szechuan pepper

1.5kg (3lb 3oz) chicken, jointed into 6 pieces

1 onion

COAT THE CHICKEN

1 Toast the Szechuan pepper in a small dry pan over very low heat for 3-5 minutes, shaking until it smells aromatic. Put the pepper in a plastic bag and crush finely with a rolling pin (or crush in a mortar and pestle). Coat the chicken pieces with the pepper, patting to coat evenly. Set aside.

CHOP THE ONION

2 Peel the onion, leaving on the root to hold it together. Cut in half and lay one half on a chopping board. Make a series of horizontal cuts from the stalk to the root (cut just to the root of the onion but not through it).

3 Make a series of lengthways vertical cuts, cutting just to the root but not through it. Try to tuck your fingertips under and use your knuckles to guide the blade.

4 Slice the onion across into fine dice, again keeping your fingers slightly tucked under to avoid any cuts.

SAUTÉ THE CHICKEN

5 **Heat the oil** and butter in a sauté pan over moderate heat until foaming. Add the chicken legs, skin side down, and sauté for about 5 minutes, until they begin to brown. Add the breast pieces and continue cooking gently for about 10-15 minutes longer, until very brown. Turn and brown the other side.

6 **Push the chicken** to one side of the pan and add the onion to the other. Stir, scraping the pan, and sauté for about 3 minutes, until soft but not brown. Spread out the chicken again and add half the stock. Cover and cook for 15-25 minutes, until tender.

7 **To check if the chicken is cooked,** pierce the meat with a 2-pronged fork or the tip of a knife. The juices should run clear. If some pieces cook before others, remove them from the pan and keep warm.

MAKE THE SAUCE

8 **Remove all the chicken pieces** from the pan and keep warm in a very low oven, covered loosely with aluminium foil to keep in as much of the moisture as possible. Add the remaining stock to the pan, increase the heat to very high and boil the pan juices, stirring so they don't catch on the base of the pan, until they are reduced to a shiny glaze.

9 **Add the cream** and shake the pan gently to mix it well into the sauce, then bring to the boil once more, stirring, for 1–2 minutes, until it tastes rich and has slightly thickened. Taste for seasoning. Return all the chicken pieces to the pan and heat through gently for 1-2 minutes until piping hot and well combined with the sauce. Serve with a mixture of wild and white rices, and sprinkle with very finely sliced spring onion, if liked.

Sweet-sour duck with cherries

TART CHERRIES ARE KEY to this dish from Limousin, in central France, where cherries grow wild in the hedgerows. A mixture of caramel and red wine, added to the pan at the end of cooking, lends the sweet-sour flavour to the wonderful cherry sauce.

SERVES	PREP	COOK
SERVES 2-3	30-35 MINS	1¼-1½ HRS

Ingredients

1 duck, weighing about 1.8kg (4lb)

salt and pepper

1 tbsp vegetable oil

60g (2oz) granulated sugar

75ml (2½fl oz) red wine vinegar

375ml (13fl oz) rich chicken stock

375g (13oz) tart cherries, stoned

parsley sprigs, to serve (optional)

TRUSS THE DUCK

1 **Wipe the inside of the duck** with kitchen paper, and season inside and out. Pull off and discard any loose bits of fat. With a small knife, remove the wishbone to make the duck easier to carve later.

2 **Set the duck breast-side up.** Push the legs back and down. Push a trussing needle into the flesh at the knee joint, through the bird and out, through the other knee joint.

3 **Turn the duck** over. Pull the neck skin over the neck cavity, and tuck the wing tips over it. Push the needle through one of the wings into the neck skin. Continue under the backbone of the duck, to the other side. Repeat with the second wing.

4 **Turn the duck** on to its side. Pull the ends of the string firmly together, and tie them together securely. Turn the duck breast-side up. Tuck the tail into the cavity of the bird, and fold over the top skin. Push the needle through the skin.

5 **Loop the string** around one of the drumsticks, under the breastbone and over the other drumstick. Tie the ends of string together.

ROAST THE DUCK

6 **Preheat the oven** to 220°C (425°F/Gas 7). Heat the oil in a roasting tin. Set the duck on its side, and roast in the oven for 15 minutes. Turn the duck on to the opposite side and roast for another 15 minutes.

7 **Spoon the fat** from the roasting tin; discard it. Prick the skin all over to release the fat. Reduce the temperature to 190°C (375°F/Gas 5). Turn the duck on to its breast, and roast for 15 minutes longer. Discard any melted fat.

8 **Finally,** set the duck on its back, and continue roasting for 15-20 minutes longer, until the juices run clear. Transfer to a warmed platter, and cover with foil to rest and keep warm.

PREPARE THE CARAMEL VINEGAR SAUCE

9 **Put 75ml (2½fl oz) water** and the sugar into a small heavy-based saucepan, and heat gently until the sugar is dissolved, stirring occasionally. Increase the heat and boil, without stirring, until the syrup starts to turn golden. Reduce the heat, and cook to a deep golden caramel. Remove from the heat and let the bubbles subside.

10 **Pour in the vinegar.** Simmer, stirring occasionally, for 3-5 minutes, until the caramel is dissolved and the mixture is reduced by half. Remove from the heat and set aside.

11 **In a medium saucepan,** combine the caramel vinegar and the stock.

12 **Add the cherries** to the pan, and simmer for 3-5 minutes, until just tender. Transfer the cherries to a bowl with a slotted spoon.

FINISH THE DISH

13 **Discard any remaining fat** from the duck roasting tin. Add the caramel sauce and bring to a boil, stirring to dissolve the pan juices. Simmer until reduced by half.

14 **Strain the liquid** back into a saucepan. With a wooden spoon, press two-thirds of the cherries through a sieve into the liquid. Add the remaining cherries, bring to a boil, then season to taste.

15 **Discard the trussing string,** and carve the duck. Arrange the meat on warmed plates, and spoon over some of the cherry sauce. Decorate with parsley sprigs, if you like, and serve at once. Serve the remaining cherry sauce separately.

Sauté of chicken with mussels

UNUSUAL BUT QUITE DELICIOUS, and a distant cousin of paella (p178). The mussel juices lend an intense flavour. If you want to get ahead, the chicken can be sautéed up to the end of step 2 and kept with the wine sauce, tightly covered, in the refrigerator for up to 2 days. It's then very quick to finish the recipe for a mid-week dinner.

SERVES	PREP	COOK
SERVES 4	30-35 MINS	40-50 MINS

Ingredients

1.5kg (3lb 3oz) chicken, jointed into 6

30g (1oz) plain flour

salt and pepper

1 tbsp vegetable oil

15g (½ oz) butter

4 tbsp dry white wine

375g (13oz) French beans, trimmed

18-24 mussels, cleaned (p41)

125ml (4fl oz) chicken stock

1 small bunch of chives, snipped

SAUTÉ THE CHICKEN

1 **Dip the chicken** in the flour and seasoning and pat off the excess. Heat the oil and butter in a sauté pan over moderate heat, until foaming. Add the chicken legs, skin down, and sauté for about 5 minutes. Add the breasts, and cook gently for 10-15 minutes, until very brown. Turn and brown the other side.

2 **Add the wine.** Cover and cook for 10-20 minutes, until almost tender. To test, pierce the meat with a fork: the chicken should fall easily from the fork. If some pieces cook before others, remove them, and keep warm.

COOK THE FRENCH BEANS

3 **Bring a large saucepan** of salted water to the boil. Add the beans and cook for 5 minutes, until just tender (tiny, slender beans may take as little as 3 minutes).

4 **Drain the beans** in a colander, rinse under cold running water to stop them cooking, then leave them to drain again thoroughly.

FINISH THE DISH

5 **Set the mussels on top** of the chicken pieces in the sauté pan, cover, and cook for about 5 minutes, until the mussels open. Discard any mussels that haven't opened.

6 **Transfer the mussels** and chicken to a baking dish. Cover with foil, and keep warm in a low oven. Add the stock to the pan and boil for 3-5 minutes, until the sauce is reduced and slightly syrupy, stirring occasionally.

7 **Return the chicken,** mussels, and French beans to the sauté pan with the chives, and heat gently for 2-3 minutes. Taste for seasoning. Serve on warmed plates with the sauce spooned over and around.

Sauté of chicken with prawns

A SEEMINGLY UNUSUAL COMBINATION, but traditional in Burgundy. A dash of marc de Bourgogne, a favourite Burgundian spirit, adds a rich flavour, though brandy would be equally good. Make sure the prawns have been properly deveined before starting to cook this dish.

| **SERVES** | **PREP** | **COOK** |
| SERVES 4-6 | 25-30 MINS | 45-55 MINS |

Ingredients

30g (1oz) butter

2 tbsp vegetable oil

375g (13oz) raw large prawns

1.8kg (4lb) chicken, cut into 8 pieces

salt and pepper

1 onion, finely chopped

2 shallots, finely chopped

2 garlic cloves, finely chopped

3 tbsp marc de Bourgogne, or brandy

200g (7oz) canned chopped tomatoes

1 tbsp tomato purée

1 bouquet garni made with 5-6 parsley stalks, 2-3 thyme sprigs, and 1 bay leaf

4 tbsp dry white wine

125ml (4fl oz) chicken stock

leaves from 4-6 parsley sprigs, finely chopped

COOK THE CHICKEN AND PRAWNS

1 **Heat the butter** and oil in a large sauté pan. Add the prawns and sauté over high heat, stirring occasionally, for 2-3 minutes, until the prawns turn pink and begin to lose their transparency. Remove them with a slotted spoon and set aside on a plate.

2 **Season the chicken pieces** and add them to the pan, skin-side down. Brown well over medium heat for 8-10 minutes. Turn and brown the other side for 3-5 minutes.

3 **Add the onion,** shallots, and garlic, letting them fall to the bottom of the pan. Cover and cook over low heat for 10 minutes, stirring occasionally, until the vegetables are tender but not browned.

FINISH THE SAUCE

4 **Pour in the marc de Bourgogne** and bring to a boil. Hold a lighted match to the side of the pan to set the alcohol alight. Baste until the flames subside. Add the tomatoes, tomato purée, bouquet garni, wine, stock, salt, and pepper, stir well, and bring to a boil.

5 **Cover and simmer,** turning, for 10-15 minutes, until tender. Transfer the chicken to a plate and cover with foil. Bring the sauce to a boil and simmer for 8-10 minutes, until thickened. Return the chicken and prawns and reheat, stirring, for 1-2 minutes. Discard the bouquet garni. Arrange on warmed plates. Spoon the sauce over, sprinkle with parsley, and serve at once.

Butterflied leg of lamb

BUTTERFLIED, A LEG OF LAMB CAN BE COOKED in a quarter of the time needed for a whole leg. The procedure is quite simple, especially if you follow these steps, so do give it a try. You'll find it an invaluable skill to possess during barbecue season, as a marinated, butterflied leg is a wonderful addition to the usual burgers and sausages.

SERVES
SERVES 6-8

PREP
35-40 MINS
PLUS MARINATING

COOK
20-30 MINS

Ingredients

1 leg of lamb, weighing about 2.2kg (5lb)

2 tbsp olive oil

4 garlic cloves, finely chopped

leaves from 3-4 rosemary sprigs, chopped

leaves from 3-4 thyme sprigs

salt and pepper

3 tbsp red wine

BONE AND BUTTERFLY THE LAMB

1 Trim the skin and most of the fat from the lamb. Cut around the pelvic bone, freeing it at the joint and cutting through the tendons to the leg. Remove the pelvic bone. Grasp the tip of the shank bone, and cut all tendons at the base. Cut the meat away from the shank, keeping it in one piece. Locate the knee, and scrape away meat and fat to expose the joint.

2 Cut the tendons at the joint, and remove the shank bone. With the knife, gently release each end of the leg bone from the meat. Cut and scrape to clean the leg bone, easing it out as you work. Twist the bone and pull it out. Lift and carefully cut away the tendons from the meat.

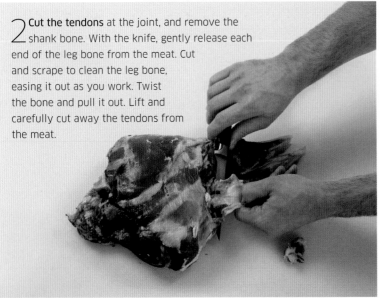

3 Insert the blade of a sharp knife into the cavity left by the leg bone. Holding the blade horizontal, cut outwards to slit open one side.

4 Lift up the flap created by cutting open one side, and spread out the meat into a "butterfly" shape. Working from the centre, make a cut in the thick muscle so the leg can be opened out flat.

MARINATE AND GRILL THE LAMB

5 Brush the grill rack and both sides of the lamb with oil. Rub half the garlic and herbs into the top. Marinate for 1 hour at room temperature, or up to 4 hours in the refrigerator.

6 Heat the grill to high. Sprinkle the lamb with salt and pepper, and grill 7.5cm (3in) from the heat for 10–15 minutes, until brown and slightly charred. Turn the lamb over.

7 Sprinkle the lamb with the remaining garlic, herbs, salt, and pepper, and continue grilling for 10–15 minutes, until a skewer inserted in the thickest part for 30 seconds is warm to the touch when withdrawn. Remove the lamb from the rack, cover it loosely with foil, and let it rest in a warm place for 5 minutes; reserve the juices in the pan.

MAKE THE SAUCE

8 Add the red wine to the grill pan and heat on top of the stove, stirring to dissolve the pan juices. Cut the lamb in thick diagonal slices. Divide the slices between warmed plates, and spoon over the sauce. Serve with new potatoes.

 VARIATION: Butterflied loin of pork

Dijon mustard permeates the meat for flavour.

1 Butterfly a 1.4kg (3lb) boneless loin of pork: unroll the flap of meat left from boning, and set the pork on a chopping board, fat-side down. Make a horizontal slit in the meat, cutting almost through to the other side. Open it out like a book.

2 Press the loin into a flat rectangle, and cover with baking parchment. Pound with a rolling pin to tenderize and achieve an even thickness throughout the loin. Evenly brush the pork with 2 tbsp Dijon mustard on each side, and sprinkle with double the quantity of oil. Prepare double quantities of chopped garlic and herbs, then rub half into the top of the pork; marinate as directed in the main recipe.

3 Grill the pork 13cm (5in) from the heat for 12–15 minutes. Turn and sprinkle with the remaining garlic and herbs. Grill until a skewer inserted in the thickest part for 30 seconds is hot to the touch when withdrawn; it should take 12–15 minutes. Cut through the thickest part of the meat to double-check: the pork should have no trace of pink. Make the sauce as directed, replacing the red wine with white, and adding 2 tsp Dijon mustard.

Fillet of beef with mushrooms

A DISH FOR A SPECIAL OCCASION: lean, tender, and easy to carve. Here, a fillet is stuffed with an intensely flavoured "duxelles" of mushrooms, parsley, garlic, and bacon. The Madeira sauce adds an edge of depth and sweetness to complement the meat perfectly. Make sure you buy properly aged beef from a reputable butcher.

SERVES SERVES 8-10	**PREP** 50-55 MINS PLUS COOLING	**COOK** 1-1¼ HRS

Ingredients

FOR THE BEEF

1 fillet of beef, 1.6kg (3½lb) trimmed weight

salt and pepper

2 tbsp vegetable oil

750ml (1¼ pints) beef stock

8-10 large button mushrooms

30g (1oz) butter

juice of ½ lemon

1 tbsp arrowroot or cornflour

125ml (4fl oz) Madeira

1 bunch of watercress

FOR THE STUFFING

2 shallots

125g (4½oz) streaky bacon

3 garlic cloves

500g (1lb 2oz) mushrooms

leaves from 1 bunch of parsley, finely chopped

PREPARE AND ROAST THE BEEF

1 **Preheat the oven** to 230°C (450°F/Gas 8). Tie a piece of string lengthways around the fillet. Using separate pieces of string, tie the roll across at 2.5cm (1in) intervals.

2 **Sprinkle the beef with salt** and pepper. Heat the oil in a large roasting tin on top of the stove until very hot, then brown the fillet well on all sides. Transfer the beef to the heated oven.

3 **Roast,** allowing 12-15 minutes for rare meat or 18-20 minutes for medium. For rare, a skewer inserted in the centre of the meat will be cool to the touch when withdrawn after 30 seconds; for medium, it will be warm. Or test with a meat thermometer: it will register 52°C (125°F) for rare meat and 60°C (140°F) for medium.

4 **Remove the beef,** let it cool, then chill it for at least 2 hours until cold. Discard any fat from the roasting tin. Add half the stock and bring to a boil, stirring to dissolve the juices in the tin. Strain the juices back into the remaining stock and set aside.

PREPARE THE STUFFING

5 **Peel the shallots** and cut into quarters. Slice the bacon rashers into 2.5cm (1in) pieces. Peel the garlic. Put the shallots, garlic, and bacon into a food processor and chop to a paste. Transfer to a frying pan.

6 **Wipe the mushroom caps** with damp kitchen paper and trim the stalks. Cut the caps into quarters. Chop them in the food processor, using the pulse button.

7 **Heat the shallot,** garlic, and bacon mixture in the frying pan, stirring, for 2-3 minutes, until the mixture begins to brown. Add the mushrooms, salt, and pepper and cook over high heat, stirring occasionally, for 10-15 minutes, until all the moisture has evaporated. Stir in the chopped parsley. Taste the stuffing for seasoning. Let it cool, then chill.

STUFF AND REHEAT THE BEEF

8 **Preheat the oven** to 220°C (425°F/Gas 7). When the fillet is cold, remove and discard the strings. Slice the beef at 1cm (½in) intervals, cutting not quite through the fillet so that the underside remains attached.

9 **Set the fillet** on top of a sheet of heavy-duty foil. With a palette knife, spread 1–2 tbsp of the stuffing between each slice and press the fillet back into its original shape.

10 **Wrap the fillet** in the foil, making a neat cylinder and twisting the ends to make handles. Set on a baking sheet and put in the oven. For rare beef, allow 15–20 minutes; a skewer inserted in the centre will be cool to the touch when withdrawn after 30 seconds and a meat thermometer will register 52°C (125°F). For medium, allow 20–25 minutes; the skewer will be warm when withdrawn and a thermometer will register 60°C (140°F).

FINISH THE DISH

11 **Put the mushrooms** in a frying pan with the butter, lemon juice, salt, pepper, and enough water to cover them partially. Fold a square of baking parchment in half then in half again to make a triangle. Fold over once or twice or more to form a slender cone. Holding the tip of the cone over the centre of the pan, cut the cone, using the edge of the pan as a guide. Unfold the round.

12 **Butter the baking parchment** round and place it over the mushrooms in the frying pan, buttered-side down (this piece of improvised cooking equipment is known as a "cartouche"). Simmer until the mushrooms are tender – it will take 15–20 minutes, but stir occasionally and check the mushrooms are not scorching on the base of the pan – then remove with a slotted spoon and keep warm.

13 **Put the stock** in the saucepan and add the mushroom cooking liquid. Bring to a boil and cook until it has reduced by half. Put the arrowroot or cornflour in a small bowl and stir in 2 tbsp of the Madeira to form a smooth paste.

14 **Whisk the arrowroot paste** into the stock. It will thicken at once, but keep whisking to avoid the formation of lumps. Stir in the remaining Madeira and taste the sauce for seasoning. Cut a slit in one end of the foil parcel surrounding the beef and carefully drain all of its juices into the sauce. Whisk to mix in the juices, then keep the sauce warm over very low heat while you serve the dish.

15 **Carve the fillet** into slices, following the slices you made earlier while stuffing the joint, and arrange them on a warmed platter or on individual warmed plates. Garnish with the sautéed mushroom caps and watercress, and pass the sauce separately.

Poussins in vine leaves

A DISH VERY CLOSE TO THE VINEYARD! The white wine in the sauce completes the theme. Poussins are a great idea to serve for a dinner party, as each bird makes a very substantial single portion and gives a feeling of generosity and plenty. The allspice and tarragon contained in the stuffing complement the dish perfectly and the recipe is always popular; you may find this soon becomes part of your regular repertoire.

SERVES	PREP	COOK
SERVES 4	45–50 MINS	60–80 MINS

Ingredients

FOR THE STUFFING

4 slices of white bread, crusts cut off

1 chicken liver

2 streaky bacon rashers, sliced

1 shallot, finely chopped

1 tbsp brandy

leaves from 3–5 tarragon sprigs, finely chopped

leaves from 3–5 parsley sprigs, finely chopped

1 pinch of ground allspice

FOR THE POUSSINS

4 poussins, each weighing about 500g (1lb 2oz)

8–12 preserved vine leaves

4 streaky bacon rashers

2 tbsp vegetable oil

1 tbsp brandy

250ml (9fl oz) dry white wine

250ml (9fl oz) chicken stock

salt and pepper

MAKE THE STUFFING

1 **Roughly tear the bread** into pieces and work them in a food processor to form crumbs. Trim any membrane from the chicken liver with a small knife, then coarsely chop the liver.

2 **Put the bacon** into a small frying pan and cook, stirring occasionally, for 3–5 minutes, until crisp and the fat has rendered. With a slotted spoon, transfer to a bowl.

3 **Add the shallot** to the pan and cook for 2–3 minutes, until soft. Add the chicken liver, sprinkle it with pepper, and cook, stirring, for 1–2 minutes, until brown. Pour in the brandy and simmer for 1 minute.

4 **Combine the liver mixture** with the bacon. Stir in the breadcrumbs, herbs, and allspice. Season the stuffing with pepper to taste; salt may not be needed as the bacon is salty.

STUFF AND TIE THE POUSSINS

5 **Wipe the insides of the poussins** with kitchen paper, and season inside and out with salt and pepper. Spoon one-quarter of the stuffing into the cavity of each bird.

6 **Rinse the vine leaves** thoroughly in cold water. Drain in a colander. Place the leaves between sheets of kitchen paper and pat gently to dry.

7 **Wrap 2 or 3 vine leaves** over the breast of each poussin, then top with a folded slice of bacon. Tie each poussin with string like a parcel.

COOK THE POUSSINS

8 **Preheat the oven** to 180°C (350°F/Gas 4). Heat the oil in a casserole on top of the stove. Add the poussins and brown all over, turning, for 5–10 minutes. Cover and transfer to the oven. Bake until tender, and a metal skewer inserted into the stuffing for 30 seconds is hot to the touch when withdrawn. It should take 45–55 minutes. Make sure the juices run clear when the skewer is removed; if there is any trace of pink, continue cooking for 5 minutes more and then test again.

9 **Transfer the poussins** to a warmed platter. Discard the trussing strings if liked (though they can look pretty as part of a rustic presentation), and cover with foil to keep warm. Spoon the fat from the casserole, then add the brandy and white wine.

10 **Bring to a boil and** simmer, stirring, until reduced by half. This should take 5–7 minutes. Add the stock and reduce again by half, it will take 5–7 minutes longer. Spoon the sauce through a sieve into a small bowl. Taste for seasoning.

11 **Set the poussins** on warmed plates and spoon over the wine sauce. Leave each guest to remove the string, if it has been left on, and their own wrappings of bacon and vine leaves. The leaves should not be eaten; they have already done their job by adding a subtle fragrance to the roasting birds.

Roast monkfish with two sauces

BOTH GARLIC AND CHILLI SAUCES show off this excellent, firm fish. The fillets are roasted whole, then sliced to serve, showing off their pristine white flesh. If monkfish is out of your budget, reasonably priced huss makes a good substitute.

SERVES	PREP	COOK
SERVES 6	25–30 MINS PLUS MARINATING	12–15 MINS

Ingredients

FOR THE MONKFISH

6 skinned monkfish fillets, total weight 1.4kg (3lb)

2 tbsp olive oil

leaves from 5–7 oregano sprigs, chopped

leaves from 5–7 thyme sprigs

salt and pepper

FOR THE GARLIC AND CHILLI SAUCES

45g (1½oz) butter

3 tbsp plain flour

8 garlic cloves, or to taste, peeled

4 eggs, hard-boiled and separated

125ml (4fl oz) olive oil

leaves from 6–9 parsley sprigs

2 red chillies

2 tsp tomato purée

cayenne pepper (optional)

MARINATE THE MONKFISH

1 Rinse the fillets with cold water, then pat dry with kitchen paper. Put them in a shallow dish and sprinkle with the oil, herbs, salt, and pepper. Toss so the fillets are coated. Cover and refrigerate for 2 hours.

MAKE THE SAUCES

2 Melt the butter in a saucepan. Whisk in the flour and cook for about 1 minute, until foaming. Take from the heat and whisk in 250ml (8fl oz) boiling water. The sauce will thicken at once. Return the saucepan to the heat and cook for 1 minute, whisking.

3 Transfer the sauce to a food processor. Add the garlic, hard-boiled egg yolks, salt, and pepper and purée until smooth. With the blades turning, pour in the oil in a thin stream, so the sauce thickens and becomes creamy. Taste for seasoning. Put half of the sauce in a bowl.

4 Add the parsley to the remaining sauce in the processor. Purée briefly. Transfer to a second bowl. Cover and chill until serving.

5 Rinse out the food processor. Core, deseed, and chop 1 chilli. Put in the processor. Add the tomato purée and reserved sauce. Purée until smooth. Season with cayenne, if you like. Transfer to a bowl, cover and chill. Core, deseed, and thinly slice the second chilli into rings.

ROAST THE FISH

6 **Preheat the oven** to 230°C (450°F/Gas 8). Line a baking sheet with aluminium foil. Arrange the monkfish fillets, side by side, on the foil, spacing them out evenly so they are not squashed together. Spoon the marinade from the dish over the fillets.

7 **Roast the fillets** in the heated oven, brushing occasionally with the juices which have collected on the foil, for 12-15 minutes, until they are browned and the fish is no longer rare in the centre (the flesh should just flake when tested with a fork).

8 **Arrange the fish** on warmed plates, and add a little of each sauce. Decorate with the rings of chilli, or thyme sprigs, if you like. Serve the remaining sauces separately. Roasted cherry tomatoes make welcome embellishments to the plates.

 VARIATION: Grilled monkfish escalopes with garlic and chilli sauces

A griddle will give great marks to the fish.

1 Rinse and pat dry the monkfish fillets. Holding each fillet steady, cut diagonal slices about 1cm (½in) thick, working towards the tail and keeping the slices as even as possible.

2 Marinate the fish as directed, using twice the amount of herbs. Meanwhile, make the sauces as directed. Omit the rings of chilli. Grill the escalopes about 7.5cm (3in) from the heat for 4 minutes; you won't need to turn them, or griddle them in a very hot griddle pan for 2 minutes each side.

3 Make pools of garlic and chilli sauces on warmed plates. Arrange the fish around the edge of each plate. Decorate with herbs.

Chinese roast duck

AROMATIC AND UNIVERSALLY POPULAR. This is traditionally made with a whole duck, head attached, as often seen hanging in the windows of Chinatown shops and restaurants. Luckily, a duck without its head can also be used! The duck can be dried, uncovered, overnight in the refrigerator.

SERVES	PREP	COOK
SERVES 4	45 MINS PLUS AIR-DRYING	1¾–2 HRS

Ingredients

FOR THE DUCK

1 duck, weighing about 2.25kg (5lb)

1 tbsp maltose or honey

FOR THE AROMATIC SEASONING

1 tsp Szechuan peppercorns

2 tbsp ground bean sauce or black bean sauce

1 tbsp Chinese rice wine or dry sherry

2 tsp caster sugar

½ tsp five-spice powder

2 tbsp light soy sauce

1 tsp oil

3 garlic cloves, finely chopped

2.5cm (1in) piece fresh root ginger, finely chopped

4 spring onions, sliced

leaves from 1 small bunch of coriander, chopped, plus more sprigs for serving, if liked

AIR-DRY THE DUCK

1 **Rinse the duck** thoroughly inside and out with cold water and pat dry with kitchen paper. Pull away and discard any fat from the body cavity. Tie heavy string around the flap of skin at the neck opening, looping it several times.

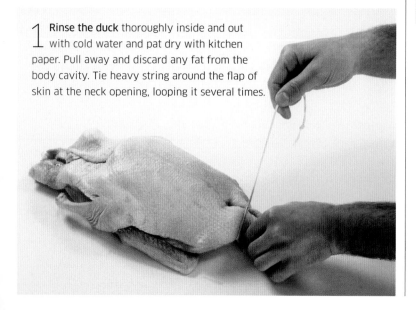

2 **Half-fill a wok** with water and bring to a boil. Hold the duck by the string and immerse it in the water. Using a ladle, pour water over the breast for 1 minute until the duck skin becomes taut. Remove the duck and pat dry with kitchen paper.

3 **Hang the duck** by the string in a cool (10–13°C/50–55°F), airy place. Place a dish underneath to catch any drips. Leave for about 2 hours, until the skin is dry. Drying time will vary depending on the weather.

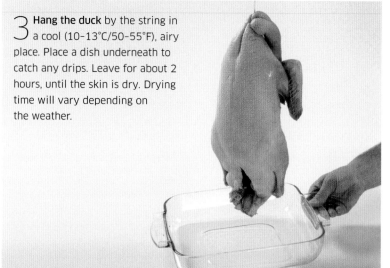

PREPARE THE AROMATIC SEASONING

4 **Heat a wok** over medium heat until hot. Add the Szechuan peppercorns and cook, stirring, for 1–2 minutes, until they smoke slightly. Transfer to a small sturdy bowl or mortar and pound to a coarse powder.

5 **Put the peppercorn powder** in a bowl and add the bean sauce, rice wine, sugar, five-spice powder, and soy sauce. Stir together.

6 **Heat the wok** again, over medium heat, until very hot. Drizzle in the oil to coat the bottom and sides. Continue heating until the oil is very hot, then add the garlic, ginger, and spring onions, and stir-fry for about 30 seconds, until fragrant.

7 **Add the sauce mixture** and the coriander. Bring to a boil, then reduce the heat to low, and simmer for about 1 minute. Transfer to a bowl and let cool to room temperature.

SEASON AND ROAST THE DUCK

8 About 45 minutes before roasting the duck, put a bamboo skewer into a bowl of cold water and let soak. Preheat the oven to 200°C (400°F/Gas 6). Spoon the aromatic seasoning into the body cavity.

9 Overlap the skin to close the cavity and thread the skewer 2–3 times from the top of the cavity through both layers of skin, then through the tail. To close tightly, tie string around the tail and the top of the skewer to bring the tail up. Set the duck, breast-side up, on a rack set in a roasting tin. Roast in the heated oven for 15 minutes.

10 Meanwhile, combine the maltose or honey and 4 tbsp boiling water in a small bowl, stirring to dissolve the maltose completely. Remove the duck from the oven, and brush the maltose mixture generously all over the skin, being sure to cover it all.

11 Reduce the oven temperature to 180°C (350°F/Gas 4) and continue roasting, brushing every 15 minutes with the maltose mixture, until dark brown and the leg meat feels soft when pinched, 1½–1¾ hours.

12 Transfer the duck to a chopping board and let stand for about 15 minutes, then carefully remove the string and skewer. Set a sieve over a bowl. Pour the seasoning from the duck cavity into the sieve. Skim off and discard the fat; reserve the liquid.

13 Carve the duck and chop the pieces up into 2.5cm (1in) pieces with a cleaver. Arrange on a warmed platter, to resemble the original shape of the duck if you like. Pour the seasoning over and decorate the platter with sliced spring onions and coriander sprigs, if you want. Serve immediately.

Hindle Wakes chicken with prunes

TRADITION HAS IT that this dish was created to reward those who kept watch (or "wake") on the eve of a great festival in Yorkshire. Try to get hold of a mature chicken for this recipe, as it will respond better to the cooking process; a good butcher should be able to help you source the perfect bird. Really top-quality prunes will lift the whole dish, giving a deep, sweet, fruity quality to the sauce.

SERVES
SERVES 4

PREP
30 MINS
PLUS SOAKING

COOK
1¼–1½ HRS

Ingredients

FOR THE STUFFING

250g (9oz) large stoneless prunes

125g (4½oz) butter

1 small onion, finely chopped

10 slices of white bread

leaves from 1 bunch of parsley, finely chopped

zest, finely grated, and juice of 1 lemon

125ml (4fl oz) chicken stock

FOR THE CHICKEN

1.8kg (4lb) boiling fowl, with liver if possible

2 carrots, quartered

1 bouquet garni

2 cloves

1 onion

2 garlic cloves

1 tsp black peppercorns

300ml (10fl oz) medium dry white wine

1.5 litres (2¾ pints) chicken stock or water

salt and pepper

FOR THE VELOUTÉ SAUCE

75g (2½ oz) butter

45g (1½ oz) flour

175ml (6fl oz) double cream

lemon juice, to taste

PREPARE THE STUFFING

1 **Put the prunes** in a bowl and cover with hot water. Allow to soak for about 1 hour, until softened and plump, then drain. Set aside 8–12 of the firmest to be stuffed; chop the rest.

2 **Heat half the butter** in a small saucepan, add the onion and fry for 2–3 minutes, until soft but not brown. Cut any membrane from the chicken liver, if using, then chop it. Stir the liver into the onion and cook for 1–2 minutes, until brown. Turn into a bowl.

3 **Break up the bread** and work it in a food processor to make crumbs. Melt the remaining butter in a small saucepan. Add the chopped prunes, breadcrumbs, parsley, and lemon zest to the bowl. Stir in the chicken stock, lemon juice, and melted butter. Season well to taste. Set aside.

POACH THE CHICKEN

4 **Put the chicken** into a casserole. Add the carrots and bouquet garni. Stick the cloves into the onion, and add to the casserole with the garlic and peppercorns. Add the white wine with enough stock to cover the chicken above its legs.

5 **Bring to a boil,** skimming well, then cover and simmer over low heat, skimming occasionally, for 1¼–1½ hours. Turn halfway through. The chicken is done when the thigh meat is tender, and no pink juice runs out when it is pierced. Remove from the casserole, wrap in foil, and keep warm. Reserve the cooking liquid.

COOK THE PRUNES AND STUFFING

6 **Preheat the oven** to 190°C (375°F/Gas 5). Fill the whole prunes with stuffing. Butter a baking dish. Spread the remaining stuffing in it. Arrange the stuffed prunes on top and cover with foil. Bake for 30–40 minutes. Take out and keep warm.

MAKE THE VELOUTÉ SAUCE

7 **Skim off and discard any fat** from the cooking liquid. Boil the liquid until reduced by half. Strain and measure it: there should be about 750ml (1¼ pints). Add more stock or water if necessary. Discard the vegetables and bouquet garni.

8 **Melt the butter** in a medium saucepan. Whisk in the flour. Cook the mixture for 1–2 minutes, until foaming but not browned, whisking well.

9 **Add the cooking liquid** and whisk constantly, until the sauce comes to the boil and thickens. Add the cream and simmer for 2 minutes. Take from the heat, stir in lemon juice and seasoning to taste, and keep warm. Carve the chicken, arrange on warmed plates and coat with sauce. Place a serving of stuffing next to it and pass the remaining sauce separately.

Chicken Pojarski

ONCE A FAVOURITE of the Russian royal family, and said to be named after the innkeeper who invented it. If you don't want to deep-fry the Pojarski, simply omit step 4 and bake them in the oven for a lighter dish. You can prepare them up to the end of step 3 a day in advance, cover, and refrigerate.

SERVES	**PREP**	**COOK**
SERVES 4	35–40 MINS	40–50 MINS

Ingredients

FOR THE CHICKEN

6 individual brioches, total weight about 250g (9oz)

125ml (4fl oz) milk

420g (15oz) skinless, boneless chicken breasts

3 tbsp double cream

ground nutmeg

salt and pepper

30g (1oz) seasoned flour

1 egg

vegetable oil, for deep-frying

FOR THE SAUCE

2 tbsp vegetable oil

1 small onion, chopped

125g (4½oz) mushrooms, sliced

1 x 400g (14oz) can tomatoes

1 tbsp tomato purée

1 garlic clove, finely chopped

1 bouquet garni

a pinch of sugar, to taste

PREPARE THE CHICKEN

1 **Cut 4 of the brioches** into dice and set aside. Break apart the remaining brioches and put them in a small bowl. Pour the milk over and soak for 5 minutes. Squeeze any excess milk from the brioches.

2 **Cut the chicken** into chunks. Work it through the fine blade of a mincer with the soaked brioches. Beat the cream into the minced chicken mixture with a pinch of nutmeg and salt and pepper. To test the mixture for seasoning, fry a little piece in the frying pan and taste; it should be well seasoned, so add more salt and pepper if required.

SHAPE AND COOK THE POJARSKI

3 **With wet hands,** shape into 4 balls and flatten slightly. Dip them in the flour and pat off the excess. Beat the egg and brush on to the rounds, draining off any excess. Coat the balls in diced brioches to completely cover. Chill, uncovered, for 30 minutes.

4 **Preheat the oven** to 190°C (375°F/Gas 5). Heat the oil in a deep-fat fryer to 180°C (350°F) (a cube of bread should turn golden in 1 minute). Add 1–2 Pojarski and fry until brown, 2–3 minutes. With a slotted spoon, transfer to a baking sheet. Fry the remaining Pojarski in the same way.

BAKE THE POJARSKI AND MAKE THE SAUCE

5 Bake in the heated oven for 25–30 minutes, until a skewer inserted in the centre is hot to the touch when withdrawn. If they brown too quickly, cover them loosely with foil.

6 **Meanwhile, heat half the vegetable oil** in a sauté pan, add the onion and mushrooms, and cook for 2–3 minutes, until brown. Stir in the tomatoes, tomato purée, garlic, bouquet garni, salt, pepper, and sugar, and cook, stirring occasionally, until fairly thick, 8–10 minutes. Serve with the Pojarski.

Roast leg of pork with orange

THIS IS EASY TO ADAPT for a cooked ham or gammon on the bone (bake for 1 hour only). This dish is also excellent cold, so worth making in its entirety (as it's a cheap cut) even if you don't have a crowd to feed. The leftovers are almost more delicious than the hot dish itself!

SERVES	**PREP**	**COOK**
SERVES 8-10	20-25 MINS	3½-4 HRS

Ingredients

FOR THE PORK

1 leg of pork, weighing about 4.5kg (10lb)

8 oranges

1 tbsp Dijon mustard

180g (6oz) dark soft brown sugar

20 cloves

1 bunch of watercress

FOR THE SAUCE

4 tbsp Grand Marnier

½ tsp grated nutmeg

½ tsp ground cloves

ROAST THE PORK

1 **Preheat the oven** to 180°C (350°F/Gas 4). Wipe the pork with kitchen paper, then set it in a roasting tin. Halve 6 of the oranges and squeeze out the juice. There should be about 500ml (16fl oz).

2 **Pour some of the orange juice** over the pork and roast in the heated oven for 3-3½ hours, pouring more orange juice over about every 30 minutes to keep it moist. Slice the remaining oranges, discarding any pips.

3 **To test if the pork is cooked,** insert a metal skewer for 30 seconds near the centre of the leg; it should be warm to the touch when withdrawn. A meat thermometer should show 77°C (170°F).

GLAZE THE PORK

4 **Take the pork** from the oven and let it cool slightly. Increase the heat to 200°C (400°F/Gas 6). Cut through the skin around the bone end of the joint. With a knife, peel the skin from the fat, starting from the wider end of the joint.

5 **Mix the mustard** and sugar together. Spread and press over the pork. Overlap the orange slices over the joint. Stud each piece with a clove. Roast for 30-45 minutes, basting with the juices every 10 minutes. Transfer to a warmed serving platter. Remove the orange slices and arrange next to the pork. Cover with foil and keep warm.

MAKE THE SAUCE

6 **Pour the Grand Marnier** into the roasting tin. Bring to a boil and whisk to dissolve the juices. Add the nutmeg and cloves and mix them in. Transfer to a sauce boat.

7 **Carve the pork** on to warmed plates with the orange slices, adding a little watercress, if you like. Pass the sauce separately.

Monkfish Americaine

A FIRM, LOBSTER-LIKE TEXTURE has made monkfish hugely popular, and so enough of a treat to impress your friends. The richness of the sauce used here, with its tomato, garlic and Cognac, makes it a suitable dish for the colder months.

SERVES	PREP	COOK
SERVES 4-6	45-50 MINS	35-40 MINS

Ingredients

1.4kg (3lb) piece of monkfish, on the bone

2 onions, chopped

125ml (4fl oz) white wine or juice of ½ lemon

1 tsp peppercorns

3-5 parsley sprigs

30g (1oz) plain flour

salt and pepper

2 tbsp olive oil

125g (4½oz) butter

FOR THE AMERICAINE SAUCE

3-4 tarragon sprigs

1 carrot, in 1cm (½in) dice

2 garlic cloves, finely chopped

400g can chopped plum tomatoes

150ml (¼ pint) white wine

3 tbsp Cognac

pinch of cayenne pepper (optional)

1 bouquet garni

4 tbsp double cream

1 tbsp tomato purée

pinch of sugar (optional)

FOR THE PILAF

2 tbsp vegetable oil

1 onion, chopped

300g (10oz) long-grain rice

PREPARE THE MONKFISH

1 If necessary, skin the monkfish: using a filleting knife, cut and release the black skin, then pull it off.

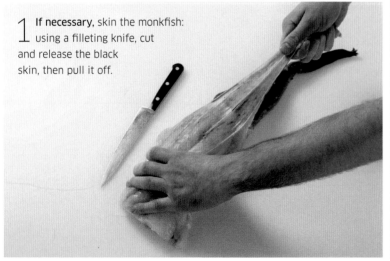

2 **Cut away the thin membrane** that covers the fish, cutting close to the flesh with a filleting knife, and pulling the membrane away with your fingers. Cut along one side of the backbone to remove 1 fillet. Repeat the process on the other side. Rinse the fillets with cold water and pat dry with kitchen paper.

3 **With a sharp, heavy knife,** cut the bone in pieces and reserve the pieces for the fish stock.

4 **Cut each fillet** into 1cm (½in) slices. Slightly flatten each slice into escalopes with the side of a knife.

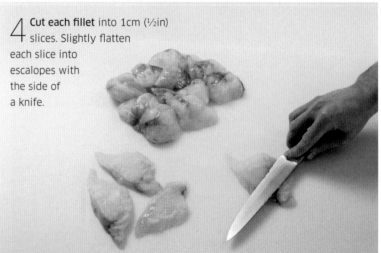

MAKE THE STOCK AND PREPARE THE SAUCE INGREDIENTS

5 **Put half the chopped onions** in a large saucepan and add the fish bones, wine, peppercorns, parsley and 500ml (16fl oz) water. Bring slowly to a boil, then simmer, uncovered, for 20 minutes. Never cook fish stock for any longer than this, or it may become bitter. Strain into a bowl and cool. You should have about 500ml (16fl oz) of fish stock.

6 **Strip the tarragon leaves** from the stalks and pile them on a chopping board. Coarsely chop the leaves and reserve for garnish. Set aside the stalks for the sauce.

COOK THE PILAF

7 **Heat the oil** in a heavy-based saucepan, add the onion, and cook stirring, for 1–2 minutes, until soft but not brown. Add the rice and cook, stirring, for 2–3 minutes, until the oil has been absorbed and the rice looks a little more translucent.

8 **Pour in 750ml (1¼ pints) water,** season and bring to a boil. Cover, reduce the heat, and simmer for about 20 minutes, or until all the liquid has been absorbed and the rice is tender. Let stand, still covered, 10 minutes, then stir with a fork to fluff up the grains.

COOK THE FISH AND MAKE THE SAUCE

9 **Meanwhile,** put the flour on a plate and season. Lightly coat the fish slices, patting to cover evenly. Heat the oil and a quarter of the butter in a sauté pan, add half the fish and sauté, turning once, for 2–3 minutes, until brown on both sides. Transfer to a plate. Sauté the remaining fish in the same way.

10 **Add the carrot,** garlic, and the remaining onion to the pan and cook, stirring to mix in the browned flour from the bottom of the pan, for 3–5 minutes, until soft but not brown.

11 **Add the tomatoes,** wine, Cognac, tarragon stalks, salt and pepper and a pinch of cayenne pepper, if you like. Tie the bouquet garni to the pan handle. Pour in the stock. Bring to a boil and simmer for 15–20 minutes, until slightly thickened.

12 **Sieve the sauce** into a large saucepan, pressing with a ladle to extract all the liquid. Boil for 5–10 minutes, until thickened. Whisk in the cream and tomato purée. Taste, adding a pinch of sugar if it is too acidic.

13 **Add the monkfish slices** to the sauce and simmer for 5–10 minutes, until just tender. Take the saucepan from the heat and add the remaining butter, in small pieces, shaking so the butter melts into the sauce. Serve the monkfish, sprinkled with the chopped tarragon, on warmed plates. Accompany with the rice pilaf.

Yellow flower pork

A STIR-FRIED PORK and egg mixture from northern China, wrapped in thin pancakes. Stir-fried dishes that contain eggs are known as "mu shu" in China, after the fragrant yellow flower of that name (this dish would be called mu shu rou). If you don't have any Chinese rice wine, use dry sherry instead.

SERVES	**PREP**	**COOK**
SERVES 4	35-45 MINS PLUS SOAKING	15-20 MINS

Ingredients

FOR THE PANCAKES

250g (9oz) plain flour, plus more to dust

1 tbsp dark sesame oil

4 tbsp hoisin sauce

FOR THE FILLING

45g (1½oz) dried Chinese mushrooms

250g (9oz) boneless loin of pork

2 tsp cornflour

2 tbsp light soy sauce, plus more if needed

2 tbsp Chinese rice wine

2 tsp dark sesame oil

3 eggs

3 tbsp flavourless oil

30g (1oz) bamboo shoots

2 spring onions, in 5cm (2in) slices

MAKE THE PANCAKE DOUGH

1 **Sift the flour** into a large bowl and make a well in the centre. Slowly pour 175ml (6fl oz) boiling water into the well, mixing until the water is absorbed and the mixture forms a rough mass.

2 **Let stand until cool** enough to handle. Gather the dough together and press into a ball. Turn on to a lightly floured surface and knead for about 5 minutes, adding more flour as necessary, until smooth and elastic. Cover loosely with a tea towel and let rest for 30 minutes.

PREPARE THE FILLING

3 **Put the mushrooms** in a bowl and cover with 250ml (9fl oz) warm water; let soak for 30 minutes. Trim off any fat from the pork. Cut it across into 5mm (¼in) slices. Cut each slice into 3mm (⅛in) strips.

4 **Drain the mushrooms,** reserving the liquid. Trim off the hard, woody stems, then slice the caps. Line a sieve with kitchen paper and hold it over a measuring jug. Pour in the mushroom soaking liquid to strain; reserve 125ml (4fl oz) of the mushroom liquid.

5 **Put the cornflour** into a small bowl. Add the reserved mushroom liquid and mix until smooth; then stir in the soy sauce, rice wine, and sesame oil. In a small bowl, beat the eggs.

MAKE THE PANCAKES

6 **On a lightly floured surface,** roll the dough into a cylinder about 30cm (12in) long. Dust a cleaver or broad knife with flour, and cut the cylinder into 12 equal pieces. Cover the pieces with a dampened tea towel.

7 **Roll each piece of dough** into a ball. Flatten each ball to make a 7.5cm (3in) round and cover with the dampened tea towel. Brush 1 side of each round lightly with sesame oil. Press the oiled sides of 2 rounds together to form 6 pairs. Lightly flour a work surface and rolling pin. Roll out each pair of rounds into a thin pancake, about 17.5cm (7in) in diameter.

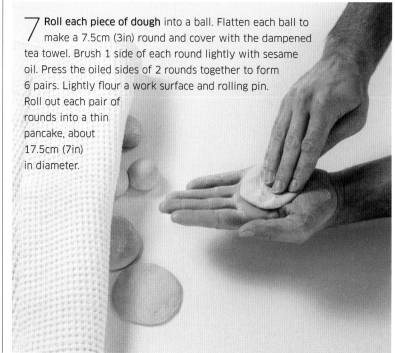

8 **Heat a wok** until very hot. Add 1 pancake and cook until blistered and puffed, about 1 minute. Turn and cook the other side, pressing down until brown spots appear on the underside, about 30 seconds. Remove, then peel the halves apart to make 2 very thin pancakes. Repeat with the remainder. Once the pancakes are cooked, stack them on a plate; cover with a dampened tea towel to keep warm.

STIR-FRY THE FILLING

9 **Heat the wok** over medium heat until hot. Drizzle in 1 tbsp oil to coat the sides. When the oil is hot, pour in the eggs. Cook to form a thin omelette, set in the centre and slightly crisp around the edge.

10 **Carefully turn the omelette.** Cook for 15–30 seconds, until the other side is lightly browned. Slide on to a chopping board and let cool slightly. Roll up loosely and cut across into 5mm (¼in) strips.

11 **Reheat the wok** over high heat. Drizzle in the remaining oil and continue heating until very hot. Add the pork and cook for 2–3 minutes, stirring and tossing, until no longer pink.

12 **Add the mushrooms** and bamboo shoots and stir-fry until mixed and heated through. Stir the cornflour mixture again, then pour it into the pork mixture.

13 **Stir-fry until the vegetables** are hot and the sauce thickens, about 2 minutes. Add the spring onions and omelette and taste, adding more soy sauce if needed. Stir-fry for 1 minute. Spoon into a warmed serving dish. Arrange the pancakes on a plate. Put the hoisin sauce in a small bowl. Each guest spreads sauce on a pancake, tops it with some filling, and rolls it up.

Sole turbans with wild mushrooms

AN OLD-FASHIONED CLASSIC, well worth reviving for today's palates. The mushroom mousse can be made up to 1 day ahead and kept, covered, in the refrigerator. Bake the sole turbans just before serving. The choice of mushrooms is entirely down to your taste and budget; substitute cultivated mushrooms for some of the total if you like, but do try to use a few wild mushrooms as well for their gutsy, earthy flavours.

SERVES	PREP	COOK
SERVES 4	20–25 MINS PLUS CHILLING	35–45 MINS

Ingredients

FOR THE WILD MUSHROOM MOUSSE

30g (1oz) butter, plus more for dishes and foil

150g (5½oz) wild mushrooms, sliced

salt and pepper

1 egg, plus 1 egg yolk

1 tbsp Madeira

leaves from 2–3 coriander sprigs, chopped

125ml (4fl oz) double cream

FOR THE SOLE AND SAUCE

6 skinless lemon sole fillets, total weight about 500g (1lb 2oz)

125ml (4fl oz) dry white wine

125g (4½oz) butter, chilled

leaves from 3–5 coriander sprigs, finely chopped, plus more for garnish

MAKE THE WILD MUSHROOM MOUSSE

1 **Heat the butter** in a frying pan. Add the mushrooms with salt and pepper. Cook, stirring constantly, until the mushrooms have given up their liquid, and it has all evaporated. It may take 3–5 minutes, but do persevere, as otherwise the mousse will be soggy. Remove from the heat and let the mushrooms cool slightly.

2 **Put the mushrooms** in a food processor and purée them. With the blade turning, add the whole egg and egg yolk. Purée until smooth. Add the Madeira and coriander, and purée just until combined.

3 **Season,** then transfer to a bowl. Cover and chill for about 1 hour. Fold the cream into the mushroom mixture. Preheat the oven to 190°C (375°F/Gas 5). Brush the inside of a soufflé dish with melted butter.

4 **Transfer the chilled mousse** to the prepared dish. Set it in a baking dish. Pour in sufficient hot water to come halfway up the side of the soufflé dish. Bake for 20–25 minutes, until just set when lightly pressed. Reduce the oven temperature to 180°C (350°F/Gas 4).

PREPARE THE SOLE TURBANS

5 **Rinse the sole fillets** and carefully pat dry with kitchen paper. Cut them lengthways in half. Shape each fillet half into a 7.5cm (3in) ring, skinned-side in, tail end around the outside. Secure with cocktail sticks. Brush a shallow baking dish with melted butter, then arrange the sole in the dish.

6 **Fold the top of a piping bag,** fitted with a large star nozzle, over your hand to form a collar. Spoon in the mousse. Twist the top of the bag, then pipe the mousse in a swirl into each sole ring to fill completely.

7 **Carefully pour the white wine** around the sole turbans in the baking dish. Butter a piece of foil and use to cover. Bake for 15–20 minutes, until the fish is white and opaque, and the mousse is firm. Keep the sole warm, and reserve the cooking liquid. Remove the cocktail sticks.

MAKE THE CORIANDER SAUCE

8 **Cut the chilled butter** into small even-sized pieces. Pour the cooking liquid from the dish into a small frying pan. Place over a high heat and boil until it is reduced right down to only about 2 tbsp of strongly flavoured liquid. Take the pan from the heat and add the butter, a little at a time, whisking constantly. The sauce should thicken a little more each time another piece of butter is added. Do not stop whisking, or the emulsified sauce will split. If it cool too much, return it to a very gentle heat for a moment.

9 **Whisk in the coriander** and taste the sauce for seasoning; you may want more salt, pepper, wine, or even a touch of Madeira, to marry in with the flavours of the mushroom mousse (though if you choose the latter 2 options, cook off the alcohol by boiling in a separate pan before whisking into the sauce and continuing). Pour the sauce over and around the sole turbans to enrich the dish. Garnish with some finely chopped coriander leaf, if you like.

 VARIATION: Turbans of plaice with spinach mousse

Lovely bright greens and reds here, with a tomato-butter sauce.

1 Bring a large pan of water to a boil, add salt, then 750g (1lb 10oz) trimmed spinach, and blanch for 1 minute. Drain in a colander, rinse with cold water, and squeeze to remove all water.

2 Make the mousse as directed, replacing the mushrooms with spinach and omitting the Madeira. Add a pinch of ground coriander with the salt and pepper. Replace the sole with 6 plaice fillets, weighing about 500g (1lb 2oz), and prepare and shape as directed.

3 Fill the plaice rings with the spinach mousse and bake as directed. Make the sauce, omitting the coriander. Whisk in 1 tbsp tomato purée after the butter. Serve on warmed plates with the butter sauce.

Leg of lamb with roasted garlic

THE FLAVOURS OF GARLIC and shallots sweeten and mellow when they are slowly roasted. The garlic will soften to a delicious purée that tastes wonderful spread either on the meat, or on a piece of crusty baguette served alongside. Make sure you get hold of really good-quality meat for this simple recipe, as the lamb takes centre stage.

SERVES	PREP	COOK
SERVES 8	15–20 MINS	1¼–2 HRS

Ingredients

1 small leg of lamb, weighing about 2.25kg (5lb)

2 heads of garlic

500g (1lb 2oz) shallots

5–7 thyme sprigs

2 tbsp olive oil

salt and pepper

125ml (4fl oz) dry white wine

250ml (9fl oz) chicken or beef stock

PREPARE THE INGREDIENTS

1 **Preheat the oven** to 230°C (450°F/Gas 8). Trim all but a thin layer of fat from the lamb. With the heel of your hand, press sharply down on the heads of garlic to loosen the cloves. Separate the cloves, and discard the root and any loose skin.

2 **With a small knife,** trim the tops and roots from the shallots but do not peel them. Strip the thyme leaves from half the sprigs, and reserve the remaining sprigs for garnish.

ROAST THE LAMB AND VEGETABLES

3 **Put the lamb** into a roasting tin and spoon over the oil. Sprinkle with thyme leaves, salt, and pepper. Roast in the heated oven for 10–15 minutes, until browned.

4 **Reduce the oven temperature** to 180°C (350°F/Gas 4). Add the garlic and shallots to the roasting tin with 125ml (4fl oz) water and stir to mix.

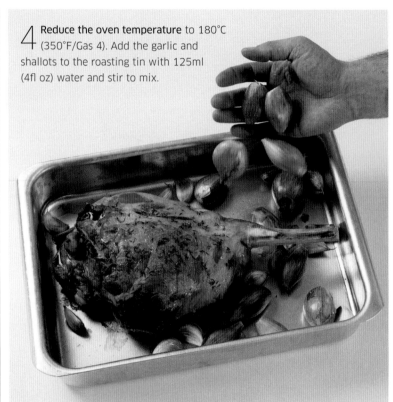

5 **Continue cooking,** basting often, and adding more water if necessary, for 1–1¼ hours for rare meat or 1¼–1½ hours for medium. Remove the lamb from the tin, cover with foil, and keep warm. Remove the garlic and shallots, cover and keep warm. Let the lamb stand for 10–15 minutes.

6 **Discard the fat** from the tin. Add the wine and bring to a boil, stirring to dissolve the pan juices. Simmer for 3–5 minutes. Stir in the stock, and continue simmering for 2–3 minutes longer. Taste for seasoning. Carve the meat and serve with the garlic, shallots, and gravy, sprinkling with the reserved thyme.

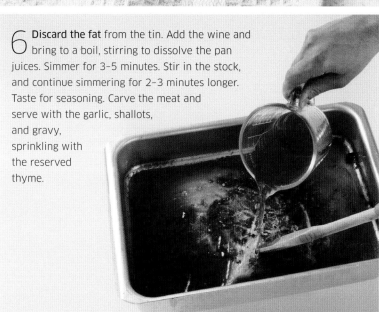

VARIATION: Leg of lamb with potatoes

Before every home had an oven, this French dish would have been cooked by the local baker.

1 Omit the shallots, water, and wine. Peel four garlic cloves. Finely chop two and cut the other two into thin slivers. Make incisions in the lamb and insert the slivers. Thinly slice 500g (1lb 2oz) onions and 1kg (2¼lb) potatoes. Strip the thyme from the stalks, and mix with the potatoes.

2 Heat 2 tbsp oil in a frying pan and soften the onions and garlic. Stir the onions into the potatoes with a pinch of nutmeg, salt, and pepper. Preheat the oven to 230°C (450°F/Gas 8). Brown the lamb as directed. Transfer to a plate. Spread the potatoes over the dish. Add 500ml (16fl oz) beef stock. Set the lamb on top, lower the heat to 180°C (350°F/Gas 4), and continue roasting as directed.

3 If necessary, remove the lamb, keep warm, and continue baking the potato mixture until golden. Carve the lamb and serve with the potatoes and gravy.

Poached salmon, watercress sauce

POACHING IN AN AROMATIC COURT BOUILLON is the ideal way to cook a whole salmon, adding flavour and keeping it moist. This is a great dish to impress, and makes a stunning centrepiece for a cold table. If you prefer, omit the watercress from the sauce and instead add a mixture of fragrant herbs: tarragon, parsley, dill, or chervil are all delicious with salmon. Experiment with the sauce to find a version that suits your palate: here, it is lightened with yogurt, but you may prefer a richer sauce with the addition of mayonnaise, or even soured cream for an extra layer of tangy flavour.

SERVES
SERVES 4–6

PREP
25–30 MINS

COOK
15–20 MINS

Ingredients

FOR THE COURT BOUILLON

1 onion, sliced

1 carrot, sliced

6 peppercorns

250ml (8fl oz) dry white wine

1 bouquet garni made with 5–6 parsley stalks, 2–3 thyme sprigs and 1 bay leaf

FOR THE FISH

1.8kg (4lb) salmon, scaled and trimmed

salt and pepper

FOR THE WATERCRESS SAUCE

250ml (8fl oz) double cream

250ml (8fl oz) plain yogurt

1 bunch of watercress, trimmed and chopped

Tabasco sauce

1 lemon

MAKE THE COURT BOUILLON

1 **Combine the onion**, carrot, peppercorns, wine, 1.5 litres (2¾ pints) water, and 1 tsp salt in a roasting tin. Add the bouquet garni. Bring to a boil and simmer for 20 minutes. Let cool.

PREPARE AND POACH THE SALMON

2 **With a filleting knife**, working inside the belly of the fish, slit between the ribcage bones and flesh as carefully as possible. Work towards the backbone, loosening the flesh from the bones on both sides of the ribcage without cutting through the skin. It is a tricky job, but just do the best you can and work as neatly as possible.

3 **Using scissors**, snip the backbone at the head to release it. Pull the bone out. Snip the bone at the tail end to release it there, too. Cut the bone into pieces and reserve. With tweezers, remove any visible bones that remain in the cavity of the fish, then run your fingers along the inside to check they have all been removed. Rinse the fish inside and out, and pat dry with kitchen paper.

4 **Add the reserved pieces** of bone to the cold court bouillon. Sprinkle the inside of the fish with salt and pepper. Cut and fold a piece of foil slightly larger than the fish, and lay the fish on it. Set it in a large, deep roasting tin so the body of the fish is in the liquid.

5 **If necessary,** add water to the court bouillon so the fish is completely immersed. Cover the roasting tin with foil and bring the liquid very slowly to a boil; this should take about 15 minutes. Simmer for 1 minute, then let the salmon cool to tepid in the liquid.

MAKE THE SAUCE

6 **Whip the cream** until soft peaks form. In another bowl, whisk the yogurt until smooth. Add the yogurt to the cream and stir gently to mix. Add the watercress and a dash of Tabasco. Squeeze the juice from the lemon and add to the sauce. Stir the sauce until evenly blended. Add salt and pepper to taste. Cover the bowl and chill until ready to serve.

FINISH THE SALMON

7 **Holding the ends** of the foil, carefully lift the salmon out of the liquid; let drain. Lift the fish off the foil. Using a small knife, slit the skin neatly around the head. Repeat around the tail.

8 **Peel off the skin** from the body, pulling it gently with the help of a small knife. Leave the head and tail intact. Scrape along the back ridge of the fish to remove the line of bones.

9 **Using a small knife**, gently scrape off any dark flesh from the length of the salmon. Carefully transfer the fish to a platter. Serve the watercress sauce in a bowl on the side.

Beef rendang

AN INTENSELY FLAVOURED Indonesian speciality, originally made with water buffalo. It can be made up to 2 days ahead and kept, covered, in the refrigerator. Bring to room temperature, then reheat on top of the stove before serving.

SERVES	PREP	COOK
SERVES 6	40–50 MINS	3½–4 HRS

Ingredients

FOR THE CURRY PASTE

2.5cm (1in) piece cinnamon stick

12 cloves

2 stalks lemongrass, trimmed and roughly chopped

6 shallots, quartered

7.5cm (3in) piece fresh root ginger, roughly chopped

6 garlic cloves, peeled

6 red chillies, finely chopped

1 tsp ground turmeric

FOR THE RENDANG

3 x 400g (14oz) cans coconut milk

4 bay leaves

1.4kg (3lb) beef chuck steak, in 5cm (2in) cubes

1½ tsp salt

PREPARE THE CURRY PASTE

1 **Crumble or break** the cinnamon stick into small pieces and put them in a mortar with the cloves. Pound them with the pestle until coarsely crushed.

2 **Put the cinnamon** and cloves in the food processor with the remaining curry paste ingredients. Process to a coarse paste. If the mixture is very thick, add about 4 tbsp of the coconut milk.

MAKE THE CURRY

3 **Combine the curry paste** and coconut milk in a wok and stir until well mixed. Add the bay leaves and bring to a boil over high heat, stirring occasionally.

4 **Reduce the heat** to medium and cook the sauce, stirring occasionally, for about 15 minutes. Add the beef and salt, stir, and return to a boil over high heat. Reduce the heat to medium and simmer, uncovered, stirring occasionally, for 2 hours.

FINISH THE CURRY

5 **Reduce the heat** to very low and continue cooking for 1½–2 hours, until the beef is tender and the sauce quite thick. Stir frequently to prevent sticking.

6 **Skim off all the fat.** Taste the curry and add salt if necessary. It will be very thick and rich. Towards the end of cooking, oil will separate from the sauce and the beef will fry in it. Arrange a bed of cooked rice on warmed plates or shallow bowls, and spoon the curried beef on top.

Osso bucco

A CLASSIC DISH from Milan. A zesty mixture called "gremolata" is sprinkled on top just before serving. This dish is traditionally served with a risotto made with saffron and Parmesan cheese, which is delicious though very rich.

SERVES	**PREP**	**COOK**
SERVES 4-6	30-35 MINS	1½-2 HRS

Ingredients

FOR THE STEW

400g(14oz) can Italian plum tomatoes

30g (1oz) plain flour

salt and pepper

4-6 pieces of veal shin with bones, about 1.8kg (4lb)

2 tbsp vegetable oil

30g (1oz) butter

1 carrot, thinly sliced

2 onions, finely chopped

250ml (9fl oz) white wine

1 garlic clove, finely chopped

zest of 1 orange, finely grated

125ml (4fl oz) chicken or veal stock, plus more if needed

FOR THE GREMOLATA

leaves from 1 small bunch of parsley, finely chopped

zest of 1 lemon, finely grated

1 garlic clove, finely chopped

PREPARE THE INGREDIENTS

1 **Preheat the oven** to 180°C (350°F/Gas 4). Tip the canned tomatoes into a sieve set over a bowl and drain off as much liquid as possible. Transfer the tomatoes to a chopping board and coarsely chop.

2 **Put the flour** on a large plate, season with salt and pepper, and stir to combine. Lightly coat the veal pieces with the seasoned flour, patting to ensure the flour adheres.

BRAISE THE VEAL

3 **Heat the oil** and butter in a sauté pan, add the veal pieces, in batches if necessary so the pan is never crowded, and brown thoroughly on all sides. Transfer to a plate with a slotted spoon.

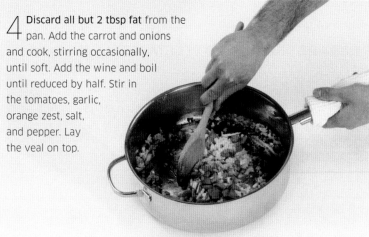

4 **Discard all but 2 tbsp fat** from the pan. Add the carrot and onions and cook, stirring occasionally, until soft. Add the wine and boil until reduced by half. Stir in the tomatoes, garlic, orange zest, salt, and pepper. Lay the veal on top.

5 **Pour in the stock**, cover the pan and cook in the oven for 1½-2 hours, until very tender. Add more stock during cooking if the pan gets dry. The sauce should be thick and rich. If necessary, boil to reduce and thicken it.

MAKE THE GREMOLATA

6 **Mix the parsley**, lemon, and garlic in a small bowl. Put the veal on warmed plates, spoon the sauce on top and sprinkle with the gremolata.

Korean grilled beef (bulgogi)

A GREAT MEAL FOR ENTERTAINING; guests grill their own meat in a table-top burner. These hot pickled vegetables (*kimchee*) are served with most Korean meals, and need to be started 4 days ahead of your meal.

SERVES	PREP	COOK
SERVES 4	50 MINS PLUS MARINATING	10 MINS

Ingredients

FOR THE PICKLED VEGETABLES

½ small Chinese cabbage (about 250g/9oz)

100g (3½oz) salt

1 tbsp chilli powder or 1 tsp cayenne

2 tbsp fish sauce

1 tsp sugar

4 garlic cloves, finely chopped

4 spring onions, chopped

2.5cm (1in) piece fresh root ginger, finely chopped

10cm (4in) piece of daikon, weighing about 175g (6oz), cut into 3mm (⅛in) strips

FOR THE BULGOGI

625g (1lb 6oz) piece of beef fillet

1 tbsp sesame seeds

4 spring onions, chopped

3 garlic cloves, finely chopped

2 tsp Japanese rice wine

3 tbsp Korean or Japanese soy sauce

2 tbsp sugar

1 tbsp dark sesame oil

¼ tsp freshly ground black pepper

oil for brazier or grill rack

boiled long-grain white rice, to serve

PREPARE THE PICKLED VEGETABLES

1 **Rinse the cabbage.** Put 1 litre (1¾ pints) water and all but ¼ tsp of the salt in a large bowl and stir until the salt has dissolved. Add the cabbage and weight it with a plate to keep it covered. Let soak for 8–10 hours.

2 **In a bowl,** mix the chilli powder or cayenne with the fish sauce, sugar, and remaining salt. Add the garlic, spring onions, ginger, and daikon and stir until the mixture is red in colour.

3 **Drain the cabbage,** rinse, and squeeze to remove the moisture. Pack the daikon mixture between each leaf, then push the cabbage into a jar. Pour any leftover daikon on top. Cover and leave in a cool place to ferment for at least 3 days. Each day, open the jar to release any gas, and push the cabbage down into the liquid. After 3 days, taste a cabbage leaf to test if it is sufficiently sour. When it's ready, cut it into 2.5cm (1in) slices and refrigerate until ready to serve.

PREPARE, MARINATE, AND GRILL THE BEEF

4 Wrap the piece of beef and freeze it for about 1 hour. Heat a frying pan over medium-high heat. Add the sesame seeds and cook, stirring, for 1–2 minutes, until golden brown. Transfer to a spice grinder and work until fine but not reduced to a paste. (Or crush in a pestle and mortar.)

5 Combine the spring onions, garlic, toasted sesame seeds, rice wine, 2 tbsp water, soy sauce, sugar, sesame oil, and pepper in a bowl and stir well to mix.

6 When the beef is partially frozen, cut it across the grain into 5mm (¼in) slices. Arrange the slices, overlapping, on a large plate. Pour the marinade over to cover each slice evenly, cover tightly and let marinate at room temperature for about 1 hour.

7 Lightly oil the cooking surface of a table-top brazier. Heat over high heat until sizzling hot. Arrange as many slices of beef as will fit in a single layer on the brazier (though do not squash them too tightly together), or allow each of your guests to do so for themselves. Cook until the beef is well-browned (about 1 minute). Turn and brown the other side for about 1 minute longer. The beef slices should remain pink in the centre though be well browned and even crusty on the outside.

8 Each guest takes a slice of beef directly from the brazier, to eat with a portion of the pickled vegetables and some plain boiled rice. Do not be scared that the pickles will be unpopular; you'll find that most people, once they have discovered kimchee, become worryingly addicted to it. Continue cooking the remaining beef when the first batch is finished, until it is all used up, allowing guests to take as much as they want.

Pork loin with garlic and rosemary

THE ITALIAN NAME for this recipe, *arista*, translates as "the best" – what more is there to say? This pork dish, with its pungent stuffing, is also delicious served at room temperature, so any leftovers will find a warm welcome. Make sure you do not cook it too long, as pork loin is lean and should remain juicy, not dry, once carved.

SERVES	PREP	COOK
SERVES 6-8	15-20 MINS	1-1½ HRS

Ingredients

10 garlic cloves, peeled

leaves from 1 small bunch of rosemary

2 tsp black peppercorns

salt

2 tbsp olive oil

1.4kg (3lb) boned loin of pork

MAKE THE STUFFING

1 Put the garlic in a food processor. Add the rosemary, peppercorns, and salt. Pulse-blend until finely chopped, or coarse, as you prefer.

PREPARE AND STUFF THE PORK

2 Preheat the oven to 200°C (400°F/Gas 6). Brush a roasting tin with olive oil. Make a deep horizontal slit through the meat, almost to the other side, and spread half the garlic and rosemary stuffing over. Fold the flap back, and reshape the loin.

ROAST THE PORK

3 Using separate pieces of string, tie the pork at 2.5cm (1in) intervals to hold its shape during cooking. Set in the prepared tin and spread the remaining stuffing over the outside. Sprinkle with olive oil.

4 Roast until it starts to brown (20–25 minutes). Remove from the oven and pour 125ml (4fl oz) water over the pork.

5 Turn the meat over. Continue roasting for 45–60 minutes longer, turning 2 or 3 times so it browns evenly, and adding more water when the tin becomes dry.

6 **The pork is cooked** when a skewer inserted into its centre for 30 seconds is very hot to the touch when withdrawn. Transfer to a chopping board, cover with foil, and stand for 10 minutes to allow the juices to be reabsorbed before carving.

FINISH THE DISH

7 **Spoon out** and discard some of the fat from the roasting tin. Add 100ml (3½fl oz) water and boil, stirring, to dissolve the juices in the roasting tin. Taste for seasoning. As you gain in cooking confidence, you may feel you want to flavour the gravy in a more complex way. The first step is to substitute chicken stock for the water used in this simple version. You may also want to add white wine, or even Madeira, for a sweeter result. Any alcoholic liquids used in the gravy must be boiled for long enough to evaporate all traces of the alcohol, or the flavour of the sauce will be tainted. You can easily find out whether you have boiled off the alcohol by tasting carefully as you cook.

8 **Discard the strings** from the pork, being careful not to pull the loin apart, and cut the meat into fairly even slices, each about a generous 1cm (½in) thick. Arrange the slices on a warmed serving dish or serve them straight on to warmed plates; spooning over the cooking juices. Steamed green vegetables make a lovely accompaniment; sweet leeks and broad beans are particularly appropriate with the succulent pork.

Bouillabaisse

A DELICIOUS SOUP for a special occasion. Purists maintain that a true bouillabaisse cannot be made anywhere but in the Mediterranean. However, you can create an excellent version based on local fish, with fabulous flavours.

SERVES
SERVES 8-10

PREP
50-55 MINS
PLUS MARINATING

COOK
50-60 MINS

Ingredients

FOR THE BOUILLABAISSE

1.4 kg (3 lb) mixed white fish, cleaned, on the bone, with heads

1kg (2¼lb) mixed oily fish, cleaned, scaled, on the bone

2 large pinches of saffron

5-6 garlic cloves

125ml (4fl oz) olive oil

1 orange

2 onions, thinly sliced

2 leeks, thinly sliced

2 celery sticks, thinly sliced

1 fennel bulb, thinly sliced

400g (14oz) can chopped tomatoes in thick juice

leaves from 10-12 parsley sprigs, chopped

1 bouquet garni

1 tbsp tomato purée

1 tbsp Pernod or other aniseed-flavoured liqueur

FOR THE CROUTES

1 baguette

olive oil, to brush

FOR THE CHILLI MAYONNAISE

1 red chilli, deseeded

4 garlic cloves, peeled

salt and pepper

175ml (6fl oz) mayonnaise

1 tsp tomato purée

cayenne pepper (optional)

PREPARE THE FISH, MARINADE, AND STOCK

1 **Rinse the fish** inside and out, drain, and pat dry. Keeping the white and oily fish separate, cut all the fish into 5cm (2in) chunks. Reserve the heads and tails for the stock (rinse the heads thoroughly).

2 **Put 1 large pinch of saffron** in a small bowl and add 2 tbsp boiling water. Let soak for 10 minutes. Peel and finely chop 2 garlic cloves. Combine the saffron, its liquid, the chopped garlic, and 3 tbsp olive oil in a bowl.

3 **Put the white** and oily fish separately in 2 large non-metallic bowls. Add half the marinade to each. Toss, cover, chill, and marinate for 1-2 hours.

4 **Meanwhile,** make the stock: put the fish heads and tails in a large saucepan, add water barely to cover, and bring to a boil. Simmer for 20 minutes. Pour through a sieve into a bowl and set aside.

PREPARE THE BROTH

5 **Peel a wide strip of zest** from the orange with a vegetable peeler. Peel and coarsely chop the remaining garlic cloves. Soak the remaining pinch of saffron in 3-4 tbsp boiling water for 10 minutes.

6 **Heat the remaining oil** in a casserole. Add the onions, leeks, celery, and fennel. Cook, stirring, for 5-7 minutes. Add the tomatoes, orange zest, garlic, and parsley to the casserole.

7 **Tie the bouquet garni** to the handle of the casserole. Pour in the stock. Add the saffron with its liquid and season. Bring to a boil. Simmer for 30-40 minutes, until thickened and the flavour is mellow, stirring occasionally.

MAKE THE CROUTES AND MAYONNAISE

8 **Preheat the oven** to 180°C (350°F/Gas 4). Cut the baguette into 2cm (¾in) slices and place them on a baking sheet, spacing them evenly apart. Brush each slice lightly with oil, using a pastry brush. Turn and brush the other side as well. Bake in the hot oven until the slices are light brown. It should take 10–12 minutes, but check often, turning the baking sheet, so all the slices brown evenly and none of them threaten to scorch. Remove any slices that brown before the rest.

9 **To make the mayonnaise,** put the chilli, garlic, and salt and pepper into the bowl of a food processor and pulse-blend until everything is finely chopped. Add the mayonnaise and the tomato puree and work until the mayonnaise is smooth. Taste and add cayenne pepper, if you like, though be cautious as the sauce should be pungent but not fierily hot. Chill, covered, until ready to serve.

FINISH THE BOUILLABAISSE

10 **Bring the broth back** to a boil. Add the oily fish and boil fiercely for 7 minutes. Shake the casserole from time to time to prevent the mixture from sticking to the base of the pan; do not stir or the pieces of fish will disintegrate.

11 **Add the white fish.** Set the most delicate types of fish on top, so they will receive the least heat. Continue boiling until the fish just flakes easily with a fork; it should take 5–8 minutes. If necessary, add more water so the fish remains covered, but don't add too much or the broth will be watery; it should remain highly flavoured.

12 **Discard the bouquet garni** and orange zest from the broth and whisk in the tomato purée and Pernod. Taste for seasoning. Ladle the broth into a soup tureen and serve at once, with the croutes and chilli mayonnaise.

Poussins with mushroom sauce

PERFECT FOR A ROMANTIC DINNER. Once split and flattened, the birds will remain moist naturally under the grill because the bones disperse the heat. If you are using a large chicken, you will need to baste it more frequently. A pair of poultry shears will make the job of splitting the birds far easier; though sturdy kitchen scissors can be used. A bigger chicken to serve 2 can be used in place of the poussins This is even more delicious if you serve the birds with a glass of the same wine you used in the mushroom sauce.

SERVES	PREP	COOK
SERVES 2	30–40 MINS	35–40 MINS

Ingredients

FOR THE POUSSINS

2 poussins

oil for the grill rack

30g (1oz) butter

salt and pepper

1 tbsp Dijon mustard

15g (½oz) dried breadcrumbs

bunch of watercress, to garnish

FOR THE MUSHROOM SAUCE

60g (2oz) butter

15g (½oz) flour

150g (5½oz) mushrooms, sliced

2 shallots, finely chopped

1 garlic clove, finely chopped

4 tbsp medium dry white wine

4 tbsp white wine vinegar

1½ tbsp Dijon mustard, or to taste

375ml (13fl oz) chicken stock

SPLIT AND FLATTEN THE POUSSINS

1 **Set one bird breast side down** on a board. With poultry shears, cut along each side of the backbone and discard it. Trim any flaps of skin and cut off the wing tips.

2 **Force the bird open** and snip the wishbone. Wipe the inside of the bird with kitchen paper. Turn breast up with the legs turned in. With the heel of your hand, push down sharply on the breast to break the breastbone and flatten the bird.

3 **Make a small cut** in the skin between the leg and breastbone and tuck in the leg knuckles.

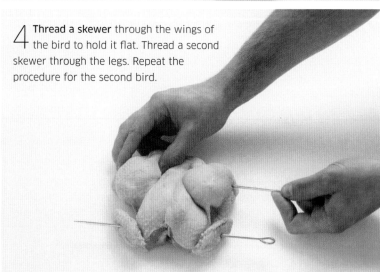

4 **Thread a skewer** through the wings of the bird to hold it flat. Thread a second skewer through the legs. Repeat the procedure for the second bird.

COOK THE POUSSINS

5 **Heat the grill**. Brush the grill rack generously with oil. Melt the butter in a small saucepan and keep it close to hand for basting. Brush the poussins evenly with half the melted butter and sprinkle with salt and a good amount of pepper.

6 **Put the poussins** on the grill rack, skin side up. Grill them about 7.5cm (3in) from the heat for about 15 minutes, basting once with butter during this time. Turn, brush the underside of the birds with the remaining butter and grill for another 10 minutes.

7 **Turn again** so the birds are breast side up once more. Brush the skin with the mustard then sprinkle evenly with the breadcrumbs. Grill, skin side up, until tender, about 10 minutes longer. If they brown too quickly, or the breadcrumbs threaten to scorch, lower the rack further from the heat.

MAKE THE MUSHROOM SAUCE

8 **In a shallow dish**, mash half the butter with the flour until soft. Melt half the remaining butter in a saucepan. Add the mushrooms and cook, stirring occasionally, for 3–5 minutes, until tender and lightly browned.

9 **Melt the remaining butter** in another saucepan, add the shallots and garlic, and cook until softened. Add the wine and vinegar and simmer until reduced to about 2 tbsp.

10 **Add the mustard** and stock and stir to combine. Stir in the mushrooms and simmer for 5 minutes. Whisk in the flour paste a small piece at a time, until the sauce lightly coats the back of a spoon. Season to taste.

11 **Remove the skewers** from the poussins. Arrange the birds on warmed plates and decorate with sprigs of watercress, if you like. Spoon on a little sauce and serve the rest separately.

Trout with orange-mustard glaze

GRILLED WHOLE FISH is a dream for the cook, quick to prepare, and easy to present. Small fish are best because their bones keep them moist and their skin protects them from the intense heat of the grill. You could barbecue the fish for this dish, but do not use strongly-flavoured wood for the fuel, as it can overpower the trout. The glaze can be made up to 1 week ahead and kept, covered, in the refrigerator.

SERVES	PREP	COOK
SERVES 6	15-20 MINUTES	20-30 MINS

Ingredients

FOR THE TROUT

6 trout, each weighing 375g (13oz), cleaned through the gills

6-8 tarragon sprigs

3-4 tbsp vegetable oil, for grill rack

3 large sweet onions, in 1cm (½in) slices

250g (9oz) mushrooms, trimmed

3 ripe tomatoes, cored and halved

FOR THE ORANGE AND MUSTARD GLAZE

4 tbsp Dijon mustard

2 tsp honey

juice of 2 oranges

4 tbsp vegetable oil

salt and pepper

PREPARE THE FISH

1 Make sure your fishmonger cleans the fish through the gills; if its stomach is slit, it may curl. Rinse inside and out and pat dry with kitchen paper. Slash diagonally 3-4 times on both sides. Make the slashes about 1cm (½in) deep to allow heat to penetrate.

2 Strip the tarragon leaves from the stalks, then tuck a leaf in each slash. Set the fish aside in a cool place.

MAKE THE GLAZE

3 Whisk the Dijon mustard and honey together in a bowl until smooth and liquid in consistency, then whisk in the orange juice until it is evenly combined. Gradually pour in the oil, whisking constantly until the glaze emulsifies and thickens slightly. Season with salt and pepper. Taste for seasoning; you may find you want to add more mustard, honey, or orange. Adjust the balance of flavourings until they suit your palate perfectly (though be careful not to add too much mustard, as it could overpower the taste of the delicate fish).

GRILL THE VEGETABLES AND FISH

4 **Heat the grill.** Brush the rack generously with oil. Arrange the onion slices and mushrooms on the rack. Brush with a little of the glaze and season. Grill about 7.5cm (3in) from the heat, brushing with more glaze and turning, allowing about 3 minutes for the mushrooms and 5-7 minutes for the onions; they should be slightly charred. Remove and keep warm.

5 **Cook the tomatoes** skin-side towards the heat for 5-7 minutes, or until warmed through and the skin is slightly charred; do not turn. Remove and keep warm.

6 **Place the fish** on the rack (in 2 batches if necessary). Brush with glaze; sprinkle with salt and pepper. Grill for 4-7 minutes, until browned.

FINISH AND SERVE THE DISH

7 Carefully turn the fish, being careful not to tear the skin, and brush each generously with more of the glaze. Continue grilling until the flesh just flakes easily when tested with a fork and there is no opaque flesh near the spine (serve the fish with the tested side downwards for the neatest presentation). They could take anything from 4–7 minutes more to cook, depending on the thickness of the fish and the strength of the grill. As a general guide, for every 2.5cm (1in) of a fish at its thickest part, allow 10 minutes cooking, whether on a barbecue or under a grill. (If cooking on a barbecue, make sure the fish is placed over a coolish part or it will burn on the outside before the flesh is cooked through.) Place the fish on warmed plates and serve with a stack of the grilled vegetables. Spoon any remaining glaze over the fish.

 VARIATION: Grilled cod steaks with maitre d'hotel butter

Try to use farmed fish rather than the endangered wild cod.

1 Omit the glaze. Finely chop 1 shallot and 8–10 parsley stalks. Cream 75g (2½oz) butter. Mix in the shallot and parsley, the juice of ½ lemon, salt, and pepper. Spoon the butter on to a piece of baking parchment and shape into a roll, twisting the ends to seal. Refrigerate until firm.

2 Rinse and dry 6 cod steaks. Brush with 3–4 tbsp olive oil, season and grill for 3–5 minutes on each side. After turning, brush with more olive oil and sprinkle with more salt and pepper.

3 Set a slice of the maître d'hôtel butter on top of each cod steak and serve.

Very garlicky sautéed chicken

THE FLAVOUR OF GARLIC mellows as it cooks, and it acts as a thickening agent for the sauce. This sauté has a piquant sauce made from red wine vinegar and chopped tomatoes. Don't worry if the amount of garlic seems excessive; all your guests will love the bold flavours of this dish. Herb and other flavoured vinegars can be used in this recipe, each will add its own distinctive taste. If you choose balsamic vinegar, use only half the quantity.

SERVES SERVES 4	**PREP** 15–20 MINS	**COOK** 1–1¼ HRS

Ingredients

1.5kg (3lb 3oz) chicken, jointed into 6 pieces, or 6 chicken joints

salt and pepper

1 tbsp vegetable oil

90g (3oz) butter

15 garlic cloves

250ml (9fl oz) red wine vinegar

1 tbsp tomato purée

1 bouquet garni

2 tomatoes, coarsely chopped

250ml (8fl oz) chicken stock

SAUTÉ THE CHICKEN AND GARLIC

1 **Season the chicken** with salt and pepper. Heat the oil and 15g (½oz) of the butter in a sauté pan over moderate heat until foaming. Add the chicken legs, skin side down, and sauté for about 5 minutes, until they begin to brown.

2 **Add the chicken breasts** and continue cooking gently for 10–15 minutes, until very brown. Turn and brown the other side.

3 **Add the unpeeled garlic cloves**. Shake the pan gently to distribute the garlic in among the chicken joints, then cover and cook over low heat for 20 minutes.

ADD THE OTHER INGREDIENTS

4 **Stir in the vinegar** and simmer, uncovered, until reduced by half; it will take about 10 minutes to get to this stage. Add the tomato purée to the pan and stir to mix with the juices, scraping the base of the pan with a wooden spoon to incorporate all the chicken flavours. Cook the tomato purée briefly to eliminate any raw taste, making sure it does not stick to the pan or the flavour of the sauce will be spoiled. Add the bouquet garni and tomatoes to the pan and mix into the chicken.

5 **Cover again** and simmer for 5–10 minutes longer, until the chicken joints are tender when pierced with a 2-pronged fork and the juices run clear. If there is any trace of pink in the juices, return the chicken to the pan for a few minutes longer before testing again. If some joints are done before others, remove them from the pan, put them on a plate, loosely cover with foil, and keep them warm in a very low oven; overcooking the chicken will result in tough meat.

MAKE THE GARLIC AND VINEGAR SAUCE

6 **Remove all the chicken** from the pan and keep warm in a very low oven. Add the stock to the juices in the pan and boil for 3–5 minutes, stirring occasionally, until well reduced and concentrated in flavour, again scraping the base of the pan with a wooden spoon to release all the flavour. Strain the sauce through a sieve back into the saucepan, pressing hard on the garlic to extract the pulp.

7 **Cut the remaining butter** into small pieces. Bring the sauce back to a boil, then remove from the heat and add the butter, a few pieces at a time, whisking constantly and moving the pan on and off the heat. You should see the sauce beginning to thicken, and develop a glossy sheen. Do not boil; the butter should make the sauce creamy and rich without melting to oil, as it will if it boils. Taste for seasoning. Arrange the chicken on warmed plates and spoon over a generous amount of the sauce, serving the remaining sauce on the side.

 VARIATION: Very garlicky sautéed guinea fowl with blackberries

A gamier bird, the flavours here are sharpened by tangy berries.

1 Joint the guinea fowl into 6 pieces, or get your butcher to do it for you. Brown the pieces as directed in the main recipe, then add the garlic.

2 Omit the red wine vinegar. Stir in 120ml (4fl oz) sherry vinegar and reduce as directed, then add the bouquet garni. Omit the tomato purée and tomatoes. Simmer as directed until the guinea fowl is cooked through, then remove the pieces and keep them warm.

3 Add the stock to the pan and reduce as directed, and strain the sauce back into the pan, pressing on the garlic. Add the butter. Pick through 120g (4oz) blackberries, washing them only if they are dirty. Add the berries to the sauce and heat them through. Taste for seasoning; you may need a pinch of sugar if the berries are very tart. Serve with the guinea fowl pieces.

Comfort food

Hearty, homely, and deeply nourishing dishes

Rib of beef with Yorkshire pudding

AS TRADITIONAL AS IT GETS, and irresistible with the crisp, golden Yorkshire puddings. Carving a rib of beef takes a little skill: set the joint upright on a carving board and, holding it steady with a carving fork, cut away the rib bones at the base of the meat, removing as little beef as possible as you do so. With the joint on its side, carve into even slices.

SERVES	PREP	COOK
SERVES 6-8	25-30 MINS	1¼-2¼ HRS

Ingredients

FOR THE YORKSHIRE PUDDING

180g (6oz) plain flour

2 eggs, beaten

300ml (10fl oz) milk

vegetable oil, if needed

FOR THE BEEF AND GRAVY

2kg (4½lb) beef rib roast (2 ribs)

salt and pepper

1-2 tbsp plain flour

500ml (16fl oz) beef stock

MAKE THE BATTER

1 **Sift the flour** into a large bowl. Make a well in the centre and add the eggs, with some salt and pepper.

2 **Slowly whisk in the milk,** drawing in the flour to make a smooth paste. Stir in 90ml (3fl oz) water. Cover with a tea towel, and let stand at room temperature for at least 15 minutes.

PREPARE AND ROAST THE BEEF

3 **Meanwhile,** preheat the oven to 230°C (450°F/Gas 8). Sprinkle the meat with salt and pepper, and set it in a large roasting tin, ribs pointing up. Roast for 15 minutes. Reduce the oven temperature to 180°C (350°F/Gas 4). Continue roasting for 50 minutes for rare beef, or 65 minutes for medium-done, basting often.

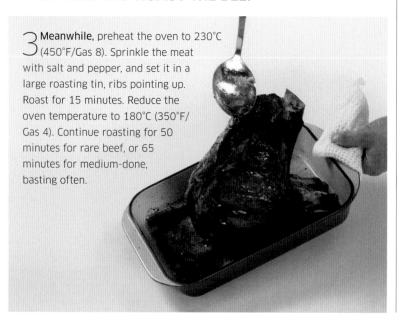

4 **When the meat is rare,** a metal skewer inserted into the centre for 30 seconds will be cool to the touch when withdrawn (a meat thermometer will show 52°C/125°F). When medium-done, the skewer will be warm (a meat thermometer will show 60°C/140°F).

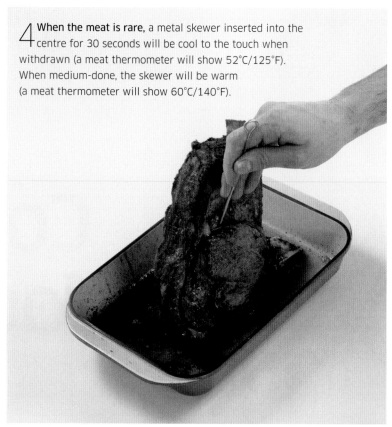

5 **Transfer the meat** to a board, cover loosely with foil and leave in a warm place, while you make the Yorkshire pudding and gravy. Tilt the baking dish, and spoon off the fat with a large metal spoon. Reserve the fat.

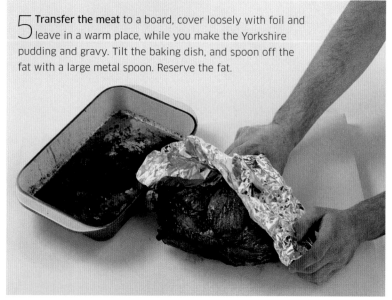

MAKE THE YORKSHIRE PUDDINGS

6 Increase the oven temperature to 230°C (450°F/Gas 8). Pour a teaspoon of the beef fat into each of 12 Yorkshire pudding, or deep bun, tins, topping up with vegetable oil if necessary. Heat in the oven for about 5 minutes until very hot. Pour in the batter to half-fill each of the tins; it should sizzle as it hits the hot fat. Bake in the hot oven for 15–20 minutes, until puffed and golden brown. Do not open the oven during this time, or the Yorkshire puddings may sink.

7 Meanwhile, make the gravy: stir 1–2 tbsp plain flour into the juices in the roasting tin and cook, stirring, for 2–3 minutes, until very brown. Add the beef stock. Bring to a boil, stirring, and simmer for 2 minutes. Strain and season to taste.

8 Carve the joint (see the recipe introduction) and arrange on warmed plates, with the Yorkshire puddings and vegetables of your choice. Serve the gravy separately.

 VARIATION: Rib of beef pebronata

With a Corsican tomato and red pepper sauce.

1 Prepare and roast the beef as directed in the main recipe. Meanwhile, finely chop 1 onion and 4 garlic cloves. Chop the leaves from 3 sprigs each thyme and parsley. Roast, peel, and core 3 red peppers.

2 Heat 2 tbsp olive oil and sauté the onion, garlic and herbs. Stir in 2 x 400g (14oz) cans chopped tomatoes, season, and cook for 25 minutes. Heat another 2 tbsp oil in a second pan and add the red pepper, 1 bay leaf, and 4 juniper berries. Cook for 10 minutes. Stir in 2 tbsp plain flour, then the tomato mixture. Simmer for 10 minutes, until thick. Stir in 250ml (9fl oz) red wine.

3 Cover the beef and let rest, as directed in the main recipe. Spoon off the fat from the roasting tin. Stir a further 250ml (9fl oz) red wine into the tin and bring to a boil. Strain into the pebronata sauce and serve with the carved beef.

Chilli con carne

IN TEXAS, YOU WILL NEVER FIND RED BEANS in a chilli; they are served on the side, as in this authentic recipe. Do mix them in with the meat, if you prefer. This is great to have in hand for a cold night; it will keep for 3 days in the refrigerator. For a real Texan touch, serve it with cornbread (p386).

SERVES
SERVES 6

PREP
35-40 MINUTES

COOK
2-2½ HOURS

Ingredients

3 garlic cloves

2-4 dried red chillies

3 tbsp vegetable oil, plus more if needed

1.4kg (3lb) braising steak, in 1cm (½in) cubes

3 onions, chopped

2 x 400g (14oz) cans chopped tomatoes

leaves from 5-6 oregano sprigs, chopped or 1 tbsp dried oregano

2 tbsp chilli powder

1 tbsp paprika

2 tsp ground cumin

1-2 tsp Tabasco sauce, or to taste

salt and pepper

1 tbsp fine cornmeal (polenta)

2 x 400g (14oz) cans red kidney beans

PREPARE THE GARLIC AND CHILLI

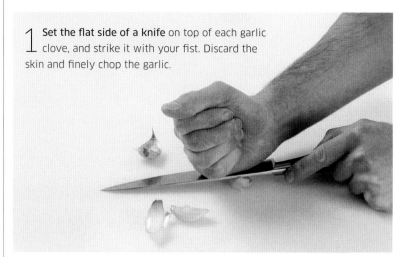

1 **Set the flat side of a knife** on top of each garlic clove, and strike it with your fist. Discard the skin and finely chop the garlic.

2 **Trim and split the chillies** lengthways. Discard the seeds, then finely chop or crumble them. The seeds are the hottest part; if you like your chilli extra hot, you can leave them in.

COOK THE CHILLI

3 **Heat half the oil** in a casserole, add about a quarter of the beef, and cook over high heat, stirring, until browned. Using a slotted spoon, transfer the meat to a plate. Brown the remaining beef cubes in 3 batches, adding more oil as needed.

4 **Return all the browned meat,** with the juices, to the casserole. Add the onions, garlic, and tomatoes, and cook, stirring, for 8-10 minutes, until the onions are just soft.

5 **Pour in 500ml (16fl oz) water,** and stir into the casserole with the chillies, oregano, chilli powder, paprika, cumin, Tabasco sauce, salt, and pepper. Bring just to a boil, then cover and simmer for about 2-2½ hours, until the meat is very tender, stirring occasionally.

6 **About 30 minutes** before the end of cooking, stir in the cornmeal. At the end of cooking, the chilli should be thick and rich. Taste for seasoning, and serve it hot from the casserole, with boiled white long-grain rice, and bowls of warmed red kidney beans alongside for each diner.

Herbed roast chicken

THIS IS A CLASSIC, juicy roast chicken, with herbs inside for flavour. Though it is a simple dish, you will find it is everyone's favourite meal. The butter used in cooking the chicken goes into the gravy so the more butter you use, the richer the gravy will be! Roast potatoes - crisp on the outside and tender within - are the perfect accompaniment. Use the very best chicken you can afford.

SERVES	PREP	COOK
SERVES 4-6	20-30 MINS	1-1¼ HRS

Ingredients

2kg (4½lb) chicken

salt and pepper

2-3 large thyme sprigs

2-3 large rosemary sprigs

1 bay leaf

60-75g (2-2½oz) butter

500ml (16fl oz) chicken stock

PREPARE THE CHICKEN

1 **Preheat the oven** to 220°C (425°F/Gas 7). Wipe the inside of the chicken with kitchen paper. Remove the wishbone for easier carving. Season the chicken inside and out. Put the herbs inside the chicken.

2 **Set the bird breast** up and push the legs back and down. Insert a metal skewer near the knee joint and push through the bird and out through the other leg. Turn the bird breast down. Pull the neck skin over the cavity and tuck the wing tips over it.

3 **Push a second skewer** through both sections of the wing, through the neck and out through the other wing. Tie the ends of the legs together with kitchen string.

ROAST THE CHICKEN

4 **Put the chicken** in a roasting tin, breast up. Cut the butter into slices and arrange them on the breast. Roast in the heated oven for 1-1¼ hours, basting with the juices in the tin every 10-15 minutes.

5 **Turn the chicken** on to its breast to keep it moist after it starts to brown. Return it breast up about 15 minutes before the end of cooking. Transfer to a carving board and cover with foil to keep warm.

MAKE THE GRAVY AND SERVE

6 **Add the stock** to the roasting tin and boil over high heat, stirring to dissolve the juices. Continue boiling until thoroughly reduced and concentrated. Taste for seasoning, then strain through a sieve into a gravy boat or serving bowl. Serve with the carved chicken.

Lamb chops in paper with fennel

CHOPS ENCLOSED IN BAKING PARCHMENT steam in their own juices, using the minimum fat for the maximum flavour. The paper parcels puff up and turn golden brown in the oven and, when opened, release wafts of delicious, gentle aniseed aroma.

SERVES SERVES 4	**PREP** 25–30 MINS	**COOK** 35–40 MINS

Ingredients

1kg (2¼lb) fennel bulbs

4 tbsp olive oil

2 garlic cloves, finely chopped

400g (14oz) can chopped tomatoes

3 tbsp pastis

salt and pepper

4 lamb loin chops, each 2.5cm (1in) thick, total weight about 625g (1lb 6oz)

melted butter, to brush

1 egg

PREPARE THE FENNEL

1 Trim off and discard the fennel stalks and root, alnog with any tough outer layers from the bulb. Reserve some green fronds for decoration. Thinly slice each fennel bulb.

2 Heat half the oil in a frying pan, add the fennel and garlic, and sauté for 6–8 minutes, until the fennel begins to soften.

3 Add three-quarters of the tomatoes, the pastis, salt, and pepper to the pan and cook, stirring occasionally, for 20-25 minutes, until the mixture is thick, and most of the moisture has evaporated. Taste for seasoning.

PREPARE THE LAMB

4 Meanwhile, cut the "tail" from each chop and season. Heat the remaining oil in another frying pan, add the chops and tails, and cook over high heat for 1-2 minutes, until well browned. Turn and brown the other side.

5 Fold a large sheet of baking parchment measuring about 30x37.5cm (12x15in) in half, and draw a curve to make a heart shape when unfolded, large enough to leave a 7.5cm (3in) border around a chop.

MAKE THE PAPER CASES

6 Cut out the heart shape with scissors. Repeat to make 4 paper hearts. Open out and brush each one with melted butter, leaving a border of about 2.5cm (1in) unbuttered.

7 Beat the egg with ½ tsp salt. Brush the egg glaze on the unbuttered border of each paper heart.

FILL THE PAPER CASES AND **BAKE**

8 Heat the oven to 190°C (375°F/Gas 5). Spoon a bed of the fennel mixture on 1 half of a paper heart.

9 Set a lamb chop and tail on top of the fennel mixture. Spoon a little of the reserved tomato over, and lay a fennel frond on top.

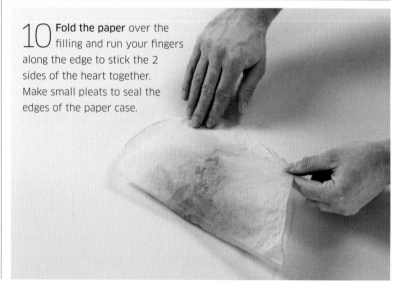

10 Fold the paper over the filling and run your fingers along the edge to stick the 2 sides of the heart together. Make small pleats to seal the edges of the paper case.

11 **Twist the ends** of the paper case to finish. Repeat the process with the remaining ingredients to make 4 paper parcels. Place on a baking sheet and bake for 10–14 minutes, until puffed and brown. Serve at once, allowing each diner to open their own parcel.

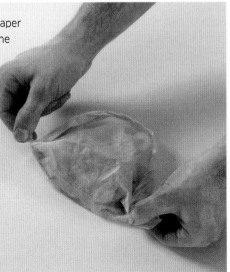

 VARIATION: Lamb chops in paper cases with leeks

This version is sweet flavoured and scented with herbs.

1 Omit the fennel. Trim 500g (1lb 2oz) leeks, discarding the root and tough green tops. Slit lengthways, wash thoroughly, drain well, and slice.

2 Strip the leaves from 3–5 rosemary or thyme sprigs, setting aside 4 small sprigs. Finely chop the leaves. Heat the oil in a frying pan and add the garlic, leeks, and all the tomatoes with 125ml (4fl oz) dry white wine, salt, and pepper. Continue as directed, omitting the pastis. Stir in the herbs at the end of cooking.

3 Brown the lamb chops, make the paper cases, and fill as directed, topping each chop with a reserved herb sprig. Bake and serve immediately.

Indonesian fried rice (nasi goreng)

WONDERFULLY RESTORATIVE and a good way to use up leftover cooked rice. This dish, from Java, is seasoned with hot chillies and sweet soy sauce. You can cook the rice and make the chilli-onion paste 1 day ahead; keep them separate, covered, in the refrigerator. Done like this, it is a great way to prepare for a very quick-to-make evening meal. Leave out the chicken and prawns and add mixed vegetables and tofu for a vegetarian version.

SERVES SERVES 4	**PREP** 40–45 MINS PLUS STANDING	**COOK** 10–15 MINS

Ingredients

250g (9oz) long-grain white rice

3 tbsp oil, plus more for the tray

1 onion, finely chopped

1 garlic clove, coarsely chopped

1 tsp dried prawn paste

1 tsp crushed chillies

2 eggs

125g (4½oz) raw, peeled large prawns

1 skinless, boneless chicken breast, weighing about 175g (6oz), very thinly sliced

2 spring onions, thinly sliced

2 tbsp sweet soy sauce, or 2 tbsp dark soy sauce plus 1 tbsp brown sugar, more if needed

COOK THE RICE

1 **Put the rice** in a large bowl, cover with cold water, and stir with your fingertips until the water has turned a milky white. Pour off the water. Repeat once or twice until the water is fairly clear. Drain in a sieve.

2 **Put the drained rice** in a saucepan and add 500ml (16fl oz) water. Bring to a boil over high heat. Stir, cover, then reduce the heat to low and simmer until all the water has been absorbed and the rice is tender; it should take about 15 minutes.

3 **Remove from the heat** and let the rice stand, without lifting the lid, for 15 minutes. Uncover, and stir to fluff it up. Lightly oil a baking sheet. Transfer the rice to the sheet and spread it out evenly so the steam can escape. Let it cool to room temperature.

MAKE THE CHILLI-ONION PASTE

4 **In a mortar**, pound the chopped onion with a pestle until pulpy. Add the garlic, prawn paste, and crushed chillies and pound until the mixture forms a coarse paste. Alternatively, purée the ingredients in a food processor. Set the paste aside.

MAKE THE OMELETTE STRIPS

5 **Beat the eggs** in a small bowl. Heat a wok over medium heat until hot. Drizzle in 1 tbsp of the oil to coat the bottom and sides of the wok. Continue heating until hot, then pour in the eggs.

6 **Quickly tilt the wok** so that the egg spreads over the bottom in an even layer. Cook for 1–2 minutes, until set in the centre and slightly crisp around the edge. Turn the omelette. Cook until the other side is lightly browned (15–30 seconds). Slide the omelette on to a chopping board. Let cool slightly. Roll it up loosely and cut into 1cm (½in) strips.

PREPARE THE PRAWNS

7 **Make a** shallow cut along the back of each prawn with a small, sharp knife and remove the dark intestinal vein. Rinse the prawns and pat them dry with kitchen paper.

STIR-FRY THE CHICKEN AND PRAWNS

8 **Heat the wok** over medium-high heat. Drizzle in 1 tbsp oil to coat the bottom and sides. When the oil is hot, stir in the chilli-onion paste; cook for about 30 seconds, until fragrant.

9 **Increase the heat** to high. Add the chicken slices and stir-fry for 2–3 minutes, until they are opaque.

10 **Add the prawns** and stir-fry until they turn pink, about 1–2 minutes. Using the spatula, transfer the chicken and prawns from the wok to a bowl and keep warm.

FINISH THE DISH

11 **Reduce the heat** to medium. Heat the remaining oil in the wok. Add the cooled rice and stir-fry until each grain is separate. You will need to keep turning it over and over with a flat spoon or a wok spatula, but be very gentle so the grains remain whole and do not begin to break up into a mush. Cover and cook the rice until it softens; this should only take about 3 minutes, stirring once or twice to prevent it from browning at the bottom of the wok.

12 **Add the spring onion**, sweet soy sauce, and a little salt, and stir-fry for about 1 minute longer until the flavourings are well dispersed throughout the rice. Return the omelette strips, chicken, and prawns to the wok; stir-fry over high heat until thoroughly combined and very hot all the way through, being very gentle so as not to break up any of the component parts. This should take about 2–3 minutes, but continue for as long as is necessary to get all the ingredients piping hot and steaming, continuing to stir so that nothing catches or browns at the bottom of the wok. Taste for seasoning, adding more soy sauce, if needed. The dish should be intensely flavoured with a good kick from the chilli. Serve at once.

Perfect fish and chips

DOUBLE-FRIED CHIPS are fluffy within and crisp without. The light beer batter makes the crust extra brittle and delicious. The traditional accompaniment to the dish is tartare sauce, and the recipe here beats anything you can buy in a jar hands down, so do give it a try.

SERVES
SERVES 4

PREP
45–50 MINS
PLUS STANDING

COOK
20–25 MINS

Ingredients

FOR THE TARTARE SAUCE

125ml (4fl oz) mayonnaise

1 hard-boiled egg, coarsely chopped

1 tsp drained capers, chopped

2 gherkins, coarsely chopped

1 small shallot, finely chopped

leaves from 2–3 parsley sprigs, chopped

leaves from 2–3 chervil or tarragon sprigs, chopped

FOR THE FISH AND CHIPS

6 potatoes, total weight about 750g (1lb 10oz)

vegetable oil for deep-frying

30g (1oz) plain flour

salt and pepper

4 skinned cod fillets, total weight 750g (1lb 10oz)

1 lemon, cut into wedges, to serve

FOR THE BATTER

1½ tsp dried yeast (or 9g/⅓oz fresh yeast)

150g (5½oz) plain flour

1 tbsp vegetable oil

175ml (6fl oz) bitter ale

1 egg white

MAKE THE TARTARE SAUCE

1 Mix together the mayonnaise, egg, capers, gherkins, shallot, and herbs, and taste for seasoning. Cover the refrigerate until serving.

PREPARE THE POTATOES AND BATTER

2 Peel the potatoes and, with a knife, square off the sides and ends of each. Cut lengthways into 1cm (½in) sticks. Put in a bowl of cold water to soak for 30 minutes. This removes starch, so the chips will be crisp when fried. Meanwhile, sprinkle the dried or crumble the fresh yeast over 4 tbsp warm water and let stand for about 5 minutes, until dissolved.

3 Sift the flour and a pinch of salt into a large bowl and make a well in the centre. Add the yeast mixture, oil, and two-thirds of the beer; stir to form a smooth paste. Stir in the remaining beer. Do not overmix. Let the batter stand in a warm place for 30–35 minutes, until it has thickened and become frothy, showing the yeast is working.

PART-FRY THE CHIPS

4 While the batter is standing, heat the vegetable oil in a deep-fat fryer until it is at 180°C (350°F) on an oil thermometer. Drain the potatoes, transfer to kitchen paper and pat dry.

5 Dip the empty frying basket in the hot oil (this will prevent the potatoes sticking). Lift the basket out of the oil and add the potatoes. Carefully lower the basket back and deep-fry for 5–7 minutes, until just tender when pierced with the tip of a knife, and just starting to brown. Lift out and let drain over the deep fryer, then tip on to a plate lined with kitchen paper.

COAT AND DEEP-FRY THE FISH

6 Heat the oven to low. Heat the oil to 190°C (375°F). Put the flour on a plate and season with salt and pepper. Coat the pieces of fish with the flour, patting with your hands so they are evenly coated.

7 Beat the egg white in a medium metal bowl until stiff peaks form when the whisk is lifted. Gently fold the whisked egg white into the batter, using a wooden spoon, until combined.

8 Using a 2-pronged fork, dip a piece of fish in the batter, turning to coat thoroughly. Lift out the fish and hold it over the bowl for 5 seconds so excess batter can drip off.

9 Carefully lower the fish into the hot oil and deep-fry, turning once, until golden brown and crisp, 6–8 minutes depending on the thickness of the fillets. Coat and deep-fry the remaining fish, 1 or 2 pieces at a time.

FINISH THE CHIPS

10 As the fish is deep-fried, transfer to a baking sheet lined with kitchen paper so that excess oil is absorbed. Keep the fish warm in the oven, loosely covered with aluminium foil to keep in the moisture.

11 Put the partially cooked chips back in the frying basket and deep-fry for 1–2 minutes more, until very hot and golden brown. Drain on kitchen paper to soak up any excess oil from the chips.

12 Divide the fish and chips among warmed plates. Sprinkle the chips with a little salt to add flavour. Decorate the plates with the lemon wedges and serve at once, accompanied by the tartare sauce.

Onion confit and gorgonzola pizzas

ONIONS AND GORGONZOLA are delicious together, topping a crust made crunchy with polenta. To make an onion confit, sliced red onions are cooked very slowly in their own juices, with red wine added for colour and another depth of flavour.

SERVES	PREP	COOK
MAKES 6	40–45 MINS PLUS RISING	15–20 MINS

Ingredients

FOR THE DOUGH

1½ tsp dried yeast or 10g (⅓oz) fresh yeast

250g (9oz) unbleached strong white flour, plus more if needed

75g (2¾oz) polenta (fine yellow cornmeal), plus more for the foil

1 tsp salt

2 tbsp olive oil

FOR THE TOPPING

2 tbsp olive oil

750g (1lb 10oz) red onions, thinly sliced

2 tsp sugar

pepper

4 tbsp red wine

leaves from 5–7 oregano sprigs, finely chopped

175g (6oz) gorgonzola cheese

MAKE THE DOUGH

1 In a small bowl, sprinkle or crumble the yeast over 4 tbsp lukewarm water. Let stand for about 5 minutes until dissolved, stirring once.

2 Put the flour on to a work surface with the polenta and salt. Make a large well in the centre and add 150ml (5fl oz) lukewarm water, the oil and dissolved yeast.

3 With your fingertips, work the ingredients in the well until thoroughly mixed. Draw in the flour mixture, working it into the other ingredients with your hand to form a smooth dough. It should be soft and slightly sticky.

4 Sprinkle the dough and your hands with flour, and begin to knead by holding the dough with one hand and pushing it away from you with the other. Give the dough a quarter turn and knead for 5–7 minutes, until it is very smooth, elastic, and forms a ball. If the dough sticks while kneading, flour the work surface.

5 Brush a large bowl with oil and put in the dough, flipping it so the surface is lightly oiled. Cover with a damp tea towel, or clingfilm, and let rise in a warm place until doubled in bulk (1–1½ hours). To test the dough, press it gently but firmly with your forefinger. If the dough holds the impression of your finger, it has risen sufficiently.

MAKE THE RED ONION CONFIT

6 Heat the oil in a frying pan. Add the onions, sugar, salt, and pepper. Cook over medium heat, stirring often, for 5–7 minutes, until the onions are soft and lightly brown.

7 Add the wine and continue cooking until it has evaporated. Reduce the heat, press a piece of foil on top of the onions, and cover with a lid.

8 **Cook the onions** over very low heat, stirring occasionally, for 15–20 minutes, or until they are soft enough to cut with a spoon. Let cool. Stir in the oregano.

ASSEMBLE AND BAKE THE PIZZAS

9 **Preheat the oven** to 230°C (450°F/Gas 8). Put 2 baking sheets on separate racks in the bottom half of the oven to heat. Cut six 23cm (9in) squares of foil, and sprinkle each generously with polenta.

10 **Turn the dough** on to a lightly floured work surface and knead with your hand just to knock out the air. Cover the dough, and let rest for about 5 minutes.

11 **With your hands,** roll the dough into a cylinder about 5cm (2in) in diameter. Cut the cylinder in half, and then cut each half into 3 equal pieces. Shape the pieces of dough into balls.

12 **Roll a ball of dough** into an 18cm (7in) round. Transfer the round to 1 of the squares of foil. Repeat to shape the remaining dough. Press up the edges of the rounds with your fingertips to form shallow rims, if you like. Spread the rounds with the onion confit.

13 **Top the rounds with cheese,** and let rise in a warm place for about 15 minutes, until the dough is puffed. Bake the pizzas, on the foil, on the baking sheets, for 15–20 minutes, until lightly browned and crisp. Switch the baking sheets after 7 minutes so the pizzas brown evenly.

14 **Serve the pizzas** hot from the oven. Brush the crusts with olive oil, and top with the oregano sprigs, if you like.

Cold chicken and ham pie

A FOND MEMORY FROM CHILDHOOD. The tasty butter and lard crust encases a plentiful, juicy filling. This is wonderful to take on a picnic, served with chutney and a crisp green salad. It can be made up to 3 days ahead and kept refrigerated.

SERVES
SERVES 8-10

PREP
50-60 MINS
PLUS COOLING

COOK
1½ HRS

Ingredients

FOR THE PASTRY

500g (1lb 2oz) plain flour

2 tsp salt

75g (2½oz) butter

75g (2½oz) lard

FOR THE FILLING

4 skinless, boneless chicken breasts, total weight about 750g (1lb 10oz)

375g (13oz) lean boneless pork

1 lemon

9 eggs

1 tsp dried thyme

1 tsp dried sage

ground nutmeg

salt and pepper

375g (13oz) cooked lean ham

butter for the pan

MAKE THE PASTRY

1 **Sift the flour** and salt into a large bowl. Make a well in the centre. Put the butter and lard in the well and cut them into small pieces with round-bladed knives. Rub with your fingertips until it forms fine crumbs.

2 **Make a well** in the centre again, add 150ml (¼ pint) water and mix quickly with a knife to form crumbs. If the mixture seems dry, add 1–2 tbsp more water. Mix with your fingers; it should be soft but not sticky.

3 **Turn the dough** on to a floured surface and knead lightly with the heel of your hand for 5–10 seconds, until smooth. Wrap the dough in clingfilm and chill for 30 minutes in the refrigerator.

MAKE THE FILLING

4 **Cut 2 of the chicken breasts** and the pork into chunks. Work the pork and chicken chunks through the fine blade of a mincer, or work in a food processor (not too finely). Put the minced meats in a large bowl.

5 **Grate the zest** from half of the lemon on to the minced meats. With a fork, beat 2 eggs; add to the minced meats with the thyme, sage, nutmeg, salt, and pepper. Beat the filling until it pulls from the side of the bowl.

6 **To test for seasoning,** fry a piece in a pan, and taste. It should be well seasoned, so add more salt and pepper if required. Cut the reserved chicken breasts and ham into 2cm (¾in) cubes and stir into the filling.

LINE THE TIN

7 **Butter the bottom a**nd side of a 20–23cm (8–9in) springform tin. Cut off about three-quarters of the dough and shape it into a ball; keep the remaining dough covered. On a floured surface, roll out the ball of dough into a 5mm (¼in) thick circle large enough to line the tin with dough left to overhang.

8 **Loosely roll the dough** around the rolling pin and unroll it over the tin. Do not stretch the dough or it will shrink during baking. Ease the dough into the tin, pressing it well into the bottom and side. Try to avoid pleats in the side. Trim the edges of the dough with scissors, leaving about 1cm (½in) overhanging. Add the trimmings to the remaining dough.

ASSEMBLE AND BAKE THE PIE

9 **Put 6 eggs in a saucepan** of cold water, bring to the boil and simmer for 10 minutes. Run cold water into the pan to stop the cooking, then allow the eggs to cool. Drain the eggs; tap them on a work surface to crack the shells all over, then peel. Preheat the oven to 200°C (400°F/Gas 6).

10 **Spread half the filling** in the pastry case. Arrange the eggs on top, gently pushing them into the filling. Cover with the remaining chicken mixture, ensuring all the gaps are filled. Fold over the trimmed dough overhang. Beat the remaining egg with pinch of salt for the glaze. Brush the edge of the dough with egg glaze.

11 **Roll out the remaining dough** to a circle about 5mm (¼in) thick. Set the tin on top and cut around the base to form a lid of dough the diameter of the tin. Lay the lid over the filling and press the edges of dough together to seal.

12 **Using a metal skewer,** poke a hole in the lid and insert a roll of foil to form a chimney, so the steam can escape during baking. Use the pastry trimmings to decorate the top, if you wish, glaze with beaten egg, and bake for 1 hour, until golden brown. Reduce the heat to 180°C (350°F/Gas 4) and bake for 30 minutes, until very brown. Allow to cool, discard the foil chimney and chill for 3–4 hours. Unmould and allow to come to room temperature before serving.

Roast leg of lamb with haricot beans

A GOOD ROAST LEG OF LAMB is unbeatable for flavour and succulence. This recipe comes from Brittany, and is accompanied by the haricot beans for which that region is famous. It's worth the effort of soaking dried beans for their superior texture.

SERVES	**PREP**	**COOK**
SERVES 6-8	35-40 MINS PLUS SOAKING	1½-2 HRS

Ingredients

FOR THE BEANS

500g (1lb 2oz) dried haricot beans

1 onion

2 cloves

1 carrot, quartered

1 bouquet garni

2-3 parsley sprigs (optional)

FOR THE LAMB

2.7kg (6lb) leg of lamb

2 garlic cloves

1 onion, quartered

1 carrot, quartered

3 tbsp olive oil

leaves from 2-3 rosemary sprigs, chopped

salt and pepper

125ml (4fl oz) white wine

250ml (9fl oz) lamb stock or water, plus more if needed

SOAK AND COOK THE BEANS

1 Put the haricot beans in a bowl, pour in cold water to cover, and let soak overnight.

2 Peel the onion and stud with the cloves. Drain the beans and put them in a casserole; add the clove-studded onion, carrot, bouquet garni, and enough fresh water to cover by at least 2.5cm (1in).

3 Bring to a boil, cover and simmer, skimming as necessary, for 1½-2 hours. Add hot water, as needed, to keep the beans covered. Season halfway through cooking. When cooked, the beans should be tender, but not mushy. Remove the onion, carrot, and bouquet garni, and discard.

PREPARE AND ROAST THE LAMB

4 **Preheat the oven** to 230°C (450°F/Gas 8). Trim any skin and fat from the lamb. Peel the garlic and cut each clove into 4–5 thin slivers. Make several shallow incisions in the lamb with the point of a small knife. Insert the slivers of garlic.

5 **Put the onion** and carrot in a roasting tin. Set the lamb on top. Pour the oil over the lamb and sprinkle with the rosemary, salt, and pepper. Sear in the heated oven for 10–15 minutes, until browned.

6 **Reduce the oven temperature** to 180°C (350°F/Gas 4) and roast, basting often, 1–1¼ hours for rare meat or 1¼–1½ hours for medium. When rare, a skewer inserted for 30 seconds will be cool to the touch when withdrawn. A meat thermometer will show 52°C (125°F). When the meat is medium, the skewer will be warm and a meat thermometer will show 60°C (140°F).

FINISH THE DISH

7 **Transfer the lamb** to a warmed serving platter. Cover with foil and let it stand for 10–15 minutes, for the meat to rest and the juices to settle (this "resting" time makes for the most succulent meat). Make the gravy. Discard the excess fat from the roasting tin, leaving the carrot and onion.

8 **Add the wine** to the tin and boil until it has reduced by half. Add the stock and boil, stirring to dissolve the juices from the bottom of the tin, until the gravy is concentrated and well flavoured. It will take 5–10 minutes. Keep warm over a gentle heat.

9 **Reheat the beans** if necessary. Finely chop the parsley and sprinkle it on the beans, if you like. Carve the tender lamb into thin slices and arrange them on warmed plates. Spoon a mound of the beans next to it. Serve the gravy separately.

Chicken en cocotte with Parmesan

COOKED IN A COVERED CASSEROLE to keep moist and with a simple, piquant sauce sharpened with lemon and given richness from cream. These small chickens are incredibly moist. Serve them with a selection of crisply cooked vegetables. The chickens can be cooked and kept with their pan juices, covered, in the refrigerator up to 24 hours. Reheat them for about 20 minutes in an oven preheated to 180°C (350°F/Gas 4), then make the sauce just before serving.

SERVES	**PREP**	**COOK**
SERVES 4	15-20 MINUTES	45-55 MINUTES

Ingredients

FOR THE CHICKEN

2 x 1kg (2¼lb) chickens

salt and pepper

2 lemons

45g (1½oz) butter

FOR THE CHEESE SAUCE

125ml (4fl oz) chicken stock

125ml (4fl oz) double cream

1 tsp cornflour or arrowroot

30g (1oz) grated Parmesan cheese

TRUSS THE CHICKENS

1 **Wipe the inside of the birds** with kitchen paper and season inside and out. With a small knife, remove the wishbone. Set each bird breast up and push the legs back and down. Insert a threaded trussing needle at the knee joint and push it through the bird and out through the other knee joint.

2 **Turn the bird over** so it is breast down. Pull the neck skin over the cavity and tuck the wing tips over it. Push the needle through both sections of 1 wing and into the neck skin. Continue under the backbone of the bird to the other side. Push the needle through the second wing in the same way, through both wing bones.

3 **Turn the bird on to its side**. Pull the ends of the string firmly together and tie them securely. Turn the bird breast up. Tuck the tail into the cavity of the bird and fold over the top skin. Push the needle through the skin.

4 **Loop the string** around 1 drumstick, under the breastbone and over the other drumstick. Tie the ends of the string together. Repeat with the other bird. Chickens hold a better shape and are easier to carve if you truss them.

COOK THE CHICKENS

5 **Heat the oven** to 190°C (375°F/Gas 5). Pare the zest from the lemons with a vegetable peeler, then cut the pieces into fine julienne, discarding any of the bitter white pith.

6 **Melt the butter** in the casserole. Add 1 chicken and brown it on all sides for 5-10 minutes. Transfer it to the platter and brown the second chicken. Return the first chicken to the casserole. Add the lemon zest and cover. Cook in the oven, turning occasionally so they cook evenly.

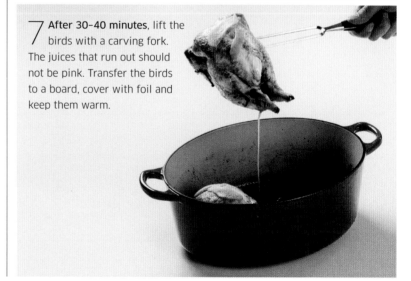

7 **After 30-40 minutes**, lift the birds with a carving fork. The juices that run out should not be pink. Transfer the birds to a board, cover with foil and keep them warm.

8 Remove the excess fat from the casserole and discard.

MAKE THE CHEESE SAUCE

9 **Add the stock t**o the casserole and bring to the boil, stirring to dissolve the pan juices. Boil for about 5 minutes, until well reduced. Strain it into a saucepan. Add the cream and whisk to mix, then bring just to a boil.

10 **Stir the cornflour** or arrowroot and 1 tbsp water together in a small bowl to form a smooth paste. Whisk in enough of the paste to thicken the sauce. It should lightly coat the back of a spoon.

11 **Take the sauce** from the heat and whisk in the Parmesan. Taste for seasoning. Keep warm.

FINISH THE CHICKEN

12 **Discard the trussing strings** from the chickens. Set a bird breast up on the board. Slice closely along the breastbone with a thin, sharp knife to loosen the meat. Cut along 1 side of the breastbone with poultry shears. Turn the bird over; cut along each side of the backbone and discard it. Repeat with the other bird. Set each chicken half on a warmed serving plate and spoon over the sauce.

Spicy tomato-bacon pasta

RED CHILLI BRINGS WARMTH to this dish. On the whole, Italians don't use a lot of chilli, but this arrabbiata sauce is an exception. The sauce can be made up to 2 days ahead, covered and refrigerated. Reheat it on top of the stove and cook the pasta just before serving.

SERVES	PREP	COOK
SERVES 6	35–40 MINS	30–40 MINS

Ingredients

125g (4½oz) thick-cut bacon rashers, sliced, or bacon lardons

375g (13oz) mushrooms, trimmed and sliced

2 garlic cloves, finely chopped

1 red chilli, deseeded and finely diced

leaves from 5–7 oregano sprigs, finely chopped

2 x 400g (14oz) cans chopped plum tomatoes

salt and pepper

500g (1lb 2oz) pasta quills

30g (1oz) butter

60g (2oz) grated Parmesan cheese

MAKE THE SAUCE

1 **Put the bacon** into a frying pan. Fry over low heat, stirring occasionally, for 5–7 minutes, until the bacon is lightly browned and the fat is rendered. Spoon off all but 3 tbsp of the fat. Increase the heat and add the mushrooms. Cook, stirring, for 3–5 minutes, until mushrooms have softened and most of the liquid has evaporated.

2 **Add the garlic,** chilli, oregano, chopped tomatoes, salt, and pepper. Bring to a boil, cover and simmer, stirring occasionally, for 25–30 minutes, until thick and rich. If necessary to thicken the sauce, continue to cook, uncovered, for a few minutes longer. Taste the sauce for seasoning.

COOK THE PASTA

3 **Fill a large pan** with cold water, bring to a boil, and add 1 tbsp salt. Add the pasta quills. Simmer until *al dente*, tender but still chewy, stirring occasionally. It should take 5-8 minutes, or cook according to the package directions. Drain in a colander.

FINISH THE DISH

4 **Put the quills** into a warmed serving bowl, and add the butter. Toss together until well coated. Spoon over the sauce and half the cheese. Toss together, then sprinkle over a little more Parmesan. Serve immediately, with the remaining cheese.

Pork chops with mustard sauce

WONDERFULLY COMFORTING, especially with mashed potatoes or buttered tagliatelle. Use a frying pan that will hold the pork chops snugly. If the pan is too big, the simmering liquid will not cover them sufficiently and they will dry out and may become tough. Use good-quality Dijon mustard here.

SERVES	PREP	COOK
SERVES 4	20-25 MINS	50-60 MINS

Ingredients

4 x 175g (6oz) pork chops

salt and pepper

125g (4½oz) streaky bacon rashers, sliced

30g (1oz) butter

1 tbsp plain flour

250ml (9fl oz) dry white wine

250ml (9fl oz) chicken stock or water, plus more if needed

1 bouquet garni

4 tbsp double cream

1 tbsp Dijon mustard, or to taste

leaves from 5-7 parsley sprigs, finely chopped

PREPARE THE PORK CHOPS

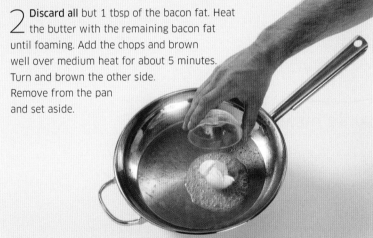

1 **Trim excess fat** from the chops and sprinkle them with pepper. Heat the bacon in a frying pan and cook, stirring occasionally, for 3-5 minutes, until crisp and the fat has rendered. With a slotted spoon, remove from the pan and drain on kitchen paper.

2 **Discard all** but 1 tbsp of the bacon fat. Heat the butter with the remaining bacon fat until foaming. Add the chops and brown well over medium heat for about 5 minutes. Turn and brown the other side. Remove from the pan and set aside.

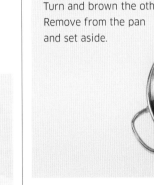

COOK THE CHOPS

3 **Remove the pan** from the heat and let cool slightly, then sprinkle in the flour, and cook, stirring, for 2-3 minutes. Whisk in the wine and stock or water. Add the bouquet garni and pepper and bring to a boil. Return the chops and bacon to the pan. Cover and simmer, stirring occasionally, for 5-10 minutes, until tender when pierced with a fork.

FINISH THE DISH

4 **Transfer the pork chops** to a plate and keep warm. Add the cream to the pan and bring just to a boil. Return the chops to the pan and heat gently for 2-3 minutes, so that the flavours blend.

5 **Arrange the chops,** bones pointing upwards, on a warmed platter. Taste the sauce for seasoning, whisking in more mustard if you like. Spoon the sauce over the chops, then sprinkle with the parsley.

Fisherman's pie

A HEARTY HOT MEAL and a traditional favourite. You'll find that everyone loves a good fish pie, and there are never any leftovers. One of the best ever dishes for entertaining, it can be made 1 day ahead and kept, covered, in the refrigerator.

SERVES	**PREP**	**COOK**
SERVES 6	35-45 MINS	20-30 MINS

Ingredients

625g (1lb 6oz) potatoes

salt and pepper

1 litre (1¾ pints) plus 4 tbsp milk

60g (2oz) butter

1 small onion

10 peppercorns

2 bay leaves

750g (1lb 10oz) skinned haddock fillets

90g (3oz) butter, plus more for the dish

60g (2oz) plain flour

leaves from 5-7 parsley sprigs, chopped

3 eggs, hard-boiled

125g (4½oz) cooked, peeled prawns

MAKE THE MASHED POTATO

1 **Wash and peel the potatoes.** Cut them into pieces. Half-fill a saucepan with water, add salt, then the potatoes, and bring to a boil. Simmer for 15-20 minutes, until tender. Drain thoroughly, then mash.

2 **Heat 4 tbsp milk** in a small saucepan. Add the butter, salt, and pepper and stir until mixed. Pour the hot milk mixture into the potatoes. Beat over medium heat for a few minutes, until fluffy. Taste for seasoning. Set aside.

COOK THE FISH

3 **Peel and quarter the onion.** Pour the remaining milk into a sauté pan, then add the peppercorns, bay leaves, and onion quarters.

4 **Bring to a boil,** then remove from the heat. Cover and let stand in a warm place to infuse for about 10 minutes.

5 **With a sharp knife,** cut each of the fillets across into pieces. Add the fish to the milk, cover and simmer for 5-10 minutes, depending on thickness; it should flake easily when tested with a fork .

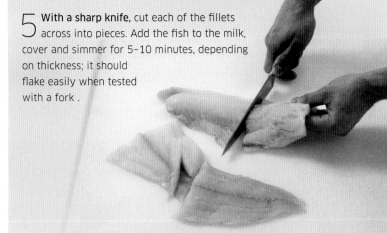

6 **Transfer the fish** to a large plate, using a slotted spoon; reserve the cooking liquid. Let the fish cool, then flake with a fork.

MAKE THE SAUCE

7 Gently melt the butter in a saucepan over medium heat. Whisk in the flour and cook for 30-60 seconds, until foaming. Remove from the heat. Pour the reserved fish cooking liquid through a sieve into the butter and flour mixture.

8 Whisk the liquid into the sauce, then return to the heat and cook, whisking constantly, until the sauce boils and thickens. Season with salt and pepper and simmer for 2 minutes. Stir in the parsley.

ASSEMBLE AND BAKE THE PIE

9 Preheat the oven to 180°C (350°F/Gas 4). Melt some butter and use it to butter a 2 litre (3½ pint) pie dish. Coarsely chop the hard-boiled eggs. Ladle a third of the sauce into the bottom of the dish.

10 Spoon the flaked haddock on top of the sauce, in an even layer. Cover with the remaining sauce, then distribute the prawns evenly on the surface. Sprinkle the chopped hard-boiled eggs over the top.

11 Spread the mashed potatoes on top, so it is covered completely. Bake in the heated oven for 20-30 minutes, until the potato topping is brown and the sauce bubbles around the edge. Serve hot from the dish, on to warmed plates.

 VARIATION: Individual fish crumbles

Rolled oats and Parmesan cheese add texture and flavour to this version of fish pies.

1 Follow the main recipe, replacing the potato topping with crumble topping. To make the crumble, sift 150g (5½oz) plain flour into a bowl. Cut 90g (3oz) butter into small pieces in the flour. Rub in the butter with your fingertips, lifting the mixture up so it is aerated as it floats back down into the bowl, until the mixture resembles fine crumbs. Make sure there are no large pieces of butter remaining in the mixture.

2 Chop the leaves from 3-5 additional parsley sprigs. Stir 40g (1½oz) rolled oats into the butter and flour, with the additional chopped parsley, 1 tbsp grated Parmesan cheese (or to taste), salt, and pepper. Stir together gently but very well, until all the flavours are evenly distributed throughout the crumble topping.

3 Butter 6 individual casserole dishes or large ramekins and layer the ingredients as directed in the main recipe. Sprinkle the crumble topping evenly over the pies and bake them for 20-25 minutes. If necessary, brown the individual fish crumbles under the grill for 1-2 minutes more, until golden and the sauce bubbles around the edges, being careful not to scorch the crumble.

Cabbage with chestnut and pork

AN OLD FAVOURITE, ideal for a cold day. It is far easier than you might imagine to assemble the dish, and everyone loves the rich stuffing. A tomato and mushroom sauce is the perfect complement.

SERVES	PREP	COOK
SERVES 6	35–40 MINS	50–60 MINS

Ingredients

FOR THE CABBAGE

1.4kg (3lb) head of Savoy cabbage

salt and pepper

125g (4½oz) lean, boneless pork

1 onion

2 slices of white bread

60g (2oz) butter

2 celery sticks, peeled and thinly sliced

500g (1lb 2oz) canned or vacuum-packed unsweetened chestnuts, chopped

leaves from 10 parsley sprigs, chopped

10–12 sage leaves, finely chopped

finely grated zest of 1 lemon

2 eggs

FOR THE SAUCE

2 tbsp vegetable oil

1 small onion, finely chopped

500g (1lb 2oz) tomatoes, chopped

1 tbsp tomato purée

1 garlic clove, finely chopped

1 bouquet garni

granulated sugar

125g (4½oz) mushrooms, sliced

PREPARE THE CABBAGE

1 **Cut the outside leaf** from the base of the cabbage stalk, and carefully peel the leaf from the head, being careful not to tear it. Repeat, until you have removed the ten largest cabbage leaves. Wash the leaves very well in cold water to remove any soil or grit.

2 **Bring a large saucepan** of water to a boil. Add salt, then immerse the ten large cabbage leaves in the water and blanch for 1 minute, to soften them. With a slotted spoon, transfer the leaves to a bowl of cold water to stop the cooking.

3 **Trim and discard** the stalk from the remaining cabbage head, and cook it in the boiling water for 3-4 minutes. Transfer it to a bowl of cold water to stop the cooking. When cool, remove and drain thoroughly, stalk-end down, in the colander.

4 **When the leaves are cool,** drain and carefully pat each dry with kitchen paper. Remove and discard the thick rib at the centre of each large cabbage leaf with a sharp knife. Slice the cabbage head in half. Cut a wedge around the core in each half of cabbage and remove and discard it. Shred the leaves reasonably fine.

MAKE THE STUFFING

5 **Cut the pork** into 2-3 pieces and the onion into quarters. Work the pork and onion through the fine blade of a mincer, or in a food processor.

6 **Trim and discard** the crusts from the bread. Work to crumbs in a food processor. Melt the butter in a frying pan, add the shredded cabbage, and cook, stirring, for 7–10 minutes, until tender. Transfer to a large bowl.

7 **Put the minced pork** and onion into the frying pan with the celery. Cook, stirring occasionally, until the minced pork is crumbled and brown; it should take 5–7 minutes.

8 **Add the breadcrumbs,** chestnuts, chopped herbs, lemon zest, salt, and pepper to the shredded cabbage. Add the pork and stir well together. Taste for seasoning. Lightly beat the eggs and stir into the stuffing.

STUFF AND COOK THE CABBAGE

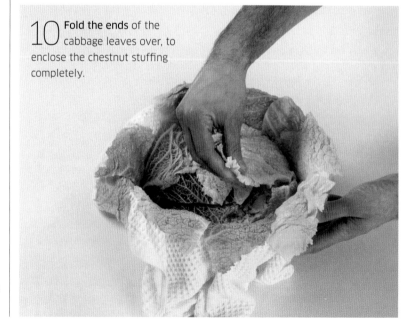

9 **Line a large bowl** with a damp tea towel. Arrange 9 blanched cabbage leaves in an overlapping layer around the inside. Allow about 5cm (2in) of the leaves to extend above the rim. Set the last leaf in the bottom of the bowl. Spoon in the stuffing, then press it down gently.

10 **Fold the ends** of the cabbage leaves over, to enclose the chestnut stuffing completely.

MAKE THE SAUCE

11 **Gather the ends** of the cloth over the top of the cabbage, and tie them together with a piece of the string to make a tight ball.

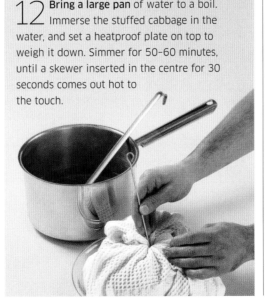

12 **Bring a large pan** of water to a boil. Immerse the stuffed cabbage in the water, and set a heatproof plate on top to weigh it down. Simmer for 50–60 minutes, until a skewer inserted in the centre for 30 seconds comes out hot to the touch.

13 **Heat half the oil** in a frying pan. Add the onion and cook, stirring, for 2–3 minutes, until soft. Stir in the tomatoes, tomato purée, garlic, bouquet garni, salt, pepper, and a pinch of sugar, and cook, stirring occasionally, for 8–10 minutes, until fairly thick.

14 **Sieve the tomato mixture** into a bowl, pressing down to extract the pulp. Wipe the frying pan, heat the remaining oil, and sauté the mushrooms until tender. Stir in the tomato sauce and taste for seasoning.

15 **Lift the cabbage** from the pan, drain and let cool slightly. Unwrap and set it, stalk down, on a warmed plate. Cut into wedges to serve. Serve the sauce separately.

Baked rigatoni with meatballs

A PERENNIAL FAMILY FAVOURITE. Italians would use finger-length macaroni called mezzani, but other shapes of pasta tubes, such as penne, make a fine alternative. This is a very convenient recipe as the whole dish can be baked 1 day ahead, covered, and kept refrigerated. Reheat it in an oven at 190°C (375°F/Gas 5) for 20 minutes.

SERVES
SERVES 6-8

PREP
45-50 MINS

COOK
30-40 MINS

Ingredients

FOR THE SAUCE AND PASTA

2 x 400g cans chopped plum tomatoes

3 garlic cloves, finely chopped

leaves from 1 bunch of basil, chopped

salt and pepper

375g (13oz) rigatoni

FOR THE MEATBALLS

500g (1lb 2oz) lean minced beef

125g (4½oz) grated Parmesan cheese

leaves from 3-5 flat-leaf parsley sprigs, chopped

juice of ½ lemon

1 egg

3 tbsp olive oil, plus more for the dish

MAKE THE TOMATO-BASIL SAUCE

1 Put the tomatoes in a frying pan and add two-thirds of the garlic, basil, and salt. Stir over medium heat for 10-12 minutes, until thickened. Transfer to a food processor, and purée. Set aside. Wipe the frying pan clean.

MAKE THE MEATBALLS

2 Put the minced beef, a quarter of the Parmesan, the parsley, remaining garlic, lemon juice, salt, and pepper in a bowl. Add the egg. Mix all the ingredients in the bowl with your hands until they are thoroughly combined.

3 Test the mixture for seasoning: heat 1 tbsp oil in a frying pan, add a small spoon of meat mixture, and fry until brown on both sides. Taste and adjust the seasoning of the remaining mixture, if necessary. Shape the mixture into meatballs about 2cm (¾in) in diameter, wetting the palms of your hands so shaping the meat is easier.

4 Heat the remaining oil in the frying pan. Add the meatballs, making sure they are not crowded. (If necessary, fry them in batches.) Fry the meatballs briskly, turning, for 2-4 minutes, until they are brown on the outside and still pink inside. Transfer to a large plate with a slotted spoon. Set aside.

MAKE THE PASTA AND **BAKE**

5 **Preheat the oven** to 190°C (375°F/Gas 5). Brush the inside of a 2 litre (3½ pint) deep baking dish or souffle dish lightly with a little olive oil.

6 **Fill a large saucepan** with water, bring to a boil, and add 1 tbsp salt. Add the pasta to the pan and simmer for 8–10 minutes, until *al dente*, tender but still chewy, or according to package directions. Stir occasionally to keep from sticking.

7 **Drain the pasta** in a colander, rinse with hot water, and drain again thoroughly. Return the pasta to the saucepan and pour in the tomato-basil sauce. Gently stir the pasta and sauce together, until the pasta is well coated.

8 **Spoon about a third** of the pasta and sauce into the prepared dish, and level the surface. Spoon half the meatballs on top. Sprinkle with a third of the remaining cheese. Top with half the remaining pasta, and then the rest of the meatballs. Sprinkle with half the remaining Parmesan.

9 **Add the remaining pasta** and top with the remaining Parmesan. Bake in the heated oven for 30–40 minutes, until very hot and the top is browned. Let stand for about 15 minutes, so the flavours blend together. Sprinkle with a little shredded basil, if you like, and serve warm.

 VARIATION: Baked ziti with mozzarella and olives

Anchovies spice the sauce in this version.

1 Chop eight anchovy fillets very finely. Make the tomato sauce as directed in the main recipe, adding the chopped anchovies to the tomatoes with the garlic. You will find the anchovies disappear as they will 'melt' into the sauce. Omit the basil and the meatballs. Stone 195g (6¾oz) oil-cured black olives. Cut 250g (9oz) mozzarella cheese into small, fairly even cubes. Oil the dish as directed.

2 Cook 375g (13oz) chunky ziti as for the pasta in the main recipe, or according to the package directions, and drain thoroughly. Layer the pasta, sauce, and fillings as directed, using the olives in place of the meatballs and the mozzarella cubes in place of the Parmesan, spreading it throughout the dish and using it as a topping as well.

3 Bake as directed for 20–25 minutes, until the pasta dish is very hot, golden brown and bubbling, and the cheese has melted. Set aside to rest for about 15 minutes, then serve on warmed plates. The piquancy given from the olives and anchovies is delicious next to the creamy, sweet mozzarella.

Aunt Sally's meat loaf

A TRUE AMERICAN CLASSIC, great with mashed potatoes and ketchup or cranberry sauce. It makes an excellent dish for family gatherings, as it can be made 2 days ahead and kept, covered, in the refrigerator. Reheat it for 20 minutes in an oven preheated to 180°C (350°F/Gas 4) for a hot dish, though this is also excellent sliced and served cold as part of a buffet spread.

SERVES	PREP	COOK
SERVES 4-6	25-30 MINS	1-1½ HRS

Ingredients

175g (6oz) spinach

salt and pepper

375g (13oz) streaky bacon rashers

2 eggs

6 slices of white bread

750g (1lb 10oz) minced beef

250g (9oz) minced veal

1 large onion, finely chopped

4 garlic cloves, finely chopped

leaves from 3-4 thyme sprigs

leaves from 3-4 rosemary sprigs, chopped

1 tbsp Worcestershire sauce

PREPARE THE INGREDIENTS

1 **Remove the tough ribs** and stalks from the spinach. Wash it well in a sink of water, then repeat, until all traces of grit and soil are gone. Half-fill a saucepan with water and bring to a boil. Add salt, then the spinach and simmer for 2-3 minutes, just until tender. Do not overcook, or the spinach will lose its vivid colour and the flavour will dull.

2 **Drain the spinach** in a colander, rinse with cold water to stop the cooking and retain the bright green colour, and drain again thoroughly. Squeeze the spinach hard between your hands to remove all excess water from the leaves, then chop.

3 **Cut the bacon** into tiny strips, reserving 4 neat rashers for the top of the meat loaf. Lightly beat the eggs in a small bowl until evenly blended. Trim off and discard the crusts from the bread. Work the bread slices in the food processor or a blender, using the pulse button, until they form even crumbs, then tip them into a large bowl that is big enough to comfortably hold all the remaining ingredients.

MIX AND BAKE THE MEAT LOAF

4 **Preheat the oven** to 180°C (350°F/Gas 4). Add the minced meat, chopped spinach, onion, garlic, thyme, rosemary, Worcestershire sauce, salt, and pepper to the large bowl and mix.

5 **Add the beaten eggs** and lightly mix them in. To test for seasoning, fry a spoonful of the mixture in a frying pan until browned on both sides. Taste it and add more seasoning to the remaining mixture if necessary.

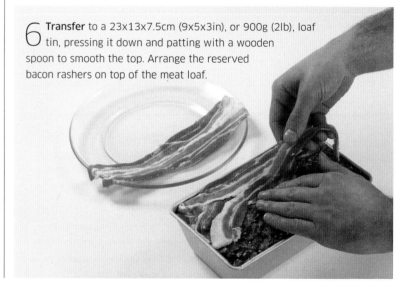

6 **Transfer** to a 23x13x7.5cm (9x5x3in), or 900g (2lb), loaf tin, pressing it down and patting with a wooden spoon to smooth the top. Arrange the reserved bacon rashers on top of the meat loaf.

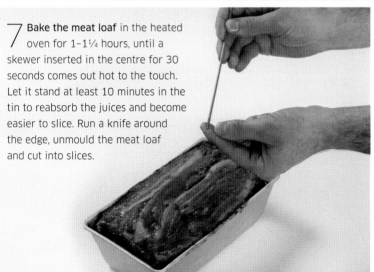

7 Bake the meat loaf in the heated oven for 1–1¼ hours, until a skewer inserted in the centre for 30 seconds comes out hot to the touch. Let it stand at least 10 minutes in the tin to reabsorb the juices and become easier to slice. Run a knife around the edge, unmould the meat loaf and cut into slices.

VARIATION: Pork loaf with apricots

A sweet yet savoury version.

1 Soak 150g (5½oz) dried apricots in hot water to cover until plump. It should take about 15 minutes, but can be left for longer as they will only plump up more. Coarsely chop three-quarters of the volume of apricots and cut the rest in half.

2 Prepare the meat loaf ingredients as directed, omitting the spinach and bacon, and substituting minced pork for minced beef.

3 Put half the meat loaf mixture in the pan and spread the chopped apricots on top. Cover with the remaining meat and arrange the apricot halves on top. Bake and finish as directed in the main recipe. Take care that the apricots on top of the loaf do not threaten to burn; if they do, cover with a layer of foil.

Spinach gnocchi in tomato cream

THESE NEVER FAIL to please. The shape of the gnocchi, which are made with potato for a light texture, ensures that they both cook evenly and hold on to the sauce well. The tomato sauce can be made to the end of step 2 up to 1 day ahead and kept, tightly covered, in the refrigerator. Add the cream and bake the spinach gnocchi just before serving the dish.

SERVES
SERVES 6-8

PREP
50-55 MINS

COOK
30-40 MINS

Ingredients

FOR THE SAUCE

45g (1½oz) butter, plus more for the dish

1 small onion, finely chopped

1 carrot, finely chopped

1 celery stick, finely chopped

2 x 400g (14oz) cans chopped plum tomatoes

salt and pepper

250ml (8fl oz) double cream

1 pinch of ground nutmeg

FOR THE GNOCCHI

1kg (2¼lb) baking potatoes

250g (9oz) fresh or 150g (5½oz) defrosted spinach

125g (4½oz) plain flour, plus more if needed

MAKE THE SAUCE

1 **Melt the butter** in a frying pan. Add the onion, carrot, and celery, and cook over medium heat, stirring, for 7-10 minutes, until tender.

2 **Add the tomatoes** to the pan with any juice, salt, and pepper, and simmer, stirring occasionally, for 25-35 minutes, until thick. Transfer to a food processor and purée until smooth. Wipe the frying pan clean.

MAKE THE GNOCCHI

3 **Peel the potatoes,** and cut each one into several pieces. Put them in a saucepan of cold, salted water, cover and bring to a boil. Simmer for 15-20 minutes, until very tender when pierced with the tip of a knife.

4 **Drain the potatoes** until completely dry. If the potatoes seem at all moist, spread them on a baking sheet and let dry in a low oven with the door open for 5-10 minutes. Mash the potatoes in the pan until there are no lumps remaining.

5 **Prepare the fresh spinach,** if using: discard the tough ribs and stalks, then wash the leaves. Bring another saucepan of cold, salted water to a boil. Add the spinach and simmer for 1-2 minutes. Drain the spinach, rinse with cold water, and drain again.

6 **Squeeze the cooked fresh spinach,** or defrosted spinach, in your fist to remove all excess water. Purée the spinach in a food processor, or chop it finely with a sharp knife.

7 **Add the spinach** to the potatoes with the flour, salt, and pepper, and mix together well. Taste for seasoning. Transfer to a lightly floured work surface, and knead lightly to form a dough, working in a little more flour to bind the mixture, if necessary.

8 **To test the consistency,** roll a 2cm (¾in) ball of dough, drop it into a saucepan of simmering water, and cook until it floats to the surface. If the gnocchi falls apart, add about 2 tbsp more flour to the dough, then test again. If the gnocchi holds, shape the remaining dough.

SHAPE AND COOK THE GNOCCHI

9 **Divide the dough** into 12 equal pieces. Lightly flour your hands; roll each piece into a cylinder about 1cm (½in) in diameter. Then cut each into logs 2cm (¾in) long. Lightly flour a baking sheet. Hold a fork in one hand with the concave side towards you. With the thumb of your other hand, roll each piece of dough along the prongs, then drop on to the baking sheet.

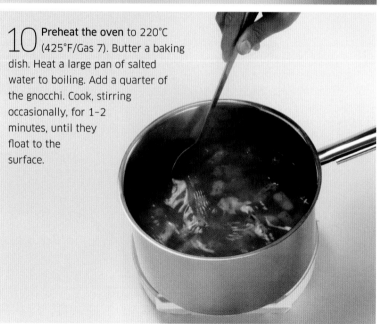

10 **Preheat the oven** to 220°C (425°F/Gas 7). Butter a baking dish. Heat a large pan of salted water to boiling. Add a quarter of the gnocchi. Cook, stirring occasionally, for 1-2 minutes, until they float to the surface.

11 **Transfer the gnocchi** to drain on paper towels, then place in the baking dish. Continue cooking the gnocchi in batches.

ASSEMBLE AND BAKE THE DISH

12 **Reheat the sauce** in a frying pan until it is piping hot, but not boiling. Remove from the heat, and evenly stir in the cream. Do not heat the sauce on the stove top again after this point, or it may separate. Season to taste with salt, pepper, and a little nutmeg. If your tomatoes were not very sweet, you may also find you need to add a pinch of sugar, so check it and see what you would prefer.

13 **Spoon the sauce** evenly over the gnocchi in the baking dish, making sure some runs under the dumplings as well as on top. This will prevent the gnocchi from sticking to the dish when in the oven. Bake in the heated oven until very hot and the top is starting to brown; it should only take about 5-7 minutes. Check that the dish is hot all the way to the centre: insert a metal skewer right to the middle of the dish; the tip should be very hot to the touch when withdrawn. Serve the gnocchi immediately on to warmed plates, sprinkled with chopped flat-leaf parsley to add a splash of colour, if you like.

Chicago deep-dish pizza

A HEARTY PIZZA, dating back to 1940s Chicago. Not only will the kneading prove enormously therapeutic, but the pizza's generous depths of Italian sausage and melting mozzarella could have been designed to soothe the soul. The dough can be made, kneaded, and left to rise in the refrigerator overnight, if it's more convenient.

SERVES
SERVES 6-8

PREP
35-40 MINS
PLUS RISING

COOK
20-25 MINS

Ingredients

FOR THE DOUGH

2½ tsp dried yeast, or 15g (½oz) fresh yeast

500g (1lb 2oz) unbleached strong white flour, plus more if needed

2 tsp salt

3 tbsp olive oil, plus more for the bowl and pan

2-3 tbsp polenta (fine yellow cornmeal)

FOR THE SAUCE

375g (13oz) mild Italian sausage

1 tbsp olive oil

3 garlic cloves, finely chopped

2 x 400g cans chopped plum tomatoes

pepper

leaves from 7-10 flat-leaf parsley sprigs, chopped

175g (6oz) mozzarella cheese

MAKE THE DOUGH

1 In a small bowl, sprinkle or crumble the yeast over 4 tbsp lukewarm water. Let stand until dissolved for about 5 minutes, stirring once.

2 Put the flour on to a work surface with the salt. Make a large well in the centre and add the dissolved yeast, 300ml (½ pint) lukewarm water, and the oil. With your fingertips, work the liquid ingredients in the centre of the well until thoroughly and evenly mixed. Begin to draw in the flour.

3 Continue to draw in the flour and work it into the other ingredients, to form a smooth dough. It should be soft and slightly sticky.

4 Sprinkle the dough and your hands with flour, and begin to knead by holding the dough with 1 hand, and pushing it away from you with the other. Peel the dough from the surface, give it a quarter turn, and knead for 5-7 minutes, until very smooth, elastic and forms a ball. If the dough sticks while kneading, flour the work surface.

5 Brush a large bowl with oil. Put the dough in the bowl and flip it so the surface is lightly oiled. Cover with a damp tea towel and let the dough rise in a warm place for 1-1½ hours, until doubled in bulk.

MAKE THE SAUCE

6 Slit the side of each sausage and push out the meat, discarding the casing. Heat the oil in a sauté pan. Add the sausage meat, and fry over medium-high heat, breaking up the meat with the wooden spoon, for 5-7 minutes, until cooked. Reduce the heat to medium, remove the meat from the pan, and pour off all but 1 tbsp of the fat.

7 Stir the garlic into the pan and fry for about 30 seconds, until fragrant. Return the sausage and stir in the tomatoes, salt, pepper, and all but 1 tbsp of the parsley.

8 Cook, stirring occasionally, for 10-15 minutes, until the sauce has thickened. Remove the sauce from the heat, taste for seasoning, and let cool completely. Chop or tear the mozzarella into small chunks.

ASSEMBLE AND BAKE THE PIZZA

9 Brush a 35cm (14in) pizza pan, or 2 x 23cm (9in) cake tins, with oil. Sprinkle the polenta in the pan or tins, and turn it to coat the bottom and side, then turn upside down and tap to remove the excess. Turn the dough on to a lightly floured work surface and knock out the air for 15-20 seconds. Cover, and let rest for about 5 minutes.

10 Shape the dough into a loose ball. With a rolling pin, roll the ball into a round or rounds to fit your pan or tins. Working carefully, wrap the dough around the rolling pin and drape it over the pan or tins.

11 **With your hands,** press the dough into the bottom of the pan or tins, and 2.5cm (1in) up the side, to form a rim.

12 **Cover with a dry tea towel,** and let rise for about 20 minutes. Preheat the oven to 230°C (450°F/Gas 8). Heat a baking sheet in the oven. Spread the sauce over the dough, leaving a border. Sprinkle over the cheese and remaining parsley. Bake for 20–25 minutes, until crisp and golden.

Spiced lamb pies

A LEAVENED DOUGH WRAPPED around a delicious lamb filling, similar to snacks found all around the Middle East. The filling can be prepared, covered and refrigerated up to 1 day ahead. You can also make the dough in an electric mixer fitted with a dough hook, to save kneading.

SERVES	PREP	COOK
MAKES 12	40-45 MINS PLUS RISING	20-25 MINS

Ingredients

FOR THE DOUGH

1 tsp dried yeast, or 6g (⅕oz) fresh yeast

2 tsp olive oil, plus more for bowl and baking sheet

1 tsp salt

60g (2oz) strong wholemeal flour

250g (9oz) unbleached strong, white flour, plus more if needed

FOR THE FILLING

2 tbsp olive oil

375g (13oz) minced lamb

salt and pepper

3 large garlic cloves, finely chopped

1cm (½in) piece of fresh root ginger, finely chopped

1 onion, finely chopped

½ tsp ground coriander

¼ tsp ground cumin

¼ tsp ground turmeric

large pinch of cayenne pepper

2 tomatoes, peeled, deseeded, and chopped

leaves from 5-7 coriander sprigs, finely chopped

MAKE THE DOUGH AND LET IT RISE

1 **In a bowl**, sprinkle the yeast over 4 tbsp warm water. Let stand, stirring once, for 5 minutes. Put the yeast, 250ml (8fl oz) lukewarm water, oil, and salt in a bowl. Mix in the wholemeal with half the strong white flour.

2 **Add the remaining** strong white flour, 60g (2oz) at a time, mixing after each addition, until the dough pulls away from the side of the bowl. Turn on to a floured work surface.

3 **Holding the dough** with one hand, press firmly down into the dough with the heel of your other hand, pushing away from you. Peel it from the work surface in one piece, fold it over, and give it a quarter turn.

4 **Continue kneading** the dough, until very smooth and elastic. If the dough sticks while kneading, flour the work surface. Press the dough with your finger; it will spring back when it has been sufficiently kneaded.

5 **Wash a large bowl** and brush it with oil. Put the dough in the bowl, and flip it, so the surface is lightly oiled. Cover with a damp tea towel and let rise in a warm place for 1-1½ hours, until doubled in bulk.

PREPARE THE FILLING

6 **Heat the oil** in a sauté pan. Add the lamb, season and stir over medium-high heat, until evenly browned. With a slotted spoon, transfer to a bowl. Reduce the heat to medium, and pour off all but 2 tbsp of the fat.

7 **Add the garlic** and ginger and fry for 30 seconds, until fragrant. Add the onion and stir until soft. Add the ground coriander, cumin, turmeric, cayenne, lamb and tomatoes, cover and cook for 10 minutes, until thickened.

8 **Remove the pan** from the heat. Stir in the chopped coriander leaves and taste for seasoning. Let the filling cool, then taste again: it should be well seasoned, so adjust if necessary.

SHAPE THE PIES

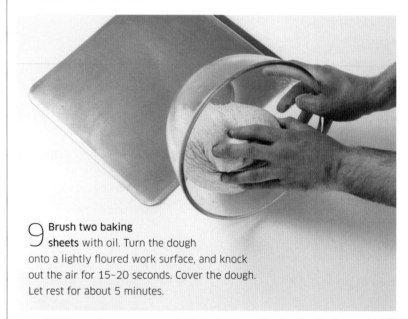

9 **Brush two baking sheets** with oil. Turn the dough onto a lightly floured work surface, and knock out the air for 15-20 seconds. Cover the dough. Let rest for about 5 minutes.

10 **Cut the dough** in half. Shape one piece into a cylinder about 5cm (2in) in diameter. Cut into six pieces, and cover them. Repeat to shape and divide the remaining dough.

11 **Shape a piece of dough** into a ball. With a rolling pin, roll into a 10cm (4in) round. Spoon some of the lamb into the centre of the round, leaving a 2.5cm (1in) border. Lift the dough up and over the filling, to form a triangular parcel.

12 **Pinch the edges** with your fingers to seal. Place the pie on a prepared baking sheet. Repeat to shape and fill the remaining dough.

BAKE THE PIES

13 **Cover the pies** with a clean, dry tea towel, and let rise in a warm place until they have puffed up once more. It should take about 20 minutes, but will depend on the weather, humidity, and the temperature of the room, so be patient and experiment until your knowledge increases. Do not give up and bake them before they have properly risen! Meanwhile, preheat the oven to 230°C (450°F/Gas 8).

14 **Bake the pies** in the heated oven until the bottoms are golden brown and ring hollow when tapped with a finger. It will take 10–15 minutes. Serve the pies warm from the oven, with a spoonful or two of Greek yogurt on the side, if you like.

Spinach-stuffed veal

A STUFFING OF SPINACH, Parmesan, and walnuts enlivens this Italian favourite. If you like, you can substitute beef, pork, chicken, or turkey for the veal here. The rolls can be cooked up to 2 days ahead, covered and refrigerated, or they can be frozen. Their flavour will mellow.

SERVES	PREP	COOK
SERVES 4	45–50 MINS	30–40 MINS

Ingredients

FOR THE STUFFING

500g (1lb 2oz) fresh or 300g (10½oz) frozen and defrosted spinach

2 tbsp olive oil

8 garlic cloves, finely chopped

45g (1½oz) walnuts, chopped

30g (1oz) grated Parmesan cheese

salt and pepper

freshly grated nutmeg

FOR THE VEAL

8 veal escalopes, total weight about 625g (1lb 6oz)

2 tbsp olive oil, plus more if needed

1 onion, thinly sliced

1 carrot, thinly sliced

2 celery sticks, thinly sliced

250ml (9fl oz) dry white wine

250ml (9fl oz) chicken stock, plus more if needed

MAKE THE STUFFING

1 **If using fresh spinach**, trim and wash it. Bring a saucepan of water to the boil, add the spinach and simmer for 1–2 minutes, then drain. Squeeze either fresh or defrosted spinach to remove excess water, then chop.

2 **Heat the oil** in a frying pan, and add the spinach. Stir until any moisture has evaporated. Remove from the heat, add half the garlic, the walnuts, Parmesan, salt, pepper, and nutmeg. Stir well, and taste for seasoning.

MAKE THE VEAL ROLLS

3 **If necessary**, flatten the escalopes: put the veal slices between two sheets of baking parchment. Gently pound to 3mm (⅛in) thick with a rolling pin. Lay one escalope on a work surface and season. Spread about one-eighth of the spinach stuffing on top.

4 **Roll up the meat**, tucking in the ends. Repeat with the remaining escalopes and stuffing. Tie up the rolls in neat packages, or secure each with a wooden toothpick, threading it in and out along the seam.

COOK THE VEAL

5 **Heat the olive oil** in a sauté pan, and add the veal rolls. Cook over high heat, turning occasionally, until well browned on all sides, 2–3 minutes. Transfer to a plate and set aside; slice to serve when the sauce is ready.

6 **Stir the onion** and remaining garlic into the pan, and cook until softened. Add the carrot and celery. Reduce the heat and cook for 8–10 minutes, until tender. Pour in the wine, bring to a boil and simmer to reduce by half.

7 **Return the veal** to the pan, and add the stock. Cover and simmer for 30–40 minutes, until tender. Strain the liquid into a saucepan, reserving the vegetables, and boil until reduced to 175ml (6fl oz); taste and serve.

Prawn risotto

SMOOTH AND CREAMY, but slightly firm to the bite. Perfect for a cold night. You have to stir a risotto constantly, to release the starch from the grains of rice and achieve the blissfully smooth texture, but the results are well worth it. Serve it the moment it is ready.

SERVES	PREP	COOK
SERVES 6	15-20 MINS	25-30 MINS

Ingredients

500g (1lb 2oz) small or medium raw prawns

90ml (3fl oz) olive oil

2 garlic cloves, finely chopped

leaves from 1 small bunch of flat-leaf parsley, chopped

salt and pepper

4 tbsp dry white wine

1 litre (1¾ pints) fish or chicken stock

1 onion, finely chopped

420g (15oz) arborio rice

PREPARE THE PRAWNS AND COOKING LIQUID

1 **Make a shallow cut** along the back of each prawn with a small knife, and remove the dark intestinal vein. Heat a third of the oil in a saucepan, and add the peeled prawns, garlic, parsley, salt, and pepper.

2 **Cook, stirring,** just until the prawns turn pink (a matter of 1–2 minutes). Pour in the wine and stir thoroughly. Transfer the prawns to a bowl; set aside. Simmer the liquid in the pan for 2–3 minutes, until reduced by three-quarters. Add the stock and 250ml (9fl oz) water, and heat to boiling. Keep the liquid simmering.

MAKE THE RISOTTO

3 **Heat half the remaining oil** in a large saucepan. Add the onion and cook, stirring, for 2–3 minutes, until soft but not brown. Add the rice, and stir until shiny and coated with oil. Ladle in just enough of the simmering liquid to cover the rice.

4 **Stir the rice** constantly until all the liquid is absorbed. Add more liquid just to cover the rice and simmer, stirring, until completely absorbed. Continue adding liquid to the rice in this way. Stop when the rice is *al dente*: just tender, but firm to the bite; it should take 25–30 minutes.

FINISH THE DISH

5 **Stir in the prawns** and the remaining olive oil, and season with salt and pepper, to taste (you may not need much salt). Spoon the risotto into warmed bowls, and serve immediately.

Ham with prunes in a wine sauce

PRUNES ADD SWEETNESS TO THIS DISH, from the Chablis region of France. A white Chablis is the obvious choice for the sauce, though any good-quality flinty dry white will do. It may sound like an unusual dish, but it is deeply comforting. Serve with mashed potatoes on a cold night.

SERVES	PREP	COOK
SERVES 6	40–45 MINS	20–25 MINS

Ingredients

**FOR THE VINEGAR
AND CARAMEL SYRUP**

100g (3½oz) caster sugar

125ml (4fl oz) red wine vinegar

FOR THE SAUCE

135g (5oz) stoned prunes

4 tbsp marc de Bourgogne, or brandy

45g (1½oz) butter

4 shallots, finely chopped

2 tbsp plain flour

250ml (9fl oz) dry white wine

250ml (9fl oz) chicken or beef stock

½ tsp black peppercorns, coarsely crushed

salt

125ml (4fl oz) double cream

1kg (2¼lb) piece of cooked ham

MAKE THE VINEGAR AND CARAMEL SYRUP

1 **Gently heat the sugar** with 125ml (4fl oz) water in a heavy-based saucepan until dissolves. Increase the heat and boil, without stirring, until the syrup starts to turn golden at the edge.

2 **Reduce the heat,** and cook until the syrup becomes a deep golden caramel. Remove the saucepan from the heat, and let the bubbles subside.

3 **Slowly add the vinegar,** standing well back to avoid the strong fumes and spluttering syrup. Simmer, stirring occasionally, for 5–8 minutes, to dissolve the caramel and reduce by half. Remove from the heat.

PREPARE THE SAUCE

4 Halve the prunes, and put them in a small saucepan with the marc or brandy. Heat gently for 5-8 minutes, or until they plump up. Using a slotted spoon, transfer the prunes to a plate; reserve the delicious, fruity and boozy liquid.

5 Melt the butter in a medium saucepan. Add the shallots and cook, stirring occasionally, for 3-5 minutes, until softened but not browned. Stir in the flour and cook for 30-60 seconds, until foaming; stir constantly, so the flour does not catch on the bottom of the pan. Remove the saucepan from the heat, and let cool slightly.

6 Whisk in the wine, return to the heat, and simmer for 1 minute. Add the stock, prune soaking liquid, crushed peppercorns, and salt. Simmer, whisking constantly, for 10-12 minutes, until the sauce thickens and lightly coats the back of a spoon.

7 Whisk the vinegar and caramel syrup into the sauce, and continue simmering, until it is again thick enough to coat the back of a spoon; it should take 5-10 minutes longer. Be gentle, as you don't want the caramel to darken any further. Stir in the cream. Reserving a few prunes for garnish, add the rest to the pan, and taste for seasoning.

FINISH THE DISH

8 Preheat the oven to 180°C (350°F/Gas 4). Brush a gratin dish with melted butter, to keep the ham from sticking to the dish. Cut the ham into 6 equal slices with a finely serrated or very sharp knife, making sure to err on the side of thick, generous slices. Remember this is supposed to be comfort food, after all.

9 Arrange the ham slices evenly in the dish, overlapping them slightly. Ladle over the rich wine sauce to coat every slice of ham, bearing in mind that any uncoated pieces are more likely to catch and burn in the oven. Bake in the heated oven until the dish is hot all the way through and the sauce is gently bubbling. It should take 20-25 minutes, but check occasionally that the ham is not scorching on the top; this dish should have a sweet, mellow flavour and it may be tainted by any charring. If you see that the top is threatening to burn before the dish is hot all the way through, cover it loosely with a sheet of foil.

10 Garnish the ham with the reserved prune halves, and serve from the gratin dish with mashed or parsley potatoes, if you like. Due to the sweetness of the ham and prunes, mashed potatoes flavoured with a little Dijon mustard, to cut through the richness, would make an excellent accompaniment.

Country terrine

A RICH MIXTURE, deeply reassuring to have at hand in the refrigerator in case of unexpected guests or hunger pangs. Even better, it can be made up to 5 days ahead and kept, covered, in the refrigerator. The flavour will only improve.

SERVES SERVES 8-10	**PREP** 1¼ HRS PLUS CHILLING	**COOK** 1¼-1½ HRS

Ingredients

1 thick slice cooked ham, weighing about 125g (4½oz)

2 tbsp brandy

salt and pepper

15g (½oz) butter

1 onion, very finely chopped

2 garlic cloves, finely chopped

leaves from 2-3 thyme sprigs

125g (4½oz) chicken livers, trimmed and chopped

625g (1lb 6oz) minced pork, part fat, part lean

250g (9oz) minced veal

¼ tsp ground allspice

pinch of ground nutmeg

pinch of ground cloves

2 eggs

250g (9oz) fat bacon rashers

1 bay leaf

45g (1½oz) plain flour

8-10 gherkins, to serve

crusty bread, to serve

MARINATE THE HAM

1 Place the slice of cooked ham on a chopping board and slice it into long strips about 1cm (½in) wide. Combine the ham, brandy and salt and pepper in a bowl. Cover and let marinate for 1 hour. Meanwhile, prepare the remaining ingredients.

MAKE THE TERRINE MIX

2 Melt the butter in a frying pan, add the onion and cook, stirring occasionally, for 3-5 minutes, until soft and brown. Turn into a bowl; let cool.

3 Add the garlic, thyme, chicken livers, minced pork, minced veal, allspice, nutmeg, cloves, and salt and pepper. Mix with a wooden spoon. Crack the eggs into a small bowl, beat to mix, then add them to the meat. Add the marinade from the ham.

4 Beat the mixture for 1-2 minutes, until it draws from the side of the bowl. Wipe the frying pan with kitchen paper. Add a little of the meat and fry for 1-2 minutes, until browned on both sides. Taste, and add more spices and salt and pepper if needed. It should be quite spicy.

ASSEMBLE AND BAKE THE TERRINE

5 Preheat the oven to 180°C (350°F/Gas 4). Set aside a third of the bacon and use the rest to line the bottom and longer sides of a 30x7.5x7.5cm (12x3x3in) terrine mould.

6 Spoon half the meat mixture into the terrine, then arrange the ham strips lengthways, end to end, on the top. Spread on the remaining meat mixture, fold over the bacon overhanging the sides, then top with the reserved bacon and bay leaf. Cover.

7 Put the flour and 2-3 tbsp water into a small bowl and mix together to make a soft smooth paste. Using your fingers, seal the gap between the rim of the mould and the lid with the paste.

8 **Set the mould** in a roasting tin. Add boiling water to come halfway up the sides. Bring this water bath to a boil on top of the stove, then carefully transfer the terrine in the tin to the oven.

9 **Bake** for 1¼–1½ hours, until a metal skewer inserted into the terrine for 30 seconds is hot to the touch when withdrawn. Remove the terrine from the water bath and let it cool to tepid. Remove the lid, cover the terrine, and set a 500g (1lb 2oz) weight on top. Chill for at least 1 day to allow the flavours to mellow.

FINISH THE TERRINE

10 **With a metal spoon,** scrape away and discard any fat from the top of the terrine. Dip a small knife into hot water and run it around the sides of the terrine to make it easter to turn out.

11 **Holding the terrine mould** with both hands, turn out the terrine on to a chopping board. Cut into slices about 1cm (½in) thick. Arrange the slices on plates or a large platter and serve with gherkins and crusty bread.

 VARIATION: Game terrine

Try this with pheasant or rabbit instead of venison.

1 Omit the ham, veal, and gherkins. Cut a 125g (4½oz) piece of venison into chunky strips, each about 1cm (½in) wide. Crush 3 juniper berries. Combine the juniper, brandy, and salt and pepper in a bowl. Add the venison strips and marinate as directed for the ham in the main recipe.

2 Make the meat mixture as directed, using 250g (9oz) minced venison in place of the veal and adding 60g (2oz) shelled pistachio nuts with the minced meat. The pistachios give this terrine beautiful flashes of bright green and crunches of texture. Cook a small portion of the meat mixture as directed, then taste for seasoning. Correct it if necessary, adding more pistachios if that would suit your palate.

3 Assemble the terrine, lining the mould with the 250g (9oz) bacon rashers and replacing the ham with the venison strips. Bake and unmould the terrine and slice as directed.

Steak and wild mushroom pie

AS COMFORTING as it gets. A quick puff pastry recipe is incredibly useful to have in your repertoire, very easy once you get the hang of it, and pleasingly impressive to your diners. But do substitute bought puff pastry if you're short of time.

SERVES	PREP	COOK
SERVES 4-6	50-55 MINS PLUS CHILLING	2½-3 HRS

Ingredients

FOR THE QUICK PUFF PASTRY

250g (9oz) plain flour

salt and pepper

175g (6oz) unsalted butter

1 egg, to glaze

FOR THE FILLING

500g (1lb 2oz) mixed wild mushrooms, sliced, or 75g (2½oz) dried wild mushrooms

35g (1¼oz) plain flour

1kg (2¼lb) braising steak, cut into 2.5cm (1in) cubes

900ml (1½ pints) beef stock or water, plus more if needed

4 shallots, finely chopped

leaves from 6 parsley sprigs, finely chopped

PREPARE THE QUICK PUFF PASTRY

1 **Sift the flour** and ½ tsp salt into a bowl. Rub in a third of the butter to form coarse crumbs. Make a well in the centre and pour in 100ml (3½fl oz) water; mix to a rough dough. Form a ball, wrap, and chill for 15 minutes.

FINISH THE PASTRY

2 **Roll out the dough** on a lightly floured surface to a 15x38 cm (6x15in) rectangle. Cut the remaining butter into small pieces, then dot the pieces over two-thirds of the dough rectangle. Fold the unbuttered dough over half of the buttered portion.

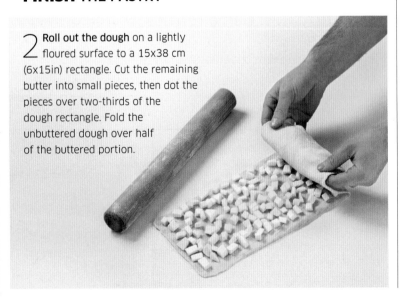

3 **With both hands,** fold the dough again so the butter pieces are completely enclosed in layers of dough. Turn the folded dough over and press the edges with the rolling pin to seal. Wrap and chill the dough 15 minutes.

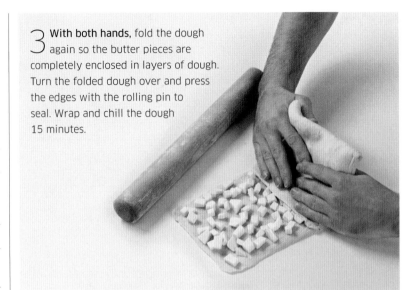

4 **Roll out the dough** to a 15x45cm (6x18in) rectangle, keeping the corners square. Work quickly, moving the dough on the floured surface so that it does not stick. Fold the rectangle in thirds again, so it forms a square, bringing the final fold towards you.

5 **Turn the dough** 90° so that the folded edge is to your left. Gently press the seams with the rolling pin to seal. This completes the first 'turn'. Repeat from step 4, to complete a second turn, then wrap tightly and chill for 15 minutes. Give the dough 2 more turns and chill for another 15 minutes.

PREPARE THE FILLING

6 Preheat the oven to 180°C (350°F/Gas 4). If using dried mushrooms, soak in a bowl of warm water for about 30 minutes, until they are plump. Drain thoroughly, slice any large mushrooms, and continue as for fresh mushrooms.

7 Season the flour with salt and pepper. Toss the steak in the flour to coat, discarding the excess. Put the floured cubes into a casserole. Pour in the stock. Add the mushrooms and shallots and stir well so all the ingredients and flavours are well combined. Bring to a boil on top of the stove, stirring constantly both to evenly warm the ingredients and to prevent any of the mixture sticking to the bottom of the casserole.

8 Cover the casserole and transfer to the heated oven. Cook, stirring occasionally, until the meat is tender enough to crush with your finger and the sauce is the consistency of single cream, 2–2¼ hours. The meat should be almost covered with gravy. If necessary, add additional stock or water during cooking.

9 Stir in the parsley and season to taste with salt and pepper. Spoon the pie filling into a 2 litre (3½ pint) pie dish with a pie funnel in the centre. Let cool completely. Increase the oven heat to 220°C (425°F/Gas 7).

FINISH AND BAKE THE PIE

10 Lightly flour a work surface and roll out three-quarters of the chilled dough to a rough shape at least 2.5cm (1in) larger than the dish. Trim the edges and cut a strip the width of the dish rim from the edge of the dough.

11 Using a pastry brush, brush the flat rim of the pie dish with a little water, just to moisten. Lay the strip of dough on the rim of the dish and press it down on to the rim. Lightly beat the egg with ½ tsp salt and brush the strip of dough with egg glaze.

12 Roll the large piece of dough around the rolling pin and drape it over the pie. Do not stretch the dough. With your fingertips, press the dough firmly to seal it to the strip of dough on the rim of the pie dish. Trim off any excess to make a neat finish.

13 Brush the top of the pie with the egg glaze. Cut a hole in the centre of the dough lid, over the funnel, to allow steam to escape. Use the pastry trimmings to decorate the pie, if you like, and glaze any decorations with egg, too.

14 Chill the pie for 15 minutes, then bake it in the heated oven for 25–35 minutes, until the top is golden brown. If the top browns too quickly, cover it with foil. Serve the pie hot from the dish.

Scallops with lemon-herb potatoes

BECAUSE SOMETIMES YOU JUST NEED TO TREAT YOURSELF! Scallops are expensive, so this is a dish to reserve for a special occasion. Because of their cost – but mostly due to their exquisite texture and flavour – scallops need to be cooked very carefully. Overcooked scallops will be dry and rubbery, whereas properly seared scallops are juicy, silky in texture, and bursting with saline flavours. Everything must be cooked just before serving for the best results.

SERVES	PREP	COOK
SERVES 6	45–50 MINS	20 MINS

Ingredients

FOR THE LEMON-HERB POTATOES

500g (1lb 2oz) potatoes

salt and pepper

4–6 parsley sprigs

4–6 tarragon sprigs

60g (2oz) butter

finely grated zest of 1 lemon

75ml (2½fl oz) milk, plus more if needed

FOR THE SCALLOPS

500g (1lb 2oz) large scallops

30g (1oz) plain flour

30g (1oz) butter

2 tbsp oil

lemon wedges and rocket leaves, to serve

PREPARE THE MASHED POTATOES

1 **Peel the potatoes** and cut into pieces. Put them in a saucepan of cold salted water, cover and bring to a boil. Simmer for 15–20 minutes, until tender.

2 **Strip the parsley** and tarragon leaves from the stalks.

3 **Put the butter,** herb leaves, and lemon zest in a food processor. Purée until the herbs are chopped finely.

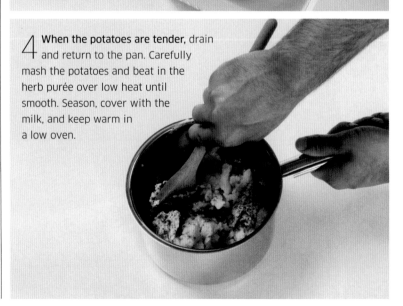

4 **When the potatoes are tender,** drain and return to the pan. Carefully mash the potatoes and beat in the herb purée over low heat until smooth. Season, cover with the milk, and keep warm in a low oven.

PREPARE AND SAUTÉ THE SCALLOPS

5 If necessary, discard the tough, crescent-shaped membrane at the side of each scallop. Put the flour on a plate and season. Roll the scallops in the flour and pat off the excess.

6 Heat the butter and oil in a frying pan. Sauté the scallops, turning them once, until just crisp and brown, 2–3 minutes.

FINISH THE DISH

7 Meanwhile, stir the milk into the potatoes, adding 2–3 tsp more, if needed. Remove the scallops from the pan and squeeze in the juice of half a lemon. Arrange the mashed potatoes and scallops on warmed serving plates and spoon over the pan juices. Serve at once, with the lemon wedges and rocket leaves.

 VARIATION: Poached scallops in cider sauce

Served in the shells with piped mashed potato.

1 Cook the potatoes as directed. Make the herbed butter, omitting the lemon zest and adding 2 garlic cloves. Mash the potatoes and spoon into a piping bag fitted with a star nozzle. Pipe them around the edges of 6 scallop shells.

2 Prepare the scallops as directed. Dice 2 shallots and squeeze the juice from 2 lemons. Put them in a saucepan with 120ml (4fl oz) each cider and white wine and 250ml (8fl oz) water. Add the scallops and heat to simmering. Poach for 30 seconds, then remove from the heat,

3 Reduce the scallop liquid to 250ml (9fl oz) and whisk in 2 tbsp plain flour, then 2 egg yolks beaten with 120ml (4fl oz) double cream. Return the scallops to the sauce, spoon them in the shells and grill for 3 minutes.

Quiche Lorraine

SERVE WARM or at room temperature, but never very hot as the custard will be too soft. This famous recipe, from Lorraine in eastern France, is as contentious as most of the traditional Gallic repertoire. Purists say it should be flavoured only with bacon, but the Gruyère cheese used in this version adds another welcome layer of flavour. The pastry can be made up to 2 days ahead and kept, tightly wrapped, in the refrigerator.

SERVES SERVES 6	**PREP** 45–50 MINS PLUS CHILLING	**COOK** 30–35 MINS

Ingredients

FOR THE PÂTE BRISÉE DOUGH

175g (6oz) plain flour, plus more to dust

1 egg yolk

½ tsp salt

90g (3oz) unsalted butter

FOR THE FILLING

250g (9oz) thick-cut bacon rashers, sliced

500ml (16fl oz) single cream

1 pinch of ground nutmeg

salt and pepper

1 egg yolk plus 3 eggs

75g (2½oz) Gruyère cheese, grated

MAKE THE PÂTE BRISÉE DOUGH

1 **Sift the flour** on to a work surface and make a well in the centre. Put the egg yolk, salt, and 3 tbsp cold water into the well. Using a rolling pin, pound the butter to soften it slightly, then add it to the well in the flour. With your fingertips, work the ingredients in the well together gently, until thoroughly mixed.

2 **Draw in the flour** and work it into the other ingredients until coarse crumbs form, trying to work the dough as little as possible so the pastry will be light and tender. Press the dough lightly into a ball. If the crumbs seem a little dry, sprinkle them with a very little more water before pressing the dough together.

3 **Lightly flour the work surface**, then blend the dough by pushing it away from you with the heel of your hand. Gather it up and continue to blend until it is very smooth and peels away from the work surface in one piece. It should only take 1–2 minutes to get to this stage. Try not to overwork it, or it will be tough; stop as soon as it forms a homogenous whole. Shape it gently into a ball, wrap tightly in clingfilm, and chill in the refrigerator until firm. It will take at least 30 minutes, or you can chill it for up to 2 days, if that is more convenient.

LINE THE TIN

4 **Brush a 25cm (10in) tin** with removable base with melted butter. Lightly flour a work surface. Roll out the chilled dough into a 30cm (12in) round. Wrap the dough around the rolling pin and unroll it so that it drapes over the tin and hangs over the edge. Do not stretch the dough or it will shrink when baked.

5 **Gently lift the edge** of the dough with one hand and press it well into the bottom edge of the tin with the forefinger of the other hand. Roll the rolling pin over the top of the tin, pressing down to cut off the excess dough.

6 **With your forefingers and thumb**, press the dough evenly up the side, from the bottom, to increase the height of the dough shell. Prick the bottom of the shell lightly with a fork to prevent air bubbles from forming during baking. Chill for at least 15 minutes, until firm.

BAKE THE PASTRY SHELL BLIND

7 **Preheat the oven** to 200°C (400°F/Gas 6). Put a baking sheet into the oven to heat. Line the pastry shell with a double thickness of foil, pressing it well into the bottom. Trim if necessary so it stands about 4cm (1½in) above the edge of the tin. Spread a layer of dried beans or rice over the foil to weigh down the dough while it is baking.

8 **Place the tin** on the baking sheet and bake the pastry shell in the heated oven for about 10 minutes, until set and the rim starts to brown. Carefully remove the foil and beans or rice.

9 Reduce the oven temperature to 190°C (375°F/Gas 5). Continue baking for 5-8 minutes longer, until the pastry is lightly browned. Remove the pastry shell from the oven and let cool slightly. Leave the oven on.

MAKE THE FILLING AND BAKE THE QUICHE

10 Put the bacon into a frying pan and cook for 3-4 minutes, stirring occasionally, until lightly browned. Using a slotted spoon, lift the bacon out of the frying pan and transfer to kitchen paper to drain. Put the cream, nutmeg, and salt and pepper into a bowl. Add the egg yolk and eggs and whisk until thoroughly mixed.

11 Sprinkle the bacon and cheese evenly over the bottom of the pastry shell. Set the tin on the hot baking sheet in the oven. Whisk the custard mixture and ladle it carefully over the bacon and cheese. Bake the quiche in the heated oven for 30-35 minutes, until lightly browned and the custard is lightly set.

12 Let the quiche cool slightly on a wire rack, then set the tin on a bowl to loosen and remove the side. Transfer to a chopping board or serving platter. Serve warm or at room temperature.

Home-made straw and hay pasta

GREEN AND WHITE FETTUCCINE REPRESENT straw and hay, and pasta is very soothing to make on a quiet afternoon. It is far easier than you think; all you need is a pasta machine and a little time, and everyone will be immeasurably impressed that you made it yourself, so you'll get an ego boost too!

SERVES	PREP	COOK
SERVES 6	55–60 MINS PLUS STANDING	10 MINS

Ingredients

FOR THE PLAIN FETTUCCINE

150g (5½oz) strong plain flour, plus more if needed

2 eggs

FOR THE SPINACH FETTUCCINE

2 tbsp defrosted spinach

220g (8oz) strong plain flour, plus more if needed

2 eggs

FOR THE SAUCE

60g (2oz) butter

1 small onion, finely chopped

250g (9oz) mushrooms, trimmed and sliced

salt and pepper

125g (4½oz) cooked ham, sliced into strips

100g (3½oz) shelled fresh or defrosted peas

250ml (9fl oz) double cream

1 pinch of ground nutmeg

60g (2oz) freshly grated Parmesan cheese, to serve

MAKE THE PLAIN AND SPINACH PASTA DOUGHS

1 **For the plain pasta**, sift the flour on to a work surface in a mound. With your fingers, make a well in the centre. Lightly beat the eggs with a fork, and add to the well, with ½ tsp salt.

2 **Gradually mix in the flour** from the sides to make a firm dough. If the dough is sticky, add more flour. As you mix, use a palette knife to scrape up any dough that sticks to the work surface. The dough may appear dry and floury at first, but will become more moist as the flour absorbs the eggs.

3 **On a floured work surface**, press the dough into a ball. Knead it with the heel of your hand to blend. Cover the dough with a bowl, and leave to rest for 1 hour. Meanwhile, make the spinach pasta dough.

4 **For the spinach pasta dough**, squeeze the defrosted spinach to remove all the water, then finely chop. Make as for the plain dough, adding the spinach with the eggs and salt. Leave the dough to rest, covered with a bowl, for 1 hour.

5 **Cut each ball of dough** into three or four roughly equal pieces, and set your pasta machine rollers to their widest setting.

MAKE THE FETTUCCINE

6 **Flour one piece of dough** lightly, and feed it through the rollers of the machine. Fold the dough strip into thirds to make a square, then feed it through the machine again, dusting with flour if it sticks. Repeat this folding and rolling process 7–10 times, until the dough is smooth and elastic.

7 **Tighten the pasta machine rollers** one notch, and feed the dough through them. Continue rolling the pasta dough, tightening the rollers one notch each time, ending with the narrowest setting. Lightly dust the dough with flour if necessary, so it does not stick. The dough will be satiny smooth and no longer crack at the sides as it comes out of the rollers.

8 **Hang the pasta sheet** over a clean broom handle and let dry for 5–10 minutes, until it has a leathery look. Meanwhile, knead and roll the remaining pieces of dough, and hang them over the broom handle. With a knife or scissors, cut the sheets of dough into lengths of about 30cm (12in).

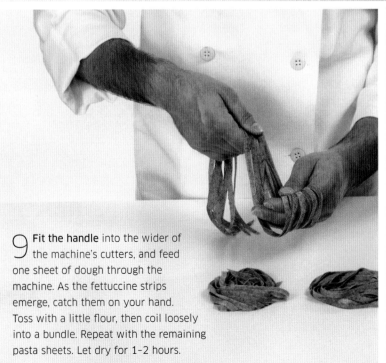

9 **Fit the handle** into the wider of the machine's cutters, and feed one sheet of dough through the machine. As the fettuccine strips emerge, catch them on your hand. Toss with a little flour, then coil loosely into a bundle. Repeat with the remaining pasta sheets. Let dry for 1-2 hours.

MAKE THE SAUCE

10 **Heat half the butter** in a large frying pan. Add the onion and cook, stirring occasionally, for 3-5 minutes, until soft. Add the mushrooms with salt and pepper, and continue cooking for 5-7 minutes, until the liquid has completely evaporated.

11 **Add the ham**, peas, and cream to the onions and mushrooms. Stir and heat to boiling, then simmer for 1-2 minutes, until slightly reduced. Add the ground nutmeg and taste for seasoning.

COOK THE PASTA AND FINISH THE DISH

12 **Fill a large pan** with water, bring to a boil and add 1 tbsp salt. Add the fettuccine and simmer for 1-2 minutes, until just tender but still chewy, stirring occasionally to prevent sticking. Drain thoroughly.

13 **Melt the remaining butter** in the pan, and add the fettuccine. Toss over medium heat, then add the sauce and toss for 1-2 minutes, until coated and very hot. Take from the heat, sprinkle generously with some of the Parmesan, and toss again. Pile the pasta in warmed bowls, and serve with the remaining Parmesan.

Sole bonne femme

AN OLD-FASHIONED CLASSIC and the most delicious of fish dishes. The bones from the filleted sole are used to make the stock, which itself is the basis for the recipe's creamy sauce. The fish stock can be prepared 4 hours ahead and chilled.

SERVES SERVES 4	**PREP** 30–35 MINS	**COOK** 25–30 MINS

Ingredients

FOR THE FISH STOCK

Heads and bones from 2 Dover sole

1 onion, sliced

3–5 parsley sprigs

1 tsp peppercorns

250ml (9fl oz) white wine or juice of 1 lemon

FOR THE FISH

15g (½oz) butter

250g (9oz) mushrooms, sliced

salt and pepper

2 shallots, finely chopped

2 Dover sole, 1kg (2¼lb) each, filleted, heads and bones reserved for the stock

FOR THE VELOUTÉ SAUCE

30g (1oz) butter

2 tbsp plain flour

3 tbsp double cream

3 egg yolks

juice of ½ lemon, or to taste

MAKE THE FISH STOCK

1 **Cut the washed fish heads** and bones into 4–5 pieces with a strong knife. Put in a medium saucepan. Add the onion, 500ml (16fl oz) water, parsley, and peppercorns. Pour in the wine.

2 **Bring to a boil** and simmer for about 20 minutes, skimming occasionally with a large, flat spoon. Pour the stock through a sieve into a second saucepan. Do not season; the flavours will intensify when it is reduced.

POACH THE SOLE

3 **Preheat the oven** to 180°C (350°F/Gas 4). Melt the butter in a frying pan; add the mushrooms, salt, pepper, and 3–4 tbsp water. Cover with buttered foil and cook for 5 minutes, until tender. Set aside.

4 **Butter a baking dish** and sprinkle the shallots over the bottom. Fold each sole fillet in half, skinned side inwards, and arrange on the shallots, tail upwards. Season. Ladle enough stock over to half-cover. Top with buttered foil. Poach the fish in the oven for 15–18 minutes, until it just flakes easily when tested with a fork. With a fish slice, transfer to kitchen paper to drain, reserving the cooking liquid. Keep the fillets warm while making the sauce.

MAKE THE SAUCE

5 **Add the fish cooking liquid** with the shallots to the remaining stock; boil until reduced to 375ml (12fl oz). Melt the butter in a separate saucepan. Whisk in the flour. Cook for 1–2 minutes, until foaming. Remove the pan from the heat and let cool slightly.

6 **Strain the reduced stock** into the butter and flour mixture. Bring to a boil, whisking constantly until thickened. Reduce the heat and let simmer for 5 minutes. Remove the sauce from the heat. Add the mushrooms with their cooking liquid, and stir to mix. Whisk the cream and egg yolks in a small bowl.

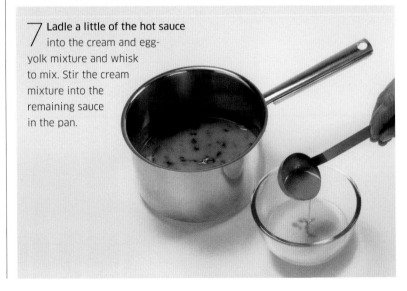

7 **Ladle a little of the hot sauce** into the cream and egg-yolk mixture and whisk to mix. Stir the cream mixture into the remaining sauce in the pan.

8 **Return to the heat** and cook gently, stirring, for 2–3 minutes, or until it thickens enough to coat the back of the spoon (your finger will leave a trail). Do not boil or it will curdle. Remove from the heat. Add lemon juice, salt and pepper to taste. Heat the grill. Arrange 2 fillets on each of 4 flameproof plates. Ladle the sauce over. Grill for 1–2 minutes, until lightly browned and glazed. Serve at once.

VARIATION: Fillets of sole with mushrooms and tomatoes

A colourful variation.

1 Peel, deseed, and finely chop 2 tomatoes. Prepare the sole, fish stock, and mushrooms as directed. Poach the sole fillets as directed, adding the tomatoes to the baking dish with the shallots.

2 Strip the leaves from 10–12 parsley sprigs and finely chop. Make the sauce, adding the fish cooking liquid to 125ml (4½fl oz) white wine instead of the remaining stock. Pour the reduced liquid into the butter and flour mixture without straining. When the sauce thickens, whisk in 1½ tbsp tomato purée.

3 Add the chopped parsley with the mushrooms and their liquid. Ladle the sauce over the fish arranged on flameproof plates and grill as directed.

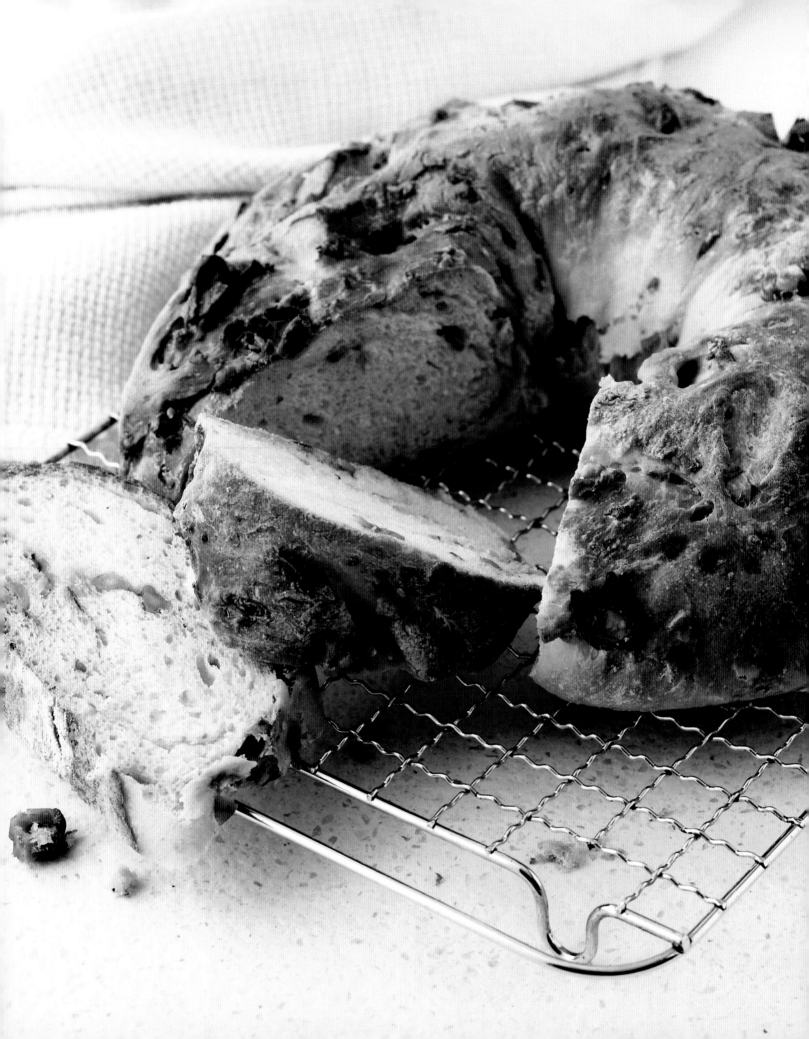

Bread

Loaves, buns, and rolls
made easy

Split-top white bread

A STAPLE RECIPE for novice and practiced bakers alike. The flour "sponge" used here is a fermented batter that adds a characteristic flavour and improves the texture of the bread. The loaves are rich in taste, and have an even, tender crumb. White loaves are best on the day of baking, but can be frozen very successfully. The dough can also be made, kneaded, and refrigerated to rise overnight.

SERVES	PREP	COOK
MAKES 2 LOAVES	2½–3 HRS PLUS FERMENTING	35–40 MINS

Ingredients

FOR THE SPONGE

2½ tsp dried yeast, or 15g (½oz) fresh yeast

125g (4½oz) unbleached, strong white flour, plus more to sprinkle

FOR THE BREAD

500ml (16fl oz) milk, plus more to glaze

750g (1lb 10oz) unbleached, strong white flour, plus more if needed

1 tbsp salt

PREPARE THE SPONGE

1 **In a small bowl,** sprinkle or crumble the yeast over 4 tbsp taken from 250ml (9fl oz) lukewarm water. Let stand for about 5 minutes, until dissolved, stirring once. Put the yeast and remaining water into a large bowl. Stir in the flour and mix vigorously, using your hand as a paddle, for 30-60 seconds.

2 **Sprinkle the sponge** with about 2 tbsp flour, covering most but not all of the surface. Cover the bowl with a damp tea towel, and let the sponge ferment in a warm place until the bubbles break through the flour; it will take anything from 30-60 minutes, depending on the heat of the room, the weather, or even the humidity. Even the most experienced bakers find the time hard to estimate, as each batch of flour is different.

MAKE THE DOUGH

3 **Meanwhile,** bring the milk just to a boil, and let it cool to lukewarm. When the sponge has risen, add the milk and mix it in with your hand. Stir in half the flour and the salt, and mix well with your hand. Add the remaining flour, 125g (4½oz) at a time, mixing well after each addition. Keep adding flour until the dough pulls away from the side of the bowl in a ball. It should be soft and slightly sticky. You may not need to use all the flour, so stop adding it when you feel the dough has the correct texture.

KNEAD THE DOUGH AND LET IT RISE

4 **Turn the dough** on to a floured work surface. Sprinkle the dough and your hands with flour, and begin to knead by holding the dough with one hand, and pushing it away from you with the other.

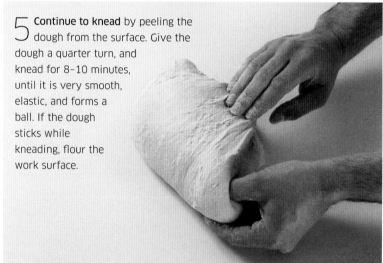

5 **Continue to knead** by peeling the dough from the surface. Give the dough a quarter turn, and knead for 8-10 minutes, until it is very smooth, elastic, and forms a ball. If the dough sticks while kneading, flour the work surface.

6 **Wash a large bowl** and brush it with melted butter. Put the kneaded dough in the bowl, and flip it so the surface is lightly buttered. Cover the bowl with a damp tea towel, and let the dough rise in a warm place for 1-1½ hours, until doubled in bulk.

SHAPE THE LOAVES

7 Brush 2 x 20x10x5cm (8x4x2in) loaf tins with melted butter. Turn the dough on to a lightly floured work surface, and knead with your hand for 15–20 seconds, just to knock out the air. Cover the dough and let rest for about 5 minutes.

8 Cut the dough in half. Cover one piece while shaping the other. Flour your hands, and pat the dough into a 25x20cm (10x8in) rectangle. Starting with a long side, roll into a cylinder. With the cylinder seam-side up, fold the ends over, making it the length of the tin.

9 Drop the loaf, seam-side down, into one of the prepared tins. Repeat to shape the remaining dough. Cover the tins with a dry tea towel, and let the loaves rise in a warm place for 45 minutes, until the tins are just full.

GLAZE AND BAKE THE LOAVES

10 Preheat the oven to 220°C (425°F/Gas 7). Brush the loaves with milk. With a very sharp knife or scalpel, make a slash about 1cm (½in) deep in each loaf. Bake for 20 minutes, and then lower the heat to 190°C (375°F/Gas 5) and bake for 15–20 minutes longer, until well browned.

11 Remove the loaves from the tins. Turn them over and tap the bottoms with your knuckles. The bread should sound hollow and the sides should feel crisp when pressed. Let the loaves cool completely.

 VARIATION: Cinnamon swirl bread

Each slice reveals a dark spiral of spice.

1 Make and knead the dough, and let it rise as directed in the main recipe. Brush two loaf tins very well with melted butter. In a small bowl, combine 1 tbsp ground cinnamon with 100g (3½oz) sugar. Set 2 tsp of the mixture aside for the glaze. Melt 45g (1½oz) unsalted butter in a small saucepan and let it cool completely.

2 Knock the air out of the dough, and let rest as directed in the main recipe. Cut the dough in half, and cover one piece while shaping the other. Roll the dough into a 30x20cm (12x8in) rectangle. Brush with some of the melted butter, and sprinkle with half the cinnamon and sugar mixture. This will combine to give a moist and delicious spiral seam throughout the loaves. Starting with a short end, roll the rectangle into an even cylinder and pinch the seam and ends to seal them together. Drop the loaf, seam-side down, into one of the prepared tins. Repeat to shape the remaining dough into another cinnamon swirl loaf.

3 Cover the loaves, and let rise as directed. Do not let the loaves rise longer than directed, or the cinnamon swirl may separate. Heat the oven to 220°C (425°F/Gas 7). Brush each loaf evenly with melted butter, sprinkle with the remaining cinnamon and sugar, and bake as directed in the main recipe. Serve warm, or toasted and spread with butter.

Wholemeal bread

STONE-GROUND WHOLEMEAL FLOUR varies from mill to mill and batch to batch so experiment with this recipe, using various flours and adding more or less water. A little white flour has been added to this recipe to bring the crumb of the loaf a lighter texture. Don't feel bound to shape the dough into these cottage loaves. Make them into long ovals or normally shaped sandwich rectangles, if it suits your purpose better. This bread is best eaten on the day it is baked, though it freezes very successfully.

SERVES	PREP	COOK
MAKES 2 LOAVES	35–40 MINS PLUS RISING	40–45 MINS

Ingredients

60g (2oz) unsalted butter

3 tbsp honey

1 tbsp dried yeast, or 20g (¾oz) fresh yeast

1 tbsp salt

125g (4½oz) unbleached strong white flour, plus more if needed

625g (1lb 6oz) stone-ground wholemeal flour

MAKE THE DOUGH AND LET IT RISE

1 **Melt the butter** in a small saucepan. Stir in 1 tbsp of the honey, along with 4 tbsp taken from 500ml (16fl oz) lukewarm water, in a small bowl until mixed. Sprinkle or crumble the yeast over the honey and water mixture and let stand for about 5 minutes until dissolved, stirring once.

2 **Put the melted butter,** remaining honey and water, dissolved yeast and salt into a large bowl. Stir in the white flour with half of the wholemeal, and mix with your hand.

3 **Add the remaining wholemeal flour,** 125g (4½oz) at a time, mixing well after each addition. Keep adding wholemeal flour until the dough pulls away from the side of the bowl in a ball. It should be soft and slightly sticky.

4 **Turn the dough** on to a floured work surface. Sprinkle it with white flour, and begin to knead by holding the dough with one hand and pushing it away from you with the other. Give the dough a quarter turn and knead for 8–10 minutes, until it is very smooth, elastic, and forms a ball. If the dough sticks while kneading, flour the work surface.

5 **Wash out the large bowl** and brush it with melted butter. Put the kneaded dough in the bowl, and flip it so the surface of the dough is lightly buttered. Cover the bowl with a damp tea towel and let the dough rise in a warm place for 1–1½ hours, or until doubled in bulk.

SHAPE AND **BAKE** THE LOAVES

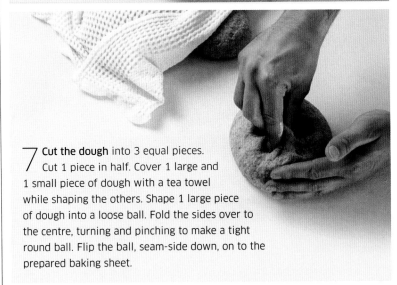

6 **Once the dough has doubled** in bulk, brush a baking sheet with melted butter. Turn the dough on to a lightly floured work surface and knead with your hand just to knock out the air. Cover the dough and let rest for about 5 minutes.

7 **Cut the dough** into 3 equal pieces. Cut 1 piece in half. Cover 1 large and 1 small piece of dough with a tea towel while shaping the others. Shape 1 large piece of dough into a loose ball. Fold the sides over to the centre, turning and pinching to make a tight round ball. Flip the ball, seam-side down, on to the prepared baking sheet.

8 **Shape 1 small piece** of dough into a ball. Fold the sides over to the centre, turning and pinching to make a tight round ball. Set it, seam-side down, on top of the first ball. With a finger, press through the centre of the 2 balls down to the bottom of the baking sheet and rotate your finger to enlarge the hole slightly. Repeat to shape the remaining 2 balls of dough.

9 **Cover the loaves** with a tea towel and leave in a warm place for about 45 minutes, or until doubled in bulk. Meanwhile, preheat the oven to 190°C (375°F/Gas 5). Bake the loaves for 40-45 minutes, until well browned. Turn them over and rap with your knuckles; They should sound hollow. Transfer to a wire rack until completely cool.

 VARIATION: Double wheat bread

Bulghur wheat adds flavour to this bread baked in flower pots.

1 Put 125g (4½oz) bulghur in a bowl and cover with water. Soak for 30 minutes, then drain, pressing to extract excess water. Melt the butter and dissolve the yeast as directed. Put the bulghur in a large bowl. Add the melted butter, dissolved yeast, and salt. Stir in the white and wholemeal flours, knead, and let rise as directed.

2 Preheat the oven to 150°C (300°F/Gas 2). Soak 2 x 750ml (1¼ pints) clean clay flower pots in water for 5 minutes. Put in the oven to dry. Repeat this process twice. Knock the air out of the dough and let rest. Cut it in half, and shape each piece into a ball. Drop into the prepared flower pots and let rise until the pots are just full; it should take about 45 minutes.

3 Preheat the oven to 190°C (375°F/Gas 5). Bake as directed. Remove the loaves from the pots to test if they are ready: the bread should sound hollow when tapped. Serve the bread in the flowerpots, if you like.

Sourdough bread

THIS BREAD HAS A WONDERFUL TANG, and is worth the trouble of making the "starter", which must be assembled 3–5 days ahead of time. You may find, as have many bakers, that creating the perfect sourdough bread becomes a bit of an obsession... The tightly wrapped loaves will freeze very successfully.

SERVES	PREP	COOK
MAKES 2 LOAVES	45–50 MINS PLUS RISING	40–45 MINS

Ingredients

FOR THE SOURDOUGH STARTER

1 tbsp dried yeast, or 20g (¾oz) fresh yeast

250g (9oz) unbleached strong white flour

FOR THE SPONGE

250g (9oz) unbleached strong white flour, more to sprinkle

FOR THE DOUGH

1½ tsp dried yeast, or 10g (⅓oz) fresh yeast

375g (13oz) unbleached strong white flour, plus more for bowls

1 tbsp salt

vegetable oil, for the bowl

polenta (fine yellow cornmeal) for the baking sheet

MAKE THE SOURDOUGH STARTER

1 This starter can be used within 3–5 days. Let the starter ferment for a day at room temperature, then use or refrigerate as directed below. Discard it if mould appears, or if it gives off a bad (rather than sour) odour.

2 In a large jar, sprinkle the yeast over 500ml (16fl oz) lukewarm water. Let stand for 5 minutes, stirring once. Stir in the flour, cover, and ferment in a warm place for 24 hours. It will be frothy with a distinct, sour aroma.

3 Stir the starter, cover, and stir each day for 2–4 days. Use or refrigerate. Replenish after each use. If a recipe calls for 250ml (9fl oz) starter, use it as directed. Then stir in 125g (4½oz) flour and 250ml (9fl oz) water.

MAKE THE SPONGE

4 Pour 250ml (9fl oz) lukewarm water into a large bowl, and spoon in 250ml (9fl oz) sourdough starter. Stir in the flour and mix vigorously with your hand for 30–60 seconds.

5 Sprinkle the sponge with 3 tbsp flour, cover the bowl with a damp tea towel, and let ferment in a warm place for 5–8 hours, or overnight. If you prefer a more sour flavour, let the sponge ferment overnight.

MAKE AND KNEAD THE DOUGH AND LET IT RISE

6 In a bowl, sprinkle the yeast over 4 tbsp lukewarm water. Let stand 5 minutes. Add to the sponge, and mix. Mix in half the flour and the salt. Add the remaining flour, 60g (2oz) at a time, mixing after each addition.

7 Turn the dough on to a floured work surface. Sprinkle the dough and your hands with flour. Knead for 8–10 minutes, until it is very smooth, elastic, and forms a ball, flouring the work surface if necessary.

8 Wash a large bowl. Brush it with oil. Put the kneaded dough in the bowl and flip it, so it is lightly oiled. Cover the bowl with a damp tea towel, and let the dough rise in a warm place for 1–1½ hours, until doubled in bulk.

SHAPE AND BAKE THE LOAVES

9 Line 2 x 20cm (8in) bowls with cotton cloth, and sprinkle generously with flour. Turn the dough on to a lightly floured work surface and knock out the air. Cover, and let rest for 5 minutes.

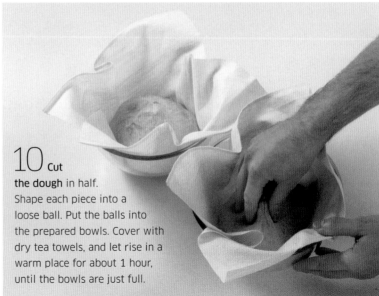

10 Cut the dough in half. Shape each piece into a loose ball. Put the balls into the prepared bowls. Cover with dry tea towels, and let rise in a warm place for about 1 hour, until the bowls are just full.

11 **Preheat the oven** to 200°C (400°F/Gas 6). Set a roasting tin to heat on the floor of the oven or on the lowest oven rack. Sprinkle 2 baking sheets with polenta. Turn the loaves on to the prepared baking sheets. With a very sharp knife, cut 3 slashes, 1cm (½in) deep, on the top of each loaf, then make 3 more to form a criss-cross pattern.

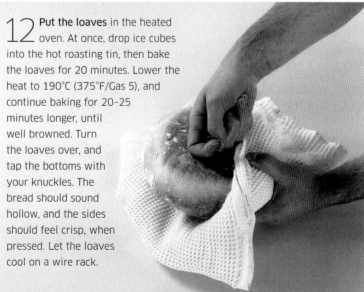

12 **Put the loaves** in the heated oven. At once, drop ice cubes into the hot roasting tin, then bake the loaves for 20 minutes. Lower the heat to 190°C (375°F/Gas 5), and continue baking for 20–25 minutes longer, until well browned. Turn the loaves over, and tap the bottoms with your knuckles. The bread should sound hollow, and the sides should feel crisp, when pressed. Let the loaves cool on a wire rack.

Cornbread

A TRADITIONAL AMERICAN LOAF baked in a cast-iron frying pan and studded with sweetcorn kernels. It is easily cut into wedges and can be served from the pan, if you like. The crust is deliciously crisp, and the bread is a brilliant accompaniment to baked hams or Southern Fried Chicken (p248).

SERVES	PREP	COOK
SERVES 8	15–20 MINS	20–25 MINS

Ingredients

2 fresh corn cobs, or 200g (7oz) defrosted and drained sweetcorn kernels

60g (2oz) unsalted butter

150g (5½oz) polenta (fine yellow cornmeal)

125g (4½oz) unbleached strong white flour

50g (1¾oz) sugar

1 tbsp baking powder

1 tsp salt

2 eggs

250ml (9fl oz) milk

MAKE THE BATTER

1 **Preheat the oven** to 220°C (425°F/Gas 7). If using fresh corn, hold each cob vertically and cut away all the kernels, from the tip down, with a sharp knife. Turn and continue cutting, removing as many whole kernels as possible.

2 **Put all the kernels** into a small bowl and, working over the bowl, use the back of a knife to scrape each cob and remove the deliciously sweet corn pulp. Mix this in with the kernels.

3 **Brush a 23cm (9in) flameproof cast-iron frying pan** with melted butter. Melt the butter for the batter in a small saucepan.

4 **Sift the polenta,** flour, sugar, baking powder, and salt into a large bowl, and make a well in the centre. Add the sweetcorn kernels to the well. In a medium bowl, whisk the eggs, melted butter, and milk until thoroughly combined. Pour three-quarters of the milk mixture into the well in the flour, and begin to stir.

FINISH AND BAKE THE BREAD

5 **Gradually draw in the dry ingredients,** adding the remaining milk mixture, and stirring to make a smooth batter. Do not overstir the batter or the bread will be heavy.

6 **Pour the cornbread batter** into the prepared frying pan and brush the top generously with melted butter. Bake for 20–25 minutes, until the bread starts to shrink from the side of the pan and a metal skewer inserted in the centre comes out clean. Let the cornbread cool slightly on a wire rack. Serve warm.

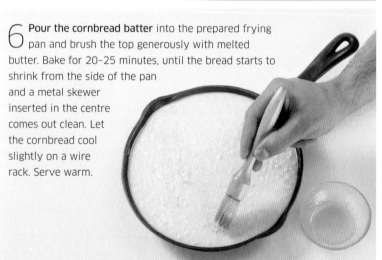

Sesame grissini

BREADSTICKS IN THE SICILIAN STYLE. The Italian tradition has it that the breadsticks should be pulled to the length of the baker's outstretched arm, though there's no need to go that far (and who has an oven big enough to cook them?). Sesame seeds are immensely popular in Sicilian food, and provide a great crunch and depth of flavour to the recipe.

SERVES MAKES 32	**PREP** 40-45 MINS PLUS RISING	**COOK** 15-18 MINS

2 tsp salt
2 tbsp olive oil
45g (1½oz) sesame seeds

Ingredients

2½ tsp dried yeast, or 15g (½oz) fresh yeast

425g (15oz) unbleached strong white flour, plus more if needed

1 tbsp sugar

MAKE AND KNEAD THE DOUGH AND LET IT RISE

1 **In a small bowl,** sprinkle or crumble the yeast over 4 tbsp taken from 300ml (10fl oz) lukewarm water. Let stand for about 5 minutes until dissolved, stirring once. Put the flour on to a work surface with the sugar and salt. Make a large well in the centre and add the dissolved yeast, remaining water, and oil.

2 **With your fingertips,** draw in the flour and work it into the other ingredients to form a smooth dough. It should be soft and slightly sticky. Sprinkle the dough and your hands with flour, and knead for 5-7 minutes, until the dough is very smooth and elastic, and forms a ball.

3 **Cover the dough** with a damp tea towel and let rest for about 5 minutes. Flour your hands and pat the dough into a rectangle on a well-floured work surface. With a rolling pin, roll the dough to a 40x15cm (16x6in) rectangle, pressing evenly so the breadsticks will be uniform in thickness. Brush the dough lightly with oil.

4 **Cover the** dough with the damp tea towel, and let rise for 1-1½ hours, or until doubled in bulk. (Rising time will depend on the temperature of the room.) Meanwhile, preheat the oven to 220°C (425°F/Gas 7).

CUT AND BAKE THE BREADSTICKS

5 **Brush 3 baking sheets with oil.** Gently lift the dough to prevent it from sticking to the work surface. Lightly brush with water. Sprinkle with the sesame seeds and press them down gently into the surface. With a sharp knife, cut the dough across into 32 strips, each about 1cm (½in) wide.

6 **Stretch 1 strip of dough** to the width of a baking sheet. Set it on 1 of the prepared baking sheets, letting the dough come just to the edges. Repeat with the remaining strips, arranging them 2cm (¾in) apart. Bake for 15-18 minutes, until golden and crisp. Transfer to a wire rack and let cool completely.

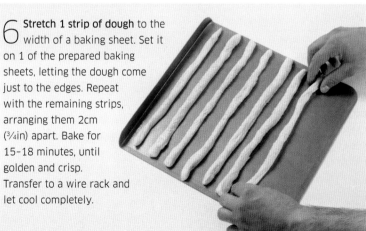

Multi-grain breakfast bread

A HEARTY BREAD with rolled oats, wheat bran, and polenta, the texture of this recipe is softened with buttermilk. This bread is best on the day of baking, but can be tightly wrapped and kept for up to 2 days, or it can be frozen successfully. Sunflower seeds add crunch, but you can use any of your favourite seeds instead, or a mixture, if you prefer. You could even use finely crushed bran cereal flakes in place of the wheat bran, for the perfect breakfast loaf.

SERVES MAKES 2 LOAVES	**PREP** 45–50 MINS PLUS RISING	**COOK** 40–45 MINS

Ingredients

75g (2½oz) sunflower seeds

425ml (15fl oz) buttermilk

2½ tsp dried yeast, or 15g (½oz) fresh yeast

45g (1½oz) rolled oats

45g (1½oz) wheat bran

75g (2½oz) polenta (fine yellow cornmeal), plus more for the baking sheet

45g (1½oz) soft brown sugar

1 tbsp salt

250g (9oz) strong wholemeal flour

250g (9oz) unbleached strong white flour, plus more if needed

1 egg white, to glaze

MAKE THE DOUGH

1 **Preheat the oven** to 180°C (350°F/Gas 4). Spread the seeds on a baking sheet, and toast in the heated oven for 5–7 minutes, until lightly browned, stirring occasionally, so they colour evenly. Let cool, then coarsely chop.

2 **Pour the buttermilk** into a saucepan. Heat just to lukewarm (too hot, and it will curdle). Sprinkle or crumble the yeast over 4 tbsp lukewarm water, and set aside for 2 minutes. Stir gently, then leave for 2–3 minutes more, until completely dissolved.

3 **Put the sunflower seeds**, rolled oats, wheat bran, polenta, brown sugar, and salt in a large bowl. Add the dissolved yeast and buttermilk, and mix with your hand. Stir in the wholemeal flour with half of the strong white flour, and mix well with your hand.

4 **Add the remaining strong white flour,** 60g (2oz) at a time, mixing well after each addition. Keep adding strong white flour until the dough pulls away from the side of the bowl in a ball. It should be soft and slightly sticky.

KNEAD THE DOUGH AND LET IT RISE

5 Turn the dough on to a floured work surface. Sprinkle the dough and your hands with strong white flour. Knead by holding the dough with one hand, and pushing it away from you with the other. Peel the dough from the surface, give it a quarter turn, and knead for 8–10 minutes, until it is very smooth, elastic, and forms a ball. If the dough sticks while kneading, flour the work surface.

6 Wash a large bowl and brush it with melted butter. Put the kneaded dough in the bowl and flip it, so the surface is lightly buttered. Cover the bowl with a damp tea towel, and let rise in a warm place for 1½–2 hours, until doubled in bulk.

SHAPE AND BAKE THE LOAVES

7 Sprinkle 2 baking sheets with polenta. Turn the dough on to a lightly floured work surface, and knead with your hand just to knock out the air. Cover the dough, and let rest for about 5 minutes.

8 With a sharp knife, cut the dough in half. Flour your hands and pat one piece of dough into a rough 38x10 cm (15x4in) rectangle, leaving the corners rounded. Fold the rectangle in half, gently pressing the halves together. Transfer to 1 of the prepared baking sheets, and repeat to shape the remaining dough.

9 Cover with a dry tea towel, and let the loaves rise in a warm place for about 1 hour, until doubled in bulk. You may find that this takes slightly longer; it will depend on the weather, the humidity, the temperature of the room, and even of the qualities of the batch of flour you have used (flours will differ from batch to batch). Meanwhile, preheat the oven to 190°C (375°F/Gas 5). Make the glaze: beat the egg white just until frothy. Brush the loaves with the glaze.

10 Bake the loaves in the heated oven until well browned. It will take 40–45 minutes. To test if they are ready, turn the loaves over and tap on the bottoms with your knuckles. The bread should sound hollow, and the sides should feel crisp. Transfer to a wire rack and let cool completely. This bread is completely delicious for breakfast, with eggs and bacon, or just thickly spread with good butter.

Baguette

THE MOST RENOWNED of French breads. It is left to rise three times for an open crumb and yeasty flavor – well worth it! Once you have fallen in love with home-made baguettes (and you will), you may want to invest in a baguette frame. We have shown you how to use that equipment here, though it is by no means necessary to own one in order to make this wonderful bread.

SERVES	PREP	COOK
MAKES 3	40-45 MINS PLUS RISING	25-30 MINS

Ingredients

2½ tsp dried yeast, or 15g (½oz) fresh yeast

500g (1lb 2oz) unbleached strong white flour, plus more if needed

2 tsp salt

MAKE AND KNEAD THE DOUGH AND LET IT RISE

1 **In a small bowl,** sprinkle or crumble the yeast over 4 tbsp taken from 425ml (15fl oz) lukewarm water. Let stand for about 5 minutes until dissolved, stirring once. Put the flour on to a work surface with the salt. Make a large well in the centre of the flour and add the dissolved yeast and remaining water. With your fingertips, work the ingredients in the well.

2 **Gradually draw in the flour** and work it into the liquid ingredients with your hand to form a smooth dough. It should be soft and slightly sticky. Sprinkle the dough with flour and begin to knead by holding the dough with one hand and pushing it away from you with the other. Continue for 5-7 minutes, until very smooth, elastic and forms a ball.

3 **Brush a large bowl** with melted butter. Put the kneaded dough in the bowl, and flip it so the surface is lightly buttered. Cover the bowl with a damp tea towel and let rise in a warm place for 2-2½ hours, until tripled in bulk. Turn the dough on to a lightly floured work surface and knead with your hand just to knock out the air. Return it to the bowl, cover and let rise for 1-1½ hours, or until doubled in bulk.

4 **For the next stage,** use a baguette frame if you are planning on making baguettes often. Otherwise, use a cotton cloth and baking sheet, and flour generously. Pleat the cloth between the baguettes, and let rise. To bake, roll the loaves from the cloth on to the baking sheet.

SHAPE AND BAKE THE BAGUETTES

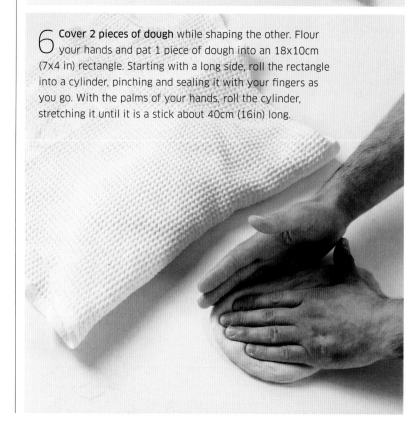

5 **Sprinkle the baguette** frame or cloth with flour. Turn the dough on to a lightly floured work surface and knead with your hand just to knock out the air. Cover and let rest for about 5 minutes. With a sharp knife, cut straight down through the dough, dividing it into 3 equal pieces.

6 **Cover 2 pieces of dough** while shaping the other. Flour your hands and pat 1 piece of dough into an 18x10cm (7x4 in) rectangle. Starting with a long side, roll the rectangle into a cylinder, pinching and sealing it with your fingers as you go. With the palms of your hands, roll the cylinder, stretching it until it is a stick about 40cm (16in) long.

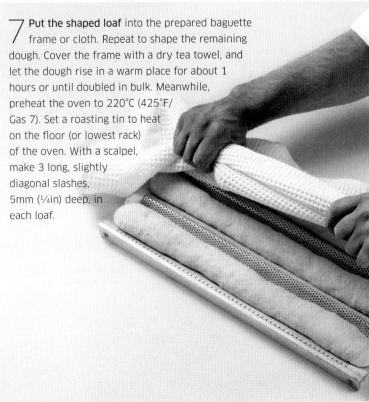

7 **Put the shaped loaf** into the prepared baguette frame or cloth. Repeat to shape the remaining dough. Cover the frame with a dry tea towel, and let the dough rise in a warm place for about 1 hours or until doubled in bulk. Meanwhile, preheat the oven to 220°C (425°F/ Gas 7). Set a roasting tin to heat on the floor (or lowest rack) of the oven. With a scalpel, make 3 long, slightly diagonal slashes, 5mm (¼in) deep, in each loaf.

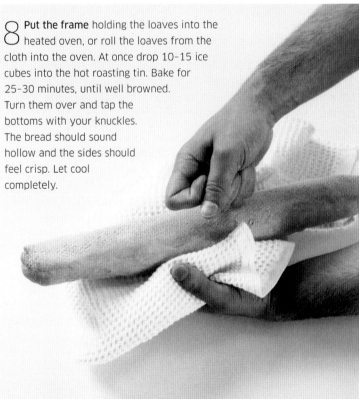

8 **Put the frame** holding the loaves into the heated oven, or roll the loaves from the cloth into the oven. At once drop 10–15 ice cubes into the hot roasting tin. Bake for 25–30 minutes, until well browned. Turn them over and tap the bottoms with your knuckles. The bread should sound hollow and the sides should feel crisp. Let cool completely.

Focaccia with rosemary

THIS MOIST ITALIAN BREAD is at its simplest and best in this recipe. Its shape, and the ingredients with which it is flavoured, differ from region to region. It can be sweet or savoury, is most often baked, but sometimes fried. These days you can buy all sorts of flavoured focaccias, but they do not always add much to the original. This is a good-tempered dough, and can be made, kneaded, and left in the refrigerator to rise overnight. Shape the dough, let it come to room temperature, then bake as directed.

SERVES	PREP	COOK
SERVES 6-8	30-35 MINS PLUS RISING	15-20 MINS

Ingredients

leaves from 5-7 rosemary sprigs	2 tsp salt
1 tbsp dried yeast, or 20g (¾oz) fresh yeast	90ml (3fl oz) olive oil
	¼ tsp freshly ground black pepper
425g (15oz) unbleached strong white flour, plus more if needed	

MAKE AND KNEAD THE DOUGH AND LET IT RISE

1 **Finely chop** two-thirds of the rosemary leaves. Reserve the remaining whole rosemary leaves for topping the focaccia. In a small bowl, sprinkle the dried or crumble the fresh yeast over 4 tbsp taken from 300ml (½ pint) lukewarm water. Let stand for about 5 minutes until dissolved, stirring once.

2 **Put the flour** on to a work surface with the salt. Make a large well in the centre of the mound and add the chopped rosemary, dissolved yeast, 4 tbsp of the oil, the freshly ground pepper, and the remaining water. With your fingertips, work together all the ingredients in the well until they are thoroughly mixed.

3 **Gradually draw in the flour** and work it into all the other ingredients with your hand to form a smooth dough. It should be soft and sticky. Do not be tempted to add more flour to dry it out as you want a moist loaf after baking. Sprinkle the dough and your hands with flour and knead, lifting the dough up and throwing it down for 5-7 minutes, until it is very smooth, elastic, and forms a ball. This bread can be made in a food processor using the dough hook attachment, but making it by hand is very satisfying and more than a little therapeutic

4 **Brush a large bowl** with olive oil. Put the kneaded dough in the bowl and flip it so the surface is lightly oiled. Cover the bowl with a damp tea towel and let rise in a warm place for 1–1½ hours, or until doubled in bulk. Alternatively, let the dough rise in the refrigerator overnight, loosely covered with clingfilm, ensuring no strong flavours can taint the mixture (it is best to ensure the refrigerator contains no pungent foods).

SHAPE AND BAKE THE FOCACCIA

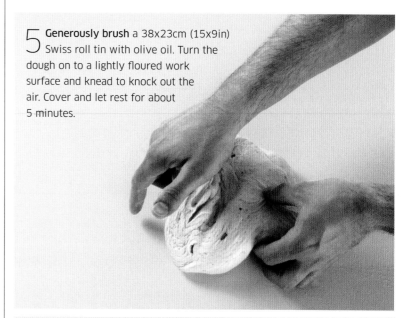

5 **Generously brush** a 38x23cm (15x9in) Swiss roll tin with olive oil. Turn the dough on to a lightly floured work surface and knead to knock out the air. Cover and let rest for about 5 minutes.

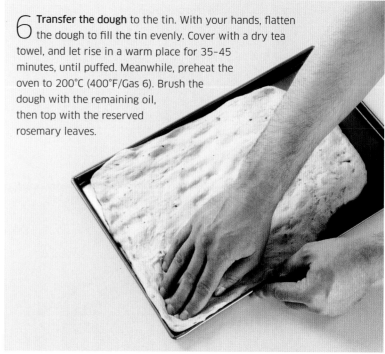

6 **Transfer the dough** to the tin. With your hands, flatten the dough to fill the tin evenly. Cover with a dry tea towel, and let rise in a warm place for 35-45 minutes, until puffed. Meanwhile, preheat the oven to 200°C (400°F/Gas 6). Brush the dough with the remaining oil, then top with the reserved rosemary leaves.

7 With your fingertips, poke the dough all over to make deep dimples. Bake for 15–20 minutes, until crisp-crusted underneath and lightly browned on top. Transfer to a wire rack and let cool slightly. Cut or break the focaccia into pieces, and serve warm as a snack, or as an appetizer at an informal supper.

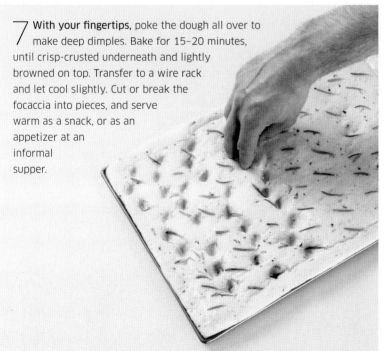

🍲 VARIATION: Focaccia with sage

1 Omit the rosemary and the freshly ground black pepper. Finely chop the leaves from 3–5 sage sprigs, discarding the stalks. (Do not be tempted to add more sage, as it is a strong flavour and can easily overpower). Make the focaccia dough, adding the chopped sage to the well in place of the rosemary. Knead the dough, and let rise as directed in the main recipe. Brush a baking sheet evenly with olive oil.

2 Knock the air out of the dough, and let rest as directed. With a rolling pin and your hands, roll and pull the dough into a rough 35cm (14in) oval. Transfer to the oiled baking sheet.

3 With a scalpel or very sharp knife, make diagonal slashes through the dough to resemble the veins of a leaf, pulling the slits apart slightly with your fingers. If your knife if not very sharp, the dough will tear and the loaf will not rise so well. The focaccia will bake to a beautiful leaf shape. Let the dough rise as directed in the main recipe, then brush it evenly with 1 tbsp well-flavoured olive oil. Bake as directed. This is delicious with a herbed roast loin of pork, or simply with good-quality ham.

Seeded rye bread

A CRUSTY LOAF full of flavour, accented by aromatic caraway seeds. Rye flour is darker than wheat flour and low in gluten, so here it is mixed with strong white flour (slightly higher in gluten) to lighten the texture of the loaf. Rye bread is best eaten on the day of baking, but can be tightly wrapped and kept for up to 2 days, or it freezes very successfully. You can make this loaf in an electric mixer fitted with a dough hook, or in a food processor, if you would rather not knead it by hand.

SERVES	PREP	COOK
MAKES 1 LOAF	35–40 MINS PLUS RISING	50–55 MINS

Ingredients

2½ tsp dried yeast, or 15g (½oz) fresh yeast

1 tbsp black treacle

1 tbsp vegetable oil

1 tbsp caraway seeds

2 tsp salt

250ml (9fl oz) lager

250g (9oz) rye flour

175g (6oz) unbleached strong white flour, plus more if needed

polenta (fine yellow cornmeal), for the baking sheet

1 egg white, to glaze

MAKE AND KNEAD THE DOUGH AND LET IT RISE

1 **In a small bowl,** sprinkle or crumble the yeast over 4 tbsp lukewarm water. Let stand for about 5 minutes, until dissolved, stirring once. Put the dissolved yeast, black treacle, oil, two-thirds of the caraway seeds, and the salt into a large bowl. Pour in the lager. Stir in the rye flour and mix everything together well with your hand.

2 **Add the strong white flour,** 60g (2oz) at a time, mixing well after each addition, until the dough pulls away from the side of the bowl in a ball. It should be soft and slightly sticky. Turn on to a floured surface. Sprinkle the dough with flour, and knead for 8–10 minutes, until it is very smooth, elastic, and forms a ball.

3 **Wash out the large bowl** and brush it with oil. Put the kneaded dough in the bowl, and flip it so the surface is lightly oiled. Cover the bowl with a damp tea towel and let rise in a warm place for 1½–2 hours, or until about doubled in bulk.

SHAPE AND BAKE THE LOAF

4 **Sprinkle a baking sheet** with polenta. Turn the dough on to a lightly floured work surface and knead just to knock out the air. Cover and let rest for about 5 minutes. Flour your hands and pat the dough into an oval about 25cm (10in) long.

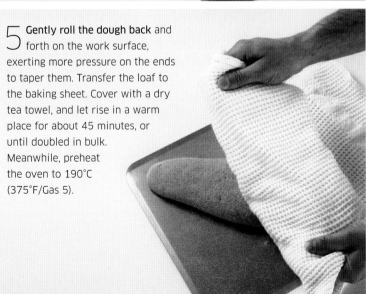

5 **Gently roll the dough back** and forth on the work surface, exerting more pressure on the ends to taper them. Transfer the loaf to the baking sheet. Cover with a dry tea towel, and let rise in a warm place for about 45 minutes, or until doubled in bulk. Meanwhile, preheat the oven to 190°C (375°F/Gas 5).

 VARIATION: Horseshoe rye bread

1 Omit the caraway seeds. Make and knead the dough, and let it rise as directed. Sprinkle a baking sheet with polenta. Knock the air out of the dough, and let rest as directed. Flour your hands and pat the dough into a 25x20cm (10x8in) rectangle.

2 Starting with a long side, roll the rectangle into a cylinder, pinching and sealing it with your fingers as you go. With the palms of your hands, roll the cylinder until it is about 45cm (18in) long and of an even thickness. Transfer the cylinder, seam-side down, to the baking sheet, then curve the ends around to form a horseshoe shape.

3 Cover the loaf and let rise as directed. Heat the oven to 190°C (375°F/Gas 5). Make the glaze and brush the loaf with egg white as directed. With a scalpel, make a slash, 5mm (¼in) deep, along the top, following the curve of the loaf. Bake the loaf, and let cool as directed.

6 **Beat the egg white** until frothy. Brush the loaf with the glaze. Sprinkle the loaf with the remaining caraway seeds, and press them into the dough.

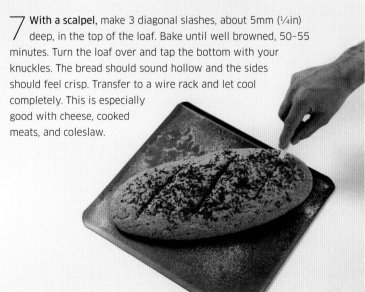

7 **With a scalpel,** make 3 diagonal slashes, about 5mm (¼in) deep, in the top of the loaf. Bake until well browned, 50–55 minutes. Turn the loaf over and tap the bottom with your knuckles. The bread should sound hollow and the sides should feel crisp. Transfer to a wire rack and let cool completely. This is especially good with cheese, cooked meats, and coleslaw.

Dinner rolls

AN EGG-ENRICHED DOUGH, easy to shape. You can shape the rolls however you like, though an assortment of different forms looks very nice in a basket. The dough can be made, shaped, and frozen ahead of time. Defrost, then bake just before serving. Freshly baked rolls also freeze well.

SERVES MAKES 16	**PREP** 45–55 MINS PLUS RISING	**COOK** 15–18 MINS

Ingredients

FOR THE ROLLS

150ml (9fl oz) milk

60g (2oz) unsalted butter

2 tbsp sugar

2½ tsp dried yeast, or 15g (½oz) fresh yeast

2 eggs

2 tsp salt

550g (1¼lb) unbleached strong white flour, plus more if needed

FOR THE GLAZE

1 egg yolk

poppy seeds, to sprinkle (optional)

MAKE AND KNEAD THE DOUGH AND LET IT RISE

1 **Put the milk** into a saucepan, and bring just to a boil. Pour 4 tbsp of the milk into a small bowl, and let cool to lukewarm. Meanwhile, cut the butter into pieces. Add the butter and sugar to the remaining milk in the pan, stirring occasionally, until the butter is melted. Let cool to lukewarm.

2 **Sprinkle the yeast** over the 4 tbsp milk and let stand, stirring once, for about 5 minutes, until dissolved. In a large bowl, beat the eggs just until mixed. Add the cooled sweetened milk, salt, and dissolved yeast.

3 **Stir in half the flour** and mix well with your hand. Add the remaining flour, 60g (2oz) at a time, mixing well after each addition. Keep adding flour until the dough pulls away from the side of the bowl in a ball. It should be soft and slightly sticky.

4 **Turn the dough** on to a floured work surface. Knead for 5–7 minutes, until it is very smooth, elastic, and forms a ball. If the dough sticks while kneading, flour the work surface.

5 **Wash a large bowl** and brush it with melted butter. Put the dough in the bowl, and flip it so the surface is lightly buttered. Cover with a damp tea towel and let rise in a warm place for 1–1½hours, until doubled in bulk,.

6 **Brush two baking sheets** with melted butter. Turn the dough onto a lightly floured work surface and knead to knock out the air. Cover and let rest for about 5 minutes. Cut the dough in half. With your hands, roll one piece of the dough into a cylinder about 5cm (2in) in diameter. Cut the cylinder into eight equal pieces. Repeat with the remaining dough.

SHAPE THE ROLLS

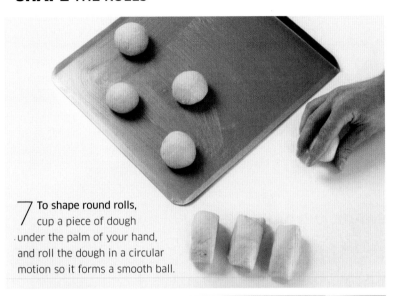

7 **To shape round rolls,** cup a piece of dough under the palm of your hand, and roll the dough in a circular motion so it forms a smooth ball.

8 **For a baker's knot,** roll a piece of dough into a long rope. Shape into a figure of eight, and tuck the ends through the holes.

9 **For a twist,** roll a piece of dough into a long rope, fold it in half and twist. Arrange on a baking sheet and press down the ends.

10 **For a snail,** roll a piece of dough into a long rope and wind it around in a spiral, tucking the end underneath. Arrange eight rolls on each baking sheet. Cover with a dry tea towel and let rise in a warm place for about 30 minutes, until doubled in bulk.

BAKE THE ROLLS

11 **Meanwhile,** preheat the oven to 220°C (425°F/Gas 7). Make the glaze: beat the egg yolk with 1 tbsp water just until it looks frothy. Brush the rolls with the glaze, sprinkle evenly with poppy seeds, if you like, then bake until the rolls are golden brown. It should take just 15–18 minutes, but do check them often (without opening the oven door), as their small size means they can scorch easily. As your baking confidence increases, experiment by sprinkling with different seeds (try sesame, or sunflower), or add a swirl of pesto, anchovy, or tomato purée to a "snail" roll before twisting it into its final spiral shape.

12 **Turn over the rolls** and tap the bottoms with your knuckles to test if they are ready. They should sound hollow. Allow to cool slightly and release any steam on a wire rack, then serve the rolls warm, piled in a basket, with plenty of good butter for spreading.

Onion and walnut crown

WONDERFUL FLAVOURS from the south-west of France come together in this simple white loaf. The onions are first sautéed, and the walnuts toasted, before being kneaded into the dough. This bread is perfect to go alongside a cheeseboard, ideally accompanied by a glass of mellow red wine, for a simple – though very classy – weekend lunch. It freezes very successfully.

SERVES MAKES 1 LARGE LOAF	**PREP** 40-45 MINS, PLUS 1¾-2¼ HOURS	**COOK** 45-50 MINUTES

Ingredients

425ml (15fl oz) milk, plus more to glaze

2½ tsp dried yeast, or 15g (½oz) fresh yeast

2 tbsp vegetable oil, plus more for the bowl and baking sheet

2 tsp salt

500g (1lb 2oz) unbleached strong white flour, plus more if needed

1 large onion, finely chopped

pepper

60g (2oz) walnut pieces

MAKE AND KNEAD THE DOUGH AND LET IT RISE

1 **Bring the milk** just to a boil. Pour 4 tbsp of the milk into a small bowl and let it cool to lukewarm. Sprinkle or crumble the yeast over the 4 tbsp milk and let stand for about 5 minutes, stirring once, until dissolved.

2 **Put the dissolved yeast,** remaining milk, half the oil, and the salt into a large bowl. Stir in half the flour and mix well with your hand. Add the remaining flour, 60g (2oz) at a time, mixing well after each addition, until the dough pulls away from the side of the bowl in a ball. It should be soft and slightly sticky.

3 **Turn the dough** on to a floured work surface. Sprinkle the dough and your hands with flour, and knead for 5-7 minutes, until very smooth, elastic, and forms a ball. If the dough sticks while kneading, flour the work surface.

4 **Wash out the large bowl** and brush it with melted butter. Flip the dough in the bowl so it is lightly buttered. Cover with a damp tea towel and let rise in a warm place for 1-1½ hours, or until doubled in bulk.

PREPARE THE ONION AND WALNUTS

5 **Preheat the oven** to 180°C (350°F/Gas 4). Heat the remaining oil in a frying pan. Add the onion with salt and pepper and cook, stirring, for 5-7 minutes, or until soft and light brown. Taste for seasoning and leave to cool.

6 **Spread the walnut pieces** on a baking sheet and toast in the heated oven, stirring occasionally, for 8-10 minutes, until lightly browned. Let the nuts cool, then coarsely chop them.

SHAPE THE CROWN

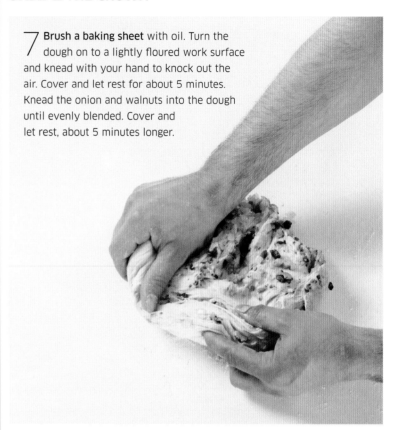

7 **Brush a baking sheet** with oil. Turn the dough on to a lightly floured work surface and knead with your hand to knock out the air. Cover and let rest for about 5 minutes. Knead the onion and walnuts into the dough until evenly blended. Cover and let rest, about 5 minutes longer.

8 **Shape the dough** into a loose ball. Fold the sides over to the centre, turning and pinching to make a tight round ball. Flip the ball, seam-side down, on to the work surface. Make a hole in the centre of the ball with two fingers. With your fingers, enlarge the hole, turning to make an even ring. Gradually enlarge the ring to a diameter of 25-30cm (10-12in).

9 **Lift the ring** on to the prepared baking sheet. Cover with a dry tea towel and let rise in a warm place for about 45 minutes, or until doubled in bulk. Meanwhile, preheat the oven to 200°C (400°F/Gas 6). Brush the ring with milk. With kitchen scissors, snip around the top of the ring in a zig-zag design.

10 **Bake the loaf** in the heated oven for 45–50 minutes, until well browned. Turn the loaf over and tap the bottom with your knuckles. The bread should sound hollow and the sides should feel crisp when pressed. Transfer the bread to a wire rack and let cool completely.

Pesto garland bread

A FRAGRANT AND BEAUTIFUL LOAF. The rye-flavoured dough is rolled into a cylinder, then cut before baking to reveal spirals of the pesto filling. This bread is best fresh, but it can be baked 1 day ahead and the flavour will mellow. Store it wrapped in foil, then warm in a low oven before serving.

SERVES MAKES 1 LOAF	**PREP** 35–40 MINS PLUS RISING	**COOK** 30–35 MINS

Ingredients

FOR THE BREAD

2½ tsp dried yeast, or 15g (½oz) fresh yeast

125g (4½oz) rye flour

300g (10oz) unbleached strong white flour, plus more if needed

2 tsp salt

FOR THE FILLING

leaves from 1 large bunch of basil

3 garlic cloves, peeled

3 tbsp olive oil

30g (1oz) pine nuts, coarsely chopped

60g (2oz) freshly grated Parmesan cheese

freshly ground black pepper

MAKE AND KNEAD THE DOUGH AND LET IT RISE

1 **In a small bowl,** sprinkle or crumble the yeast over 4 tbsp taken from 300ml (10fl oz) lukewarm water. Let stand for about 5 minutes, until dissolved, stirring once.

2 **Put the rye flour,** and half the strong white flour in the bowl of a food processor, with the salt. Combine the dissolved yeast and remaining water and pour in, pulse-blending just until mixed. Add the remaining flour, 60g (2oz) at a time. Mix after each addition, until the dough pulls away from the bowl in a ball. It should be soft and slightly sticky.

3 **Continue working** the dough until it is very smooth and elastic; it will take 60 seconds longer. Turn the dough on to a lightly floured work surface, and remove the blade. Shape into a ball. Brush a large bowl with oil, put in the dough, and flip so it is lightly oiled. Cover with a damp tea towel and let rise in a warm place for 1–1½ hours, until doubled in bulk.

MAKE THE PESTO

4 **Put the basil** in a food processor or blender with the garlic. Work until coarsely chopped. With the blades turning, gradually add the oil until smooth. Transfer the pesto mixture to a bowl and stir in the pine nuts, Parmesan, and plenty of black pepper. Taste for seasoning.

SHAPE AND BAKE THE LOAF

5 **Brush a baking sheet** with oil. Turn the dough on to a lightly floured work surface, and knead to knock out the air. Cover and let rest for about 5 minutes. Flatten the dough, then roll it into a 40x30cm (16x12in) rectangle with a rolling pin. Use your hands to shape the rectangle.

6 **With a spatula,** spread the pesto evenly over the dough, leaving a 1cm (½in) border. Starting with a long end, roll up the rectangle into an even cylinder. Running the length of the cylinder, pinch the seam firmly together. Do not seal the ends.

7 **Transfer the cylinder,** seam-side down, to the prepared baking sheet. Curve the cylinder into a ring, overlapping and sealing the ends. With a sharp knife, make a series of deep cuts around the ring, about 5cm (2in) apart. Pull the slices apart slightly, and twist them over to lie flat. Cover with a dry tea towel, and let rise in a warm place for about 45 minutes, until doubled in bulk. Meanwhile, preheat the oven to 220°C (425°F/Gas 7).

8 **Brush the loaf** with oil and bake for 10 minutes. Reduce the heat to 190°C (375°F/Gas 5), and continue baking for 20–25 minutes longer, until well browned. Carefully transfer to a wire rack and let cool slightly.

VARIATION: Sun-dried tomato spiral

A gutsy, intensely flavoured bread.

1 Make the dough, and let it rise as directed in the main recipe. Drain 75g (2½oz) oil-packed sun-dried tomatoes, reserving 2 tbsp of the oil; then coarsely chop the tomatoes. Chop the pine nuts. Peel and finely chop 2 garlic cloves. Strip the leaves from 5–10 basil sprigs and finely chop.

2 Put the sun-dried tomatoes in a small bowl with the pine nuts, garlic, basil, and the grated Parmesan cheese. Stir in 1 tbsp of the reserved tomato oil, and season with plenty of black pepper. Brush a 20cm (8in) round cake tin with the remaining oil. Sprinkle 1–2 tbsp polenta in the tin, and turn it to coat the bottom and side; turn the tin upside down, and tap to remove excess cornmeal.

3 Knock the air out of the dough, and let rest as directed. Roll the dough into a rectangle, spread the filling and shape a cylinder. Flip so it is seam-side down, curve it into a spiral and tuck the end underneath. Drop it into the tin, cover, and let rise as directed. Bake as directed, allowing 25–30 minutes at 190°C (375°F/Gas 5). Unmould and let cool.

Irish soda bread

This has a surprisingly light, almost cake-like texture. Stone-ground flour makes a great difference to the flavour, and it takes very little time to make. As an added bonus, it requires no kneading, so is a wonderfully effort-free loaf. It is best eaten warm from the oven, with lots of butter and either very good mature cheese or jam.

SERVES	PREP	COOK
MAKES 1 LOAF	10–15 MINS	35–40 MINS

Ingredients

500g (1lb 2oz) stoneground strong wholemeal flour

1½ tsp bicarbonate of soda

1½ tsp salt

500ml (16fl oz) buttermilk, plus more if needed

MAKE THE DOUGH

1 **Preheat the oven** to 200°C (400°F/Gas 6). Brush a baking sheet with melted butter. Sift the flour, bicarbonate of soda, and salt into a large bowl, tipping the bran from the sieve into the bowl. Mix with your hand to combine the dry ingredients, and make a well in the centre.

2 **In a steady stream,** pour the buttermilk into the centre of the well. With your hand, quickly draw the flour into the buttermilk to make a soft dough. It should be slightly sticky. Do not overwork the dough or the bread will be heavy. Add a little more buttermilk if the dough seems dry.

SHAPE AND BAKE THE LOAF

3 **Turn the dough** on to a lightly floured work surface, and quickly shape it into a round loaf. Put the loaf on the prepared baking sheet and pat it down with the palms of your hands to form a round, about 5cm (2in) high.

4 **With a scalpel** or a very sharp knife, make an "x", 1cm (½in) deep, in the top of the loaf. This is the traditional decoration for this bread, and the deep slashes allow steam to escape during baking.

5 **Bake the loaf** in the heated oven for 35–40 minutes, until brown. Turn the loaf over and tap the bottom with your knuckles. The bread should sound hollow. Transfer the bread to a wire rack and let cool slightly.

6 **Cut the bread** into slices or wedges and serve warm, with plenty of butter. Soda bread is a traditional accompaniment to soup or stew, and also makes very good toast.

Buttermilk scones

ONE OF THE SIMPLEST and best teatime treats. Buttermilk adds flavour and makes the lightest scones. Serve these hot, with generous toppings of butter, jam, and clotted cream, if you like. The only drawback to the recipe is that they must be made and eaten on the same day, though that shouldn't prove too taxing!

SERVES MAKES 8-10 **PREP** 15-20 MINS **COOK** 12-15 MINS

Ingredients

60g (2oz) unsalted butter	2 tbsp caster sugar
250g (9oz) unbleached strong white flour	175ml (6fl oz) buttermilk, plus more if needed
2 tsp baking powder	
½ tsp salt	

MAKE THE DOUGH

1 **Preheat the oven** to 220°C (425°F/Gas 7). Brush a baking sheet with melted butter. Sift the flour, baking powder, and salt into a medium bowl. Stir in the sugar. Add the butter and cut it into small pieces using 2 round-bladed knives (this keeps the butter cool).

2 **Rub the mixture** with your fingertips until it forms fine crumbs, lifting and crumbling to aerate it. Work quickly so the warmth of your hands does not melt the butter. In a slow, steady stream, pour the buttermilk into the centre of the well.

3 **Quickly toss the flour mixture** and buttermilk with a fork to form crumbs. Do not overmix the dough or the scones will be heavy. Add a little more buttermilk if the crumbs seem dry.

4 **Stir the mixture** just until the crumbs hold together and form a dough. It is important not to work this dough any more than absolutely necessary, for the best results, so take care.

SHAPE AND BAKE THE SCONES

5 **Turn the dough** on to a floured work surface and knead lightly for 3-5 seconds. Don't be tempted to make the dough smooth. The rougher the dough remains, the lighter the scones will be. Pat the dough out to a round, 1cm (½in) thick. Cut out rounds with a 7cm (2¾in) pastry cutter, patting out the trimmings and cutting additional rounds until all the dough has been used.

6 Arrange the scones 5cm (2in) apart on the baking sheet. Bake for 12-15 minutes, until lightly browned. Pile the scones in a basket and serve them hot with jam, butter, and clotted cream.

Pitta bread

A MIDDLE EASTERN BREAD, delicious when stuffed with salad. The cumin seeds in the dough add a subtle crunch and pungent flavour, but the breads will be equally delicious if you don't have any, or prefer to leave them out. If you would rather not knead the bread by hand, it can be made in a food processor fitted with a dough hook, or in a heavy-duty electric mixer.

SERVES	PREP	COOK
MAKES 6	20–30 MINS PLUS RISING	5 MINS

Ingredients

1 tsp dried yeast, or 6g (⅕oz) fresh yeast

2 tsp olive oil

1 tsp salt

60g (2oz) strong wholemeal flour

250g (9oz) unbleached strong white flour, plus more if needed

2 tsp cumin seeds

MAKE AND KNEAD THE DOUGH AND LET IT RISE

1 In a small bowl, sprinkle or crumble the yeast over 4 tbsp taken from 250ml (9fl oz) lukewarm water. Let stand for about 5 minutes until dissolved, stirring once.

3 Add the remaining strong white flour, 60g (2oz) at a time, mixing well after each addition. Keep adding flour until the dough pulls away from the side of the bowl in a ball. It should be soft and slightly sticky. Turn the dough on to a floured work surface, and knead until very smooth and elastic.

2 Put the dissolved yeast, remaining water, oil, and salt in a large bowl. Stir in the wholemeal flour with half of the strong white flour and the cumin seeds, and mix well with your hand.

4 Wash a large bowl and brush it with oil. Put the kneaded dough in the bowl, and flip it, so the surface is lightly oiled. Cover the bowl with a damp tea towel, and let rise in a warm place for 1–1½ hours, until doubled in bulk.

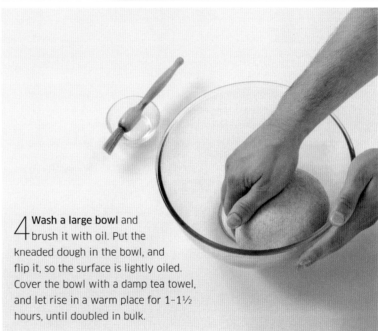

SHAPE THE PITTA BREADS

5 Generously flour 2 baking sheets. Turn the dough on to a lightly floured work surface, and knead with your hand just to knock out the air. Cover the dough and let rest for about 5 minutes. Shape the dough into a cylinder about 5cm (2in) in diameter, then cut the cylinder into 6 pieces.

6 Take 1 piece of the dough, and cover the rest while you work. Shape the piece of dough into a ball, then roll the ball into an 18cm (7in) round or oval with a rolling pin. Transfer the round to a prepared baking sheet. Repeat to shape the remaining dough. Cover the pitta breads with a dry tea towel, and let rise in a warm place for about 20 minutes, until puffed. Meanwhile, preheat the oven to its maximum setting.

7 Put an additional baking sheet in the oven to heat. With a palette knife, gently loosen the rounds or ovals from 1 of the baking sheets. Slide the loosened rounds all at once on to the heated baking sheet in the oven, and bake them until puffed; it should only take about 5 minutes. You only want the tops to be tinged with brown; they should not be golden or crispy, so err on the side of undercooked rather than overcooked. Crisped pitta breads will be impossible to fill.

8 Transfer the cooked breads to a wire rack, and brush the tops lightly with water, in order to keep the very thin pittas moist as they cool. Bake the remaining rounds or ovals from the second baking sheet. Brush any excess flour from the bottom of each pitta, and serve while still warm: break each open, and stuff with salad.

Potato-chive monkey bread

BREAD MADE WITH MASHED POTATO has a soft crust and moist centre, and is an American favourite. Potato bread is delicious warm from the oven, but the dough can be made, kneaded, and left to rise in the refrigerator overnight. Shape the dough, let it come to room temperature, then bake as directed.

SERVES	PREP	COOK
MAKES 1 LOAF	50-55 MINS PLUS RISING	40-45 MINS

Ingredients

250g (9oz) potatoes

2½ tsp dried yeast, or 15g (½oz) fresh yeast

125g (4½oz) unsalted butter, plus more for the bowl and mould

1 large bunch of chives, snipped

2 tbsp sugar

2 tsp salt

425g (15oz) unbleached strong white flour, plus more if needed

PREPARE THE DOUGH

1 **Peel the potatoes** and cut them into 2-3 pieces. Put them in a saucepan with plenty of cold water, cover, and bring to a boil. Simmer gently for 15-20 minutes, or just until the potatoes are tender when pierced with the tip of a knife.

2 **Drain the potatoes,** reserving 250ml (9fl oz) of the cooking liquid. Mash the potatoes well, ensuring there are no lumps. Let the reserved liquid and potatoes cool. In a small bowl, sprinkle or crumble the yeast over 4 tbsp lukewarm water. Let stand for about 5 minutes until dissolved, stirring once.

3 **Melt half the butter** in a saucepan. Put the reserved potato liquid, mashed potato, dissolved yeast, and melted butter into a large bowl. Add the snipped chives, sugar, and salt and mix with your hand, until all the ingredients are evenly spread through the mixture.

4 **Stir in half the flour** and mix well with your hand. Add the remaining flour, 60g (2oz) at a time, mixing well after each addition. Keep adding flour until the dough pulls away from the side of the bowl in a ball. It should be soft and slightly sticky.

KNEAD THE DOUGH AND LET IT RISE

5 **Turn the dough** on to a floured work surface. Sprinkle the dough and your hands with flour and knead for 5-7 minutes, until it is very smooth and elastic, and forms a ball. If the dough sticks while kneading, flour the work surface sparingly.

6 **Wash out the large bowl** and brush it with melted butter. Put the dough in the bowl and flip it so the surface is lightly buttered. Cover with a damp tea towel and let the dough rise in a warm place for 1-1½ hours, or until doubled in bulk.

SHAPE AND BAKE THE LOAF

7 **Brush a 1.7 litre (3 pint) ring mould** with melted butter. Melt the remaining 60g (2oz) butter and pour it into a shallow dish. Turn the dough on to a lightly floured work surface and knead just to knock out the air. Cover and let rest for about 5 minutes. Flour your hands and pinch off walnut-sized pieces of dough, making about 30 pieces.

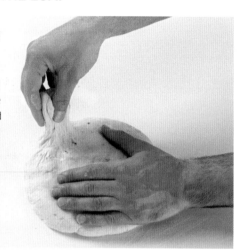

8 **Roll each piece of dough** between the palms of your hands to shape into smooth balls. Put a few balls of dough into the dish of melted butter and turn them with a spoon until coated.

9 **Transfer the balls** of dough to the prepared mould. Repeat with the remaining dough. Cover the mould with a dry tea towel and let rise in a warm place for about 40 minutes, until the mould is full. Preheat the oven to 190°C (375°F,/Gas 5).

10 **Bake the loaf** in the heated oven for 40-45 minutes, until golden brown and the bread starts to shrink from the side of the mould. Let cool slightly on a wire rack, then carefully unmould. With your fingers, pull the bread apart while still warm. It is delicious with roast chicken.

VARIATION: Soured cream and dill potato bread

1 Omit the melted butter for coating, and omit the chives. Strip the leaves from 5-7 dill sprigs and coarsely chop. Prepare the potatoes and make the dough, using 60g (2oz) butter and adding the dill in place of the chives. Knead, and let rise as directed.

2 Brush a ring mould with melted butter. Put 75ml (2½fl oz) soured cream into a small bowl in place of the melted butter for coating. Knock the air out of the dough, and rest as directed. Cut the dough in half. Roll the pieces of dough into cylinders about 5cm (2in) in diameter. Cut each into 4 pieces. Lightly flour the work surface. Roll a piece of dough into a smooth ball. Drop it into the mould.

3 Brush the sides and top of the ball of dough with the soured cream. Repeat with the remaining dough, arranging the balls evenly in the mould. Let the loaf rise as directed. Heat the oven to 190°C (375°F/Gas 5). Bake, cool, and unmould the bread as directed.

Walnut, bacon, and herb kugelhopf

FROM ALSACE, the most easterly province of France, this egg-rich bread is traditionally baked in a ring mould to give the characteristic shape. Make sure that your walnuts and bacon are of the best quality, as they will give the bread its definite taste. Buy walnuts from France, if you can, for the sweetest and most delicious results. The bread freezes successfully; make sure that you get it into the freezer as soon as it is completely cold.

SERVES
MAKES 1
LOAF

PREP
45–50 MINS
PLUS RISING

COOK
45–50 MINS

Ingredients

150ml (5fl oz) milk

150g (5½oz) unsalted butter

1 tbsp sugar

1 tbsp dried yeast, or 20g (¾oz) fresh yeast

3 eggs

500g (1lb 2oz) unbleached strong white flour

1 tsp salt

60g (2oz) walnut halves

125g (4½oz) thick-cut bacon rashers, sliced

3–5 sage sprigs, chopped

3–5 thyme sprigs, chopped

MAKE AND KNEAD THE DOUGH AND LET IT RISE

1 **Bring the milk** just to a boil, pour 4 tbsp into a bowl and let cool to lukewarm. Cut the butter into pieces. Add the butter and sugar to the milk in the pan and stir until melted.

3 **With your fingertips,** work the ingredients in the well until thoroughly mixed. Gradually draw in the flour and work it into the other ingredients with your hand to form a smooth dough.

2 **Sprinkle the yeast** over the 4 tbsp milk and let stand for 5 minutes until dissolved, stirring once. Beat the eggs just until mixed. Sift the flour and salt into a large bowl. Make a well in the centre and add the dissolved yeast, eggs, and the cooled sweetened milk.

4 **Beat the dough:** cupping your hand like a spoon, lift the dough, then let it fall back into the bowl with a slap. Continue beating for 5–7 minutes, until very elastic. Do not be tempted to add more flour; it should be very sticky. Cover the bowl with a damp tea towel and let rise in a warm place for 1–1½ hours, or until doubled in bulk.

PREPARE THE OTHER INGREDIENTS

5 Brush a 1 litre (1¾ pint) kugelhopf or ring mould with melted butter. Freeze the mould until the butter is hard (about 10 minutes) then butter it again. Set 5 walnut halves aside for decoration and coarsely chop the rest.

6 Cook the bacon in a frying pan, stirring occasionally, for 3–4 minutes, until lightly browned. With a slotted spoon, transfer the bacon to kitchen paper and let drain.

FINISH AND BAKE THE KUGELHOPF

7 Beat the dough lightly with your hand to knock out the air. Add the herbs, chopped walnuts, and bacon and beat with your hand until well combined. Arrange the reserved walnut halves in a circle in the bottom of the prepared mould, placing them rounded-side down.

8 Drop the dough into the mould, filling it evenly. Cover with a clean, dry tea towel and let the dough rise in a warm place until it comes just above the top of the mould. It should take about 30–40 minutes, but it will depend on the heat of the room, or even the humidity of the atmosphere. Sometimes it can take a lot longer, depending on the flour used (flour can vary greatly). Preheat the oven to 190°C (375°F/Gas 5) when the bread has risen to the required height.

9 Bake the kugelhopf in the heated oven until puffed and very brown, and the bread starts to shrink from the side of the mould. It should take 45–50 minutes. Watch carefully so that the bread does not scorch, as this will taint the flavour. Let it cool slightly. Unmould the bread on to a wire rack and let cool completely. Serve the kugelhopf as an accompaniment to soups or simple salads.

Small brioches

A CLASSIC FRENCH BREAD, rich with eggs and butter. You'll need 10 x 7.5cm (3in) brioche moulds. You can choose whether or not to place a round "head" on top of each brioche; it is traditional, but the golden, shining domes are just as beautiful if you leave them off. The dough can be made up to the end of step 5, kneaded, and left in the refrigerator to rise overnight. Let the dough come to room temperature, knead in the butter, and finish the brioche as directed.

SERVES
MAKES 10

PREP
45–50 MINS
PLUS RISING

COOK
15–20 MINS

Ingredients

FOR THE BRIOCHES

2½ tsp dried yeast, or 15g (½oz) fresh yeast

5 eggs

375g (13oz) unbleached strong white flour, plus more if needed

2 tbsp sugar

1½tsp salt

175g (6oz) unsalted butter, softened, plus more for the bowl and moulds

FOR THE GLAZE

1 egg

½ tsp salt

MAKE AND KNEAD THE DOUGH AND LET IT RISE

1 In a small bowl, sprinkle or crumble the yeast over 2 tbsp lukewarm water. Let stand for about 5 minutes, until dissolved, stirring once. In another small bowl, beat the eggs with a fork just until mixed.

2 Sift the flour on to a work surface with the sugar and salt. Make a large well in the centre, and add the eggs and dissolved yeast. With your fingertips, work the ingredients in the well until thoroughly mixed.

3 Gradually draw in the flour, and work it into the other ingredients with your hand to form a smooth dough. It should be soft and sticky. Sprinkle the dough with flour and knead, lifting the dough up and throwing it down, for 8-10 minutes, until it is very elastic and resembles chamois leather.

4 Work in more flour, so the dough is slightly sticky; it will become less sticky while kneading, so add flour sparingly. Brush a bowl with butter. Put in the dough and roll it against the side, so the surface is lightly buttered.

5 Cover the bowl with a damp tea towel, and let rise in a warm place for 1-1½ hours, until doubled in bulk. Alternatively, put the covered bowl of dough in the refrigerator, and leave it up to 8 hours or overnight. It will rise slowly during that time.

KNEAD IN THE BUTTER

6 Brush 10 x 7.5cm (3in) brioche moulds with melted butter. Set the moulds on a baking sheet. Turn the dough onto a lightly floured work surface, and knead with your hand to knock out the air. Cover the dough and let rest for about 5 minutes.

7 Knead in the softened butter, pinching and squeezing the dough with both hands. Knead the dough on the floured work surface for 3-5 minutes, until smooth again. Cover, and let rest for 5 minutes more.

SHAPE AND BAKE THE BRIOCHES

8 Divide the dough in half. Roll one piece of dough into a cylinder about 5cm (2in) in diameter. Cut the cylinder into five pieces. Repeat to shape and divide the remaining dough. Lightly flour the work surface. Cup each piece of dough under the palm of your hand and roll the dough so it forms a smooth ball.

9 Pinch about one-quarter of each ball between your thumb and forefinger, almost dividing it from the remaining dough, to form the head. Holding the head, lower each ball into a mould, twisting and pressing the head on to the base of the brioche.

10 With your forefinger, press down 2-3 times around the head to seal it to the base of the brioche. Cover the moulds with a dry tea towel, and let rise in a warm place for about 30 minutes, until the moulds are full and the dough is puffed. Meanwhile, preheat the oven to 220°C (425°F/Gas 7).

11 Lightly beat the egg with the salt. Brush the brioches with egg glaze. Bake the brioches in the heated oven for 15-20 minutes, until puffed and brown. Unmould one of the brioches, turn it over and tap the bottom; it should sound hollow. Let the brioches cool slightly, then unmould. Transfer to a wire rack and let cool completely. Brioches make a special breakfast or afternoon tea, served plain, or with jam.

Yule bread

IF YOU WANT TO EAT THIS BREAD at Christmas, you will need to make it 1 month before, to give it time to moisten and mellow. Eat it with a well-aged Stilton cheese. To store the loaf, wrap it first in baking parchment, and then in foil, and seal it in an airtight container. It will be fine for up to 4 weeks, and you won't have to worry about it.

SERVES
MAKES 1
LARGE LOAF

PREP
50-55 MINS,
PLUS RISING

COOK
60-65 MINS

Ingredients

1 English breakfast tea bag	2 eggs
90g (3oz) sultanas	530g (1lb 3oz) unbleached strong white flour, plus more if needed
90g (3oz) currants	½ tsp ground cinnamon
45g (1½oz) candied orange peel	½ tsp ground cloves
2½ tsp dried yeast, or 15g (½oz) fresh yeast	3 tbsp granulated sugar
	1 tsp salt
	125g (4½oz) unsalted butter, plus more for the bowl and tin
	2 tbsp fine brown sugar crystals, to glaze

MAKE THE DOUGH

1 Bring 300ml (½ pint) of water to a boil. Take from the heat, add the tea bag and let soak for 5 minutes. Put the sultanas and currants in a medium bowl. Discard the tea bag. Pour over the warm tea, and let the fruit soak for 10-15 minutes, until plump.

2 Strain the fruit, reserving the tea. Chop the candied orange peel. Set all the fruit aside. In a small bowl, sprinkle or crumble the yeast over 4 tbsp lukewarm water. Let stand for about 5 minutes, until dissolved, stirring once. In another small bowl, beat the eggs with a fork just until mixed.

3 Sift the flour, cinnamon, and cloves into a large bowl, and add the sugar and salt. Make a well in the centre and add the reserved tea, eggs and dissolved yeast. Work the ingredients in the well until thoroughly mixed.

4 Gradually draw in the flour, and work it into the other ingredients with your hand, to form a smooth dough. It should be soft and slightly sticky. Turn on to a floured work surface. Knead for 5-7 minutes, until it is very smooth, elastic, and forms a ball.

5 Wash a large bowl. Brush the bowl with melted butter. Put the dough in the bowl, and flip it so that the surface is lightly buttered. Cover the bowl with a damp tea towel, and let the dough rise in a warm place for 1-1½ hours, until doubled in bulk.

KNEAD IN THE BUTTER AND SHAPE THE LOAF

6 Brush a 23x12x7.5cm (9x5x3in) loaf tin with melted butter. Turn the dough on to a lightly floured work surface and knead to knock out the air. Cover and let rest for about 5 minutes. Knead in the softened butter, pinching and squeezing the dough with both hands. Knead the dough on the floured work surface for 3-5 minutes, until smooth again. Cover and let rest for about 5 minutes longer.

7 Knead the sultanas, currants, and candied orange peel into the dough until evenly blended. Cover and let rest for about 5 minutes. Flour your hands and pat the dough into a 25x20cm (10x8in) rectangle, on the floured work surface. Starting with a long side, roll the rectangle into a cylinder, sealing it with your fingers as you go.

8 Roll the cylinder, stretching it until it is about 45cm (18in) long. Working with the cylinder seam-side up, fold the ends over to meet, making it the length of the tin. Drop the loaf, seam-side down, into the tin. Cover with a dry tea towel and let rise in a warm place for about 45 minutes, until the tin is just full.

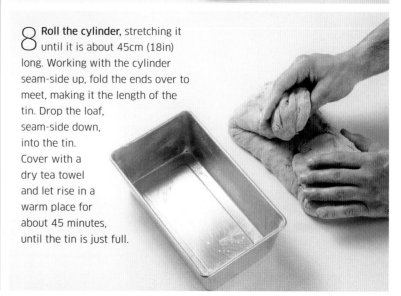

9 **Put the sugar crystals** in a plastic bag. Crush them with a rolling pin; they should be rather fine. Preheat the oven to 200°C (400°F/Gas 6). Brush the top of the loaf with water. Sprinkle the loaf with the sugar crystals, spreading them evenly over the surface.

BAKE THE LOAF

10 **Bake the loaf** on the center shelf of the oven until it puffs up and begins to brown; it will take about 15 minutes. Reduce the heat to 180°C (350°F/Gas 4) and continue baking until a metal skewer inserted in the centre comes out clean. It should take 45–50 minutes longer. This is a long baking time, so if the top of the bread browns too quickly before it is fully baked (which is quite likely), cover it loosely with a sheet of aluminium foil to protect the surface from scorching. Be sure to check the bread, without opening the oven door, frequently, so that it does not threaten to burn. If your oven is particularly fast, it may help to put a small ovenproof bowl of water on to the bottom rack, to keep the air inside the oven moist; this can help prevent scorching.

11 **Remove the bread** from the tin. To check if it is ready, turn it over and firmly tap the bottom with your knuckles. The bread should sound hollow, and the sides should feel crisp when gently squeezed. Transfer the bread to a wire rack and let it cool completely. This is good for breakfast, served plain or toasted, and spread with butter. Or eat it with a full-flavoured, mature cheese; it's especially good with blue cheese, as a festive snack or as a savoury, after the main course.

Chocolate bread

A DELICIOUS DESSERT BREAD. Try it spread with mascarpone and eaten with a glass of red wine. The recipe comes from Italy, and is a cousin of the more famous panettone. It is very important to use good-quality chocolate for the best flavour. This is a wonderful bread to serve when you have a house full of guests; it's unlikely they will have seen its like before, and everyone loves it.

SERVES MAKES 1 LOAF	PREP 35-40 MINS PLUS RISING	COOK 45-50 MINS

Ingredients

2½ tsp dried yeast, or 15g (½oz) fresh yeast

15g (½oz) unsalted butter, softened

30g (1oz) cocoa powder

500g (1lb 2oz) unbleached strong white flour

2 tsp salt

60g (2oz) sugar

125g (4½oz) good-quality dark chocolate

MIX AND KNEAD THE DOUGH IN A FOOD MIXER

1 **In a small bowl,** sprinkle or crumble the yeast over 4 tbsp taken from 375ml (13fl oz) lukewarm water. Let stand for 5 minutes, until dissolved, stirring once. Put the dissolved yeast, softened butter and cocoa powder into the food mixer bowl. Pour in the remaining water and mix with the paddle on low speed to combine.

3 **Attach the dough hook.** On medium speed, knead the dough for 3-5 minutes, until very smooth and elastic. If necessary, add more flour while kneading. If the dough climbs up the hook, stop the machine, and push the dough back down.

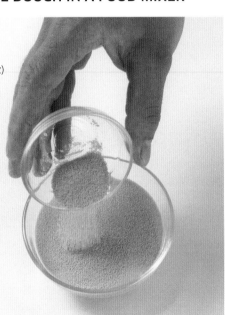

2 **Add half the flour** to the bowl with the salt and sugar, and beat with the paddle just until combined. Add the remaining flour, 60g (2oz) at a time, beating after each addition. Keep adding flour until the dough pulls away from the side of the bowl in a ball. It should be soft and slightly sticky.

4 **Remove the kneaded dough** from the dough hook, and shape it into a ball. Brush a large bowl with melted butter. Put the dough in the bowl and flip it so the surface is lightly buttered. Cover with a damp tea towel and let rise in a warm place for 1-1½ hours, or until doubled in bulk.

 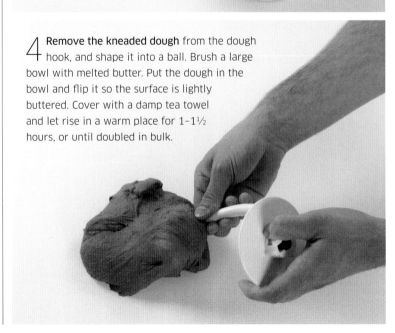

FINISH THE DOUGH

5 Brush a 1.5 litre (2¾ pint) soufflé dish with melted butter. Set aside. Cut the chocolate into large chunks, then coarsely chop them. Chill the chocolate, so it won't melt when kneaded into the dough. Once the dough has risen, turn it from the bowl on to a lightly floured work surface.

6 Knead the dough with your hand just to knock out the air. Cover and let rest for about 5 minutes. Knead the chopped chocolate into the dough until evenly blended. Cover and let rest again for about 5 minutes more. Shape the dough into a loose ball. Fold the sides over to the centre, turning and pinching to make a tight round ball.

7 Carefully put the ball of dough, seam-side down, into the prepared dish. Cover with a dry tea towel and let rise in a warm place until the soufflé dish is just full. It should take about 45 minutes. Meanwhile, preheat the oven to 220°C (425°F/Gas 7).

BAKE THE LOAF

8 Brush the loaf with water and lightly sprinkle with sugar to glaze. Bake for 20 minutes. Reduce the heat to 190°C (375°F/Gas 5) and bake for 25-30 minutes longer, until well browned. Remove the loaf from the dish. Turn it over and tap the bottom. The bread should sound hollow, and the sides should feel crisp. Using a dry tea towel, carefully transfer the bread to a wire rack and let cool completely.

 VARIATION: Chocolate and orange rolls

Grated orange zest adds a wonderful tang to this bread.

1 Omit the cocoa powder. Finely grate the zest of 2 oranges, making sure to include none of the bitter white pith. Make the dough, adding the orange zest to the softened butter and liquid ingredients in place of the cocoa powder. Knead and let the dough rise as directed in the main recipe. Chop and chill the chocolate. Brush 2 baking sheets with melted butter.

2 Knock the air out of the dough and let it rest for about 5 minutes. Knead in the chocolate and let the dough rest again, for about 5 minutes more. Cut the dough in half. Roll 1 piece of dough into a cylinder about 5cm (2in) in diameter. Cut the cylinder into 4 pieces. Shape and divide the remaining dough. Lightly flour a work surface. Roll each piece of dough into a smooth ball. Set the ball on a prepared baking sheet. Shape the remaining pieces. Cover and let rise in a warm place until the rolls have doubled in bulk. It will probably take about 30 minutes.

3 Preheat the oven to 220°C (425°F/Gas 7). Glaze the rolls as directed, and bake them in the heated oven for 15 minutes, until they begin to brown. Reduce the heat to 190°C (375°F/Gas 5) and bake until well browned and the rolls sound hollow when tapped. It could take 15-20 minutes longer, but keep a close eye on them so that the rolls do not scorch. Cover them with foil if they threaten to do so. Makes 8 rolls.

Pies, tarts, and cakes

Sweet baked goodies,
for dessert or with tea

Blackberry and apple pie

BECAUSE THEY RIPEN TOGETHER in early autumn, blackberries and apples are a popular combination. Traditionally, cooking apples are used, but this recipe contains eating apples for their sweeter flavour. Serve the pie warm, with double cream. The shortcrust pastry dough can be made up to 2 days ahead and kept, tightly wrapped with clingfilm, in the refrigerator. The pie itself is best eaten on the day it is baked, but that shouldn't prove too difficult to achieve!

SERVES SERVES 4-6	**PREP** 35-40 MINS PLUS CHILLING	**COOK** 50-60 MINS

Ingredients

FOR THE PASTRY

215g (7½oz) plain flour

1½ tbsp caster sugar (optional)

¼ tsp salt

45g (1½oz) white vegetable fat, chilled

60g (2oz) unsalted butter, chilled

FOR THE FILLING

500g (1lb 2oz) blackberries

1 lemon

875g (1lb 15oz) eating apples

150g (5½oz) caster sugar, or to taste

MAKE THE PASTRY

1 **Sift the flour**, sugar, if using, and salt into a medium bowl. Cut the chilled vegetable fat and butter into pieces, and add it to the flour mixture; then cut the fats into the mixture with 2 round-bladed table knives to keep the mixture as cool as possible. (You can use your hands, but this will warm up the pastry, which should be avoided.)

2 **Rub in the fat** with your fingertips until the mixture forms coarse crumbs, lifting and crumbling to help aerate it. Try to make this process as quick as possible, to avoid warming up the pastry misture. Sprinkle 3-4 tbsp cold water over the mixture, 1 tbsp at a time, and mix in with a fork. Stop as soon as the crumbs begin to cling together in moist clumps. Do not use too much water, or the dough will be sticky and the pastry may be tough once baked.

3 **Continue mixing** the pastry with the fork, to keep the mixture cool and prevent the fat from melting, until the crumbs are moist enough to start sticking together. Press the dough lightly into a ball – again being very careful not to let it come into too much contact with your warm palms – then wrap it tightly, and chill until firm in the refrigerator. It will take at least 30 minutes, but can be chilled for up to 3 days, if this is more convenient.

PREPARE THE PIE FILLING

4 **Pick over the blackberries**; wash them only if dirty. Squeeze the lemon and set the juice aside. Peel the apples with a vegetable peeler. Cut out the stalk and flower ends from each apple.

5 **Halve 1 apple**, and scoop out the core from each half with a teaspoon or a melon baller, ensuring all the hard fibres and membranes are removed. Repeat for the remaining apples.

6 **Set 1 apple half**, cut-side down, on the chopping board. Cut it lengthways in half, then slice it across into 6 equal chunks. Repeat for the remaining apple halves. Put the apples in a bowl. Add the lemon juice and all but 2 tbsp of the sugar; toss to combine.

7 **Add the blackberries** to the apple chunks and toss again lightly. Taste the fruit mixture, adding more sugar if necessary. How much you will need depends whether the apples are sweet or tart.

ASSEMBLE THE PIE

8 **Lightly flour a work surface.** Roll out the dough, and trim to a shape 7.5cm (3in) larger than the top of your chosen pie dish. The dish can be any shape as long as it has a 1 litre (1¾ pint) capacity. Reserve the trimmings.

9 **Invert the pie dish** on to the pastry. Cut a 2cm (¾in) strip from the edge of the dough, leaving a shape 4cm (1½in) larger than the dish. Place a pie funnel in the centre and spoon the fruit around it into a mound.

10 **With a pastry brush,** lightly moisten the edge of the pie dish with cold water. Lift the strip from around the dough and transfer it to the edge of the pie dish, pressing it down firmly. Brush the strip with cold water.

11 **Roll up the pastry** around the rolling pin and unroll it over the filling. Press the edge down on to the dough strip to seal it. With the tip of a small knife, cut a hole in the dough over the pie funnel, to allow steam to escape. Trim the edges; use the trimmings to decorate the pie, if you like.

BAKE THE PIE

12 **Chill the pie** until firm, about 15 minutes. Meanwhile, preheat the oven to 190°C (375°F/Gas 5). Bake the pie for 50-60 minutes, until the pastry is lightly browned and crisp, and the apples are tender when pierced with a metal skewer. Remove from the oven and sprinkle with the reserved sugar. Serve hot or warm, with double cream, if you like.

Lemon meringue pie

TART LEMON CURD WITH SWEET MERINGUE PEAKS is a combination few can resist. It's not surprising that this pie has achieved international fame. The pastry shell can be baked and the lemon curd made 1 day ahead.

SERVES	PREP	COOK
SERVES 6-8	45–50 MINS PLUS CHILLING	30–35 MINS

Ingredients

FOR THE PASTRY

215g (7½oz) plain flour

¼ tsp salt

90g (3oz) white vegetable fat

1½ tbsp caster sugar (optional)

FOR THE LEMON CURD

5 lemons

3 egg yolks

2 eggs

125g (4½oz) unsalted butter

150g (5½oz) caster sugar

FOR THE ITALIAN MERINGUE

100g (3½oz) caster sugar

3 egg whites

MAKE THE PASTRY AND BAKE BLIND

1 **Sift the flour** and salt into a bowl. Cut in the fat with 2 knives. With your fingertips, rub in the fat until the mixture forms coarse crumbs. Add the sugar, if using. Mix in 3–4 tbsp cold water, 1 tbsp at a time. When the crumbs stick together, press lightly into a ball, wrap, and chill for 30 minutes.

2 **Brush a 23cm (9in) pie dish** with melted butter. On a floured surface, roll the pastry into a round 5cm (2in) larger than the dish. Using the rolling pin, drape the dough over the dish. Gently lift the edge of the pastry with your fingertips and press it well into the bottom and up the side of the pie dish. Press to seal any cracks.

3 **Using kitchen scissors** or a round-bladed table knife, trim the dough so that it extends 1cm (½in) out from the edge of the dish. Fold under the excess pastry to make a thicker edge. Flute the edge of the pastry shell: press your thumbs together diagonally into it to make a ridge. Continue around the edge in this way until the fluting is completed.

4 **Prick the bottom of the pastry shell** with a fork to prevent air bubbles forming during cooking. Chill for about 15 minutes, until firm. Meanwhile, preheat the oven to 200°C (400°F/Gas 6). Heat a baking sheet in the oven. Line the pastry with a double thickness of foil, pushing well into the bottom. Half-fill with dried beans or rice. Bake on the baking sheet for about 15 minutes, until set and the rim starts to brown.

5 **Remove the foil** and beans, and reduce the oven temperature to 190°C (375°F/Gas 5). Bake for 5–10 minutes longer, until golden. Transfer to a wire rack and let cool before adding the filling. Leave the oven on and the baking sheet in the oven.

MAKE THE LEMON CURD

6 **Finely grate the zest** from 2 of the lemons on to baking parchment. Set aside. Halve all the lemons. Squeeze the juice and strain it into a measuring jug. There should be about 250ml (8fl oz). Whisk the egg yolks with the whole eggs until evenly mixed together. Cut the butter into small pieces.

7 **Put the sugar,** zest, and butter into a heavy-based saucepan. Add the lemon juice. Whisk over fairly low heat for 2–3 minutes, until the sugar has dissolved. Off the heat, whisk in the beaten eggs until evenly combined with the lemon mixture.

8 **Return to the heat and cook gently,** so the curd thickens slowly and does not curdle, stirring constantly with a wooden spoon, for 4–6 minutes, or until it is thick enough to coat the back of the spoon.

9 Sieve the lemon curd into a bowl to remove any bits of egg or zest and set aside to cool. Spoon the lemon curd into the pastry shell. Bake on the baking sheet for 10-12 minutes, just until the mixture starts to set. Transfer to a wire rack and let cool, then chill. The curd will set further when cold.

MAKE THE MERINGUE AND **FINISH** THE PIE

10 **Heat the sugar** in 75ml (2½fl oz) water until dissolved. Boil, without stirring, until it reaches hard ball stage (120°C/248°F on a sugar thermometer, or until a small spoonful forms a firm, pliable ball).

11 **Meanwhile, put the egg whites** into a metal bowl and whisk with an electric mixer or by hand. Begin whisking slowly, but increase the speed when the egg whites become foamy and white. Continue whisking the egg whites until stiff peaks form when the beaters are lifted.

12 **Gradually pour the hot sugar syrup** into the beaten egg whites, beating constantly. Be sure to pour the syrup directly into the egg whites so that it does not stick to the side of the bowl. Continue beating for about 5 minutes, until the meringue is cool and stiff.

13 **Heat the grill.** With a palette knife, spread the meringue over the filling to cover (or pipe it on, if you prefer). Grill the pie 7.5cm (3in) from the heat for 1-2 minutes, until the meringue is golden brown. Transfer to a serving platter and serve from the pie dish while the meringue is warm and the filling is chilled. Cut it into wedges with a knife dipped in hot water to cut cleanly.

Rhubarb and strawberry tart

TART RHUBARB AND SWEET STRAWBERRIES go into this wonderful pie, which is delicious warm or at room temperature. Ice cream would make a good accompaniment. The pastry can be made up to 2 days ahead and kept, tightly wrapped, in the refrigerator. The pie is best eaten on the day it is baked. Make this in late spring, when both rhubarb and strawberries are at their best.

SERVES	PREP	COOK
SERVES 6-8	30-35 MINS PLUS CHILLING	50-55 MINS

Ingredients

FOR THE PASTRY

330g (11oz) plain flour

½ tsp salt

150g (5½oz) white vegetable fat

2 tbsp caster sugar (optional)

FOR THE FILLING

375g (13oz) strawberries

1 orange

1kg (2¼lb) rhubarb, sliced

250g (9oz) caster sugar

¼ tsp salt

30g (1oz) plain flour

15g (½oz) unsalted butter

FOR THE GLAZE

1 tbsp milk

1 tbsp caster sugar

MAKE THE PASTRY AND LINE THE PIE DISH

1 **Sift the flour** and salt into a bowl. Add the fat, cutting it with 2 round-bladed knives. With your fingertips, rub the fat into the flour until the mixture forms coarse crumbs, lifting and crumbling the mixture to help aerate it. Add the sugar, if using. Sprinkle 6-7 tbsp cold water over the mixture, 1 tbsp at a time, mixing lightly with a fork. When the crumbs start sticking together, press the dough lightly into a ball, wrap it tightly, and chill until firm, about 30 minutes.

2 **Brush a 23cm (9in) pie dish** with melted butter. Lightly flour a work surface. Roll out two-thirds of the dough into a round, 5cm (2in) larger than the top of the dish. Using the rolling pin, drape the pastry over the dish. Gently lift the edge of the dough and press it well into the bottom and up the side of the pie dish.

3 **Lift the dish** and trim the pastry even with the outer edge of the dish, using a table knife. Reserve the trimmings. Chill the pastry shell for about 15 minutes, until firm.

PREPARE THE FILLING

4 **Hull the strawberries,** washing only if dirty. Halve or quarter them according to size. Using the medium grid of a grater, grate the zest from the orange on to a sheet of baking parchment.

5 **In a bowl,** combine the rhubarb, orange zest, sugar, salt, and flour, and stir to mix. Add the strawberries and toss gently. Spoon the fruit mixture into the lined pie dish, doming it slightly. Cut the butter into small pieces and dot the pieces over the filling.

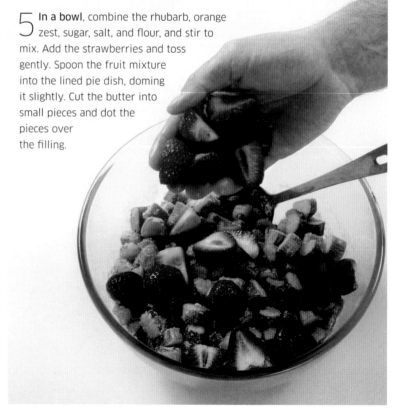

FINISH AND BAKE THE PIE

7 **Use the pastry trimmings** to decorate the top of the pie, if you like. With a small knife, cut steam vents around the top crust of the pie. (If you don't do this, the pastry topping may become a little soggy while baking, as it will soak up all the moisture from the fruit.) Scallop the edge of the pie, if you like: place the forefinger of one hand on the edge of the dough, pointing outwards. With the forefinger and thumb of your other hand, push the dough inwards to form scallops. Repeat around the pie.

8 **Brush the top crust** with milk, and sprinkle evenly with the sugar. Chill the pie until firm; it should take about 15 minutes. Meanwhile, preheat the oven to 220°C (425°F/Gas 7). Put a baking sheet in the centre of the oven to heat up.

9 **Bake the pie** on the baking sheet in the oven, 20 minutes. Baking on a hot metal baking sheet will mean the base of the pie is in instant contact with direct heat from the moment it goes into the oven, so the bottom crust will be as crisp as possible. Reduce the oven temperature to 180°C (350°F/Gas 4). Bake until the rhubarb is tender when pierced with a skewer through a steam vent, and the crust is browned. It should take 30–35 minutes longer. If the top crust threatens to scorch before the pie is ready, cover it loosely with a sheet of foil and continue to bake until the fruit is completly tender. Transfer to a wire rack, and let cool. Serve in generous slices, with ice cream or pouring cream.

6 **Brush the edge** of the pastry shell with cold water. Roll out the remaining dough into a 28cm (11in) round. Wrap it around the rolling pin and drape it over the filling. With a small knife, trim the top crust even with the bottom crust. Press the edges together to seal them.

Pear pie with walnut pastry

IN THIS SPECIALITY from central France, wedges of pear are sandwiched between a double crust of walnut pastry. The pastry dough can be made up to 2 days ahead and kept, tightly wrapped, in the refrigerator. Serve the pie warm, with crème fraiche or whipped cream.

SERVES	**PREP**	**COOK**
SERVES 6-8	35-40 MINS PLUS CHILLING	35-40 MINS

Ingredients

FOR THE WALNUT PASTRY

60g (2oz) walnut pieces

135g (4¾oz) caster sugar

250g (9oz) plain flour, plus more if needed

150g (5½oz) unsalted butter

1 egg

½ tsp salt

1 tsp ground cinnamon

FOR THE FILLING

1 lemon

875g (1lb 15oz) pears

½ tsp freshly ground black pepper

1 tbsp caster sugar

MAKE THE WALNUT PASTRY DOUGH

1 **Put the walnut** pieces in a food processor. Add about half the sugar, and finely grind. Sift the flour on to a work surface, add the ground walnut and sugar mixture, then make a large well in the centre of the ingredients. Using the rolling pin, pound the butter to soften it slightly.

2 **Put the egg**, remaining sugar, butter, salt, and ground cinnamon into the well. With your fingertips, work the ingredients in the well until they are all thoroughly mixed together. Draw in the flour, working it into the other ingredients with your fingers, until coarse crumbs form.

3 **Press the dough** gently into a ball. It should be quite soft, but if it is too sticky, add a little more flour. Sprinkle the work surface lightly with flour. Knead the dough for 1-2 minutes, until it is very smooth and peels away from the work surface in one piece. Shape into a smooth ball, wrap tightly, and chill for 1 hour, until firm.

LINE THE TIN

4 **Brush a 23cm (9in) flan tin** with removable base, with melted butter. Lightly flour the work surface. Roll out two-thirds of the chilled dough into a 28cm (11in) round. Rewrap and return the unrolled dough to the refrigerator. Wrap the rolled dough around the rolling pin. Gently drape it over the tin.

5 **Gently press the dough** into the bottom of the tin. Roll the rolling pin over the top, pressing down to cut off excess dough. Add the trimmings to the reserved portion of dough and return to the refrigerator. With your thumbs, press the dough evenly up the tin side to increase the height of the shell. Chill for about 1 hour, until very firm.

PREPARE THE PEARS

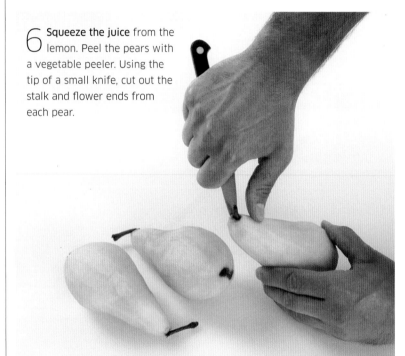

6 **Squeeze the juice** from the lemon. Peel the pears with a vegetable peeler. Using the tip of a small knife, cut out the stalk and flower ends from each pear.

7 **Cut each pear** into quarters, then scoop out the central stalks and cores with a small knife, being sure to remove all the hard fibres and working gently to keep the pear quarters intact.

8 **Put the pear wedges** into a bowl. Add the black pepper and the lemon juice. Toss until the pear wedges are coated. The lemon juice will stop the fruit from discolouring.

FILL AND **BAKE** THE PIE

9 **Shaking off any excess lemon juice,** arrange the pear wedges evenly in a cartwheel pattern on the bottom of the pastry shell. Roll out the remaining dough into a 25cm (10in) round; stamp out a 5cm (2in) round from the centre, using a cutter or a glass as a guide. This will provide very crisp pastry and allow a tantalizing glimpse into the pie filling.

10 **Wrap the dough** around the rolling pin, and drape it carefully over the pear wedges. With a small sharp knife, trim the top round even with the filled pastry shell, using the tin as a guide. Press the dough edges together firmly with the back of a fork to seal the top and bottom of the pastry shell together.

11 **Brush the top** of the pie with water and sprinkle evenly with the sugar. Chill the pie until firm; it should take about 15 minutes. Meanwhile, preheat the oven to 190°C (375°F/Gas 5). Heat a baking sheet in the oven. Put the pie on the baking sheet so the heat starts to cook the pastry base immediately, and bake the pie until the pastry is browned, and the pears are tender when pierced with a metal skewer, 35-40 minutes. If the top crust threatens to scorch before the pie is ready, cover it loosely with foil and continue to bake until the fruit is completely tender.

Almond and raspberry tart

NOW A VIENNESE SPECIALITY, this tart of buttery almond pastry and raspberry filling probably originated in the town of Linz, in Austria. It is ideal for entertaining, as it actually mellows, becoming more delicious, if it is baked a day or 2 ahead and stored in an airtight container. Sprinkle with icing sugar only about 30 minutes before serving, or it will sink into the pastry and may make it soft.

SERVES
SERVES 6-8

PREP
30-35 MINS
PLUS CHILLING

COOK
40-45 MINS

Ingredients

FOR THE ALMOND PASTRY DOUGH

1 lemon
175g (6oz) whole blanched almonds
125g (4½oz) plain flour, plus more if needed
½ tsp ground cinnamon
1 pinch of ground cloves

125g (4½oz) unsalted butter
1 egg yolk
100g (3½oz) caster sugar
¼ tsp salt

FOR THE FILLING

375g (13oz) raspberries
125g (4½oz) caster sugar
1-2 tbsp icing sugar

MAKE THE ALMOND PASTRY DOUGH

1 **Grate the zest** from the lemon on to a piece of baking parchment. Halve the lemon, and squeeze about 1½ tbsp juice. Put the whole almonds in a food processor, and add half the flour to prevent them from becoming oily. Finely grind.

2 **Sift the remaining flour** on to a work surface, with the cinnamon and cloves. Mix in the nuts, then make a well. Pound the butter to soften it. Put the butter, egg yolk, sugar, salt, lemon juice, and zest into the well.

3 **Using your fingertips,** work the ingredients in the well until thoroughly mixed. Draw in the flour and work it into the other ingredients, until coarse crumbs form. Press the dough into a ball, adding a little more flour if it is sticky. Lightly flour the work surface.

4 **Blend the dough** by pushing it away from you with the heel of your hand. Then gather it up and continue to blend for 1-2 minutes, until it is very smooth, and peels away from the work surface in 1 piece. Shape into a ball, wrap tightly, and chill for 1-2 hours, until firm. Meanwhile, make the filling.

MAKE THE RASPBERRY FILLING

5 Pick over the raspberries; wash them only if dirty. Put the sugar and raspberries in a saucepan. Cook, stirring, for 10–12 minutes, until they form a thick pulpy jam. Set aside to cool.

6 With the back of a wooden spoon, press half of the fruit pulp through a sieve set over a bowl to remove the seeds. Stir in the remaining pulp, leaving in its seeds for a little texture.

LINE THE TIN AND FINISH THE TART

7 Brush a 23cm (9in) flan tin with removable base with melted butter. Lightly flour a work surface; roll out two-thirds of the dough into a 28cm (11in) round. Rewrap and chill the remaining dough.

8 Wrap the dough around the rolling pin, then drape it over the tin and press it into the bottom. Roll the rolling pin over the top to cut off the excess dough. Reserve the trimmings. With your thumbs, press the dough evenly up the side of the flan tin to increase the height of the shell.

9 Spread the filling in the shell. Roll out the remaining dough; trim to a 15x30cm (6x12in) rectangle. Reserve the trimmings. Cut the dough into 12x1cm (½in) strips. Arrange half the strips across the tart, about 2cm (¾in) apart. Turn the tart 45°, and arrange the remaining strips diagonally over the first to form a lattice. Trim the overhanging dough strips.

10 Roll out all the dough trimmings thinly. Cut 3–4x1cm (½in) strips, with a patterned edge if you like. Brush the edge of the tart with cold water. Press the strips around the edge. Chill for about 15 minutes, until firm. Meanwhile, preheat the oven to 190°C (375°F/Gas 5), and heat a baking sheet.

11 Bake the tart on the baking sheet for 15 minutes, until the pastry begins to brown. Reduce the oven temperature to 180°C (350°F/Gas 4) and continue baking for 25–30 minutes longer, until the tart is golden brown and just beginning to shrink from the side of the tin.

12 Transfer the tart to a wire rack, and let cool slightly. Set the tin on a bowl and remove the side. Slide the tart on to the wire rack. Let cool completely. About 30 minutes before serving, dust with icing sugar.

Bavarian plum tart

BAVARIA IS FAMOUS for its cakes and tarts. In this recipe, a quick version of brioche forms the base. Juice from the fruit mingles with the custard filling to bring about a deliciously moist result. The amount of sugar you need depends on the sweetness of the plums. Apricots or greengages are also delicious in this tart.

SERVES	**PREP**	**COOK**
SERVES 8-10	35-40 MINS PLUS RISING	50-55 MINS

Ingredients

FOR THE BRIOCHE DOUGH

1½ tsp dried yeast, or 9g (⅓oz) fresh yeast

375g (13oz) plain flour, more if needed

2 tbsp caster sugar

1 tsp salt

3 eggs

125g (4½oz) unsalted butter

FOR THE FILLING

875g (1lb 15oz) purple plums

2 tbsp dried breadcrumbs

2 egg yolks

100g (3½oz) caster sugar

60ml (2fl oz) double cream

MAKE THE BRIOCHE DOUGH

1 **Sprinkle or crumble the yeast** over 60ml (2fl oz) lukewarm water in a small bowl. Let stand for 5 minutes, until dissolved. Lightly oil a medium bowl. Sift the flour on to the work surface. Make a well in the centre and add the sugar, salt, yeast mixture, and eggs.

2 **With your fingertips,** work the ingredients in the well until they are thoroughly mixed. Work in the flour to form a soft dough; add more flour if it is very sticky. Knead on a floured work surface for 10 minutes, until very elastic. Work in more flour as needed so that the dough is slightly sticky but peels easily from the work surface.

3 **Pound the butter** with a rolling pin to soften it. Add the butter to the dough; pinch and squeeze to mix it in, then knead until smooth. Shape into a ball and put it into the oiled bowl. Cover, and let rise in the refrigerator for 1½-2 hours, until doubled in bulk. If more convenient, the dough can be left to rise overnight.

4 **Brush a 28cm (11in) quiche dish** with melted butter. Knead the chilled brioche dough lightly to knock out the air. Flour the work surface; roll out the dough into a 32cm (13in) round. Wrap the dough around the rolling pin and loosely drape it over the quiche dish.

5 **Lift the edge of the dough** with one hand and press it well into bottom and up the side of the dish with other hand. With a small knife, trim off the excess dough, using the rim of the dish as a guide. Sprinkle the breadcrumbs over the bottom of the dough shell. Preheat the oven to 220°C (425°F/Gas 7). Put a baking sheet in the oven to heat.

MAKE THE CUSTARD AND **FINISH** THE TART

6 **Meanwhile,** stone the plums. Cut each plum half into two. Arrange the plum wedges, cut side up, in concentric circles on the brioche shell. Let stand at room temperature for 30-45 minutes, until the edge of the dough is puffed. Put the egg yolks and two-thirds of the sugar into a bowl. Pour in the double cream. Whisk together.

7 **Sprinkle the plum wedges** with the remaining sugar and bake the tart on the baking sheet for 5 minutes. Reduce the heat to 180°C (350°F/Gas 4).

8 **Ladle the custard mixture** over the fruit, return the tart to the oven, and continue baking for 45–50 minutes longer, until the dough is browned, the fruit is tender, and the custard is set. Let the tart cool on a wire rack. Serve warm or at room temperature.

🍲 VARIATION: Bavarian blueberry tart

Traditionally, bilberries would be used for this tart.

1 Omit the plums. Prepare the brioche dough as directed in the main recipe. Pick over 500g (1lb 2oz) blueberries; wash them only if they are dirty, as the added moisture will be unwelcome in the finished tart. Any that have to be washed must be gently and very thoroughly patted dry. Leave the fruit whole. Assemble the tart as directed. Make the custard as directed, using 60g (2oz) sugar, 4 egg yolks, and 125ml (4fl oz) double cream.

2 Sprinkle the blueberries with 2 tbsp sugar. Bake the tart for 5 minutes, as directed. Ladle the custard evenly over the blueberries and bake for 45–50 minutes longer. Keep an eye on it as it bakes and cover with foil if the surface of the custard or the berries threaten to scorch before the tart is fully cooked.

3 Just before serving, use a sieve to sprinkle the tart with 1–2 tbsp icing sugar. Serve the blueberry tart warm or at room temperature, cut into neat wedges.

Lemon tart

THIS RECIPE, WITH ITS FILLING OF CITRUS zest and juice in a smooth custard, is from the famous Maxim's restaurant in Paris. Candy the lemon slices at least 1 day, and up to 2 days, ahead, and keep them at room temperature. The dough can be made up to 1 day ahead and refrigerated, tightly wrapped.

SERVES	PREP	COOK
SERVES 8	40–45 MINS	40–45 MINS

Ingredients

FOR THE CANDIED LEMON SLICES

2 lemons

250g (9oz) caster sugar

FOR THE PÂTE SUCRÉE DOUGH

215g (7½oz) plain flour, plus more if needed

90g (3oz) unsalted butter, plus more for the tin

60g (2oz) caster sugar

½ tsp vanilla essence

¼ tsp salt

3 egg yolks

FOR THE CUSTARD

1 orange

3 lemons

3 eggs, plus 1 egg yolk

150g (5½oz) caster sugar

CANDY THE LEMON SLICES

1 **Trim the ends** from the lemons. Cut each lemon into 3mm (⅛in) slices; discard any seeds and the small, pithy end slices of each fruit.

2 **Bring a saucepan of water** to a boil. Add the lemon slices, and simmer for 3 minutes, until they soften. With a slotted spoon, remove and let drain. Attach 3 lengths of kitchen string to an upturned round wire rack. Dissolve the sugar in 500ml (16fl oz) water in a wide shallow pan, then bring to a boil. Put the lemon slices on the rack, tie the strings together, and lower into the syrup.

3 **Press a round of greaseproof paper** on top. Bring slowly to a simmer, taking 10–12 minutes. Poach the lemon slices for about 1 hour, until tender to the bite. Add more water, if necessary, so the slices are always covered. Let the candied lemon slices cool in the syrup. Let stand, covered with the paper round, at room temperature, for 24 hours.

MAKE THE PÂTE SUCRÉE DOUGH

4 **Sift the flour** on to a work surface and make a well in the centre. Pound the butter with a rolling pin to soften it. Put the sugar, butter, vanilla, salt, and egg yolks into the well. Work the ingredients in the well until thoroughly mixed, then draw in the flour until coarse crumbs form.

5 **Press the crumbs** together to form a ball. If the dough is sticky, work in a little more flour. Lightly flour the work surface, and knead the dough for 1–2 minutes, until it is very smooth. Shape into a ball, wrap tightly and chill for about 30 minutes, until firm.

LINE THE TIN AND BAKE BLIND

6 **Brush a 25cm (10in) flan tin** with a removable base with melted butter. Lightly flour a work surface, and roll out the dough into a 30cm (12in) round. Wrap it around the rolling pin and drape it over the tin.

Gently press the dough into the tin. Roll the rolling pin over the top of
the tin to cut off excess dough. With your thumbs, press the dough
evenly up the side of the tin, from the bottom, to increase the height of the
pastry rim. Chill for about 15 minutes, until firm.

Preheat the oven to 200°C (400°F/Gas 6), and put a baking sheet in the
oven. Line the shell with foil. Half-fill with rice. Bake on the sheet for 10
minutes. Remove the foil and rice. Reduce the oven temperature to 190°C
(375°F/Gas 5). Bake for 5 minutes, until pale brown. Leave the oven on.

MAKE THE FILLING, FILL, AND FINISH THE TART

Grate the zest from the citrus, then squeeze the juice. Put the eggs, yolk,
and sugar in a bowl. Whisk in the zest and juice. Set the pastry shell on a
baking sheet. Ladle in the filling, then bake for 25–30 minutes, until set.

Transfer to a wire rack and let cool slightly. Set the tart on a bowl and
remove the side. Let cool. Lift the candied lemon slices from the syrup
and drain. Using a palette knife, arrange the slices over the filling.

 VARIATION: Lime and cardamom tart

An exotic and exciting version.

1 Substitute 4 limes for 4 of the lemons; omit the sugar and water for
candying. Make and chill the pastry dough, line the tin, and bake the shell
blind as directed in the main recipe. Pare the zest from 1 lime. Cut it into
very fine julienne strips. Bring a small saucepan of water to a boil, add the
zest strips, and simmer to blanch for 2–3 minutes. Drain, rinse in cold water,
and drain again thoroughly.

2 Grate the zest from 2 of the remaining limes and the lemon, then squeeze
the juice from the lemon and all 4 limes; there should be 175ml (6fl oz) juice.
Make the filling as directed in the main recipe, using the lime, lemon juice,
and zest, and adding 150ml (¼ pint) double cream, and ½ tsp ground
cardamom to the custard.

3 Bake, cool, and unmould the tart as directed. Sprinkle the edge of the
tart with the lime julienne, and serve with sweetened whipped cream or
crème fraîche.

Chocolate pie with crunchy crust

A VELVETY COMBINATION of dark chocolate and cream in a crisp, almond crust. The pastry recipe dates back to 18th-century England. The pie can be baked 1 day in advance. Keep it, covered, in the refrigerator and allow it to come to room temperature before serving. Omit the white chocolate decoration, if you prefer.

SERVES	**PREP**	**COOK**
SERVES 8	30–35 MINS	25–30 MINS

Ingredients

FOR THE CRUNCHY CRUST

60g (2oz) caster sugar

175g (6oz) blanched almonds

1 egg white

butter, for the tin

FOR THE FILLING

270g (10oz) good-quality plain chocolate

375ml (13fl oz) double cream

2 eggs plus 1 egg yolk

60g (2oz) white chocolate, to decorate

MAKE AND BAKE THE CRUST

1 **Put the sugar** and blanched almonds in a food processor, and finely grind. In a bowl, whisk the egg white just until frothy. Add the ground almond and sugar mixture. Stir with a wooden spoon to form a stiff paste. Shape it into a ball, wrap tightly, and chill for about 30 minutes, until firm.

2 **Melt a little butter** in a small saucepan, then brush it over a 25cm (10in) flan tin with removable base. Lightly flour a work surface, then lightly pound out the crust mixture with a rolling pin to flatten it.

3 **With the back of a spoon,** dipped into cold water, or with the heel of your hand, press the mixture into the tin, then push it well up the side. Chill for about 15 minutes, until firm. Preheat the oven to 180°C (350°F/Gas 4). Put a baking sheet in the oven to heat.

4 **Put the shell** on the sheet, and bake for 8–10 minutes, until lightly browned. Slide the shell on to a wire rack. Let the crust cool in the tin. Leave the oven on while you make the chocolate filling.

MAKE THE FILLING

5 **Chop the chocolate** and put it into a bowl. In a saucepan, bring the cream just to a boil. Pour the cream over the chocolate. Whisk until the chocolate has melted completely. Set aside to cool to tepid. Put the eggs and the egg yolk into another bowl, and whisk them together until mixed.

6 **Whisk the tepid chocolate** and cream mixture into the eggs. Carefully pour into the cooled shell. Put the tart on the baking sheet and bake in the oven for 15–20 minutes, until the filling begins to set, but is still soft in the centre. Let cool slightly on a wire rack, then carefully loosen the pastry from the side of the tin. Melt the white chocolate in a bain marie (see p472) and drizzle it on top to serve.

Rustic apple tart

EVERY FRENCH HOUSEWIFE has her own version of this tart, the recipe of which comes from Normandy, where they grow the best apples. The pastry dough can be made up to two days ahead, and kept tightly wrapped, in the refrigerator. The apple tart is at its best freshly baked.

SERVES SERVES 6-8	**PREP** 40-45 MINS PLUS CHILLING	**COOK** 30-40 MINS

Ingredients

FOR THE PÂTE SUCRÉE DOUGH

175g (6oz) plain flour, more if needed

90g (3oz) unsalted butter, more for flan tin

60g (2oz) caster sugar

½ tsp vanilla essence

¼ tsp salt

3 egg yolks

FOR THE FILLING

1.4kg (3lb) cooking apples

30g (1oz) butter

1 tsp vanilla essence

60g (2oz) caster sugar, plus more to taste

juice of ½ lemon

FOR THE GLAZE

4 tbsp apricot jam

MAKE THE DOUGH AND PREPARE THE APPLES

1 **Make and chill** the pâte sucrée dough (see p430). Peel two-thirds of the apples, core them, and cut into dice.

2 **Melt the butter** in a frying pan. Add the apples, vanilla essence, and all but 2 tbsp of the sugar. Cook, stirring, for 10–15 minutes, until almost a purée. Taste, adding more sugar if needed. Let cool. Peel, core, and thinly slice the remaining apples. Sprinkle with the lemon juice, and toss to coat.

LINE THE TIN

3 **Brush a 25cm (10in) flan tin** with removable base, with melted butter. Lightly flour a work surface, and roll the dough into a 30cm (12in) round. Wrap it around the rolling pin, then push it into the tin, trimming any excess.

4 **Press the dough** evenly up the side, from the bottom, to increase the height of the shell. Chill for about 15 minutes, until firm. Preheat the oven to 200°C (400°F/Gas 6). Heat a baking sheet in the oven.

ASSEMBLE AND BAKE THE TART

5 **Spoon the cooled apple compote** over the pastry shell. Arrange the apple slices on top in concentric circles. Sprinkle with the remaining sugar.

6 **Bake on the baking sheet** in the oven for 15-20 minutes. Reduce the oven temperature to 180°C (350°F/Gas 4), and continue baking for 15-20 minutes longer, until the apple slices are tender and the rim is golden brown. Let cool slightly on a wire rack, then remove the tin.

7 **Let the tart cool.** Heat the jam with 1-2 tbsp water; work through a sieve. Brush it over the apples and pastry. Serve with crème fraîche.

Peach pie

THIS IS AN AMERICAN CLASSIC, and rightly so. Ripe, fresh peaches and their thick juices are enclosed in a pastry lattice for a succulent and indulgent pie that will leave your guests clamouring for second helpings. Choose peaches that are ripe, and full of juice, with no green tinge. It makes the perfect summer dessert, especially when served with vanilla ice cream. The pie can be made up to 2 days ahead and kept, covered, at room temperature, but is really best eaten on the day it is baked.

SERVES	PREP	COOK
SERVES 8	40–45 MINS PLUS CHILLING	40–45 MINS

Ingredients

FOR THE PASTRY DOUGH

250g (9oz) plain flour

½ tsp salt

125g (4½oz) white vegetable fat

75g (2½oz) unsalted butter

FOR THE FILLING

4–5 ripe peaches

30g (1oz) plain flour

150g (5½oz) granulated sugar, plus more if needed

salt

1–2 tbsp lemon juice (optional)

FOR THE GLAZE

1 egg

½ tsp salt

MAKE THE PASTRY DOUGH

1 **Sift the flour** and salt into a large bowl, using a sieve. Hold the sieve a fair distance above the bowl, and knock it with your free hand, so the flour travels through it.

2 **Add the fat** and butter, and cut them into the flour with a pastry blender, if you have one. A pastry blender will keep the pastry as cool as possible, as it avoids any contact with warm hands, but if you don't have one, use 2 round-bladed knives. Keep cutting, until the mixture forms coarse crumbs.

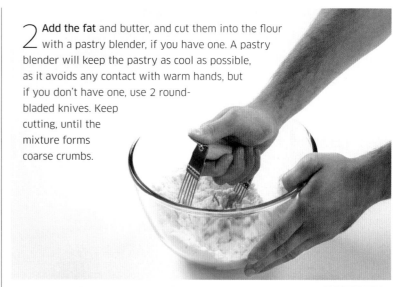

3 **Sprinkle with 3 tbsp water,** and continue blending until the dough can be gathered up into a ball. If the dough seems too dry, add more water, a little at a time. Continue kneading lightly for about 30 seconds, until mixed.

4 **Shape the dough** into a ball, handling it as little as possible. Then wrap it tightly in clingfilm, and chill it in the refrigerator for about 30 minutes, until firm.

LINE THE TIN

5 **Preheat the oven** to 200°C (400°F/Gas 6), and put in a baking sheet. Roll out two-thirds of the dough, about 5cm (2in) larger than a 23cm (9in) pie tin. Press the dough well into the tin. Chill for about 15 minutes, until firm.

PREPARE THE FILLING

6 **Immerse the peaches** in boiling water for 10 seconds, then transfer to a bowl of cold water. Halve the peaches, remove the stones, and peel off the skins. Cut the peaches into 1cm (½in) slices and put in a large bowl.

7 **Sprinkle the peaches** with the flour, sugar, a pinch of salt, and lemon juice, to taste. Carefully stir the peaches, then transfer them to the lined pie tin, with the juices in the bowl.

MAKE THE LATTICE

8 **Press any dough trimmings** into the remaining dough, and roll into a rectangle. Cut out 8 strips 1cm (½in) wide. Weave them into a lattice on top of the pie. Use the trimmings to make leaves, marking veins with a knife.

9 **Lightly beat** together the egg and salt, and use this to glaze the lattice and leaves. Bake for 40-45 minutes, until the pastry is golden brown, and the peaches soft and bubbling. Serve warm, with vanilla ice cream.

 VARIATION: Cherry pie

The most famous of American pies.

1 Stone 500g (1lb 2oz) cherries. Prepare the pie pastry dough and line the pie tin as directed in the main recipe. Stir the cherries with 200g (7oz) sugar, more if needed to taste, depending on how sweet or tart are your cherries. Add 45g (1½oz) flour to thicken the cherries, and ¼ tsp almond essence to add a subtle depth of flavour, if you like. Stir very well, so all the cherries are evenly coated in the flour mixture. Transfer these coated cherries to evenly cover the pastry in the pie tin.

2 Cut the pastry strips, using a fluted ravioli cutter, and use them to make a prettily-edged lattice as directed in the main recipe. Place the lattice carefully over the top of the cherry pie. Cut two more strips with the ravioli cutter, and lay them around the edge of the pie to cover the lattice ends neatly, pressing this strip down firmly to adhere both to the pastry rim and to the lattice strips.

3 Flute the edge of the pastry rim, pinching it with your fingers, as neatly as you possibly can. Brush with the egg and salt glaze, as directed. Bake the pie as directed in the main recipe, watching it carefully without opening the oven door to avoid any scorching of the pastry lattice. Serve at room temperature, or even slightly chilled, with scoops of vanilla ice cream or generous billowing piles of crème fraîche.

Normandy pear tart

THIS DELICIOUS TART has become a signature recipe of Normandy, where they grow some of the world's best pears. The sliced fruits are arranged like petals, and baked in a fragrant almond cream. The pears you choose should be ripe, or they will discolour during cooking.

SERVES	PREP	COOK
SERVES 6-8	40-45 MINS	40-45 MINS

Ingredients

FOR THE SWEET PASTRY DOUGH

175g (6oz) plain flour

3 egg yolks

60g (2oz) sugar

salt

75g (2½oz) unsalted butter

½ tsp vanilla essence

FOR THE ALMOND CREAM

125g (4½oz) whole blanched almonds

125g (4½oz) unsalted butter, at room temperature

100g (3½oz) caster sugar

1 egg plus 1 egg yolk

1 tbsp kirsch

2 tbsp plain flour

FOR THE PEARS

1 lemon

3-4 ripe pears

FOR THE GLAZE

150g (5½oz) apricot jam

2-3 tbsp kirsch or water

MAKE THE ALMOND CREAM

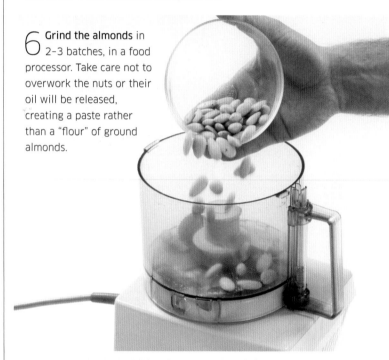

6 **Grind the almonds** in 2-3 batches, in a food processor. Take care not to overwork the nuts or their oil will be released, creating a paste rather than a "flour" of ground almonds.

7 **With an electric mixer** or wooden spoon, cream the butter. Add the sugar, and continue beating for 2-3 minutes, until fluffy and light. Do not stop beating too soon, as you want the mixture to be as aerated as possible.

MAKE THE SWEET PASTRY DOUGH

1 **Sift the flour** on to a work surface. Make a well in the centre and add the egg yolks, sugar, and a pinch of salt. Using a rolling pin, pound the butter to soften it slightly. Add the butter to the well with the vanilla. Using your fingertips, work the ingredients in the well until thoroughly mixed.

2 **With your fingers,** work the flour into the other ingredients until coarse crumbs form. If they seem dry, add a little water. Lightly flour a work surface, then knead for 1-2 minutes. Wrap, and chill for 30 minutes.

LINE THE TIN

3 **Brush the inside of a 23-25cm (9-10in) flan tin** with butter. Unwrap the dough; roll on a lightly floured work surface to a round 5cm (2in) larger than the tin. Roll the dough around the rolling pin, then unroll it over the tin.

4 **Gently press the dough** into the tin. Leave a ridge of dough just inside the edge, to make a deep shell. Cut off the excess dough. With your thumb, press the dough up the side of the tin. Neaten the edge of the dough.

5 **With both forefingers and thumbs,** pinch the dough above the side of the tin to form a fluted edge. Prick the bottom with a fork, to prevent air bubbles. Chill for at least 15 minutes, until firm.

8 **Add the egg** and egg yolk to the mixture, 1 at a time, beating well after each addition. Add the kirsch, then stir in the ground almonds and flour with a spatula, just until everything is well blended. Go gently, to keep the mixture as light as you can.

PREPARE THE PEARS

9 **Cut the lemon** in half. Peel the pears, rubbing them all over with the cut lemon to prevent discolouration. Cut the pears lengthways in half. Neatly remove the cores, and rub all the cut surfaces with the cut lemon again.

10 **Set a pear half cut-side down** on a chopping board. Using a thin-bladed knife, cut it lengthways into thin slices. Repeat with all the remaining pear halves.

ASSEMBLE AND BAKE THE TART

11 **Preheat the oven** to 200°C (400°F/Gas 6). Heat a baking sheet near the bottom of the oven. Spoon the almond cream into the pastry shell, and spread it evenly with a palette knife.

12 **Transfer the pear** slices to the tart, arranging like the petals of a flower. Set the tin on the baking sheet, and bake for 12–15 minutes. Reduce the heat to 180°C (350°F/Gas 4), and bake for 25–30 minutes more.

13 **Meanwhile,** melt the jam with the kirsch in a small pan, work it through a sieve and reheat. Unmould the tart and transfer it to a plate. Brush the top with the glaze. Serve at room temperature.

Fig and mulled wine tart

FRESH FIGS, with their deep, red flesh and delicate flavor, call for the simplest treatment. Here, they are poached briefly in mulled wine syrup. If you can't get hold of a vanilla pod, use ½ tsp of vanilla extract instead. Do not buy or use anything labelled vanilla "essence"; it is made from synthetic ingredients and tastes very little like the real thing. This is a lovely tart to serve during later summer, when figs are at the peak of their season and so reasonably priced.

SERVES SERVES 6–8	**PREP** 25–30 MINS, PLUS CHILLING	**COOK** 15–20 MINS

Ingredients

FOR THE POLENTA PASTRY

125g (4½oz) plain flour, plus more if needed

45g (1½oz) polenta (fine yellow cornmeal)

75g (2½oz) unsalted butter, plus more for the baking sheet and flan ring

1 egg

50g (1¾oz) caster sugar

¼ tsp salt

FOR THE LIGHT PASTRY CREAM

½ vanilla pod

250ml (8fl oz) milk

3 egg yolks

3 tbsp caster sugar

2 tbsp flour

10g (¼oz) unsalted butter

90ml (3fl oz) double cream

FOR THE FILLING

500g (1lb 2oz) purple figs

1 orange

1 lemon

1 nutmeg

100g (3½oz) caster sugar

5cm (2in) piece of cinnamon stick

2 whole cloves

1 tsp black peppercorns

500ml (16fl oz) dry red wine

MAKE THE DOUGH, LINE THE TIN, AND BAKE THE SHELL

1 **Sift the flour** on to a work surface. Add the polenta and make a well in the centre. Pound the butter with a rolling pin to soften it. Beat the egg to mix. Put the butter, egg, sugar, and salt into the well. With your fingertips, work the ingredients until thoroughly mixed.

2 **Draw in the flour** and polenta, and work them into the other ingredients with your fingers, until coarse crumbs form. Press the dough into a ball. If it is sticky, work in a little more flour.

3 **Lightly flour a work surface.** Knead the dough for 1–2 minutes, until it peels away from the surface. Shape into a ball, wrap tightly, and chill for 30 minutes, until firm. Preheat the oven to 190°C (375°F/Gas 5). Brush a 25cm (10in) springform tin with melted butter. Roll out the dough on a floured surface, into a 28cm (11in) round. Wrap around the rolling pin and drape over the tin.

4 **Gently press the dough** into the tin. Fold over the excess dough inside, to form a border. Chill for about 15 minutes, until firm. Bake the pastry for 15–20 minutes, until set and golden brown. Carefully slide the pastry round on to a wire rack, loosen the sides of the tin, and let cool.

MAKE THE LIGHT PASTRY CREAM

5 **Split the vanilla pod.** In a heavy-based pan, bring the milk to a boil with the pod. Remove from the heat, cover, and let stand for 10–15 minutes. Whisk the egg yolks and sugar until thick. Stir in the flour. Gradually stir in the hot milk until smooth. Pour back into the pan. Bring to a boil over medium heat, whisking constantly to keep it smooth, until thickened.

6 **Reduce the heat** and cook, still whisking, for about 2 minutes, until the pastry cream softens slightly. Remove from heat, and take out the vanilla pod. Transfer to a bowl. Rub the butter over surface of the cream to keep it from forming a skin, and chill for 30 minutes.

7 **Pour the double cream** into a chilled bowl, and whip until soft peaks form; cover and chill. Add the cream to the chilled pastry cream and fold together gently but thoroughly. Cover and chill. Meanwhile, make the syrup and poach the figs.

MAKE THE SYRUP AND POACH THE FIGS

8 **Prick each fig** two or three times with the tines of a fork, so that the syrup will penetrate the fruit. Pare the zest from the orange and lemon. Crush the nutmeg in a plastic bag with the rolling pin; it should be very aromatic.

9 **Put the zest** and nutmeg into a saucepan with the sugar, spices, and peppercorns. Add the wine. Heat, stirring, to dissolve the sugar. Bring just to a boil, then add the figs. Cover, and poach for 3-5 minutes, just until the figs are tender.

10 **Remove the figs** with a slotted spoon, allowing them to drain well, and let cool. Simmer the syrup for 25-30 minutes, until reduced to about 125ml (4fl oz). Strain and cool. Cut the stalks from the figs; cut the figs into halves. Now cut them nearly through into quarters, leaving them attached at the flower ends. Slide the pastry shell on to a serving plate. Spread the pastry cream over the pastry. Arrange the figs in concentric circles on top, and pull each half open slightly. Spoon 1-2 tbsp syrup over the figs. Just before serving, spoon the remaining syrup over.

Filo apricot turnovers

FILO IS A MULTI-PURPOSE DOUGH and not nearly as hard to work with as you might think. Here, it is folded into triangles to enclose a filling of fresh apricots, cooked with a spicy blend of cinnamon, nutmeg, and cloves. These light and flaky turnovers can be eaten with a knife and fork, or your fingers. They can be prepared up to the end of step 7, wrapped tightly and securely, and kept in the refrigerator for up to 2 days. They also freeze very well. Bake them just before serving.

SERVES
MAKES 24

PREP
35–40 MINS

COOK
12–15 MINS

Ingredients

500g (1lb 2oz) apricots	ground nutmeg
1 lemon	ground cloves
200g (7oz) caster sugar	225g (8oz) pack of filo pastry sheets
1 tsp ground cinnamon	175g (6oz) unsalted butter

MAKE THE APRICOT FILLING

1 **Cut each apricot** in half around the stone. Using both hands, give a quick, sharp twist to each half to loosen it from the stone. Scoop out the stone with a knife and discard. Cut each half into 4–5 pieces. Grate the zest from half of the lemon on to a plate.

2 **In a saucepan,** combine the apricots, lemon zest, three-quarters of the sugar, the cinnamon, and a pinch each of nutmeg and cloves. Add 2 tbsp water. Cook gently, stirring occasionally, for 20–25 minutes, until the mixture thickens to the consistency of jam. Transfer to a bowl and let cool.

PREPARE THE FILO PASTRY

3 **Preheat the oven** to 200°C (400°F/Gas 6). Lay a tea towel on the work surface, and sprinkle it lightly with water. Unroll the filo pastry sheets on the towel, and cut them lengthways in half. Cover them with a second moistened towel.

4 **Melt the butter** in a small pan. Take a half sheet of dough from the pile and set it lengthways on the work surface. Lightly brush the left-hand side of the sheet with butter, and fold the other half over on top. Brush the strip of dough with more butter.

FILL, SHAPE, AND BAKE THE TURNOVERS

5 **Spoon 1–2 tsp of the cooled filling** onto the strip of dough about 2.5cm (1in) from one end. Do not put too much apricot filling in each turnover, or they will burst during cooking. Fold a corner of the dough strip over the filling to meet the other edge of dough, forming a triangle.

6 **Continue folding the strip** over and over, to form a triangle with the filling inside. Set the triangle on a baking sheet with the final edge underneath, and cover the baking sheet with a moistened tea towel. Make sure you have closed the corners tightly so the filling does not leak.

7 **Continue making triangles** with the remaining filo pastry sheets and filling, arranging them on baking sheets and keeping them covered with moistened tea towels.

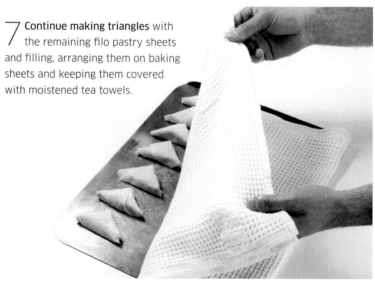

8 Brush the top of each triangle with butter, and sprinkle with the remaining sugar. Bake in the heated oven for 12–15 minutes, until golden brown and flaky. With the palette knife, transfer the turnovers to a wire rack to cool slightly, and serve warm or at room temperature.

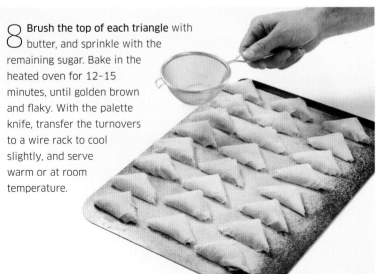

 VARIATION: Filo berry turnovers

Great for high summer, when a glut of berries brings down their usually high price.

1 Hull 250g (9oz) strawberries and pick over 175g (6oz) raspberries. Wash them only if dirty, as water will adversely affect their texture as well as introducing water into the filo pastry filling. Cut the strawberries in half or into quarters. Put all the fruit in a bowl, sprinkle with 60g (2oz) sugar and toss lightly to combine.

2 Fill each triangle with a scant 1 tbsp berries, being sure not to overfill the turnovers, or they will burst while baking. Brush with butter, sprinkle with sugar, and bake as directed in the main recipe.

3 Decorate each serving with whole raspberries and mint sprigs, if you like.

Tarte Tatin

THIS DESSERT WAS NAMED AFTER two impoverished gentlewomen from the French region of Sologne, who earned their living by baking their father's favourite apple tart. The secret of this upside-down tart lies in cooking the apples in the caramel itself, so it flavours deep inside the fruit. It is delicious served warm, with piles of sharp, refreshing crème fraîche to cut through the richness of the caramel. Make sure you use a heavy-based frying pan to make the best caramel.

SERVES	PREP	COOK
SERVES 8	45–50 MINS	20–25 MINS

Ingredients

FOR THE PASTRY DOUGH

75g (2½oz) unsalted butter

175g (6oz) plain flour

2 egg yolks

1½ tbsp caster sugar

salt

FOR THE FILLING

14–16 apples, total weight about 2.4kg (5lb 6oz)

1 lemon

125g (4½oz) unsalted butter

200g (7oz) caster sugar

crème fraîche, to serve

MAKE THE PASTRY DOUGH

1 **Using a rolling pin,** pound the butter to soften it slightly. Sift the flour on to a work surface, and make a well in the centre. Put the egg yolks, sugar, and a pinch of salt in the centre of the well, then add the softened butter and 1 tbsp water. Using your fingertips, work the ingredients in the well until thoroughly mixed.

2 **Work the flour** into the other ingredients until coarse crumbs form. If they seem dry, add a little more water. Press the dough into a ball. Lightly flour the work surface, then knead the dough for 1–2 minutes, until it is very smooth, and peels away from the work surface in 1 piece. Shape into a ball, wrap it tightly, and chill for about 30 minutes, until firm.

PREPARE THE APPLES

3 **With a vegetable peeler,** carefully peel the apples, then halve and core them. Cut the lemon in half, and rub the apples all over with the cut lemon to prevent discolouration.

CARAMELIZE THE APPLES AND BAKE THE TART

4 **Melt the butter** in a heavy-based ovenproof frying pan. Add the sugar. Cook over medium heat, stirring occasionally, for 3–5 minutes, until caramelized to a deep golden brown. Remove from the heat, and let cool to tepid. Arrange the apple halves over in concentric circles to fill the pan. They will shrink during cooking, so pack them tightly.

5 **Cook the apples** over high heat for 15–25 minutes, until caramelized. Turn once to caramelize on both sides. Take the pan from the heat, and let cool for 10-15 minutes. Meanwhile, preheat the oven to 190°C (375°F/Gas 5).

6 **Roll out the pastry** to a round, about 2.5cm (1in) larger than the pan. Roll up the dough around the rolling pin, then drape it over the pan. Tuck the edges around the apples. Bake for 20-25 minutes, until golden brown. Cool to tepid, then set a plate on top, hold firmly together, and invert. If any apples stick to the pan, replace on the tart. Spoon some caramel over the apples. Serve with crème fraîche.

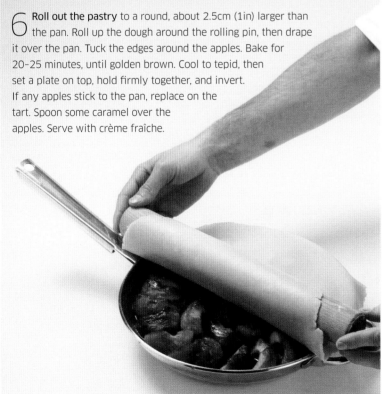

 VARIATION: Pear tarte tatin

Pears are just as delicious in this recipe.

1 Peel, halve, and core 12–14 pears (total weight about 2.4kg/5lb 6oz). Make sure they are well-flavoured but firm examples, so they will hold up to the caramelization and baking processes without disintegrating. Be careful to keep the attractive teardrop-shape of the fruits while preparing them. Rub each all over with a cut lemon, as directed in the main recipe, to prevent discolouration.

2 Caramelize the pears as directed for the apples in the main recipe, arranging them on their sides in the pan with the tapered ends towards the centre, so that they resemble the petals of a flower. Pears may produce more liquid than apples, and so could take longer to cook in the caramel until all the liquid has completely evaporated. Do not rush this step, as you need to be sure that the fruit is dry before you place on the pastry, or your tart will become soggy during baking. This is because the fruit will steam in the oven beneath its pastry lid.

3 Cover with the pastry dough, tucking it well down around the pears. Bake the tart, and unmould as directed in the main recipe. Serve with crème fraîche, and offer lemon wedges as well, because this tart will taste even sweeter than the apple version.

Cherry strudel

DON'T BE INTIMIDATED by making the ultra-thin strudel pastry; the trick is to knead the dough thoroughly so it is elastic. You will, however, need a large work table and an old, but scrupulously clean, sheet to cover it. Because strudel dough dries out easily, the strudel should be assembled and cooked at once. It is at its best eaten slightly warm on the day of baking, but can be warmed through in the oven 1 day later to mimic the just-baked taste.

SERVES
SERVES 6-8

PREP
45–50 MINS
PLUS RESTING

COOK
30–40 MINS

Ingredients

FOR THE STRUDEL DOUGH

250g (9oz) plain flour

1 egg

½ tsp lemon juice

salt

125g (4½oz) unsalted butter

FOR THE FILLING

500g (1lb 2oz) cherries

1 lemon

75g (2½oz) walnuts

100g (3½oz) light soft brown sugar

1 tsp ground cinnamon

icing sugar, to sprinkle

MAKE THE STRUDEL DOUGH

1 **Sift the flour** on to a work surface and make a well in the centre. In a bowl, beat the egg to mix with 125ml (4½fl oz) water, the lemon juice, and a pinch of salt, and pour into the well. Work the ingredients in the well, drawing in a little of the flour with your fingertips.

2 **Gradually draw in the remaining flour.** Gently knead in just enough flour so that the dough forms a ball; it should be quite soft. Work the dough in an electric mixer with dough hook for 5–7 minutes, or place on a floured work surface and knead by hand, picking it up and throwing it down, until shiny and smooth. Shape into a ball, cover with a bowl, and let rest for 30 minutes.

PREPARE THE FILLING

3 **Stone all the cherries.** Grate the zest from the lemon on to a plate. Coarsely chop the walnuts; nuts are best chopped by hand to control the finished texture, although this will always be uneven.

ROLL THE DOUGH AND BAKE THE STRUDEL

4 **Cover the work table** with a bed sheet and lightly flour it. Roll out the dough to as large a square as possible. Cover it with the damp tea towel and let rest about 15 minutes. Preheat the oven to 190°C (375°F/Gas 5) and butter a baking sheet. Melt the butter in a small saucepan.

5 **Flour your hands** and place them under the dough. Starting at the centre and working outwards, carefully stretch the dough with both hands. Continue to work outwards until the dough is as thin as possible. At once, brush the dough with about three-quarters of the melted butter.

6 **Sprinkle the buttered strudel dough** with the stoned cherries, chopped walnuts, brown sugar, lemon zest, and cinnamon. Trim the thick edge of the dough, pulling it out and pinching it off with your fingers.

7 **Roll up the strudel** with the help of the sheet. Transfer the roll to the baking sheet and shape it into a crescent. Brush with the remaining melted butter and bake for 30–40 minutes, until crisp and golden brown. Sprinkle with icing sugar and serve hot or cold, with cream or crème fraîche.

 VARIATION: Dried fruit strudel

Try this when fresh cherries are out of season.

1 Coarsely chop 500g (1lb 2oz) mixed dried fruit (apricots, prunes, dates, raisins, figs), discarding any stones you might find in the fruits. Put them into a small pan, cover with 125ml (4½fl oz) dark rum and 125ml (4½fl oz) water – or use all water if you like – and heat gently, stirring occasionally, for about 5 minutes. Remove from the heat and leave until completely cool and all the fruit has plumped up.

2 Drain the fruit thoroughly, discarding any remaining soaking liquid. Prepare and stretch the strudel dough as directed in the main recipe, brushing with the melted butter.

3 Sprinkle the dough evenly with the dried fruit, chopped walnuts, brown sugar, and cinnamon; omit the lemon zest, though orange zest can be substituted, if liked. Roll and bake the strudel as directed in the main recipe. Serve with plenty of cream.

Three-nut pie

INSPIRED BY THE TRADITIONAL AMERICAN PECAN PIE, this combines walnuts, hazelnuts, and almonds in a light filling. Choose your own combination of nuts, or just select one favourite. Serve with double cream for a real treat.

SERVES SERVES 6-8	**PREP** 35-40 MINS PLUS CHILLING	**COOK** 60-65 MINS

Ingredients

FOR THE PASTRY DOUGH

330g (11oz) plain flour

½ tsp salt

150g (5½oz) butter

FOR THE FILLING

60g (2oz) walnut halves

60g (2oz) whole blanched almonds

30g (1oz) hazelnuts

60g (2oz) unsalted butter

4 eggs

300g (10oz) light soft brown sugar

1 tsp vanilla essence

¼ tsp salt

1 tbsp milk, to glaze

MAKE THE PASTRY DOUGH

1 **Sift the flour** and salt into a bowl. Cut in the fat with 2 round-bladed table knives. With your fingertips, rub the fat into the flour until the mixture forms coarse crumbs, lifting and crumbling the mixture to help aerate it. Sprinkle 6-7 tbsp cold water over the mixture, 1 tbsp at a time, and mix lightly with a fork.

2 **When the crumbs are moist** enough to start sticking together, press the dough lightly into a ball, wrap it tightly, and chill for about 30 minutes until firm. Brush a 23cm (9in) round tin or a 20cm (8in) square tin with melted butter and preheat the oven to 200°C (400°F/Gas 6). Put a baking sheet in the oven to heat.

LINE THE TIN AND BAKE BLIND

3 **Lightly flour a work surface.** Roll out the dough and trim it either to a 25cm (10in) round or square, depending on the shape of the tin you have chosen. Wrap the dough around the rolling pin and drape it over the tin. Press it well into the bottom edges and up the sides of the tin with your fingertips. It need not reach the rim.

4 **Using a round-bladed table knife,** trim the dough inside the tin, so that the shell is 4cm (1½in) deep. Prick the bottom of the pastry shell with a fork to prevent air bubbles during cooking. Chill until firm, about 15 minutes.

5 **Line the shell** with a double thickness of foil, pressing it well into the corners. Half-fill the foil with rice. Bake the shell on the baking sheet for about 10 minutes, until set. Remove the foil and rice and continue baking for about 5 minutes longer. Let the shell cool slightly in the tin on a wire rack. Reduce the oven temperature to 180°C (350°F/Gas 4).

PREPARE THE NUT FILLING

6 **Set aside a third of the walnuts** and almonds for decoration. Spread the remainder on a baking sheet and toast in the oven, stirring occasionally, for 8-10 minutes, until lightly browned. Remove. Toast the hazelnuts as for the walnuts and almonds, allowing 12-15 minutes. Leave the oven on. While the hazelnuts are still hot, rub them in a rough tea towel to remove the skins. Let cool.

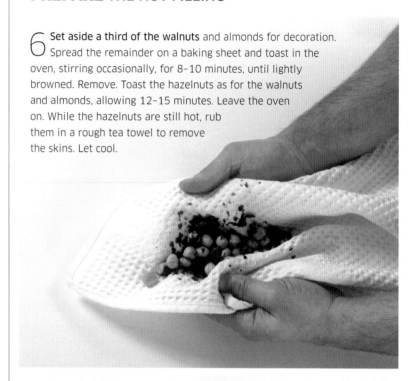

7 **Roughly chop the toasted** walnuts, almonds, and hazelnuts. Melt the butter in a small saucepan. Let cool. Put the eggs in a bowl. Add the brown sugar and whisk the eggs and sugar together until evenly mixed. Add the vanilla essence, salt, and cooled melted butter and stir until well combined.

8 Add the toasted chopped walnuts, almonds, and hazelnuts to the filling mixture. With a wooden spoon, stir the nuts into the filling mixture to distribute them evenly. Carefully pour the filling into the pastry shell.

BAKE THE PIE

9 Bake the pie on the baking sheet in the heated oven just until it starts to set. It should only take 8–10 minutes. Remove from the oven and, working quickly, brush any exposed pastry edges with the milk to glaze. Arrange the reserved nuts on top. Continue baking the pie until a metal skewer inserted in the centre comes out clean. It will probably take 35–40 minutes longer. Watch it very carefully, and cover with a sheet of foil if it threatens to scorch, as burned nuts have a bitter and very unpleasant flavour and will spoil the dish.

10 Transfer the pie to a wire rack. Let it cool to room temperature. When cool, transfer the wire rack to the top of the tin, turn both over together, then carefully lift off the tin. Make none of your motions too rapid or forceful, as this might dislodge some of the delicious, moist nutty filling from the rest of the pie. Set a second wire rack on the pie base and turn both over so the pie is right-side up once more. Slide the pie on to a serving platter. Serve just slightly warm, or at room temperature, with double cream, if desired.

Mincemeat tart with whisky butter

FRESH FRUIT IS ADDED to the traditional dried fruit for this fresh mincemeat, and the whisky butter makes this a really festive and indulgent treat for Christmas time.

SERVES	PREP	COOK
SERVES 8	40-45 MINS PLUS CHILLING	40-45 MINS

Ingredients

FOR THE SHORTCRUST PASTRY DOUGH

345g (12oz) plain flour

1½ tbsp caster sugar

½ tsp salt

60g (2oz) vegetable fat

90g (3oz) unsalted butter

1 egg, plus ½ tsp salt, to glaze

FOR THE MINCEMEAT

1 tart eating apple

1 lemon

200g (7oz) seedless grapes

1 tbsp chopped candied orange peel

20g (¾oz) slivered almonds

¼ tsp each ground cinnamon, nutmeg, and allspice

90g (3oz) each raisins and sultanas

100g (3½oz) light, soft brown sugar

3 tbsp whisky

FOR THE WHISKY BUTTER

125g (4½oz) unsalted butter

100g (3½oz) caster sugar

60ml (2fl oz) whisky

MAKE THE PASTRY AND **LINE** THE TIN

1 **Make the pastry** as for Blackberry and Apple Pie (p418). Brush a 25cm (10in) springform tin with melted butter. Lightly flour a work surface, and roll out two-thirds of the dough into a 30cm (12in) round. Wrap the rolled dough around the rolling pin, and drape it over the tin.

2 **Gently press the dough** into the tin, then roll the pin over the top to cut off excess. Press the dough up the side of the tin, to increase the height of the rim. Chill for about 15 minutes.

MAKE THE MINCEMEAT AND **FILL** THE TART

3 **Peel, core, and dice** the apple. Grate the lemon zest; squeeze the juice. Halve the grapes. Mix the apple, grapes, lemon zest and juice, candied peel, almonds, spices, dried fruit, sugar, and whisky. Spoon it into the pastry.

MAKE THE PASTRY LATTICE TOP

4 **Roll out the remaining dough** and cut into 14x2cm (¾in) strips. Form into a lattice over the pie (p427), brushing the ends with water to seal them to the shell. Lightly beat the egg and salt, and brush this on the lattice.

5 **Chill the tart** for 15 minutes. Preheat the oven to 180°C (350°F/Gas 4). Put a baking sheet in the oven to heat. Bake for 40-45 minutes, until lightly browned. Let cool slightly, remove the tin and slide on to a plate.

MAKE THE WHISKY BUTTER

6 **With an electric mixer,** beat the butter until creamy. Add the sugar, and beat for 2-3 minutes, until light and fluffy. Beat in the whisky, 1 spoon at a time. Chill for 1-2 hours, until firm. Serve with the tart.

Flaky pear tartlets

THESE ARE A PARTY FAVOURITE, a spectacular contrast of hot and cold, and need very little last-minute preparation. They are very easy to make, through they manage seriously to impress any guest. It's worth fanning out the pears on this occasion, as they look beautiful.

SERVES	PREP	COOK
SERVES 8	35-40 MINS PLUS CHILLING	30-40 MINS

Ingredients

FOR THE TARTLETS

450g (1lb) bought all-butter puff pastry

1 egg beaten with ½ tsp salt, to glaze

4 pears

juice of 1 lemon

50g (1¾oz) sugar

FOR THE CARAMEL SAUCE

150g (5½oz) caster sugar

125ml (4½fl oz) double cream

FOR THE CHANTILLY CREAM

125ml (4½fl oz) double cream

1-2 tsp icing sugar

½ tsp vanilla essence

MAKE AND BAKE THE PASTRY CASES

1 **Sprinkle 2 baking sheets** with cold water. Roll out the puff pastry dough, cut in half lengthways, then cut diagonally at 10cm (4in) intervals along the length of each piece, to make 8 diamond shapes. Transfer to the baking sheets, and brush with the glaze. With the tip of a knife, score a border around each. Chill for 15 minutes.

2 **Preheat the oven** to 220°C (425°F/Gas 7). Bake the cases for about 15 minutes, until they start to brown, then reduce the temperature to 190°C (375°F/Gas 5) and bake for 20-25 minutes more, until golden and crisp. Transfer to wire racks to cool, then cut out the lid from each case, and scoop out any under-cooked pastry from inside.

MAKE THE CARAMEL SAUCE AND CHANTILLY CREAM

3 **Put 125ml (4fl oz) water in a saucepan,** and dissolve the sugar. Boil, without stirring, until golden. Reduce the heat. Remove from the heat, stand back, and add the cream. Heat gently until the caramel dissolves. Cool.

4 **Pour the cream** for the Chantilly cream into a bowl, and whip until soft peaks form. Add the icing sugar and vanilla, and continue whipping until stiff peaks form. Chill.

PREPARE AND GRILL THE PEAR FANS

5 **Butter a baking sheet.** Heat the grill. Peel and core the pears. Thinly slice, keeping attached at the stalk end. With your fingers, flatten, transfer to the sheet, brush with lemon and sprinkle with sugar. Grill until caramelized.

ASSEMBLE THE TARTLETS

6 **Transfer the pastry cases** to plates, and place Chantilly cream and a pear fan in each. Pour a little cold caramel sauce over each fan, and partially cover with the pastry lids.

Mississippi mud pie

IN THIS POPULAR AMERICAN DESSERT, a chocolate crumb crust is filled with homemade coffee ice cream swirled with chocolate, and served with hot fudge sauce. You can use a tub of good-quality bought coffee ice cream if time is short.

SERVES	PREP	COOK
SERVES 6-8	45–50 MINS PLUS FREEZING	25–30 MINS

Ingredients

FOR THE COFFEE ICE CREAM

600ml (1 pint) milk

3 tbsp instant coffee granules

135g (5oz) caster sugar

8 egg yolks

2 tbsp cornflour

250ml (9fl oz) double cream

FOR THE CHOCOLATE CRUMB CRUST

125g (4½oz) unsalted butter

250g (9oz) plain dark crisp chocolate biscuits

3 tbsp caster sugar

FOR THE FUDGE SAUCE

60g (2oz) whole blanched almonds

150ml (5fl oz) double cream

60g (2oz) unsalted butter

100g (3½oz) caster sugar

135g (5oz) light soft brown sugar

90g (3oz) cocoa powder

salt

1 tbsp dark rum, or to taste

double cream, to serve

PREPARE THE COFFEE CUSTARD, MAKE, AND BAKE THE CRUST

1 **Put the milk** and coffee in a saucepan and heat, stirring, until the coffee dissolves. Set aside a quarter of this. Stir the sugar into the rest. In a bowl, whisk the yolks and cornflour. Whisk in the sweetened hot milk.

2 **Pour the custard back** into the saucepan and cook over medium heat, stirring constantly, just until it comes to a boil and thickens enough to coat the back of a spoon. Your finger will leave a clear trail across the spoon. It may curdle if cooked longer.

3 **Off the heat,** stir in the reserved milk until thoroughly combined. Strain into a cold bowl and cover tightly to prevent a skin forming. Let cool. Preheat the oven to 180°C (350°F/Gas 4). Put a baking sheet in to heat.

4 **Melt the butter.** Brush a 23cm (9in) pie dish with melted butter. Grind the biscuits to coarse crumbs in a food processor, using the pulse button. Transfer to a bowl and stir in the melted butter and sugar.

5 **Press the crumbs** evenly over the bottom and up the side of the pie dish. Chill until firm, about 15 minutes. Bake the crumb crust on the baking sheet in the heated oven for 15 minutes. Let cool on a wire rack. The crust will harden as it cools.

TOAST THE ALMONDS; MAKE THE FUDGE SAUCE

6 **Coarsely chop the almonds.** Spread them on the baking sheet and toast in the heated oven, stirring occasionally, for 10–12 minutes, until lightly browned. Watch carefully, as they burn easily.

7 **In a saucepan,** heat the double cream and butter, stirring occasionally, until the butter melts and the mixture comes just to a boil. Add the sugars and stir them in until dissolved. Sift the cocoa. Whisk it, with a pinch of salt, into the cream and sugar mixture, and bring back to a boil.

8 Gently simmer the fudge sauce, whisking constantly, until the cocoa powder has dissolved. Stir in the rum. Transfer 125ml (4½fl oz) of the fudge sauce to a bowl and combine with half the almonds. Let cool. Set the remaining sauce and almonds aside.

FREEZE THE ICE CREAM AND PIE

9 If the custard has formed a skin, whisk to dissolve it. Pour the coffee custard into an ice cream maker and freeze until slushy, following the manufacturer's directions. Meanwhile, chill 2 large bowls in the freezer.

10 Pour the cream into one of the chilled bowls and whisk to soft peaks. Add to the half-set custard and finish freezing in the ice cream maker. Transfer to the second chilled bowl. Add the cooled almond fudge mixture.

11 Spread the coffee ice cream and almond fudge mixture over the bottom of the crumb crust. Swirl the top with the back of a metal spoon and freeze for at least 1–2 hours, or up to 3 days.

FINISH THE PIE

12 If the pie has been frozen for more than 12 hours, let it soften in the refrigerator for 1 hour. Whip the double cream to stiff peaks. Sprinkle the reserved almonds over the pie. Reheat the fudge sauce.

13 Transfer the pie dish to a serving platter. Serve the pie directly from the dish, cut into wedges. Drizzle hot fudge sauce over the top of each serving, and serve at once, with double cream on the side.

Apple jalousie

IN FRANCE, A JALOUSIE IS A LOUVRED SHUTTER – perfect for the observation of wives by jealous husbands. In this pastry, the top layer of dough is slashed before baking to look like a shutter, revealing glimpses of the apple compote inside. The flavour of this dessert is best when made with tart eating apples, which hold their shape well. The puff pastry must be kept cold, so a marble slab is the ideal preparation surface.

SERVES
SERVES 6-8

PREP
1¼-1½ HRS
PLUS CHILLING

COOK
30-40 MINS

Ingredients

FOR THE PUFF PASTRY DOUGH

250g (9oz) plain flour

250g (9oz) unsalted butter

1 tsp salt

1 tsp lemon juice

FOR THE FILLING

1kg (2¼lb) tart eating apples

2.5cm (1in) piece of fresh root ginger

15g (½oz) unsalted butter

100g (3½oz) caster sugar

1 egg white

MAKE THE PUFF PASTRY

1 **Sift the flour** on to a work surface, and make a well in the centre. Cut 30g (1oz) of the butter into pieces, and add to the well with the salt, lemon juice, and 125ml (4fl oz) water. Gradually draw in the flour, working to form coarse crumbs. If the crumbs seem dry, add a little more water to form a dough.

2 **Cut and turn the dough** several times, until it forms a rough, slightly moist ball. At this stage, try to handle it as little as possible. Score the dough to prevent shrinkage, then wrap and chill for 15 minutes. Lightly flour the remaining butter. Pound the butter with a rolling pin, folding and pounding it until it is softened and pliable. It should be the same consistency as the dough.

3 **Shape the piece of butter** into a 12.5cm (5in) square. Roll out the chilled dough on a lightly floured work surface, to a 25cm (10in) square, slightly thicker in the centre. Set the butter diagonally in the centre, and pull the corners of the dough around to wrap it like an envelope. Pinch the edges to seal. Lightly flour the work surface again, and turn the dough package on to it, seam side down. Tap with the rolling pin to flatten.

4 **Roll out the dough** to 15x45cm (6x18in). Fold the dough into 3, bringing the top third down, and the bottom third up, like a letter. Turn it 90° to bring the seam to your right. Gently press the layered ends to seal. This is the first turn. Repeat this step to complete a second turn. Wrap and chill for 15 minutes. Repeat twice more, to make a total of 6 turns.

PREPARE THE FILLING

5 **Peel, core, and dice** the apples. Peel and finely chop the fresh root ginger. Melt the butter in a large frying pan. Add the apples, ginger, and all but 2 tbsp of the sugar. Sauté, stirring often, for 15–20 minutes, until the apples are tender and caramelized. Cook them briskly, so they do not dissolve into purée. Taste, adding more sugar if needed. Let cool.

ASSEMBLE AND BAKE THE JALOUSIE

6 **Sprinkle a baking sheet** evenly with cold water. Lightly flour a work surface, then roll out the puff pastry dough and trim it into a neat 28x32cm (11x 13in) rectangle. Cut the rectangle lengthways in half. Fold 1 half lengthways, and cut across the fold at 5mm (¼in) intervals to form the shutter effect, leaving an uncut border at the edges. Use a very sharp knife so you do not have to press down too hard, or the folded piece of pastry will be hard to unfold.

7 **Transfer the uncut rectangle** of dough to the prepared baking sheet and press it down lightly. Spoon the apple filling evenly down the centre, leaving a 2cm (¾in) border. With a pastry brush, moisten the border with cold water. Top with the slashed dough rectangle.

8 **Press the edges** together with your fingertips. With a sharp knife, trim the edges to neaten them. Holding the dough in place with a fingertip, scallop the edges at close intervals with the back of a small knife. Chill the jalousie for 15 minutes. Meanwhile, preheat the oven to 220°C (425°F/Gas 7). Bake for 20-25 minutes, until puffed and light brown. Meanwhile, whisk the egg white just until frothy.

9 **Brush the hot jalousie** with the egg white, and sprinkle the remaining sugar evenly over the top. Return to the oven and continue baking for 10-15 minutes, until the sugar glaze is crisp, and the pastry is deep golden. Transfer to a wire rack, and let cool. Cut the jalousie across into 6-8 slices. Serve warm or at room temperature.

Eggnog tart

THE AMERICAN EGGNOG, a rich drink, is transformed here into a creamy, rum-flavoured tart. The crust is made from almond-flavoured amaretti biscuits, but other crisp biscuits can also be used. This is a great tart to make around Christmas time.

SERVES	PREP	COOK
SERVES 6-8	40-45 MINS PLUS SETTING	10-15 MINS

Ingredients

FOR THE CRUST

125g (4½oz) unsalted butter

250g (9oz) amaretti biscuits

FOR THE FILLING

500ml (16fl oz) milk

1 vanilla pod or 1 tsp vanilla essence

50g (1¾oz) caster sugar

2 tbsp cornflour

4 egg yolks

125ml (4½fl oz) double cream

7g (¼oz) powdered gelatine

60ml (2fl oz) dark rum, more to taste

whole nutmeg

MAKE AND BAKE THE AMARETTI CRUST

1 **Preheat the oven** to 180°C (350°F/Gas 4). Melt the butter in a saucepan. Brush a 23cm (9in) springform tin with melted butter. Crush the biscuits to fine crumbs and stir in the melted butter. Press over the bottom and 2.5cm (1in) up the side of the tin. Chill until firm. Put a baking sheet in the oven to heat. Bake the crust on the heated baking sheet for 10-15 minutes. Let cool on a wire rack.

MAKE THE CUSTARD

2 **Put the milk** in a heavy-based saucepan. Split the vanilla pod, if using, lengthways in half and add it to the milk. Bring just to a boil, then remove from the heat, cover and let stand in a warm place, 10-15 minutes. Remove the vanilla pod, rinse it, and store to use again.

3 **Set aside** a quarter of the milk. Add the sugar to the remaining hot milk in the saucepan; stir until dissolved.

4 **Put the cornflour** and egg yolks in a medium bowl and whisk them together until smooth. Whisk the sweetened hot milk into the cornflour mixture until smooth. Pour the mixture back into the saucepan, and cook over medium heat. Stir constantly with the wooden spoon, just until it comes to a boil, and is thick enough to coat the back of the spoon. Your finger will leave a trail across the back of the spoon.

5 **Do not continue** to boil the custard or it may curdle. Off the heat, stir the reserved milk into the custard and strain it into a cold bowl. Stir in the vanilla essence, if using. Cover tightly to prevent a skin forming on the surface of the custard, and let cool to tepid.

FINISH THE FILLING

6 **Pour the cream** into a bowl and whisk until soft peaks form; chill. Sprinkle the gelatine over the rum in a small saucepan. Let soak for 5 minutes. Set over low heat and melt. Do not stir.

7 **Stir the gelatine** mixture into the tepid custard. Taste the custard, adding more rum, if you like. Set the bowl of custard in a larger bowl, half-filled with iced water, and stir gently until it starts to thicken and set.

ASSEMBLE THE TART

8 **Remove the bowl** of setting custard immediately from the bowl of iced water and whisk briskly to lighten it. Add the whipped cream to the custard and fold together gently.

9 **Pour the filling** into the crust, smooth with a palette knife, then chill until set, 2–3 hours. Run a knife around the tin; loosen and remove the side. Grate nutmeg over the top. Serve chilled, in wedges.

Pistachio and ricotta filo pie

FILO PASTRY can be used to make many different shapes. Here, sheets of filo dough are filled with layers of ricotta cheese and ground pistachios, and finished with filo rosettes. The baked pie can be kept in the refrigerator for up to 2 days. Allow it to come to room temperature before serving. Filo pastry is very easy to work with, so don't be alarmed by its apparent fragility.

SERVES	PREP	COOK
SERVES 6-8	35-40 MINS	45-50 MINS

Ingredients

FOR THE FILLING

1 tbsp unsalted butter

90g (3oz) shelled pistachio nuts

3 tbsp caster sugar

3 tbsp light soft brown sugar

2 lemons

1 egg

175g (6oz) ricotta cheese

75ml (2½fl oz) soured cream

1 tsp vanilla essence

2 tbsp honey

2 tsp plain flour

salt

45g (1½oz) raisins

FOR THE FILO PASTRY CASE

500g (1lb 2oz) filo sheets

125g (4½oz) unsalted butter

FOR THE TOPPING

1 tsp ground cinnamon

1 tbsp caster sugar

MAKE THE FILLING

1 **Melt the butter** in a saucepan. In a food processor, coarsely chop the pistachio nuts. Add the sugars and work the nuts until finely chopped. While the blade is turning, add the melted butter and work until coarse crumbs form.

2 **Finely grate the zest** from each of the lemons, using a small brush to remove any zest remaining on the grater. Set aside. In a medium bowl, stir the egg. Add the ricotta cheese.

3 **Beat the egg** and ricotta cheese with an electric mixer, or with a hand whisk, until smooth. Make sure it is completely blended, so the final filling will be easy to work with.

4 **Add the soured cream,** lemon zest, vanilla essence, honey, flour, and a pinch of salt to the egg and ricotta mixture. Continue beating for 2-3 minutes, until light and fluffy. Stir in the raisins.

ASSEMBLE AND BAKE THE PIE

5 **Preheat the oven** to 180°C (350°F/Gas 4). Put a baking sheet in the oven to heat. Brush a 20cm (8in) square cake tin with melted butter; line with a strip of double thickness foil, draping the excess over the edges. Roll up the excess to form handles. Brush with melted butter.

6 **Lay a tea towel** on the work surface and sprinkle it lightly with water. Unroll the filo sheets on to it. Trim the sheets to 20x40cm (8x16in) rectangles. Cover the sheets and trimmings with a second dampened tea towel to stop them becoming brittle.

7 **Put 1 of the sheets of dough** on top of a third dampened tea towel and brush with melted butter. Lay it in the bottom of the tin so that part of the sheet drapes over one edge of the tin.

8 **Butter a second sheet.** Lay it in the bottom of the tin so that part drapes over the edge at right angles to the first sheet. Butter the third and fourth sheets, laying and pressing them into the tin so the excess drapes over the remaining 2 sides. Cut the remaining sheets in half to make 20cm (8in) squares; cover with the dampened tea towel.

9 **Spread half of the ricotta cheese** filling evenly over the dough in the tin. Butter 3 of the squares of filo dough and lay each one, butter-side up, over the filling. Evenly distribute half the nut mixture on top of the buttered dough, reserving 2 tbsp.

10 **Butter and layer 3 more squares of pastry** on top of the nut mixture. Layer the remaining cheese and nut fillings with the buttered filo, finishing the layering with 3 squares of buttered pastry. Fold the 4 overhanging pieces of pastry over the pie and brush the top with butter. Cut the reserved trimmings into 5cm (2in) wide strips.

11 **Curl the strips to form loose rosettes** and arrange on top of the pie. Combine the cinnamon and sugar in a small bowl. Brush the pie and rosettes with the remaining melted butter and sprinkle the cinnamon, sugar, and reserved pistachios over the top. Bake on the baking sheet until golden brown and flaky, 45–50 minutes. Let cool slightly in the tin. Transfer to a wire rack; let cool to room temperature and discard the foil. Drizzle with honey to serve.

Cherry clafoutis

THIS PUDDING COMES FROM LIMOUSIN in central France. Cherries are baked in batter that puffs up, and turns golden. Tart cherries give the most flavour, and contrast beautifully with the sweet batter. The cherry stones can be removed before cooking if you prefer, though this is not traditional, and the stones will lend the dessert a surprising, subtle taste reminiscent of bitter almonds. Crème fraîche is a really delicious accompaniment to this pudding. This is a dish for the early summer, when cherries are at the peak of their season.

SERVES SERVES 6-8	**PREP** 20-25 MINS	**COOK** 30-35 MINS

Ingredients

100g (3½oz) caster sugar, plus more for the dish

625g (1lb 6oz) cherries

45g (1½oz) plain flour

salt

150ml (5fl oz) milk

75ml (2½fl oz) double cream

4 eggs, plus 2 egg yolks

3 tbsp kirsch

2 tbsp icing sugar

PREPARE THE DISH AND CHERRIES

1 **Brush a 2 litre (3½ pint) baking dish** with melted butter. Sprinkle some caster sugar into the dish. Turn the dish around and shake it, to coat the bottom and side evenly. Turn the dish upside-down and tap the base with your knuckles to remove any excess sugar.

2 **Stone the fresh cherries**, either with a cherry stoner or the tip of a vegetable peeler, or leave the stones in if you like. Spread the cherries in an even layer over the bottom of the prepared baking dish.

MAKE THE BATTER

3 **Sift the flour** and a pinch of salt into a bowl, holding the sieve up high to aerate the flour. Make a well in the centre with your fingers to take the wet ingredients.

4 **Pour the milk** and cream into the well at the same time, and stir with a whisk, gradually drawing in the flour and whisking constantly, to make a smooth paste and work out any lumps.

5 **Add the eggs**, egg yolks to add richness, and caster sugar, and continue whisking to make a smooth batter.

ASSEMBLE AND BAKE THE CLAFOUTIS

6 Preheat the oven to 180°C (350°F/Gas 4). Just before baking, ladle the batter evenly over the cherries - it should partially cover them - then sprinkle over the kirsch.

7 Bake the clafoutis in the heated oven for 30–35 minutes, until beautifully puffed up, and beginning to turn golden brown. If it threatens to scorch before it is cooked, cover with foil. When cooked, the clafoutis will begin slightly to pull away from the side of the baking dish. Just before serving, sift icing sugar over the top. Serve warm or at room temperature, with a pile of crème fraîche or whipped cream, if you like.

 VARIATION: Plum clafoutis

With cherries, clafoutis is a dish of early summer. This variation is for autumn or winter.

1 Omit the cherries. Prepare the baking dish and make the batter as directed.

2 Cut 625g (1lb 6oz) small plums in half around the stone. Using both hands, give a quick, sharp twist to each half to loosen it from the stone. Scoop out the stone with the tip of a small knife and discard it.

3 Arrange the plums, cut-side up, in the bottom of the prepared baking dish. Assemble, bake, and decorate the clafoutis as directed.

Hazelnut, chocolate, and orange tart

THE ITALIAN SWEET PASTRY pasta frolla acts as a container for a rich filling flavoured with ground hazelnuts, plain chocolate, and candied orange zest, all topped with a chocolate glaze. A most delicious recipe for a special occasion.

SERVES
SERVES 6-8

PREP
45-50 MINS
PLUS CHILLING

COOK
35-40 MINS

Ingredients

FOR THE PASTA FROLLA DOUGH

1 orange

150g (5½oz) plain flour, plus more if needed

75g (2½oz) unsalted butter, plus more for the tin

50g (1¾oz) caster sugar

¼ tsp salt

1 egg

FOR THE FILLING

2 oranges

125g (4½oz) hazelnuts

150g (5½oz) caster sugar

60g (2oz) plain chocolate

150g (5½oz) unsalted butter

2 tsp plain flour

2 egg yolks, plus 1 egg

FOR THE CHOCOLATE GLAZE

125g (4½oz) plain chocolate

75g (2½oz) unsalted butter

2 tsp Grand Marnier

MAKE THE PASTA FROLLA DOUGH

1 Grate the zest from the orange. Sift the flour on to a work surface and make a well in the centre. Pound the butter with a rolling pin to soften. Put the softened butter, sugar, salt, orange zest, and egg into the well.

2 With your fingertips, work the ingredients in the well until thoroughly mixed. Work the flour in with your fingertips until coarse crumbs form. Press the dough into a ball. If it is sticky, work in a little more flour.

3 Lightly flour the work surface. Knead the dough for 1-2 minutes, until it is very smooth and peels away from the work surface in one piece. Shape into a ball, wrap it tightly and chill until firm, about 30 minutes.

LINE THE TIN

4 Brush a 23cm (9in) springform tin with melted butter. Lightly flour a work surface, and roll the dough into a 28cm (11in) round. Wrap it around the rolling pin and gently press into the tin, sealing any cracks.

5 Roll the rolling pin over the top of the tin, pressing down to cut off excess. With your thumbs, press the dough evenly up the side of the tin, to increase the height of the rim. Prick the bottom of the shell with a fork to prevent air bubbles forming. Chill for 15 minutes, until firm.

MAKE THE FILLING

6 With a vegetable peeler, pare the zest from the oranges; cut it into very fine julienne strips. Bring a small saucepan of water to a boil, add the zest and simmer for 2 minutes. Drain in a sieve and set aside.

7 Preheat the oven to 180°C (350°F/Gas 4). Spread out the nuts on a baking sheet, and toast in the heated oven until they are lightly browned, 6-15 minutes, depending on whether they are whole or chopped. Stir occasionally, so they colour evenly. To remove their skins, rub in a tea towel while still hot. Discard the skins. Let cool. Leave the oven on.

8 Put a third of the sugar into a pan, add 60ml (2fl oz) water and heat gently until dissolved, shaking the pan once or twice. Add the zest and simmer for 8-10 minutes, until all the water has evaporated and the strips are transparent and tender. With a fork, transfer the candied zest to a piece of baking parchment and let cool slightly. Coarsely chop two-thirds of it.

9 Put a baking sheet in the oven to heat. Cut the chocolate into chunks, then finely chop (or chop it in a food processor). Put the remaining sugar in a food processor, add the hazelnuts and finely grind.

10 Beat the butter until creamy. Add the flour and the hazelnut mixture and continue beating for 2-3 minutes, until light and fluffy. Add the yolks and egg, one at a time, beating after each addition. Mix in the chocolate and chopped candied orange zest. Spread the filling over the pastry shell and smooth the top. Bake the tart on the baking sheet in the heated oven until a metal skewer inserted in the centre comes out clean; it should take 35-40 minutes. Let cool on a wire rack.

MAKE THE CHOCOLATE GLAZE AND FINISH THE TART

11 While the tart is cooling, cut the chocolate into chunks. Heat the chocolate in a bowl set over a saucepan of hot water (make sure the base of the bowl does not touch the water), stirring occasionally, just until melted.

12 **Cut the butter** into small pieces and gently stir it into the warm melted chocolate in 2–3 batches. Work quickly, but do not beat, or the butter may turn oily.

13 **Add the Grand Marnier.** Let cool to tepid. Set the tart tin on a bowl to loosen and remove the side. Pour the glaze on to the tart and spread it smoothly over the top. Slide the tart from the tin base on to a plate. Decorate with the remaining candied orange zest.

Amelia Simmons' pumpkin pie

BASED ON a recipe from the first American cook book, written in 1796. Miss Simmons suggested sweetening the filling with blackstrap molasses, but a little sugar – as well as some treacle – is more suited to our tastes today. You can use a 400g (14oz) can of pumpkin purée instead of fresh if you prefer, though the flavour will not be as good. This pie is best eaten on the day it is baked, though the dough can be made and the pumpkin cooked up to 2 days ahead and stored in the refrigerator.

SERVES	PREP	COOK
SERVES 6	45-50 MINS PLUS CHILLING	60-75 MINS

Ingredients

FOR THE SHORTCRUST PASTRY

215g (7½oz) plain flour

¼ tsp salt

1½ tbsp caster sugar (optional)

45g (1½oz) white vegetable fat

60g (2oz) unsalted butter

FOR THE FILLING

1.15-1.4kg (2½-3lb) piece of pumpkin

2 eggs

175ml (6fl oz) double cream

50g (1¾oz) caster sugar

½ tsp ground ginger

½ tsp ground nutmeg

¼ tsp ground mace

60ml (2fl oz) black treacle

MAKE THE PASTRY DOUGH

1 **Put the flour** into a food processor. Add the salt and sugar, if using, and blend for about 5 seconds only. Cut the fat and butter into small, even pieces and add it to the flour. (Use all butter instead of the white vegetable fat, if you prefer a richer flavour.) Pulse-blend until the mixture resembles coarse crumbs; it should take only 10-15 seconds.

2 **Sprinkle 3-4 tbsp cold water** over the mixture, 1 tbsp at a time, pulse-blending all the while, just until the crumbs start sticking together in larger clumps. Don't try to add too much water at once, as it is impossible to remove excess water from a dry dough, but easy to add a drop more. Transfer the dough to a work surface and press lightly into a ball. Do not handle the dough too much at this stage, or the pastry will be tough. Wrap tightly in clingfilm and chill until firm, about 30 minutes, or for up to 2 days.

COOK THE PUMPKIN

3 **Scoop out and discard** the seeds and fibres from the pumpkin. Cut the skin and flesh into wedges, then into large chunks and put into a large pan. Pour in enough water to come a quarter of the way up the pumpkin. Cover and simmer for 25-30 minutes, until tender.

4 **With a slotted spoon**, transfer to a colander and discard the cooking water. With a metal spoon, scrape the pumpkin flesh into a bowl and discard the skin.

5 **Put the pumpkin into a food processor** or blender and purée until smooth. Work it through a sieve to remove any fibres. There should be about 375g (13oz) of pumpkin purée.

MAKE THE PIE BASE

6 Brush a 23cm (9in) pie dish with melted butter. Lightly flour a work surface and roll out the dough into a round 5cm (2in) larger than the dish. Wrap the dough around the rolling pin and drape it over the dish.

7 Gently press the dough into the dish, then trim off excess with a knife. Chill the trimmings. Pinch the dough edge between thumb and finger to make it stand up. With scissors, make 1cm (½in) diagonal cuts around the rim at 1cm (½in) intervals.

8 With your fingertips, push one point towards the centre and the next point towards the edge. Continue around the edge. Prick the bottom of the shell with a fork. Chill for about 15 minutes, until firm. Meanwhile, preheat the oven to 200°C (400°F/Gas 6) and put in a baking sheet.

9 Line the prepared shell with a double thickness of foil, then half-fill it with dried beans or rice. Roll out the pastry trimmings and cut out 3 maple leaf shapes, if you like, scoring them with the back of a knife to resemble veins. Set the pie on a plate and chill.

10 Bake on the baking sheet for 10 minutes, or until the rim just starts to brown. Remove the foil and beans and reduce the oven temperature to 180°C (350°F/Gas 4). Bake for 5 minutes longer, until lightly browned.

PREPARE THE FILLING AND BAKE THE PIE

11 Beat the eggs lightly. Add the cream and eggs to the pumpkin. Beat with an electric mixer or hand whisk until thoroughly mixed. Add the sugar, ginger, nutmeg, and mace. Pour in the treacle and beat to combine. Pour into the shell and bake on the baking sheet for 20 minutes.

12 Add the leaves to the baking sheet, if using, and continue baking for 25–30 minutes, until the filling is firm and a metal skewer inserted into the centre comes out clean. Transfer the pie (and leaves) to a wire rack and let cool. Set the leaves on the filling, if liked, and serve at room temperature, with lightly whipped cream.

Apple cake

A FIRM DESSERT APPLE is best for this moist and dense Italian cake, which is perfect for picnics. Any flavourful apple that holds its shape during cooking is suitable. The cake is best eaten warm from the oven, but it can be stored for up to 2 days in an airtight container. Try to buy unwaxed lemons or, if not available, scrub lemons before using their zest.

SERVES	PREP	COOK
SERVES 8	20-25 MINS	1¼-1½ HRS

Ingredients

175g (6oz) unsalted butter

175g (6oz) plain flour

½ tsp salt

1 tsp baking powder

1 lemon
625g (1lb 6oz) apples
200g (7oz) sugar, plus 60g (2oz) to glaze
2 eggs
4 tbsp milk

PREPARE THE INGREDIENTS

1 **Preheat the oven** to 180°C (350°F/Gas 4). Brush a 23-25cm (9-10in) springform tin with melted butter, and sprinkle with a little flour, discarding the excess. Sift the measured flour with the salt and baking powder. Grate the zest from the lemon.

2 **Peel, core, and thinly slice the apples** lengthways. Squeeze the lemon juice over the apple slices and toss well, ensuring they are all covered to prevent discolouration.

MAKE AND BAKE THE CAKE

3 **With an electric mixer,** beat the butter in a large bowl until soft and creamy. Add the sugar and zest, and beat until light and crumbly. Add the eggs one by one, beating well after each addition. Gradually beat in the milk until the batter is very smooth.

4 **Sift in the flour mixture** and stir gently until evenly mixed. Stir in half the apple slices. Spoon the batter into the prepared tin and smooth the top. Arrange the remaining apple slices in concentric circles on top. Bake the cake in the heated oven for 1¼-1½ hours.

MAKE THE GLAZE AND FINISH THE CAKE

5 **Meanwhile,** make the glaze: heat 4 tbsp water, and the sugar to glaze, in a small saucepan over low heat, until the sugar has dissolved. Bring to a boil and simmer for 2 minutes, without stirring, then let cool.

6 **The cake is done** when it shrinks slightly from the side of the tin, and a skewer inserted in the centre comes out clean. It will still be moist. Brush the sugar syrup glaze on top of the cake as soon as it comes out of the oven. Let the cake cool in the tin. Remove the side of the tin, then transfer the cake to a serving plate.

Walnut cake with caramel topping

ANOTHER SIMPLE ITALIAN CAKE, this time with a crisp layer of caramel topping. This rich cake is flavoured with grappa or rum, so is great for a celebration. This recipe is perfect for entertaining, as it actually benefits from being made up to 2 days ahead, and stored in an airtight container; the flavours will mellow beautifully. Add the caramel topping just before serving.

SERVES	**PREP**	**COOK**
SERVES 8	25–30 MINS	1–1¼ HRS

Ingredients

1 lemon

2 slices of white bread

175g (6oz) walnut halves

4 eggs

125g (4½oz) unsalted butter

135g (5oz) caster sugar, plus 100g (3½oz) more for the caramel

2 tbsp grappa or rum

PREPARE AND BAKE THE CAKE

1 **Preheat the oven** to 180°C (350°F/Gas 4). Brush a 23cm (9in) cake tin with melted butter and line the base with baking parchment. Brush the paper with more butter. Grate the zest from the lemon. Toast the bread in the oven for 5–7 minutes, or until very dry; don't let it brown.

2 **Break the bread** into pieces and put them in a food processor. Work until finely ground. Separately grind 8 walnut halves for garnish. Add the remaining walnuts to the food processor and grind until quite fine.

3 **Separate the eggs.** Cream the butter in an electric mixer. Add two-thirds of the sugar and beat until light and fluffy. Add the egg yolks, beating well. Beat in the zest and grappa. Add the breadcrumb mixture and stir well.

4 **Whisk the** egg whites until stiff. Sprinkle with the remaining sugar and whisk until glossy. Gently fold a spoonful into the batter. Now fold the walnut mixture into the remaining whites. Spoon into the tin and smooth the top. Bake for 1–1¼ hours, until a skewer inserted in the centre comes out clean. Let cool slightly, invert on to a wire rack and leave until cold.

MAKE THE CARAMEL TOPPING

5 **Heat 4 tbsp water** and the sugar for caramel in a saucepan over low heat until the sugar has dissolved. Boil, without stirring, until the syrup starts to turn golden. Do not stir, or it may crystallize. Reduce the heat and continue cooking, swirling the syrup in the pan once or twice so it colours evenly.

6 **Cook** until the caramel is deep golden for best flavour. Do not overcook or the caramel may burn. Quickly plunge the base of the pan into a bowl of cold water to stop the cooking. As soon as the caramel has stopped bubbling, pour it over the cake. Using a palette knife, spread it quickly in a thin layer. Immediately arrange the reserved walnuts on top.

Lemon-blueberry muffins

FEATHERLIGHT MUFFINS glazed with lemon juice and sugar for an extra burst of lemon flavour. Absolutely delicious. These are best freshly baked and glazed to serve warm. The most important thing to remember when making muffins is to stir the batter as little as possible, only just to combine.

SERVES MAKES 12	**PREP** 20-25 MINS	**COOK** 15-20 MINS

Ingredients

60g (2oz) unsalted butter

280g (10oz) unbleached strong white flour

1 tbsp baking powder

½ tsp salt

100g (3½oz) caster sugar

1 egg

juice and zest, finely grated, of 1 lemon

1 tsp vanilla essence

250ml (8fl oz) milk

225g (8oz) blueberries

MAKE THE BATTER

1 Preheat the oven to 220°C (425°F/Gas 7). Melt the butter in a saucepan. Sift the flour, baking powder, and salt into a large bowl. Set 2 tbsp sugar aside and stir the rest into the flour. Make a well in the centre.

2 In a bowl, beat the egg just until mixed. Add the melted butter, lemon zest, vanilla, and milk and beat until foamy. In a slow, steady stream, pour the egg mixture into the well in the flour.

3 Stir with a rubber spatula, gradually drawing in the dry ingredients to make a smooth batter. Gently fold in the blueberries, taking care not to bruise them. Do not overmix, or the muffins will be tough.

BAKE AND GLAZE THE MUFFINS

4 **Place 12 muffin cases** in a medium-sized muffin tin. Spoon the batter evenly between the cases and bake until a metal skewer inserted in the centre of a muffin comes out clean. It may take up to 15–20 minutes, but start checking after 12, as some ovens can be faster than others. (Be sure, though, not to check too often, or you will let out the heat and prevent even baking.) Let the muffins cool slightly on a wire rack.

5 **In a small bowl,** stir the reserved sugar with the lemon juice. While the muffins are still warm, dip the crown of each into the sugar and lemon mixture and set upright on a wire rack to continue cooling. The fact that the muffins are warm will mean they absorb the maximum amount of the wonderful lemony glaze. Serve the glazed muffins while still warm.

 ## VARIATION: Lemon poppy-seed muffins

The poppy seeds add a pleasing crunch.

1 Omit the blueberries. Heat the oven to 220°C (425°F/Gas 7), and place 9 muffin cases in a muffin tin. Melt the butter for the batter as directed. Grate the zest from the lemon and squeeze the juice.

2 Sift the flour, baking powder, and salt into a large bowl. Stir in all the sugar. In a medium bowl, beat the egg just until mixed. Add the melted butter, vanilla, and milk, and whisk as directed. Stir in 2 tbsp poppy seeds, then add the lemon zest and lemon juice.

3 Combine the ingredients as directed and spoon the mixture into the muffin cases. Sprinkle the muffins with 2 tsp sugar and bake as directed. Makes 9.

Rich chocolate cake

THIS TRIPLE-LAYER CHOCOLATE CAKE has got everything the chocolate and cake lover could wish for: moist sponge, fluffy vanilla cream, and unctuous, shiny chocolate icing. It's a surefire hit for any special occasion. Best of all, it is very simple to make: even a novice baker will be able to produce their own masterpiece. Because of the fresh cream, eat this in one sitting (that shouldn't prove difficult); any leftovers should be refrigerated.

SERVES
SERVES 12

PREP
15 MINS
PLUS COOLING

COOK
30-35 MINS

Ingredients

FOR THE CAKE

300g (10oz) self-raising flour

4 tbsp cocoa powder

1 heaped tsp bicarbonate of soda

300g (10oz) unsalted butter, softened

300g (10oz) golden caster sugar

5 large eggs

1 tsp vanilla essence

4 tbsp milk

FOR THE CHOCOLATE CURLS, FILLING, AND ICING

175g (6oz) plain chocolate

450ml (15fl oz) double cream

a knob of unsalted butter

1 tbsp caster sugar

a few drops of vanilla essence

PREPARE THE TINS

1 Preheat the oven to 180°C (350°F/Gas 4). Lightly butter 3 x 20cm (8in) sandwich tins and line the bases with baking parchment.

MAKE AND BAKE THE CAKES

2 Sift the flour, cocoa, and bicarbonate of soda together into a bowl. Place the butter and sugar in another bowl together, then use an electric whisk to beat them until pale and fluffy.

3 Add the sifted flour, eggs, vanilla, and milk, then whisk for 1 minute, until the mixture is uniform and fluffy. Divide the mixture evenly between the 3 cake tins and use the back of a spoon to level the surface. Bake in the hot oven for 30–35 minutes, or until the centre of the sponge springs back when lightly pressed with your finger. Leave the cakes to cool in the tins for 5 minutes. Remove from the tins, transfer to a wire rack, and leave until cold.

MELT THE CHOCOLATE FOR THE CURLS

4 Break 50g (2oz) of the chocolate into pieces and place in a heatproof bowl. Put it over a pan of gently simmering water, making sure the base of the bowl does not touch the water, and stir until the chocolate is melted and smooth. Pour on to a baking sheet - or a marble slab if you have one - and leave to set in a cool place.

DECORATE THE CAKE

5 When the chocolate has set, (or just use a bar of chocolate if you're short on time), push a sharp knife or vegetable peeler across the surface at a 45° angle, so that curls of chocolate form. Set aside in a cool place.

6 Measure 150ml (5fl oz) of the cream into a heatproof bowl. Break the remaining chocolate into squares and add to the bowl. Place over a pan of gently simmering water, making sure the base of the bowl does not touch the water, and stir until the chocolate melts and a smooth shiny icing forms. Remove from the heat, stir in the butter, and leave to cool.

7 **Pour the remaining cream** into a large bowl, add the sugar and vanilla and whisk until the cream forms soft peaks. Divide the cream between 2 of the cakes, stack them on top of each other, then cover with the third cake.

8 **Spoon the cooled chocolate icing** over the top, allowing a little to ooze down the sides of the cake. Scatter over the chocolate curls and serve.

Chocolate orange pound cake

FOR A TREAT, candy your own peel. To save time, you can substitute 125g (4½oz) of bought peel; if it seems dry, soak in boiling water for 5–10 minutes to plump it up, then drain and dry very well before chopping. The cake can be stored for up to 1 week in an airtight container; it will become moist and sticky the longer it is kept.

SERVES	**PREP**	**COOK**
SERVES 6-8	2 HRS PLUS CANDIED PEEL	50-60 MINS

Ingredients

FOR THE CANDIED PEEL

2 oranges

200g (7oz) caster sugar

FOR THE CAKE

125g (4½oz) plain flour

3 tbsp cocoa powder

1 tsp baking powder

salt

175g (6oz) unsalted butter

200g (7oz) caster sugar

3 eggs

FOR THE ORANGE ICING

60g (2oz) icing sugar

2–3 tsp orange juice (reserved from orange for peel)

MAKE THE CANDIED PEEL

1 Roll each orange gently on a work surface to loosen the peel. Score the orange peel lengthways into quarters with a small knife, then strip away the peel and pith with your fingers.

2 Cut the peel into 5mm (¼in) strips with a sharp knife. Cut one orange in half and squeeze the juice; reserve it for the icing.

3 Heat the sugar with 250ml (9fl oz) water in a saucepan until dissolved, then bring just to a boil, and tip in the peel. Press a circle of baking parchment on top, and weigh it down with a plate. Heat slowly to a simmer, then poach for about 1 hour, until tender. Allow it to soak at room temperature for 24 hours, then drain on a rack placed over a tray for 3–5 hours longer.

MAKE THE CAKE

4 Reserve several pieces of peel for decoration, and finely chop the rest. Preheat the oven to 180°C (350°F/Gas 4). Butter, line, and flour a 21x11x7.5cm (8½x4½x3in) loaf tin. Sift the flour into a bowl with the cocoa powder, baking powder, and a pinch of salt.

5 With an electric mixer, cream the butter. Add the sugar and continue beating for 2–3 minutes, until light and fluffy. Add the eggs one by one, beating thoroughly with the electric mixer after each addition. Stir the finely chopped candied orange peel evenly into the mixture.

6 Stir in the flour and cocoa powder mixture until just mixed. Transfer the mixture to the prepared loaf tin. Tap the tin on a work surface to level the surface, and knock out large air bubbles. Bake in the heated oven for 50–60 minutes, until it shrinks slightly from the sides of the tin, and a skewer inserted in the centre comes out clean.

MAKE THE ICING AND **FINISH** THE CAKE

7 Remove the cake from the oven. Run a small knife round the sides of the loaf tin to loosen the cake, then invert the tin and transfer the cake to a wire rack, keeping a baking sheet below the rack to catch any drips from the icing later. Carefully remove the baking parchment. Leave the cake to cool completely.

8 Sift the icing sugar into a small bowl, and stir in enough of the orange juice to make a soft paste. Adjust the consistency by adding more icing sugar if it seems too thin, or more orange juice if it's a little too thick, adding just a very little of either at a time as it's a finely balanced process to get the consistency just right. Place the bowl in a saucepan of hot (not simmering) water, and heat until the icing is warm, and will pour easily from the spoon. Drizzle the icing evenly over the cake, then top with the reserved candied peel. Leave to stand for about 1 hour, until the icing has set. Serve the cake in generous slices, with afternoon tea.

 VARIATION: Chocolate orange marble pound cake

An attractive cake with a swirl of plain orange mixture.

1 Make the candied orange peel as directed, then chop all of it. Sift the flour with the baking powder, and salt, and divide evenly between 2 bowls. Sift 3 tbsp cocoa powder into 1 of the bowls.

2 Continue making the cake mixture as directed until the end of step 5, then divide it in half. Stir the cocoa mixture into 1 portion, and the plain flour mixture into the other. Pour the plain mixture into the prepared loaf tin.

3 Pour the chocolate mixture over the plain mixture in the tin. Using the tip of a knife, swirl the mixtures together in a marbled pattern, taking care not to overmix them or the marbled effect will be lost. Bake and ice the cake as directed.

Marbled chocolate cheesecake

THIS ALL-AMERICAN FAVOURITE has swirls of plain and chocolate cheesecake fillings flavoured with vanilla, in a crumbled biscuit base. The marbled filling is dense and rich, making it an indulgent finishing touch to a dinner party. Even better, the cheesecake can be made up to 3 days ahead and kept, tightly wrapped, in the refrigerator, so you have far less to prepare on the day. The filling has very few ingredients, so you must use the very best quality chocolate you can afford.

SERVES
SERVES 8-10

PREP
35-40 MINS
PLUS COOLING
AND CHILLING

COOK
50-60 MINS

Ingredients

FOR THE BISCUIT BASE

75g (2½oz) unsalted butter, plus more, melted, for the tin

150g (5½oz) digestive biscuits

FOR THE CHEESECAKE FILLING

150g (5½oz) good-quality plain chocolate

500g (1lb 2oz) cream cheese, softened

150g (5½oz) caster sugar

1 tsp vanilla essence

2 eggs

MAKE THE BISCUIT BASE

1 **Generously brush** the inside of a 20cm (8in) springform tin with melted butter, and chill it. Work the digestive biscuits to fine crumbs in a food processor (or crush with a rolling pin); transfer to a bowl. Melt the butter in a small saucepan; add to the crumbs.

2 **Stir with a wooden spoon** until all the crumbs are moistened with melted butter. Press the crumb mixture evenly over the bottom and up the side of the prepared tin. Chill for 30-60 minutes, until firm.

MAKE THE CHEESECAKE FILLING

3 **Preheat the oven** to 180°C (350°F/Gas 4). Cut the chocolate into large chunks with a sharp knife, or in a food processor using the pulse button. Melt the chocolate in a bowl suspended over – but not touching the surface of – a pan of simmering water, stirring as little as possible until smooth, then allow to cool.

4 **Beat the cream cheese** with an electric mixer or wooden spoon for 2-3 minutes, until smooth. Add the sugar and vanilla essence, and beat just until smooth once more. Add the eggs one by one, beating very well after each addition.

ASSEMBLE AND MARBLE THE CHEESECAKE

5 **Pour half of the filling** into the biscuit base. It will be nowhere near full, as the chocolate mixture is still to come. It is fine if the surface is not level, as you will be marbling the fillings later.

6 **Mix the cooled, melted chocolate** into the remaining filling. It is important to have waited long enough for the melted chocolate to become cool, otherwise there is a risk that the eggs in the mixture may begin to scramble.

7 **Slowly spoon** a ring of the chocolate filling over the plain filling. Don't worry about neatness here; as long as you make a rough, even band of chocolate filling, the cheesecake will look great.

8 Using a table knife, swirl the fillings together to make a marbled pattern. Don't over-mix, or the marbled effect will be lost. Bake in the oven for 50–60 minutes, until the side is set but the centre remains soft. Turn off the oven and leave the cheesecake there until completely cool, or it may crack. Refrigerate for at least 4 hours. Run a knife round the side of the cheesecake to loosen it, remove the tin and transfer to a serving plate.

VARIATION: All-chocolate cheescake

You have 2 options here: either use all plain, or all white chocolate, depending on which you would prefer.

1 Make the base as directed. Chop and melt 300g (10oz) plain chocolate, or 250g (9oz) white chocolate, as directed, making sure that the base of the bowl containing the chocolate does not touch the simmering water, or there is a risk the chocolate may "seize" and be spoiled.

2 Prepare the filling as directed, using only 100g (3½oz) sugar and stirring in all the cooled, melted plain or white chocolate after the eggs, without dividing the mixture into 2 portions.

3 Pour all the filling into the prepared base, level the surface, and bake as directed. Let cool, then serve with fresh raspberries.

Spectacular desserts

Impressive, indulgent,
and delicious puddings

Chocolate orange truffle cake

A LAYER OF CHOCOLATE SPONGE CAKE, crowned with chocolate ganache, and flavoured with Grand Marnier. Orange segments steeped in Grand Marnier provide the perfect accompaniment. Make sure you leave yourself at least 6 hours' chilling time.

SERVES
SERVES 10-12

PREP
35-40 MINS
PLUS CHILLING

COOK
40 MINS

Ingredients

FOR THE CHOCOLATE CAKE

60g (2oz) butter

100g (3½oz) plain flour

30g (1oz) cocoa powder

salt

4 eggs

135g (5oz) caster sugar

4-5 tbsp Grand Marnier

FOR THE CHOCOLATE GANACHE

375g (13oz) plain chocolate

375ml (13fl oz) double cream

3 tbsp Grand Marnier

TO DECORATE AND FINISH

6 oranges

3 tbsp Grand Marnier

3 tbsp cocoa powder

MAKE THE CAKE

1 **Preheat the oven** to 220°C (425°F/Gas 7). Butter a 25cm (10in) round cake tin, and line the bottom with baking parchment. Butter the parchment. Sprinkle in 2-3 tbsp flour, and turn the tin to coat the bottom and side; tap the tin upside down to remove excess flour. Melt the butter and allow to cool.

2 **Sift together** the flour, cocoa powder, and a pinch of salt. Put the eggs in a large bowl, and beat with an electric mixer for a few seconds. Add the sugar and continue beating at high speed for about 5 minutes, until the mixture leaves a ribbon trail when the beaters are lifted.

3 **Sift about a third of the flour** and cocoa mixture over the egg mixture, and fold together as lightly as possible. Add another third of the flour and cocoa mixture, and fold together in the same way. Add the remaining flour and cocoa mixture, and the cooled, melted butter, and fold them in gently but quickly.

4 **Pour the mixture** into the prepared tin, then gently tap the tin on the work surface to level the mixture, and knock out any large air bubbles. Bake in the heated oven for about 40 minutes, until the cake is risen and just firm to the touch. Turn the cake out on to a wire rack. Peel off the paper. Leave the cake to cool.

PREPARE THE BASE

5 **Trim the cooled cake** to fit a 23cm (9in) springform tin, using the base of the tin as a guide. Lightly butter the bottom and side. Carefully transfer the trimmed cake to the tin. Sprinkle 4-5 tbsp Grand Marnier evenly over the top of the cake. Cover and set aside while making the chocolate ganache.

MAKE THE CHOCOLATE GANACHE

6 **Cut the chocolate** into large chunks with a sharp knife, or in a food processor. Put the chocolate in a large bowl. Heat the cream until almost boiling, then pour it over the chopped chocolate. Stir until the chocolate has melted. Allow to cool, stirring occasionally.

7 **Add the 3 tbsp Grand Marnier** to the cream and chocolate mixture, and stir until blended. Do not stir too vigorously, as melted chocolate should always be treated gently and with care. Using the electric mixer, beat the chocolate ganache for 5-10 minutes, until fluffy. Do not overbeat the mixture, or it will be very stiff and hard to spread. You just want to incorporate a little air.

8 With a rubber spatula, or a wooden spoon, turn out the chocolate ganache on top of the cake, and smooth the surface. Cover with cling film and chill for at least 6 hours, until firm.

PREPARE THE DECORATION AND FINISH THE CAKE

9 Using a citrus zester, remove the zest from 3 of the oranges, working over a sheet of baking parchment to catch all the essential oils. Be careful not to include any of the white pith. Set aside on a plate in the refrigerator until needed.

10 Trim both ends of each orange, set the fruits upright on a chopping board, and cut away all the remaining peel and the white pith, following the curve of the oranges. Working over a bowl, cut down between each side of the orange segments to separate them from the thin membranes. Put the segments in a bowl and squeeze each empty orange shell over, to extract all the remaining juice and flavour. Sprinkle with the Grand Marnier.

11 Just before serving, take the cake from the refrigerator. Stand it on top of a bowl, then release the side of the tin. Carefully remove the base of the tin, using a palette knife. Place the cake on a wire rack with a baking sheet beneath. Sift cocoa powder over the top, using a stencil if you like, then transfer to a serving plate, and sprinkle with the reserved orange zest. Serve the orange segments and liquid in small bowls alongside.

Strawberry shortcakes

REAL STRAWBERRY SHORTCAKE, MADE WITH A SCONE-LIKE DOUGH. This is a rich version of the dish, but a tangy strawberry coulis mingles well with the shortcakes and cream, and cuts through the richness. These are best eaten fresh from the oven.

SERVES
SERVES 6

PREP
15–20 MINS

COOK
12–15 MINS

Ingredients

FOR THE SHORTCAKES

250g (9oz) plain flour

1 tbsp baking powder

½ tsp salt

45g (1½oz) caster sugar

60g (2oz) unsalted butter, cut into pieces

175ml (6fl oz) double cream, plus more if needed

FOR THE STRAWBERRY COULIS

500g (1lb 2oz) strawberries

2–3 tbsp icing sugar

2 tbsp kirsch (optional)

FOR THE STRAWBERRIES

500g (1lb 2oz) strawberries

45g (1½oz) caster sugar

FOR THE CHANTILLY CREAM (optional)

250ml (9fl oz) double cream

2–3 tbsp caster sugar

1 tsp vanilla essence

PREPARE THE SHORTCAKES

1 **Preheat the oven** to 220°C (425°F/Gas 7). Butter a baking sheet. Sift the flour into a bowl with the baking powder, salt, and caster sugar.

2 **Cut the butter** into the flour mixture using 2 round-bladed knives. Rub with your fingertips to form fine crumbs. Add the cream, and toss quickly to form crumbs. Add a little more cream if it seems dry.

BAKE THE SHORTCAKES

3 **Press all the crumbs** together with your hands, to form a rough ball of dough. It doesn't matter at this stage if it seems a little crumbly, as that will disappear once you work the dough. Remember to handle it lightly at all times.

4 **Turn the dough** on to a floured surface and knead lightly for a few seconds; the dough should remain quite rough, but all the ingredients should be evenly mixed, without any big lumps. Pat the dough out to a round 1cm (½in) thick.

5 **Cut out rounds** with an 8cm (3in) pastry cutter, or a glass of the same diameter. Pat out the trimmings, and cut additional rounds, for a total of 6 rounds. Transfer to the prepared baking sheet, spacing them out evenly.

6 **Bake until very lightly browned:** it should take 12–15 minutes. Transfer them to a wire rack to cool.

MAKE THE COULIS

7 Hull and pick over the strawberries, washing them only if dirty. Purée them in a food processor. Transfer to a bowl and stir in the icing sugar and kirsch, if using. It should be thick enough to coat the back of a spoon.

PREPARE THE STRAWBERRIES AND CHANTILLY CREAM

8 Hull the strawberries and cut into slices, reserving 6 small whole berries. Sprinkle the sliced strawberries with the caster sugar and let stand to soften for 5-10 minutes. Slice the reserved strawberries and set aside.

9 Pour the cream into a chilled bowl. Set the bowl over iced water, if your kitchen is hot. Whip until soft peaks form. Add the sugar and vanilla and whip until it forms stiff peaks.

ASSEMBLE THE SHORTCAKES

10 Cut the cooled shortcakes in half, with a serrated knife. Spoon the strawberries on the bottom halves. Pile on the cream, and top each with its lid and the reserved sliced strawberries. Spoon the coulis around.

 VARIATION: Lemon shortcakes with blueberries

The lemon here accents the blueberry filling.

1 Make the shortcakes as directed in the main recipe, adding the grated zest and juice of 1 unwaxed lemon along with the unsalted butter. Remember to handle the shortcake dough as lightly and gently as possible at all times during the making and cutting out process, or they will be tough. Use the trimmings to make miniature shortcakes.

2 Pick over 500g (1lb 2oz) firm and plump blueberries, discarding any that are very soft; they do not need to be sprinkled with sugar unless they are very tart. Taste a berry to check how sweet yours are, and take a view on whether you would like to sweeten them or not; you know your palate better than anyone else.

3 Assemble the shortcakes as directed in the main recipe, piling the Chantilly cream on top of the blueberries, then decorate the top of each shortcake with an edible flower or a herb sprig. Lemon verbena, if you can get hold of it, or you grow it in the garden, would be a good choice of herb to use here. Otherwise sprinkle with the leaves stripped from a sprig of lemon thyme.

Orange and cinnamon crème brûlée

IN THIS DESSERT, translated as "burnt cream", a rich custard is sprinkled with sugar just before serving, and then grilled. The top will crack when tapped with a spoon, while the cinnamon and orange give complexity to the satin-smooth baked cream. Fresh berries or a peach compote would make a perfect accompaniment. It can be made up to the end of step 5 and refrigerated for up to 8 hours.

SERVES	**PREP**	**COOK**
SERVES 8	15-20 MINS PLUS CHILLING	30-35 MINS

1 litre (1¾ pints) whipping cream
8 egg yolks
200g (7oz) granulated sugar

Ingredients

1 orange
1 cinnamon stick

MAKE THE ORANGE-CINNAMON CUSTARD

1 **Preheat the oven** to 190°C (375°F/Gas 5). Grate the zest from the orange. Snap the cinnamon stick in half and place in a saucepan. Warm over low heat for 40-60 seconds, until you can smell the spice. Let cool slightly, then add the cream and grated orange zest. Bring just to a boil. Remove from the heat, cover, and let the cream infuse for 10-15 minutes.

2 **Put the yolks** and a third of the sugar in a large bowl. Whisk just until mixed, using an electric mixer or a hand whisk. Slowly pour the cream mixture into the egg yolks, whisking constantly until evenly mixed. You must continue to whisk all the time, or there is a risk that the egg yolks will start to scramble, splitting the custard base.

BAKE THE CUSTARD

3 **Ladle the cream mixture** through a large sieve into a 1.5 litre (2¾pint) gratin dish. Fold an old, clean tea towel, and put it on the bottom of a roasting tin. Then set the gratin dish on the towel.

4 **Pour enough hot water** into the roasting tin to come about halfway up the sides of the gratin dish. Bring the water bath to a boil on top of the stove, then carefully transfer to the heated oven.

5 **Bake for 30-35 minutes, until a thin skin forms** on top and the cream underneath is almost firm when the dish is gently moved from side to side. Remove from the roasting tin. Let cool to room temperature. Chill for 3-8 hours.

CARAMELIZE THE CREAM

6 **Heat the grill** to its highest setting. Sprinkle the remaining sugar over the surface of the cream in an even layer. Half-fill a roasting tin with cold water, and set the gratin dish in it. Add some ice cubes to the water to keep the custard cool. Grill for 3 minutes, until the sugar melts and caramelizes on top. Let cool a few minutes so the caramel becomes crisp, then serve.

Tiramisu

THIS RICH ITALIAN DESSERT has many versions. The name means "pick me up". To be truly authentic, use espresso coffee. This can be assembled 2 days ahead and kept, covered, in the refrigerator. Add the cocoa and coffee decoration just before serving.

SERVES SERVES 8-10	**PREP** 35-40 MINS PLUS CHILLING	**COOK** 30-40 MINS

Ingredients

FOR THE MASCARPONE MIXTURE

6 egg yolks

60g (2oz) caster sugar

500g (1lb 2oz) mascarpone cheese

1 tsp vanilla essence

TO SOAK AND TOP THE TIRAMISU

150ml (5fl oz) espresso coffee

4 tbsp Tia Maria or Kahlúa (coffee liqueur)

4 tbsp brandy

32 sponge fingers (preferably Savoiarde)

1 tbsp cocoa powder

1 tbsp coffee powder

icing sugar, to serve (optional)

PREPARE THE MASCARPONE MIXTURE

1 **Put the egg yolks** and sugar in a large heatproof bowl and beat them with an electric mixer. Set the bowl over a saucepan of hot, but not simmering, water. Make sure the base of the bowl does not touch the water. Whisk for 3–5 minutes, until pale and thick enough to leave a "ribbon" trail when the whisk is lifted.

2 **Take the bowl** from the pan of hot water, and continue beating for 1–2 minutes, until the mixture has cooled slightly. Let cool completely. Combine the mascarpone and vanilla essence in another bowl, and stir with a rubber spatula until smooth and creamy. Add the egg yolk and sugar mixture to the mascarpone, and fold them together.

ASSEMBLE THE TIRAMISU

3 **Combine the espresso,** Tia Maria, and brandy in a shallow dish. Dip each of the sponge fingers, cut-side down, in the coffee, then place in the bottom of a large serving dish.

4 **Continue to moisten** a third of the sponge fingers, to make a single layer. Sprinkle them with 2 tbsp of the remaining coffee mixture.

5 **Spoon one-third of the mascarpone mixture** over the sponge fingers to cover them completely. Continue layering the moistened cake fingers and mascarpone mixture, ending with a layer of mascarpone.

6 **Smooth the surface** with a large metal spoon. Cover and chill for at least 6 hours. Mix together the cocoa and coffee powders. Sift them over the top of the tiramisu, then sift over a little icing sugar, if using, and serve.

Pavlova with tropical fruit

A GIANT MERINGUE PUFF, with a crisp outside and a soft, chewy interior, filled with whipped cream and fruit. This luscious dessert was created for the famous ballerina Anna Pavlova, and originates from Australia and New Zealand. This recipe makes a huge meringue, but you will find it disappears very rapidly! The meringue can be baked up to the end of step 3 and kept for up to 1 week in a large airtight container. It can also be frozen. Assemble the pavlova just before serving.

SERVES	PREP	COOK
SERVES 6-8	25-30 MINS	2-2½ HRS

Ingredients

FOR THE MERINGUE

6 egg whites

350g (12oz) caster sugar

1 tbsp cornflour

1 tsp distilled malt vinegar

2 tbsp chopped pistachios, to serve

FOR THE FRUIT

3 mangoes, total weight about 1kg (2¼lb)

5 kiwi fruit

1 pineapple, weighing about 750g (1lb 10oz)

45g (1½oz) caster sugar

2 tbsp kirsch

FOR THE CREAM

375ml (13fl oz) double cream

45-60g (1½-2oz) caster or icing sugar

1 tsp vanilla essence

MAKE THE MERINGUE

1 **Line a baking sheet** with baking parchment. Using a 20cm (8in) cake tin as a guide, draw a circle on the paper. Preheat the oven to 130°C (250°F/ Gas ½). Whisk the egg whites until stiff. Sprinkle in 75g (2½oz) of the sugar, and continue whisking for about 20 seconds until glossy. Sift the cornflour and remaining sugar over, and add the vinegar.

2 **Fold the mixture** together until thoroughly mixed. Pile the meringue in the centre of the circle drawn on the paper, making sure it keeps within the line. With the back of a large metal spoon, spread out the meringue to an even round, making a deep hollow in the centre. Bake in the oven for 2-2½ hours, until firm and very lightly coloured. If it starts to brown during cooking, reduce the heat and cover loosely with foil.

3 **Let the pavlova cool** to lukewarm, then lift it off the baking sheet with two large palette knives, and set it on a wire rack to cool completely. When cold, peel off the paper. The exterior of the baked meringue will become crisp as it cools, while the interior stays moist and chewy.

PREPARE THE MANGO

4 **Removing the flat, central stone** and cubing mango flesh is easy, if you use this method. Cut each mango into two pieces lengthways, slightly off-centre, to just miss the stone. Cut the flesh away from the other side of the stone. Discard the stone.

5 **Slash one piece** - or "cheek" - in a lattice, cutting through the flesh but not the skin. Repeat with the other mango cheeks. Try to keep the lattice as even as possible.

6 **Holding a mango cheek** flesh side upwards, push the centre of the skin with your fingers to turn it inside out, opening the cuts of the flesh to reveal cubes. It will look a little like a hedgehog. Cut the cubes away from the skin.

PREPARE THE REMAINING FILLING

7 **Pour the cream** into a chilled bowl, and whip until soft peaks form. Add the sugar and vanilla essence, and continue whipping until stiff peaks form. Set aside.

8 **With a small knife, trim** the ends of the kiwi fruit. Set the fruit upright and trim off the skin in strips, working from top to bottom. Cut the kiwi fruit into neat slices.

9 **Cut off the plume** and base of the pineapple, then peel it, working from top to bottom following the curve of the fruit. Cut the pineapple lengthways in half, then into quarters. Cut out the core from each quarter. Cut the quarters lengthways into strips, then across into neat chunks.

10 **Put all the fruit** in a large bowl. Sprinkle the fruit with the sugar and kirsch. Stir very gently with a scrupulously clean wooden spoon (now is not the time for a scent of garlic!) to distribute the flavourings evenly, taking care not to break up any of the fruit pieces.

ASSEMBLE THE PAVLOVA

11 **Put the cooled pavlova** on a serving plate and spoon in the sweetened vanilla cream to form an even layer. Arrange the mixed fruit neatly over the top, sprinkle with the chopped pistachios, and serve immediately. Do not leave it to stand, or the cream will seep into the meringue, and make it soggy.

Cold lemon soufflé

A FAVOURITE ENDING to a grand dinner, this dessert is cool, light, and fluffy, with just the right balance of tart and sweet. Choose unwaxed lemons that feel heavy for their size, indicating they are full of juice. If unwaxed lemons are unavailable, scrub the fruits very well with a small, stiff brush before cooking with the zest.

SERVES	PREP	COOK
SERVES 8	35–40 MINS PLUS CHILLING	15–20 MINS

Ingredients

250g (9oz) caster sugar	
250ml (9fl oz) double cream	

FOR THE SOUFFLÉ

10g (¼oz) powdered gelatine
4 large lemons
4 eggs, and 2 egg whites

FOR THE CANDIED ZEST

2 tbsp caster sugar

FOR THE CHANTILLY CREAM

125ml (4½fl oz) double cream
1–2 tbsp caster sugar
½ tsp vanilla essence

PREPARE THE SOUFFLÉ DISH

1 **Cut a piece of foil,** 5cm (2in) longer than the circumference of a 1 litre (1¾ pint) soufflé dish. Fold the foil lengthways in half. Wrap the foil around the dish. It should stand well above the rim, so the soufflé will appear to have "risen". Secure with tape.

MAKE THE SOUFFLÉ BASE

2 **Put 75ml (2½fl oz) water** in a small saucepan, sprinkle the gelatine on top, and set aside for about 5 minutes, to soften until spongy. Make sure every crystal is soaked in water, or there will be crystals in the final soufflé.

3 **Grate the zest** from 3 of the lemons. Pare strips of zest from the remaining lemon, and reserve it to candy. Squeeze the juice from all 4 lemons – there should be 150ml (5fl oz). Separate the whole eggs. In a saucepan, mix together the egg yolks, grated lemon zest, lemon juice, and two-thirds of the sugar until blended.

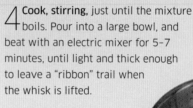

4 **Cook, stirring,** just until the mixture boils. Pour into a large bowl, and beat with an electric mixer for 5–7 minutes, until light and thick enough to leave a "ribbon" trail when the whisk is lifted.

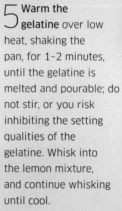

5 **Warm the gelatine** over low heat, shaking the pan, for 1–2 minutes, until the gelatine is melted and pourable; do not stir, or you risk inhibiting the setting qualities of the gelatine. Whisk into the lemon mixture, and continue whisking until cool.

FINISH AND CHILL THE SOUFFLÉ

6 **Pour the cream** into a bowl, and whip until soft peaks form; chill. Heat the remaining sugar with 125ml (4fl oz) water, until dissolved. Boil without stirring until it reaches the hard-ball stage: to test, remove a teaspoon of syrup. Take it between finger and thumb; it should form a firm, pliable ball. (Or it should register 120°C (248°F) on a sugar thermometer.)

7 **While the syrup is boiling,** put the 6 egg whites in a bowl and whisk. until stiff peaks form when the whisk is lifted. Gradually pour the hot sugar syrup into the egg whites, whisking constantly.

8 **Continue whisking** for about 5 minutes, until the meringue is cool and stiff. Set the bowl of lemon mixture in a larger bowl of iced water, and stir the mixture gently until it starts to thicken. Remove the bowl from the ice bath. Gently fold in the chilled whipped cream, then fold in the meringue in 2 batches.

9 **Pour the soufflé** mixture into the prepared dish; it should come at least 5cm (2in) above the rim of the dish, but below the edge of the foil collar. Chill the soufflé for at least 2 hours, until firmly set.

CANDY THE LEMON ZEST

10 **Cut the pared lemon** zest into very fine strips. Bring a small pan of water to the boil, add the zest and simmer for 2 minutes, then drain. In the same pan, gently heat the sugar with 2 tbsp water until dissolved. Add the zest and simmer for 8–10 minutes, until the moisture has evaporated. Remove with a fork, gently separate, and set on baking parchment to cool.

MAKE THE CHANTILLY CREAM

11 **To make the Chantilly cream,** pour the cream into a chilled bowl, and whip until soft peaks form. Add the sugar and vanilla, and continue whipping until the cream forms stiff peaks.

12 **Transfer the Chantilly cream** into a serving bowl. Remove the soufflé from the refrigerator, and allow to stand at room temperature for 30 minutes to lose its chilled stiffness, Sprinkle with the candied lemon zest, carefully remove the foil collar, being gentle so as not to spoil the appearance of the "risen" sides, and serve with the Chantilly cream.

Chocolate ice cream

HOME-MADE ICE CREAM still beats them all. Serve with langues de chats biscuits, or even a colourful assortment of seasonal fruit, if you like. Strawberries and peaches are especially good. The ice cream can be made 2 weeks ahead and kept in a covered container in the freezer. It will become very hard, so soften it in the refrigerator before serving.

SERVES SERVES 6-8	**PREP** 15-20 MINS PLUS FREEZING	**COOK** 10-15 MINS

Ingredients

250g (9oz) good-quality plain chocolate

600ml (1 pint) milk

125g (4½oz) caster sugar

8 egg yolks

2 tbsp cornflour

250ml (9fl oz) double cream

1 bar plain chocolate for chocolate curls (optional)

MAKE THE CHOCOLATE CUSTARD

1 **With a sharp knife,** cut the chocolate into large chunks, then chop finely with a knife or in a food processor using the pulse button. Put the milk in a saucepan, add the chocolate and heat, stirring, until smooth. Make sure you stir constantly, so the chocolate does not stick and burn on the pan.

2 **Add the sugar** to the chocolate milk, and stir until it has completely dissolved. In a bowl, whisk the egg yolks with the cornflour until smooth. Gradually whisk three-quarters of the chocolate milk into the egg yolk mixture, until smooth. Reserve the remainder in a measuring jug. Do not overwhisk, or the custard will be frothy instead of smooth.

COOK THE CHOCOLATE CUSTARD

3 **Return the mixture** to the saucepan, and cook over medium heat, stirring constantly, until the custard thickens enough to coat the back of the spoon. Stir in the reserved chocolate milk. Strain the chocolate custard sauce into a cold bowl, and leave to cool. If the custard forms a skin, whisk to dissolve it back into the mixture.

FREEZE THE ICE CREAM

4 **Pour the custard** into an ice-cream maker, and churn, according to the manufacturer's instructions. Meanwhile, chill 2 large bowls in the freezer. Whip the cream in 1 chilled bowl until it forms peaks, and holds its shape.

5 **Add the whipped cream** to the partially-set chocolate custard, and continue freezing until firm. Transfer the ice cream to the second chilled bowl, cover, and freeze for at least 4 hours.

6 **Make the chocolate curls,** if wanted: the chocolate bar should be at room temperature. With a vegetable peeler, shave curls on to a sheet of baking parchment. Scoop out the ice cream, and sprinkle with chocolate curls.

Blackberry fool

THE NAME "FOOL" dates back at least to 16th-century England, and probably comes from the French "fouler", meaning to purée. Fools are traditionally made with a tart fruit. There are simpler versions, but this is a delicious recipe.

SERVES	PREP	COOK
SERVES 8	20-25 MINS PLUS CHILLING	15-20 MINS

Ingredients

FOR THE BLACKBERRIES

500g (1lb 2oz) blackberries

60-75g (2-2½oz) caster sugar, plus more if needed

250ml (9fl oz) double cream

fresh mint sprigs, to decorate

FOR THE PASTRY CREAM

375ml (13fl oz) milk

1 vanilla pod, or 2 tsp vanilla essence

5 egg yolks

60g (2oz) caster sugar

30g (1oz) plain flour

knob of unsalted butter

MAKE THE BLACKBERRY PURÉE

1 **Pick over the blackberries,** and set aside 8 for decoration. Put the berries in a saucepan with 4 tbsp water. Simmer over medium heat, stirring, for 8-10 minutes, until soft but thick. Transfer to a food processor, and purée to a fairly coarse texture.

2 **Press the purée** through a sieve to remove the pips. There should be 375ml (13fl oz). Stir in sugar to taste, and set the purée aside to cool. The flavours will blend and develop.

MAKE THE PASTRY CREAM

3 **Put the milk** in a small saucepan and add the split vanilla pod, if using. Bring to a boil, then remove from the heat, cover, and let stand for 10-15 minutes. In a large bowl, whisk the yolks, sugar, and flour just to mix. Whisk the hot milk into the egg yolk mixture until thoroughly combined.

4 **Return the mixture** to the pan, and cook over low heat, whisking constantly, for 2-3 minutes, until the flour has cooked and the pastry cream has thickened. Simmer over low heat for 2 minutes longer. Transfer to a bowl and remove the vanilla pod, if using, or stir in the vanilla essence. Using the fork, rub the butter over the surface to prevent a skin from forming. Set aside to cool.

FINISH THE FOOL

5 **Pour the cream** into a chilled bowl. Whip until stiff peaks form, and the whisk leaves clear marks in the cream. Set aside. Add the blackberry purée to the cooled pastry cream, and stir to mix thoroughly.

6 **Fold in the whipped cream** gently. Taste; add more sugar if necessary. Spoon into stemmed glasses. Cover and chill for at least 2 hours. Decorate each fool with a blackberry and a mint sprig, and serve chilled.

Caramelized mango tartlets

THE FAME OF TARTE TATIN (p442) has spread worldwide, but this modern version, using mangoes, is equally good. The tartlets are turned out to serve upside-down, and are best eaten warm.

SERVES	PREP	COOK
SERVES 6	40-45 MINS	20-25 MINS

60g (2oz) caster sugar

¼ tsp salt

Ingredients

FOR THE PÂTE SUCRÉE DOUGH

90g (3oz) unsalted butter

3 egg yolks

½ tsp vanilla essence

215g (7½oz) plain flour, plus more if needed

FOR THE FILLING

200g (7oz) caster sugar

4 mangoes, total weight about 1.5kg (3lb 3oz)

juice of ½ lime, or to taste

1-2 tbsp icing sugar (optional)

MAKE THE DOUGH

1 **Cut the butter** into pieces. In a small bowl, mix the egg yolks with the vanilla. Put the flour in a food processor with the sugar and salt, and blend for about 5 seconds. Add the butter and pulse-blend to coarse crumbs,.

2 **Add the egg yolks**, and work until the mixture resembles small peas. If it is dry, work in 1-2 tbsp water. Transfer to a floured work surface. Work with the heel of your hand until smooth. Chill for 30 minutes, until firm.

MAKE THE CARAMEL SYRUP

3 **Put the sugar** and 125ml (4fl oz) water in a saucepan, and heat gently until dissolved, stirring occasionally. Boil, without stirring, until the mixture starts to turn golden around the edge. Do not stir the sugar syrup during boiling, or it may crystallize.

4 **Lower the heat** and continue cooking, swirling the saucepan once or twice so the syrup colours evenly, until the caramel is golden. Cook the caramel only until medium gold; if it gets too dark, it will become bitter in the oven.

5 **Remove the saucepan** from the heat, and immediately plunge the base of the saucepan into a bowl of cold water, until cooking stops. Stand back in case of splashes: there are few things hotter than caramel.

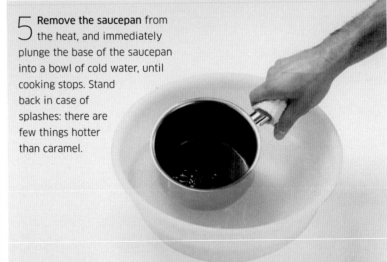

6 **Pour about one-sixth of the caramel** into the bottom of a 10cm (4in) baking dish. Working quickly, tilt the dish so the bottom is coated with a thin, even layer. Repeat with 5 more dishes. Let cool.

PREPARE THE MANGOES

7 **Peel each of the mangoes** with a small knife, taking care to remove the minimum amount of mango flesh with the skin. Cut each lengthwise on both sides of the stone, so the knife just misses the stone. Cut the remaining flesh away from each stone in 2 long slices, and set aside for the coulis. Discard the stones.

8 **Cut each of the large pieces** of mango into 3 diagonal slices. Arrange 3 slices, cut-side up, on top of the caramel in 1 dish. Repeat until all the dishes are filled. Add the remaining slices to the mango for the coulis.

ASSEMBLE AND BAKE THE TARTLETS

9 **Preheat the oven** to 200°C (400°F/Gas 6). Lightly flour a work surface. With your hands, shape the dough into a cylinder about 30cm (12in) long. Cut it into 6 equal pieces. Shape each piece into a ball.

10 **Roll out each ball** into a 12cm (5in) round. Drape one of the rounds over a baking dish, and tuck the edge down around the mango slices. Repeat for the remaining tartlets. Chill for 15 minutes, until the dough is firm. Bake for 20–25 minutes.

MAKE THE MANGO COULIS

11 **Put the reserved mango** flesh into a food processor or a blender, and purée it until smooth. Transfer to a bowl; add the lime juice, and stir it in. Taste and add icing sugar, if necessary, or even more lime juice if you prefer. Chill the coulis.

12 **Remove the tartlets** from the oven when golden brown. Let cool in the dishes for 2–3 minutes. To unmould, set a small plate on top and invert. If any mango slices stick to the dish, remove with a palette knife and replace on the tartlet. Repeat for the remaining tartlets. Serve at once with lime wedges, if you like. Pass the coulis separately.

Ricotta cheesecake

THIS IS PERFECTION: a classic Italian dish of ricotta, flavoured with candied orange peel and almonds, baked in a sweet, lemon pastry. The fresher the cheese, the better the cake.

SERVES	PREP	COOK
SERVES 8-10	35-40 MINS PLUS CHILLING	1-1¼ HRS

Ingredients

FOR THE SWEET PASTRY DOUGH

175g (6oz) unsalted butter

250g (9oz) plain flour, plus more if needed

1 lemon

50g (1¾oz) caster sugar

4 egg yolks

1 whole egg, to glaze

FOR THE FILLING

1 orange

2 tbsp chopped candied orange peel

1.25kg (2¾lb) ricotta cheese

100g (3½oz) caster sugar

1 tbsp plain flour

salt

1 tsp vanilla essence

45g (1½oz) sultanas

30g (1oz) slivered almonds

4 egg yolks

MAKE THE SWEET PASTRY DOUGH

1 **With a rolling pin,** pound the butter between 2 sheets of baking parchment to soften it slightly. Sift the flour on to a work surface, and make a large well in the centre. Grate the zest from the lemon. Put the butter, grated lemon zest, sugar, egg yolks, and a pinch of salt in the well.

2 **Using your fingertips,** work together all the ingredients in the well, until they are thoroughly mixed. Gradually draw the flour into the other ingredients. Press the dough into a ball. Lightly flour the work surface, then knead the dough for 1-2 minutes, until it is very smooth, and peels away from the work surface in one piece. Shape into a ball, wrap, and refrigerate for about 30 minutes, until firm.

ROLL OUT THE DOUGH AND LINE THE TIN

3 **Brush the bottom** and side of a 23-25cm (9-10in) springform tin with melted butter. Lightly flour the work surface, and roll out three-quarters of the dough, to make a 35-37cm (14-15in) round. Roll up the dough around the rolling pin, then unroll it loosely so that it drapes over the tin.

4 **Press the dough** gently into the bottom of the tin, then press it gently up the side of the tin with your fingers. Using a table knife, trim excess dough even with the outer edge of the tin. Chill the shell, together with the remaining dough and trimmings, for 15 minutes. Meanwhile, make the filling.

MAKE THE FILLING

5 **Grate the zest** from the orange on to a small plate. Finely chop the candied orange peel.

6 **Place the ricotta** in a large bowl and beat in the sugar, flour, and ½ tsp salt. Make sure all the ingredients are well mixed into the ricotta, so you have a smooth base for the cheesecake filling, without any lumps.

7 **Add the grated orange zest,** candied peel, vanilla essence, sultanas, slivered almonds, and egg yolks to the ricotta. Beat the mixture together thoroughly to combine, again being very sure that everything is very well blended.

8 **Spoon the filling** into the chilled pastry shell. Tap the tin on the work surface, to eliminate any air pockets that might remain through the ricotta mixture. Smooth the top of the filling, using the back of a wooden spoon.

MAKE THE LATTICE TOP AND BAKE THE CHEESECAKE

9 **Press any dough trimmings** into the remaining dough, and roll it into a 25cm (10in) round on a lightly floured surface. Using a sharp knife, cut into strips about 1cm (½in) wide. Use them to make a lattice on top of the cheesecake.

10 **Make an egg glaze:** lightly beat the whole egg with ½ tsp salt. Moisten the ends of each of the strips with the glaze, then seal them firmly to the pastry rim. Brush the lattice with the glaze, and chill the cheesecake for 15–30 minutes, or until firm. Meanwhile, preheat the oven to 180°C (350°F/Gas 4), and put in a baking sheet near the bottom.

11 **Bake the cheesecake** on the heated baking sheet, until the top is firm and golden brown. It will take 1–1¼ hours. Let cool in the tin until just warm, then remove the side of the tin and let the cake cool completely. Serve at room temperature.

 VARIATION: Chocolate ricotta pie

Discovered in a pastry shop in Assisi.

1 Make the pastry as directed in the main recipe, with 175g (6oz) flour, 3 egg yolks, 45g (1½oz) sugar, and 125g (4½oz) butter; omit the lemon zest. Roll out to line a 33x23x5cm (13x9x2in) buttered baking dish.

2 Finely chop 125g (4½oz) plain chocolate in a food processor. Make the filling as directed, adding the chocolate and grated orange zest in place of the candied fruit, sultanas, and almonds. Fill the pastry shell, chill, and bake as directed for 35–40 minutes. Let cool completely in the baking dish.

3 Chop 30g (1oz) more chocolate. Melt it in a bowl in a saucepan of hot water, until smooth. Stir in ½ tsp vegetable oil. Dip a fork in the chocolate and flick over the top.

Creamy rice pudding with peaches

THE LENGTHY COOKING FOR THIS RICE PUDDING results in a golden dessert. In summer, serve it just warm, with the chilled peaches macerated in red wine. Both the rice and the peaches can be prepared 1 day ahead and kept, covered, in the refrigerator. Let the rice come to room temperature, or warm it in a low oven, before serving.

SERVES	PREP	COOK
SERVES 4–6	15–20 MINUTES PLUS MACERATING AND STANDING	3 HOURS

Ingredients

FOR THE PEACHES

4 ripe peaches

60g (2oz) caster sugar, plus more if needed

250ml (9fl oz) dry red wine, plus more if needed

FOR THE RICE PUDDING

65g (2¼oz) short-grain rice

1 litre (1¾pints) milk, plus more if needed

5cm (2in) cinnamon stick

50g (1¾oz) caster sugar

salt

PREPARE THE PEACHES

1 **Peel and stone** the peaches: bring a saucepan of water to a boil. Immerse the peaches in the water for 10 seconds, then transfer them to a bowl of cold water to stop the cooking. If the peaches are very ripe, you may not need to blanch them in boiling water before peeling.

2 **Using a small knife,** cut each peach in half, using the indentation on 1 side as a guide. With both hands, give a sharp twist to each half, then lift out the stones. Carefully peel the skin from the peaches; it should come away easily. The skinned peaches will absorb more wine during macerating.

MACERATE THE PEACHES IN RED WINE

3 **Cut each peach half** into 2 wedges, and put them into a non-metallic bowl. Sprinkle the peaches with sugar; they may need more or less sugar than specified, depending on their sweetness.

4 **Pour over the red wine,** to cover the fruit completely. Set a plate on top. Leave to macerate in the refrigerator for at least 2 and up to 24 hours. Strain the liquid into a saucepan, bring to a boil, and simmer for 2 minutes, until syrupy. Stir it back into the peaches.

MAKE THE RICE PUDDING AND SERVE

5 **Preheat the oven** to 150°C (300°F/Gas 2). In the ovenproof bowl, stir the rice, milk, cinnamon, sugar, and a pinch of salt. Bake, stirring gently every 30 minutes, for 3 hours.

6 **Remove the pudding** from the oven. Carefully slip a spoon down the side, and stir from the bottom. Let stand for 1 hour. Discard the cinnamon. Serve with the peaches and wine syrup.

Ginger cheesecake

CLASSIC CHEESECAKE LENDS ITSELF to an assortment of delicious flavourings. Chopped stem ginger adds sparkle to the rich, smooth filling, baked in a crumbly biscuit crust. During baking, the ginger sinks to make a delicate layer in the creamy filling.

SERVES SERVES 8-10	**PREP** 40-45 MINS PLUS CHILLING	**COOK** 50-60 MINS

Ingredients

FOR THE CRUST

150g (5½oz) digestive biscuits

75g (2½oz) unsalted butter

FOR THE FILLING

500g (1lb 2oz) cream cheese, at room temperature

125g (4½oz) pieces of preserved stem ginger in syrup, plus 3 tbsp syrup

1 lemon

250ml (9fl oz) soured cream

150g (5½oz) granulated sugar

1 tsp vanilla essence

4 eggs

FOR THE TOPPING (optional)

150ml (5fl oz) double cream

MAKE THE CRUMB CRUST

1 **Generously butter the bottom** and side of a 20cm (8in) springform tin, then chill, to set the butter. Work the biscuits in a food processor to form crumbs (or crush with a rolling pin in a plastic bag). Put them in a bowl.

2 **Melt the butter** in a saucepan, and add it to the crumbs. Stir with a wooden spoon until all the crumbs are moistened. Press the crumb mixture evenly over the bottom, and 4cm (1½in) up the side of the tin. Chill for 30-60 minutes, until firm. Meanwhile, make the filling.

MAKE THE FILLING

3 **Using a wooden spoon,** beat the cream cheese in a bowl until soft and smooth. Chop the stem ginger. Reserve 2 tbsp ginger for the topping. Finely grate the lemon zest and squeeze out 2 tsp of juice.

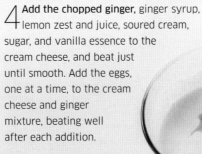

4 **Add the chopped ginger,** ginger syrup, lemon zest and juice, soured cream, sugar, and vanilla essence to the cream cheese, and beat just until smooth. Add the eggs, one at a time, to the cream cheese and ginger mixture, beating well after each addition.

BAKE AND FINISH THE CHEESECAKE

5 **Preheat the oven** to 180°C (350°F/Gas 4). Pour the filling into the crust, and gently shake to level the surface. Place the tin on a baking sheet.

6 **Bake the cheesecake** for 50-60 minutes. Turn off the oven; leave the cheesecake in for 1½ hours to prevent cracks, then chill for 4 hours.

7 **Whip the double cream,** if using, to soft peaks. Run a knife round the cheesecake, then remove the tin. Swirl the cream on top, if liked. Scatter with the reserved chopped stem ginger.

Chocolate walnut torte

IN THE TRUE TRADITION of flourless cakes, this is based on ground walnuts and chocolate, lightened with meringue. The mixture is baked slowly in a low oven so the edges of the cake do not dry, and the result is beautifully moist.

SERVES	**PREP**	**COOK**
SERVES 8	20–25 MINS PLUS CHILLING	60–70 MINS

Ingredients

FOR THE CAKE

125g (4½oz) unsalted butter

30g (1oz) plain flour, for the tin

375g (13oz) plain chocolate

250g (9oz) walnut pieces

4 eggs

200g (7oz) caster sugar

FOR THE CHANTILLY CREAM (optional)

250ml (9fl oz) double cream

1 tbsp caster sugar

½ tsp vanilla essence

LINE THE TIN

1 **Melt 30g (1oz) of the butter,** and use to brush the base and sides of a 23cm (9in) springform tin. Line the base with a circle of baking parchment, and butter that too. Sprinkle in 30g (1oz) plain flour, then turn and shake the tin to evenly coat. Shake out the excess. Set aside.

MAKE THE TORTE MIXTURE

2 **Preheat the oven** to 150°C (300°F/Gas 2). Chop 110g (3¾oz) of the chocolate and set a few walnuts aside. Grind the chocolate with half the remaining walnuts in a food processor. Repeat with another 110g (3¾oz) chocolate and the remaining nuts. Separate the eggs. With a wooden spoon, cream the butter. Add three-quarters of the sugar, and beat for 2–3 minutes, until light and fluffy.

3 **Add the egg yolks** one by one, beating thoroughly after each addition to avoid the risk of the mixture curdling. Stir in both batches of the ground chocolate and walnut mixture.

4 **Whisk the egg whites** until stiff. Sprinkle in the remaining sugar, and continue whisking until glossy. Add the meringue to the chocolate mixture, and fold them together.

BAKE THE TORTE

5 **Transfer the torte mixture** to the prepared tin and smooth the top. Bake until a skewer inserted in the centre of the torte comes out clean. It should take 60–70 minutes.

6 **Allow the torte** to cool completely in the tin. When completely cold, release the hinge on the side of the cake tin, and lift it gently away from the cake. The torte is so delicate, it is best served still on the base of the cake tin.

7 **You can choose** to serve the torte now, as it is, or dusted with icing sugar, or cocoa powder. Serve crème fraiche or lightly whipped cream on the side. If you wish to make it more spectacular, however, follow the next steps to finish the decoration.

FINISH THE TORTE

8 **Make the Chantilly cream,** if wanted: whip the cream in a bowl set within a larger bowl of iced water, until soft peaks form. Add the sugar and vanilla, and whip until soft peaks form again. Taste, to see if it is sweet enough; you may want to add more sugar.

9 **With a palette knife,** spread the cream evenly over the top of the cake. Place the cake on a serving plate and chill for about 1 hour. For the topping, chop the remaining chocolate, and melt it in a bowl placed in a saucepan of hot water (make sure the base of the bowl does not touch the water). Meanwhile, chop the reserved walnuts. Make a baking parchment piping cone and fill with the chocolate. Pipe the chocolate lightly over the cake, and sprinkle with the walnuts.

 VARIATION: Chocolate almond torte

Almonds add crunch to this variation.

1 Replace the walnuts with the same quantity of whole blanched almonds. Toast the almonds before grinding, and make the cake as directed.

2 Omit the Chantilly cream and chocolate topping, and decorate the cake as follows: cut 4–5 x 2cm (¾in) wide strips of thin card, and lay them on top of the cake. Sprinkle with icing sugar. Carefully lift off the strips and discard the excess sugar.

3 Lay the strips back on the cake to make a diagonal lattice on the sugar bands. Sift cocoa powder generously over the top, and carefully lift off the card strips, discarding the excess cocoa powder.

Oeufs à la neige

A TIME-HONOURED FRENCH DESSERT, where simple meringues are poached, then served on a pool of vanilla custard, decorated with flaked almonds and trails of caramel. If you don't have a vanilla pod, use 1 tsp vanilla extract instead for this recipe. Never buy anything labelled 'vanilla essence'; it is synthetic and tastes nothing like the real thing. The custard can be made 1 day ahead and kept, covered, in the refrigerator.

SERVES	**PREP**	**COOK**
SERVES 8	35–40 MINS	45–50 MINS

Ingredients

FOR THE VANILLA CUSTARD

750ml (1¼ pints) milk

1 vanilla pod, or 1 tsp vanilla extract

100g (3½oz) caster sugar

8 egg yolks

2 tbsp cornflour

FOR THE MERINGUE

8 egg whites

salt

400g (14oz) caster sugar

FOR THE DECORATION

45g (1½oz) flaked almonds

200g (7oz) caster sugar

MAKE THE CUSTARD AND TOAST THE ALMONDS

1 Pour the milk into a saucepan. Cut the vanilla pod, if using, lengthways, and add to the milk. Bring the milk just to a boil, then remove the pan from the heat. Cover, and let stand in a warm place for 10–15 minutes.

2 Set aside one-quarter of the milk. Add the sugar to the remaining hot milk, and stir until dissolved. Beat the egg yolks with the cornflour in a bowl. Whisk in the sweetened hot milk just until the mixture is smooth.

3 Pour the custard back into the saucepan and cook over medium heat, stirring constantly, until it comes just to a boil and is thick enough to coat the back of the spoon; the custard will curdle if boiled further.

4 Remove the pan from the heat, stir in the reserved milk, then strain into a bowl. Rinse the vanilla pod, dry, and store to use again. Stir in the vanilla extract, if using. Cover tightly with clingfilm to prevent a skin from forming on the surface of the custard, and let cool. Finally, chill the custard sauce.

5 Preheat the oven to 180°C (350°F/Gas 4). Spread the almonds on a baking sheet, and toast in the oven for 10–12 minutes, until lightly browned, stirring occasionally so that they colour evenly. Set aside.

MAKE AND POACH THE MERINGUES

6 Put the egg whites into a metal bowl with a pinch of salt, and whisk until stiff. Sprinkle in 60–75g (2–2½oz) of the sugar, and continue whisking for about 30 seconds, until glossy, to make a light meringue. Fold in the remaining sugar gradually and thoroughly.

7 Bring a large, wide pan of water to a simmer. Dip a dessert spoon into the water, then use it to scoop out a large spoonful of meringue. Use a second spoon to shape the meringue into a neat oval, turning the spoons one against the other.

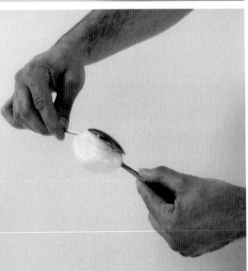

8 Drop the meringue into the simmering water. Quickly continue shaping 6–7 more, dipping the spoons into the water so that they do not stick. Poach for 5–7 minutes, until firm and puffed.

9 Lift the meringues out of the water with a slotted spoon; drain on kitchen paper. Shape and cook the remaining meringue in the same way. The meringues will deflate slightly as they cool.

MAKE THE CARAMEL AND FINISH THE DISH

10 Pour the chilled custard into a wide, shallow serving dish. Using a slotted spoon, arrange the meringues over the custard. Make the caramel: put the sugar and 125ml (4fl oz) water into a small frying pan, and heat gently until the sugar is dissolved, stirring occasionally. Bring to a boil, and boil without stirring, until the syrup starts to turn golden around the edge; it should take 8–10 minutes, but watch it like a hawk as it can easily burn.

11 Reduce the heat, and continue cooking until the caramel is a deep golden brown, swirling the pan once or twice so it colours evenly. Remove from the heat, and immediately plunge the base of the pan into a bowl of cold water to stop the caramel cooking. Delicately drizzle the caramel over the meringues. Sprinkle with the toasted almonds and serve immediately.

Baked peaches with amaretti

A CLASSIC FROM NORTHERN ITALY, as delicious as it is easy to prepare, this can be served hot or cold. Amaretti biscuits, with their hint of bitter almonds, pick up the sweetness of the peaches. Choose fruits that feel heavy for their size, showing they contain lots of juice.

SERVES	PREP	COOK
SERVES 6	15–20 MINS	1–1¼ HRS

Ingredients

FOR THE PEACHES

7 large peaches, total weight about 1kg (2¼lb)

8–10 amaretti biscuits

60g (2oz) caster sugar

1 egg yolk

unsalted butter, for the dish

FOR THE FLAVOURED CREAM

125ml (4fl oz) double cream

1–2 tbsp caster sugar

1–2 tbsp amaretto liqueur

SCALD, STONE, AND PEEL 1 PEACH

1 **Bring a small saucepan** of water to a boil. Immerse 1 peach in the water for 10 seconds. Remove and plunge into iced water. With a small knife, cut the peach in half, using the indentation on one side of the peach, as a guide.

2 **Using both hands,** give a quick, sharp twist to each half to loosen it from the stone. Scoop out the stone with a small knife. Peel the skin from the peach halves. Discard the stone and skin.

PREPARE THE FILLING

3 **Preheat the oven** to 180°C (350°F/Gas 4). Crush the amaretti in a plastic bag with a rolling pin and pour them into a bowl. Put the 2 peeled peach halves in the food processor. Process to a thick, smooth purée.

4 **Transfer the peach purée** to a large bowl, scraping it from the food processor with a spatula. Add the sugar, egg yolk, and amaretti crumbs to the peach, and mix well.

PREPARE, FILL, AND BAKE THE PEACHES

5 **Butter a baking dish.** Halve and remove the stone from the remaining peaches, without peeling them. If necessary, spoon out a little of the flesh from the centre of each, so the cavity is large enough for the filling.

6 **Set the peach halves,** cut-side up, in the baking dish. Spoon some filling into each. Bake for 1–1¼ hours, until tender. Meanwhile, whip together the cream, sugar, and liqueur until stiff peaks form. Transfer the hot peaches to individual serving plates, and spoon any juices over. Serve the flavoured cream in a separate bowl.

Profiteroles with ice cream

LIGHT AND AIRY CHOUX PASTRY PUFFS are filled with chocolate ice cream for extra decadence, and topped with a hot chocolate sauce. The choux puffs can be kept in an airtight container for up to 3 days. Assemble the profiteroles just before serving.

SERVES SERVES 8	**PREP** 25–30 MINS	**COOK** 25–30 MINS

Ingredients

FOR THE ICE CREAM

¾ quantity chocolate ice cream (p486), or 750ml (1¼ pints) bought good-quality chocolate ice cream

FOR THE CHOUX PASTRY

75g (2½oz) unsalted butter

½ tsp salt

100g (3½oz) plain flour, sifted

4 eggs

FOR THE EGG GLAZE

1 egg

½ tsp salt

FOR THE CHOCOLATE SAUCE

375g (13oz) good-quality plain chocolate

250ml (9fl oz) double cream

2 tbsp Cognac (optional)

PREPARE THE CHOUX PASTRY

1 **Preheat the oven** to 200°C (400°F/Gas 6). Brush a baking sheet with butter. Cut the butter into pieces. Put them into a saucepan, with 175ml (6fl oz) water and the salt. Heat until melted. Bring just to a boil. Add the flour all at once and beat vigorously, until smooth. Return to low heat and beat to dry out the dough, then remove from the heat.

2 **Mix in** and beat 3 of the eggs, 1 at a time, beating thoroughly after each addition. Beat the remaining egg in a small bowl, and add it little by little until the dough is shiny and soft. You may not need it all. Fit a piping bag with a plain nozzle, and add the choux dough. Squeeze out the dough in 30–35 x 2.5cm (1in) mounds on the baking sheet, spaced well apart.

MAKE THE GLAZE; BAKE THE PROFITEROLES

3 **Beat the egg** with the salt; leave for 2–3 minutes until smooth. Brush some on each profiterole. Press down lightly on each round with the tines of a fork, in one direction and then in the other, for a criss-cross pattern.

4 **Bake in the heated oven** for 25–30 minutes, until firm and brown. Transfer to a wire rack. With a sharp knife, make a slit in each to release steam. Let cool. Meanwhile, allow the ice cream to soften in the refrigerator.

MAKE THE CHOCOLATE SAUCE AND FINISH THE PROFITEROLES

5 **Chop the chocolate** and put in a medium heavy-based saucepan with the cream. Heat gently, stirring with a wooden spoon, until the chocolate has melted and the mixture is smooth and thick.

6 **If using Cognac**, stir it into the chocolate-and-cream mixture. Keep the sauce warm. Fill each profiterole with a ball of ice cream. Pile in a shallow dish, pour the warm chocolate sauce over and serve immediately.

Apricot and hazelnut ice cream

VANILLA ICE CREAM IS TRANSFORMED by hazelnuts and dried apricots in this Burgundian recipe. A hazelnut liqueur, such as Frangelico, adds sparkle to the recipe. Use apricot brandy instead, if you prefer. The ice cream can be made up to 2 weeks ahead; but if it has been frozen for more than 12 hours, let it soften for about 30 minutes in the refrigerator before serving.

SERVES	PREP	COOK
SERVES 6	2½–3 HRS PLUS FREEZING	25–30 MINS

Ingredients

90g (3oz) dried apricots

175ml (6fl oz) hazelnut liqueur

125g (4½oz) hazelnuts

600ml (1 pint) milk

1 vanilla pod

135g (5oz) caster sugar

8 egg yolks

2 tbsp cornflour

250ml (8fl oz) double cream

1tsp vanilla essence (optional)

PREPARE THE APRICOTS AND HAZELNUTS

1 **Put the apricots** into a bowl, and pour over enough boiling water to cover them. Let soak for 10–15 minutes. Drain and put into a small jar. Pour over the liqueur and cover tightly. Let soak for at least 2 hours, and up to 2 days. Strain, reserving the liqueur. Purée the apricots in a food processor and set aside.

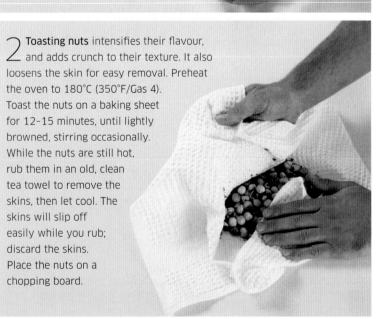

2 **Toasting nuts** intensifies their flavour, and adds crunch to their texture. It also loosens the skin for easy removal. Preheat the oven to 180°C (350°F/Gas 4). Toast the nuts on a baking sheet for 12–15 minutes, until lightly browned, stirring occasionally. While the nuts are still hot, rub them in an old, clean tea towel to remove the skins, then let cool. The skins will slip off easily while you rub; discard the skins. Place the nuts on a chopping board.

3 **With a sharp knife,** coarsely chop the hazelnuts. Reserve half the nuts for serving. If you are making the ice cream well ahead of time, store both the reserved hazelnuts and the liqueur in airtight containers.

MAKE THE VANILLA CUSTARD

4 **Pour the milk** into a heavy saucepan. Cut the vanilla pod lengthways, if using. Add to the pan. Bring the milk just to a boil. Remove from the heat. Cover, and let stand in a warm place for 10–15 minutes. Set aside one-quarter of the milk. Add the sugar to the remaining hot milk, and stir until dissolved.

5 **Beat the egg yolks** with the cornflour in a bowl. Add the sweetened hot milk, and whisk just until smooth. Pour the custard back into the saucepan and cook over medium heat, stirring constantly with a wooden spoon, until it comes just to a boil and thickens enough to coat the back of the spoon. Your finger will leave a clear trail across the spoon.

6 **Remove the pan** from the heat, stir in the reserved milk, then strain into a bowl. Stir in the vanilla essence, if using. Cover tightly with clingfilm to prevent a skin forming on the surface of the custard, and let cool. The vanilla pod can be rinsed and dried to use again.

FREEZE THE ICE CREAM

7 If the custard has formed a skin, whisk to dissolve it back into the mixture. Pour the custard into an ice-cream maker and churn it until slushy, following the manufacturer's directions. Meanwhile, chill 2 bowls in the freezer. Pour the cream into 1 of the chilled bowls, and whip until soft peaks form. Do not over-whip until it is too stiff, or the cream may separate; you are aiming for a floppy consistency.

8 Add half the hazelnuts and the apricot purée to the slushy vanilla ice cream, and stir until evenly mixed. Add the whipped cream, stir lightly, and continue freezing in the ice-cream maker until firm. Transfer the ice cream to the second chilled bowl. Cover tightly and store in the freezer until needed. If necessary, bring it from the freezer and allow to soften in the refrigerator before serving. Scoop the ice cream into chilled glasses or bowls, spoon over the reserved apricot soaking liqueur, top with the reserved hazelnuts, and serve at once.

 VARIATION: Prune and Armagnac ice cream

A combination of 2 Gascon favourites, prunes and Armagnac, makes this a fine end to a festive meal.

1 Omit the apricots, hazelnut liqueur, and hazelnuts. Put 150g (5½oz) pitted prunes into a small bowl. Pour over 175ml (6fl oz) Armagnac, and let the prunes soak as directed for the apricots. Strain the prunes, reserving the liqueur. Purée the prunes.

2 Make and chill the vanilla custard as directed. Make and freeze the ice cream as directed, substituting the prunes and Armagnac for the apricots and hazelnut liqueur.

3 Serve the ice cream with the reserved liqueur as directed, topped with more pitted prunes, if you like.

Strawberry-raspberry hazelnut tart

TRADITIONALLY, ITALIAN FRUIT TARTS ARE SIMPLE, often nothing more than fresh fruit on a pastry base. This *crostata* is packed with delicious Marsala-flavoured whipped cream. The hazelnut pastry dough can be made up to 2 days ahead and refrigerated, or it can be frozen.

SERVES
SERVES 6-8

PREP
35-40 MINS

COOK
30-35 MINS

Ingredients

FOR THE HAZELNUT PASTRY DOUGH

125g (4½oz) hazelnuts

75g (2½oz) granulated sugar

125g (4½oz) plain flour, plus more if needed

125g (4½oz) unsalted butter

1 egg

FOR THE FILLING

250ml (9fl oz) double cream

3-4 tbsp icing sugar, plus more to dust

2 tbsp Marsala wine

125g (4½oz) raspberries

300g (10oz) strawberries

MAKE THE HAZELNUT PASTRY DOUGH

1 **Toast and skin the hazelnuts** (p500). Reserve a few for decoration. In a food processor, grind the remaining hazelnuts, with the sugar, to a fine powder. Do not overwork or the oil from the nuts will create a paste. Sift the flour on to a work surface, add the ground nut mixture, and make a large well in the centre.

2 **Cut the butter** into pieces, and add to the well with the egg. Using your fingertips, work the ingredients in the well until soft and thoroughly mixed, then draw in the hazelnut powder and the flour. Work with your fingers until you form coarse crumbs that start sticking together. Lightly press the crumbs together to form a ball of dough.

3 **Lightly flour** the work surface, then blend the dough by pushing it away from you with the heel of your hand. Gather it up and continue to blend, until it peels easily from the work surface. Shape into a ball, wrap, and chill for at least 30 minutes, until firm.

BAKE THE PASTRY SHELL

4 **Preheat the oven** to 180°C (350°F/Gas 4). Brush a 23-25cm (9-10in) springform tart tin with melted butter. With the back of a spoon, or the heel of your hand, press the dough into the tin to make an even shell. Chill for at least 15 minutes, until firm. Bake for 30-35 minute until golden brown and shrinking slightly from the tin. Cool, then remove the sides of the tin.

ASSEMBLE THE TART

5 **Make the Marsala whipped cream:** using a whisk, whip the double cream in a chilled bowl until it forms soft peaks. Add the icing sugar and Marsala. Continue whipping until the cream forms stiff peaks.

6 **Pick over the raspberries.** Hull the strawberries, and wash them only if they are dirty (washing softens strawberries). With a small knife, cut the strawberries in half, or into quarters if they are large.

7 **Using a palette knife,** spread two-thirds of the Marsala whipped cream evenly over the cooled hazelnut pastry, just to the edge. Ensure your pastry is completely cold before you start.

8 **Arrange most of the strawberries** and raspberries evely over the Marsala whipped cream. Top with the remaining Marsala cream, then scatter with the remaining fruits and the reserved hazelnuts. Chill, then sift over a little icing sugar to serve.

Raspberry soufflés, kirsch custard

A HOT, BAKED SOUFFLÉ need not be intimidating. What could be simpler than puréed fruit folded into meringue and baked? Given the few ingredients of this recipe, it is important that the raspberries be as sweet, juicy, and highly flavoured as possible.

SERVES	PREP	COOK
SERVES 6	20-25 MINS	10-12 MINS

Ingredients

FOR THE KIRSCH CUSTARD

375ml (13fl oz) milk

50g (1¾oz) caster sugar

5 egg yolks

1 tbsp cornflour

2-3 tbsp kirsch

FOR THE SOUFFLÉS

100g (3½oz) caster sugar

500g (1lb 2oz) raspberries

5 egg whites

2-3 tbsp icing sugar, to serve

MAKE THE CUSTARD

1 **Pour the milk** into a heavy-based saucepan and bring just to a boil over medium heat. Set aside a quarter of the milk. Add the sugar to the remaining milk, and stir until dissolved. Put the yolks and cornflour into a bowl. Whisk together lightly, until the mixture is smooth. Add the sweetened milk to the egg yolks, whisking until just smooth.

2 **Cook the custard** over medium heat, stirring constantly, until it comes just to a boil and thickens enough to coat the back of a spoon. (Your finger will leave a clear trail across the spoon.) Remove from the heat. Stir the reserved milk into the custard, then strain into a cold bowl and let cool. If it forms a skin, whisk to dissolve. Stir in the kirsch. Cover tightly and refrigerate.

PREPARE AND BAKE THE PUDDINGS

3 **Brush 6 ramekins** with butter. Sprinkle with sugar, tilting to coat evenly. Preheat the oven to 190°C (375°F/Gas 5). Purée the raspberries with half the sugar in a food processor. Taste; add more sugar if the purée is tart.

4 **Using a small ladle,** work the purée through a sieve into a large bowl to remove the pips. Whisk the egg whites until stiff. Sprinkle in the remaining caster sugar and continue whisking for about 20 seconds, until glossy, to form a light meringue.

5 **Add about one-quarter** of the meringue to the raspberry purée, and stir. Add this mixture to the remaining meringue and fold together, until the mixture is an even colour.

6 **Spoon the mixture** into the prepared ramekins. Set them on a baking sheet for easy handling. Bake in the oven for 10-12 minutes, until puffed and lightly browned on top. Sift over the icing sugar, and serve immediately, with the kirsch custard on the side.

Gratin of fresh berries with sabayon

FLUFFY SABAYON SAUCE HERE IS FLAVOURED with lemon zest and Grand Marnier or Marsala, and is grilled to an attractive golden brown. Use a blow torch instead of a grill, if you have one. Be sure to choose berries that are plump, and full of flavour.

SERVES	PREP	COOK
SERVES 4	15-20 MINS	1-2 MINS

3 egg yolks

50g (1¾oz) caster sugar

90ml (3fl oz) Grand Marnier or Marsala

Ingredients

375g (13oz) mixed berries, such as raspberries, strawberries, blackberries, or blueberries

1 lemon

PREPARE THE BERRIES

1 **Pick over the berries,** washing them only if they are dirty. Hull the strawberries. Cut any large berries into halves or quarters. Divide the berries evenly among 4 individual gratin dishes or heatproof dessert plates, and chill in the refrigerator.

MAKE THE SABAYON

2 **Heat the grill.** Grate the zest from half the lemon. Put the egg yolks, sugar, and Grand Marnier in a large heatproof bowl, and whisk them to mix. Set the bowl over a saucepan half-filled with hot but not simmering water (the base of the bowl must not touch the water), and start to whisk.

3 **Continue whisking** for 5-8 minutes, until the mixture is frothy and thick enough to leave a ribbon trail. Take the sauce from the pan of hot water, whisk in the zest, and continue whisking for 1-2 minutes until slightly cooled.

BROWN THE GRATIN

4 **Arrange the gratin dishes** on a baking sheet, and spoon the sabayon over and around the berries. Grill about 15cm (6in) from the heat for 1-2 minutes, until the sabayon is golden brown and the fruit is warm.

5 **Put each of the hot dishes** on to plates to prevent burning you or your guests' hands. Serve immediately while the berries are juicy, and the dishes still crackling from the heat of the grill.

Chocolate decadence

RICH AND DENSE, this cake relies wholly on melted chocolate, butter, and eggs, with only 2 spoons of sugar and 1 of flour, so your ingredients – most especially the chocolate – must be of the very best quality you can afford to make this dessert a show-stopper. A tart raspberry coulis cuts through the richness of the dish. This cake can be stored for up to 1 week in an airtight container (it will become even more moist), and it also freezes well.

SERVES	PREP	COOK
SERVES 8	30-40 MINS PLUS CHILLING	20 MINS

Ingredients

FOR THE CAKE

500g (1lb 2oz) plain chocolate

150g (5½oz) unsalted butter

6 eggs

2 tbsp caster sugar

1 tbsp plain flour, plus more for the tin

FOR THE RASPBERRY COULIS

750g (1lb 10oz) raspberries, plus more to serve

2-3 tbsp icing sugar

TO SERVE

crème fraîche or whipped double cream

MAKE THE CHOCOLATE CAKE

1 **Preheat the oven** to 200°C (400°F/Gas 6). Butter and base line a 23cm (9in) springform tin. Sprinkle in 2-3 tbsp flour, turn and shake to coat, then tap to remove excess. Coarsely pulse-chop the chocolate in a food processor. Cut the butter into pieces, and put them in a large heatproof bowl with the chocolate. Set over a pan of hot, but not simmering, water. Stir until melted and smooth. Let cool, stirring occasionally.

2 **Separate the eggs.** Beat the egg yolks into the chocolate mixture with the wooden spoon, until evenly mixed. It is vital that the chocolate should be cool before you attempt this, or the eggs will cook and split the mixture.

3 **Put the egg whites** in a scrupulously clean metal bowl, and beat with a hand whisk or electric mixer, until stiff. Add the sugar; continue whisking for about 20 seconds, until glossy, to make a light meringue.

4 **Stir the flour** into the chocolate mixture, then fold in one-third of the egg whites to lighten it. Fold in the remaining whisked egg whites in 2 batches. Transfer to the cake tin. Tap on the work surface to knock out any air bubbles. Bake for about 20 minutes, until crusty on top but soft in the centre. Let cool completely in the tin, set on a wire rack. When cold, chill for 2 hours. Unmould and peel off the paper.

PREPARE THE RASPBERRY COULIS

5 **Pick over the raspberries**, washing them only if they are dirty. Put the raspberries in a food processor or blender. Work the raspberries in the machine until they are puréed. Add icing sugar to taste. Purée again until the sugar is evenly blended.

6 **Work the puréed raspberries** through a sieve into a bowl to remove the seeds. Discard the seeds. If making in advance, wrap tightly and store in the refrigerator, being sure to bring the coulis to room temperature before serving.

FINISH THE CAKE

7 **Using a serrated knife,** cut the cake into 8 wedges. Set 1 wedge in the centre of each plate. Dipping the knife in hot water between slices makes it easy to cut neat wedges. Ladle a small pool of raspberry coulis on to each plate, near the tip of the wedge of cake.

8 **If you like,** dip the tip of a small knife into some double cream, and drizzle a curved line on the coulis. Pull the tip of the knife across the cream to make a feathered design. Decorate each plate with a few whole raspberries, and serve with crème fraîche or whipped cream.

 VARIATION: Chocolate decadence with passion fruit sauce

If passion fruit are not available, substitute 2 ripe mangoes.

1 Omit the raspberries and the raspberry coulis. Make and bake the cake exactly as directed in the main recipe.

2 Make a passion fruit sauce: halve 18-20 passion fruit, and scrape the orange pulp and black seeds into a fine sieve set over a bowl. (When buying passion fruit, be sure to buy those with wrinkled skins. This may seem counterintuitive, but the wrinkled fruits are the ripest, and contain the maximum delicious juice and pulp.) Now you can choose how you would prefer your sauce: either rub the pulp through a sieve, with a wooden spoon, then discard the seeds, or don't sieve the pulp and keep in the crunchy seeds. Some people love their crunch; others find them too hard to eat. Beat 30-37g (1-1¼oz) icing sugar into the passion fruit pulp and taste, adding more sugar if you would prefer to have a sweeter sauce. Chill, tightly covered, until ready to serve.

3 Serve the cake as directed, on a pool of the orange passion fruit sauce. Serve whipped cream or crème fraîche in a pile next to each slice of cake, if you like.

Crêpes Suzette

IN THIS MOST CLASSIC OF FRENCH DESSERTS, thin crêpes are spread with orange butter, sautéed to caramelize, then flamed just before serving. A sure way to create culinary drama, as well as a nostalgic treat. The crêpes can be made up to 3 days ahead; they won't suffer if you layer them up with a sheet of baking parchment between each one and store in a plastic bag in the refrigerator.

SERVES	PREP	COOK
SERVES 6-8	40-50 MINS PLUS STANDING	45-60 MINS

Ingredients

FOR THE CRÊPES

90g (3oz) unsalted butter, plus more if needed

175g (6oz) plain flour

1 tbsp caster sugar

½ tsp salt

4 eggs

375ml (13fl oz) milk, plus more if needed

FOR THE ORANGE BUTTER

175g (6oz) unsalted butter, at room temperature

30g (1oz) icing sugar

3 large oranges

1 tbsp Grand Marnier (optional)

FOR FLAMING

75ml (2½fl oz) brandy

75ml (2½fl oz) Grand Marnier

MAKE THE CRÊPE BATTER

1 **Melt the butter** in a small saucepan, and set aside to cool; do not skip this step, as the butter needs to be cool when it is added to the rest of the batter ingredients, or it could begin to cook the eggs. Sift the flour into a large bowl, holding the sieve up high to aerate the flour as it falls down. Add the caster sugar and the salt, and stir so everything is evenly mixed. Make a well in the centre of the flour, and break the eggs into the well. Whisk the eggs together in the well just until mixed.

2 **Pour half the milk** into the eggs in a slow, steady stream, whisking constantly and gradually drawing in the flour from the sides of the well, to make a smooth batter. Gradually whisk in half the cooled, melted butter, still drawing in the flour, until all has been incorporated. Whisk the mixture well, until it is completely smooth. Now add enough of the remaining milk to give a batter that is about the consistency of single cream (you may not need all the milk). Cover and let the batter stand at room temperature for at least 30 minutes.

MAKE THE ORANGE BUTTER AND ORANGE JULIENNE

3 **Put the butter** and icing sugar in a bowl, and cream them together with a wooden spoon. This may take up to 5 minutes, as you must make sure the mixture is smooth, light, and airy.

4 **Finely grate the zest** from 2 of the oranges. With a vegetable peeler, pare the zest from the remaining orange; set aside. Cut the pith and skin from all 3 oranges. Slide the knife down both sides of each segment to cut it free. Reserve the segments and their juice. Add the zest, and 2 tbsp of juice, to the butter with the Grand Marnier, if using. Beat until smooth. Cover, and keep at room temperature.

5 **Make the orange julienne:** cut the pared orange zest lengthways into the thinnest possible julienne strips. Bring a small pan of cold water to a boil, add the strips, and simmer for 2 minutes. Drain, rinse, and drain again. Reserve the strips for decoration.

FRY THE CRÊPES

6 **If necessary,** stir a little more milk into the batter to make it the consistency of single cream again (it may have thickened on standing). Add the remaining melted butter to the crêpe pan and heat gently, then pour any excess butter into a small bowl, leaving a thin film in the pan.

7 **Reheat the pan,** then add a drop of batter to test the temperature: when it splatters briskly, it is hot enough for frying. Stir the batter in the bowl briefly, then quickly ladle a little (2–3 tbsp) into the pan. Do not add too much, or the crêpe will be thick. If too little is added, it will have holes.

8 **Immediately tilt the pan** with a twist of the wrist, shaking so the base is evenly covered with batter. Fry over medium-high heat for about 1 minutes, until set on top, and brown underneath. Gently loosen the edge of the crêpe with a palette knife.

9 **Turn the crêpe** quickly: either slide the palette knife underneath and flip it over, or use the fingertips of both hands. You can also toss the crêpe, if you are feeling brave. Continue frying over medium-high heat for 30–60 seconds, until brown on the other side. Slide on to a plate, with the side cooked first facing up. Continue frying the crêpes, buttering the pan sparingly again only when the crêpes start to stick, until all the batter has been used up.

ASSEMBLE AND FLAME THE CRÊPES

10 **Spread the orange butter** over the side of each crêpe that was cooked first, stacking the buttered crêpes up again on another plate. Heat the frying pan over medium heat. Add 1 crêpe, orange-butter-side down. Cook briskly for about 1 minute, until very hot.

11 **Using a palette knife,** fold the crêpe in half and then into quarters to make a triangle. Transfer the folded crêpe to a plate, and add another crêpe to the pan, again orange-butter-side down. Continue to fry and fold the crêpes in this way, overlapping them around the side of the plate.

12 **Arrange the caramelized crêpes** in the hot frying pan, distributing them evenly. If the pan becomes too full, you may have to flame them in 2 batches (keep the first batch warm while you flame the remaining crêpes). Heat the brandy and Grand Marnier in a small saucepan, then pour them over the crêpes.

13 **Hold a lighted match** to the side of the pan, to set the alcohol alight. Baste the crêpes with the alcohol until the flames die; it should only take 2–3 minutes. (Stand back and keep your hair and face away from the pan). Divide the flamed crêpes among warmed plates, and spoon the sauce from the pan over them. Decorate with the orange segments and orange julienne, and serve immediately.

Apple and almond galettes

THIS ELEGANT DESSERT IS DECEPTIVELY SIMPLE to make. A delicate layer of marzipan adds richness to the thin, crisp pastry bases, and the galettes are caramelized halfway through baking by a sprinkling of sugar, forming the only decoration necessary. A scoop of ice-cold Apple and Calvados Sorbet (p515) would make the perfect finishing touch. The galettes must be baked just before serving.

SERVES SERVES 8	**PREP** 25-30 MINS	**COOK** 20-30 MINS

1 lemon
8 small, tart, green eating apples
50g (1¾oz) granulated sugar

Ingredients

500g (1lb 2oz) puff pastry
215g (7½oz) marzipan

PREPARE THE PUFF PASTRY ROUNDS

1 **Lightly flour** a work surface. Roll out half the pastry to a 35cm (14in) square, about 3mm (⅛in) thick. Using a 15cm (6in) plate as a guide, cut out 4 rounds. Sprinkle 2 baking sheets with water. Set the rounds on 1 baking sheet, and prick each with a fork, avoiding the edge. Repeat with the remaining dough. Chill for 15 minutes. Divide the marzipan into 8, and roll each portion into a ball.

2 **Spread a sheet** of baking parchment on the work surface. Set 1 ball of marzipan on the parchment, and cover with another sheet. Roll out the marzipan to a 12.5cm (5in) round between the sheets. Set on top of a pastry dough round, leaving a 1cm (½in) border. Repeat with the remaining marzipan and pastry bases. Chill, until ready to bake.

PREPARE THE APPLES

3 **Cut the lemon** in half, and squeeze the juice from 1 half into a small bowl. Peel the apples, then halve and core them. Rub them with the remaining lemon half, to prevent them from turning brown. Cut into thin slices, brushing with lemon juice as you work.

FINISH AND BAKE THE GALETTES

4 **Preheat the oven** to 220°C (425°F/Gas 7). Arrange the apple slices, overlapping them slightly, in a ring on the marzipan rounds, covering them completely. Leave a thin border of puff pastry dough around the edge.

5 **Bake the apple** and almond galettes for 15-20 minutes, until the pastry edges have risen around the marzipan, and are light golden. Sprinkle the apples evenly with the sugar.

6 **Return to the oven,** and continue baking for 5-10 minutes, or until the apples are golden brown, caramelized around the edges and just tender when tested with the tip of a small knife. Transfer to warmed individual serving plates, and serve at once.

Grapefruit granita, almond biscuits

A REFRESHING END to a rich dinner. Unlike a smooth sorbet, the texture should resemble coarse snow. This effect is achieved by whisking during the freezing process. The almond All Souls' Day biscuits are a lovely accompaniment.

SERVES	PREP	COOK
SERVES 4	15-20 MINS PLUS FREEZING	35-40 MINS

Ingredients

FOR THE GRANITA

3 grapefruit

½ lemon

50g (1¾oz) sugar, plus more to taste

FOR THE ALL SOULS' DAY BISCUITS

90g (3oz) plain flour

15g (½oz) butter

1 lemon

150g (5½oz) ground almonds

125g (4½oz) caster sugar

1 tbsp brandy

1 egg

12-15 whole, blanched almonds

MAKE AND FREEZE THE GRANITA

1 **Thinly pare the zest** from half a grapefruit, leaving behind the white pith. Reserve the pared zest. Squeeze the juice from all the grapefruits. Strain the juice into a non-metallic bowl, along with the lemon juice. Add half the sugar and stir until dissolved. Taste, adding more sugar if you like.

2 **Freeze the liquid** for 45-60 minutes, until ice starts to form on top. Whisk to break the ice. Continue freezing, whisking the mixture to break the ice about once an hour, until the granita is slushy and slightly granular. Allow 4-5 hours.

MAKE THE BISCUITS

3 **Preheat the oven** to 180°C (350°F/Gas 4). Butter a baking sheet and sprinkle with flour. Sift the flour into a bowl. Add butter, grated lemon zest, ground almonds, sugar, and brandy. Whisk the egg and stir into the flour mixture to form a dough.

4 **Wet your hands** and roll the dough into 2.5cm (1in) balls. Place on the baking sheet, leaving 2.5cm (1in) between the biscuits. Press an almond into each. Bake for 15-20 minutes, until light brown. Let cool on a wire rack.

PREPARE THE ZEST

5 **With a very sharp knife,** cut the pared grapefruit zest into fine julienne. In a small pan, dissolve the remaining 2 tbsp sugar in 2 tbsp water. Add the zest. Simmer for 12-15 minutes, until the water has evaporated and the zest is translucent. Spread on baking parchment. Let cool.

6 **Spoon the grapefruit granita** into 4 chilled glasses or bowls. Pile the candied zest on top, and serve at once, with the biscuits on the side.

Hazelnut meringue gâteau

THIS CLASSIC CAKE IS A SPECIALITY of Dax, a town in the foothills of the Pyrenees, and is known as a Dacquoise. Crisp rounds of hazelnut meringue are sandwiched with buttercream, flavoured with kirsch, in delicate tones of ivory and white. Use apricot brandy if you don't have any kirsch; it will be equally delicious.

SERVES
SERVES 6-8

PREP
50-60 MINS
PLUS CHILLING

COOK
40-50 MINS

Ingredients

FOR THE HAZELNUT MERINGUE

250g (9oz) hazelnuts

300g (10oz) caster sugar

2 tbsp cornflour

6 egg whites

icing sugar, to dust

FOR THE BUTTERCREAM

100g (3½oz) caster sugar

4 egg yolks

250g (9oz) unsalted butter, at room temperature

2 tbsp kirsch, plus more if needed

MAKE THE HAZELNUT MERINGUE

1 **Brush 3 baking sheets** with melted butter, and line with baking parchment. Butter the paper and sprinkle with flour, discarding the excess. Trace 1 circle on each baking sheet, using a 20cm (8in) round cake tin as a guide. Toast the hazelnuts in the oven for 12-15 minutes, then skin (p500). Reserve a third for decoration. Put half the sugar and the remaining nuts in a food processor.

2 **Process, until the mixture is quite fine.** Do not overwork the nuts or they will release their oil, creating a paste. (Grinding with sugar helps prevent this.) Transfer the ground hazelnuts and sugar to a bowl, and stir in the cornflour.

3 **Put the egg whites** in a metal bowl. Beat with a whisk or electric mixer until stiff peaks form. Sprinkle in the remaining caster sugar and continue whisking, until glossy, to make a light meringue. Add a third of the hazelnut mixture, and fold together as lightly as possible. Fold in the remaining hazelnut mixture, in 2 batches.

BAKE THE MERINGUES

4 **Preheat the oven** to 130°C (250°F/Gas ½). Divide the hazelnut meringue evenly among the traced circles on the baking parchment, and spread it out with a palette knife to make 3 even, flat discs. Bake them in the oven, rotating the baking sheets occasionally for even cooking, for 40-50 minutes, or until the rounds are all lightly browned, and feel dry to the touch. Remove the baking sheets from the oven. Carefully peel the paper from the meringue rounds while they are still warm, transfer the meringues to a wire rack, and let cool completely.

MAKE THE BUTTERCREAM

5 **Put 150ml (5fl oz) water** and the caster sugar in a saucepan, and heat until dissolved. Boil the syrup without stirring, until it reaches the soft ball stage. To test, take the pan from the heat, dip a teaspoon in the hot syrup, remove, and let cool a few seconds. Take a little syrup between your finger and thumb; it should form a soft ball. (A sugar thermometer should register 115°C/239°F.)

6 **While the syrup is boiling,** beat the egg yolks with an electric mixer or whisk, just until mixed. Gradually pour the hot sugar syrup into the egg yolks in a steady stream, beating constantly. Continue beating at high speed for about 5 minutes, until the mixture is cool, and forms a thick mousse.

7 **Put the butter** in a bowl and beat it with an electric mixer or wooden spoon, until it is smooth and creamy. Gradually add the butter to the cool egg mousse, and beat to combine. (Be sure the egg mousse has cooled, or it will melt the butter). Beat in the kirsch, adding more to taste, if necessary.

ASSEMBLE THE GÂTEAU

8 Cut a round of cardboard to fit the gâteau. Add a dab of buttercream, set 1 meringue round (choose the ugliest) on the cardboard, and press down lightly so it sticks. Place the cardboard on an upturned cake tin, to raise it a little off the work surface, if you like.

9 Spoon about a half the buttercream on to the meringue round, and spread it out with a palette knife to cover the meringue evenly. Place a second meringue round on top, and spread it with all the remaining buttercream. Cover with the third, most attractive, of the meringue rounds, making sure all 3 rounds are stacked neatly.

DECORATE THE GÂTEAU

10 With a small sieve, cover the top of the gâteau thickly with a layer of sifted icing sugar. Finely chop the reserved hazelnuts. Sprinkle them on top of the gâteau. Chill for at least 1 hour, until firm. Transfer to a cake stand or serving plate.

 VARIATION: Almond meringue gâteau

Armagnac-flavoured butter cream and almond meringue combine in a punchy version of the classic Dacquoise.

1 Make the meringue mixture as directed in the main recipe, substituting 150g (5½oz) ground, toasted almonds for the hazelnuts. Shape and bake the meringue rounds as directed.

2 Make the buttercream as directed, substituting Armagnac or cognac for the kirsch. Alternatively, flavour the buttercream with coffee: dissolve 2 tbsp instant coffee granules in 2 tbsp hot water, cool it slightly, and beat into the buttercream.

3 Toast 90g (3oz) flaked almonds in the oven, watching carefully so that they do not catch and burn. Assemble the cake as directed. Decorate with the toasted almonds instead of the hazelnuts, and sprinkle with a few chocolate-coated coffee beans, if you like (these are especially appropriate if you chose to make a coffee-flavoured buttercream).

Trio of sorbets

WHAT BETTER WAY TO ENJOY the essence of fresh fruit? This trio makes a pretty picture in a bowl, complete with fresh fruit and berries. If you prefer, choose your favourite fruit, and increase the quantities to make just 1 sorbet. The sorbets can be kept for up to 1 week in the freezer. If they have been frozen for more than 1 day, remember to let them soften for 30 minutes in the refrigerator before serving, both to improve the texture and release the full flavour of the fruits.

SERVES	PREP	COOK
SERVES 8	40–50 MINS PLUS FREEZING	15–20 MINS

Ingredients

FOR THE SUGAR SYRUP

300g (10oz) granulated sugar, plus more if needed

FOR THE SORBETS

400g (14oz) raspberries, plus more if needed

3 lemons, plus more if needed

750g (1lb 10oz) ripe pears

2 tbsp Poire Williams liqueur, or to taste

625g (1lb 6oz) ripe peaches

PREPARE THE SUGAR SYRUP

1 **Combine the sugar** and 375ml (13fl oz) water in a saucepan, and heat until the sugar has dissolved. Bring to a boil, and boil without stirring for 2–3 minutes, until the syrup is clear. Pour the sugar syrup into a measuring jug, and let cool completely.

MAKE THE RASPBERRY SORBET

2 **Pick over the raspberries,** washing them only if they are dirty. Purée them in a food processor. Work the purée through a sieve held over a bowl, to remove the seeds. There should be 175ml (6fl oz) purée. If necessary, purée a few more berries.

3 **Squeeze the lemons;** there should be just over 125ml (4fl oz) juice. Keep the lemon halves. Add 4 tbsp water, 2 tbsp of the lemon juice, and one-third of the sugar syrup, to the raspberry purée. Taste, and stir in more lemon or sugar if needed. Chill, then taste again. Remember, flavours are blunted by the cold, so be sure they are concentrated.

4 **Pour the raspberry mixture** into an ice-cream maker, and churn until firm, following the manufacturer's directions. Meanwhile, chill a bowl in the freezer. Transfer the sorbet to the chilled bowl. Cover and freeze for at least 4 hours, to allow the flavour to mellow.

MAKE THE PEAR SORBET

5 **Pour half the remaining sugar syrup** into a small saucepan. Add 2 tbsp of the lemon juice. Peel the pears, then cut out the flower and stalk ends with a small knife. Cut each pear in half, then into quarters, and cut out the core. Rub all over with the reserved, squeezed lemon halves.

6 **Cut the pear quarters** into chunks, and drop them immediately into the saucepan of syrup. Bring to a boil, then simmer the pears for 5–10 minutes, until soft and translucent, depending on ripeness. Purée the pears with their syrup in a food processor, or purée them in 2 batches, in a blender. Always remember not to fill a blender jug too full; it could cause splashes and burns.

7 **Work the purée** through a sieve held over a bowl. There should be nearly 500ml (16fl oz) pear purée. Stir in the liqueur, and taste, adding more liqueur, lemon juice, or sugar if needed. Freeze the pear sorbet, as for the raspberry sorbet.

PREPARE THE PEACH SORBET

8 Immerse the peaches in a pan of boiling water for 10–20 seconds, depending on ripeness. Transfer them immediately to a bowl of cold water with a slotted spoon. Cut each in half. Using both hands, give a quick twist to each half, to loosen it from the stone. Discard the stone. With a small knife, peel off the skin; it should come off easily.

9 Cut the skinned peach halves into chunks, put them into a food processor, and add the remaining sugar syrup and lemon juice. Purée until smooth. There should be nearly 500ml (16fl oz) purée. Taste, and add more lemon juice, or sugar, if needed. Freeze as for the raspberry sorbet.

10 Soften all the sorbets in the refrigerator for 30 minutes before serving, so the texture is pleasing, and the true flavours emerge. Scoop the sorbets into bowls, and serve with fresh fruit, if liked.

 VARIATION: Apple and Calvados sorbet

A rich and indulgent scoopful.

1 Omit the raspberries, pears, Poire Williams liqueur, peaches, and all but ½ lemon. Make the sugar syrup as directed in the main recipe, using 200g (7oz) sugar and 250ml (9fl oz) water.

2 Peel 1.4kg (3lb) tart apples (they should be quite tart for the maximum flavour), quarter, and core. Rub each quarter with the lemon half so they do not discolour. Continue as directed for the pear sorbet, adding 2 tbsp Calvados in place of the Poire Williams liqueur.

3 Scoop small balls of the sorbet into shallow glasses or bowls. If you like, add a spoonful of Calvados to each glass, and serve with a crisp biscuit. This amount of sorbet will serve 6 people.

Chocolate mousse with hazelnuts

TOASTED HAZELNUTS CREATE TEXTURE, and whisky gives zip, to this version of classic dark chocolate mousse. If you prefer, you can substitute almost any spirit or liqueur for the whisky used in the recipe. Rum, brandy, or Grand Marnier taste particularly good with chocolate, but you may well have your own favourite.

SERVES	PREP	COOK
SERVES 6	20–25 MINS	20–25 MINS

Ingredients

FOR THE MOUSSE	FOR THE WHISKY CREAM (optional)
60g (2oz) hazelnuts	125ml (4fl oz) double cream
250g (9oz) plain chocolate	1 tbsp caster sugar
15g (½oz) unsalted butter	2 tsp whisky

	3 eggs
	2 tbsp whisky
	50g (1¾oz) caster sugar

TOAST AND GRIND THE NUTS

1 **Preheat the oven** to 180°C (350°F/Gas 4). Spread the nuts on a baking sheet and bake until lightly browned. Rub in a rough towel while hot, to remove the skins. Grind in a food processor, reserving a few for decoration.

MAKE THE CHOCOLATE MIX

2 **Cut the chocolate** into large chunks. Chop with a sharp knife, or in a food processor, then place in a heavy-based saucepan and add 65ml (2¼fl oz) water. Heat gently, stirring, for 3–5 minutes, until melted and the consistency of double cream.

3 **Remove the chocolate** from the heat, and stir in the butter, cut in pieces. Separate the eggs. Whisk the yolks into the chocolate one by one. Whisk over low heat for 4 minutes to ensure the yolks are cooked. Remove from the heat, and whisk in the hazelnuts and whisky. Allow to cool to tepid.

FINISH THE MOUSSE

4 **Meanwhile,** put 60ml (2fl oz) water in a small pan, add the sugar and heat until dissolved. Boil without stirring until syrup is 120°C (248°F) on a sugar thermometer, or a teaspoon of it forms a firm, pliable ball.

5 **Whisk the egg whites** until stiff. Gradually whisk in the syrup, until the meringue is cool and stiff. Stir a quarter into the tepid chocolate, then fold in the remaining meringue. Spoon into glasses, and chill for 1 hour.

MAKE THE WHISKY CREAM, IF LIKED

6 **Whisk the cream** until soft peaks form, adding the sugar and whisky. Top each mousse with the reserved hazelnuts and serve with the cream.

Poires belle Hélène

THIS DESSERT OF POACHED PEARS, vanilla ice cream, and hot chocolate sauce dates from the 19th century when it was created for the star of Offenbach's opera, *La Belle Hélène*. If you're pressed for time, just use good-quality bought vanilla ice cream.

SERVES
SERVES 6

PREP
30–35 MINS
PLUS FREEZING

COOK
25–35 MINS

Ingredients

FOR THE VANILLA ICE CREAM

600ml (1 pint) milk

1 vanilla pod

150g (5½oz) caster sugar

8 egg yolks

2 tbsp cornflour

250ml (9fl oz) double cream

FOR THE PEARS

2 lemons

6 firm pears

1 vanilla pod (optional)

150g (5½oz) caster sugar

FOR THE CHOCOLATE SAUCE

250g (9oz) good-quality plain chocolate, chopped

1 tbsp brandy

MAKE THE ICE CREAM

1 **Put the milk** in a saucepan. Split and add the vanilla pod. Bring to a boil. Remove from the heat, and let stand for 10–15 minutes. Set aside a quarter of it. Add the sugar to the remaining milk and stir until dissolved.

2 **Put the egg yolks** and cornflour in a bowl. Whisk in the milk. Stir over medium heat, until thick enough to coat the back of a spoon. Stir in the reserved milk. Cool, pour into an ice-cream maker, and churn. Whip the cream to soft peaks. Add to the custard, and freeze for at least 4 hours.

PREPARE THE PEARS

3 **Cut 1 lemon** in half. Peel the pears, leaving the stalks intact. Rub the lemon all over the pears. From the bottom, scoop out the pips and core.

POACH THE PEARS

4 **Make the poaching syrup:** combine 750ml (1¼ pints) water, the vanilla pod, if using, the zest and juice from the remaining lemon, and sugar in a shallow pan, wide enough to take all 6 pears in a single layer. Heat until the sugar has dissolved, then bring to a boil. Remove from the heat. Carefully add the pears. If necessary, add more water to cover them.

5 **Cut a disk** of baking parchment the same diameter as the pan. Dampen it, then place it on top of the pears to keep them submerged. Simmer gently for 25–35 minutes, depending on ripeness, until tender when pierced with a small knife. Let cool in the liquid.

MAKE THE CHOCOLATE SAUCE

6 **Mix the chocolate** with 125ml (4fl oz) water in a pan. Melt over gentle heat. Add the brandy. Serve warm with the pears and ice cream.

Grand Marnier soufflé

RISEN TO LOFTY HEIGHTS, this impressive dessert will make a truly grand ending to a special meal. As with all soufflés, it should be baked only until soft in the centre, forming a fluffy accompaniment to the crisper outside. It's served here with a refreshing compote of orange segments, to help cut through the richness. If you would prefer to make a non-alcoholic version of the soufflé, simply substitute the same amount of fresh orange juice for the Grand Marnier in the recipe.

SERVES	PREP	COOK
SERVES 6	30–35 MINS	20–25 MINS

Ingredients

FOR THE SOUFFLÉ

375ml (13fl oz) milk

4 egg yolks

150g (5½oz) caster sugar

45g (1½oz) plain flour

75ml (2½fl oz) Grand Marnier

6 egg whites

icing sugar, to serve

FOR THE ORANGE COMPOTE

4 oranges

2 tbsp orange marmalade

1 tbsp Grand Marnier

MAKE THE ORANGE COMPOTE

1 With a vegetable peeler, pare the zest from 1 of the oranges, taking care not to include any bitter white pith. Cut the zest lengthways into the finest possible julienne strips. Bring a small saucepan of water to a boil. Add the julienne strips and simmer for 2 minutes. Drain, rinse under cold running water, and drain again. Transfer the strips to a bowl. Finely grate the zest from a second orange into a dish, and reserve for the soufflé.

2 Segment all 4 oranges, working over a bowl to catch the juice: with a sharp knife, cut away both ends of the oranges, set upright on a chopping board and, working from top to bottom, cut away the zest and pith, following the curve of the fruit. Slide the knife down both sides of a segment, cutting it from the membrane, and let it slide into the bowl.

3 Add the orange segments to the julienned zest. Put the juice from segmenting the oranges, and the marmalade, into a small saucepan. Heat gently until the marmalade has melted, stirring occasionally. Remove from the heat and let cool slightly. Add the marmalade mixture to the orange segments and julienne, and stir to mix. Stir in the Grand Marnier. Cover, and chill until ready to serve.

MAKE THE PASTRY CREAM BASE

4 Scald the milk, bringing it just to a boil in a saucepan. Meanwhile, whisk the egg yolks with three-quarters of the caster sugar for 2–3 minutes, until thick and light coloured. Make sure the mixture is really airy and foamy.

5 Stir in the flour with a whisk. Then gradually stir in the hot milk until the mixture is smooth. Make sure you are constantly beating the mixture, as otherwise there is a risk that the egg yolks may cook and scramble.

6 Pour the pastry cream back into the saucepan. Bring to a boil over medium heat, whisking constantly until it thickens. If lumps form, remove from the heat at once and whisk until the cream is smooth again. Reduce the heat to low and cook the pastry cream, still whisking constantly, for about 2 minutes, until it softens slightly. Remove the pan from the heat. Add the reserved grated orange zest and the Grand Marnier, and stir in with the whisk.

FINISH AND BAKE THE SOUFFLÉ

7 Preheat the oven to 200°C (400°F/Gas 6). Generously butter a 1.5 litre (2¾ pint) soufflé dish. If necessary, reheat the pastry cream until hot to the touch. Whisk the egg whites in a metal bowl until stiff. Sprinkle in the remaining caster sugar, and continue whisking for about 20 seconds to form a glossy light meringue. Fold the meringue and pastry cream base together.

8 Gently pour into the prepared dish. Tap on the table to eliminate any pockets of air. The mixture should fill the dish to within 1cm (½in) of the rim. Smooth the top, then run your thumb around the edge to make a shallow indentation. Place in the oven and bake for 20-25 minutes, until puffed and golden brown. When gently shaken, the soufflé should be firm outside but still slightly soft and wobbly in the centre.

9 Sift icing sugar over the top of the soufflé, working quickly, as the soufflé will lose volume within minutes as it cools. Serve at once, with the fresh orange compote in a separate bowl.

 VARIATION: Hot coffee soufflé

This classic soufflé takes an innovative turn with a flavouring of cardamom, echoing true Turkish coffee.

1 Omit the orange compote. Put 375ml (13fl oz) single cream in a saucepan; add 2 lightly crushed cardamom pods. Bring just to a boil. Remove from the heat and infuse for 10-15 minutes. When cool, strain and chill, covered.

2 For the pastry cream base, add 30g (1oz) coarsely ground coffee to the milk before heating, then cover, and set aside to infuse for 10-15 minutes. Whisk the egg yolks, sugar, and flour, then strain in the milk. Continue as directed, omitting the zest and replacing the Grand Marnier with Tia Maria.

3 Butter the soufflé dish. Finish and bake the soufflé as directed. Quickly sift cocoa powder over the top of the soufflé and serve immediately, with the spiced cardamom cream as an accompanying sauce.

Tri-chocolate terrine

MAURICE FERRE WAS THE PASTRY CHEF at Maxim's in Paris. This is his frozen terrine, with three sumptuously flavoured chocolate layers, served with a pool of delicate mint custard. Use very good-quality chocolate and be extra careful to buy only white chocolate containing cocoa butter, not other tropical fats, whenever you are intending to use it for cooking.

SERVES	PREP	COOK
MAKES 12–16 SLICES	35–40 MINS PLUS FREEZING	20–25 MINS

Ingredients

FOR THE CHOCOLATE TERRINE

vegetable oil

125g (4½oz) good-quality plain chocolate

9 tbsp double cream

6 eggs

135g (5oz) unsalted butter

6 egg whites

3 tbsp caster sugar

150g (5½oz) good-quality white chocolate

150g (5½oz) good-quality milk chocolate

FOR THE MINT CUSTARD

1 bunch of mint

500ml (16fl oz) milk

60g (2oz) caster sugar

6 egg yolks

1½ tbsp cornflour

MAKE THE DARK CHOCOLATE LAYER

1 **Lightly brush the sides** and bottom of a 30x7.5x7.5cm (12x3x3in) terrine with oil. Using the base of the terrine as a guide, draw and then cut out 2 strips of baking parchment. Use one to line the bottom of the terrine, and reserve the other.

2 **Cut the plain chocolate** into large chunks. Chop them with a sharp knife, or in a food processor using the pulse button. Melt the chocolate in a large bowl placed in a saucepan half-filled with hot water (make sure the base of the bowl does not touch the water).

3 **In a small saucepan,** bring 3 tbsp of the double cream to boiling point, then whisk it into the chocolate. Separate 2 of the eggs. Whisk the egg yolks into the chocolate one at a time, stirring well between each addition.

4 **Cut 45g (1½oz)** of the butter into small pieces, and add a few pieces at a time, whisking so the butter melts smoothly into the warm mixture. In another large bowl, whisk 2 of the egg whites until stiff.

5 **Sprinkle in 1 tbsp** of the sugar and whisk until glossy, to make a light meringue. Fold the meringue into the chocolate mixture as lightly as possible. This can be done in 2 batches, if you like.

ASSEMBLE AND FREEZE THE TERRINE

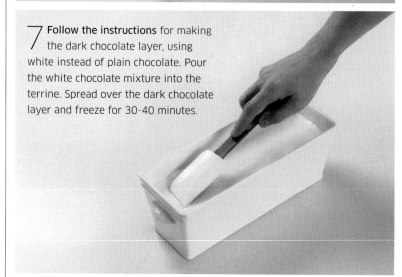

6 **Pour the dark chocolate** mixture into the terrine. Spread the chocolate mixture in the terrine, pushing it into the corners and smoothing the top evenly. Freeze for 30–40 minutes while preparing the remaining layers.

7 **Follow the instructions** for making the dark chocolate layer, using white instead of plain chocolate. Pour the white chocolate mixture into the terrine. Spread over the dark chocolate layer and freeze for 30–40 minutes.

8 **Make the milk chocolate layer,** using the same process as for the preceding layers, and pour it into the terrine on top of the white chocolate layer. Smooth the top layer, using a rubber spatula.

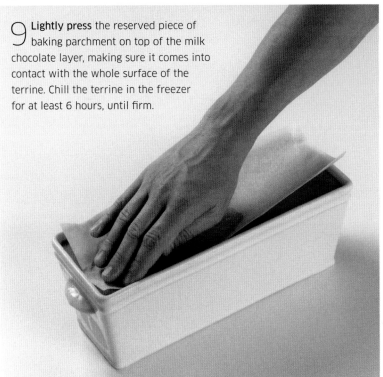

9 **Lightly press** the reserved piece of baking parchment on top of the milk chocolate layer, making sure it comes into contact with the whole surface of the terrine. Chill the terrine in the freezer for at least 6 hours, until firm.

MAKE THE MINT CUSTARD

10 **Rinse the mint** and trim the ends of the stalks. Reserve 12–16 sprigs for decoration, and lightly crush the remainder with a rolling pin. Put the milk in a heavy-based saucepan, and bring just to a boil. Add the crushed mint, cover and leave to infuse in a warm place for 10–15 minutes.

11 **Strain the milk** into a measuring jug or bowl, and discard the crushed mint. Stir in the sugar until dissolved. Whisk the egg yolks with the cornflour in a bowl. Add the infused milk, reserving about 125ml (4fl oz). Whisk until just smooth, then return the custard to the saucepan.

12 **Cook over moderate heat**, stirring constantly with a wooden spoon, until the custard just comes to a boil and thickens enough to coat the back of the spoon. (Your finger will leave a clear trail across the spoon.) Stir in the reserved milk. Strain the custard into a chilled bowl, and leave to cool.

TURN OUT THE TERRINE

13 **Fill a roasting tin** with hot water. Dip the base of the terrine into the hot water for 10–15 seconds, then lift it out. Peel off the baking parchment. Set a dish on top of the terrine, and turn them over together. Remove the terrine. Serve sliced, with the custard and mint sprigs.

Mango sorbet

THE KEY TO GOOD SORBET is smoothness: the ice crystals that form naturally during freezing must be removed by stirring the mixture constantly, usually by machine. As freezing any food will diminish its flavour, be sure the fruit is at its peak of ripeness. The citrus juices in this recipe heighten the taste and balance the mango's sweetness.

SERVES	PREP	COOK
SERVES 6	25–30 MINS PLUS FREEZING	2–3 MINS

Ingredients

100g (3½oz) caster sugar, plus more if needed

3 mangoes, total weight 1.25–1.4kg (2¾–3lb)

juice of 1 lemon

juice of 1 orange

lime zest, to serve

MAKE THE SUGAR SYRUP

1 **Combine the sugar** and 125ml (4fl oz) water in a small saucepan. Heat until the sugar has dissolved, then boil the syrup for 2–3 minutes, until it is clear. Set aside to cool.

MAKE THE SORBET MIXTURE

2 **Peel the mangoes.** Cut each mango lengthwise into 2 pieces, slightly off-centre just to miss the stone (p482). Cut the flesh away from the other side of the stone.

3 **Cut the remaining thin layer** of flesh from the stone. Cut all the mango into cubes. Purée it in batches, in a food processor. It must be very smooth for the best results.

4 **With all the pureé** in the food processor, and the blade turning, pour in the cooled syrup and citrus juices. Taste, adding more sugar if it is tart, remembering the flavours will be dulled by freezing.

FREEZE THE SORBET

5 **Pour the sorbet mixture** into an ice-cream maker and freeze until firm, following the manufacturer's directions. Meanwhile, chill a bowl in the freezer.

6 **Transfer the sorbet** to the chilled bowl. Cover it and freeze for at least 4 hours to allow the flavour to mellow. If necessary, transfer the sorbet to the refrigerator to soften slightly. Scoop the sorbet into chilled glasses and serve immediately, sprinkled with lime zest.

Chocolate soufflés

THE CHOCOLATE IS SO THICK AND RICH that it holds the whisked egg white without any flour. Be careful not to overcook the soufflés; the best part is the soft, creamy centre that forms a sauce for the crisp outside layer. Serve them with crisp biscuits for extra texture, if you like. Never open the oven while cooking a soufflé, or it may deflate.

SERVES	PREP	COOK
SERVES 4	20-25 MINS	15-18 MINS

Ingredients

125g (4½oz) plain chocolate

125ml (4fl oz) double cream

3 eggs, plus 2 egg whites

2 tbsp brandy

½ tsp vanilla essence

3 tbsp caster sugar

2-3 tbsp icing sugar, to dust (optional)

START THE CHOCOLATE MIXTURE

1 **Brush 4 ramekins** with melted butter. Preheat the oven to 220°C (425°F/Gas 7). Cut the chocolate into large chunks. Chop them with a knife, or in a food processor using the pulse button. Put the chocolate in the saucepan, add the cream, stir to mix, then heat gently, stirring, for about 5 minutes, until melted and smooth.

2 **If the mixture is a little thin,** simmer it until it is the consistency of double cream. Remove the pan from the heat. Separate the eggs. Whisk the yolks into the hot mixture 1 at a time, stirring well after each addition.

FINISH THE CHOCOLATE MIXTURE

3 **Whisk the chocolate mixture** over low heat for about 4 minutes to ensure that the egg yolks are cooked. Remove from the heat and whisk in the brandy and vanilla essence. If necessary, reheat the chocolate mixture until it's hot to the touch.

4 **Whisk the 5 egg whites** until stiff. Sprinkle in the sugar and continue whisking for about 20 seconds until glossy, to form a light meringue. Fold the meringue and chocolate mixtures together.

BAKE THE CHOCOLATE SOUFFLÉS

5 **Gently pour the soufflé mixture** into the ramekins. Carefully place the soufflés in the heated oven and bake for about 10 minutes, until puffed.

6 **Remove the soufflés** from the oven and sift over icing sugar, if you like. Take to the table immediately, before the soufflés have a chance to deflate, and serve with crisp biscuits, if you like.

Amaretti and chocolate bombe

AN ICE CREAM BOMBE, with its attractive shape and contrasting centre, is always festive. Here, amaretto ice cream surrounds an amaretti biscuit and chocolate filling. This is a great dessert for entertaining, as it can be prepared ahead and frozen, with only the chocolate sauce to be made before serving. There's no need to invest in a special bombe mould, as a Pyrex dish will serve the purpose just as well.

SERVES
SERVES 8-10

PREP
40-60 MINS
PLUS FREEZING

COOK
20-25 MINS

Ingredients

FOR THE AMARETTO ICE CREAM

600ml (1 pint) milk

125g (4½oz) caster sugar

8 egg yolks

2 tbsp cornflour

3 tbsp amaretto liqueur

250ml (8fl oz) double cream

FOR THE CHOCOLATE FILLING

100g (3½oz) caster sugar

4 egg yolks

125ml (4fl oz) double cream

125g (4½oz) plain chocolate

100g (3½oz) small amaretti biscuits, plus more to serve

FOR THE CHOCOLATE SAUCE

250g (9oz) plain chocolate

MAKE THE AMARETTO ICE CREAM

1 **Put the milk in a saucepan** and bring just to a boil. Remove from the heat, set aside one-quarter of the milk, and add the sugar to the remainder. Stir until the sugar has completely dissolved into the milk. Put the egg yolks and cornflour in another bowl. Whisk together very well, until smooth and evenly combined, with no lumps.

2 **Pour the sweetened milk** into the egg yolk mixture, whisking just until evenly blended. Be sure to whisk constantly, so the hot milk does not begin to cook the egg. Return the mixture to the pan and cook over medium heat, stirring constantly, until the custard comes just to a boil and thickens enough to coat the back of a spoon; your finger, when drawn across the spoon, should leave a clear trail. Remove the saucepan from the heat.

3 **Stir the reserved milk** into the custard. Strain into a bowl and let cool completely. If a skin has formed, whisk to dissolve it, then whisk in the amaretto liqueur. Pour the cooled custard into an ice-cream maker and churn it until slushy, following the manufacturer's directions.

CONSTRUCT THE BOMBE SHELL

4 Chill a 2 litre (3½ pint) bombe mould or Pyrex bowl in the freezer. Pour the cream into a chilled bowl, and whip until it forms soft peaks and just holds a shape. Add the whipped cream to the half-frozen custard, and continue freezing until the ice cream is firm but still soft enough to spread. The cream will soften the texture.

5 Line the bombe mould or bowl with cling film, then spoon the ice cream into the mould, and spread it over the bottom and side in an even layer about 4cm (1½in) thick.

6 Make a neat, even hollow in the centre of the ice cream. Make sure it is well centred, so each serving of bombe will have an even amount of amaretto ice cream and chocolate filling. Cover and freeze for 30-60 minutes, until firm. Meanwhile, make the bombe filling.

MAKE THE CHOCOLATE FILLING AND FREEZE THE BOMBE

7 Put the sugar and 125ml (4fl oz) water in a small saucepan, and heat until dissolved, stirring occasionally. Boil without stirring until the syrup reaches the soft-ball stage. To test, dip a teaspoon in the hot syrup. Let the syrup cool a few seconds, then take a little between finger and thumb; it should form a soft ball. If using a sugar thermometer, it should register 115°C (239°F).

8 While the syrup is boiling, lightly beat the egg yolks in a large bowl. Gradually pour the hot sugar syrup into the egg yolks, beating constantly with an electric mixer or hand whisk for about 5 minutes, until the mixture is cool, very thick, and pale. Pour the cream into a chilled bowl, and whip until it forms soft peaks and just holds a shape.

9 Add the whipped cream to the egg yolk mousse, and fold the mixtures together. Make sure the mousse is completely cool before adding the cream. Grate the chocolate. Put 7–8 amaretti biscuits in a plastic bag, and crumble them coarsely by pounding with a rolling pin. Reserve the remaining biscuits for decoration.

10 Add the grated chocolate and crumbled biscuits to the filling mixture, and fold in. Remove the ice-cream-lined mould from the freezer, and spoon in the bombe filling. Smooth the top with the palette knife. Cover with baking parchment and the lid, or a piece of foil, and freeze for at least 8 hours, until very firm.

MAKE THE CHOCOLATE SAUCE

11 Cut the chocolate into large chunks. Chop them in a food processor using the pulse button, or with a sharp knife. Combine the chocolate and 175ml (6fl oz) water in a small saucepan, and stir over gentle heat until the sauce is smooth, making sure that the chocolate does not catch on the bottom of the pan. Simmer until thickened slightly to the consistency of single cream; it should only take 2–3 minutes to reach this stage. Remove from the heat, and keep warm.

UNMOULD AND SERVE

12 Remove the lid or foil from the bombe, and dip the mould in a bowl of cool water for 30–60 seconds; this should help loosen the bombe from its mould. Lift the mould out and wipe it dry. Run the small knife around the inside edge of the mould. Peel off the baking parchment. Set a chilled serving plate on top of the bombe then, holding both firmly, invert. Wrap a damp cloth around the mould for a few moments, then lift it off. The bombe should fall out on to the plate. Keep the bombe chilled in the freezer until ready to serve.

13 Serve the bombe immediately with the warm chocolate sauce and reserved amaretti biscuits. Sprinkle with chocolate shavings as well, if you like. Cut the bombe into wedges at the table.

Chocolate and pear tartlets

THESE TARTLETS ARE SUPERBLY FLAVOURED.
The pastry can be made up to 2 days in advance,
tightly wrapped, and kept in the refrigerator, or it
can be frozen. The tartlets can be kept for 6–8
hours, but are best eaten the day they are baked.
Make sure your pears are fully ripe and juicy.

SERVES	PREP	COOK
MAKES 8	30–35 MINS PLUS CHILLING	25–30 MINS

Ingredients

FOR THE PASTRY

175g (6oz) plain flour

90g (3oz) unsalted butter

60g (2oz) caster sugar

½ tsp salt

½ tsp vanilla essence

3 egg yolks

FOR THE FILLING

150g (5½oz) plain chocolate

2 large, ripe pears

1–2 tbsp caster sugar, to sprinkle

FOR THE CUSTARD

1 egg

125ml (4½fl oz) single cream

1 tbsp kirsch (optional)

MAKE THE PASTRY

1. Sift the flour on to a work surface, tapping
the side of the sieve. Put the butter
between 2 sheets of baking parchment and
pound with a rolling pin to soften it slightly.
Make a well in the centre of the flour
with your hand. Put the sugar, salt,
and vanilla essence in the well.
Add the butter to the
ingredients in the well.
With your fingertips,
work the ingredients
in the well
together until
thoroughly mixed.

2. Add the egg yolks and work into
the ingredients in the well. Draw
in the flour with a palette knife. With
your fingers, work the flour into the
other ingredients until coarse
crumbs form. Press the dough
into a ball. Sprinkle the
work surface lightly
with flour, then
blend the dough
by pushing the
ball away from
you with the heel
of your hand.

3. Gather up the dough and continue to
blend for 1–2 minutes, until it is very
smooth and peels away from the work
surface in 1 piece. Shape the dough into
a ball again, wrap in cling film, and
chill for about 30 minutes, until
firm. Pastry doughs made with
sugar are particularly
delicate. Be sure to chill
the dough well before
rolling out.

LINE THE TARTLET TINS

4. Brush the insides of 8 x 10cm (4in) tartlet tins with melted butter. Group
4 of the tartlet tins together, with their edges nearly touching. Sprinkle
the work surface lightly with flour. Divide the ball of dough in half, and roll
1 piece out to 3mm (⅛in) thick. Roll the dough loosely round the rolling pin,
and drape it over the 4 tins to cover them completely.

5. Tear off a small piece of dough from the edge, form it into a ball, dip it in
flour, and use it to push the dough into the tins. Roll the rolling pin over
the tops of the tins to cut off excess dough (it can be rolled out again and
used to line the remaining tartlet tins). Repeat with the 4 remaining tins and
the second piece of dough.

FILL AND **BAKE** THE TARTLETS

6. Preheat the oven to 200°C (400°F/Gas 6). Heat a baking sheet on an
oven shelf near the bottom of the oven. Cut the chocolate into large
chunks. Finely chop them with a sharp knife, or in a food processor using the
pulse button. Sprinkle into each tartlet shell.

7 **To make the custard,** whisk the egg, cream, and kirsch, if using, together until thoroughly mixed. For an extra-smooth custard, rub the mixture through a sieve. Spoon 2–3 tbsp of the kirsch custard over the chocolate in each tartlet shell.

8 **Peel the pears,** cut them in half, and remove the cores. With a small knife, cut each pear half across into very thin slices. Arrange the slices on the custard so that they overlap. Press them down very lightly into the custard, so it will bake up around the fruit, then sprinkle each tartlet evenly with the sugar.

9 **Place the tartlet tins** on the heated baking sheet. Bake them for 10 minutes, then reduce the heat to 180°C (350°F/Gas 4) and continue baking until the pastry is golden and the custard has set. It should take 15–20 minutes longer.

10 **Leave the tartlets** to cool slightly. Once cool enough to handle, unmould them carefully, and place the tartlets on to individual plates to serve.

 VARIATION: Chocolate and apple tartlets

A touch of cinnamon adds spice to this version.

1 Prepare the pastry dough and carefully line the tartlet tins as directed in the main recipe. Peel and core 3 apples, total weight about 500g (1lb 2oz). Cut them into small chunks. Each time you prepare apples for cooking, do so at the last minute, to prevent discolouration.

2 Heat about 2 tbsp unsalted butter in a large saucepan. Tip in all the apple chunks and sprinkle them with 1–2 tbsp sugar and 2 tsp ground cinnamon. Sauté briskly for 3–5 minutes, until slightly softened and caramelized, stirring occasionally. Make sure you get some good colour on the apples, for a deeper flavour.

3 Sprinkle the chopped chocolate evenly into the tartlet shells and spoon the custard over the top. Spread the apples on the custard, pressing them down lightly. Bake as directed, on a hot baking sheet. (The hot baking sheet will conduct heat immediately to the base of the tarts and cook the pastry.)

Almond milk curd with exotic fruit

MADE FROM SWEETENED MILK AND ALMOND ESSENCE, this dish resembles a Chinese bean curd dessert in appearance, but its delicate texture and flavour make it far friendlier to Western palates, and a perfect light finish to a meal. A heavy-based saucepan is essential, so the milk does not scorch.

SERVES	PREP	COOK
SERVES 8	40 MINS PLUS CHILLING	15 MINS

Ingredients

FOR THE ALMOND MILK CURD

600ml (1 pint) milk

60g (2oz) caster sugar

2 tbsp powdered gelatine

1 tsp almond essence

FOR THE SUGAR SYRUP

60g (2oz) caster sugar

FOR THE FRUIT

4 ripe, crinkly passion fruits

500g (1lb 2oz) lychees

1 small mango

PREPARE THE ALMOND MILK CURD

1 **Combine the milk and sugar** in a heavy-based saucepan, and slowly bring to a boil over medium heat, stirring occasionally until the sugar has completely dissolved. Sprinkle the gelatine over 2 tbsp water in a small saucepan and let stand for about 5 minutes, until spongy. Warm the pan over very low heat, shaking it occasionally, but not stirring, until the gelatine is melted.

2 **Off the heat, stir the gelatine** into the milk mixture, then stir in the almond essence. Pour the almond-flavoured mixture into a 20cm (8in) square cake tin. Let cool to room temperature, then cover tightly, and refrigerate for 3–4 hours, until the almond milk curd has set.

MAKE THE SYRUP

3 **For the syrup,** combine 125ml (4fl oz) and the sugar in a small saucepan and heat, stirring occasionally, until the sugar has dissolved. Bring to a boil and simmer the syrup for 1 minute. Remove from the heat and let cool.

PREPARE THE FRUIT

4 **Cut the passion fruits** in half and scrape the seeds and pulp into a bowl. Peel the lychees, slit them on one side and remove the stone. Add to the bowl. Peel and slice the mango (p482), and add to the bowl. Pour the sugar syrup over the fruits. Toss gently, cover and chill for at least 1 hour.

FINISH THE DISH

5 **With a small, sharp knife,** cut the almond curd in the tin into 4cm (1½in) diamonds or squares, as you prefer. Run a knife around the inside edge of the tin. Spoon the chilled fruit in to serving bowls. Loosen the almond curd and carefully lift out the pieces with a palette knife. Arrange them beside the fruit salad.

Chocolate mocha sorbet

THIS HAS A SURPRISINGLY CREAMY TEXTURE. You can leave the sorbet plain, or decorate it with a sprinkling of chocolate-covered coffee beans. Though the sorbet can be stored in the freezer for up to 1 week, the texture may coarsen, so do not make it too far in advance of serving. As there are so few ingredients in this recipe, the chocolate has to be of the best quality you can afford.

SERVES	PREP	COOK
SERVES 6-8	25-30 MINS PLUS FREEZING	15-20 MINS

Ingredients

90g (3oz) good-quality plain chocolate

2-3 tbsp instant coffee powder

300g (10oz) caster sugar

MAKE THE SORBET BASE

1 **Cut the chocolate** into large chunks, then finely chop in a food processor using the pulse button. Put 375ml (13fl oz) water in a medium heavy-based saucepan, add the chocolate and the coffee, and heat, stirring, until melted and smooth.

2 **Add the sugar** and 375ml (13fl oz) more water and heat, stirring, until the sugar has dissolved. Bring to a boil and simmer for 8-10 minutes, stirring; the mixture should thicken very slightly. Remove from the heat, and allow to cool completely.

FREEZE THE SORBET

3 **Pour the sorbet mixture** into an ice-cream maker and churn until slushy, following the manufacturer's instructions. Meanwhile, chill a large bowl in the freezer to store your sorbet.

4 **Transfer the sorbet** to the chilled bowl, cover it, and freeze for at least 4 hours to allow the flavour to mellow. Freezing time varies greatly depending on the machine you use.

5 **If the sorbet has been frozen** for more than 12 hours, it will need to soften for 15-20 minutes in the refrigerator before serving. This will allow the flavours to come out, and the texture to mellow and smoothen.

6 **Serve in chilled glasses**, in scoops or quenelles. To make a quenelle, dip 2 metal spoons in cold water. Use one spoon to scoop out a generous spoonful of sorbet, then use the other to shape the mixture into a neat oval, turning each spoon against the other.

Hazelnut torte with strawberries

AN IMPRESSIVE THREE-LAYER CASTLE of hazelnut pastry, sandwiched with strawberries and whipped cream. A tart raspberry coulis makes the ideal accompaniment. The pastry can be baked up to 2 days ahead and kept in an airtight container, or can be frozen. The torte should be assembled no more than 4 hours ahead of serving, and should be kept refrigerated.

SERVES	PREP	COOK
SERVES 8	40-45 MINS PLUS CHILLING	15-18 MINS

Ingredients

FOR THE HAZELNUT PASTRY

250g (9oz) hazelnuts

135g (5oz) caster sugar

125g (4½oz) plain flour, plus more to dust

½ tsp salt

150g (5½oz) unsalted butter

1 egg yolk

FOR THE RASPBERRY COULIS

500g (1lb 2oz) raspberries

2-3 tbsp icing sugar, or to taste

1-2 tbsp kirsch (optional)

FOR THE CHANTILLY CREAM

375ml (13fl oz) double cream

1½ tbsp caster sugar

1 tsp vanilla essence

FOR THE STRAWBERRIES AND DECORATION

750g (1lb 10oz) strawberries

mint sprigs, to decorate

MAKE THE HAZELNUT PASTRY DOUGH

1 **Preheat the oven** to 180°C (350°F/Gas 4). Spread the hazelnuts on a baking sheet. Toast for 8-10 minutes, until lightly browned, stirring occasionally so the nuts colour evenly. While still hot, rub the nuts in a clean tea towel to remove the skins, then leave to cool.

2 **In a food processor**, grind the hazelnuts with the caster sugar to a fine powder. Put the ground nut mixture on a work surface and sift the flour and salt on top. Make a well in the centre of the ingredients and add the butter and egg yolk.

3 **Using your fingertips**, work the butter and egg yolk together in the well, drawing in a little of the ground nut and flour mixtures, until soft and thoroughly mixed. Press the dough into a ball. Sprinkle the work surface lightly with flour; place the dough on the work surface and knead the dough gently until very smooth.

4 **Shape the dough** into a ball, wrap it tightly, and chill for at least 30 minutes, until firm. Pastry doughs made with nuts are particularly delicate, so be sure to give the dough enough time to chill.

SHAPE AND BAKE THE PASTRY LAYERS

5 **Preheat the oven** to 200°C (400°F/Gas 6). Divide the chilled dough into 3 equal pieces. With the heel of your hand or the back of a spoon, press each piece into a 20cm (8in) round on a baking sheet. (Use a pan lid or an upturned cake tin as a guide.) You can cook 2 pastry layers on 1 sheet, but space the rounds about 2.5cm (1in) apart, as they expand during baking.

6 **Bake the pastry** in the heated oven for 15-18 minutes, until the edges begin to brown. While they are still warm, trim them with a very sharp knife into neat rounds, using a pan lid or cake tin as a guide. Do not let the pastry cool before trimming, or the rounds may break.

7 **Using a sharp knife,** cut 1 of the layers across into 8 equal wedges. Let all the layers and wedges cool to tepid on the baking sheets. Carefully transfer to wire racks to cool completely.

MAKE THE COULIS, CREAM AND DECORATION

8 **To make the raspberry** coulis, pick over the berries, then purée them in a food processor. Stir in icing sugar to taste, and the kirsch, if you like. Work the purée through a sieve to remove the pips.

9 **Hull the strawberries,** washing them only if they are dirty. Set aside 8 small berries for decoration. Halve the remaining strawberries, or quarter them if they are large.

10 **To make the Chantilly** cream, pour the cream into a chilled bowl and whip until soft peaks form. Add the sugar and vanilla and whip until the cream forms stiff peaks and the whisk leaves clear marks in the cream.

ASSEMBLE THE TORTE

11 **Set a round of pastry** on a serving plate. Cover with about one-quarter of the Chantilly cream, and arrange half the strawberries on top. Work neatly, as the final look of this torte is important.

12 **Cover the strawberries** with more Chantilly cream, spreading lightly with a rubber spatula. Try not to dislodge any of the strawberries on the bottom layer, and do not press, or they will begin to leak their juices.

13 **Set the second round of pastry** on top, and spread with half the remaining Chantilly cream. Slide the pastry round directly from the wire rack to avoid breaking it. Remember it is quite fragile.

14 **Cover with the remaining strawberries,** and spread the rest of the Chantilly cream on top. Top with the wedges of pastry, setting them at an angle. Put the whole strawberries on top. To serve, cut into wedges, and drizzle each individual serving with the coulis.

Chocolate chestnut roll

A WINTER FAVOURITE, especially over the Christmas period, this is filled with a rich chestnut purée mixed with whipped cream. Be as elaborate or simple as you like with the decoration. Once assembled, it will keep for up to 2 days in the refrigerator; add decorations just before serving.

SERVES SERVES 8-10	PREP 50-55 MINS	COOK 5-7 MINS

Ingredients

FOR THE CHOCOLATE SPONGE ROLL

35g (1¼oz) cocoa powder

1 tbsp plain flour

salt

5 eggs

150g (5½oz) caster sugar

FOR THE FILLING

175ml (6fl oz) double cream

125g (4½oz) chestnut purée

2 tbsp dark rum

30g (1oz) plain chocolate

caster sugar, to taste (optional)

TO FINISH AND DECORATE (optional)

25g (1oz) caster sugar

2 tbsp dark rum

8-10 marrons glacés

90g (3oz) plain chocolate

MAKE THE CHOCOLATE CAKE MIXTURE

1 **Preheat the oven** to 220°C (425°F/Gas 7). Brush a 30x37cm (12x15in) baking sheet with melted butter, line with baking parchment, and butter the parchment. Sift the cocoa powder, flour, and a pinch of salt into a bowl.

2 **Separate the eggs.** Beat the egg yolks with two-thirds of the sugar until light, and the mixture leaves a ribbon trail when the whisk is lifted; it will take 3-5 minutes.

3 **Whisk the egg whites** until stiff. Your bowl and whisk must be completely free of any trace of water, grease, or egg yolk, or the egg whites will not whisk to full volume. Sprinkle in the remaining sugar and whisk for about 20 seconds, until glossy, to make a light meringue.

4 **Sift about one-third of the cocoa mixture** over the egg-yolk mixture. Add one-third of the meringue. Fold the mixtures together as lightly as possible. Add the remaining cocoa mixture and meringue in the same way in 2 batches.

BAKE AND ROLL THE SPONGE

5 **Pour the chocolate mixture,** all at once, on to the prepared baking sheet. Use a spatula to scrape out the bowl. Spread the mixture evenly on the baking sheet almost to the edges. Put in the heated oven, near the bottom, and bake for 5-7 minutes. The cake is done when it is risen, and just firm to the touch. Do not overbake or it will be difficult to roll.

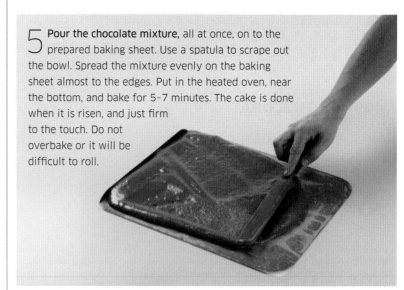

6 **Dampen a tea towel.** Remove the cake from the oven, and immediately cover with the tea towel. Take a second baking sheet and set it on top of the cake. Quickly invert the cake so the original baking sheet is on top. Place the cake on the work surface, and carefully remove the uppermost baking sheet.

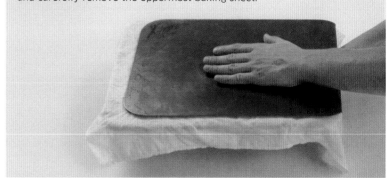

7 **Holding the baking parchment** by its edges, carefully peel it off the cake. Be very careful about this, as the cake is quite fragile and you don't want to tear the sponge. It will be easier if you work as quickly as you can. Starting at the short end nearest you, tightly roll up the cake and towel lengthways. Be very careful and work quickly, as it will be easier when hot. Set aside to cool

MAKE THE FILLING

8 **Pour the cream** into a chilled bowl, and whip until it forms soft peaks and just holds a shape. Put the chestnut purée in another bowl, and add the rum. Cut the chocolate into large chunks, then chop in a food processor.

9 **Melt the chocolate** in a bowl placed in a saucepan half-filled with hot water (make sure the base of the bowl does not touch the water). Add the melted chocolate to the chestnut purée, and stir well with a wooden spoon to remove any lumps.

FINISH AND DECORATE THE CAKE

10 **Leave the chocolate to cool** slightly; if it is too hot when added to the cream, the cream may become oily. Stir about 2 tbsp of the whipped cream into the chocolate mixture to soften it, then fold the remaining chocolate and chestnut mixture into the whipped cream. If necessary, add sugar to taste.

11 **Make a rum syrup:** in a small saucepan, over low heat, heat the sugar in 60ml (2fl oz) of water until it dissolves. Simmer the syrup for 1 minute. Allow to cool, then stir in the rum.

12 **Unroll the cake,** then roll it up again without the towel. Place the cake on a sheet of baking parchment and unroll it. The smooth top will be on the outside. Brush the cake with the cooled rum syrup. Using a palette knife, spread the chestnut filling evenly over. Using the paper underneath, carefully roll up the filled cake as tightly as possible.

13 **Bring the paper** up over the cake; fold it in tightly. Insert the edge of the baking sheet against the fold, and push away from you to tighten the roll. With a serrated knife, trim each end of the cake neatly. Transfer the cake to a serving plate.

14 **Chop the marrons glacés.** Arrange them on top of the roll, sprinkling them randomly or placing in a neat line, as you prefer. Melt the chocolate in the same way as in step 9, cool it slightly, then place into a small piping bag. Pipe the melted chocolate back and forth over the roll, being as freeform as you like.

Sticky rice with mangoes

A WELL-KNOWN THAI DESSERT, this is simply a coconut-flavoured rice pudding, with slices of ripe, juicy mango. You should use pudding rice – or even glutinous or sticky rice if you can get hold of it from Asian stores – all are starchy varieties ideal for making creamy desserts. If you like, reserve about 4 tbsp of the thick "cream" that rises to the top of the coconut milk in its tin, then spoon it over the rice to finish the dish.

SERVES	PREP	COOK
SERVES 6	40 MINS PLUS SOAKING	40–50 MINS

Ingredients

400g (14oz) pudding rice

100g (3½oz) caster sugar

½ tsp salt

300ml (10fl oz) canned coconut milk

3 large, ripe mangoes, total weight about 1kg (2¼lb)

lime zest, to serve

PREPARE THE RICE

1 **Put the rice** in a bowl, and pour cold water over. Cover, and let soak for at least 3 hours or overnight. Pour the rice into a sieve to drain off the liquid. Rinse thoroughly with cold water, to remove excess starch.

COOK THE RICE

2 **Pour enough water** into a wok so it almost touches the bottom of a bamboo steamer basket, when the basket is placed inside the wok. Cover the wok with its lid, and bring the water to a boil. Line the bottom and side of the basket with a double thickness of damp muslin.

3 **Tip the rice** into the basket, and spread it evenly. Uncover the wok, and place the basket of rice over the boiling water. Cover the basket with its lid. Reduce the heat to medium. Steam the rice for 40–50 minutes, until tender. The longer it has been soaked, the faster it will cook.

MAKE THE STICKY RICE

4 **In a saucepan, combine the sugar** and salt with the coconut milk. Bring slowly to a boil, stirring, until the sugar dissolves. Remove from the heat. Stir in the rice. Cool to room temperature.

PREPARE THE MANGOES AND FINISH THE DISH

5 **Peel the mangoes** with a small knife. Carefully cut the mangoes lengthways on both sides of the stone, so the knife just misses the stone. Slice them into 5mm (¼in) slices.

6 **Mound the rice** in a serving dish, and arrange the mango around it. Decorate with curls of lime zest, and a few more mango slices, and serve at room temperature.

Chocolate charlotte

A DREAM COME TRUE for chocolate lovers. Half fudge, half cake, this is a wonderful recipe to have in your repertoire. Decorate with chocolate curls (p486), or crystallized violets, if you like. The charlotte can be prepared as much as 1 week ahead and kept, covered, in the refrigerator; it can also be frozen very successfully.

SERVES SERVES 6-8	**PREP** 40-45 MINS PLUS CHILLING	**COOK** 70 MINS

Ingredients

FOR THE CHARLOTTE

250g (9oz) good-quality plain chocolate

175ml (6fl oz) strong black coffee

250g (9oz) unsalted butter

200g (7oz) caster sugar

4 eggs

cocoa powder, to dust

FOR THE CHANTILLY CREAM (optional)

375ml (13fl oz) double cream

1½ tbsp caster sugar

¾ tsp vanilla extract

MAKE THE CHOCOLATE CHARLOTTE

1 Brush a 1 litre (1¾ pint) mould or Pyrex bowl with melted butter. Line the bottom with baking parchment, and butter the paper. Chill. Preheat the oven to 180°C (350°F/Gas 4). Pulse-chop the chocolate in a food processor. Put into a heavy saucepan, add the coffee, and heat, stirring, until smooth. Add the butter and sugar, and melt. Bring almost to a boil, stirring well.

2 Remove the saucepan from the heat and whisk in the eggs, one by one, whisking well after each addition. The eggs will cook and thicken in the heat of the mixture. Strain into the prepared mould or bowl.

BAKE THE CHARLOTTE

3 **Bake for 70 minutes, until a thick crust forms** on top, watching so it does not scorch. Allow to cool, cover, and refrigerate for at least 24 hours. The charlotte will shrink slightly. Under the crust, it will still be quite soft.

TURN OUT THE CHARLOTTE

4 **Run a thin-bladed knife** between the charlotte and the mould, to loosen it. Dip the mould briefly in warm water, then dry the mould.

5 **Hold a serving plate** over the mould, invert, then lift off the mould. Peel off the paper. Chill the charlotte, tightly wrapped, until ready to serve.

MAKE THE CHANTILLY CREAM (OPTIONAL)

6 **Pour the cream** into a chilled bowl and whip to soft peaks. Add the sugar and vanilla, and whip to stiff peaks. Serve the charlotte, dusted with cocoa, with the Chantilly cream, or with crème fraîche.

Baked Alaska

THIS STRIKING DESSERT IS A FESTIVE WAY to conclude a celebration. The surprise of still-frozen ice cream hidden beneath hot, lightly browned meringue never fails to excite. The secret is the cake base, which insulates the ice cream from the oven's heat. Assemble the Alaska carefully, and seal it properly, to achieve the best results after baking. Make this recipe when you have a large crowd to feed, as it needs to be eaten straight from the oven.

SERVES	PREP	COOK
SERVES 8-10	45-50 MINS	30-40 MINS

Ingredients

FOR THE CAKE

60g (2oz) unsalted butter

125g (4½oz) plain flour

pinch of salt

4 eggs135g (5oz) caster sugar

1 tsp vanilla extract

FOR THE FILLING

300g (10oz) strawberries

2-3 tbsp icing sugar, to taste

1.5 litres (2¾ pints) vanilla ice cream

FOR THE MERINGUE

450g (1lb) caster sugar, plus more to sprinkle

9 egg whites

MAKE THE CAKE

1 Preheat the oven to 180°C (350°F/Gas 4). Butter a 20cm (8in) square cake tin, and line the bottom with baking parchment. Butter the paper. Sprinkle in 2 tbsp flour and turn the tin to coat the bottom and sides; turn the tin upside down, and tap to remove excess flour.

2 Sift the flour with the salt. Melt the butter in a small saucepan, and let cool. Put the eggs in a large bowl, and beat with an electric mixer for a few seconds, to mix. Add the sugar, and beat at high speed for about 5 minutes, or until the mixture is pale and thick, and leaves a ribbon trail when the beaters are lifted. Beat in the vanilla extract.

3 Sift about a third of the flour over the egg mixture, and fold them together as lightly as possible. Add another third of the flour and fold it in. Fold in the remaining flour and the cooled, melted butter. Pour into the tin, then tap on the work surface to level the mixture and knock out any air bubbles.

4 Bake in the heated oven for 30-40 minutes, until the cake has risen, and is just firm to the touch. Run a knife around the edge of the cake, and unmould it on to a wire rack. Peel off the paper, and allow to cool.

MAKE THE STRAWBERRY COULIS

5 Hull the strawberries with a small knife, washing them only if dirty. Purée in a food processor or blender, then pour into a bowl. Stir in icing sugar, to taste. You should have about 375ml (13fl oz) strawberry coulis.

PREPARE THE MERINGUE

6 Heat the sugar with 250ml (9fl oz) water in a saucepan, until dissolved. Boil without stirring until the syrup reaches the hard ball stage. To test, dip a teaspoon in the syrup. Take a little between finger and thumb; it should form a pliable ball. On a sugar thermometer, it should register 120°C (248°F).

7 Meanwhile, put the egg whites in a bowl and beat with an electric mixer for 3-5 minutes, until stiff peaks form. Gradually pour in the hot syrup, beating constantly for about 5 minutes, until the meringue is cool and stiff.

PREPARE THE BASE

8 Lightly butter a large heatproof serving plate. Remove the ice cream from the freezer, and leave until soft enough to scoop. Trim a 2.5cm (1in) strip from each side of the cake, leaving a 15cm (6in) square. Using a serrated knife, split the cake horizontally into 2 layers. Set the 2 squares of cake, cut side up and end to end, on the serving plate, to make a rectangle.

9 Work the cake trimmings in a food processor to form even crumbs. Add 250ml (9fl oz) of the strawberry coulis to the cake crumbs, and blend briefly to mix together.

ASSEMBLE AND BAKE THE DESSERT

10 Spread the remaining coulis over the cake. Scoop the ice cream into balls, and arrange them in a layer on the cake. Scoop and arrange a second layer of ice-cream balls. (Dip the scoop in warm water to prevent sticking).

11 **Quickly smooth the ice cream** layers with the palette knife, to even the surface and edges. Without delay, cover the top of the ice cream layer with the prepared strawberry cake crumbs.

12 **Using a large metal spoon,** spoon the meringue on top of the cake. Work quickly now, as the ice cream must stay as firm as possible at this point before baking.

13 **Spread the meringue** over the top and sides to cover completely, and seal it to the plate to insulate the ice cream. Keep in the freezer for up to 2 hours. Preheat the oven to 220°C (425°F/Gas 7). Take the dessert from the freezer, sprinkle with sugar, and let stand for 1 minute. Bake for just 3–5 minutes, until lightly browned. Serve at once.

INDEX

*Index entries in italics
refer to techniques*

Dorling Kindersley would like to thank:

Photographers: David Murray, William Reavell, William Shaw, Jon Whitaker

Prop stylist: Liz Belton

Food stylists: Lizzie Harris, Sal Henley, Cara Hobday, Jane Lawrie, Phil Mundy, Jenny White

Art directors: Nicky Collings, Anne Fisher, Luis Peral

Indexer: Hilary Bird

Proofreader: Irene Lyford

All photographs © Dorling Kindersley

Useful information

Refrigerator and freezer storage guidelines

FOOD	REFRIGERATOR	FREEZER
Raw poultry, fish, and meat (small pieces)	2–3 days	3 months
Raw minced beef and poultry	1–3 days	3 months
Cooked whole roasts or whole poultry	2–3 days	9 months
Cooked poultry pieces	2–3 days	3 months
Soups and stocks	2–3 days	3–6 months
Stews	2–3 days	3 months
Pies	2–3 days	3–6 months

Oven temperature equivalents

CELSIUS	FAHRENHEIT	GAS	DESCRIPTION
110°C	225°F	¼	Cool
130°C	250°F	½	Cool
140°C	275°F	1	Very low
150°C	300°F	2	Very low
160°C	325°F	3	Low
180°C	350°F	4	Moderate
190°C	375°F	5	Moderately hot
200°C	400°F	6	Hot
220°C	425°F	7	Hot
230°C	450°F	8	Very hot
240°C	475°F	9	Very hot

The Complete
Illustrated
Works of

LEWIS
CARROLL

The Complete
Illustrated
Works of
LEWIS
CARROLL

CHANCELLOR
PRESS

Alice's Adventures in Wonderland, illustrated by John Tenniel, was first published in Great Britain in 1865.

Phantasmagoria and Other Poems was first published in Great Britain in 1869. (first published with illustrations by Arthur B. Frost in *Rhyme? and Reason?* in 1883).

Through the Looking-Glass, illustrated by John Tenniel, was first published in Great Britain in 1872.

The Hunting of the Snark, illustrated by Henry Holiday, was first published in Great Britain in 1876.

A Tangled Tale, illustrated by Arthur B. Frost, was first published in Great Britain in 1885.

Sylvie and Bruno, illustrated by Harry Furniss, was first published in Great Britain in 1889.

Sylvie and Bruno Concluded, illustrated by Harry Furniss, was first published in Great Britain in 1893.

Three Sunsets and Other Poems, illustrated by E. Gertrude Thomson, was first published in Great Britain in 1898.

This edition first published in Great Britain in 1982 by

Chancellor Press
Michelin House
81 Fulham Road
London SW3 6RB

Reprinted 1983, 1984, 1985, 1986, 1987, 1989

© 1982 Arrangement and Design Octopus Books Ltd.

All rights Reserved

ISBN 0 907486 21 5

Printed in Austria

Contents

I

ALICE'S ADVENTURES
IN WONDERLAND

II

THROUGH THE
LOOKING GLASS

III

SYLVIE AND BRUNO

IV
SYLVIE AND BRUNO
CONCLUDED

V
A TANGLED TALE

VI

THE HUNTING OF
THE SNARK

VII

PHANTASMAGORIA
AND OTHER POEMS

VIII

THREE SUNSETS
AND OTHER POEMS

❦ I ❦

Alice's Adventures in Wonderland

with forty-two illustrations by
Sir John Tenniel

ALL in the golden afternoon
　　Full leisurely we glide;
For both our oars, with little skill,
　　By little arms are plied
While little hands make vain pretence
　　Our wanderings to guide.

Ah, cruel Three! In such an hour
　　Beneath such dreamy weather,
To beg a tale of breath too weak
　　To stir the tiniest feather!
Yet what can one poor voice avail
　　Against three tongues together?

Imperious Prima flashes forth
　　Her edict 'to begin it':
In gentler tone Secunda hopes
　　'There will be nonsense in it!'
While Tertia interrupts the tale
　　Not *more* than once a minute.

Anon, to sudden silence won,
　　In fancy they pursue
The dream-child moving through a land
　　Of wonders wild and new,
In friendly chat with bird or beast —
　　And half believe it true.

And ever, as the story drained
　　The wells of fancy dry,
And faintly strove that weary one
　　To put the subject by,
'The rest next time—' 'It *is* next time!'
　　The happy voices cry.

Thus grew the tale of Wonderland:
   Thus slowly, one by one,
Its quaint events were hammered out —
   And now the tale is done,
And home we steer, a merry crew
   Beneath the setting sun.

Alice! a childish story take,
   And with a gentle hand
Lay it where Childhood's dreams are twined
   In Memory's mystic band,
Like pilgrim's wither'd wreath of flowers
   Pluck'd in a far-off land.

CHRISTMAS-GREETINGS

[FROM A FAIRY TO A CHILD]

LADY dear, if Fairies may
　　For a moment lay aside
Cunning tricks and elfish play,
　　'Tis at happy Christmas-tide.

We have heard the children say—
　　Gentle children, whom we love—
Long ago, on Christmas-Day,
　　Came a message from above.

Still, as Christmas-tide comes round,
　　They remember it again—
Echo still the joyful sound
　　"Peace on earth, good-will to men!"

Yet the hearts must child-like be
　　Where such heavenly guests abide;
Unto children, in their glee,
　　All the year is Christmas-tide.

Thus, forgetting tricks and play
　　For a moment, Lady dear,
We would wish you, if we may,
　　Merry Christmas, glad New Year!

Christmas, 1867.

CHAPTER 1

Down the Rabbit-hole

ALICE was beginning to get very tired of sitting by her sister on the bank, and of having nothing to do; once or twice she had peeped into the book her sister was reading, but it had no pictures or conversations in it, "and what is the use of a book," thought Alice, "without pictures or conversations?"

So she was considering in her own mind (as well as she could, for the hot day made her feel very sleepy and stupid), whether the pleasure of making a daisy-chain would be worth the trouble of getting up and picking the daisies, when suddenly a White Rabbit with pink eyes ran close by her.

There was nothing so *very* remarkable in that: nor did Alice think it so *very* much out of the way to hear the Rabbit say to itself, "Oh dear! Oh dear! I shall be too late!" (When she thought it over afterwards, it occurred to her that she ought to have wondered at this, but at the time it all seemed quite natural); but when the Rabbit actually *took a watch out of its waistcoat-pocket*, and looked at it, and then hurried on, Alice started to her feet, for it flashed across her mind that she had never before seen a rabbit with either a waistcoat-pocket or a watch to take out of it, and burning with curiosity, she ran across the field after it, and was just in time to see it pop down a large rabbit-hole under the hedge.

In another moment down went Alice after it, never once considering how in the world she was to get out again.

The rabbit-hole went straight on like a tunnel for some way, and then dipped suddenly down, so suddenly that Alice had not a moment to think about stopping herself before she found herself falling down what seemed to be a very deep well.

Either the well was very deep, or she fell very slowly, for she had plenty of time as she went down to look about her, and to wonder what was going to happen next. First, she tried to look down and make out what she was coming to, but it was too dark to see anything: then she looked at the sides of the well, and noticed that they were filled with cupboards and book-shelves: here and there she saw maps and pictures hung upon pegs. She took down a jar from one of the shelves as she passed: it was labelled "ORANGE MARMALADE," but to her great disappointment it was empty: she did not like to drop the jar for fear of killing somebody underneath, so managed to put it into one of the cupboards as she fell past it.

"Well!" thought Alice to herself. "After such a fall as this, I shall think nothing of tumbling down-stairs! How brave they'll all think me at home! Why, I wouldn't say anything about it, even if I fell off the top of the house!" (Which was very likely true.)

Down, down, down. Would the fall *never* come to an end? "I wonder how many miles I've fallen by this time?" she said aloud. "I must be getting somewhere near the centre of the earth. Let me see: that would be four thousand miles down, I think –" (for, you see, Alice had learnt several things of this sort in her lessons in the schoolroom, and though this was not a *very* good opportunity for showing off her knowledge, as there was no one to listen to her, still it was good practice to say it over) "– yes, that's about the right distance – but then I wonder what Latitude or Longitude I've got to?" (Alice had not the slightest idea what Latitude was, or Longitude either, but she thought they were nice grand words to say.)

Presently she began again. "I wonder if I shall fall right *through* the earth! How funny it'll seem to come out among the people that walk with their heads downwards! The Antipathies, I think –" (she was rather glad there *was* no one listening, this time, as it didn't sound at all the right word) "– but I shall have to ask them what the name of the country is, you know. Please, Ma'am, is this New Zealand? Or Australia?" (and she tried to curtsey as she spoke – fancy *curtseying* as you're falling through the air! Do you think she could manage it?) "And what an ignorant little girl she'll think me for asking! No, it'll never do to ask: perhaps I shall see it written up somewhere."

Down, down, down. There was nothing else to do, so Alice soon began talking again. "Dinah'll miss me very much to-night, I should think!" (Dinah was the cat.) "I hope they'll remember her saucer of milk at tea-time. Dinah, my dear! I wish you were down here with me! There are no mice in the air, I'm afraid, but you might catch a bat, and that's very like a mouse, you know. But do cats eat bats, I wonder?"

And here Alice began to get rather sleepy, and went on saying to herself, in a dreamy sort of way, "Do cats eat bats? Do cats eat bats?" and sometimes, "Do bats eat cats?", for, you see, as she couldn't answer either question, it didn't much matter which way she put it. She felt that she was dozing off, and had just begun to dream that she was walking hand in hand with Dinah, and was saying to her very earnestly, "Now, Dinah, tell me the truth: did you ever eat a bat?", when suddenly, thump! thump! down she came upon a heap of sticks and dry leaves, and the fall was over.

Alice was not a bit hurt, and she jumped up on to her feet in a moment: she looked up, but it was all dark overhead: before her was another long passage, and the White Rabbit was still in sight, hurrying down it. There was not a moment to be lost: away went Alice like the wind, and was just in time to hear it say, as it turned a corner, "Oh my ears and whiskers, how late it's getting!" She was close behind it when she turned the corner, but the Rabbit was no longer to be seen: she found herself in a long, low hall, which was lit up by a row of lamps hanging from the roof.

There were doors all round the hall, but they were all locked; and when Alice had been all the way down one side and up the other trying every door, she walked sadly down the middle, wondering how she was ever to get out again.

Suddenly she came upon a little three-legged table, all made of solid glass: there was nothing on it but a tiny golden key, and Alice's first idea was that this might belong to one of the doors of the hall; but, alas! either the locks were too large, or the key was too small, but at any rate it would not open any of them. However, on the second time round, she came upon a low curtain she had noticed before, and behind it was

a little door about fifteen inches high: she tried the little golden key in the lock, and to her great delight it fitted.

Alice opened the door and found that it led into a small passage, not much larger than a rat-hole: she knelt down and looked along the passage into the loveliest garden you ever saw. How she longed to get out of that dark hall, and wander about among those beds of bright flowers and those cool fountains, but she could not even get her head through the doorway: "and even if my head *would* go through," thought poor Alice, "it would be of very little use without my shoulders. Oh, how I wish I could shut up like a telescope! I think I could, if I only knew how to begin." For, you see, so many out-of-the-way things had happened lately, that Alice had begun to think that very few things indeed were really impossible.

There seemed to be no use in waiting by the little door, so she went back to the table, half hoping she might find another key on it, or at any rate a book of rules for shutting people up like telescopes: this time she found a little bottle on it ("which certainly was not here before," said Alice), and tied round the neck of the bottle was a paper label, with the words "DRINK ME" beautifully printed on it in large letters.

It was all very well to say "Drink me," but the wise little Alice was not going to do *that* in a hurry. "No, I'll look first," she said, "and see whether it's marked '*poison*' or not"; for she had read several nice little stories about children who had got burnt, and eaten up by wild beasts, and other unpleasant things, all because they *would* not remember the simple rules their friends had taught them: such as, that a red-hot poker will burn you if you hold it too long; and that, if you cut your finger *very* deeply with a knife, it usually bleeds; and she had never forgotten that, if you drink much from a bottle marked "poison", it is almost certain to disagree with you, sooner or later.

However, this bottle was *not* marked "poison", so Alice ventured to taste it, and finding it very nice (it had, in fact, a sort of mixed flavour of cherry-tart, custard, pineapple, roast turkey, toffy, and hot buttered toast), she very soon finished it off.

* * * * *

* * * *

* * * * *

"What a curious feeling!" said Alice. "I must be shutting up like a telescope!"

And so it was indeed: she was now only ten inches high, and her face brightened up at the thought that she was now the right size for going through the little door into that lovely garden. First, however, she waited for a few minutes to see if she was going to shrink any further: she felt a little nervous about this; "for it might end, you know," said Alice to herself, "in my going out altogether, like a candle. I wonder what I should be like then?" And she tried to fancy what the flame of a candle looks like after the candle is blown out, for she could not remember ever having seen such a thing.

After a while, finding that nothing more happened, she decided on going into the garden at once; but, alas for poor Alice! when she got to the door, she found she had forgotten the little golden key, and when she went back to the table for it, she found she could not possibly reach it: she could see it quite plainly through the glass and she tried her best to climb up one of the legs of the table, but it was too slippery; and when she had tired herself out with trying, the poor little thing sat down and cried.

"Come, there's no use in crying like that!" said Alice to herself, rather sharply. "I advise you to leave off this minute!" She generally gave herself very good advice (though she very seldom followed it), and sometimes she scolded herself so severely as to bring tears into her eyes; and once she remembered trying to box her own ears for having cheated herself in a game of croquet she was playing against herself, for this curious child was very fond of pretending to be two people. "But it's no use now," thought poor Alice, "to pretend to be two people! Why, there's hardly enough of me left to make *one* respectable person!"

Soon her eye fell on a little glass box that was lying under the table: she opened it, and found in it a very small cake, on which the words "EAT ME" were beautifully marked in currants. "Well I'll eat it," said Alice, "and if it makes me grow larger, I can reach the key; and if it makes me grow smaller, I can creep under the door: so either way I'll get into the garden, and I don't care which happens!"

She ate a little bit, and said anxiously to herself, "Which way? Which way?", holding her hand on the top of her head to feel which way it was growing; and she was quite surprised to find that she remained the same size. To be sure, this is what generally happens when one eats cake; but Alice had got so much into the way of expecting nothing but out-of-the-way things to happen, that it seemed quite dull and stupid for life to go on in the common way.

So she set to work, and very soon finished off the cake.

* * * * *

* * * *

* * * * *

CHAPTER 2

The Pool of Tears

"CURIOUSER and curiouser!" cried Alice (she was so much surprised, that for the moment she quite forgot how to speak good English). "Now I'm opening out like the largest telescope that ever was! Goodbye, feet!" (for when she looked down at her feet, they seemed to be almost out of sight, they were getting so far off). "Oh, my poor little feet, I wonder who will put on your shoes and stockings for you now, dears? I'm sure I sha'n't be able! I shall be a great deal too far off to trouble myself about you: you must manage the best way you can – but I must be kind to them," thought Alice, "or perhaps they wo'n't walk the way I want to go! Let me see. I'll give them a new pair of boots every Christmas."

And she went on planning to herself how she would manage it. "They must go by the carrier," she thought; "and how funny it'll seem, sending presents to one's own feet! And how odd the directions will look!

> *Alice's Right Foot, Esq.*
> *Hearthrug,*
> *near the Fender*
> *(with Alice's love).*

Oh dear, what nonsense I'm talking!"

Just at this moment her head struck against the roof of the hall: in fact she was now rather more than nine feet high, and she at once took up the little golden key and hurried off to the garden door.

Poor Alice! It was as much as she could do, lying down on one side, to look through into the garden with one eye; but to get through was more hopeless than ever: she sat down and began to cry again.

"You ought to be ashamed of yourself," said Alice, "a great girl like you" (she might well say this), "to go on crying in this way! Stop this moment, I tell you!" But she went on all the same, shedding gallons of

tears, until there was a large pool all round her, and four inches deep and reaching half down the hall.

After a time she heard a little pattering of feet in the distance, and she hastily dried her eyes to see what was coming. It was the White Rabbit returning, splendidly dressed, with a pair of white kid-gloves in one hand and a large fan in the other: he came trotting along in a great hurry, muttering to himself as he came, "Oh! the Duchess, the Duchess! Oh! *Wo'n't* she be savage if I've kept her waiting!" Alice felt so desperate that she was ready to ask help of any one: so, when the Rabbit came near her, she began, in a low, timid voice, "If you please, Sir——" The Rabbit started violently, dropped the white kid-gloves and the fan, and skurried away into the darkness as hard as he could go.

Alice took up the fan and gloves, and, as the hall was very hot, she kept fanning herself all the time she went on talking. "Dear, dear! How queer everything is today! And yesterday things went on just as usual. I wonder if I've been changed in the night? Let me think: *was* I the same when I got up this morning? I almost think I can remember feeling a little different. But if I'm not the same, the next question is, 'Who in the world am I?' Ah, *that's* the great puzzle!" And she began thinking over all the children she knew that were of the same age as herself, to see if she could have been changed for any of them.

"I'm sure I'm not Ada," she said, "for her hair goes in such long ringlets, and mine doesn't go in ringlets at all; and I'm sure I ca'n't be Mabel, for I know all sorts of things, and she, oh! she knows such a very little! Besides, *she's* she, and *I'm* I, and – oh dear, how puzzling it all is! I'll try if I know all the things I used to know. Let me see: four times five is twelve, and four times six is thirteen, and four times seven is – oh dear! I shall never get to twenty at that rate! However, the Multiplication Table doesn't signify: let's try Geography. London is the capital of Paris, and Paris is the capital of Rome, and Rome – no, *that's* all wrong, I'm certain! I must have been changed for Mabel! I'll try and say '*How doth the little*——'," and she crossed her hands on her lap as if she were saying lessons, and began to repeat it, but her voice sounded hoarse and strange, and the words did not come the same as they used to do:—

> *How doth the little crocodile*
> *Improve his shining tail,*
> *And pour the waters of the Nile*
> *On every golden scale!*
>
> *How cheerfully he seems to grin,*
> *And neatly spreads his claws,*
> *And welcomes little fishes in,*
> *With gently smiling jaws!*

"I'm sure those are not the right words," said poor Alice, and her eyes filled with tears again as she went on. "I must be Mabel, after all, and I shall have to go and live in that poky little house, and have next to no toys to play with, and oh, ever so many lessons to learn! No, I've made up my mind about it: if I'm Mabel, I'll stay down here! It'll be no use their putting their heads down and saying 'Come up again, dear!' I shall only look up and say 'Who am I then? Tell me that first, and then, if I like being that person, I'll come up: if not, I'll stay down here till I'm somebody else' – but, oh dear!" cried Alice, with a sudden burst of tears, "I do wish they *would* put their heads down! I am so *very* tired of being all alone here!"

As she said this she looked down at her hands, and was surprised to see that she had put on one of the Rabbit's little white kid-gloves while she was talking. "How *can* I have done that?" she thought. "I must be growing small again." She got up and went to the table to measure herself by it, and found that, as nearly as she could guess, she was now about two feet high, and was going on shrinking rapidly: she soon found out that the cause of this was the fan she was holding, and she dropped it hastily, just in time to save herself from shrinking away altogether.

"That *was* a narrow escape!" said Alice, a good deal frightened at the sudden change, but very glad to find herself still in existence. "And now for the garden!" And she ran with all speed back to the little door; but, alas! the little door was shut again, and the little golden key was lying on the glass table as before, "and things are worse than ever," thought the poor child, "for I never was so small as this before, never! And I declare it's too bad, that it is!"

As she said these words her foot slipped, and in another moment, splash! she was up to her chin in salt water. Her first idea was that she had somehow fallen into the sea, "and in that case I can go back by railway," she said to herself. (Alice had been to the seaside once in her life, and had come to the general conclusion, that wherever you go to on the English coast you find a number of bathing machines in the sea, some children digging in the sand with wooden spades, then a row of lodging houses, and behind them a railway-station.) However, she soon made out that she was in the pool of tears which she had wept when she was nine feet high.

"I wish I hadn't cried so much!" said Alice, as she swam about, trying to find her way out. "I shall be punished for it now, I suppose, by being drowned in my own tears! That *will* be a queer thing, to be sure! However, everything is queer to-day."

Just then she heard something splashing about in the pool a little way off, and she swam nearer to make out what it was: at first she thought it must be a walrus or hippopotamus, but then she remembered how small she was now, and she soon made out that it was only a mouse that had slipped in like herself.

"Would it be of any use now," thought Alice, "to speak to this mouse? Everything is so out-of-the-way down here, that I should think very likely it can talk: at any rate, there's no harm in trying." So she

began: "O Mouse, do you know the way out of this pool? I am very tired of swimming about here, O Mouse!" (Alice thought this must be the right way of speaking to a mouse: she had never done such a thing before, but she remembered having seen in her brother's Latin Grammar, "A mouse – of a mouse – to a mouse – a mouse – O mouse") The mouse looked at her rather inquisitively, and seemed to her to wink with one of its little eyes, but it said nothing.

"Perhaps it doesn't understand English," thought Alice. "I daresay it's a French mouse, come over with William the Conqueror." (For, with all her knowledge of history, Alice had no clear notion how long ago anything had happened.) So she began again: "Où est ma chatte?" which was the first sentence in her French lesson-book. The Mouse gave a sudden leap out of the water, and seemed to quiver all over with fright. "Oh, I beg your pardon!" cried Alice hastily, afraid that she had hurt the poor animal's feelings. "I quite forgot you didn't like cats."

"Not like cats!" cried the Mouse, in a shrill, passionate voice. "Would *you* like cats, if you were me?"

"Well, perhaps not," said Alice in a soothing tone: "don't be angry about it. And yet I wish I could show you our cat Dinah. I think you'd take a fancy to cats if you could only see her. She is such a dear quiet

thing," Alice went on half to herself, as she swam lazily about in the pool, "and she sits purring so nicely by the fire, licking her paws and washing her face – and she is such a nice soft thing to nurse – and she's such a capital one for catching mice—— oh, I beg your pardon!" cried Alice again, for this time the Mouse was bristling all over, and she felt certain it must be really offended. "We wo'n't talk about her any more if you'd rather not."

"We, indeed!" cried the Mouse, who was trembling down to the end of its tail. "As if *I* would talk on such a subject! Our family always *hated* cats: nasty, low, vulgar things! Don't let me hear the name again!"

"I won't indeed!" said Alice, in a great hurry to change the subject of conversation "are you – are you fond – of – of dogs?" The Mouse did not answer, so Alice went on eagerly: "There is such a nice little dog near our house I should like to show you! A little bright-eyed terrier, you know, with oh, such long curly brown hair! And it'll fetch things when you throw them, and it'll sit up and beg for its dinner, and all sorts of things – I ca'n't remember half of them – and it belongs to a farmer, you know, and he says it's so useful, it's worth a hundred pounds! He says it kills all the rats and – oh dear!" cried Alice in a sorrowful tone, "I'm afraid I've offended it again!" For the Mouse was swimming away from her as hard as it could go, and making quite a commotion in the pool as it went. So she called softly after it. "Mouse dear! Do come back again, and we wo'n't talk about cats or dogs either, if you don't like them!" When the Mouse heard this, it turned round and swam slowly back to her: its face was quite pale (with passion, Alice thought), and it said in a low trembling voice, "Let us get to the shore, and then I'll tell you my history, and you'll understand why it is I hate cats and dogs."

It was high time to go, for the pool was getting quite crowded with the birds and animals that had fallen into it: there was a Duck and a Dodo, a Lory and an Eaglet, and several other curious creatures. Alice led the way, and the whole party swam to the shore.

CHAPTER 3

A Caucus-race and a Long Tale

THEY were indeed a queer-looking party that assembled on the bank – the birds with draggled feathers, the animals with their fur clinging close to them, and all dripping wet, cross, and uncomfortable.

The first question of course was, how to get dry again: they had a consultation about this, and after a few minutes it seemed quite natural to Alice to find herself talking familiarly with them, as if she had known them all her life. Indeed, she had quite a long argument with the Lory, who at last turned sulky, and would only say "I am older than you, and must know better." And this Alice would not allow without knowing how old it was, and, as the Lory positively refused to tell its age, there was no more to be said.

At last the Mouse, who seemed to be a person of some authority among them, called out "Sit down, all of you, and listen to me! *I'll* soon make you dry enough!" They all sat down at once in a large ring, with the Mouse in the middle. Alice kept her eyes anxiously fixed on it, for she felt sure she would catch a bad cold if she did not get dry very soon.

"Ahem!" said the Mouse with an important air. "Are you all ready? This is the driest thing I know. Silence all round, if you please! "William the Conqueror, whose cause was favoured by the pope, was soon submitted to by the English, who wanted leaders, and had been of late much accustomed to usurpation and conquest. Edwin and Morcar, the earls of Mercia and Northumbria——'"

"Ugh!" said Lory, with a shiver.

"I beg your pardon!" said the Mouse, frowning, but very politely. "Did you speak?"

"Not I!" said the Lory hastily.

"I thought you did," said the Mouse. "I proceed. 'Edwin and Morcar, the earls of Mercia and Northumbria, declared for him; and even Stigand, the patriotic archbishop of Canterbury, found it advisable——'"

"Found *what*?" said the Duck.

"Found *it*," the mouse replied rather crossly: "of course you know what 'it' means."

"I know what 'it' means well enough, when *I* find a thing," said the Duck: "it's generally a frog or a worm. The question is, what did the archbishop find?"

The Mouse did not notice this question, but hurriedly went on, "'found it advisable to go with Edgar Atheling to meet William and offer him the crown. William's conduct at first was moderate. But the insolence of his Normans——' How are you getting on now, my dear?" it continued, turning to Alice as it spoke.

"As wet as ever," said Alice in a melancholy tone: "it doesn't seem to dry me at all."

"In that case," said the Dodo solemnly, rising to its feet, "I move that the meeting adjourn, for the immediate adoption of more energetic remedies——"

"Speak English!" said the Eaglet. "I don't know the meaning of half those long words, and, what's more, I don't believe you do either!" And the Eaglet bent down its head to hide a smile: some of the other birds tittered audibly.

"What I was going to say," said the Dodo in an offended tone, "was, that the best thing to get us dry would be a Caucus-race."

"What *is* a Caucus-race?" said Alice; not that she much wanted to know, but the Dodo had paused as if it thought that *somebody* ought to speak, and no one else seemed inclined to say anything.

"Why," said the Dodo, "the best way to explain it is to do it." (And, as you might like to try the thing yourself some winter day, I will tell you how the Dodo managed it.)

First it marked out a race-course, in a sort of circle ("the exact shape doesn't matter," it said), and then all the party were placed along the course, here and there. There was no "One, two, three, and away," but they began running when they liked, and left off when they liked, so that it was not easy to know when the race was over. However, when they had been running half an hour or so, and were quite dry again, the Dodo suddenly called out "The race is over!" and they all crowded round it, panting, and asking "But who has won?"

This question the Dodo could not answer without a great deal of thought, and it stood for a long time with one finger pressed upon its forehead (the position in which you usually see Shakespeare, in the pictures of him), while the rest waited in silence. At last the Dodo said "*Everyone* has won, and *all* must have prizes."

"But who is to give the prizes?" quite a chorus of voices asked.

"Why, *she* of course," said the Dodo, pointing to Alice with one finger; and the whole party at once crowded round her, calling out in a confused way, "Prizes! Prizes!"

Alice had no idea what to do, and in despair she put her hand in her pocket, and pulled out a box of comfits (luckily the salt water had not got into it), and handed them round as prizes. There was exactly one apiece all round.

"But she must have a prize herself, you know," said the Mouse.

"Of course," the Dodo replied very gravely. "What else have you got in your pocket?" it went on, turning to Alice.

"Only a thimble," said Alice sadly.

"Hand it over here," said the Dodo.

Then they all crowded round her once more, while the Dodo solemnly presented the thimble, saying, "We beg your acceptance of this elegant thimble"; and, when it had finished this short speech, they all cheered.

Alice thought the whole thing very absurd, but they all looked so grave that she did not dare to laugh; and, as she could not think of anything to say, she simply bowed, and took the thimble, looking as solemn as she could.

The next thing was to eat the comfits: this caused some noise and confusion, as the large birds complained that they could not taste theirs, and the small ones choked and had to be patted on the back. However, it was over at last, and they sat down again in a ring, and begged the Mouse to tell them something more.

"You promised to tell me your history, you know," said Alice, "and why it is you hate – C and D," she added in a whisper, half afraid that it would be offended again.

"Mine is a long and sad tale!" said the Mouse turning to Alice, and sighing.

"It *is* a long tail, certainly," said Alice, looking down with wonder at the Mouse's tail; "but why do you call it sad?" And she kept on puzzling about it while the Mouse was speaking, so that her idea of the tale was something like this:—

"Fury said to
a mouse, That
he met in the
house, 'Let
us both go
to law: *I*
will prose-
cute *you*.—
Come, I'll
take no de-
nial: We
must have
the trial;
For really
this morn-
ing I've
nothing
to do.'
Said the
mouse to
the cur.
'Such a
trial, dear
Sir. With
no jury
or judge,
would
be wast-
ing our
breath.'
'I'll be
judge.
I'll be
jury,'
said
cun-
ning
old
Fury:
'I'll
try
the
whole
cause,
and
con-
demn
you to
death.'"

"You are not attending!" said the Mouse to Alice severely. "What are you thinking of?"

"I beg your pardon," said Alice very humbly; "you had got to the fifth bend, I think?"

"I had *not*!" cried the Mouse, sharply and very angrily.

"A knot!" said Alice, always ready to make herself useful, and looking anxiously about her. "Oh, do let me help to undo it!"

"I shall do nothing of the sort," said the Mouse, getting up and walking away. "You insult me by talking such nonsense!"

"I didn't mean it!" pleaded poor Alice. "But you're so easily offended, you know!"

The Mouse only growled in reply.

"Please come back and finish your story!" Alice called after it. And the others all joined in chorus. "Yes, please do!" But the Mouse only shook its head impatiently and walked a little quicker.

"What a pity it wouldn't stay!" sighed the Lory, as soon as it was quite out of sight. And an old Crab took the opportunity of saying to her daughter "Ah, my dear! Let this be a lesson to you never to lose *your* temper!" "Hold your tongue, Ma!" said the young Crab, a little snappishly. "You're enough to try the patience of an oyster!"

"I wish I had our Dinah here, I know I do!" said Alice aloud, addressing nobody in particular. "*She'd* soon fetch it back!"

"And who is Dinah, if I might venture to ask the question?" said the Lory.

Alice replied eagerly, for she was always ready to talk about her pet: "Dinah's our cat. And she's such a capital one for catching mice, you ca'n't think! And oh, I wish you could see her after the birds! Why, she'll eat a little bird as soon as look at it!"

The speech caused a remarkable sensation among the party. Some of the birds hurried off at once: one old Magpie began wrapping itself up very carefully, remarking "I really must be getting home: the night-air doesn't suit my throat!" and a Canary called out in a trembling voice to its children "Come away, my dears! It's high time you were all in bed!" On various pretexts they all moved off, and Alice was soon left alone.

"I wish I hadn't mentioned Dinah!" she said to herself in a melancholy tone. "Nobody seems to like her, down here, and I'm sure she's the best cat in the world! Oh, my dear Dinah! I wonder if I shall ever see you any more!" And here poor Alice began to cry again, for she felt very lonely and low-spirited. In a little while, however, she again heard a little pattering of footsteps in the distance, and she looked up eagerly, half hoping that the Mouse had changed his mind, and was coming back to finish his story.

CHAPTER 4

The Rabbit Sends in a Little Bill

IT was the White Rabbit, trotting slowly back again, and looking anxiously about as it went, as if it had lost something; and she heard it muttering to itself, "The Duchess! The Duchess! Oh my dear paws! Oh my fur and whiskers! She'll get me executed, as sure as ferrets are ferrets! Where *can* I have dropped them, I wonder?" Alice guessed in a moment that it was looking for the fan and the pair of white kid-gloves, and she very good-naturedly began hunting about for them, but they were nowhere to be seen – everything seemed to have changed since her swim in the pool, and the great hall, with the glass table and the little door, had vanished completely.

Very soon the Rabbit noticed Alice, as she went hunting about, and called out to her in an angry tone, "Why, Mary Ann, what *are* you doing out here? Run home this moment, and fetch me a pair of gloves and a fan! Quick, now," and Alice was so much frightened that she ran off at once in the direction it pointed to, without trying to explain the mistake that it had made.

"He took me for his housemaid," she said to herself as she ran. "How surprised he'll be when he finds out who I am! But I'd better take him his fan and gloves – that is, if I can find them." As she said this she came upon a neat little house, on the door of which was a bright brass plate with the name "W. RABBIT" engraved upon it. She went in without knocking, and hurried up stairs, in great fear lest she should meet the real Mary Ann, and be turned out of the house before she had found the fan and gloves.

"How queer it seems," Alice said to herself, "to be going messages for a rabbit! I suppose Dinah'll be sending me on messages next!" And she began fancying the sort of thing that would happen: "'Miss Alice! Come here directly, and get ready for your walk!' 'Coming in a minute, nurse! But I've got to watch this mouse-hole till Dinah comes back, and see that the mouse doesn't get out.' Only I don't think," Alice went on, "that they'd let Dinah stop in the house if it began ordering people about like that!"

By this time she had found her way into a tidy little room with a table in the window, and on it (as she had hoped) a fan and two or three pairs of tiny white kid-gloves: she took up the fan and a pair of the gloves, and was just going to leave the room, when her eyes fell upon a little bottle that stood near the looking-glass. There was no label this time with the words "DRINK ME," but nevertheless she uncorked it and put it to her lips. "I know *something* interesting is sure to happen," she said to herself, "whenever I eat or drink anything: so I'll just see what this bottle does. I do hope it'll make me grow large again, for really I'm quite tired of being such a tiny little thing!"

It did so indeed, and much sooner than she had expected: before she had drunk half the bottle she found her head pressing against the ceiling, and had to stoop to save her neck from being broken. She hastily put down the bottle. saying to herself "That's quite enough – I hope I sha'n't grow any more – As it is, I ca'n't get out at the door – I do wish I hadn't drunk quite so much!"

Alas! it was too late to wish that! She went on growing, and growing, and very soon had to kneel down on the floor: in another minute there was not even room for this, and she tried the effect of lying down with one elbow against the door, and the other arm curled round her head. Still she went on growing, and, as a last resource, she put one arm out of the window, and one foot up the chimney, and said to herself "Now I can do no more, whatever happens. What *will* become of me?"

Luckily for Alice, the little magic bottle had now had its full effect, and she grew no larger: still it was very uncomfortable, and, as there seemed to be no sort of chance of her ever getting out of the room again, no wonder she felt unhappy.

"It was much pleasanter at home," thought poor Alice, "when one wasn't always growing larger and smaller, and being ordered about by mice and rabbits. I almost wish I hadn't gone down that rabbit-hole – and yet – and yet – it's curious, you know, this sort of life! I do wonder what *can* have happened to me! When I used to read fairy-tales, I fancied that kind of thing never happened, and now here I am in the middle of one! There ought to be a book written about me, that there ought! And when I grow up, I'll write one – but I'm grown up now," she added in a sorrowful tone: "at least there's no room to grow up any more *here*."

"But then," thought Alice, "shall I *never* get any older than I am now? That'll be a comfort, one way – never to be an old woman – but then – always to have lessons to learn! Oh, I shouldn't like *that*!"

"Oh, you foolish Alice!" she answered herself. "How can you learn lessons in here? Why, there's hardly room for *you*, and no room at all for any lesson-books!"

And so she went on, taking first one side and then the other. and making quite a conversation of it altogether; but after a few minutes she heard a voice outside, and stopped to listen.

"Mary Ann! Mary Ann!" said the voice. "Fetch me my gloves this moment!" Then came a little pattering of feet on the stairs. Alice knew it was the Rabbit coming to look for her, and she trembled till she shook the house, quite forgetting that she was now about a thousand times as large as the Rabbit, and had no reason to be afraid of it.

Presently the Rabbit came up to the door, and tried to open it; but, as the door opened inwards, and Alice's elbow was pressed hard against it, that attempt proved a failure. Alice heard it say to itself "Then I'll go round and get in at the window."

"*That* you wo'n't!" thought Alice, and, after waiting till she fancied

she heard the Rabbit just under the window, she suddenly spread out her hand, and made a snatch in the air. She did not get hold of anything, but she heard a little shriek and a fall, and a crash of broken glass, from which she concluded that it was just possible it had fallen into a cucumber-frame, or something of the sort.

Next came an angry voice – the Rabbit's – "Pat! Pat! Where are you?" And then a voice she had never heard before, "Sure then I'm here! Digging for apples, yer honour!"

"Digging for apples, indeed!" said the Rabbit angrily. "Here! Come and help me out of *this*!" (Sounds of more broken glass.)

"Now tell me, Pat, what's that in the window?"

"Sure, it's an arm, yer honour!" (He pronounced it "arrum.")

"An arm, you goose! Who ever saw one that size? Why, it fills the whole window!"

"Sure, it does, yer honour: but it's an arm for all that."

"Well, it's got no business there, at any rate: go and take it away!"

There was a long silence after this, and Alice could only hear whispers now and then; such as, "Sure, I don't like it, yer honour, at all, at all!" "Do as I tell you, you coward!" and at last she spread out her hand again, and made another snatch in the air. This time there were *two* little shrieks, and more sounds of broken glass. "What a number of cucumber-frames there must be!" thought Alice. "I wonder what they'll do next! As for pulling me out of the window, I only wish they *could*! I'm sure *I* don't want to stay in here any longer!"

She waited for some time without hearing anything more: at last came a rumbling of little cart-wheels, and the sound of a good many voices all talking together: she made out the words: "Where's the other ladder? – Why, I hadn't to bring but one. Bill's got the other – Bill! Fetch it here, lad! – Here, put 'em up at this corner – No, tie 'em together first – they don't reach half high enough yet – Oh! they'll do well enough. Don't be particular – Here, Bill! Catch hold of this rope – Will the roof bear? – Mind that loose slate – Oh, it's coming down! Heads below!" (a loud crash) – "Now, who did that? – It was Bill, I fancy – Who's to go down the chimney? – Nay, *I* sha'n't! *You* do it! – *That* I won't, then! – Bill's got to go down – Here, Bill! The master says you've got to go down the chimney!"

"Oh! So Bill's got to come down the chimney, has he?" said Alice to herself. "Why, they seem to put everything upon Bill! I wouldn't be in Bill's place for a good deal: this fireplace is narrow, to be sure; but I *think* I can kick a little!"

She drew her foot as far down the chimney as she could, and waited till she heard a little animal (she couldn't guess of what sort it was) scratching and scrambling about in the chimney close above her: then saying to herself "This is Bill," she gave one sharp kick, and waited to see what would happen next.

The first thing she heard was a general chorus of "There goes Bill!" then the Rabbit's silence, and then another confusion of voices – "Hold up his head – Brandy now – Don't choke him – How was it, old fellow? What happened to you? Tell us all about it!"

At last came a little feeble, squeaking voice ("That's Bill," thought Alice), "Well, I hardly know – No more, thank ye; I'm better now – but

I'm a deal too flustered to tell you – all I know is, something comes at me like a Jack-in-the-box, and up I goes like a sky-rocket!"

"So you did, old fellow!" said the others.

"We must burn the house down!" said the Rabbit's voice. And Alice called out as loud as she could, "If you do I'll set Dinah at you!"

There was a dead silence instantly, and Alice thought to herself "I wonder what they *will* do next! If they had any sense, they'd take the roof off." After a minute or two they began moving about again, and Alice heard the Rabbit say, "A barrowful will do, to begin with."

"A barrowful of *what*?" thought Alice. But she had not long to doubt, for the next moment a shower of little pebbles came rattling in at the window, and some of them hit her in the face. "I'll put a stop to this," she said to herself, and shouted out, "You'd better not do that again!" which produced another dead silence.

Alice notices with some surprise that the pebbles were all turning into little cakes as they lay on the floor, and a bright idea came into her head. "If I eat one of these cakes," she thought, "it's sure to make *some* change in my size; and, as it ca'n't possibly make me larger, it must make me smaller, I suppose."

So she swallowed one of the cakes, and was delighted to find that she began shrinking directly. As soon as she was small enough to get through the door, she ran out of the house, and found quite a crowd of little animals and birds waiting outside. The poor little Lizard, Bill, was in the middle, being held up by two guinea-pigs, who were giving it something out of a bottle. They all made a rush at Alice the moment she appeared; but she ran off as hard as she could, and soon found herself safe in a thick wood.

"The first thing I've got to do," said Alice to herself, as she wandered about in the wood, "is to grow to my right size again; and the second thing is to find my way into that lovely garden. I think that will be the best plan."

It sounded an excellent plan, no doubt, and very neatly and simply arranged; the only difficulty was, that she had not the smallest idea how to set about it; and, while she was peering about anxiously among the trees, a little sharp bark just over her head made her look up in a great hurry.

An enormous puppy was looking down at her with large round eyes, and feebly stretching out one paw, trying to touch her. "Poor little thing!" said Alice, in a coaxing tone, and she tried hard to whistle to it; but she was terribly frightened all the time at the thought that it might

be hungry, in which case it would be very likely to eat her up in spite of all her coaxing.

Hardly knowing what she did, she picked up a little bit of stick, and held it out to the puppy: whereupon the puppy jumped into the air off all its feet at once, with a yelp of delight, and rushed at the stick, and made believe to worry it: then Alice dodged behind a great thistle, to keep herself from being run over; and, the moment she appeared on the other side, the puppy made another rush at the stick, and tumbled head over heels in its hurry to get hold of it: then Alice, thinking it was very like having a game of play with a cart-horse, and expecting every moment to be trampled under its feet, ran round the thistle again: then the puppy began a series of short charges at the stick, running a very little way forwards each time and a long way back, and barking hoarsely all the while, till at last it sat down a good way off, panting, with its tongue hanging out of its mouth, and its great eyes half shut.

This seemed to Alice a good opportunity for making her escape: so she set off at once, and ran till she was quite tired and out of breath, and till the puppy's bark sounded quite faint in the distance.

"And yet what a dear little puppy it was!" said Alice, as she leant against a buttercup to rest herself, and fanned herself with one of the leaves, "I should have liked teaching it tricks very much, if – if I'd only been the right size to do it! Oh dear! I'd nearly forgotten that I've got to grow up again! Let me see – how *is* it to be managed? I suppose I ought to eat or drink something or other; but the great question is, 'What?'"

The great question certainly was, "What?" Alice looked all round her at the flowers and the blades of grass, but she could not see anything that looked like the right thing to eat or drink under the circumstances. There was a large mushroom growing near her, about the same height as herself; and, when she had looked under it, and on both sides of it, and behind it, it occurred to her that she might as well look and see what was on top of it.

She stretched herself up on tiptoe, and peeped over the edge of the mushroom, and her eyes immediately met those of a large blue caterpillar, that was sitting on the top with its arms folded, quietly smoking a long hookah, and taking not the smallest notice of her or of anything else.

CHAPTER 5

Advice from a Caterpillar

THE Caterpillar and Alice looked at each other for some time in silence: at last the Caterpillar took the hookah out of its mouth, and addressed her in a languid, sleepy voice.

"Who are *you*?" said the Caterpillar.

This was not an encouraging opening for a conversation. Alice replied, rather shyly, "I – I hardly know, Sir, just at present – at least I know who I *was* was when I got up this morning, but I think I must have been changed several times since then."

"What do you mean by that?" said the Caterpillar sternly. "Explain yourself!"

"I ca'n't explain *myself*, I'm afraid, Sir," said Alice, "because I'm not myself, you see."

"I don't see," said the Caterpillar.

"I'm afraid I ca'n't put it more clearly," Alice replied very politely, "for I ca'n't understand it myself to begin with; and being so many different sizes in a day is very confusing."

"It isn't," said the Caterpillar.

"Well, perhaps you haven't found it so yet," said Alice; "but when you have to turn into a chrysalis – you will some day, you know – and then after that into a butterfly, I should think you'll feel it a little queer, wo'n't you?"

"Not a bit," said the Caterpillar.

"Well, perhaps *your* feelings may be different," said Alice; "all I know is, it would feel very queer to *me*."

"You!" said the Caterpillar contemptuously. "Who are *you*?"

Which brought them back again to the beginning of the conversation. Alice felt a little irritated at the Caterpillar's making such *very* short remarks, and she drew herself up and said, very gravely, "I think you ought to tell me who *you* are, first."

"Why?" said the Caterpillar.

Here was another puzzling question; and, as Alice could not think of any good reason, and the Caterpillar seemed to be in a *very* unpleasant state of mind, she turned away.

"Come back!" the Caterpillar called after her. "I've something important to say!"

This sounded promising, certainly. Alice turned and came back again.

"Keep your temper," said the Caterpillar.

"Is that all?" said Alice, swallowing down her anger as well as she could.

"No," said the Caterpillar.

Alice thought she might as well wait, as she had nothing else to do, and perhaps after all it might tell her something worth hearing. For some minutes it puffed away without speaking; but at last it unfolded its arms, took the hookah out of its mouth again, and said "So you think you're changed, do you?"

"I'm afraid I am, Sir," said Alice. "I ca'n't remember things as I used – and I don't keep the same size for ten minutes together!"

"Ca'n't remember *what* things?" said the Caterpillar.

"Well, I've tried to say '*How doth the little busy bee*,' but it all came different!" Alice replied in a very melancholy voice.

"Repeat '*You are old, Father William*,'" said the Caterpillar.

Alice folded her hands, and began:—

"You are old, Father William," the young man said,
  "And your hair has become very white;
And yet you incessantly stand on your head –
  Do you think, at your age, it is right?"

"In my youth," Father William replied to his son,
  "I feared it might injure the brain;
But, now that I'm perfectly sure I have none,
  Why, I do it again and again."

"You are old," said the youth, "as I mentioned before,
  And have grown most uncommonly fat;
Yet you turned a back-somersault in at the door –
  Pray, what is the reason of that?"

"In my youth," said the sage, as he shook his grey locks,
  "I kept all my limbs very supple
By the use of this ointment – one shilling the box –
  Allow me to sell you a couple?"

"You are old," said the youth, "and your jaws are too weak
  For anything tougher than suet;
Yet you finished the goose, with the bones and the beak –
  Pray, how did you manage to do it?"

"In my youth," said his father, "I took to the law
  And argued each case with my wife;
And the muscular strength, which it gave to my jaw,
  Has lasted the rest of my life."

"You are old," said the youth, "one would hardly suppose
    That your eye was as steady as ever;
Yet you balanced an eel on the end of your nose –
    What made you so awfully clever?"

"I have answered three questions, and that is enough,"
    Said his father; "don't give yourself airs!
Do you think I can listen all day to such stuff?
    Be off, or I'll kick you down stairs!"

"That is not said right," said the Caterpillar.

"Not *quite* right, I'm afraid," said Alice, timidly: "Some of the words have got altered."

"It is wrong from beginning to end," said the Caterpillar decidedly, and there was silence for some minutes.

The Caterpillar was the first to speak.

"What size do you want to be?" it asked.

"Oh, I'm not particular as to size," Alice hastily replied; "only one doesn't like changing so often, you know."

"I *don't* know," said the Caterpillar.

Alice said nothing: she had never been so much contradicted in all her life before, and she felt that she was losing her temper.

"Are you content now?" said the Caterpillar.

"Well, I should like to be a *little* larger, Sir, if you wouldn't mind," said Alice: "three inches is such a wretched height to be."

"It is a very good height indeed!" said the Caterpillar angrily, rearing itself upright as it spoke (it was exactly three inches high).

"But I'm not used to it!" pleaded poor Alice in a piteous tone. And she thought to herself, "I wish the creatures wouldn't be so easily offended!"

"You'll get used to it in time," said the Caterpillar; and it put the hookah into its mouth and began smoking again.

This time Alice waited patiently until it chose to speak again. In a minute or two the Caterpillar took the hookah out of its mouth and yawned once or twice, and shook itself. Then it got down off the mushroom, and crawled away into the grass, merely remarking as it went, "One side will make you grow taller, and the other side will make you grow shorter."

"One side of *what*? The other side of *what*?" thought Alice to herself.

"Of the mushroom," said the Caterpillar, just as if she had asked it aloud; and in another moment it was out of sight.

Alice remained looking thoughtfully at the mushroom for a minute, trying to make out which were the two sides of it; and as it was perfectly round, she found this a very difficult question. However, at last she stretched her arms round it as far as they would go, and broke off a bit of the edge with each hand.

"And now which is which?" she said to herself, and nibbled a little of the right-hand bit to try the effect: the next moment she felt a violent blow underneath her chin: it had struck her foot!

She was a good deal frightened by this very sudden change, but she felt that there was no time to be lost, as she was shrinking rapidly: so she set to work at once to eat some of the other bit. Her chin was pressed so closely against her foot, that there was hardly room to open her mouth; but she did it at last, and managed to swallow a morsel of the left-hand bit.

*   *   *   *   *

*   *   *   *

"Come, my head's free at last!" said Alice in a tone of delight, which changed into alarm in another moment, when she found that her shoulders were nowhere to be found: all she could see, when she looked down, was an immense length of neck, which seemed to rise like a stalk out of a sea of green leaves that lay far below her.

"What *can* all that green stuff be?" said Alice. "And where *have* my shoulders got to? And oh, my poor hands, how is it I ca'n't see you?" She was moving them about as she spoke, but no result seemed to follow, except a little shaking among the distant green leaves.

As there seemed to be no chance of getting her hands up to her head, she tried to get her head down to *them*, and was delighted to find that her neck would bend about easily in any direction, like a serpent. She had just succeeded in curving it down into a graceful zigzag, and was going to dive in among the leaves, which she found to be nothing but the tops of the trees under which she had been wandering, when a sharp hiss made her draw back in a hurry: a large pigeon had flown into her face, and was beating her violently with its wings.

"Serpent!" screamed the Pigeon.

"I'm *not* a serpent!" said Alice indignantly. "Let me alone!"

"Serpent, I say again!" repeated the Pigeon, but in a more subdued tone, and added with a kind of sob, "I've tried every way, but nothing seems to suit them!"

"I haven't the least idea what you're talking about," said Alice.

"I've tried the roots of trees, and I've tried banks, and I've tried hedges," the Pigeon went on, without attending to her; "but those serpents! There's no pleasing them!"

Alice was more and more puzzled, but she thought there was no use in saying anything more till the Pigeon had finished.

"As if it wasn't trouble enough hatching the eggs," said the Pigeon; "but I must be on the look-out for serpents night and day! Why, I haven't had a wink of sleep these three weeks!"

"I'm very sorry you've been annoyed," said Alice, who was beginning to see its meaning.

"And just as I'd taken the highest tree in the wood," continued the Pigeon, raising its voice to a shriek, "and just as I was thinking I should be free of them at last, they must needs come wriggling down from the sky! Ugh, Serpent!"

"But I'm *not* a serpent, I tell you!" said Alice. "I'm a—— I'm a——"

"Well! *What* are you?" said the Pigeon. "I can see you're trying to invent something!"

"I – I'm a little girl," said Alice, rather doubtfully, as she remembered the number of changes she had gone through, that day.

"A likely story indeed!" said the Pigeon, in a tone of the deepest contempt. "I've seen a good many little girls in my time, but never *one* with such a neck as that! No, no! You're a serpent; and there's no use denying it. I suppose you'll be telling me next that you never tasted an egg!"

"I *have* tasted eggs, certainly," said Alice, who was a very truthful child; "but little girls eat eggs quite as much as serpents do, you know."

"I don't believe it," said the Pigeon; "but if they do, why, then they're a kind of serpent: that's all I can say."

This was such a new idea to Alice, that she was quite silent for a minute or two, which gave the Pigeon the opportunity of adding, "You're looking for eggs, I know *that* well enough; and what does it matter to me whether you're a little girl or a serpent?"

"It matters a good deal to *me*," said Alice hastily; "but I'm not looking for eggs, as it happens; and, if I was, I shouldn't want *yours*: I don't like them raw."

"Well, be off, then!" said the Pigeon in a sulky tone, as it settled down again into its nest. Alice crouched down among the trees as well as she could, for her neck kept getting entangled among the branches, and every now and then she had to stop and untwist it. After a while she remembered that she still held the pieces of mushroom in her hands, and she set to work very carefully, nibbling first at one and then at the other, and growing sometimes taller, and sometimes shorter, until she had succeeded in bringing herself down to her usual height.

It was so long since she had been anything near the right size, that it felt quite strange at first; but she got used to it in a few minutes, and began talking to herself, as usual, "Come, there's half my plan done now! How puzzling all these changes are! I'm never sure what I'm going to be, from one minute to another! However, I've got back to my right size: the next thing is, to get into that beautiful garden – how *is* that to be done, I wonder?" As she said this, she came suddenly upon an open place, with a little house in it about four feet high. "Whoever lives there?" thought Alice; "it'll never do to come upon them *this* size: why, I should frighten them out of their wits!" So she began nibbling at the right-hand bit again, and did not venture to go near the house till she had brought herself down to nine inches high.

CHAPTER 6

Pig and Pepper

FOR a minute or two she stood looking at the house, and wondering what to do next, when suddenly a footman in livery came running out of the wood – (she considered him to be a footman because he was in livery: otherwise, judging by his face only, she would have called him a fish) – and rapped loudly at the door with his knuckles. It was opened by another footman in livery, with a round face, and large eyes like a frog; and both footmen, Alice noticed, had powdered hair that curled all over their heads. She felt very curious to know what it was all about, and crept a little way out of the wood to listen.

The Fish-Footman began by producing from under his arm a great letter, nearly as large as himself, and this he handed over to the other, saying, in a solemn tone, "For the Duchess. An invitation from the Queen to play croquet." The Frog-Footman repeated, in the same solemn tone, only changing the order of the words a little, "From the Queen. An invitation for the Duchess to play croquet."

Then they both bowed low, and their curls got entangled together.

Alice laughed so much at this, that she had to run back into the wood for fear of their hearing her; and, when she next peeped out, the Fish-Footman was gone, and the other was sitting on the ground near the door, staring stupidly up into the sky.

Alice went timidly up to the door, and knocked.

"There's no sort of use in knocking," said the Footman, "and that for two reasons. First, because I'm on the same side of the door as you are: secondly, because they're making such a noise inside, no one could possibly hear you." And certainly there *was* a most extraordinary noise going on within – a constant howling and sneezing, and every now and then a great crash, as if a dish or kettle had been broken to pieces.

"Please, then," said Alice, "how am I to get in?"

"There might be some sense in your knocking," the Footman went on, without attending to her, "if we had the door between us. For instance, if you were *inside*, you might knock, and I could let you out, you know." He was looking up into the sky all the time he was speaking, and this Alice thought decidedly uncivil. "But perhaps he ca'n't help it," she said to herself; "his eyes are so *very* nearly at the top of his head. But at any rate he might answer questions – How am I to get in?" she repeated, aloud.

"I shall sit here," the Footman remarked, "till tomorrow——"

At this moment the door of the house opened, and a large plate came skimming out, straight at the Footman's head: it just grazed his nose, and broke to pieces against one of the trees behind him.

"—— or next day, maybe," the Footman continued in the same tone, exactly as if nothing had happened.

"How am I to get in?" asked Alice again, in a louder tone.

"*Are* you to get in at all?" said the Footman. "That's the first question, you know."

It was, no doubt: only Alice did not like to be told so. "It's really dreadful," she muttered to herself, "the way all the creatures argue. It's enough to drive one crazy!"

The Footman seemed to think this a good opportunity for repeating his remark with variations. "I shall sit here," he said, "on and off, for days and days."

"But what am *I* to do?" said Alice.

"Anything you like," said the Footman, and began whistling.

"Oh, there's no use in talking to him," said Alice desperately: "he's perfectly idiotic!" And she opened the door and went in.

The door led right into a large kitchen, which was full of smoke from one end to the other: the Duchess was sitting on a three-legged stool in the middle, nursing a baby: the cook was leaning over the fire, stirring a large cauldron which seemed to be full of soup.

"There's certainly too much pepper in that soup!" Alice said to herself, as well as she could for sneezing.

There was certainly too much of it in the *air*. Even the Duchess sneezed occasionally; and as for the baby, it was sneezing and howling alternately without a moment's pause. The only two creatures in the kitchen that did *not* sneeze, were the cook, and a large cat, which was lying on the hearth and grinning from ear to ear.

"Please would you tell me," said Alice, a little timidly, for she was not quite sure whether it was good manners for her to speak first, "why your cat grins like that?"

"It's a Cheshire-Cat," said the Duchess, "and that's why. Pig!"

She said the last word with such sudden violence that Alice quite jumped; but she saw in another moment that it was addressed to the baby, and not to her, so she took courage, and went on again:—

"I didn't know that Cheshire-Cats always grinned; in fact, I didn't know that cats *could* grin."

"They all can," said the Duchess; "and most of 'em do."

"I don't know of any that do," Alice said very politely, feeling quite pleased to have got into a conversation.

"You don't know much," said the Duchess; "and that's a fact."

Alice did not at all like the tone of this remark, and thought it would be as well to introduce some other subject of conversation. While she was trying to fix on one, the cook took the cauldron of soup off the fire, and at once set to work throwing everything within her reach at the Duchess and the baby – the fire-irons came first; then followed a shower of saucepans, plates, and dishes. The Duchess took no notice of them even when they hit her; and the baby was howling so much already, that it was quite impossible to say whether the blows hurt it or not.

"Oh, *please* mind what you're doing!" cried Alice, jumping up and

down in an agony of terror. "Oh, there goes his *precious* nose!" as an unusually large saucepan flew close by it, and very nearly carried it off.

"If everybody minded their own business," the Duchess said, in a hoarse growl, "the world would go round a deal faster than it does."

"Which would *not* be an advantage," said Alice, who felt very glad to get an opportunity of showing off a little of her knowledge. "Just think what work it would make with the day and night! You see, the earth takes twenty-four hours to turn round on its axis——"

"Talking of axes," said the Duchess, "chop off her head!"

Alice glanced rather anxiously at the cook, to see if she meant to take the hint; but the cook was busily stirring the soup, and seemed not to be listening, so she went on again: "Twenty-four hours, I *think*; or is it twelve? I——"

"Oh, don't bother *me*!" said the Duchess. "I never could abide figures!" And with that she began nursing her child again, singing a sort of lullaby to it as she did so, and giving it a violent shake at the end of every line:—

> *Speak roughly to your little boy,*
> *And beat him when he sneezes:*
> *He only does it to annoy,*
> *Because he knows it teases.*

CHORUS

(in which the cook and the baby joined):—
Wow! wow! wow!

While the Duchess sang the second verse of the song, she kept tossing the baby violently up and down, and the poor little thing howled so, that Alice could hardly hear the words:—

> *I speak severely to my boy,*
> *I beat him when he sneezes;*
> *For he can thoroughly enjoy*
> *The pepper when he pleases!*

CHORUS

Wow! wow! wow!

"Here! You may nurse it a bit, if you like!" the Duchess said to Alice, flinging the baby at her as she spoke. "I must go and get ready to

play croquet with the Queen," and she hurried out of the room. The cook threw a frying-pan after her as she went, but it just missed her.

Alice caught the baby with some difficulty, as it was a queer-shaped little creature, and held out its arms and legs in all directions, "just like a starfish," thought Alice. The poor little thing was snorting like a steam-engine when she caught it, and kept doubling itself up and straightening itself out again, so that altogether, for the first minute or two, it was as much as she could do to hold it.

As soon as she had made out the proper way of nursing it (which ˙ to twist it up into a sort of knot, and then keep tight hold of its righ and left foot, so as to prevent its undoing itself), she carried it c the open air. "If I don't take this child away with me," thought Alice, "they're sure to kill it in a day or two. Wouldn't it be murder to leave it behind?" She said the last words out loud, and the little thing grunted in reply (it had left off sneezing by this time). "Don't grunt," said Alice; "that's not at all a proper way of expressing yourself."

The baby grunted again, and Alice looked very anxiously into its face to see what was the matter with it. There could be no doubt that it had a *very* turn-up nose, much more like a snout than a real nose: also its eyes were getting extremely small for a baby: altogether Alice did not like the look of the thing at all. "But perhaps it was only sobbing," she thought, and looked into its eyes again, to see if there were any tears.

No, there were no tears. "If you're going to turn into a pig, my dear," said Alice, seriously, "I'll have nothing more to do with you. Mind now!" The poor little thing sobbed again (or grunted, it was impossible to say which), and they went on for some while in silence.

Alice was just beginning to think to herself, "Now, what am I to do with this creature, when I get it home?" when it grunted again, so violently, that she looked down into its face in some alarm. This time there could be *no* mistake about it: it was neither more or less than a pig, and she felt that it would be quite absurd for her to carry it any further.

So she set the little creature down, and felt quite relieved to see it trot away quietly into the wood. "If it had grown up," she said to herself, "it would have made a dreadfully ugly child: but it makes rather a handsome pig, I think." And she began thinking over other children she knew, who might do very well as pigs, and was just saying to herself "if one only knew the right way to change them——" when she was a little startled by seeing the Cheshire-Cat sitting on a bough of a tree a few yards off.

The Cat only grinned when it saw Alice. It looked good-natured, she thought: still it had *very* long claws and a great many teeth, so she felt that it ought to be treated with respect.

"Cheshire-Puss," she began rather timidly, as she did not at all know whether it would like the name: however, it only grinned a little wider. "Come, it's pleased so far," thought Alice, and she went on. "Would you tell me, please, which way I ought to go from here?"

"That depends a good deal on where you want to get to," said the Cat.

"I don't much care where——" said Alice.

"Then it doesn't matter which way you go," said the Cat.

"—— so long as I get *somewhere*," Alice added as an explanation.

"Oh, you're sure to do that," said the Cat, "if you only walk long enough."

Alice felt that this could not be denied, so she tried another question. "What sort of people live about here?"

"In *that* direction," the Cat said, waving its right paw round, "lives a Hatter: and in *that* direction," waving the other paw, "lives a March Hare. Visit either you like: they're both mad."

"But I don't want to go among mad people," Alice remarked.

"Oh, you ca'n't help that," said the Cat: "we're all mad here. I'm mad. You're mad."

"How do you know I'm mad?" said Alice.

"You must be," said the Cat, "or you wouldn't have come here."

Alice didn't think that proved it at all: however, she went on: "And how do you know that you're mad?"

"To begin with," said the Cat, "a dog's not mad. You grant that?"

"I suppose so," said Alice.

"Well, then," the Cat went on, "you see a dog growls when it's angry, and wags its tail when it's pleased. Now *I* growl when I'm pleased, and wag my tail when I'm angry. Therefore I'm mad."

"*I* call it purring, not growling," said Alice.

"Call it what you like," said the Cat. "Do you play croquet with the Queen to-day?"

"I should like it very much," said Alice, "but I haven't been invited yet."

"You'll see me there," said the Cat, and vanished.

Alice was not much surprised at this, she was getting so well used to queer things happening. While she was still looking at the place where it had been, it suddenly appeared again.

"By-the-bye, what became of the baby?" said the Cat. "I'd nearly forgotten to ask."

"It turned into a pig," Alice answered very quietly, just as if the Cat had come back in a natural way.

"I thought it would," said the Cat, and vanished again.

Alice waited a little, half expecting to see it again, but it did not appear, and after a minute or two she walked on in the direction in which the March Hare was said to live. "I've seen hatters before," she said to herself: "the March Hare will be much the most interesting, and perhaps, as this is May, it wo'n't be raving mad – at least not so mad as it was in March." As she said this, she looked up, and there was the Cat again, sitting on a branch of a tree.

"Did you say 'pig', or 'fig'?" said the Cat.

"I said 'pig'," replied Alice; "and I wish you wouldn't keep appearing and vanishing so suddenly: you make one quite giddy!"

"All right," said the Cat; and this time it vanished quite slowly, beginning with the end of the tail, and ending with the grin, which remained some time after the rest of it had gone.

"Well! I've often seen a cat without a grin," thought Alice; "but a grin without a cat! It's the most curious thing I ever saw in all my life!"

She had not gone much farther before she came in sight of the house of the March Hare: she thought it must be the right house, because the chimneys were shaped like ears and the roof was thatched with fur. It was so large a house, that she did not like to go nearer till she had nibbled some more of the left-hand bit of mushroom, and raised herself to about two feet high: even then she walked up towards it rather timidly, saying to herself "Suppose it should be raving mad after all! I almost wish I'd gone to see the Hatter instead!"

CHAPTER 7

A Mad Tea-Party

THERE was a table set out under a tree in front of the house, and the March Hare and the Hatter were having tea at it: a Dormouse was sitting between them, fast asleep, and the other two were using it as a cushion, resting their elbows on it, and talking over its head. "Very uncomfortable for the Dormouse," thought Alice; "only as it's asleep, I suppose it doesn't mind."

The table was a large one, but the three were all crowded together at one corner of it. "No room! No room!" they cried out when they saw Alice coming. "There's *plenty* of room!" said Alice indignantly, and she sat down in a large arm-chair at one end of the table.

"Have some wine," the March Hare said in an encouraging tone.

Alice looked all round the table, but there was nothing on it but tea. "I don't see any wine," she remarked.

"There isn't any," said the March Hare.

"Then it wasn't very civil of you to offer it," said Alice angrily.

"It wasn't very civil of you to sit down without being invited," said the March Hare.

"I didn't know it was *your* table," said Alice: "it's laid for a great many more than three."

"Your hair wants cutting," said the Hatter. He had been looking at Alice for some time with great curiosity, and this was his first speech.

"You should learn not to make personal remarks," Alice said with some severity: "it's very rude."

The Hatter opened his eyes very wide on hearing this; but all he *said* was "Why is a raven like a writing-desk?"

"Come, we shall have some fun now!" thought Alice. "I'm glad they've begun asking riddles – I believe I can guess that," she added aloud.

"Do you mean that you think you can find out the answer to it," said the March Hare.

"Exactly so," said Alice.

"Then you should say what you mean," the March Hare went on.

"I do," Alice hastily replied; "at least – at least I mean what I say – that's the same thing, you know."

"Not the same thing a bit!" said the Hatter. "Why, you might just as well say that 'I see what I eat' is the same thing as 'I eat what I see'!"

"You might just as well say," added the March Hare, "that 'I like what I get' is the same thing as 'I get what I like'!"

"You might just as well say," added the Dormouse, which seemed to be talking in its sleep, "that 'I breathe when I sleep' is the same thing as 'I sleep when I breathe'!"

"It *is* the same thing with you," said the Hatter, and here the conversation dropped, and the party sat silent for a minute, while Alice thought over all she could remember about ravens and writing-desks, which wasn't much.

The Hatter was the first to break the silence. "What day of the month is it?" he said, turning to Alice: he had taken his watch out of his pocket, and was looking at it uneasily, shaking it every now and then, and holding it to his ear.

Alice considered a little, and then said, "The fourth."

"Two days wrong!" sighed the Hatter. "I told you butter wouldn't suit the works!" he added, looking angrily at the March Hare.

"It was the *best* butter," the March Hare meekly replied.

"Yes, but some crumbs must have got in as well," the Hatter grumbled: "you shouldn't have put it in with the bread-knife."

The March Hare took the watch and looked at it gloomily; then he dipped it into his cup of tea, and looked at it again: but he could think of nothing better to say than his first remark, "It was the *best* butter, you know."

Alice had been looking over his shoulder with some curiosity. "What a funny watch!" she remarked. "It tells the day of the month, and doesn't tell what o'clock it is!"

"Why should it?" muttered the Hatter. "Does *your* watch tell you what year it is?"

"Of course not," Alice replied very readily: "but that's because it stays the same year for such a long time together."

"Which is just the case with *mine*," said the Hatter.

Alice felt dreadfully puzzled. The Hatter's remark seemed to her to have no sort of meaning in it, and yet it was certainly English. "I don't quite understand you," she said, as politely as she could.

"The Dormouse is asleep again," said the Hatter, and he poured a little hot tea upon its nose.

The Dormouse shook its head impatiently, and said, without opening its eyes, "Of course, of course: just what I was going to remark myself."

"Have you guessed the riddle yet?" the Hatter said, turning to Alice again.

"No, I give it up," Alice replied. "What's the answer?"

"I haven't the slightest idea," said the Hatter.

"Nor I," said the March Hare.

Alice sighed wearily. "I think you might do something better with the time," she said, "than wasting it in asking riddles that have no answers."

"If you knew Time as well as I do," said the Hatter, "you wouldn't talk about wasting *it*. It's *him*."

"I don't know what you mean," said Alice.

"Of course you don't," the Hatter said, tossing his head contemptuously. "I dare say you never even spoke to Time!"

"Perhaps not," Alice cautiously replied; "but I know I have to beat time when I learn music."

"Ah! That accounts for it," said the Hatter. "He wo'n't stand beating. Now, if you only kept on good terms with him, he'd do almost anything you liked with the clock. For instance, suppose it were nine o'clock in the morning, just time to begin lessons: you'd only have to whisper a hint to Time, and round goes the clock in a twinkling! Half-past one, time for dinner!"

("I only wish it was," the March Hare said to itself in a whisper.)

"That would be grand, certainly," said Alice thoughtfully; "but then – I shouldn't be hungry for it, you know."

"Not at first, perhaps," said the Hatter: "but you could keep it to half-past one as long as you liked."

"Is that the way *you* manage?" Alice asked.

The Hatter shook his head mournfully. "Not I!" he replied. "We quarrelled last March – just before *he* went mad, you know——" (pointing with his teaspoon at the March Hare,) "——it was at the great concert given by the Queen of Hearts, and I had to sing

> *Twinkle, twinkle, little bat!*
> *How I wonder what you're at!"*

You know the song, perhaps?"

"I've heard something like it," said Alice.

"It goes on, you know," the Hatter continued, "in this way:—

> *Up above the world you fly,*
> *Like a tea-tray in the sky.*
> *Twinkle, twinkle——"*

Here the Dormouse shook itself and began singing in its sleep *"Twinkle, twinkle, twinkle, twinkle——"* and went on so long that they had to pinch it to make it stop.

"Well, I'd hardly finished the first verse," said the Hatter, "when the Queen bawled out, 'He's murdering the time! Off with his head!'"

"How dreadfully savage!" exclaimed Alice.

"And ever since that," the Hatter went on in a mournful tone, "he wo'n't do a thing I ask! It's always six o'clock now."

A bright idea came into Alice's head. "Is that the reason so many tea-things are put out here?" she asked.

"Yes, that's it," said the Hatter with a sigh: "it's always tea-time, and we've no time to wash the things between whiles."

"Then you keep moving round, I suppose?" said Alice.

"Exactly so," said the Hatter: "as the things get used up."

"But what happens when you come to the beginning again?" Alice ventured to ask.

"Suppose we change the subject," the March Hare interrupted, yawning. "I'm getting tired of this. I vote the young lady tells us a story."

"I'm afraid I don't know one," said Alice, rather alarmed at the proposal.

"Then the Dormouse shall!" they both cried. "Wake up, Dormouse!" And they pinched it on both sides at once.

The Dormouse slowly opened its eyes. "I wasn't asleep," it said in a hoarse, feeble voice, "I heard every word you fellows were saying."

"Tell us a story!" said the March Hare.

"Yes, please do!" pleaded Alice.

"And be quick about it," added the Hatter, "or you'll be asleep again before it's done."

"Once upon a time there were three little sisters," the Dormouse began in a great hurry; "and their names were Elsie, Lacie, and Tillie; and they lived at the bottom of a well——"

"What did they live on?" said Alice, who always took a great interest in questions of eating and drinking.

"They lived on treacle," said the Dormouse, after thinking a minute or two.

"They couldn't have done that, you know," Alice gently remarked. "They'd have been ill."

"So they were," said the Dormouse; "*very* ill."

Alice tried a little to fancy to herself what such an extraordinary way of living would be like, but it puzzled her too much: so she went on: "But why did they live at the bottom of a well?"

"Take some more tea," the March Hare said to Alice, earnestly.

"I've had nothing yet," Alice replied in an offended tone: "so I ca'n't take more."

"You mean you ca'n't take *less*," said the Hatter: "it's very easy to take *more* than nothing."

"Nobody asked *your* opinion," said Alice.

"Who's making personal remarks now?" the Hatter asked triumphantly.

Alice did not quite know what to say to this: so she helped herself to some tea and bread-and-butter, and then turned to the Dormouse, and repeated her question. "Why did they live at the bottom of a well?"

The Dormouse again took a minute or two to think about it, and then said "It was a treacle-well."

"There's no such thing!" Alice was beginning very angrily, but the Hatter and the March Hare went "Sh! Sh!" and the Dormouse sulkily remarked "If you ca'n't be civil, you'd better finish the story for yourself."

"No, please go on!" Alice said very humbly. "I wo'n't interrupt you again. I dare say there may be *one*."

"One, indeed!" said the Dormouse indignantly. However, he consented to go on. "And so these three little sisters – they were learning to draw, you know——"

"What did they draw?" said Alice, quite forgetting her promise.

"Treacle," said the Dormouse, without considering at all, this time.

"I want a clean cup," interrupted the Hatter: "let's all move one place on."

He moved on as he spoke, and the Dormouse followed him: the March Hare moved into the Dormouse's place, and Alice rather unwillingly took the place of the March Hare. The Hatter was the only one who got any advantage from the change; and Alice was a good deal worse off than before, as the March Hare had just upset the milk-jug into his plate.

Alice did not wish to offend the Dormouse again, so she began very cautiously: "But I don't understand. Where did they draw the treacle from?"

"You can draw water out of a water-well," said the Hatter; "so I should think you could draw treacle out of a treacle-well – eh, stupid?"

"But they were *in* the well," Alice said to the Dormouse, not choosing to notice this last remark.

"Of course they were," said the Dormouse: "well in."

This answer so confused poor Alice, that she let the Dormouse go on for some time without interrupting it.

"They were learning to draw," the Dormouse went on, yawning and rubbing its eyes, for it was getting very sleepy; "and they drew all manner of things – everything that begins with an M——"

"Why with an M?" said Alice.

"Why not?" said the March Hare.

Alice was silent.

The Dormouse had closed its eyes by this time, and was going off into a doze; but, on being pinched by the Hatter, it woke up again with a little shriek, and went on: "——that begins with an M, such as mouse-traps, and the moon, and memory, and muchness – you know you say things are 'much of a muchness' – did you ever see such a thing as a drawing of a muchness?"

"Really, now you ask me," said Alice, very much confused, "I don't think——"

"Then you shouldn't talk," said the Hatter.

This piece of rudeness was more than Alice could bear: she got up in great disgust, and walked off: the Dormouse fell asleep instantly, and neither of the others took the least notice of her going, though she looked back once or twice, half hoping that they would call after her: the last time she saw them, they were trying to put the Dormouse into the teapot.

"At any rate I'll never go *there* again!" said Alice, as she picked her way through the wood. "It's the stupidest tea-party I ever was at in all my life!"

Just as she said this, she noticed that one of the trees had a door leading right into it. "That's very curious!" she thought. "But everything's curious to-day. I think I may as well go in at once." And in she went.

Once more she found herself in the long hall, and close to the little glass table. "Now, I'll manage better this time," she said to herself, and began by taking the little golden key, and unlocking the door that led into the garden. Then she set to work nibbling at the mushroom (she had kept a piece of it in her pocket) till she was about a foot high; then she walked down the little passage: and *then* – she found herself at last in the beautiful garden, among the bright flower-beds and the cool fountains.

CHAPTER 8

The Queen's Croquet-Ground

A LARGE rose-tree stood near the entrance of the garden: the roses growing on it were white, but there were three gardeners at it, busily painting them red. Alice thought this a very curious thing, and she went nearer to watch them, and, just as she came up to them, she heard one of them say "Look out now, Five! Don't go splashing paint over me like that!"

"I couldn't help it," said Five, in a sulky tone. "Seven jogged my elbow."

On which Seven looked up and said "That's right, Five! Always lay the blame on others!"

"*You'd* better not talk!" said Five. "I heard the Queen say only yesterday you deserved to be beheaded."

"What for?" said the one who had spoken first.

"That's none of *your* business, Two!" said Seven.

"Yes, it *is* his business!" said Five. "And I'll tell him – it was for bringing the cook tulip-roots instead of onions."

Seven flung down his brush, and had just begun "Well, of all the unjust things——" when his eye chanced to fall upon Alice, as she stood watching them, and he checked himself suddenly: the others looked round also, and all of them bowed low.

"Would you tell me, please," said Alice, a little timidly, "why you are painting those roses?"

Five and Seven said nothing, but looked at Two. Two began, in a low voice, "Why, the fact is, you see, Miss, this here ought to have been a *red* rose-tree, and we put a white one in by mistake; and, if the Queen was to find it out, we should all have our heads cut off, you know. So you see, Miss, we're doing our best, afore she comes, to——" At this moment, Five, who had been anxiously looking across the garden, called out "The Queen! The Queen!" and the three gardeners instantly threw themselves flat upon their faces. There was a sound of many footsteps, and Alice looked round, eager to see the Queen.

First came ten soldiers carrying clubs: these were all shaped like the three gardeners, oblong and flat, with their hands and feet at the corners: next the ten courtiers: these were ornamented all over with diamonds, and walked two and two, as the soldiers did. After these came the royal children: there were ten of them, and the little dears came jumping merrily along, hand in hand, in couples: they were all ornamented with hearts. Next came the guests, mostly Kings and

Queens, and among them Alice recognised the White Rabbit: it was talking in a hurried nervous manner, smiling at everything that was said, and went by without noticing her. Then followed the Knave of Hearts, carrying the King's crown on a crimson velvet cushion; and, last of all this grand procession, came THE KING AND THE QUEEN OF HEARTS.

Alice was rather doubtful whether she ought not to lie down on her face like the three gardeners, but she could not remember ever having heard of such a rule at processions; "and besides, what would be the use of a procession," thought she, "if people had all to lie down on their faces, so that they couldn't see it?" So she stood where she was, and waited.

When the procession came opposite to Alice, they all stopped and looked at her, and the Queen said, severely, "Who is this?" She said it to the Knave of Hearts, who only bowed and smiled in reply.

"Idiot!" said the Queen, tossing her head impatiently; and, turning to Alice, she went on: "What's your name, child?"

"My name is Alice, so please your Majesty," said Alice very politely; but she added, to herself, "Why, they're only a pack of cards, after all. I needn't be afraid of them!"

"And who are *these*?" said the Queen, pointing to the three gardeners who were lying round the rose-tree; for, you see, as they were lying on their faces, and the pattern on their backs was the same as the rest of the pack, she could not tell whether they were gardeners, or soldiers, or courtiers, or three of her own children.

"How should *I* know," said Alice, surprised at her own courage. "It's no business of *mine*."

The Queen turned crimson with fury, and, after glaring at her for a moment like a wild beast, began screaming "Off with her head! Off with——"

"Nonsense!" said Alice, very loudly and decidedly, and the Queen was silent.

The King laid his hand upon her arm, and timidly said "Consider, my dear: she is only a child!"

The Queen turned angrily away from him, and said to the Knave "Turn them over!"

The Knave did so, very carefully, with one foot.

"Get up!" said the Queen in a shrill, loud voice, and the three gardeners instantly jumped up, and began bowing to the King, the Queen, the royal children, and everybody else.

"Leave off that!" screamed the Queen. "You make me giddy." And then, turning to the rose-tree, she went on "What *have* you been doing here?"

"May it please your Majesty," said Two, in a very humble tone, going down on one knee as he spoke, "we were trying——"

"*I* see!" said the Queen, who had meanwhile been examining the roses. "Off with their heads!" and the procession moved on, three of the soldiers remaining behind to execute the unfortunate gardeners, who ran to Alice for protection.

"You sha'n't be beheaded!" said Alice, and she put them into a large flower-pot that stood near. The three soldiers wandered about for a minute or two, looking for them, and then quietly marched off after the others.

"Are their heads off?" shouted the Queen

"Their heads are gone, if it please your Majesty!" the soldiers shouted in reply.

"That's right!" shouted the Queen. "Can you play croquet?"

The soldiers were silent, and looked at Alice, as the question was evidently meant for her.

"Yes!" shouted Alice.

"Come on, then!" roared the Queen, and Alice joined the procession, wondering very much what would happen next.

"It's – it's a very fine day!" said a timid voice at her side. She was walking by the White Rabbit, who was peeping anxiously into her face.

"Very," said Alice. "Where's the Duchess?"

"Hush! Hush!" said the Rabbit in a low hurried tone. He looked anxiously over his shoulder as he spoke, and then raised himself upon tiptoe, put his mouth close to her ear, and whispered "She's under sentence of execution."

"What for?" said Alice.

"Did you say 'What a pity!'?" the Rabbit asked.

"No, I didn't," said Alice. "I don't think it's at all a pity. I said 'What for?'"

"She boxed the Queen's ears——" the Rabbit began. Alice gave a little scream of laughter. "Oh, hush!" the Rabbit whispered in a frightened tone. "The Queen will hear you! You see, she came rather late, and the Queen said——"

"Get to your places!" shouted the Queen in a voice of thunder, and people began running about in all directions, tumbling up against each other: however, they got settled down in a minute or two, and the game began.

Alice thought she had never seen such a curious croquet-ground in her life: it was all ridges and furrows: the croquet balls were live hedgehogs, and the mallets live flamingoes, and the soldiers had to double themselves up and stand on their hands and feet, to make the arches.

The chief difficulty Alice found at first was in managing her flamingo: she succeeded in getting its body tucked away, comfortably enough, under her arm, with its legs hanging down, but generally, just as she had got its neck nicely straightened out, and was going to give the hedgehog a blow with its head, it *would* twist itself round and look up in her face, with such a puzzled expression that she could not help bursting out laughing; and, when she had got its head down, and was going to begin again, it was very provoking to find that the hedgehog had unrolled itself, and was in the act of crawling away: besides all this, there was generally a ridge or a furrow in the way whenever she wanted to send the hedgehog to, and, as the doubled-up soldiers were always getting up and walking off to other parts of the ground, Alice soon came to the conclusion that it was a very difficult game indeed.

The players all played at once, without waiting for turns, quarrelling all the while, and fighting for the hedgehogs; and in a very short time the Queen was in a furious passion, and went stamping about, and shouting "Off with his head!" or "Off with her head!" about once a minute.

Alice began to feel very uneasy: to be sure, she had not as yet had any dispute with the Queen, but she knew that it might happen any minute. "And then," thought she, "what would become of me? They're dreadfully fond of beheading people here: the great wonder is, that there's any one left alive!"

She was looking about for some way of escape, and wondering whether she could get away without being seen, when she noticed a curious appearance in the air: it puzzled her very much as first, but after watching it a minute or two she made it out to be a grin, and she said to herself "It's the Cheshire-Cat: now I shall have somebody to talk to."

"How are you getting on?" said the Cat, as soon as there was mouth enough for it to speak with.

Alice waited till the eyes appeared, and then nodded. "It's no use speaking to it," she thought, "till its ears have come, or at least one of them." In another minute the whole head appeared, and then Alice put down her flamingo, and began an account of the game, feeling very glad she had some one to listen to her. The Cat seemed to think that there was enough of it now in sight, and no more of it appeared.

"I don't think they play at all fairly," Alice began, in rather a complaining tone, "and they all quarrel so dreadfully one ca'n't hear oneself speak – and they don't seem to have any rules in particular: at least, if there are, nobody attends to them – and you've no idea how confusing it is all the things being alive: for instance, there's the arch I've got to go through next walking about at the other end of the ground – and I should have croqueted the Queen's hedgehog just now, only it ran away when it saw mine coming!"

"How do you like the Queen?" said the Cat in a low voice.

"Not at all," said Alice: "she's so extremely—" Just then she noticed that the Queen was close behind her, listening: so she went on "—likely to win, that it's hardly worth while finishing the game."

The Queen smiled and passed on.

"Who *are* you talking to?" said the King, coming up to Alice, and looking at the Cat's head with great curiosity.

"It's a friend of mine – a Cheshire-Cat," said Alice: "allow me to introduce it."

"I don't like the look of it at all," said the King: "however, it may kiss my hand, if it likes."

"I'd rather not," the Cat remarked.

"Don't be impertinent," said the King, "and don't look at me like that!" He got behind Alice as he spoke.

"A cat may look at a king," said Alice. "I've read that in some book, but I don't remember where."

"Well, it must be removed," said the King very decidedly; and he called to the Queen who was passing at the moment, "My dear! I wish you would have this cat removed!"

The Queen had only one way of settling all difficulties, great or small. "Off with his head!" she said without even looking round.

"I'll fetch the executioner myself," said the King eagerly, and he hurried off.

Alice thought she might as well go back and see how the game was going on, and she heard the Queen's voice in the distance, screaming with passion. She had already heard her sentence three of the players to be executed for having missed their turns, and she did not like the look of things at all, as the game was in such confusion that she never knew whether it was her turn or not. So she went off in search of her hedgehog.

The hedgehog was engaged in a fight with another hedgehog, which seemed to Alice an excellent opportunity for croqueting one of them with the other: the only difficulty was, that her flamingo was gone across to the other side of the garden, where Alice could see it trying in a helpless sort of way to fly up into a tree.

By the time she had caught the flamingo and brought it back, the fight was over, and both the hedgehogs were out of sight: "but it doesn't matter much," thought Alice, "as all the arches are gone from this side of the ground." So she tucked it away under her arm, that it might not escape again, and went back to have a little more conversation with her friend.

When she got back to the Cheshire-Cat, she was surprised to find quite a large crowd collected round it: there was a dispute going on between the executioner, the King, and the Queen, who were all talking at once, while all the rest were quite silent, and looked very uncomfortable.

The moment Alice appeared, she was appealed to by all three to settle the question, and they repeated their arguments to her, though, as they all spoke at once, she found it very hard to make out exactly what they said.

The executioner's argument was, that you couldn't cut off a head unless there was a body to cut it off from: that he had never had to do such a thing before, and he wasn't going to begin at *his* time of life.

The King's argument was that anything that had a head could be beheaded, and that you weren't to talk nonsense.

The Queen's argument was that, if something wasn't done about it in less than no time, she'd have everybody executed, all round. (It was this last remark that had made the whole party look so grave and anxious.)

Alice could think of nothing else to say but "It belongs to the Duchess: you'd better ask *her* about it."

"She's in prison," the Queen said to the executioner: "fetch her here." And the executioner went off like an arrow.

The Cat's head began fading away the moment he was gone, and, by the time he had come back with the Duchess, it had entirely disappeared: so the King and the executioner ran wild up and down, looking for it, while the rest of the party went back to the game.

CHAPTER 9

The Mock Turtle's Story

"You ca'n't think how glad I am to see you again, you dear old thing!" said the Duchess, as she tucked her arm affectionately into Alice's, and they walked off together.

Alice was very glad to find her in such a pleasant temper, and thought to herself that perhaps it was only the pepper that had made her so savage when they met in the kitchen.

"When *I'm* a Duchess," she said to herself (not in a very hopeful tone, though), "I wo'n't have any pepper in my kitchen *at all*. Soup does very well without – Maybe it's always pepper that makes people hot-tempered," she went on, very much pleased at having found out a new kind of rule, "and vinegar that makes them sour – and camomile that makes them bitter – and – and barley-sugar and such things that make children sweet-tempered. I only wish people knew *that*: then they wouldn't be so stingy about it, you know——"

She had quite forgotten the Duchess by this time, and was a little startled when she heard her voice close to her ear. "You're thinking about something, my dear, and that makes you forget to talk. I ca'n't tell you just now what the moral of that is, but I shall remember it in a bit."

"Perhaps it hasn't one," Alice ventured to remark.

"Tut, tut, child!" said the Duchess. "Every thing's got a moral, if only you can find it." And she squeezed herself up closer to Alice's side as she spoke.

Alice did not much like her keeping so close to her: first, because the Duchess was *very* ugly; and secondly, because she was exactly the right height to rest her chin on Alice's shoulder, and it was an uncomfortably sharp chin. However, she did not like to be rude: so she bore it as well as she could.

"The game's going on rather better now," she said, by way of keeping up the conversation a little.

"'Tis so," said the Duchess: "and the moral of that is – 'Oh, 'tis love, 'tis love, that makes the world go round!'"

"Somebody said," Alice whispered, "that it's done by everybody minding their own business!"

"Ah, well! It means much the same thing," said the Duchess, digging her sharp little chin into Alice's shoulder as she added "and the moral of *that* is – 'Take care of the sense, and the sounds will take care of themselves.'"

"How fond she is of finding morals in things!" Alice thought to herself.

"I dare say you're wondering why I don't put my arm round your waist," the Duchess said, after a pause: "the reason is, that I'm doubtful about the temper of your flamingo. Shall I try the experiment?"

"He might bite," Alice cautiously replied, not feeling at all anxious to have the experiment tried.

"Very true," said the Duchess: "flamingoes and mustard both bite. And the moral of that is – 'Birds of a feather flock together.'"

"Only mustard isn't a bird," Alice remarked.

"Right, as usual," said the Duchess: "what a clear way you have of putting things!"

"It's a mineral, I *think*," said Alice.

"Of course it is," said the Duchess, who seemed ready to agree to everything that Alice said: "there's a large mustard-mine near here. And the moral of that is – 'The more there is of mine, the less there is of yours.'"

"Oh, I know!" exclaimed Alice, who had not attended to this last remark. "It's a vegetable. It doesn't look like one, but it is."

"I quite agree with you," said the Duchess; "and the moral of that is – 'Be what you would seem to be' – or, if you'd like it put more simply –

'Never imagine yourself not to be otherwise than what it might appear to others that what you were or might have been was not otherwise than what you had been would have appeared to them to be otherwise.'"

"I think I should understand that better," Alice said very politely, "if I had it written down: but I ca'n't quite follow it as you say it."

"That's nothing to what I could say if I chose," the Duchess replied, in a pleased tone.

"Pray don't trouble yourself to say it any longer than that," said Alice.

"Oh, don't talk about trouble!" said the Duchess. "I make you a present of everything I've said as yet."

"A cheap sort of present!" thought Alice. "I'm glad people don't give birthday-presents like that!" But she did not venture to say it out loud.

"Thinking again?" the Duchess asked, with another dig of her sharp little chin.

"I've a right to think," said Alice sharply, for she was beginning to feel a little worried.

"Just about as much right," said the Duchess, "as pigs have to fly; and the m——"

But here, to Alice's great surprise, the Duchess's voice died away, even in the middle of her favourite word "moral," and the arm that was linked into hers began to tremble. Alice looked up, and there stood the Queen in front of them, with her arms folded, frowning like a thunderstorm.

"A fine day, your Majesty," the Duchess began in a low, weak voice.

"Now, I give you fair warning," shouted the Queen, stamping on the ground as she spoke; "either you or your head must be off, and that in about half no time! Take your choice!"

The Duchess took her choice, and was gone in a moment.

"Let's go on with the game," the Queen said to Alice; and Alice was too much frightened to say a word, but slowly followed her back to the croquet-ground.

The other guests had taken advantage of the Queen's absence, and were resting in the shade: however, the moment they saw her, they hurried back to the game, the Queen merely remarking that a moment's delay would cost them their lives.

All the time they were playing the Queen never left off quarrelling with the other players, and shouting "Off with his head!' or "Off with her head!" Those whom she sentenced were taken into custody by the soldiers, who of course had to leave off being arches to do this, so that, by the end of half an hour or so, there were no arches left, and all the players, except the King, the Queen, and Alice, were in custody and under sentence of execution.

Then the Queen left off, quite out of breath, and said to Alice, "Have you seen the Mock Turtle yet?"

"No," said Alice. "I don't even know what a Mock Turtle is."

"It's the thing Mock Turtle Soup is made from," said the Queen.

"I never saw one, or heard of one," said Alice.

"Come on, then," said the Queen, "and he shall tell you his history."

As they walked off together, Alice heard the King say in a low voice, to the company generally, "You are all pardoned." "Come, *that's* a good thing!" she said to herself, for she had felt quite unhappy at the number of executions the Queen had ordered.

They very soon came upon a Gryphon, lying fast asleep in the sun. (If you don't know what a Gryphon is, look at the picture.) "Up, lazy thing!" said the Queen, "and take this young lady to see the Mock Turtle, and to hear his history. I must go back and see after some executions I have ordered"; and she walked off, leaving Alice alone

with the Gryphon. Alice did not quite like the look of the creature, but on the whole she thought it would be quite as safe to stay with it as to go after that savage Queen: so she waited.

The Gryphon sat up and rubbed his eyes: then it watched the Queen till she was out of sight: then it chuckled. "What fun!" said the Gryphon, half to itself, half to Alice.

"What *is* the fun?" said Alice.

"Why, *she*," said the Gryphon. "It's all her fancy, that: they never executes nobody, you know. Come on!"

"Everybody says 'come on!' here," thought Alice, as she went slowly after it: "I never was so ordered about before, in all my life, never!"

They had not gone far before they saw the Mock Turtle in the distance, sitting sad and lonely on a little ledge of rock, and, as they came nearer, Alice could hear him sighing as if his heart would break. She pitied him deeply. "What is his sorrow?" she asked the Gryphon. And the Gryphon answered, very nearly in the same words as before, "It's all his fancy, that: he hasn't got no sorrow, you know. Come on!"

So they went up to the Mock Turtle, who looked at them with large eyes full of tears, but said nothing.

"This here young lady," said the Gryphon, "she wants for to know your history, she do."

"I'll tell it her," said the Mock Turtle in a deep, hollow tone. "Sit down, both of you, and don't speak a word till I've finished."

So they sat down, and nobody spoke for some minutes. Alice thought to herself "I don't see how he can *ever* finish, if he doesn't begin." But she waited patiently.

"Once," said the Mock Turtle at last, with a deep sigh, "I was a real Turtle."

These words were followed by a very long silence, broken only by an occasional exclamation of "Hjckrrh!" from the Gryphon, and the constant heavy sobbing of the Mock Turtle. Alice was very nearly getting up and saying "Thank you, Sir, for your interesting story," but she could not help thinking there *must* be more to come, so she sat still and said nothing.

"When we were little," the Mock Turtle went on at last, more calmly, though still sobbing a little now and then, "we went to school in the sea. The master was an old Turtle – we used to call him Tortoise——"

"Why did you call him Tortoise, if he wasn't one?" Alice asked.

"We called him Tortoise because he taught us," said the Mock Turtle angrily. "Really you are very dull!"

"You ought to be ashamed of yourself for asking such a simple

question," added the Gryphon; and then they both sat silent and looked at poor Alice, who felt ready to sink into the earth. At last the Gryphon said to the Mock Turtle "Drive on, old fellow! Don't be all day about it!", and he went on in these words:—

"Yes, we went to school in the sea, though you mayn't believe it ——"

"I never said I didn't!" interrupted Alice.

"You did," said the Mock Turtle.

"Hold your tongue!" added the Gryphon, before Alice could speak again. The Mock Turtle went on.

"We had the best of educations – in fact, we went to school every day——"

"*I've* been to a day-school, too," said Alice. "You needn't be so proud as all that."

"With extras?" asked the Mock Turtle, a little anxiously.

"Yes," said Alice: "we learned French and music."

"And washing?" said the Mock Turtle.

"Certainly not!" said Alice indignantly.

"Ah! Then yours wasn't a really good school," said the Mock Turtle in a tone of great relief. "Now, at *ours*, they had, at the end of the bill, 'French, music, *and washing* – extra.'"

"You couldn't have wanted it much," said Alice; "living at the bottom of the sea."

"I couldn't afford to learn it," said the Mock Turtle with a sigh. "I only took the regular course."

"What was that?" inquired Alice.

"Reeling and Writhing, of course, to begin with," the Mock Turtle replied; "and then the different branches of Arithmetic – Ambition, Distraction, Uglification, and Derision."

"I never heard of 'Uglification,'" Alice ventured to say, "What is it?"

The Gryphon lifted up both its paws in surprise. "Never heard of uglifying!" it exclaimed. "You know what to beautify is, I suppose?"

"Yes," said Alice doubtfully: "it means – to – make – anything – prettier."

"Well, then," the Gryphon went on, "if you don't know what to uglify is you *are* a simpleton."

Alice did not feel encouraged to ask any more questions about it: so she turned to the Mock Turtle, and said "What else had you to learn?"

"Well, there was Mystery," the Mock Turtle replied, counting off the subjects on his flappers, – "Mystery, ancient and modern, with Seaography: then Drawling – the Drawling-master was an old conger-eel, that used to come once a week: *he* taught us Drawling, Stretching, and Fainting in Coils."

"What was *that* like?" said Alice.

"Well, I ca'n't show it you, myself," the Mock Turtle said: "I''m too stiff. And the Gryphon never learnt it."

"Hadn't time," said the Gryphon: "I went to the classical master, though. He was an old crab, *he* was."

"I never went to him," the Mock Turtle said with a sigh. "He taught Laughing and Grief, they used to say."

"So he did, so he did," said the Gryphon, sighing in his turn; and both creatures hid their faces in their paws.

"And how many hours a day did you do lessons?" said Alice, in a hurry to change the subject.

"Ten hours the first day," said the Mock Turtle: "nine the next, and so on."

"What a curious plan!" exclaimed Alice.

"That's the reason they're called lessons," the Gryphon remarked: "because they lessen from day to day."

This was quite a new idea to Alice, and she thought it over a little before she made her next remark. "Then the eleventh day must have been a holiday?"

"Of course it was," said the Mock Turtle.

"And how did you manage on the twelfth?" Alice went on eagerly.

"That's enough about lessons," the Gryphon interrupted in a very decided tone. "Tell her something about the games now."

CHAPTER 10

The Lobster-Quadrille

THE Mock Turtle sighed deeply, and drew the back of one flapper across his eyes. He looked at Alice and tried to speak, but, for a minute or two, sobs choked his voice. "Same as if he had a bone in his throat," said the Gryphon; and it set to work shaking him and punching him in the back. At last the Mock Turtle recovered his voice, and, with tears running down his cheeks, he went on again:—

"You may not have lived much under the sea—" ("I haven't," said Alice) "—and perhaps you were never even introduced to a lobster—" (Alice began to say "I once tasted——" but checked herself hastily, and said "No, never") "—so you can have no idea what a delightful thing a Lobster-Quadrille is!"

"No, indeed," said Alice. "What sort of a dance is it?"

"Why," said the Gryphon, "you first form into a line along the sea-shore——"

"Two lines!" cried the Mock Turtle. "Seals, turtles, salmon, and so on: then, when you've cleared all the jelly-fish out of the way——"

"*That* generally takes some time," interrupted the Gryphon.

"—you advance twice——"

"Each with a lobster as a partner!" cried the Gryphon.

"Of course," the Mock Turtle said: "advance twice, set to partners——"

"—change lobsters, and retire in same order," continued the Gryphon.

"Then, you know," the Mock Turtle went on, "you throw the——"

"The lobsters!" shouted the Gryphon, with a bound into the air.

"—as far out to sea as you can——"

"Swim after them!" screamed the Gryphon.

"Turn a somersault in the sea!" cried the Mock Turtle, capering wildly about.

"Change lobsters again!" yelled the Gryphon at the top of its voice.

"Back to land again, and – that's all the first figure," said the Mock Turtle, suddenly dropping his voice; and the two creatures, who had been jumping about like mad things all this time, sat down again very sadly and quietly, and looked at Alice.

"It must be a very pretty dance," said Alice timidly.

"Would you like to see a little of it?" said the Mock Turtle.

"Very much indeed," said Alice.

"Come, let's try the first figure!" said the Mock Turtle to the Gryphon. "We can do it without lobsters, you know. Which shall sing?"

"Oh, *you* sing," said the Gryphon. "I've forgotten the words."

So they began solemnly dancing round and round Alice, every now and then treading on her toes when they passed too close, and waving their fore-paws to mark the time while the Mock Turtle sang this, very slowly and sadly:——

"Will you walk a little faster?" said a whiting to a snail,
"There's a porpoise close behind us, and he's treading on my tail.
See how eagerly the lobsters and the turtles all advance!
They are waiting on the shingle – will you come and join the dance?
 Will you, wo'nt you, will you, wo'nt you, will you join the
  dance?
 Will you, wo'nt you, will you, wo'nt you, wo'nt you join the
  dance?

"You can really have no notion how delightful it will be
When they take us up and throw us, with the lobsters, out to sea!"
But the snail replied "Too far, too far!", and gave a look askance—
Said he thanked the whiting kindly, but he would not join the dance.
    Would not, could not, would not, could not, would not join the
        dance.
    Would not, could not, would not, could not, could not join the
        dance.

"What matters it how far we go?" his scaly friend replied.
"There is another shore, you know, upon the other side.
The further off from England the nearer is to France—
Then turn not pale, beloved snail, but come and join the dance.
    Will you, wo'nt you, will you, wo'nt you, will you join the
        dance?
    Will you, wo'nt you, will you, wo'nt you, wo'nt you join the
        dance.

"Thank you, it's a very interesting dance to watch," said Alice, feeling very glad that it was over at last: "and I do so like that curious song about the whiting!"

"Oh, as to the whiting," said the Mock Turtle, "they – you've seen them, of course?"

"Yes," said Alice, "I've often seen them at dinn——" she checked herself hastily.

"I don't know where Dinn may be," said the Mock Turtle; "but, if you've seen them so often, of course you know what they're like?"

"I believe so," Alice replied thoughtfully. "They have their tails in their mouths – and they're all over crumbs."

"You're wrong about the crumbs," said the Mock Turtle: "crumbs would all wash off in the sea. But they *have* their tails in their mouths; and the reason is——" here the Mock Turtle yawned and shut his eyes. "Tell her about the reason and all that," he said to the Gryphon.

"The reason is," said the Gryphon, "that they *would* go with the lobsters to the dance. So they got thrown out to sea. So they had to fall a long way. So they got their tails fast in their mouths. So they couldn't get them out again. That's all."

"Thank you," said Alice, "it's very interesting. I never knew so much about a whiting before."

"I can tell you more than that, if you like," said the Gryphon. "Do you know why it's called a whiting?"

"I never thought about it," said Alice. "Why?"

"*It does the boots and shoes,*" the Gryphon replied very solemnly.

Alice was thoroughly puzzled. "Does the boots and shoes!" she repeated in a wondering tone.

"Why, what are *your* shoes done with!" said the Gryphon. "I mean, what makes them so shiny?"

Alice looked down at them, and considered a little before she gave her answer. "They're done with blacking, I believe."

"Boots and shoes under the sea," the Gryphon went on in a deep voice, "are done with whiting. Now you know."

"And what are they made of?" Alice asked in a tone of great curiosity.

"Soles and eels, of course," the Gryphon replied, rather impatiently: "any shrimp could have told you that."

"If I'd been the whiting," said Alice, whose thoughts were still running on the song, "I'd have said to the porpoise 'Keep back, please! We don't want *you* with us!'"

"They were obliged to have him with them," the Mock Turtle said. "No wise fish would go anywhere without a porpoise."

"Wouldn't it, really?" said Alice, in a tone of great surprise

"Of course not," said the Mock Turtle. "Why, if a fish came to *me*, and told me he was going a journey, I should say 'With what porpoise?'"

"Don't you mean 'purpose'?" said Alice.

"I mean what I say," the Mock Turtle replied, in an offended tone. And the Gryphon added "Come, let's hear some of *your* adventures."

"I could tell you my adventures – beginning from this morning," said Alice a little timidly; "but it's no use going back to yesterday, because I was a different person then."

"Explain all that," said the Mock Turtle.

"No, no! The adventures first," said the Gryphon in an impatient tone: "explanations take such a dreadful time."

So Alice began telling them her adventures from the time when she first saw the White Rabbit. She was a little nervous about it, just at first, the two creatures got so close to her, one on each side, and opened their eyes and mouths so *very* wide; but she gained courage as she went on. Her listeners were perfectly quiet till she got to the part about her repeating, "*You are old, Father William,*" to the Caterpillar, and the words all coming different, and then the Mock Turtle drew a long breath, and said "That's very curious!"

"It's all about as curious as it can be," said the Gryphon.

"It all came different!" the Mock Turtle repeated thoughtfully. "I

should like to hear her try and repeat something now. Tell her to begin." He looked at the Gryphon as if he thought it had some kind of authority over Alice.

"Stand up and repeat "'*Tis the voice of the sluggard*,'" said the Gryphon.

"How the creatures order one about, and make one repeat lessons!" thought Alice. "I might just as well be at school at once." However, she got up, and began to repeat it, but her head was so full of the Lobster-Quadrille, that she hardly knew what she was saying; and the words came very queer indeed:—

'Tis the voice of the Lobster: I heard him declare
    "You have baked me too brown, I must sugar my hair."
As a duck with its eyelids, so he with his nose
    Trims his belt and his buttons, and turns out his toes.
When the sands are all dry, he is gay as a lark,
    And will talk in contemptuous tones of the Shark:
But, when the ride rises and sharks are around,
    His voice has a timid and tremulous sound.

"That's different from what *I* used to say when I was a child," said the Gryphon.

"Well, *I* never heard it before," said the Mock Turtle; "but it sounds uncommon nonsense."

Alice said nothing: she had sat down with her face in her hands, wondering if anything would *ever* happen in a natural way again.

"I should like to have it explained," said the Mock Turtle.

"She ca'n't explain it," said the Gryphon hastily. "Go on with the next verse."

"But about his toes?" the Mock Turtle persisted. "How *could* he turn them out with his nose, you know?"

"It's the first position in dancing," Alice said; but she was dreadfully puzzled by the whole thing, and longed to change the subject.

"Go on with the next verse," the Gryphon repeated: it begins '*I passed by his garden.*'"

Alice did not dare to disobey though she felt sure it would all come wrong, and she went on in a trembling voice:—

I passed by his garden, and marked, with one eye,
    How the Owl and the Panther were sharing a pie:
The Panther took pie-crust, and gravy, and meat,
    While the Owl had the dish as its share of the treat.
When the pie was all finished, the Owl, as a boon,
    Was kindly permitted to pocket the spoon:
While the Panther received knife and fork with a growl,
    And concluded the banquet by——

"What *is* the use of repeating all that stuff?" the Mock Turtle interrupted, "if you don't explain it as you go on? It's by far the most confusing thing *I* ever heard!"

"Yes, I think you'd better leave off," said the Gryphon, and Alice was only too glad to do so.

"Shall we try another figure of the Lobster-Quadrille?" the Gryphon went on. "Or would you like the Mock Turtle to sing you another song?"

"Oh, a song, please, if the Mock Turtle would be so kind," Alice replied, so eagerly that the Gryphon said, in a rather offended tone, "Hm! No accounting for tastes! Sing her '*Turtle Soup*,' will you, old fellow?"

The Mock Turtle sighed deeply, and began, in a voice choked with sobs, to sing this:—

> *Beautiful Soup, so rich and green,*
> *Waiting in a hot tureen!*
> *Who for such dainties would not stoop?*
> *Soup of the evening, beautiful Soup!*
> *Soup of the evening, beautiful Soup!*
> > *Beau—ootiful Soo—oop!*
> > *Beau—ootiful Soo—oop!*
> *Soo—oop of the e—e—evening,*
> > *Beautiful, beautiful Soup!*
> *Beautiful Soup! Who cares for fish,*
> *Game, or any other dish!*
>
> *Who would not give all else for two p*
> *ennyworth only of beautiful Soup?*
> *Pennyworth only of beautiful Soup?*
> > *Beau—ootiful Soo—oop!*
> > *Beau—ootiful Soo—oop!*
> *Soo—oop of the e—e—evening,*
> > *Beautiful, beauti—FUL SOUP!*

"Chorus again!" cried the Gryphon, and the Mock Turtle had just begun to repeat it, when a cry of "The trial's beginning!" was heard in the distance.

'Come on!" cried the Gryphon, and, taking Alice by the hand, it hurried off, without waiting for the end of the song.

"What trial is it?" Alice panted as she ran; but the Gryphon only answered "Come on!" and ran the faster, while more and more faintly came, carried on the breeze that followed them, the melancholy words:—

> *Soo—oop of the e—e—evening,*
> > *Beautiful, beautiful Soup!*

CHAPTER 11

Who Stole the Tarts?

THE King and Queen of Hearts were seated on their throne when they arrived, with a great crowd assembled about them – all sorts of little birds and beasts, as well as the whole pack of cards: the Knave was standing before them, in chains, with a soldier on each side to guard him; and near the King was the White Rabbit, with a trumpet in one hand, and a scroll of parchment in the other. In the very middle of the court was a table, with a large dish of tarts upon it: they looked so good, that it made Alice quite hungry to look at them – "I wish they'd get the trial done," she thought, "and hand round the refreshments!" But there seemed to be no chance of this; so she began looking at everything about her to pass away the time.

Alice had never been in a court of justice before, but she had read about them in books, and she was quite pleased to find that she knew the name of nearly everything there. "That's the judge," she said to herself, "because of his great wig."

The judge, by the way, was the King; and, as he wore his crown over the wig (look at the frontispiece if you want to see how he did it), he did not look at all comfortable, and it was certainly not becoming.

"And that's the jury-box," thought Alice; "and those twelve creatures," (she was obliged to say "creatures," you see, because some of them were animals, and some were birds,) "I suppose they are the jurors." She said this last word two or three times over to herself, being rather proud of it: for she thought, and rightly too, that very few little girls of her age knew the meaning of it at all. However, "jurymen" would have done just as well.

The twelve jurors were all writing very busily on slates. "What are they doing?" Alice whispered to the Gryphon. "They ca'n't have anything to put down yet, before the trial's begun."

"They're putting down their names," the Gryphon whispered in reply, "for fear they should forget them before the end of the trial."

"Stupid things!" Alice began in a loud indignant voice; but she stopped herself hastily, for the White Rabbit cried out "Silence in the Court!", and the King put on his spectacles and looked anxiously round, to make out who was talking.

Alice could see, as well as if she were looking over their shoulders, that all the jurors were writing down "Stupid things!" on their slates, and she could even make out that one of them didn't know how to spell "stupid," and that he had to ask his neighbour to tell him. "A nice muddle their slates'll be in, before the trial's over!" thought Alice.

One of the jurors had a pencil that squeaked. This, of course, Alice could *not* stand, and she went round the court and got behind him, and very soon found an opportunity of taking it away. She did it so quickly that the poor little juror (it was Bill, the Lizard) could not make out at all what had become of it; so, after hunting all about for it, he was obliged to write with one finger for the rest of the day; and this was of very little use, as it left no mark on the slate.

"Herald, read the accusation!" said the King.

On this the White Rabbit blew three blasts on the trumpet, and then unrolled the parchment-scroll, and read as follows:—

> *The Queen of Hearts, she made some tarts,*
> *All on a summer day:*
> *The Knave of Hearts, he stole those tarts*
> *And took them quite away!*

"Consider your verdict," the King said to the jury.

"Not yet, not yet!" the Rabbit hastily interrupted. "There's a great deal to come before that!"

"Call the first witness," said the King; and the White Rabbit blew three blasts on the trumpet, and called out "First witness!"

The first witness was the Hatter. He came in with a teacup in one hand and a piece of bread-and-butter in the other. "I beg pardon, your Majesty," he began, "for bringing these in; but I hadn't quite finished my tea when I was sent for."

"You ought to have finished," said the King. "When did you begin?"

The Hatter looked at the March Hare, who had followed him into the court, arm-in-arm with the Dormouse. "Fourteenth of March, I *think* it was," he said.

"Fifteenth," said the March Hare.

"Sixteenth," said the Dormouse.

"Write that down," the King said to the jury; and the jury eagerly wrote down all three dates on their slates, and then added them up, and reduced the answer to shillings and pence.

"Take off your hat," the king said to the Hatter.

"It isn't mine," said the Hatter.

"*Stolen!*" the King exclaimed, turning to the jury, who instantly made a memorandum of the fact.

"I keep them to sell," the Hatter added as an explanation. "I've none of my own. I'm a hatter."

Here the Queen put on her spectacles, and began staring hard at the Hatter, who turned pale and fidgeted.

"Give your evidence," said the King; "and don't be nervous, or I'll have you executed on the spot."

This did not seem to encourage the witness at all: he kept shifting from one foot to the other, looking uneasily at the Queen, and in his confusion he bit a large piece out of his teacup instead of the bread-and-butter.

Just at this moment Alice felt a very curious sensation, which puzzled her a good deal until she made out what it was: she was beginning to grow larger again, and she thought at first she would get up and leave the court; but on second thoughts she decided to remain where she was as long as there was room for her.

"I wish you wouldn't squeeze so," said the Dormouse, who was sitting next to her. "I can hardly breathe."

"I ca'n't help it," said Alice very meekly: "I'm growing."

"You've no right to grow *here*," said the Dormouse.

"Don't talk nonsense," said Alice more boldly: "you know you're growing too."

"Yes, but *I* grow at a reasonable pace," said the Dormouse: "not in that ridiculous fashion." And he got up very sulkily and crossed over to the other side of the court.

All this time the Queen had never left off staring at the Hatter, and, just as the Dormouse crossed the court, she said, to one of the officers of the court, "Bring me the list of the singers in the last concert!" on which the wretched Hatter trembled so, that he shook off both his shoes.

"Give your evidence," the King repeated angrily, "or I'll have you executed, whether you're nervous or not."

"I'm a poor man, your Majesty," the Hatter began, in a trembling voice, "and I hadn't begun my tea – not above a week or so – and what with the bread-and-butter getting so thin – and the twinkling of the tea——"

"The twinkling of *what*?" said the King.

"It *began* with the tea," the Hatter replied.

"Of course twinkling *begins* with a T!" said the King sharply. "Do you take me for a dunce? Go on!"

"I'm a poor man," the Hatter went on, "and most things twinkled after that – only the March Hare said——"

"I didn't!" the March Hare interrupted in a great hurry.

"You did!" said the Hatter.

"I deny it!" said the March Hare.

"He denies it," said the King: "leave out that part."

"Well, at any rate, the Dormouse said——" the Hatter went on, looking anxiously round to see if he would deny it too; but the Dormouse denied nothing, being fast asleep.

"After that," continued the Hatter, "I cut some more bread-and-butter——"

"But what did the Dormouse say?" one of the jury asked.

"That I ca'n't remember," said the Hatter.

"You *must* remember," remarked the King, "or I'll have you executed."

The miserable Hatter dropped his teacup and bread-and-butter, and went down on one knee. "I'm a poor man, your Majesty," he began.

"You're a *very* poor *speaker*," said the King.

Here one of the guinea-pigs cheered, and was immediately suppressed by the officers of the court. (As that is rather a hard word, I will just explain to you how it was done. They had a large canvas bag, which tied up at the mouth with strings: into this they slipped the guinea-pig, head first, and then sat upon it.)

"I'm glad I've seen that done," thought Alice. "I've so often read in the newspapers, at the end of trials, 'There was some attempt at applause, which was immediately suppressed by the officers of the court,' and I never understood what it meant till now."

"If that's all you know about it, you may stand down," continued the King.

"I ca'n't go no lower," said the Hatter: "I'm on the floor, as it is."

"Then you may *sit* down," the King replied.

Here the other guinea-pig cheered and was suppressed.

"Come, that finishes the guinea-pigs!" thought Alice. "Now we shall get on better."

"I'd rather finish my tea," said the Hatter, with an anxious look at the Queen, who was reading the list of singers.

"You may go," said the King, and the Hatter hurriedly left the court, without even waiting to put his shoes on.

"——and just take his head off outside," the Queen added to one of the officers; but the Hatter was out of sight before the officer could get to the door.

"Call the next witness!" said the King.

The next witness was the Duchess's cook. She carried the pepper-box in her hand, and Alice guessed who it was, even before she got into the court, by the way the people near the door began sneezing all at once.

"Give your evidence," said the King.

"Sha'n't," said the cook.

The King looked anxiously at the White Rabbit, who said, in a low voice, "Your Majesty must cross-examine *this* witness."

"Well, if I must, I must," the King said with a melancholy air; and, after folding his arms and frowning at the cook till his eyes were nearly out of sight, he said, in a deep voice, "What are tarts made of?"

"Pepper, mostly," said the cook.

"Treacle," said a sleepy voice behind her.

"Collar that Dormouse!" the Queen shrieked out. "Behead that Dormouse! Turn that Dormouse out of court! Suppress him! Pinch him! Off with his whiskers!"

For some minutes the whole court was in confusion, getting the Dormouse turned out, and, by the time they had settled down again, the cook had disappeared.

"Never mind!" said the King, with an air of great relief. "Call the next witness." And, he added, in an under-tone to the Queen, "Really, my dear, *you* must cross-examine the next witness. It quite makes my forehead ache!"

Alice watched the White Rabbit as he fumbled over the list, feeling very curious to see what the next witness would be like, "—for they haven't got much evidence *yet*," she said to herself. Imagine her surprise, when the White Rabbit read out, at the top of his shrill little voice, the name "Alice!"

CHAPTER 12

Alice's Evidence

"HERE!" cried Alice, quite forgetting in the flurry of the moment how large she had grown in the last few minutes, and she jumped up in such a hurry that she tipped over the jury-box with the edge of her skirt, upsetting all the jurymen on to the heads of the crowd below, and there they lay sprawling about, reminding her very much of a globe of gold-fish she had accidentally upset the week before.

"Oh, I *beg* your pardon!" she exclaimed in a tone of great dismay, and began picking them up again as quickly as she could, for the accident of the gold-fish kept running in her head, and she had a vague sort of idea that they must be collected at once and put back into the jury-box, or they would die.

"The trial cannot proceed," said the King, in a very grave voice, "until all the jurymen are back in their proper places – *all*," he repeated with great emphasis, looking hard at Alice as he said so.

Alice looked at the Jury-box, and saw that, in her haste, she had put the Lizard in head downwards, and the poor little thing was waving its tail about in a melancholy way, being quite unable to move. She soon got it out again, and put it right; "not that it signifies much," she said to herself; "I should think it would be *quite* as much use in the trial one way up as the other."

As soon as the jury had a little recovered from the shock of being upset, and their slates and pencils had been found and handed back to them, they set to work very diligently to write out a history of the accident, all except the Lizard, who seemed too much overcome to do anything but sit with its mouth open, gazing up into the roof of the court.

"What do you know about this business?" the King said to Alice.

"Nothing," said Alice.

"Nothing *whatever*?" persisted the King.

"Nothing whatever," said Alice.

"That's very important," the King said, turning to the jury. They were just beginning to write this down on their slates, when the White Rabbit interrupted: "*Un*important, your Majesty means, of course," he said, in a very respectful tone, but frowning and making faces at him as he spoke.

"*Un*important, of course, I meant," the King hastily said, and went on to himself in an under-tone, "important – unimportant – unimportant – important——" as if he were trying which word sounded best.

Some of the jury wrote it down "important," and some "unimportant." Alice could see this, as she was near enough to look over their slates; "but it doesn't matter a bit," she thought to herself.

At this moment the King, who had been for some time busily writing in his note-book, called out "Silence!", and read out from his book, "Rule Forty-two. *All persons more than a mile high to leave the court.*"

Everybody looked at Alice.

"*I'm* not a mile high," said Alice.

"You are," said the King.

"Nearly two miles high," added the Queen.

"Well, I sha'n't go, at any rate," said Alice: "besides, that's not a regular rule: you invented it just now."

"It's the oldest rule in the book," said the King.

"Then it ought to be Number One," said Alice.

The King turned pale, and shut his note-book hastily. "Consider your verdict," he said to the jury, in a low trembling voice.

"There's more evidence to come yet, please your Majesty," said the White Rabbit, jumping up in a great hurry: "this paper had just been picked up."

"What's in it?" said the Queen.

"I haven't opened it yet," said the White Rabbit; "but it seems to be a letter, written by the prisoner to – to somebody."

"It must have been that," said the King, "unless it was written to nobody, which isn't usual, you know."

"Who is it directed to?" said one of the jurymen.

"It isn't directed at all," said the White Rabbit: "in fact, there's nothing written on the *outside*." He unfolded the paper as he spoke, and added "It isn't a letter, after all: it's a set of verses."

"Are they in the prisoner's handwriting?" asked another of the jurymen.

"No, they're not," said the White Rabbit, "and that's the queerest thing about it." (The jury all looked puzzled.)

"He must have imitated somebody else's hand," said the King. (The jury all brightened up again.)

"Please your Majesty," said the Knave, "I didn't write it, and they ca'n't prove that I did: there's no name signed at the end."

"If you didn't sign it," said the King, "that only makes the matter worse. You *must* have meant some mischief, or else you'd have signed your name like an honest man."

There was a general clapping of hands at this: it was the first really clever thing the King had said that day.

"That *proves* his guilt, of course," said the Queen: "so, off with——"

"It doesn't prove anything of the sort!" said Alice. "Why, you don't even know what they're about!"

"Read them," said the King.

The White Rabbit put on his spectacles. "Where shall I begin, please your Majesty?" he asked.

"Begin at the beginning," the King said, very gravely, "and go on till you come to the end: then stop."

There was dead silence in the court, whilst the White Rabbit read out these verses:—

> *They told me you had been to her,*
> *And mentioned me to him:*
> *She gave me a good character,*
> *But said I could not swim.*
>
> *He sent them word I had not gone*
> *(We know it to be true):*
> *If she should push the matter on,*
> *What would become of you?*
>
> *I gave her one, they gave him two,*
> *You gave us three or more;*
> *They all returned from him to you,*
> *Though they were mine before.*
>
> *If I or she should chance to be*
> *Involved in this affair,*
> *He trusts to you to set them free,*
> *Exactly as we were.*
>
> *My notion was that you had been*
> *(Before she had this fit)*
> *An obstacle that came between*
> *Him, and ourselves, and it.*
>
> *Don't let him know she liked them best,*
> *For this must ever be*
> *A secret, kept from all the rest,*
> *Between yourself and me.*

"That's the most important piece of evidence we've heard yet," said the King, rubbing his hands; "so now let the jury——"

"If any one of them can explain it," said Alice, (she had grown so large in the last few minutes that she wasn't a bit afraid of interrupting him,) "I'll give him sixpence. *I* don't believe there's an atom of meaning in it."

The jury all wrote down, on their slates, "*She* doesn't believe there's an atom of meaning in it," but none of them attempted to explain the paper.

"If there's no meaning in it," said the King, "that saves a world of trouble, you know, as we needn't try to find any. And yet I don't know," he went on, spreading out the verses on his knee, and looking at them with one eye; "I seem to see some meaning in them, after all. '—*said I could not swim*—' you ca'n't swim, can you?" he added, turning to the Knave.

The Knave shook his head sadly. "Do I look like it?" he said. (Which he certainly did *not*, being made entirely of cardboard.)

"All right, so far," said the King; and he went on muttering over the verses to himself: "'*We know it to be true*'—that's the jury, of course— '*If she should push the matter on*' – that must be the Queen – '*What would become of you?* – What, indeed! – '*I gave her one, they gave him two*' – why, that must be what he did with the tarts, you know——"

"But it goes on '*they all returned from him to you*,'" said Alice.

"Why, there they are!" said the King, triumphantly, pointing to the tarts on the table. "Nothing can be clearer that *that*. Then again – '*before she had this fit*' – you never had *fits*, my dear, I think?" he said to the Queen.

"Never!" said the Queen, furiously, throwing an inkstand at the Lizard as she spoke. (The unfortunate little Bill had left off writing on his slate with one finger, as he found it made no mark; but he now hastily began again, using the ink, that was trickling down his face, as long as it lasted.)

"Then the words don't *fit* you," said the King, looking round the court with a smile. There was a dead silence.

"It's a pun!" the King added in an angry tone, and everybody laughed. "Let the jury consider their verdict," the King said, for about the twentieth time that day.

"No, no!" said the Queen. "Sentence first – verdict afterwards."

"Stuff and nonsense!" said Alice loudly. "The idea of having the sentence first!"

"Hold your tongue!" said the Queen, turning purple.

"I won't!" said Alice.

"Off with her head!" the Queen shouted at the top of her voice. Nobody moved.

"Who cares for *you*? said Alice (she had grown to her full size by this time). "You're nothing but a pack of cards!"

At this the whole pack rose up into the air, and came flying down upon her; she gave a little scream, half of fright and half of anger, and tried to beat them off, and found herself lying on the bank, with her head in the lap of her sister, who was gently brushing away some dead leaves that had fluttered down from the trees upon her face.

"Wake up, Alice dear!" said her sister. "Why, what a long sleep you've had!"

"Oh, I've had such a curious dream!" said Alice. And she told her sister, as well as she could remember them, all these strange Adventures of hers that you have just been reading about; and, when she had finished, her sister kissed her, and said "It *was* a curious dream, dear, certainly; but now run in to your tea: it's getting late." So Alice got up and ran off, thinking while she ran, as well she might, what a wonderful dream it had been.

But her sister sat still just as she left her, leaning her head on her hand, watching the setting sun, and thinking of little Alice and all her wonderful Adventures, till she too began dreaming after a fashion, and this was her dream:—

First, she dreamed about little Alice herself: once again the tiny hands were clasped upon her knee, and the bright eager eyes were looking up into hers – she could hear the very tones of her voice, and see that queer little toss of her head to keep back the wandering hair that *would* always get into her eyes – and still as she listened, or seemed to listen, the whole place around her became alive with the strange creatures of her little sister's dream.

The long grass rustled at her feet as the White Rabbit hurried by – the frightened Mouse splashed his way through the neighbouring pool – she could hear the rattle of the teacups at the March Hare and his friends shared their never-ending meal, and the shrill voice of the Queen ordering off her unfortunate guests to execution – once more the pig-baby was sneezing on the Duchess's knee, while plates and dishes crashed around it – once more the shriek of the Gryphon, the squeaking of the Lizard's slate-pencil, and the choking of the suppressed guinea-pigs, filled the air, mixed up with the distant sob of the miserable Mock Turtle.

So she sat on, with closed eyes, and half believed herself in Wonderland, though she knew she had but to open them again, and all would change to dull reality – the grass would be only rustling in the wind, and the pool rippling to the waving of the reeds – the rattling teacups would change to tinkling sheep-bells, and the Queen's shrill cries to the voice of the shepherd-boy – and the sneeze of the baby, the shriek of the Gryphon, and all the other queer noises, would change (she knew) to the confused clamour of the busy farm-yard – while the lowing of the cattle in the distance would take the place of the Mock Turtle's heavy sobs.

Lastly, she pictured to herself how this same little sister of hers would, in the aftertime, be herself a grown woman; and how she would keep, through all her riper years, the simple and loving heart of her childhood; and how she would gather about her other little children, and make *their* eyes bright and eager with many a strange tale, perhaps even with the dream of Wonderland of long ago; and how she would feel with all their simple sorrows, and find a pleasure in all their simple joys, remembering her own child-life, and the happy summer days.

❦ II ❧

Through the Looking Glass

and what Alice found there

with fifty illustrations by
Sir John Tenniel

CHILD of the pure unclouded brow
　　And dreaming eyes of wonder!
Though time be fleet, and I and thou
　　Are half a life asunder,
Thy loving smile will surely hail
The love-gift of a fairy-tale.

I have not seen thy sunny face,
　　Nor heard thy silver laughter;
No thought of me shall find a place
　　In thy young life's hearafter —
Enough that now thou wilt not fail
To listen to my fairy-tale.

A tale begun in other days,
　　When summer suns were glowing —
A simple chime, that served to time
　　The rhythm of our rowing —
Whose echoes live in memory yet,
Though envious years would say 'forget'.

Come, hearken then, ere voice of dread,
　　With bitter tidings laden,
Shall summon to unwelcome bed
　　A melancholy maiden!
We are but older children, dear,
Who fret to find our bedtime near.

Without, the frost, the blinding snow,
  The storm-wind's moody madness —
Within, the firelight's ruddy glow
  And childhood's nest of gladness.
The magic words shall hold thee fast:
Thou shalt not heed the raving blast.

And though the shadow of a sigh
  May tremble through the story,
For 'happy summer days' gone by,
  And vanish'd summer glory —
It shall not touch with breath of bale
The pleasance of our fairy-tale.

DRAMATIS PERSONÆ

(As arranged before commencement of game)

WHITE			RED
PIECES	PAWNS	PAWNS	PIECES
Tweedledee	Daisy	Daisy	Humpty Dumpty
Unicorn	Haigha	Messenger	Carpenter
Sheep	Oyster	Oyster	Walrus
W. Queen	'Lily'	Tiger-lily	R. Queen
W. King	Fawn	Rose	R. King
Aged man	Oyster	Oyster	Crow
W. Knight	Hatta	Frog	R. Knight
Tweedledum	Daisy	Daisy	Lion

RED

WHITE.

White Pawn (Alice) to play, and win in eleven moves.

Preface to 1896 Edition

As the chess-problem, given on the previous page, has puzzled some of my readers, it may be well to explain that it is correctly worked out, so far as the *moves* are concerned. The *alternation* of Red and White is perhaps not so strictly observed as it might be, and the "castling" of the three Queens is merely a way of saying that they entered the palace; but the "check" of the White King at move 6, the capture of the Red Knight at move 7, and the final "checkmate" of the Red King, will be found, by any one who will take the trouble to set the pieces and play the moves as directed, to be strictly in accordance with the laws of the game.

The new words, in the poem "Jabberwocky" (see p. 134), have given rise to some differences of opinion as to their pronunciation: so it may be well to give instructions on *that* point also. Pronounce "slithy" as if it were the two words "sly, the": make the "g" *hard* in "gyre" and "gimble": and pronounce "rath" to rhyme with "bath".

For this sixty-first thousand, fresh electrotypes have been taken from the wood-blocks (which, never having been used for printing from, are in as good condition as when first cut in 1871), and the whole book has been set up afresh with new type. If the artistic qualities of this reissue fall short, in any particular, of those possessed by the original issue, it will not be for want of painstaking on the part of author, publisher, or printer.

I take this opportunity of announcing that the Nursery "Alice", hitherto priced at four shillings, net, is now to be had on the same terms as the ordinary shilling picture-books—although I feel sure that it is, in every quality (except the *text* itself, in which I am not qualified to pronounce), greatly superior to them. Four shillings was a perfectly reasonable price to charge, considering the very heavy initial outlay I had incurred: still, as the Public have practically said, "We will *not* give more than a shilling for a picture-book, however artistically got-up," I am content to reckon my outlay on the book as so much dead loss, and, rather than let the little ones, for whom it was written, go without it, I am selling it at a price which is, to me, much the same thing as *giving* it away.

Christmas, 1896

CHAPTER 1

Looking-Glass House

ONE thing was certain, that the *white* kitten had had nothing to do with it – it was the black kitten's fault entirely. For the white kitten had been having its face washed by the old cat for the last quarter of an hour (and bearing it pretty well, considering): so you see that it *couldn't* have had any hand in the mischief.

The way Dinah washed her children's faces was this: first she held the poor thing down by its ear with one paw, and then with the other paw she rubbed its face all over, the wrong way, beginning at the nose: and just now, as I said, she was hard at work on the white kitten, which was lying quite still and trying to purr – no doubt feeling that it was all meant for its good.

But the black kitten had been finished with earlier in the afternoon, and so, while Alice was sitting curled up in a corner of the great armchair, half talking to herself and half asleep, the kitten had been having a grand game of romps with the ball of worsted Alice had been trying to wind up, and had been rolling it up and down till it had all come undone again; and there it was, spread over the hearth-rug, all knots and tangles, with the kitten running after its own tail in the middle.

"Oh, you wicked wicked little thing!" cried Alice, catching up the kitten, and giving it a little kiss to make it understand that it was in disgrace. "Really, Dinah ought to have taught you better manners! You *ought*, Dinah, you know you ought!" she added, looking reproachfully at the old cat, and speaking in as cross a voice as she could manage – and then she scrambled back into the arm-chair, taking the kitten and the worsted with her, and began winding up the ball again. But she didn't get on very fast, as she was talking all the time, sometimes to the kitten, and sometimes to herself. Kitty sat very demurely on her knee, pretending to watch the progress of the winding, and now and then putting out one paw and gently touching the ball, as if it would be glad to help if it might.

"Do you know what to-morrow is, Kitty?" Alice began. "You'd have guessed if you'd been up in the window with me – only Dinah was making you tidy, so you couldn't. I was watching the boys getting in sticks for the bonfire – and it wants plenty of sticks, Kitty! Only it got so cold, and it snowed so, they had to leave off. Never mind, Kitty, we'll go and see the bonfire tomorrow." Here Alice wound two or three turns of the worsted round the kitten's neck, just to see how it would look: this led to a scramble, in which the ball rolled down upon the floor, and yards and yards of it got unwound again.

"Do you know, I was so angry, Kitty," Alice went on, as soon as they were comfortably settled again, "when I saw all the mischief you had been doing, I was very nearly opening the window, and putting you out into the snow! And you'd have deserved it, you little mischievous darling! What have you got to say for yourself? Now don't interrupt me!" she went on, holding up one finger. "I'm going to tell you all your faults. Number one: you squeaked twice while Dinah was washing your face this morning. Now you ca'n't deny it, Kitty: I heard you! What's that you say?" (pretending that the kitten was speaking). "Her paw

went into your eye? Well, that's *your* fault for keeping your eyes open –
if you'd shut them tight up, it wouldn't have happened. Now don't
make any more excuses, but listen! Number two: you pulled Snowdrop
away by the tail just as I had put down the saucer of milk before her!
What, you were thirsty, were you? How do you know she wasn't thirsty
too? Now for number three: you unwound every bit of the worsted
while I wasn't looking!

"That's three faults, Kitty, and you've not been punished for any of
them yet. You know I'm saving up all your punishments for Wednesday

week – Suppose they had saved up all *my* punishments?" she went on, talking more to herself than the kitten. "What *would* they do at the end of a year? I should be sent to prison, I suppose, when the day came. Or – let me see – suppose each punishment was to be going without a dinner: then, when the miserable day came, I should have to go without fifty dinners at once! Well, I shouldn't mind *that* much! I'd far rather go without them than eat them!

"Do you hear the snow against the window-panes, Kitty? How nice and soft it sounds! Just as if some one was kissing the window all over outside. I wonder if the snow *loves* the trees and fields, that it kisses them so gently? And then it covers them up snug, you know, with a white quilt; and perhaps it says 'Go to sleep, darlings, till the summer comes again.' And when they wake up in the summer, Kitty, they dress themselves all in green, and dance about – whenever the wind blows – oh, that's very pretty!" cried Alice, dropping the ball of worsted to clap her hands. "And I do so *wish* it was true! I'm sure the woods look sleepy in the autumn, when the leaves are getting brown.

"Kitty, can you play chess? Now, don't smile, my dear, I'm asking it seriously. Because, when we were playing just now, you watched just as if you understood it: and when I said 'Check!' you purred! Well, it *was* a nice check, Kitty, and really I might have won, if it hadn't been for that nasty Knight, that came wriggling down among my pieces. Kitty, dear, let's pretend——" And here I wish I could tell you half the things Alice used to say, beginning with her favourite phrase "Let's pretend." She had had quite a long argument with her sister only the day before – all because Alice had begun with "Let's pretend we're kings and queens;" and her sister, who liked being very exact, had argued that they couldn't, because there were only two of them, and Alice had been reduced at last to say, "Well, *you* can be one of them, then, and *I'll* be all the rest." And once she had really frightened her old nurse by shouting suddenly in her ear, "Nurse! Do let's pretend that I'm a hungry hyæna, and you're a bone!"

But this is taking us away from Alice's speech to the kitten. "Let's pretend that you're the Red Queen, Kitty! Do you know, I think if you sat up and folded your arms, you'd look exactly like her. Now do try, there's a dear!" And Alice got the Red Queen off the table, and set it up before the kitten as a model for it to imitate; however, the thing didn't succeed, principally, Alice said, because the kitten wouldn't fold its arms properly. So, to punish it, she held it up to the Looking-glass, that it might see how sulky it was, "——and if you're not good directly," she added, "I'll put you through into Looking-glass House. How would you like *that*?

"Now, if you'll only attend, Kitty, and not talk so much, I'll tell you all my ideas about Looking-glass House. First, there's the room you can see through the glass – that's just the same as our drawing-room, only the things go the other way. I can see all of it when I get upon a chair – all but the bit just behind the fire-place. Oh! I do so wish I could see *that* bit! I want so much to know whether they've a fire in the winter: you never *can* tell, you know, unless our fire smokes, and then smoke comes up in that room too – but that may be only pretence, just to make it look as if they had a fire. Well then, the books are something like our books, only the words go the wrong way: I know *that*, because I've held up one of our books to the glass, and then they hold up one in the other room.

"How would you like to live in Looking-glass House, Kitty? I wonder if they'd give you milk in there? Perhaps Looking-glass milk isn't good to drink – but oh, Kitty! now we come to the passage. You can just see a little *peep* of the passage in Looking-glass House, if you leave the door of our drawing-room wide open: and it's very like our passage as far as you can see, only you know it may be quite different on beyond. Oh, Kitty, how nice it would be if we could only get through into Looking-glass House! I'm sure it's got, oh! such beautiful things in it! Let's pretend there's a way of getting through into it, somehow, Kitty. Let's pretend the glass has got all soft like gauze, so that we can get through. Why, it's turning into a sort of mist now, I declare! It'll be easy enough to get through——" She was up on the chimney-piece while she said this, though she hardly knew how she had got there. And certainly the glass *was* beginning to melt away, just like a bright silvery mist.

In another moment Alice was through the glass, and had jumped lightly down into the Looking-glass room. The very first thing she did was to look whether there was a fire in the fireplace, and she was quite pleased to find that there was a real one, blazing away as brightly as the one she had left behind. "So I shall be as warm here as I was in the old room," thought Alice: "warmer, in fact, because there'll be no one here to scold me away from the fire. Oh, what fun it'll be, when they see me through the glass in here, and ca'n't get at me!"

Then she began looking about, and noticed that what could be seen from the old room was quite common and uninteresting, but that all the rest was as different as possible. For instance, the pictures on the wall

next the fire seemed to be all alive, and the very clock on the chimney-piece (you know you can only see the back of it in the Looking-glass) had got the face of a little old man, and grinned at her.

"They don't keep this room so tidy as the other," Alice thought to herself, as she noticed several of the chessmen down in the hearth among the cinders; but in another moment, with a little "Oh!" of

surprise, she was down on her hands and knees watching them. The chessmen were walking about, two and two!

"Here are the Red King and the Red Queen," Alice said (in a whisper, for fear of frightening them), "and there are the White King and the White Queen sitting on the edge of the shovel – and here are two castles walking arm in arm – I don't think they can hear me," she

went on, as she put her head closer down, "and I'm nearly sure they ca'n't see me. I feel somehow as if I was getting invisible——"

Here something began squeaking on the table behind Alice, and made her turn her head just in time to see one of the White Pawns roll over and begin kicking: she watched it with great curiosity to see what would happen next.

"It is the voice of my child!" the White Queen cried out, as she rushed past the King, so violently that she knocked him over among the cinders. "My precious Lily! My imperial kitten!" and she began scrambling wildly up the side of the fender.

"Imperial fiddlestick!" said the King, rubbing his nose, which had been hurt by the fall. He had a right to be a *little* annoyed with the Queen, for he was covered with ashes from head to foot.

Alice was very anxious to be of use, and, as the poor little Lily was nearly screaming herself into a fit, she hastily picked up the Queen and set her on the table by the side of her noisy little daughter.

The Queen gasped, and sat down: the rapid journey through the air had quite taken away her breath, and for a minute or two she could do nothing but hug the little Lily in silence. As soon as she had recovered her breath a little, she called out to the White King, who was sitting sulkily among the ashes, "Mind the volcano!"

"What volcano?" said the King, looking up anxiously into the fire, as if he thought that was the most likely place to find one.

"Blew – me – up," panted the Queen, who was still a little out of breath. "Mind you come up – the regular way – don't get blown up!"

Alice watched the White King as he slowly struggled up from bar to bar, till at last she said, "Why, you'll be hours and hours getting to the table at that rate. I'd far better help you, hadn't I?" But the King took no notice of the question: it was quite clear that he could neither hear her nor see her.

So Alice picked him up very gently, and lifted him across more slowly than she had lifted the Queen, that she mightn't take his breath

away: but before she put him on the table, she thought she might as well dust him a little, he was so covered with ashes.

She said afterwards that she had never seen in all her life such a face as the King made, when he found himself held in the air by an invisible hand, and being dusted: he was far too much astonished to cry out, but his eyes and his mouth went on getting larger and larger, and rounder and rounder, till her hand shook so with laughing that she nearly let him drop upon the floor.

"Oh! *please* don't make such faces, my dear!" she cried out, quite forgetting that the King couldn't hear her. "You make me laugh so that I can hardly hold you! And don't keep your mouth so wide open! All the ashes will get into it – there, now I think you're tidy enough!" she added, as she smoothed his hair, and set him upon the table near the Queen.

The King immediately fell flat on his back, and lay perfectly still; and Alice was a little alarmed at what she had done, and went round the room to see if she could find any water to throw over him. However, she could find nothing but a bottle of ink, and when she got back with it she found he had recovered, and he and the Queen were talking together in a frightened whisper – so low, that Alice could hardly hear what they said.

The King was saying, "I assure you, my dear, I turned cold to the very ends of my whiskers!"

To which the Queen replied, "You haven't got any whiskers."

"The horror of that moment," the King went on, 'I shall never, *never* forget!"

"You will, though," the Queen said, "if you don't make a memorandum of it."

Alice looked on with great interest as the King took an enormous memorandum-book out of his pocket, and began writing. A sudden thought struck her, and she took hold of the end of the pencil, which came some way over his shoulder, and began writing for him.

The poor King looked puzzled and unhappy, and struggled with the pencil for some time without saying anything; but Alice was too strong for him, and at last he panted out, "My dear! I really *must* get a thinner pencil. I ca'n't manage this one a bit: it writes all manner of things that I don't intend——"

"What manner of things?" said the Queen, looking over the book (in which Alice had put *'The White Knight is sliding down the poker. He balances very badly'*). "That's not a memorandum of *your* feelings!"

There was a book lying near Alice on the table, and while she sat watching the White King (for she was still a little anxious about him, and had the ink all ready to throw over him, in case he fainted again), she turned over the leaves, to find some part that she could read, "for it's all in some language I don't know," she said to herself.

It was like this.

JABBERWOCKY.

'Twas brillig, and the slithy toves
Did gyre and gimble in the wabe:
All mimsy were the borogoves,
And the mome raths outgrabe.

She puzzled over this for some time, but at last a bright thought struck her. "Why, it's a Looking-glass book, of course! And, if I hold it up to a glass, the words will all go the right way again."

This was the poem that Alice read.

JABBERWOCKY.

'Twas brillig, and the slithy toves
    Did gyre and gimble in the wabe:
All mimsy were the borogoves,
    And the mome raths outgrabe.

"Beware the Jabberwock, my son!
    The jaws that bite, the claws that catch!
Beware the Jubjub bird, and shun
    The frumious Bandersnatch!"

He took his vorpal sword in hand:
    Long time the manxome foe he sought –
So rested he by the Tumtum tree,
    And stood awhile in thought.

And, as in uffish thought he stood,
    The Jabberwock, with eyes of flame,
Came whiffling through the tulgey wood,
    And burbled as it came!

One, two! One, two! And through and through
    The vorpal blade went snicker-snack!
He left it dead, and with its head
    He went galumphing back.

"And hast thou slain the Jabberwock?
    Come to my arms, my beamish boy!
O frabjous day! Callooh! Callay!"
    He chortled in his joy.

'Twas brillig, and the slithy toves
    Did gyre and gimble in the wabe:
All mimsy were the borogoves,
    And the mome raths outgrabe.

"It seems very pretty," she said when she had finished it, "but it's *rather* hard to understand!" (You see she didn't like to confess, even to herself, that she couldn't make it out at all.) "Somehow it seems to fill my head with ideas – only I don't exactly know what they are! However, *somebody* killed *something*: that's clear, at any rate——

"But oh!" thought Alice, suddenly jumping up, "if I don't make

haste, I shall have to go back through the Looking-glass, before I've seen what the rest of the house is like! Let's have a look at the garden first!" She was out of the room in a moment, and ran down stairs – or, at least, it wasn't exactly running, but a new invention for getting down stairs quickly and easily, as Alice said to herself. She just kept the tips of her fingers on the hand-rail, and floated gently down without even touching the stairs with her feet: then she floated on through the hall, and would have gone straight out at the door in the same way, if she hadn't caught hold of the door-post. She was getting a little giddy with so much floating in the air, and was rather glad to find herself walking again in the natural way.

CHAPTER 2

The Garden of Live Flowers

"I SHOULD see the garden far better," said Alice to herself, "if I could get to the top of that hill: and here's a path that leads straight to it – at least, no, it doesn't do *that*——" (after going a few yards along the path, and turning several sharp corners), "but I suppose it will at last. But how curiously it twists! It's more like a corkscrew than a path! Well, *this* turn goes to the hill I suppose – no, it doesn't! This goes straight back to the house! Well then, I'll try it the other way."

And so she did: wandering up and down, and trying turn after turn, but always coming back to the house, do what she would. Indeed, once, when she turned a corner rather more quickly than usual, she ran against it before she could stop herself.

"It's no use talking about it," Alice said, looking up at the house and pretending it was arguing with her. "I'm *not* going in again yet. I know I should have to get through the Looking-glass again – back into the old room – and there'd be an end of all my adventures!"

So, resolutely turning her back upon the house, she set out once more down the path, determined to keep straight on till she got to the hill. For a few minutes all went on well, and she was just saying "I really *shall* do it this time——" when the path gave a sudden twist and shook itself (as she described it afterwards), and the next moment she found herself actually walking in at the door.

"Oh, it's too bad!" she cried. "I never saw such a house for getting in the way! Never!"

However, there was the hill full in sight, so there was nothing to be done but start again. This time she came upon a large flower-bed, with a border of daisies, and a willow-tree growing in the middle.

"O Tiger-lily!" said Alice, addressing herself to one that was waving gracefully about in the wind, "I *wish* you could talk!"

"We *can* talk," said the Tiger-lily, "when there's anybody worth talking to."

Alice was so astonished that she couldn't speak for a minute: it quite seemed to take her breath away. At length, as the Tiger-lily only went on waving about, she spoke again, in a timid voice – almost in a whisper. "And can *all* the flowers talk?"

"As well as *you* can," said the Tiger-lily. "And a great deal louder."

"It isn't manners for us to begin, you know," said the Rose, "and I really was wondering when you'd speak! Said I to myself, 'Her face has got *some* sense in it, though it's not a clever one!' Still, you're the right colour, and that goes a long way."

"I don't care about the colour," the Tiger-lily remarked. "If only her petals curled up a little more, she'd be all right."

Alice didn't like being criticized, so she began asking questions. "Aren't you sometimes frightened at being planted out here, with nobody to take care of you?"

"There's the tree in the middle," said the Rose. "What else is it good for?"

"But what could it do, if any danger came?" Alice asked.

"It could bark," said the Rose.

"It says 'Bough-wough!' cried a Daisy. "That's why its branches are called boughs!"

"Didn't you know *that*?" cried another Daisy. And here they all began shouting together, till the air seemed quite full of little shrill voices. "Silence every one of you!" cried the Tiger-lily, waving itself passionately from side to side, and trembling with excitement. "They know I ca'n't get at them!" it panted, bending its quivering head towards Alice, "or they wouldn't dare to do it!"

"Never mind!" Alice said in a soothing tone, and, stooping down to

the daises, who were just beginning again, she whispered, "If you don't hold your tongues, I'll pick you!"

There was silence in a moment, and several of the pink daisies turned white.

"That's right!" said the Tiger-lily. "The daisies are worst of all. When one speaks, they all begin together, and it's enough to make one wither to hear the way they go on!"

"How is it you can all talk so nicely?" Alice said, hoping to get it into a better temper by a compliment. "I've been in many gardens before, but none of the flowers could talk."

"Put your hand down and feel the ground," said the Tiger-lily. "Then you'll know why."

Alice did so. "It's very hard," she said; "but I don't see what that has to do with it."

"In most gardens," the Tiger-lily said, "they make the beds too soft – so that the flowers are always asleep."

This sounded a very good reason, and Alice was quite pleased to know it. "I never thought of that before!" she said.

"It's *my* opinion that you never think *at all*," the Rose said, in a rather severe tone.

"I never saw anybody that looked stupider," a Violet said, so suddenly, that Alice quite jumped; for it hadn't spoken before.

"Hold *your* tongue," cried the Tiger-lily. "As if *you* ever saw anybody! You keep your head under the leaves, and snore away there, till you know no more what's going on in the world, than if you were a bud!"

"Are there any more people in the garden besides me?" Alice said, not choosing to notice the Rose's last remark.

"There's one other flower in the garden that can move about like you," said the Rose. "I wonder how you do it——" ("You're always wondering," said the Tiger-lily), "but she's more bushy than you are."

"Is she like me?" Alice asked eagerly, for the thought crossed her mind, "There's another little girl in the garden, somewhere!"

"Well, she has the same awkward shape as you," the Rose said: "but she's redder – and her petals are shorter, I think."

"They're done up close, like a dahlia," said the Tiger-lily: "not tumbled about, like yours."

"But that's not *your* fault," the Rose added kindly. "You're beginning to fade, you know – and then one ca'n't help one's petals getting a little untidy."

Alice didn't like this idea at all: so, to change the subject, she asked, "Does she ever come out here?"

"I daresay you'll see her soon," said the Rose. "She's one of the kind that has nine spikes, you know.

"Where does she wear them?" Alice asked with some curiosity.

"Why, all round her head, of course," the Rose replied. "I was wondering *you* hadn't got some too. I thought it was the regular rule."

"She's coming!" cried the Larkspur. "I hear her footstep, thump, thump, along the gravel-walk!"

Alice looked round eagerly and found that it was the Red Queen. "She's grown a good deal!" was her first remark. She had indeed: when Alice first found her in the ashes, she had been only three inches high – and here she was, half a head taller than Alice herself!

"It's the fresh air that does it," said the Rose: "wonderfully fine air it is, out here."

"I think I'll go and meet her," said Alice, for, though the flowers were interesting enough, she felt that it would be far grander to have a talk with a real Queen.

"You ca'n't possibly do that," said the Rose: "I should advise you to walk the other way."

This sounded nonsense to Alice, so she said nothing, but set off at once towards the Red Queen. To her surprise she lost sight of her in a moment, and found herself walking in at the front-door again.

A little provoked, she drew back, and, after looking everywhere for the Queen (whom she spied out at last, a long way off), she thought she would try the plan, this time, of walking in the opposite direction.

It succeeded beautifully. She had not been walking a minute before she found herself face to face with the Red Queen, and full in sight of the hill she had been so long aiming at.

"Where do you come from?" said the Red Queen. "And where are you going? Look up, speak nicely, and don't twiddle your fingers all the time."

Alice attended to all these directions, and explained, as well as she could, that she had lost her way.

"I don't know what you mean by *your* way," said the Queen: "all the ways about here belong to *me* – but why did you come out here at all?" she added in a kinder tone. "Curtsey while you're thinking what to say. It saves time."

Alice wondered a little at this, but she was too much in awe of the Queen to disbelieve it. "I'll try it when I go home," she thought to herself, "the next time I'm a little late for dinner."

"It's time for you to answer now," the Queen said, looking at her watch: "open your mouth a *little* wider when you speak, and always say 'your Majesty.'"

"I only wanted to see what the garden was like, your Majesty——"

"That's right," said the Queen, patting her on the head, which Alice didn't like at all: "though, when you say 'garden' – *I've* seen gardens, compared with which this would be a wilderness."

Alice didn't dare to argue the point, but went on – "and I thought I'd try and find my way to the top of that hill——"

"When you say "hill,"" the Queen interrupted, "*I* could show you hills in comparison with which you'd call that a valley."

"No, I shouldn't," said Alice, surprised into contradicting her at last: "a hill *ca'n't* be a valley, you know. That would be nonsense——"

The Red Queen shook her head. "You may call it "nonsense" if you like," she said, "but *I've* heard nonsense, compared with which that would be as sensible as a dictionary!"

Alice curtseyed again, as she was afraid from the Queen's tone that she was a *little* offended: and they walked on in silence till they got to the top of the little hill.

For some minutes Alice stood without speaking, looking out in all directions over the country – and a most curious country it was. There were a number of tiny little brooks running straight across it from side to side, and the ground between was divided up into squares by a number of little green hedges, that reached from brook to brook.

"I declare it's marked out just like a large chess-board!" Alice said at last. "There ought to be some men moving about somewhere – and so there are!" she added in a tone of delight, and her heart began to beat quick with excitement as she went on. "It's a great huge game of chess that's being played – all over the world – if this *is* the world at all, you

know. Oh, what fun it is! How I *wish* I was one of them! I wouldn't mind being a Pawn, if only I might join – though of course I should *like* to be a Queen, best."

She glanced rather shyly at the real Queen as she said this, but her companion only smiled pleasantly, and said "That's easily managed. You can be the White Queen's Pawn, if you like, as Lily's too young to play; and you're in the Second Square to begin with: when you get to the Eighth Square you'll be a Queen——" Just at this moment, somehow or other, they began to run.

Alice never could quite make out, in thinking it over afterwards, how it was that they began: all she remembers is, that they were running hand in hand, and the Queen went so fast that it was all she could do to keep up with her: and still the Queen kept crying "Faster! Faster!", but Alice felt she *could not* go faster, though she had no breath left to say so.

The most curious part of the thing was, that the trees and the other things round them never changed their places at all: however fast they went, they never seemed to pass anything. "I wonder if all the things move along with us?" thought poor puzzled Alice. And the Queen seemed to guess her thoughts, for she cried "Faster! Don't try to talk!"

Not that Alice had any idea of doing *that*. She felt as if she would never be able to talk again, she was getting so much out of breath: and still the Queen cried "Faster! Faster!", and dragged her along. "Are we nearly there?" Alice managed to pant out at last.

"Nearly there!" the Queen repeated. "Why, we passed it ten minutes ago! Faster!" And they ran on for a time in silence, with the wind whistling in Alice's ears, and almost blowing her hair off her head, she fancied.

"Now! Now!" cried the Queen. "Faster! Faster!" And they went so fast that at last they seemed to skim through the air, hardly touching the ground with their feet, till suddenly, just as Alice was getting quite exhausted, they stopped, and she found herself sitting on the ground, breathless and giddy.

The Queen propped her up against a tree, and said kindly, "You may rest a little, now."

Alice looked round her in great surprise. "Why, I do believe we've been under this tree the whole time! Everything's just as it was!"

"Of course it is," said the Queen. "What would you have it?"

"Well, in *our* country," said Alice, still panting a little, "you'd generally get to somewhere else – if you ran very fast for a long time as we've been doing."

"A slow sort of country!" said the Queen. "Now, *here*, you see, it takes all the running *you* can do, to keep in the same place. If you want to get somewhere else, you must run at least twice as fast as that!"

"I'd rather not try, please!" said Alice. "I'm quite content to stay here – only I *am* so hot and thirsty!"

"I know what *you'd* like!" the Queen said good-naturedly, taking a little box out of her pocket. "Have a biscuit?"

Alice thought it would not be civil to say "No," though it wasn't at all what she wanted. So she took it, and ate it as well as she could: and it was *very* dry: and she thought she had never been so nearly choked in all her life.

"While you're refreshing yourself," said the Queen, "I'll just take the measurements." And she took a ribbon out of her pocket, marked in inches, and began measuring the ground, and sticking little pegs in here and there.

"At the end of two yards," she said, putting in a peg to mark the distance, "I shall give you your directions – have another biscuit?"

"No, thank you," said Alice: "one's *quite* enough!"

"Thirst quenched, I hope?" said the Queen.

Alice did not know what to say to this, but luckily the Queen did not wait for an answer, but went on. "At the end of *three* yards I shall repeat them – for fear of your forgetting them. At the end of *four*, I shall say good-bye. And at the end of *five*, I shall go!"

She had got all the pegs put in by this time, and Alice looked on with great interest as she returned to the tree, and then began slowly walking down the row.

At the two-yard peg she faced round and said, "A pawn goes two squares in its first move, you know. So you'll go very quickly through the Third Square – by railway, I should think – and you'll find yourself in the Fourth Square in no time. Well, *that* square belongs to Tweedledum and Tweedledee – the Fifth is mostly water – the Sixth belongs to Humpty Dumpty. – But you make no remark?"

"I – I didn't know I had to make one – just then," Alice faltered out.

"You *should* have said," the Queen went on in a tone of grave reproof, " 'It's extremely kind of you to tell me all this' – however, we'll suppose it said – the Seventh Square is all forest – however, one of the Knights will show you the way – and in the Eighth Square we shall be Queens together, and it's all feasting and fun!" Alice got up and curtseyed, and sat down again.

At the next peg the Queen turned again and this time she said, "Speak in French when you ca'n't think of the English for a thing – turn out your toes as you walk – and remember who you are!" She did not wait for Alice to curtsey, this time, but walked on quickly to the next peg, where she turned for a moment to say "Good-bye," and then hurried on to the last.

How it happened, Alice never knew, but exactly as she came to the last peg, she was gone. Whether she vanished into the air, or whether she ran quickly into the wood ("and she *can* run very fast!" thought Alice), there was no way of guessing, but she was gone, and Alice began to remember that she was a Pawn, and that it would soon be time for her to move.

CHAPTER 3

Looking-Glass Insects

OF course the first thing to do was to make a grand survey of the country she was going to travel through. "It's something very like learning geography," thought Alice, as she stood on tiptoe in hopes of being able to see a little further. Principal rivers – there *are* none. Principal mountains – I'm on the only one, but I don't think it's got any name. Principal towns – why, what *are* those creatures, making honey down there? They ca'n't be bees – nobody ever saw bees a mile off, you know——" and for some time she stood silent, watching one of them that was bustling about among the flowers, poking its proboscis into them, "just as if it was a regular bee," thought Alice.

However, this was anything but a regular bee: in fact, it was an elephant – as Alice soon found out, though the idea quite took her breath away at first. "And what enormous flowers they must be!" was her next idea. "Something like cottages with the roofs taken off, and stalks put to them – and what quantities of honey they must make! I think I'll go down and – no, I wo'n't go *just* yet," she went on, checking herself just as she was beginning to run down the hill, and trying to find some excuse for turning shy so suddenly. "It'll never do to go down among them without a good long branch to brush them away – and what fun it'll be when they ask me how I liked my walk. I shall say, 'Oh, I liked it well enough——' (here came the favourite little toss of the head), "only it *was* so dusty and hot, and the elephants *did* tease so!"

"I think I'll go down the other way,' she said after a pause; "and perhaps I may visit the elephants later on. Besides, I *do* so want to get into the Third Square!"

So, with this excuse, she ran down the hill, and jumped over the first of the six little brooks.

              *   *   *   *   *

                    *   *   *   *

              *   *   *   *   *

"Tickets, please!" said the Guard, putting his head in at the window. In a moment everybody was holding out a ticket: they were about the same size as the people, and quite seemed to fill the carriage.

"Now then! Show your ticket, child!" the Guard went on, looking angrily at Alice. And a great many voices all said together ("like the chorus of a song," thought Alice) "Don't keep him waiting, child! Why, his time is worth a thousand pounds a minute!"

"I'm afraid I haven't got one," Alice said in a frightened tone: "There wasn't a ticket-office where I came from." And again the chorus of voices went on. "There wasn't room for one where she came from. The land there is worth a thousand pounds an inch!"

"Don't make excuses," said the Guard: "you should have bought one from the engine-driver." And once more the chorus of voices went on with "The man that drives the engine. Why, the smoke alone is worth a thousand pounds a puff!"

Alice thought to herself "Then there's no use in speaking." The voices didn't join in, *this* time, as she hadn't spoken, but to her great surprise, they all *thought* in chorus (I hope you understand what *thinking in chorus* means – for I must confess that *I* don't). "Better say nothing at all. Language is worth a thousand pounds a word!"

"I shall dream about a thousand pounds to-night, I know I shall!" thought Alice.

All this time the Guard was looking at her, first through a telescope, then through a microscope, and then through an opera-glass. At last he said "You're travelling the wrong way," and shut up the window, and went away.

"So young a child," said the gentleman sitting opposite to her, (he was dressed in white paper,) "ought to know which way she's going, even if she doesn't know her own name!"

A Goat, that was sitting next to the gentleman in white, shut his eyes

and said in a loud voice, "She ought to know her way to the ticket-office, even if she doesn't know her alphabet!"

There was a Beetle sitting next the Goat (it was a very queer carriage-full of passengers altogether), and, as the rule seemed to be that they should all speak in turn, *he* went on with "She'll have to go back from here as luggage!"

Alice couldn't see who was sitting beyond the Beetle, but a hoarse voice spoke next. "Change engines——" it said, and there it choked and was obliged to leave off.

"It sounds like a horse," Alice thought to herself. And an extremely small voice, close to her ear, said "You might make a joke on that – something about 'horse' and 'hoarse,' you know."

Then a very gentle voice in the distance said, "She must be labelled 'Lass, with care,' you know——"

And after that other voices went on ("What a number of people there are in the carriage!" thought Alice), saying "She must go by post, as she's got a head on her——" "She must be sent as a message by the telegraph——" "She must draw the train herself the rest of the way——," and so on.

But the gentleman dressed in white paper leaned forwards and whispered in her ear, "Never mind what they all say, my dear, but take a return-ticket every time the train stops."

"Indeed I sha'n't!' Alice said rather impatiently, "I don't belong to this railway journey at all – I was in a wood just now – and I wish I could get back there!"

"You might make a joke on *that*," said the little voice close to her ear: "something about "you *would* if you could,' you know."

"Don't tease so," said Alice, looking about in vain to see where the voice came from. "If you're so anxious to have a joke made, why don't you make one yourself?"

The little voice sighed deeply. It was *very* unhappy, evidently, and Alice would have said something pitying to comfort it, "if it would only sigh like other people!" she thought. But this was such a wonderfully small sigh, that she wouldn't have heard it at all, if it hadn't come *quite* close to her ear. The consequence of this was that it tickled her ear very much, and quite took off her thoughts from the unhappiness of the poor little creature.

"I know you are a friend," the little voice went on: "a dear friend, and an old friend. And you won't hurt me, though I *am* an insect."

"What kind of insect?" Alice inquired, a little anxiously. What she really wanted to know was, whether it would sting or not, but she thought this wouldn't be quite a civil question to ask.

"What, then you don't——" the little voice began, when it was drowned by a shrill scream from the engine, and everybody jumped up in alarm, Alice among the rest.

The Horse, who had put his head out of the window, quietly drew it in and said "It's only a brook we have to jump over." Everybody seemed satisfied with this, though Alice felt a little nervous at the idea of trains jumping at all. "However, it'll take us into the Fourth Square, that's some comfort!" she said to herself. In another moment she felt the carriage rise straight up into the air, and in her fright she caught at the thing nearest to her hand, which happened to be the Goat's beard.

*   *   *   *   *

*   *   *   *

*   *   *   *   *

But the beard seemed to melt away as she touched it, and she found herself sitting quietly under a tree – while the Gnat (for that was the insect she had been talking to) was balancing itself on a twig just over her head, and fanning her with its wings.

It certainly was a *very* large Gnat: "about the size of a chicken," Alice thought. Still, she couldn't feel nervous with it, after they had been talking together so long. "——then you don't like *all* insects?" the Gnat went on, as quietly as if nothing had happened.

"I like them when they can talk," Alice said. "None of them ever talk, where *I* come from."

"What sort of insects do you rejoice in, where *you* come from?" the Gnat inquired.

"I don't *rejoice* in insects at all," Alice explained, "because I'm rather afraid of them – at least the large kinds. But I can tell you the names of some of them."

"Of course they answer to their names?" the Gnat remarked carelessly.

"I never knew them do it."

"What's the use of their having names," the Gnat said, "if they wo'n't answer to them?"

"No use to *them*," said Alice; "but it's useful to the people that name them, I suppose. If not, why do things have names at all?"

"I ca'n't say," the Gnat replied. "Further on, in the wood down there, they've got no names – however, go on with your list of insects: you're wasting time."

"Well, there's the Horse-fly," Alice began, counting off the names on her fingers.

"All right," said the Gnat. "Half way up that bush, you'll see a Rocking-horse-fly, if you look. It's made entirely of wood, and gets about by swinging itself from branch to branch."

"What does it live on?" Alice asked, with great curiosity.

"Sap and sawdust," said the Gnat. "Go on with the list."

Alice looked at the Rocking-horse-fly with great interest, and made up her mind that it must have been just repainted, it looked so bright and sticky; and then she went on.

"And there's the Dragon-fly."

"Look on the branch above your head," said the Gnat, "and there you'll find a Snap-dragon-fly. Its body is made of plum-pudding, its wings of holly-leaves, and its head is a raisin burning in brandy."

"And what does it live on?" Alice asked, as before.

"Frumenty and mince-pie," the Gnat replied; "and it makes its nest in a Christmas-box."

"And then there's the Butterfly," Alice went on, after she had taken a good look at the insect with its head on fire, and had thought to herself, "I wonder if that's the reason insects are so fond of flying into candles – because they want to turn into Snap-dragon-flies!"

"Crawling at your feet," said the Gnat (Alice drew her feet back in some alarm), "you may observe a Bread-and-butter-fly. Its wings are thin slices of bread-and-butter, its body is a crust, and its head is a lump of sugar."

"And what does *it* live on?"

"Weak tea with cream in it."

A new difficulty came into Alice's head. "Supposing it couldn't find any?" she suggested.

"Then it would die, of course."

"But that must happen very often," Alice remarked thoughtfully.

"It always happens," said the Gnat.

After this, Alice was silent for a minute or two, pondering. The Gnat amused itself meanwhile by humming round and round her head: at last it settled again and remarked, "I suppose you don't want to lose your name?"

"No, indeed," Alice said, a little anxiously.

"And yet I don't know," the Gnat went on in a careless tone: "only

think how convenient it would be if you could manage to go home without it! For instance, if the governess wanted to call you to your lessons, she would call out "Come here——," and there she would have to leave off, because there wouldn't be any name for her to call, and of course you wouldn't have to go, you know."

"That would never do, I'm sure," said Alice: "the governess would never think of excusing me lessons for that. If she couldn't remember my name, she'd call me 'Miss,' as the servants do."

"Well, if she said 'Miss,' and didn't say anything more," the Gnat remarked, "of course you'd miss your lessons. That's a joke. I wish *you* had made it."

"Why do you wish *I* had made it?" Alice asked. "It's a very bad one."

But the Gnat only sighed deeply, while two large tears came rolling down its cheeks.

"You shouldn't make jokes," Alice said, "if it makes you so unhappy."

Then came another of those melancholy little sighs, and this time the poor Gnat really seemed to have sighed itself away, for, when Alice looked up, there was nothing whatever to be seen on the twig, and, as she was getting quite chilly with sitting still so long, she got up and walked on.

She very soon came to an open field, with a wood on the other side of it: it looked much darker than the last wood, and Alice felt a *little* timid about going into it. However, on second thoughts, she made up her mind to go on: "for I certainly wo'n't go *back*," she thought to herself, and this was the only way to the Eighth Square.

"This must be the wood," she said thoughtfully to herself, "where things have no names. I wonder what'll become of *my* name when I go in? I shouldn't like to lose it at all – because they'd have to give me another, and it would be almost certain to be an ugly one. But then the fun would be, trying to find the creature that had got my old name! That's just like the advertisements, you know, when people lose dogs – '*answers to the name of 'Dash', had on a brass collar*' – just fancy calling everything you met 'Alice,' till one of them answered! Only they wouldn't answer at all, if they were wise."

She was rambling on in this way when she reached the wood: it looked very cool and shady. "Well, at any rate it's a great comfort," she said as she stepped under the trees, "After being so hot, to get into the – into *what*?" she went on, rather surprised at not being able to think of the word. "I mean to get under the – under the – under *this*, you know!" putting her hand on the trunk of the tree. "What *does* it call

itself, I wonder? I do believe it's got no name – why, to be sure it hasn't!"

She stood silent for a minute, thinking: then she suddenly began again. "Then it really *has* happened, after all! And now, who am I? I *will* remember, if I can! I'm determined to do it!" But being determined didn't help her much, and all she could say, after a great deal of puzzling, was "L, I *know* it begins with L!"

Just then a Fawn came wandering by: it looked at Alice with its large gentle eyes, but didn't seem at all frightened. "Here then! Here then!" Alice said, as she held out her hand and tried to stroke it; but it only started back a little, and then stood looking at her again.

"What do you call yourself?" the Fawn said at last. Such a soft sweet voice it had!

"I wish I knew!" thought poor Alice. She answered, rather sadly, "Nothing, just now."

"Think again," it said: "that wo'n't do."

Alice thought, but nothing came of it. "Please, would you tell me what *you* call yourself?" she said timidly. "I think that might help a little."

"I'll tell you, if you'll come a little further on," the Fawn said. "I can't remember *here*."

So they walked on together through the wood, Alice with her arms clasped lovingly round the soft neck of the Fawn, till they came out into another open field, and here the Fawn gave a sudden bound into the air, and shook itself free from Alice's arm. "I'm a Fawn!" it cried out in a voice of delight. "And dear me! you're a human child!" A sudden look of alarm came into its beautiful brown eyes, and in another moment it had darted away at full speed.

Alice stood looking after it, almost ready to cry with vexation at having lost her dear little fellow-traveller so suddenly. "However, I know my name now," she said: "that's *some* comfort. Alice – Alice – I wo'n't forget it again. And now, which of these finger-posts ought I to follow, I wonder?"

It was not a very difficult question to answer, as there was only one road through the wood, and the two finger-posts both pointed along it. "I'll settle it," Alice said to herself, "when the road divides and they point different ways."

But this did not seem likely to happen. She went on and on, a long way, but, wherever the road divided, there were sure to be two finger-posts pointing the same way, one marked "TO TWEEDLEDUM'S HOUSE," and the other "TO THE HOUSE OF TWEEDLEDEE."

"I do believe," said Alice at last, "that they live in the *same* house! I wonder I never thought of that before – But I ca'n't stay there long. I'll just call and say 'How d'ye do?' and ask them the way out of the wood. If I could only get to the Eighth Square before it gets dark!" So she wandered on, talking to herself as she went, till, on turning a sharp corner, she came upon two fat little men, so suddenly that she could not help starting back, but in another moment she recovered herself, feeling sure that they must be——

CHAPTER 4

Tweedledum and Tweedledee

THEY were standing under a tree, each with an arm round the other's neck, and Alice knew which was which in a moment, because one of them had "DUM" embroidered on his collar, and the other "DEE." "I suppose they've each got "TWEEDLE" round at the back of the collar," she said to herself.

They stood so still that she quite forgot they were alive, and she was just going round to see if the word "TWEEDLE" was written at the back of each collar, when she was startled by a voice coming from the one marked "DUM."

"If you think we're wax-works," he said, "you ought to pay, you know. Wax-works weren't made to be looked at for nothing. Nohow!"

"Contrariwise," added the one marked "DEE," "if you think we're alive, you ought to speak."

"I'm sure I'm very sorry," was all Alice could say; for the words of the old song kept ringing through her head like the ticking of a clock, and she could hardly help saying them out loud:—

> *Tweedledum and Tweedledee*
> *Agreed to have a battle;*
> *For Tweedledum said Tweedledee*
> *Had spoiled his nice new rattle.*
>
> *Just then flew down a monstrous crow,*
> *As black as a tar-barrel;*
> *Which frightened both the heroes so,*
> *They quite forgot their quarrel.*

"I know what you're thinking about," said Tweedledum; "but it isn't so, nohow."

"Contrariwise," continued Tweedledee, "if it was so, it might be; and if it were so, it would be; but as it isn't, it ain't. That's logic."

"I was thinking," Alice said very politely, "which is the best way out of this wood: it's getting so dark. Would you tell me, please?"

But the fat little men only looked at each other and grinned.

They looked so exactly like a couple of great schoolboys, that Alice couldn't help pointing her finger at Tweedledum, and saying "First Boy!"

"Nohow!" Tweedledum cried out briskly, and shut his mouth up again with a snap.

"Next Boy!" said Alice, passing on to Tweedledee, though she felt quite certain he would only shout out "Contrariwise!" and so he did.

"You've begun wrong!" cried Tweedledum. "The first thing in a visit is to say 'How d'ye do?' and shake hands!" And here the two brothers gave each other a hug, and then they held out the two hands that were free, to shake hands with her.

Alice did not like shaking hands with either of them first, for fear of hurting the other one's feelings; so, as the best way out of the difficulty, she took hold of both hands at once: the next moment they were dancing round in a ring. This seemed quite natural (she remembered afterwards), and she was not even surprised to hear music playing: it seemed to come from the tree under which they were dancing, and it was done (as well as she could make it out) by the branches rubbing one across the other, like fiddles and fiddle-sticks.

"But it certainly *was* funny," (Alice said afterwards, when she was telling her sister the history of all this,) "to find myself singing "*Here we go round the mulberry bush.*" I don't know when I began it, but somehow I felt as if I'd been singing it a long long time!"

The other two dancers were fat, and very soon out of breath. "Four times round is enough for one dance," Tweedledum panted out, and they left off dancing as suddenly as they had begun: the music stopped at the same moment.

Then they let go of Alice's hands, and stood looking at her for a minute: there was a rather awkward pause, as Alice didn't know how to begin a conversation with people she had just been dancing with. "It would never do to say "How d'ye do?" *now*," she said to herself: "we seem to have got beyond that, somehow!"

"I hope you're not much tired?" she said at last.

"Nohow. And thank you *very* much for asking," said Tweedledum.

"So *much* obliged!" added Tweedledee. "You like poetry?"

"Ye-es, pretty well – *some* poetry," Alice said doubtfully. "Would you tell me which road leads out of the wood?"

"What shall I repeat to her?" said Tweedledee, looking round at Tweedledum with great solemn eyes, and not noticing Alice's question.

"'*The Walrus and the Carpenter*' is the longest," Tweedledum replied, giving his brother an affectionate hug.

Tweedledee began instantly:

" *The sun was shining* ——"

Here Alice ventured to interrupt him. "If it's *very* long," she said, as politely as she could, "would you please tell me first which road——"

Tweedledee smiled gently, and began again:

> The sun was shining on the sea,
>   Shining with all his might:
> He did his very best to make
>   The billows smooth and bright —
> And this was odd, because it was
>   The middle of the night.

The moon was shining sulkily,
Because she thought the sun
Had got no business to be there
After the day was done —
'It's very rude of him,' she said,
'To come and spoil the fun!'

The sea was wet as wet could be,
The sands were dry as dry,
You could not see a cloud, because
No cloud was in the sky:
No birds were flying overhead —
There were no birds to fly.

The Walrus and the Carpenter
Were walking close at hand:
They wept like anything to see
Such quantities of sand:
'If this were only cleared away,'
They said, 'it would *be grand.'*

'If seven maids with seven mops
  Swept it for half a year,
Do you suppose,' the Walrus said,
  'That they could get it clear?'
'I doubt it,' said the Carpenter,
  And shed a bitter tear.

'O Oysters, come and walk with us!'
  The Walrus did beseech.
A pleasant walk, a pleasant talk,
  Along the briny beach:
We cannot do with more than four,
  To give a hand to each.'

The eldest Oyster looked at him,
  But never a word he said:
The eldest Oyster winked his eye,
  And shook his heavy head —
Meaning to say he did not choose
  To leave the oyster-bed.

But four young Oysters hurried up,
  All eager for the treat:
Their coats were brushed, their faces washed,
  Their shoes were clean and neat —
And this was odd, because, you know,
  They hadn't any feet.

Four other Oysters followed them,
  And yet another four;
And thick and fast they came at last,
  And more, and more, and more —
All hopping through the frothy waves,
  And scrambling to the shore.

The Walrus and the Carpenter
  Walked on a mile or so,
And then they rested on a rock
  Conveniently low:
And all the little Oysters stood
  And waited in a row.

'The time has come,' the Walrus said,
  'To talk of many things:
Of shoes — and ships — and sealing wax —
  Of cabbages — and kings —
And why the sea is boiling hot —
  And whether pigs have wings.'

'But wait a bit,' the Oysters cried,
  'Before we have our chat;
For some of us are out of breath,
  And all of us are fat!'
'No hurry!' said the Carpenter.
  They thanked him much for that.

'A loaf of bread,' the Walrus said,
  'Is what we chiefly need:
Pepper and vinegar besides
  Are very good indeed —
Now, if you're ready, Oysters dear,
  We can begin to feed.'

'But not on us!' the Oysters cried,
  Turning a little blue.
'After such kindness, that would be
  A dismal thing to do!'
'The night is fine,' the Walrus said.
  'Do you admire the view?'

'It was so kind of you to come!
  And you are very nice!'
The Carpenter said nothing but
  'Cut us another slice.
I wish you were not quite so deaf —
  I've had to ask you twice!'

'It seems a shame,' the Walrus said,
  'To play them such a trick.
After we've brought them out so far,
  And made them trot so quick!'
The Carpenter said nothing but
  'The butter's spread too thick!'

'I weep for you,' the Walrus said:
  'I deeply sympathize.'
With sobs and tears he sorted out
  Those of the largest size,
Holding his pocket-handkerchief
  Before his streaming eyes.

'O Oysters,' said the Carpenter,
  'You've had a pleasant run!
Shall we be trotting home again?'
  But answer came there none —
And this was scarcely odd, because
  They'd eaten every one.

"I like the Walrus best," said Alice: "because he was a *little* sorry for the poor oysters."

"He ate more than the Carpenter, though," said Tweedledee. "You see he held his handkerchief in front, so that the Carpenter couldn't count how many he took: contrariwise."

"That was mean!" Alice said indignantly. "Then I like the Carpenter best — if he didn't eat so many as the Walrus."

"But he ate as many as he could get," said Tweedledum.

This was a puzzler. After a pause, Alice began, "Well! They were *both* very unpleasant characters——" Here she checked herself in some alarm, at hearing something that sounded to her like the puffing of a large steam-engine in the wood near them, though she feared it was more likely to be a wild beast. "Are there any lions or tigers about here?" she asked timidly.

"It's only the Red King snoring," said Tweedledee.

"Come and look at him!" the brothers cried, and they each took one of Alice's hands, and led her up to where the King was sleeping.

"Isn't he a *lovely* sight?" said Tweedledum.

Alice couldn't say honestly that he was. He had a tall red night-cap

on, with a tassel, and he was lying crumpled up into a sort of untidy heap, and snoring loud—— "fit to snore his head off!" as Tweedledum remarked.

"I'm afraid he'll catch cold with lying on the damp grass," said Alice, who was a very thoughtful little girl.

"He's dreaming now," said Tweedledee: "and what do you think he's dreaming about?"

Alice said "Nobody can guess that."

"Why, about *you!*" Tweedledee exclaimed, clapping his hands triumphantly. "And if he left off dreaming about you, where do you suppose you'd be?"

"Where I am now, of course," said Alice.

"Not you!" Tweedledee retorted contemptuously. "You'd be nowhere. Why, you're only a sort of thing in his dream!"

"If that there King was to wake," added Tweedledum, "you'd go out – bang! – just like a candle!"

"I shouldn't!" Alice exclaimed indignantly. "Besides, if *I'm* only a sort of thing in his dream, what are *you*, I should like to know?"

"Ditto," said Tweedledum.

"Ditto, ditto!" cried Tweedledee.

He shouted this so loud that Alice couldn't help saying "Hush! You'll be waking him, I'm afraid, if you make so much noise."

"Well, it's no use *your* talking about waking him," said Tweedledum, "when you're only one of the things in his dream. You know very well you're not real."

"I *am* real!" said Alice, and began to cry.

"You won't make yourself a bit realler by crying," Tweedledee remarked: "there's nothing to cry about."

"If I wasn't real," Alice said – half laughing through her tears, it all seemed so ridiculous – "I shouldn't be able to cry."

"I hope you don't suppose those are *real* tears?" Tweedledum interrupted in a tone of great contempt.

"I know they're talking nonsense," Alice thought to herself: "and it's foolish to cry about it." So she brushed away her tears, and went on, as cheerfully as she could, "At any rate I'd better be getting out of the wood, for really it's coming on very dark. Do you think it's going to rain?"

Tweedledum spread a large umbrella over himself and his brother, and looked up into it. "No, I don't think it is," he said: "at least – not under *here*. Nohow."

"But it may rain *outside?*"

"It may – if it chooses," said Tweedledee: "we've no objection. Contrariwise."

"Selfish things!" thought Alice, and she was just going to say "Goodnight" and leave them, when Tweedledum sprang out from under the umbrella, and seized her by the wrist.

"Do you see *that*?" he said, in a voice choking with passion, and his eyes grew large and yellow all in a moment, as he pointed with a trembling finger at a small white thing lying under a tree.

"It's only a rattle," Alice said, after a careful examination of the little white thing. "Not a rattle-*snake*, you know," she added hastily, thinking that he was frightened: "only an old rattle – quite old and broken."

"I knew it was!" cried Tweedledum, beginning to stamp about wildly and tear his hair. "It's spoilt, of course!" Here he looked at Tweedledee, who immediately sat down on the ground, and tried to hide himself under the umbrella.

Alice laid her hand upon his arm, and said, in a soothing tone, "You needn't be so angry about an old rattle."

"But it *isn't* old!" Tweedledum cried, in a greater fury than ever. "It's *new*, I tell you – I bought it yesterday – my nice NEW RATTLE!" and his voice rose to a perfect scream.

All this time Tweedledee was trying his best to fold up the umbrella

with himself in it: which was such an extraordinary thing to do, that it quite took off Alice's attention from the angry brother. But he couldn't quite succeed, and it ended in his rolling over, bundled up in the umbrella, with only his head out: and there he lay, opening and shutting his mouth and his large eyes—— "looking more like a fish than anything else," Alice thought.

"Of course you agree to have a battle?" Tweedledum said in a calmer tone.

"I suppose so," the other sulkily replied, as he crawled out of the umbrella: "only *she* must help us to dress up, you know."

So the two brothers went off hand-in-hand into the wood, and returned in a minute with their arms full of things – such as bolsters, blankets, hearth-rugs, table-cloths, dish-covers, and coal-scuttles. "I hope you're a good hand at pinning and tying strings?" Tweedledum remarked. "Every one of these things has got to go on, somehow or other."

Alice said afterwards she had never seen such a fuss made about anything in all her life – the way those two bustled about – and the quantity of things they put on – and the trouble they gave her in tying strings and fastening buttons—— "Really they'll be more like bundles of old clothes than anything else, by the time they're ready!" she said to herself, as she arranged a bolster round the neck of Tweedledee, "to keep his head from being cut off," as he said.

"You know," he added very gravely, "it's one of the most serious things that can possibly happen to one in a battle – to get one's head cut off."

Alice laughed loud: but she managed to turn it into a cough, for fear of hurting his feelings.

"Do I look very pale?" said Tweedledum, coming up to have his helmet tied on. (He *called* it a helmet, though it certainly looked much more like a saucepan.)

"Well – yes – a *little*," Alice replied gently.

"I'm very brave, generally," he went on in a loud voice: "only to-day I happen to have a headache!"

"And *I've* got a toothache!" said Tweedledee, who had overheard the remark. "I'm far worse than you."

"Then you'd better not fight to-day," said Alice, thinking it a good opportunity to make peace.

"We *must* have a bit of a fight, but I don't care about going on long," said Tweedledum. "What's the time now?"

Tweedledee looked at his watch, and said, "Half-past four."

"Let's fight till six, and then have dinner," said Tweedledum.

"Very well," the other said, rather sadly: "and *she* can watch us – only you'd better not come *very* close," he added: "I generally hit every thing I can see – when I get really excited."

"And *I* hit every thing within reach," cried Tweedledum, "whether I can see it or not!"

Alice laughed. "You must hit the *trees* pretty often, I should think," she said.

Tweedledum looked round him with a satisfied smile. "I don't suppose," he said, "there'll be a tree left standing, for ever so far round, by the time we've finished!"

"And all about a rattle!" said Alice, still hoping to make them a *little* ashamed of fighting for such a trifle.

"I shouldn't have minded it so much," said Tweedledum, "if it hadn't been a new one."

"I wish the monstrous crow would come!" thought Alice.

"There's only one sword, you know," Tweedledum said to his brother; "but *you* can have the umbrella – its quite as sharp. Only we must begin quick. It's getting as dark as it can."

"And darker," said Tweedledee.

It was getting dark so suddenly that Alice thought there must be a thunderstorm coming on. "What a thick black cloud that is!" she said. "And how fast it comes! Why, I do believe it's got wings!"

"It's the crow!" Tweedledum cried out in a shrill voice of alarm; and the two brothers took to their heels and were out of sight in a moment.

Alice ran a little way into the wood, and stopped under a large tree. "It can never get at me *here*," she thought; "it's far too large to squeeze itself in among the trees. But I wish it wouldn't flap its wings so – it makes quite a hurricane in the wood – here's somebody's shawl being blown away!"

CHAPTER 5

Wool and Water

SHE caught the shawl as she spoke, and looked about for the owner; in another moment the White Queen came running wildly through the wood, with both arms stretched out wide, as if she were flying, and Alice very civilly went to meet her with the shawl.

"I'm very glad I happened to be in the way," Alice said, as she helped her to put on her shawl again.

The White Queen only looked at her in a helpless frightened sort of way, and kept repeating something in a whisper to herself that sounded like "Bread-and-butter, bread-and-butter," and Alice felt that if there was to be any conversation at all, she must manage it herself. So she began rather timidly: "Am I addressing the White Queen?"

"Well, yes, if you call that a-dressing," the Queen said, "It isn't *my* notion of the thing, at all."

Alice thought it would never do to have an argument at the very beginning of their conversation, so she smiled and said, "If your Majesty will only tell me the right way to begin, I'll do it as well as I can."

"But I don't want it done at all!" groaned the poor Queen. "I've been a-dressing myself for the last two hours."

It would have been all the better, as it seemed to Alice, if she had got some one else to dress her, she was so dreadfully untidy. "Every single thing's crooked," Alice thought to herself, "and she's all over pins! ——May I put your shawl straight for you?" she added aloud.

"I don't know what's the matter with it!" the Queen said, in a melancholy voice. "It's out of temper, I think. I've pinned it here, and I've pinned it there, but there's no pleasing it!"

"It *ca'n't* go straight, you know, if you pin it all on one side," Alice

said, as she gently put it right for her; "and, dear me, what a state your hair is in!"

"The brush has got entangled in it!" the Queen said with a sigh. "And I lost the comb yesterday."

Alice carefully released the brush, and did her best to get the hair into order. "Come, you look rather better now!" she said, after altering most of the pins. "But really you should have a lady's-maid!"

"I'm sure I'll take *you* with pleasure!" the Queen said. "Twopence a week, and jam every other day."

Alice couldn't help laughing, as she said, "I don't want you to hire *me* – and I don't care for jam."

"It's very good jam," said the Queen.

"Well, I don't want any *to-day*, at any rate."

"You couldn't have it if you *did* want it," the Queen said. "The rule is, jam to-morrow and jam yesterday – but never jam *to-day*."

"It *must* come sometimes to 'jam to-day,'" Alice objected.

"No, it ca'n't," said the Queen. "It's jam every *other* day; to-day isn't any *other* day, you know."

"I don't understand you," said Alice. "It's dreadfully confusing!"

"That's the effect of living backwards," the Queen said kindly; "it always makes one a little giddy at first——"

"Living backwards!" Alice repeated in great astonishment. "I never heard of such a thing!"

"——but there's one great advantage in it, that one's memory works both ways."

"I'm sure *mine* only works one way," Alice remarked. "I ca'n't remember things before they happen."

"It's a poor sort of memory that only works backwards," the Queen remarked.

"What sort of things do *you* remember best?" Alice ventured to ask.

"Oh, things that happened the week after next," the Queen replied in a careless tone. "For instance now," she went on, sticking a large piece of plaster on her finger as she spoke, "there's the King's Messenger. He's in prison now, being punished: and the trial doesn't even begin till next Wednesday; and of course the crime comes last of all."

"Suppose he never commits the crime?" said Alice.

"That would be all the better, wouldn't it?" the Queen said, as she bound the plaster round her finger with a bit of ribbon.

Alice felt there was no denying *that*. "Of course it would be all the better," she said: "but it wouldn't be all the better his being punished."

"You're wrong *there*, at any rate," said the Queen. "Were *you* ever punished?"

"Only for faults," said Alice.

"And you were all the better for it, I know!" the Queen said triumphantly.

"Yes, but then I *had* done the things I was punished for," said Alice; "that makes all the difference."

"But if you *hadn't* done them," the Queen said, "that would have been better still; better, and better, and better!" Her voice went higher with each "better," till it got quite to a squeak at last.

Alice was just beginning to say "There's a mistake somewhere——", when the Queen began screaming, so loud that she had to leave the sentence unfinished. "Oh, oh, oh!" shouted the Queen, shaking her hand about as if she wanted to shake it off. "My finger's bleeding! Oh, oh, oh, oh!"

Her screams were so exactly like the whistle of a steam-engine, that Alice had to hold both her hands over her ears.

"What *is* the matter?" she said, as soon as there was a chance of making herself heard. "Have you pricked your finger?"

"I haven't pricked it *yet*," the Queen said, "but I soon shall – oh, oh, oh!"

"When do you expect to do it?" Alice asked, feeling very much inclined to laugh.

"When I fasten my shawl again," the poor Queen groaned out: "the brooch will come undone directly. Oh, Oh!" As she said the words the brooch flew open, and the Queen clutched wildly at it, and tried to clasp it again.

"Take care!" cried Alice. "You're holding it all crooked!" And she caught at the brooch; but it was too late: the pin has slipped, and the Queen had pricked her finger.

"That accounts for the bleeding, you see," she said to Alice with a smile. "Now you understand the way things happen here."

"But why don't you scream *now*?" Alice asked, holding her hands ready to put over her ears again.

"Why, I've done all the screaming already," said the Queen. "What would be the good of having it all over again?"

By this time it was getting light. "The crow must have flown away, I think," said Alice: "I'm so glad it's gone. I thought it was the night coming on."

"I wish *I* could manage to be glad!" the Queen said. "Only I never can remember the rule. You must be very happy, living in this wood, and being glad whenever you like!"

"Only it is so *very* lonely here!" Alice said in a melancholy voice; and, at the thought of her loneliness, two large tears came rolling down her cheeks.

"Oh, don't go on like that!" cried the poor Queen, wringing her hands in despair. "Consider what a great girl you are. Consider what a long way you've come today. Consider what o'clock it is. Consider anything, only don't cry!"

Alice could not help laughing at this, even in the midst of her tears. "Can *you* keep from crying by considering things?" she asked.

"That's the way it's done," the Queen said with great decision:

"nobody can do two things at once, you know. Let's consider your age to begin with – how old are you?"

"I'm seven and a half, exactly."

"You needn't say 'exactly,' " the Queen remarked. "I can believe it without that. Now I'll give *you* something to believe. I'm just one hundred and one, five months and a day."

"I ca'n't believe *that*!" said Alice.

"Ca'n't you?" the Queen said in a pitying tone. "Try again: draw a long breath, and shut your eyes."

Alice laughed. "There's no use trying," she said: "one *ca'n't* believe impossible things."

"I daresay you haven't had much practice," said the Queen. "When I was your age, I always did it for half-an-hour a day. Why, sometimes I've believed as many as six impossible things before breakfast. There goes the shawl again!"

The brooch had come undone as she spoke, and a sudden gust of wind blew the Queen's shawl across a little brook. The Queen spread out her arms again, and went flying after it, and this time she succeeded in catching it for herself. "I've got it!" she cried in a triumphant tone. "Now you shall see me pin it on again, all by myself!"

"Then I hope your finger is better now?" Alice said very politely, as she crossed the little brook after the Queen.

* * * * *

* * * *

* * * * *

"Oh, much better!" cried the Queen, her voice rising into a squeak as she went on. "Much be-etter! Be-etter! Be-e-e-etter! Be-e-ehh!" The last word ended in a long bleat, so like a sheep that Alice quite started.

She looked at the Queen, who seemed to have suddenly wrapped herself up in wool. Alice rubbed her eyes, and looked again. She couldn't make out what had happened at all. Was she in a shop? And was that really – was it really a *sheep* that was sitting on the other side of the counter? Rub as she would, she could make nothing more of it: she was in a little dark shop, leaning with her elbows on the counter, and opposite to her was an old Sheep, sitting in an arm-chair, knitting, and every now and then leaving off to look at her through a great pair of spectacles.

"What is it you want to buy?" the Sheep said at last, looking up for a moment from her knitting.

"I don't *quite* know yet," Alice said very gently. "I should like to look all round me first, if I might."

"You may look in front of you, and on both sides, if you like," said the Sheep; "but you ca'n't look *all* round you, unless you've got eyes at the back of your head."

But these, as it happened, Alice had *not* got: so she contented herself with turning round, looking at the shelves as she came to them.

The shop seemed to be full of all manner of curious things – but the oddest part of it all was that, whenever she looked hard at any shelf, to make out exactly what it had on it, that particular shelf was always quite empty, though the others round it were crowded as full as they could hold.

"Things flow about so here!" she said at last in a plaintive tone, after she had spent a minute or so in vainly pursuing a large bright thing, that looked sometimes like a doll and sometimes like a work-box, and was always in the shelf next above the one she was looking at. "And this one is the most provoking of all – but I'll tell you what——" she added, as a sudden thought struck her. "I'll follow it up to the very top shelf of all. It'll puzzle it to go through the ceiling, I expect!"

But even this plan failed: the "thing" went through the ceiling as quietly as possible, as if it were quite used to it.

"Are you a child or a teetotum?" the Sheep said, as she took up another pair of needles. "You'll make me giddy soon, if you go on turning round like that.' She was now working with fourteen pairs at once, and Alice couldn't help looking at her in great astonishment.

"How *can* she knit with so many?" the puzzled child thought to herself. "She gets more and more like a porcupine every minute?"

"Can you row?" the Sheep asked, handing her a pair of knitting-needles as she spoke.

"Yes, a little – but not on land – and not with needles——" Alice was beginning to say, when suddenly the needles turned into oars in her hands, and she found they were in a little boat, gliding along between banks: so there was nothing for it but to do her best.

"Feather!" cried the Sheep, as she took up another pair of needles.

This didn't sound like a remark that needed any answer: so Alice said nothing, but pulled away. There was something very queer about the water, she thought, as every now and then the oars got fast in it, and would hardly come out again.

"Feather! Feather!" the Sheep cried again, taking more needles. "You'll be catching a crab directly."

"A dear little crab!" thought Alice. "I should like that."

"Didn't you hear me say 'Feather'?" the Sheep cried angrily, taking up quite a bunch of needles.

"Indeed I did," said Alice; "you've said it very often – and very loud. Please where *are* the crabs?"

"In the water, of course?" said the Sheep, striking some of the needles into her hair, as her hands were full. "Feather, I say!"

"*Why* do you say 'Feather' so often?" Alice asked at last, rather vexed. "I'm not a bird!"

"You are," said the Sheep: "you're a little goose."

This offended Alice a little, so there was no more conversation for a minute or two, while the boat glided gently on, sometimes among beds of weeds (which made the oars stick fast in the water, worse than ever), and sometimes under trees, but always with the same tall river-banks frowning over their heads.

"Oh, please! There are some scented rushes!" Alice cried in a sudden transport of delight. "There really are – and *such* beauties!"

"You needn't say 'please' to *me* about 'em," the Sheep said, without looking up from her knitting: "I didn't put 'em there, and I'm not going to take 'em away."

"No, but I meant – please, may we wait and pick some?" Alice pleaded. "If you don't mind stopping the boat for a minute."

"How am *I* to stop it?" said the Sheep. "If you'll leave off rowing, it'll stop of itself."

So the boat was left to drift down the stream as it would, till it glided gently in among the waving rushes. And then the little sleeves were carefully rolled up, and the little arms were plunged in elbow-deep, to get hold of the rushes a good long way down before breaking them off – and for a while Alice forgot all about the Sheep and the knitting, as she bent over the side of the boat, with just the ends of her tangled hair dipping into the water – while with bright eager eyes she caught at one bunch after another of the darling scented rushes.

"I only hope the boat won't tipple over!" she said to herself."Oh, *what* a lovely one! Only I couldn't quite reach it." And it certainly *did* seem a little provoking ("almost as if it happened on purpose,' she thought) that, though she managed to pick plenty of beautiful rushes as the boat glided by, there was always a more lovely one that she couldn't reach.

"The prettiest are always further!" she said at last, with a sigh at the obstinacy of the rushes in growing so far off, as, with flushed cheeks and dripping hair and hands, she scrambled back into her place, and began to arrange her new-found treasures.

What mattered it to her just then that the rushes had begun to fade, and to lose all their scent and beauty, from the very moment that she picked them? Even real scented rushes, you know, last only a very little while – and these, being dream-rushes, melted away, almost like snow, as they lay in heaps at her feet – but Alice hardly noticed this, there were so many other curious things to think about.

They hadn't gone much farther before the blade of one of the oars got fast in the water and *wouldn't* come out again (so Alice explained it afterwards), and the consequence was that the handle of it caught her under the chin, and, in spite of a series of little shrieks of "Oh, oh, oh!" from poor Alice, it swept her straight off the seat, and down among the heap of rushes.

However, she wasn't a bit hurt, and was soon up again: the Sheep went on with her knitting all the while, just as if nothing had happened. "That was a nice crab you caught!" she remarked, as Alice got back into her place, very much relieved to find herself still in the boat.

"Was it? I didn't see it," said Alice, peeping cautiously over the side of the boat into the dark water. "I wish it hadn't let go – I should so like a little crab to take home with me!" But the sheep only laughed scornfully, and went on with her knitting.

"Are there many crabs here?" said Alice.

"Crabs, and all sorts of things," said the Sheep: "plenty of choice, only make up your mind. Now, what *do* you want to buy?"

"To buy!" Alice echoed in a tone that was half astonished and half frightened – for the oars, and the boat, and the river, had vanished all in a moment, and she was back again in the little dark shop.

"I should like to buy an egg, please", she said timidly. "How do you sell them?"

"Fivepence farthing for one – twopence for two," the Sheep replied.

"Then two are cheaper than one?" Alice said in a surprised tone, taking out her purse.

"Only you *must* eat them both, if you buy two," said the Sheep.

"Then I'll have *one*, please," said Alice, as she put the money down on the counter. For she thought to herself, "They mightn't be at all nice, you know."

The Sheep took the money, and put it away in a box: then she said, "I never put things into people's hands – that would never do – you must get it for yourself." And so saying, she went off to the other end of the shop, and set the egg upright on a shelf.

"I wonder *why* it wouldn't do?" thought Alice, as she groped her way among the tables and chairs, for the shop was very dark towards the end. "The egg seems to get further away the more I walk towards it.

Let me see, is this a chair? Why, it's got branches, I declare! How very odd to find trees growing here! And actually here's a little brook! Well, this is the very queerest shop I ever saw!"

* * * * *

* * * *

* * * * *

So she went on, wondering more and more at every step, as everything turned into a tree the moment she came up to it, and she quite expected the egg to do the same.

CHAPTER 6

Humpty Dumpty

HOWEVER, the egg only got larger and larger, and more and more human: when she had come within a few yards of it, she saw that it had eyes and a nose and a mouth; and when she had come close to it, she saw clearly that it was HUMPTY DUMPTY himself. "It ca'n't be anybody else!" she said to herself. "I'm as certain of it, as if his name were written all over his face!"

It might have been written a hundred times, easily, on that enormous face. Humpty Dumpty was sitting, with his legs crossed like a Turk, on the top of a high wall – such a narrow one Alice quite wondered how he could keep his balance – and, as his eyes were steadily fixed in the opposite direction, and he didn't take the least notice of her, she thought he must be a stuffed figure, after all.

"And how exactly like an egg he is!" she said aloud, standing with her hands ready to catch him, for she was every moment expecting him to fall.

"It's *very* provoking," Humpty Dumpty said after a long silence, looking away from Alice as he spoke, "to be called an egg – *very!*"

"I said you *looked* like an egg, Sir," Alice gently explained. "And some eggs are very pretty, you know," she added, hoping to turn her remark into a sort of compliment.

"Some people,' said Humpty, looking away from her as usual, "have no more sense than a baby!"

Alice didn't know what to say to this: it wasn't at all like conversation, she thought, as he never said anything to *her*; in fact, his last remark was evidently addressed to a tree – so she stood and softly repeated to herself: —

> *Humpty Dumpty sat on a wall:*
> *Humpty Dumpty had a great fall.*
> *All the King's horses and all the King's men*
> *Couldn't put Humpty Dumpty in his place again.*

"That last line is much too long for the poetry," she added, almost out loud, forgetting that Humpty Dumpty would hear her.

"Don't stand chattering to yourself like that," Humpty Dumpty said, looking at her for the first time, "but tell me your name and your business."

"My *name* is Alice, but——"

"It's a stupid name enough!' Humpty Dumpty interrupted impatiently. "What does it mean?"

"*Must* a name mean something?" Alice asked doubtfully.

"Of course it must," Humpty said with a short laugh: *my* name means the shape I am – and a good handsome shape it is, too. With a name like yours, you might be any shape, almost."

"Why do you sit out here all alone?" said Alice, not wishing to begin an argument.

"Why, because there's nobody with me!" cried Humpty Dumpty. "Did you think I didn't know the answer to *that*? Ask another."

"Don't you think you'd be safer down on the ground?" Alice went on, not with any idea of making another riddle, but simply in her good-natured anxiety for the queer creature. "That wall is so *very* narrow!"

"What tremendously easy riddles you ask!" Humpty Dumpty growled out. "Of course I don't think so! Why, if ever I *did* fall off – which there's no chance of – but *if* I did——" Here he pursed up his lips, and looked so solemn and grand that Alice could hardly help laughing.

"If I *did* fall," he went on, "*the King has promised me* – ah, you may turn pale, if you like! You didn't think I was going to say that, did you? *The King has promised me – with his very own mouth – to – to*——"

"To send all his horses and all his men," Alice interrupted, rather unwisely.

"Now I declare that's too bad!" Humpty Dumpty cried, breaking into a sudden passion. "You've been listening at doors – and behind trees – and down chimneys – or you couldn't have known it!"

"I haven't, indeed!" Alice said very gently. "It's in a book."

"Ah, well! They may write such things in a *book*," Humpty Dumpty said in a calmer tone. "That's what you call a History of England, that is. Now, take a good look at me! I'm one that has spoken to a King, *I* am: mayhap you'll never see such another: and, to show you I'm not proud, you may shake hands with me!" And he grinned almost from ear to ear, as he leant forwards (and as nearly as possible fell off the wall in doing so) and offered Alice his hand. She watched him a little anxiously as she took it. "If he smiled much more the ends of his mouth might meet behind," she thought: "and then I don't know *what* would happen to his head! I'm afraid it would come off!"

"Yes, all his horses and all his men," Humpty Dumpty went on. "They'd pick me up again in a minute, *they* would! However, this conversation is going on a little too fast: let's go back to the last remark but one."

"I'm afraid I ca'n't quite remember it," Alice said, very politely.

"In that case we start afresh," said Humpty Dumpty, "and it's my turn to choose a subject——" ("He talks about it just as if it was a game!" thought Alice.) "So here's a question for you. How old did you say you were?"

Alice made a short calculation, and said "Seven years and six months."

"Wrong!" Humpty Dumpty exclaimed triumphantly. "You never said a word like it!"

"I thought you meant 'How old *are* you?'" Alice explained.

"If I'd meant that, I'd have said it," said Humpty Dumpty.

Alice didn't want to begin another argument, so she said nothing.

"Seven years and six months!" Humpty Dumpty repeated thoughtfully. "An uncomfortable sort of age. Now if you'd asked *my* advice, I'd have said 'Leave off at seven' – but it's too late now."

"I never ask advice about growing," Alice said indignantly.

"Too proud?" the other enquired.

Alice felt even more indignant at this suggestion. "I mean," she said, "that one ca'n't help growing older."

"*One* ca'n't, perhaps," said Humpty Dumpty; "but *two* can. With proper assistance, you might have left off at seven."

"What a beautiful belt you've got on!" Alice suddenly remarked. (They had had quite enough of the subject of age, she thought: and, if they really were to take turns in choosing subjects it was *her* turn now.) "At least," she corrected herself on second thoughts, "a beautiful cravat, I should have said – no, a belt, I mean – I beg your pardon!" she added in dismay, for Humpty Dumpty looked thoroughly offended, and she began to wish she hadn't chosen that subject. "If only I knew," she thought to herself, "which was neck and which was waist!"

Evidently Humpty Dumpty was very angry, though he said nothing for a minute or two. When he *did* speak again, it was in a deep growl.

"It is a – *most* – *provoking* – thing," he said at last, "when a person doesn't know a cravat from a belt!"

"I know it's very ignorant of me," Alice said, in so humble a tone that Humpty Dumpty relented.

"It's a cravat, child, and a beautiful one, as you say. It's a present from the White King and Queen. There now!"

"Is it really?" said Alice, quite pleased to find that she *had* chosen a good subject, after all.

"They gave it me," Humpty Dumpty continued thoughtfully, as he crossed one knee over the other and clasped his hands round it, "they gave it me – for an un-birthday present."

"I beg your pardon?" Alice said with a puzzled air.

"I'm not offended," said Humpty Dumpty.

"I mean, what *is* an un-birthday present?"

"A present given when it isn't your birthday, of course."

Alice considered a little. "I like birthday presents best," she said at last.

"You don't know what you're talking about!" cried Humpty Dumpty. "How many days are there in a year?"

"Three hundred and sixty-five," said Alice.

"And how many birthdays have you?"

"One."

"And if you take one from three hundred and sixty-five, what remains?"

"Three hundred and sixty-four, of course."

Humpty Dumpty looked doubtful. "I'd rather see that done on paper," he said.

Alice couldn't help smiling as she took out her memorandum-book, and worked the sum for him:

$$\frac{\begin{array}{r} 365 \\ 1 \end{array}}{364}$$

Humpty Dumpty took the book and looked at it carefully. "That seems to be done right——" he began.

"You're holding it upside down!" Alice interrupted.

"To be sure I was!" Humpty Dumpty said gaily, as she turned it round for him. "I thought it looked a little queer. As I was saying, that *seems* to be done right – though I haven't time to look it over thoroughly just now – and that shows that there are three hundred and sixty-four days when you might get un-birthday presents——"

"Certainly," said Alice.

"And only *one* for birthday presents, you know. There's glory for you!"

"I don't know what you mean by 'glory,'" Alice said.

Humpty Dumpty smiled contemptuously. "Of course you don't – till I tell you. I meant 'there's a nice knock-down argument for you!'"

"But 'glory' doesn't mean 'a nice knock-down argument,'" Alice objected.

"When *I* use a word," Humpty Dumpty said, in rather a scornful tone, "it means just what I choose it to mean – neither more nor less."

"The question is," said Alice, "whether you *can* make words mean so many different things."

"The question is," said Humpty Dumpty, "which is to be master – that's all."

Alice was too much puzzled to say anything; so after a minute Humpty Dumpty began again. "They've a temper, some of them – particularly verbs: they're the proudest – adjectives you can do anything with, but not verbs – however, *I* can manage the whole lot of them! Impenetrability! That's what *I* say!"

"Would you tell me, please," said Alice, "what that means?"

"Now you talk like a reasonable child," said Humpty Dumpty, looking very much pleased. "I meant by 'impenetrability' that we've had enough of that subject, and it would be just as well if you'd mention what you mean to do next, as I suppose you don't mean to stop here all the rest of your life."

"That's a great deal to make one word mean," Alice said in a thoughtful tone.

"When I make a word do a lot of work like that," said Humpty Dumpty, "I always pay it extra."

"Oh!" said Alice. She was too much puzzled to make any other remark.

"Ah, you should see 'em come round me of a Saturday night,"

Humpty Dumpty went on, wagging his head gravely from side to side, "for to get their wages, you know."

(Alice didn't venture to ask what he paid them with; so you see I can't tell *you*.)

"You seem very clever at explaining words, Sir," said Alice. "Would you kindly tell me the meaning of the poem called 'Jabberwocky'?"

"Let's hear it," said Humpty Dumpty. "I can explain all the poems that ever were invented – and a good many that haven't been invented just yet."

This sounded very hopeful, so Alice repeated the first verse: —

> *'Twas brillig, and the slithy toves*
> *Did gyre and gimble in the wabe:*
> *All mimsy were the borogoves,*
> *And the mome raths outgrabe.*

"That's enough to begin with," Humpty Dumpty interrupted: "there are plenty of hard words there. *'Brillig'* means four o'clock in the afternoon – the time when you begin *broiling* things for dinner."

"That'll do very well," said Alice: "and *'slithy'*?"

"Well, *'slithy'* means 'lithe and slimy.' 'Lithe' is the same as 'active.' You see it's like a portmanteau – there are two meanings packed up into one word."

"I see it now," Alice remarked thoughtfully: "and what are *'toves'*?"

"Well, *'toves'* are something like badgers – they're something like lizards – and they're something like corkscrews."

"They must be very curious-looking creatures."

"They are that," said Humpty Dumpty: "also they make their nests under sun-dials – also they live on cheese."

"And what's t. *'gyre'* and to *'gimble'*?"

"To *'gyre'* is to go round and round like a gyroscope. To *'gimble'* is to make holes like a gimlet."

"And *'the wabe'* is the grass-plot round a sundial, I suppose?" said Alice, surprised at her own ingenuity.

"Of course it is. It's called *'wabe,'* you know, because it goes a long way before it, and a long way behind it——"

·"And a long way beyond it on each side," Alice added.

"Exactly so. Well then, *'mimsy'* is 'flimsy and miserable' (there's another portmanteau for you). And a *'borogove'* is a thin shabby-looking bird with its feathers sticking out all round – something like a live mop."

"And then '*mome raths*'?" said Alice. "I'm afraid I'm giving you a great deal of trouble."

"Well, a '*rath*' is a sort of green pig: but '*mome*' I'm not certain about. I think it's short for 'from home' – meaning that they'd lost their way, you know."

"And what does '*outgrabe*' mean?"

"Well, '*outgribing*' is something between bellowing and whistling,

with a kind of sneeze in the middle; however you'll hear it done, maybe
– down in the wood yonder – and, when you've once heard it, you'll be
quite content. Who's been repeating all that hard stuff to you?"

"I read it in a book," said Alice. "But I *had* some poetry repeated to
me much easier than that, by – Tweedledee, I think it was."

"As to poetry, you know," said Humpty Dumpty, stretching out one
of his great hands, "*I* can repeat poetry as well as other folk, if it comes
to that——"

"Oh, it needn't come to that!" Alice hastily said, hoping to keep him
from beginning.

"The piece I'm going to repeat," he went on without noticing her
remark, "was written entirely for your amusement."

Alice felt that in that case she really *ought* to listen to it; so she sat
down, and said "Thank you" rather sadly.

> *In winter, when the fields are white,*
> *I sing this song for your delight——*

only I don't sing it," he added, as an explanation.

"I see you don't," said Alice.

"If you can *see* whether I'm singing or not you've sharper eyes than
most," Humpty Dumpty remarked severely. Alice was silent.

> *In spring, when woods are getting green,*
> *I'll try and tell you what I mean:*

"Thank you very much," said Alice.

> *In summer, when the days are long,*
> *Perhaps you'll understand this song:*
>
> *In autumn, when the leaves are brown,*
> *Take pen and ink, and write it down.*

"I will, if I can remember it so long," said Alice.

"You needn't go on making remarks like that," Humpty Dumpty
said; "they're not sensible, and they put me out."

> *I sent a message to the fish:*
> *I told them 'This is what I wish.'*
>
> *The little fishes of the sea,*
> *They sent an answer back to me.*
>
> *The little fishes' answer was*
> *'We cannot do it, Sir, because——'*

"I'm afraid I don't quite understand," said Alice.
"It gets easier further on," Humpty Dumpty replied.

> *I sent to them again to say*
> *'It will be better to obey.'*
>
> *The fishes answered, with a grin,*
> *'Why, what a temper you are in!'*
>
> *I told them once, I told them twice:*
> *They would not listen to advice.*
>
> *I took a kettle large and new,*
> *Fit for the deed I had to do.*
>
> *My heart went hop, my heart went thump:*
> *I filled the kettle at the pump.*
>
> *Then some one came to me and said*
> *'The little fishes are in bed.'*
>
> *I said to him, I said it plain,*
> *'Then you must wake them up again.'*
>
> *I said it very loud and clear:*
> *I went and shouted in his ear.*

Humpty Dumpty raised his voice almost to a scream as he repeated this verse, and Alice thought, with a shudder, "I wouldn't have been the messenger for *anything*!"

> *But he was very stiff and proud:*
> *He said 'You needn't shout so loud!'*
>
> *And he was very proud and stiff:*
> *He said 'I'd go and wake them, if——'*
>
> *I took a corkscrew from the shelf:*
> *I went to wake them up myself.*
>
> *And when I found the door was locked,*
> *I pulled and pushed and kicked and knocked.*
>
> *And when I found the door was shut,*
> *I tried to turn the handle, but——'*

There was a long pause.
"Is that all?" Alice timidly asked.
"That's all," said Humpty Dumpty. "Good-bye."

This was rather sudden, Alice thought: but, after such a *very* strong hint that she ought to be going, she felt that it would hardly be civil to stay. So she got up, and held out her hand. "Good-bye, till we meet again!" she said as cheerfully as she could.

"I shouldn't know you again if we *did* meet," Humpty Dumpty replied in a discontented tone, giving her one of his fingers to shake: "you're so exactly like other people."

"The face is what one goes by, generally," Alice remarked in a thoughtful tone.

"That's just what I complain of," said Humpty Dumpty. "Your face is the same as everybody has – the two eyes, so——" (marking their

places in the air with his thumb) "nose in the middle, mouth under. It's always the same. Now if you had the two eyes on the same side of the nose, for instance – or the mouth at the top – that would be *some* help."

"It wouldn't look nice," Alice objected. But Humpty Dumpty only shut his eyes, and said "Wait till you've tried."

Alice waited a minute to see if he would speak again, but, as he never opened his eyes or took any further notice of her, she said "Good-bye!" once more, and, getting no answer to this, she quietly walked away: but she couldn't help saying to herself, as she went, "Of all the unsatisfactory——" (she repeated this aloud, as it was a great comfort to have such a long word to say) "of all the unsatisfactory people I *ever* met——" She never finished the sentence, for at this moment a heavy crash shook the forest from end to end.

CHAPTER 7

The Lion and the Unicorn

THE next moment soldiers came running through the wood, at first in twos and threes, then tens or twenty together, and at last in such crowds that they seemed to fill the whole forest. Alice got behind a tree, for fear of being run over, and watched them go by.

She thought that in all her life she had never seen soldiers so uncertain on their feet: they were always tripping over something or other, and whenever one went down, several more always fell over him, so that the ground was soon covered with little heaps of men.

Then came the horses. Having four feet, these managed rather better than the foot-soldiers; but even *they* stumbled now and then; and it seemed to be a regular rule that, whenever a horse stumbled, the rider fell off instantly. The confusion got worse every moment, and Alice was very glad to get out of the wood into an open place, where she found the White King seated on the ground, busily writing in his memorandum-book.

"I've sent them all!" the King cried in a tone of delight, on seeing Alice. "Did you happen to meet any soldiers, my dear, as you came through the wood?"

"Yes, I did," said Alice: "several thousand, I should think."

"Four thousand two hundred and seven, that's the exact number," the King said, referring to his book. "I couldn't send all the horses, you know, because two of them are wanted in the game. And I haven't sent the two Messengers, either. They're both gone to the town. Just look along the road, and tell me if you can see either of them."

"I see nobody on the road," said Alice.

"I only wish *I* had such eyes," the King remarked in a fretful tone. "To be able to see Nobody! And at that distance too! Why, it's as much as *I* can do to see real people, by this light!"

All this was lost on Alice, who was still looking intently along the road, shading her eyes with one hand. "I see somebody now!" she exclaimed at last. "But he's coming very slowly – and what curious attitudes he goes into!" (For the Messenger kept skipping up and down, and wriggling like an eel, as he came along, with his great hands spread out like fans on each side.)

"Not at all," said the King. "He's an Anglo-Saxon Messenger – and those are Anglo-Saxon attitudes. He only does them when he's happy. His name is Haigha." (He pronounced it so as to rhyme with "mayor.")

"I love my love with an H," Alice couldn't help beginning, "because he is Happy. I hate him with an H, because he is Hideous. I fed him with – with – with Ham-sandwiches and Hay. His name is Haigha, and he lives——"

"He lives on the Hill," the King remarked simply, without the least idea that he was joining in the game, while Alice was still hesitating for the name of a town beginning with H. "The other Messenger's called Hatta. I must have *two*, you know – to come and go. One to come, and one to go."

"I beg your pardon?" said Alice.

"It isn't respectable to beg," said the King.

"I only meant that I didn't understand," said Alice. "Why one to come and one to go?"

"Don't I tell you?" the King repeated impatiently. "I must have *two* – to fetch and carry. One to fetch, and one to carry."

At this moment the Messenger arrived: he was far too much out of breath to say a word, and could only wave his hands about, and make the most fearful faces at the poor King.

"This young lady loves you with an H," the King said, introducing Alice in the hope of turning off the Messenger's attention from himself – but it was of no use – the Anglo-Saxon attitudes only got more extraordinary every moment, while the great eyes rolled wildly from side to side.

"You alarm me!" said the King. "I feel faint—— Give me a ham sandwich!"

On which the Messenger, to Alice's great amusement, opened a bag that hung round his neck, and handed a sandwich to the King, who devoured it greedily.

"Another sandwich!" said the King.

"There's nothing but hay left now," the Messenger said, peeping into the bag.

"Hay, then," the King murmured in a faint whisper.

Alice was glad to see that it revived him a good deal.

"There's nothing like eating hay when you're faint," he remarked to her as he munched away.

"I should think throwing cold water over you would be better," Alice suggested: "—or some sal-volatile."

"I didn't say there was nothing *better*," the King replied. "I said there was nothing *like* it." Which Alice did not venture to deny.

"Who did you pass on the road?" the King went on, holding out his hand to the Messenger for some more hay.

"Nobody," said the Messenger.

"Quite right," said the King: "this young lady saw him too. So of course Nobody walks slower than you."

"I do my best," the Messenger said in a sullen tone. "I'm sure nobody walks much faster than I do!"

"He can't do that," said the King, "or else he'd have been here first. However, now you've got your breath, you may tell us what's happened in the town."

"I'll whisper it," said the Messenger, putting his hands to his mouth in the shape of a trumpet and stooping so as to get close to the King's ear. Alice was sorry for this, as she wanted to hear the news too. However, instead of whispering, he simply shouted, at the top of his voice, "They're at it again!"

"Do you call *that* a whisper?" cried the poor King, jumping up and shaking himself. "If you do such a thing again, I'll have you buttered! It went through and through my head like an earthquake!"

"It would have to be a very tiny earthquake!" thought Alice. "Who are at it again?" she ventured to ask.

"Why, the Lion and the Unicorn, of course," said the King.

"Fighting for the crown!"

"Yes, to be sure," said the King: "and the best of the joke is, that it's *my* crown all the while! Let's run and see them." And they trotted off, Alice repeating to herself, as she ran, the words of the old song:—

> *The Lion and the Unicorn were fighting for the crown:*
> *The Lion beat the Unicorn all round the town.*
> *Some gave them white bread, some gave them brown:*
> *Some gave them plum-cake and drummed them out of town.*

"Does – the one – that wins – get the crown?" she asked, as well as she could, for the run was putting her quite out of breath.

"Dear me, no!" said the King. "What an idea!"

"Would you – be good enough——" Alice panted out, after running a little further, "to stop a minute – just to get – one's breath again?"

"I'm *good* enough," the King said, "only I'm not *strong* enough. You see, a minute goes by so fearfully quick. You might as well try to stop a Bandersnatch!"

Alice had no more breath for talking; so they trotted on in silence, till they came into sight of a great crowd, in the middle of which the Lion and Unicorn were fighting. They were in such a cloud of dust, that at first Alice could not make out which was which; but she soon managed to distinguish the Unicorn by his horn.

They placed themselves close to where Hatta, the other Messenger, was standing watching the fight, with a cup of tea in one hand and a piece of bread-and-butter in the other.

"He's only just out of prison, and he hadn't finished his tea when he was sent in," Haigha whispered to Alice: "and they only give them oyster-shells in there – so you see he's very hungry and thirsty. How are you, dear child?" he went on, putting his arm affectionately round Hatta's neck.

Hatta looked round and nodded, and went on with his bread-and-butter.

"Were you happy in prison, dear child?" said Haigha.

Hatta looked round once more, and this time a tear or two trickled down his cheek; but not a word would he say.

"Speak, ca'n't you!" Haigha cried impatiently. But Hatta only munched away, and drank some more tea.

"Speak, won't you!" cried the King. "How are they getting on with the fight?"

Hatta made a desperate effort, and swallowed a large piece of bread and butter. "They're getting on very well," he said in a choking voice: "each of them has been down about eighty-seven times."

"Then I suppose they'll soon bring the white bread and the brown?" Alice ventured to remark.

"It's waiting for 'em now," said Hatta; "this is a bit of it as I'm eating."

There was a pause in the fight just then, and the Lion and Unicorn sat down, panting, while the King called out, "Ten minutes allowed for refreshments!" Haigha and Hatta set to work at once, carrying round trays of white and brown bread. Alice took a piece to taste, but it was *very* dry.

"I don't think they'll fight any more to-day," the King said to Hatta: "go and order the drums to begin." And Hatta went bounding away like a grasshopper.

For a minute or two Alice stood silent, watching him. Suddenly she brightened up. "Look, look!" she cried, pointing eagerly. "There's the White Queen running across the country! She came flying out of the wood over yonder—— How fast those Queens *can* run!"

"There's some enemy after her, no doubt," the King said, without even looking round. "That wood's full of them."

"But aren't you going to run and help her?" Alice asked, very much surprised at his taking it so quietly.

"No use, no use!" said the King. "She runs so fearfully quick. You

might as well try to catch a Bandersnatch! But I'll make a memorandum about her, if you like——She's a dear good creature," he repeated
softly to himself, as he opened his memorandum-book. "Do you spell
'creature' with a double 'e'?"

At this moment the Unicorn sauntered by them, with his hands in his
pockets. "I had the best of it this time?" he said to the King, just
glancing at him as he passed.

"A little – a little," the King replied, rather nervously. "You
shouldn't have run him through with your horn, you know."

"It didn't hurt him," the Unicorn said carelessly, and he was going
on, when his eye happened to fall upon Alice: he turned round
instantly, and stood for some time looking at her with an air of the
deepest disgust.

"What – is – this?" he said at last.

"This is a child!" Haigha replied eagerly, coming in front of Alice to
introduce her, and spreading out both his hands towards her in an
Anglo-Saxon attitude. "We only found it to-day. It's as large as life and
twice as natural!"

"I always thought they were fabulous monsters!" said the Unicorn.
"Is it alive?"

"It can talk," said Haigha solemnly.

The Unicorn looked dreamily at Alice, and said, "Talk, child."

Alice could not help her lips curling up into a smile as she began: "Do you know, I always thought Unicorns were fabulous monsters, too? I never saw one alive before!"

"Well, now that we *have* seen each other," said the Unicorn, "if you'll believe in me, I'll believe in you. Is that a bargain?"

"Yes, if you like," said Alice.

"Come, fetch out the plum-cake, old man!" the Unicorn went on, turning from her to the King. "None of your brown bread for me!"

"Certainly – certainly!" the King muttered, and beckoned to Haigha. "Open the bag!" he whispered. "Quick! Not that one – that's full of hay!"

Haigha took a large cake out of the bag, and gave it to Alice to hold, while he got out a dish and carving-knife. How they all came out of it Alice couldn't guess. It was just like a conjuring trick, she thought.

The Lion had joined them while this was going on: he looked very

tired and sleepy, and his eyes were half shut. "What's this!" he said, blinking lazily at Alice, and speaking in a deep hollow tone that sounded like the tolling of a great bell.

"Ah, what *is* it now?" the Unicorn cried eagerly. "You'll never guess! *I* couldn't."

The Lion looked at Alice wearily. "Are you animal – or vegetable – or mineral?" he said, yawning at every other word.

"It's a fabulous monster!" the Unicorn cried out, before Alice could reply.

"Then hand round the plum-cake, Monster," the Lion said, lying down and putting his chin on his paws. "And sit down, both of you," (to the King and the Unicorn): "fair play with the cake, you know!"

The King was evidently very uncomfortable at having to sit down between the two great creatures; but there was no other place for him.

"What a fight we might have for the crown, *now*!" the Unicorn said, looking slyly up at the crown, which the poor King was nearly shaking off his head, he trembled so much.

"I should win easy," said the Lion.

"I'm not sure of that," said the Unicorn.

"Why, I beat you all round the town, you chicken!" the Lion replied angrily, half getting up as he spoke.

Here the king interrupted, to prevent the quarrel going on: he was very nervous, and his voice quite quivered. "All round the town?" he said. "That's a good long way. Did you go by the old bridge, or the market-place? You get the best view by the old bridge."

"I'm sure I don't know," the Lion growled out as he lay down again. "There was too much dust to see anything. What a time the Monster is, cutting up that cake!"

Alice had seated herself on the bank of a little brook, with the great dish on her knees, and was sawing away diligently with the knife. "It's very provoking!" she said, in reply to the Lion (she was getting quite used to being called "the Monster"). "I've cut several slices already, but they always join on again!"

"You don't know how to manage Looking-glass cakes," the Unicorn remarked. "Hand it round first, and cut it afterwards."

This sounded nonsense, but Alice very obediently got up, and carried the dish round, and the cake divided itself into three pieces as she did so. "*Now* cut it up," said the Lion, as she returned to her place with the empty dish.

"I say, this isn't fair!" cried the Unicorn, as Alice sat with the knife in her hand, very much puzzled how to begin. "The Monster has given the Lion twice as much as me!"

"She's kept none for herself, anyhow," said the Lion. "Do you like plum-cake, Monster?"

But before Alice could answer him, the drums began.

Where the noise came from, she couldn't make out: the air seemed full of it, and it rang through and through her head till she felt quite

deafened. She started to her feet and sprang across the little brook in her terror, and had just time to see the Lion and the Unicorn rise to their feet, with angry looks at being interrupted in their feast, before she dropped to her knees, and put her hands over her ears, vainly trying to shut out the dreadful uproar.

*   *   *   *   *

*   *   *   *

*   *   *   *   *

"If *that* doesn't 'drum them out of town,'" she thought to herself, "nothing ever will!"

CHAPTER 8

"It's My Own Invention"

AFTER a while the noise seemed gradually to die away, till all was dead silence, and Alice lifted up her head in some alarm. There was no one to be seen, and her first thought was that she must have been dreaming about the Lion and the Unicorn and those queer Anglo-Saxon Messengers. However, there was the great dish still lying at her feet, on which she had tried to cut the plum-cake, "So I wasn't dreaming, after all," she said to herself, "unless – unless we're all part of the same dream. Only I do hope it's *my* dream, and not the Red King's! I don't like belonging to another person's dream," she went on in a rather complaining tone: "I've a great mind to go and wake him, and see what happens!"

At this moment her thoughts were interrupted by a loud shouting of "Ahoy! Ahoy! Check!" and a Knight, dressed in crimson armour, came galloping down upon her, brandishing a great club. Just as he reached her, the horse stopped suddenly: "You're my prisoner!" the Knight cried, as he tumbled off his horse.

Startled as she was, Alice was more frightened for him than for herself at the moment, and watched him with some anxiety as he mounted again. As soon as he was comfortably in the saddle, he began once more, "You're my——" but here another voice broke in "Ahoy! Ahoy! Check!" and Alice looked round in some surprise for the new enemy.

This time it was a White Knight. He drew up at Alice's side, and tumbled off his horse just as the Red Knight had done: then he got on again, and the two Knights sat and looked at each other for some time without speaking. Alice looked from one to the other in some bewilderment.

"She's *my* prisoner, you know!" the Red Knight said at last.

"Yes, but then *I* came and rescued her!" the White Knight replied.

"Well, we must fight for her then," said the Red Knight, as he took up his helmet (which hung from the saddle, and was something the shape of a horse's head) and put it on.

"You will observe the Rules of Battle, of course?" the White Knight remarked, putting on his helmet too.

"I always do," said the Red Knight, and they began banging away at each other with such fury that Alice got behind a tree to be out of the way of the blows.

"I wonder, now, what the Rules of Battle are," she said to herself, as she watched the fight, timidly peeping out from her hiding-place. "One Rule seems to be, that if one Knight hits the other, he knocks him off his horse; and, if he misses, he tumbles off himself – and another Rule seems to be that they hold their clubs with their arms, as if they were Punch and Judy—— What a noise they make when they tumble! Just like a whole set of fire-irons falling into the fender! And how quiet the horses are! They let them get on and off them just as if they were tables!"

Another Rule of Battle, that Alice had not noticed, seemed to be that they always fell on their heads; and the battle ended with their

both falling off in this way, side by side. When they got up again, they shook hands, and then the Red Knight mounted and galloped off.

"It was a glorious victory, wasn't it?" said the White Knight, as he came up panting.

"I don't know," Alice said doubtfully. "I don't want to be anybody's prisoner. I want to be a Queen."

"So you will, when you've crossed the next brook," said the White Knight. "I'll see you safe to the end of the wood – and then I must go back, you know. That's the end of my move."

"Thank you very much," said Alice. "May I help you off with your helmet?" It was evidently more than he could manage by himself: however she managed to shake him out of it at last.

"Now one can breathe more easily," said the Knight, putting back his shaggy hair with both hands, and turning his gentle face and large mild eyes to Alice. She thought she had never seen such a strange-looking soldier in all her life.

He was dressed in tin armour, which seemed to fit him very badly, and he had a queer-shaped little deal box fastened across his shoulders, upside-down, and with the lid hanging open. Alice looked at it with great curiosity.

"I see you're admiring my little box," the Knight said in a friendly tone. "It's my own invention – to keep clothes and sandwiches in. You see I carry it upside-down, so that the rain ca'n't get in."

"But the things can get *out*," Alice gently remarked. "Do you know the lid's open?"

"I didn't know it," the Knight said, a shade of vexation passing over his face. "Then all the things must have fallen out! And the box is no use without them." He unfastened it as he spoke, and was just going to throw it into the bushes, when a sudden thought seemed to strike him, and he hung it carefully on a tree. "Can you guess why I did that?" he said to Alice.

Alice shook her head.

"In hopes some bees may make a nest in it – then I should get the honey."

"But you've got a beehive – or something like one – fastened to the saddle," said Alice.

"Yes, it's a very good beehive," the Knight said in a discontented tone, "one of the best kind. But not a single bee has come near it yet. And the other thing is a mouse-trap. I suppose the mice keep the bees out – or the bees keep the mice out, I don't know which."

"I was wondering what the mouse-trap was for," said Alice. "It isn't very likely there would be any mice on the horse's back."

"Not very likely, perhaps," said the Knight; "but, if they *do* come, I don't choose to have them running all about."

"You see," he went on after a pause, "it's as well to be provided for *everything*. That's the reason the horse has all those anklets round his feet."

"But what are they for?" Alice asked in a tone of great curiosity.

"To guard against the bites of sharks," the Knight replied. "It's an invention of my own. And now help me on. I'll go with you to the end of the wood—— What's that dish for?"

"It's meant for plum cake," said Alice.

"We'd better take that with us," the Knight said. "It'll come in handy if we find any plum cake. Help me to get it into this bag."

This took a long time to manage, though Alice held the bag open very carefully, because the Knight was so *very* awkward in putting in the dish: the first two or three times that he tried he fell in himself instead. "It's rather a tight fit, you see," he said, as they got it in at last; "there are so many candlesticks in the bag." And he hung it to the saddle, which was already loaded with bunches of carrots, and fire-irons, and many other things.

"I hope you've got your hair well fastened on?" he continued, as they set off.

"Only in the usual way," Alice said, smiling.

"That's hardly enough," he said, anxiously. "You see the wind is so *very* strong here. It's as strong as soup."

"Have you invented a plan for keeping the hair from being blown off?" Alice enquired.

"Not yet," said the Knight. "But I've got a plan for keeping it from *falling* off."

"I should like to hear it, very much."

"First you take an upright stick," said the Knight. "Then you make your hair creep up it, like a fruit-tree. Now the reason hair falls off is because it hangs *down* – things never fall *upwards*, you know. It's a plan of my own invention. You may try it if you like."

It didn't sound a comfortable plan, Alice thought, and for a few minutes she walked on in silence, puzzling over the idea, and every now and then stopping to help the poor Knight, who certainly was *not* a good rider.

Whenever the horse stopped (which it did very often), he fell off in front; and, whenever it went on again (which it generally did rather suddenly), he fell off behind. Otherwise he kept on pretty well, except that he had a habit of now and then falling off sideways; and, as he generally did this on the side on which Alice was walking, she soon found that it was the best plan not to walk *quite* close to the horse.

"I'm afraid you've not had much practice in riding," she ventured to say, as she was helping him up from his fifth tumble.

The Knight looked very much surprised, and a little offended at the remark. "What makes you say that?" he asked, as he scrambled back into the saddle, keeping hold of Alice's hair with one hand, to save himself from falling over on the other side.

"Because people don't fall off quite so often, when they've had much practice!"

"I've had plenty of practice," the Knight said very gravely: "plenty of practice!"

Alice could think of nothing better to say than "Indeed?" but she said it as heartily as she could. They went on a little way in silence after this, the Knight with his eyes shut, muttering to himself, and Alice watching anxiously for the next tumble.

"The great art of riding," the Knight suddenly began in a loud voice, waving his right arm as he spoke, "is to keep——" Here the sentence ended as suddenly as it had begun, as the Knight fell heavily on top of his head exactly in the path where Alice was walking. She was quite frightened this time, and said in an anxious tone, as she picked him up, "I hope no bones are broken?"

"None to speak of," the Knight said, as if he didn't mind breaking two or three of them. "The great art of riding, as I was saying, is – to keep your balance properly. Like this, you know——"

He let go the bridle, and stretched out both his arms to show Alice what he meant, and this time he fell flat on his back, right under the horse's feet.

"Plenty of practice!" he went on repeating, all the time that Alice was getting him on his feet again. "Plenty of practice!"

"It's too ridiculous!" cried Alice, losing all her patience this time. "You ought to have a wooden horse on wheels, that you ought!"

"Does that kind go smoothly?" the Knight asked in a tone of great interest, clasping his arms round the horse's neck as he spoke, just in time to save himself from tumbling off again.

"Much more smoothly than a live horse," Alice said, with a little scream of laughter, in spite of all she could do to prevent it.

"I'll get one," the Knight said thoughtfully to himself. "One or two – several."

There was a short silence after this, and then the Knight went on again. "I'm a great hand at inventing things. Now, I daresay you noticed, the last time you picked me up, that I was looking rather thoughtful?"

"You *were* a little grave," said Alice.

"Well, just then I was inventing a new way of getting over a gate – would you like to hear it?"

"Very much indeed," Alice said politely.

"I'll tell you how I came to think of it," said the Knight. "You see, I said to myself, 'The only difficulty is with the feet: the *head* is high enough already.' Now, first I put my head on the top of the gate – then the head's high enough – then I stand on my head – then the feet are high enough, you see – then I'm over, you see."

"Yes, I suppose you'd be over when that was done," Alice said thoughtfully: "but don't you think it would be rather hard?"

"I haven't tried it yet," the Knight said, gravely; "so I ca'n't tell for certain – but I'm afraid it *would* be a little hard."

He looked so vexed at the idea, that Alice changed the subject hastily. "What a curious helmet you've got!" she said cheerfully. "Is that your invention too?"

The Knight looked down proudly at his helmet which hung from the saddle. "Yes," he said; "but I've invented a better one than that – like a sugar-loaf. When I used to wear it, if I fell off the horse, it always touched the ground directly. So I had a *very* little way to fall, you see – But there *was* the danger of falling *into* it, to be sure. That happened to me once – and the worst of it was, before I could get out again, the other White Knight came and put it on. He thought it was his own helmet."

The Knight looked so solemn about it that Alice did not dare to laugh. "I'm afraid you must have hurt him," she said in a trembling voice, "being on the top of his head."

"I had to kick him, of course," the Knight said, very seriously. "And then he took the helmet off again – but it took hours and hours to get me out. I was as fast as – as lightning, you know."

"But that's a different kind of fastness," Alice objected.

The Knight shook his head. "It was all kinds of fastness with me, I can assure you!" he said. He raised his hands in some excitement as he said this, and indignantly rolled out of the saddle, and fell headlong into a deep ditch.

Alice ran to the side of the ditch to look for him. She was rather startled by the fall, as for some time he had kept on very well, and she was afraid that he really *was* hurt this time. However, though she could

see nothing but the soles of his feet, she was much relieved to hear that he was talking on in his usual tone. "All kinds of fastness," he repeated: "but it was careless of him to put another man's helmet on – with the man in it, too."

"How *can* you go on talking so quietly, head downwards?" Alice asked, as she dragged him out by the feet, and laid him in a heap on the bank.

The Knight looked surprised at the question. "What does it matter where my body happens to be?" he said. "My mind goes on working all the same. In fact, the more head-downwards I am, the more I keep inventing new things."

"Now the cleverest thing of the sort that I ever did," he went on after a pause, "was inventing a new pudding during the meat-course."

"In time to have it cooked for the next course?" said Alice. "Well, that *was* quick work, certainly!"

"Well, not the *next* course," the Knight said in a slow thoughtful tone: "no, certainly not the next *course*."

"Then it would have to be the next day. I suppose you wouldn't have two pudding-courses in one dinner?"

"Well, not the *next* day," the Knight repeated as before: "not the next *day*. In fact," he went on, holding his head down, and his voice getting lower and lower, "I don't believe that pudding ever *was* cooked! In fact, I don't believe that pudding ever *will* be cooked! And yet it was a very clever pudding to invent."

"What did you mean it to be made of?" Alice asked, hoping to cheer him up, for the poor Knight seemed quite low-spirited about it.

"It began with blotting-paper," the Knight answered with a groan.

"That wouldn't be very nice, I'm afraid——"

"Not very nice *alone*," he interrupted, quite eagerly: "but you've no idea what a difference it makes, mixing it with other things – such as gunpowder and sealing-wax. And here I must leave you." They had just come to the end of the wood.

Alice could only look puzzled: she was thinking of the pudding.

"You are sad," the Knight said in an anxious tone: "let me sing you a song to comfort you."

"Is it very long?" Alice asked, for she had heard a good deal of poetry that day.

"It's long," said the Knight, "but it's very, *very* beautiful. Everybody that hears me sing it – either it brings the *tears* into their eyes, or else——"

"Or else what?" said Alice, for the Knight had made a sudden pause.

"Or else it doesn't, you know. The name of the song is called
'*Haddocks' Eyes.*'"

"Oh, that's the name of the song, is it?" Alice said, trying to feel
interested.

"No, you don't understand," the Knight said, looking a little vexed.
"That's what the name is *called*. The name really *is* '*The Aged Aged
Man.*'"

"Then I ought to have said 'That's what the *song* is called'?" Alice
corrected herself.

"No, you oughtn't: that's quite another thing! The *song* is called
'*Ways And Means*': but that's only what it's *called*, you know!"

"Well, what *is* the song then?" said Alice, who was by this time
completely bewildered.

"I was coming to that," the Knight said. "The song really *is* '*A-sitting
on A Gate*': and the tune's my own invention."

So saying, he stopped his horse and let the reins fall on its neck: then,
slowly beating time with one hand, and with a faint smile lighting up his
gentle foolish face, as if he enjoyed the music of his song, he began.

Of all the strange things that Alice saw in her journey Through The
Looking-Glass, this was the one that she always remembered most
clearly. Years afterwards she could bring the whole scene back again,
as if it had been only yesterday – the mild blue eyes and kindly smile of
the Knight – the setting sun gleaming through his hair, and shining on
his armour in a blaze of light that quite dazzled her – the horse quietly
moving about, with the reins hanging loose on his neck, cropping the
grass at her feet – and the black shadows of the forest behind – all this
she took in like a picture, as, with one hand shading her eyes, she leant
against a tree watching the strange pair, and listening, in a half-dream,
to the melancholy music of the song.

"But the tune *isn't* his own invention," she said to herself: "it's '*I give
thee all, I can no more.*'" She stood and listened very attentively, but no
tears came into her eyes.

I'll tell thee everything I can:
 There's little to relate.
I saw an aged aged man,
 A-sitting on a gate.
'Who are you, aged man?' I said.
 'And how is it you live?'
And his answer trickled through my head,
 Like water through a sieve.

He said, 'I look for butterflies
  That sleep among the wheat:
I make them into mutton-pies,
  And sell them in the street.
I sell them unto men,' he said,
  'Who sail on stormy seas;
And that's the way I get my bread –
  A trifle, if you please.'

But I was thinking of a plan
  To dye one's whiskers green,
And always use so large a fan
  That they could not be seen.
So, having no reply to give
  To what the old man said,
I cried 'Come, tell me how you live!'
  And thumped him on the head.

His accents mild took up the tale:
  He said 'I go my ways,
And when I find a mountain-rill,
  I set it in a blaze;
And thence they make a stuff they call
  Rowland's Macassar-Oil –
Yet twopence-halfpenny is all
  They give me for my toil.'

But I was thinking of a way
  To feed oneself on batter,
And so go on from day to day
  Getting a little fatter.
I shook him well from side to side,
  Until his face was blue:
'Come, tell me how you live,' I cried,
  'And what it is you do!'

He said, 'I hunt for haddocks' eyes
  Among the heather bright,
And work them into waistcoat-buttons
  In the silent night.
And these I do not sell for gold
  Or coin of silvery shine,
But for a copper halfpenny,
  And that will purchase nine.

'I sometimes dig for buttered rolls,
  Or set limed twigs for crabs:
I sometimes search the grassy knolls
  For wheels of Hansom-cabs.
And that's the way' (he gave a wink)
  'By which I get my wealth –
And very gladly will I drink
  Your Honour's noble health.'

I heard him then, for I had just
  Completed my design
To keep the Menai bridge from rust
  By boiling it in wine.
I thanked him much for telling me
  The way he got his wealth,
But chiefly for his wish that he
  Might drink my noble health.

And now, if e'er by chance I put
*   My fingers into glue,*
Or madly squeeze a right-hand foot
*   Into a left-hand shoe,*
Or if I drop upon my toe
*   A very heavy weight,*
I weep, for it reminds me so
Of that old man I used to know –
Whose look was mild, whose speech was slow,
Whose hair was whiter than the snow,
Whose face was very like a crow,
With eyes, like cinders, all aglow,
Who seemed distracted with his woe,
Who rocked his body to and fro,
And muttered mumblingly and low,
As if his mouth were full of dough,
Who snorted like a buffalo—
That summer evening long ago,
*   A-sitting on a gate.*

As the Knight sang the last words of the ballad, he gathered up the reins, and turned his horse's head along the road by which they had come. "You've only a few yards to go," he said, "down the hill and over that little brook, and then you'll be a Queen——But you'll stay and see me off first?" he added as Alice turned with an eager look in the direction to which he pointed. "I sha'n't be long. You'll wait and wave your handkerchief when I get to that turn in the road! I think it'll encourage me, you see."

"Of course I'll wait," said Alice: "and thank you very much for coming so far – and for the song – I liked it very much."

"I hope so," the Knight said doubtfully: "but you didn't cry so much as I thought you would."

So they shook hands, and then the Knight rode slowly away into the forest. "It won't take long to see him *off*, I expect," Alice said to herself, as she stood watching him. "There he goes! Right on his head as usual! However, he gets on again pretty easily – that comes of having so many things hung round the horse——" So she went on talking to herself, as she watched the horse walking leisurely along the road, and the Knight tumbling off, first on one side and then on the other. After the fourth or fifth tumble he reached the turn, and then she waved her handkerchief to him, and waited till he was out of sight.

"I hope it encouraged him," she said, as she turned to run down the hill: "and now for the last brook, and to be a Queen! How grand it

sounds!" A very few steps brought her to the edge of the brook. "The Eighth Square at last!" she cried as she bounded across,

   *   *   *   *   *

    *   *   *   *

   *   *   *   *   *

and threw herself down to rest on a lawn as soft as moss, with little flower-beds dotted about it here and there. "Oh, how glad I am to get here! And what *is* this on my head?" she exclaimed in a tone of dismay, as she put her hands up to something very heavy, that fitted tight all round her head.

"But how *can* it have got there without my knowing it?" she said to herself, as she lifted it off, and set it on her lap to make out what it could possibly be.

It was a golden crown.

CHAPTER 9

Queen Alice

"WELL, this *is* grand!" said Alice. "I never expected I should be a Queen so soon – and I'll tell you what it is, your Majesty," she went on, in a severe tone (she was always rather fond of scolding herself), "it'll never do for you to be lolling about on the grass like that! Queens have to be dignified, you know!"

So she got up and walked about – rather stiffly just at first, as she was afraid that the crown might come off: but she comforted herself with the thought that there was nobody to see her, "and if I really am a Queen," she said as she sat down again, "I shall be able to manage it quite well in time."

Everything was happening so oddly that she didn't feel a bit surprised at finding the Red Queen and the White Queen sitting close to her, one on each side: she would have liked very much to ask them how they came there, but she feared it would not be quite civil. However, there would be no harm, she thought, in asking if the game was over. "Please, would you tell me——" she began, looking timidly at the Red Queen.

"Speak when you're spoken to!" the Queen sharply interrupted her.

"But if everybody obeyed that rule," said Alice, who was always ready for a little argument, "and if you only spoke when you were spoken to, and the other person always waited for *you* to begin, you see nobody would ever say anything, so that——"

"Ridiculous!" cried the Queen. "Why, don't you see, child——" Here she broke off with a frown, and, after thinking for a minute, suddenly changed the subject of the conversation. "What right have you to call yourself so? You ca'n't be a Queen, you know, till you've passed the proper examination. And the sooner we begin it, the better."

"I only said 'if'!" poor Alice pleaded in a piteous tone.

The two Queens looked at each other, and the Red Queen remarked with a little shudder, "She *says* she only said 'if——"

"But she said a great deal more than that!" the White Queen moaned, wringing her hands. "Oh, ever so much more than that!"

"So you did, you know," the Red Queen said to Alice. "Always speak the truth – think before you speak – and write it down afterwards."

"I'm sure I didn't mean——" Alice was beginning, but the Red Queen interrupted her impatiently.

"That's just what I complain of! You *should* have meant! What do you suppose is the use of a child without any meaning? Even a joke should have some meaning – and a child's more important than a joke, I hope. You couldn't deny that if you tried with both hands."

"I don't deny things with my *hands*," Alice objected.

"Nobody said you did," said the Red Queen. "I said you couldn't if you tried."

"She's in that state of mind," said the White Queen, "that she wants to deny *something* – only she doesn't know what to deny!"

"A nasty vicious temper," the Red Queen remarked: and then there was an uncomfortable silence for a minute or two.

The Red Queen broke the silence by saying, to the White Queen, "I invite you to Alice's dinner-party this afternoon."

The White Queen smiled feebly, and said, "And I invite *you*."

"I didn't know I was to have a party at all," said Alice, "but, if there *is* to be one, I think *I* ought to invite the guests."

"We gave you the opportunity of doing it," the Red Queen remarked: "but I daresay you've not had many lessons in manners yet?"

"Manners are not taught in lessons," said Alice. "Lessons teach you to do sums, and things of that sort."

"Can you do addition?" the White Queen asked. "What's one and one and one and one and one and one and one and one and one and one?"

"I don't know," said Alice. "I lost count."

"She ca'n't do Addition," the Red Queen interrupted. "Can you do Subtraction? Take nine from eight."

"Nine from eight I ca'n't, you know," Alice replied very readily: "but——"

"She ca'n't do Subtraction," said the White Queen. "Can you do Division? Divide a loaf by a knife – what's the answer to *that*?"

"I suppose——" Alice was beginning, but the Red Queen answered for her. "Bread-and-butter, of course. Try another Subtraction sum. Take a bone from a dog: what remains?"

Alice considered. "The bone wouldn't remain, of course, if I took it – and the dog wouldn't remain: it would come to bite me – and I'm sure *I* shouldn't remain!"

"Then you think nothing would remain?" said the Red Queen.

"I think that's the answer."

"Wrong, as usual," said the Red Queen: "the dog's temper would remain."

"But I don't see how——"

"Why, look here!" the Red Queen cried. "The dog would lose its temper, wouldn't it?"

"Perhaps it would," Alice replied cautiously.

"Then if the dog went away, its temper would remain!" the Queen exclaimed triumphantly.

Alice said, as gravely as she could, "They might go different ways."

But she couldn't help thinking to herself, "What dreadful nonsense we *are* talking!"

"She ca'n't do sums a *bit*!" the Queens said together, with great emphasis.

"Can *you* do sums?" Alice said, turning suddenly on the White Queen, for she didn't like being found fault with so much.

The Queen gasped and shut her eyes. "I can do Addition," she said, "if you give me time – but I ca'n't do Subtraction under *any* circumstances!"

"Of course you know your ABC?" said the Red Queen.

"To be sure I do," said Alice.

"So do I," the White Queen whispered: "we'll often say it over together, dear. And I'll tell you a secret – I can read words of one letter! Isn't *that* grand? However, don't be discouraged. You'll come to it in time."

Here the Red Queen began again. "Can you answer useful questions?" she said. "How is bread made?"

"I know *that*!" Alice cried eagerly. "You take some flour——"

"Where do you pick the flower?" the White Queen asked. "In a garden or in the hedges?"

"Well, it isn't *picked* at all," Alice explained: "it's *ground*——"

"How many acres of ground?" said the White Queen. "You mustn't leave out so many things."

"Fan her head!" the Red Queen anxiously interrupted. "She'll be feverish after so much thinking." So they set to work and fanned her with bunches of leaves, till she had to beg them to leave off, it blew her hair about so.

"She's all right again now," said the Red Queen. "Do you know Languages? What's the French for fiddle-de-dee?"

"Fiddle-de-dee's not English," Alice replied gravely.

"Who ever said it was?" said the Red Queen.

Alice thought she saw a way out of the difficulty, this time. "If you'll tell me what language 'fiddle-de-dee' is, I'll tell you the French for it!" she exclaimed triumphantly.

But the Red Queen drew herself up rather stiffly, and said, "Queens never make bargains."

"I wish Queens never asked questions," Alice thought to herself.

"Don't let us quarrel," the White Queen said in an anxious tone. "What is the cause of lightning?"

"The cause of lightning," Alice said very decidedly, for she felt quite certain about this, "is the thunder – no, no!" she hastily corrected herself. "I meant the other way."

"It's too late to correct it," said the Red Queen: "When you've once said a thing, that fixes it, and you must take the consequences."

"Which reminds me——" the White Queen said, looking down and nervously clasping and unclasping her hands, "we had *such* a thunderstorm last Tuesday – I mean one of the last set of Tuesdays, you know."

Alice was puzzled. "In *our* country," she remarked, "there's only one day at a time."

The Red Queen said, "That's a poor thin way of doing things. Now *here*, we mostly have days and nights two or three at a time, and sometimes in the winter we take as many as five nights together – for warmth, you know."

"Are five nights warmer than one night, then?" Alice ventured to ask.

"Five times as warm, of course."

"But they should be five times as *cold*, by the same rule——"

"Just so!" cried the Red Queen. "Five times as warm, *and* five times as cold – just as I'm five times as rich as you are, *and* five times as clever!"

Alice sighed and gave it up. "It's exactly like a riddle with no answer!" she thought.

"Humpty Dumpty saw it too," the White Queen went on in a low voice, more as if she were talking to herself. "He came to the door with a corkscrew in his hand——"

"What did he want?" said the Red Queen.

"He said he *would* come in," the White Queen went on, "because he was looking for a hippopotamus. Now, as it happened, there wasn't such a thing in the house, that morning."

"Is there generally?" Alice asked in an astonished tone.

"Well, only on Thursdays," said the Queen.

"I know what he came for," said Alice: "he wanted to punish the fish, because——"

Here the White Queen began again. "It was *such* a thunderstorm, you ca'n't think!" ("She *never* could, you know," said the Red Queen.) "And part of the roof came off, and ever so much thunder got in – and it went rolling round the room in great lumps – and knocking over the tables and things – till I was so frightened, I couldn't remember my own name!"

Alice thought to herself, "I never should *try* to remember my name

in the middle of an accident! Where would be the use of it?" but she did
not say this aloud, for fear of hurting the poor Queen's feelings.

"Your Majesty must excuse her," the Red Queen said to Alice,
taking one of the White Queen's hands in her own, and gently stroking
it: "She means well, but she ca'n't help saying foolish things, as a
general rule."

The White Queen looked timidly at Alice, who felt she *ought* to say
something kind, but really couldn't think of anything at the moment.

"She never was really well brought up," the Red Queen went on,
"but it's amazing how good-tempered she is. Pat her on the head, and
see how pleased she'll be!" But this was more than Alice had courage to
do.

"A little kindness – and putting her hair in papers – would do
wonders with her——"

The White Queen gave a deep sigh, and laid her head on Alice's
shoulder. "I *am* so sleepy!" she moaned.

"She's tired, poor thing!" said the Red Queen. "Smooth her hair – lend her your nightcap – and sing her a soothing lullaby."

"I haven't got a nightcap with me," said Alice, as she tried to obey the first direction: "and I don't know any soothing lullabies."

"I must do it myself, then," said the Red Queen, and she began:——

> *Hush-a-by lady, in Alice's lap!*
> *Till the feast's ready, we've time for a nap.*
> *When the feast's over, we'll go to the ball –*
> *Red Queen, and White Queen, and Alice, and all!*

"And now you know the words," she added, as she put her head down on Alice's other shoulder, "just sing it through to *me*. I'm getting sleepy, too." In another moment both Queens were fast asleep, and snoring loud.

"What *am* I to do?" exclaimed Alice, looking about in great perplexity, as first one round head, and then the other, rolled down from her shoulder, and lay like a heavy lump in her lap. "I don't think it *ever* happened before, that any one had to take care of two Queens asleep at once! No, not in all the History of England – it couldn't, you know, because there never was more than one Queen at a time. Do wake up, you heavy things!" she went on in an impatient tone; but there was no answer but a gentle snoring.

The snoring got more distinct every minute, and sounded more like a tune: at last she could even make out words, and she listened so eagerly that, when the two great heads suddenly vanished from her lap she hardly missed them.

She was standing before an arched doorway, over which were the words "QUEEN ALICE" in large letters, and on each side of the arch there was a bell-handle; one was marked "Visitors' Bell," and the other "Servants' Bell."

"I'll wait till the song's over," thought Alice, "and then I'll ring the – the – *which* bell must I ring?" she went on, very much puzzled by the names. "I'm not a visitor, and I'm not a servant. There *ought* to be one marked "Queen," you know——"

Just then the door opened a little way, and a creature with a long beak put its head out for a moment and said, "No admittance till the week after next!" and shut the door again with a bang.

Alice knocked and rang in vain for a long time; but at last a very old Frog, who was sitting under a tree, got up and hobbled slowly towards her: he was dressed in bright yellow, and had enormous boots on.

"What is it, now?" the Frog said in a deep hoarse whisper.

Alice turned round, ready to find fault with anybody. "Where's the servant whose business it is to answer the door?" she began angrily.

"Which door?" said the Frog.

Alice almost stamped with irritation at the slow drawl in which he spoke. "*This* door, of course!"

The Frog looked at the door with his large dull eyes for a minute: then he went nearer and rubbed it with his thumb, as if he were trying whether the paint would come off: then he looked at Alice.

"To answer the door?" he said. "What's it been asking of?" He was so hoarse that Alice could scarcely hear him.

"I don't know what you mean," she said.

"I speaks English, doesn't I?" the Frog went on. "Or are you deaf? What did it ask you?"

"Nothing!" Alice said impatiently. "I've been knocking at it!"

"Shouldn't do that – shouldn't do that——" the Frog muttered. "Wexes it, you know." Then he went up and gave the door a kick with one of his great feet. "You let *it* alone," he panted out, as he hobbled back to his tree, "and it'll let *you* alone, you know."

At this moment the door was flung open, and a shrill voice was heard singing:—

> *To the Looking-Glass world it was Alice that said*
> *'I've a sceptre in hand, I've a crown on my head.*
> *Let the Looking-Glass creatures, whatever they be*
> *Come and dine with the Red Queen, the White Queen, and me!'*

And hundreds of voices joined in the chorus:—

> *Then fill up the glasses as quick as you can,*
> *And sprinkle the table with buttons and bran:*
> *Put cats in the coffee, and mice in the tea –*
> *And welcome Queen Alice with thirty-times-three!*

Then followed a confused noise of cheering, and Alice thought to herself, "Thirty times three makes ninety. I wonder if any one's counting?" In a minute there was silence again, and the same shrill voice sang another verse:—

> *'O Looking-Glass creatures,' quoth Alice, 'draw near!*
> *'Tis an honour to see me, a favour to hear:*
> *'Tis a privilege high to have dinner and tea*
> *Along with the Red Queen, the White Queen, and me!'*

Then came the chorus again:--

Then fill up the glasses with treacle and ink,
Or anything else that is pleasant to drink:
Mix sand with the cider, and wool with the wine –
And welcome Queen Alice with ninety-times-nine!

"Ninety times nine!" Alice repeated in despair. "Oh, that'll never be done! I'd better go in at once——" and in she went, and there was a dead silence the moment she appeared.

Alice glanced nervously along the table, as she walked up the large hall, and noticed that there were about fifty guests, of all kinds: some were animals, some birds, and there were even a few flowers among them. "I'm glad they've come without waiting to be asked," she thought: "I should never have known who were the right people to invite!"

There were three chairs at the head of the table: the Red and White Queens had already taken two of them, but the middle one was empty. Alice sat down in it, rather uncomfortable at the silence, and longing for some one to speak.

At last the Red Queen began. "You've missed the soup and fish," she said. "Put on the joint!" And the waiters set a leg of mutton before Alice, who looked at it rather anxiously, as she had never had to carve a joint before.

"You look a little shy: let me introduce you to that leg of mutton," said the Red Queen. "Alice——Mutton: Mutton——Alice." The leg of mutton got up in the dish and made a little bow to Alice: and Alice returned the bow, not knowing whether to be frightened or amused.

"May I give you a slice?" she said, taking up the knife and fork, and looking from one Queen to the other.

"Certainly not," the Red Queen said, very decidedly: "it isn't etiquette to cut any one you've been introduced to. Remove the joint!" And the waiters carried it off, and brought a large plum-pudding in its place.

"I won't be introduced to the pudding, please," Alice said rather hastily, "or we shall get no dinner at all. May I give you some?"

But the Red Queen looked sulky, and growled, "Pudding——Alice: Alice——Pudding. Remove the Pudding!" and the waiters took it away so quickly that Alice couldn't return its bow.

However, she didn't see why the Red Queen should be the only one to give orders; so, as an experiment, she called out, "Waiter! Bring back the pudding!" and there it was again in a moment, like a conjuring trick. It was so large that she could not help feeling a *little* shy with it, as she had been with the mutton: however, she conquered her shyness by a great effort, and cut a slice and handed it to the Red Queen.

"What impertinence!" said the Pudding. "I wonder how you'd like it, if I were to cut a slice out of *you*, you creature?"

It spoke in a thick, suety sort of voice, and Alice hadn't a word to say in reply: she could only sit and look at it and gasp.

"Make a remark," said the Red Queen: "it's ridiculous to leave all the conversation to the pudding!"

"Do you know, I've had such a quantity of poetry repeated to me to-day," Alice began, a little frightened at finding that, the moment she opened her lips, there was a dead silence, and all eyes were fixed upon her; "and it's a very curious thing, I think – every poem was about fishes in some way. Do you know why they're so fond of fishes, all about here?"

She spoke to the Red Queen, whose answer was a little wide of the mark. "As to fishes," she said very slowly and solemnly, putting her mouth to Alice's ear, "her White Majesty knows a lovely riddle – all in poetry – all about fishes. Shall she repeat it?"

"Her Red Majesty's very kind to mention it," the White Queen murmured into Alice's other ear, in a voice like the cooing of a pigeon. "It would be *such* a treat. May I?"

"Please do," Alice said very politely.

The White Queen laughed with delight, and stroked Alice's cheek. Then she began:

> 'First, the fish must be caught.'
> That is easy: a baby, I think could have caught it.
> 'Next, the fish must be bought.'
> That is easy: a penny, I think, would have bought it.
>
> 'Now cook me the fish!'
> That is easy, and will not take more than a minute.
> 'Let it lie in a dish!'
> That is easy, because it already is in it.
>
> 'Bring it here! Let me sup!'
> It is easy to set such a dish on the table.
> 'Take the dish-cover up!'
> Ah! that is so hard that I fear I'm unable!
>
> For it holds it like glue –
> Holds the lid to the dish, while it lies in the middle:
> Which is easiest to do,
> Un-dish-cover the fish, or dishcover the riddle?'

"Take a minute to think about it, and then guess," said the Red Queen. "Meanwhile we'll drink your health – Queen Alice's health!" she screamed at the top of her voice, and all the guests began drinking it directly, and very queerly they managed it: some of them put their glasses upon their heads like extinguishers, and drank all that trickled down their faces – others upset the decanters, and drank the wine as it ran off the edges of the table – and three of them (who looked like kangaroos) scrambled into the dish of roast mutton, and began eagerly lapping up the gravy, "just like pigs in a trough!" thought Alice.

"You ought to return thanks in a neat speech," the Red Queen said, frowning at Alice as she spoke.

"We must support you, you know," the White Queen whispered, as Alice got up to do it, very obediently, but a little frightened.

"Thank you very much," she whispered in reply, "but I can do quite well without."

"That wouldn't be at all the thing," the Red Queen said very decidedly: so Alice tried to submit to it with a good grace.

("And they *did* push so!" she said afterwards, when she was telling her sister the history of the feast. "You would have thought they wanted to squeeze me flat!")

In fact it was rather difficult for her to keep in her place while she made her speech: the two Queens pushed her so, one on each side, that they nearly lifted her up into the air. "I rise to return thanks——" Alice began: and she really *did* rise as she spoke, several inches; but she got hold of the edge of the table, and managed to pull herself down again.

"Take care of yourself!" screamed the White Queen, seizing Alice's hair with both her hands. "Something's going to happen!"

And then (as Alice afterwards described it) all sorts of things happened in a moment. The candles all grew up to the ceiling, looking something like a bed of rushes with fireworks at the top. As to the bottles, they each took a pair of plates, which they hastily fitted on as wings, and so, with forks for legs, went fluttering about in all directions: "and very like birds they look," Alice thought to herself, as well as she could in the dreadful confusion that was beginning.

At this moment she heard a hoarse laugh at her side, and turned to see what was the matter with the White Queen; but, instead of the Queen, there was the leg of mutton sitting in the chair. "Here I am!" cried a voice from the soup-tureen, and Alice turned again, just in time to see the Queen's broad good-natured face grinning at her for a moment over the edge of the tureen, before she disappeared into the soup.

There was not a moment to be lost. Already several of the guests were lying down in the dishes, and the soup-ladle was walking up the table towards Alice's chair, beckoning to her impatiently to get out of its way.

"I ca'n't stand this any longer!" she cried, as she jumped up and seized the table-cloth with both hands: one good pull, and plates,

dishes, guests, and candles came crashing down together in a heap on the floor.

"And as for *you*," she went on, turning fiercely upon the Red Queen, whom she considered as the cause of all the mischief – but the Queen was no longer at her side – she suddenly dwindled down to the size of a little doll, and was now on the table, merrily running round and round after her own shawl, which was trailing behind her.

At any other time, Alice would have felt surprised at this, but she was far too much excited to be surprised at anything *now*. "As for *you*," she repeated, catching hold of the little creature in the very act of jumping over a bottle which had just lighted upon the table. "I'll shake you into a kitten, that I will!"

CHAPTER 10

Shaking

SHE took her off the table as she spoke and shook her backwards and forwards with all her might.

The Red Queen made no resistance whatever: only her face grew very small, and her eyes got large and green: and still, as Alice went on shaking her, she kept on growing shorter – and fatter – and softer – and rounder – and——

CHAPTER 11

Waking

——and it really *was* a kitten, after all.

CHAPTER 12

Which Dreamed It?

"Your Red Majesty shouldn't purr so loud," Alice said, rubbing her eyes, and addressing the kitten, respectfully, yet with some severity. "You woke me out of oh! such a nice dream; and you've been along with me, Kitty – all through the Looking-Glass world. Did you know it, dear?"

It is a very inconvenient habit of kittens (Alice had once made the remark) that, whatever you say to them, they *always* purr. "If they would only purr for 'yes,' and mew for 'no,' or any rule of that sort," she had said, "so that one could keep up a conversation! But how *can* you talk with a person if they *always* say the same thing?"

On this occasion the kitten only purred: and it was impossible to guess whether it meant "yes" or "no."

So Alice hunted among the chessmen on the table till she had found the Red Queen: then she went down on her knees on the hearth-rug, and put the kitten and the Queen to look at each other. "Now, Kitty!" she cried, clapping her hands triumphantly. "Confess that was what you turned into!"

("But it wouldn't look at it," she said, when she was explaining the thing afterwards to her sister: "it turned away its head, and pretended

not to see it: but it looked a *little* ashamed of itself, so I think it *must* have been the Red Queen.")

"Sit up a little more stiffly, dear!" Alice cried with a merry laugh. "And curtsey while you're thinking what to – what to purr. It saves time, remember!" And she caught it up and gave it one little kiss, "just in honour of its having been a Red Queen."

"Snowdrop, my pet!" she went on, looking over her shoulder at the White Kitten, which was still patiently undergoing its toilet, "when *will* Dinah have finished with your White Majesty, I wonder? That must be the reason you were so untidy in my dream.——Dinah! Do you know that you're scrubbing a White Queen? Really, it's most disrespectful of you!

"And what did *Dinah* turn to, I wonder?" she prattled on, as she settled comfortably down, with one elbow on the rug, and her chin in her hand, to watch the kittens. "Tell me, Dinah, did you turn to Humpty Dumpty? I *think* you did – however, you'd better not mention it to your friends just yet, for I'm not sure.

"By the way, Kitty, if only you'd been really with me in my dream, there was one thing you *would* have enjoyed——I had such a quantity of poetry said to me, all about fishes! To-morrow morning you shall have a real treat. All the time you're eating your breakfast, I'll repeat 'The Walrus and the Carpenter' to you; and then you can make believe it's oysters, dear!

"Now, Kitty, let's consider who it was that dreamed it all. This is a serious question, my dear, and you should *not* go on licking your paw like that – as if Dinah hadn't washed you this morning! You see, Kitty, it *must* have been either me or the Red King. He was part of my dream, of course – but then I was part of his dream, too! *Was* it the red King, Kitty? You were his wife, my dear, so you ought to know——Oh, Kitty, do help to settle it! I'm sure your paw can wait!" But the provoking kitten only began on the other paw, and pretended it hadn't heard the question.

Which do *you* think it was?

A BOAT, beneath a sunny sky
Lingering onward dreamily
In an evening of July –

Children three that nestle near,
Eager eye and willing ear
Pleased a simple tale to hear –

Long has paled that sunny sky:
Echoes fade and memories die:
Autumn frosts have slain July.

Still she haunts me, phantomwise,
Alice moving under skies
Never seen by waking eyes.

Children yet, the tale to hear,
Eager eye and willing ear,
Lovingly shall nestle near.

In a Wonderland they lie,
Dreaming as the days go by,
Dreaming as the summers die:

Ever drifting down the stream –
Lingering in the golden gleam –
Life, what is it but a dream?

❧ III ❧

Sylvie and Bruno

with forty-six illustrations by
Harry Furniss

Is all our Life, then, but a dream
Seen faintly in the golden gleam
Athwart Time's dark resistless stream?

Bowed to the earth with bitter woe,
Or laughing at some raree-show,
We flutter idly to and fro.

Man's little Day in haste we spend,
And, from its merry noontide, send
No glance to meet the silent end.

Preface

THE descriptions, at pp. 429, 430, of Sunday as spent by children of the last generation, are quoted *verbatim* from a speech made to me by a child-friend and a letter written to me by a lady-friend.

The Chapters, headed "Fairy Sylvie" and "Bruno's Revenge", are a reprint, with a few alterations, of a little fairy-tale which I wrote in the year 1867, at the request of the late Mrs. Gatty, for "Aunt Judy's Magazine", which she was then editing.

It was in 1874, I believe, that the idea first occurred to me of making it the nucleus of a longer story. As the years went on, I jotted down, at odd moments, all sorts of odd ideas, and fragments of dialogue, that occurred to me—who know how?—with a transitory suddenness that left me no choice but either to record them then and there, or to abandon them to oblivion. Sometimes one could trace to their source these random flashes of thought—as being suggested by the book one was reading, or struck out from the "flint" of one's own mind by the "steel" of a friend's chance remark—but they had also a way of their own, of occurring, *à propos* of nothing—specimens of that hopelessly illogical phenomenon, "an effect without a cause". Such, for example, was the last line of "The Hunting of the Snark", which came into my head (as I have already related in "The Theatre" for April, 1887) quite suddenly, during a solitary walk; and such, again, have been passages which occurred in *dreams*, and which I cannot trace to any antecedent cause whatever. There are at least *two* instances of such dream-suggestions in this book—one, my Lady's remark, "it often runs in families, just as a love for pastry does", at p. 287; the other, Eric Lindon's *badinage* about having been in domestic service, at p. 404.

And thus it came to pass that I found myself at last in possession of a huge unwieldy mass of litterature—if the reader will kindly excuse the spelling—which only needed stringing together, upon the thread of a consecutive story, to constitute the book I hoped to write. Only! The task, at first, seemed absolutely hopeless, and gave me a far clearer idea, than I ever had before, of the meaning of the word "chaos": and I think it must have been ten years, or more, before I had succeeded in classifying these odds-and-ends sufficiently to see what sort of a story they indicated: for the story had to grow out of the incidents, not the incidents out of the story.

I am telling all this, in no spirit of egoism, but because I really believe that some of my readers will be interested in these details of the "genesis" of a book, which looks so simple and straight-forward a matter, when completed, that they might suppose it to have been written straight off, page by page, as one would write a letter, beginning at the beginning and ending at the end.

It is, no doubt, *possible* to write a story in that way: and, if it be not vanity to say so, I believe that I could, myself,—if I were in the unfortunate position (for I do hold it to be a real misfortune) of being obliged to produce a given amount of fiction in a given time that I could "fulfil my task", and produce my "tale of bricks", as other slaves have done. One thing, at any rate I could guarantee as to the story so produced—that it should be utterly commonplace, should contain no new ideas whatever, and should be very very weary reading!

This species of literature has received the very appropriate name of "padding"—which might fitly be defined as "that which all can write and none can read". That the present volume contains *no* such writing I dare not avow: sometimes, in order to bring a picture into its proper place, it has been necessary to eke out a page with two or three extra lines: but I can honestly say I have put in no more than I was absolutely compelled to do.

My readers may perhaps like to amuse themselves by trying to detect, in a given passage, the one piece of "padding" it contains. While arranging the "slips" into pages, I found that the passage, which now extends from the top of p. 262 to the middle of p. 264, was 3 lines too short. I supplied the deficiency, not by interpolating a word here and a word there, but by writing in 3 consecutive lines. Now can my readers guess *which* they are?

A harder puzzle—if a harder be desired—would be to determine, as to the Gardener's Song, in *which* cases (if any) the stanza was adapted to the surrounding text, and in *which* (if any) the text was adapted to the stanza.

Perhaps the hardest thing in all literature—at least *I* have found it so: by no voluntary effort can I accomplish it: I have to take it as it comes—is to write anything *original*. And perhaps the easiest is, when once an original line has been struck out, to follow it up, and to write any amount more to the same tune. I do not know if "Alice in Wonderland" was an *original* story—I was, at least, no *conscious* imitator in writing it—but I do know that, since it came out, something like a dozen story-books have appeared, on identically the same pattern. The path I timidly explored—believing myself to be "the first that ever burst into that silent sea"—is now a beaten high-road: all the way-side flowers have long ago been trampled into the dust: and it would be courting disaster for me to attempt that style again.

Hence it is that, in "Sylvie and Bruno", I have striven—with I know not what success—to strike out yet another new path: be it bad or good, it is the best I can do. It is written, not for money, and not for fame, but in the hope of supplying, for the children whom I love, some thoughts that may suit those hours of innocent merriment which are the very life of Childhood: and also, in the hope of suggesting, to them and to others, some thoughts that may prove, I would fain hope, not wholly out of harmony with the graver cadences of Life.

If I have not already exhausted the patience of my readers, I would like to seize this opportunity—perhaps the last I shall have of addressing so many friends at once—of putting on record some ideas that have occurred to me, as to books desirable to be written—which I should much like to *attempt,* but may not ever have the time or power to carry through—in the hope that, if *I* should fail (and the years are gliding away *very* fast) to finish the task I have set myself, other hands may take it up.

First, a Child's Bible. The only real *essentials* of this would be, carefully selected passages, suitable for a child's reading, and pictures. One principle of selection, which I would adopt, would be that Religion should be put before a child as a relevation of *love*—no need to pain and puzzle the young mind with the history of crime and punishment. (On such a principle I should, for example, omit the history of the Flood.) The supplying of the pictures would involve no great difficulty: no new ones would be needed: hundreds of excellent pictures already exist, the copyright of which has long ago expired, and which simply need photo-zincography, or some similar process, for their successful reproduction. The book should be handy in size—with a pretty attractive-looking cover—in a clear legible type—and, above all, with abundance of pictures, pictures, pictures!

Secondly, a book of pieces selected from the Bible—not single texts, but passages of from 10 to 20 verses each—to be committed to memory. Such passages would be found useful, to repeat to one's self and to ponder over, on many occasions when reading is difficult, if not impossible: for instance, when lying awake at night—on a railway-journey—when taking a solitary walk—in old age, when eye-sight is failing or wholly lost—and, best of all, when illness, while incapacitating us for reading or any other occupation, condemns us to lie awake through many weary silent hours: at such a time how keenly one may realize the truth of David's rapturous cry "*O how sweet are thy words unto my throat: yea, sweeter than honey unto my mouth!*"

I have said "passages", rather than single texts, because we have no means of *recalling* single texts: memory needs *links,* and here are none: one may have a hundred texts stored in the memory, and not be able to recall, at will, more than half-a-dozen—and those by mere chance: whereas, once get hold of any portion of a *chapter* that has been committed to memory, and the whole can be recovered: all hangs together.

Thirdly, a collection of passages, both prose and verse, from books other than the Bible. There is not perhaps much, in what is called "un-inspired" literature (a misnomer, I hold: if Shakespeare was not inspired, one may well doubt if any man ever was), that will bear the process of being pondered over, a hundred times: still there *are* such passages—enough, I think, to make a goodly store for the memory.

These two books—of sacred, and secular, passages for memory—will serve other good purposes besides merely occupying vacant hours: they will help to keep at bay many anxious thoughts, worrying thoughts, uncharitable thoughts, unholy thoughts. Let me say this, in better words than my own, by copying a passage from that most interesting book, Robertson's Lectures on the Epistles to the Corinthians, Lecture XLIX. "If a man finds himself haunted by evil desires and unholy images, which will generally be at periodical hours, let him commit to memory passages of Scripture, or passages from the best writers in verse or prose. Let him store his mind with these, as safeguards to repeat when he lies awake in some restless night, or when despairing imaginations, or gloomy, suicidal thoughts, beset him. Let these be to him the sword, turning everywhere to keep the way of the Garden of Life from the intrusion of profaner footsteps."

Fourthly, a "Shakespeare" for girls: that is, an edition in which everything, not suitable for the perusal of girls of (say) from 10 to 17, should be omitted. Few children under 10 would be likely to understand or enjoy the greatest of poets: and those, who have passed out of girlhood, may safely be left to read Shakespeare, in any edition, "expurgated" or not, that they may prefer; but it seems a pity that so many children, in the intermediate stage, should be debarred from a great pleasure for want of an edition suitable to them. Neither Bowdler's, Chambers's, Brandram's, nor Cundell's "Boudoir" Shakespeare, seems to me to meet the want: they are not sufficiently "expurgated". Bowdler's is the most extraordinary of all: looking through it, I am filled with a deep sense of wonder, considering what he has left in, that he should have cut *anything* out! Besides relentlessly erasing all that is unsuitable on the score of reverence or decency, I should be inclined to omit also all that seems too difficult, or not likely to interest young readers. The resulting book might be slightly fragmentary: but it would be a real treasure to all British maidens who have any taste for poetry.

If it be needful to apologize to any one for the new departure I have taken in this story—by introducing, along with what will, I hope, prove to be acceptable nonsense for children, some of the graver thoughts of human life—it must be to one who has learned the Art of keeping such thoughts wholly at a distance in hours of mirth and careless ease. To him such a mixture will seem, no doubt, ill-judged and repulsive. And that such an Art *exists* I do not dispute: with youth, good health, and sufficient money, it seems quite possible to lead, for years together, a life of unmixed gaiety—with the exception of one solemn fact, with which we are liable to be confronted at *any* moment, even in the midst of the most brilliant company or the most sparkling entertainment. A man may fix his own times for admitting serious thought, for attending public worship, for prayer, for reading the Bible: all such matters he can defer to that "convenient season", which is so apt never to occur at all: but he cannot defer, for one single moment, the necessity of attending to a message, which may come before he has finished reading this page, *"this night shall thy soul be required of thee."*

The ever-present sense of this grim possibility has been, in all ages,[1] an incubus that men have striven to shake off. Few more interesting subjects of enquiry could be found, by a student of history, than the various weapons that have been used against this shadowy foe. Saddest of all must have been the thoughts of those who saw indeed an *existence* beyond the grave, but an existence far more terrible than annihilation—an existence as filmy, impalpable, all but invisible spectres, drifting about, through endless ages, in a world of shadows, with nothing to do, nothing to hope for, nothing to love! In the midst of the gay verses of that genial

---

[1] At the moment, when I had written these words, there was a knock at the door, and a telegram was brought me, announcing the sudden death of a dear friend.

"bon vivant" Horace, there stands one dreary word whose utter sadness goes to one's heart. It is the word *"exilium"* in the well-known passage

> *Omnes eodem cogimur, omnium*
> *Versatur urnâ serius ocius*
> *Sors exitura et nos in æternum*
> *Exilium impositura cymbæ.*

Yes, to him this present life—spite of all its weariness and all its sorrow—was the only life worth having: all else was "exile"! Does it not seem almost incredible that one, holding such a creed, should ever have smiled?

And many in this day, I fear, even though believing in an existence beyond the grave far more real than Horace ever dreamed of, yet regard it as a sort of "exile" from all the joys of life, and so adopt Horace's theory, and say "let us eat and drink, for to-morrow we die".

We go to entertainments, such as the theatre—I say "we", for *I* also go to the play, whenever I get a chance of seeing a really good one—and keep at arm's length, if possible, the thought that we may not return alive. Yet how do you know—dear friend, whose patience has carried you through this garrulous preface—that it may not be *your* lot, when mirth is fastest and most furious, to feel the sharp pang, or the deadly faintness, which heralds the final crisis—to see, with vague wonder, anxious friends bending over you—to hear their troubled whispers—perhaps yourself to shape the question, with trembling lips, "Is it serious?" and to be told "Yes: the end is near" (and oh, how different all Life will look when those words are said!)—how do you know, I say, that all this may not happen to *you*, this night?

And *dare* you, knowing this, say to yourself "Well, perhaps it *is* an immoral play: perhaps the situations *are* a little too 'risky', the dialogue a little too strong, the 'business' a little too suggestive. I don't say that conscience is *quite* easy: but the piece is so clever, I must see it this once! I'll begin a stricter life to-morrow." *To-morrow, and to-morrow, and to-morrow!*

> *"Who sins in hope, who, sinning, says,*
> *'Sorrow for sin God's judgement stays!'*
> *Against God's Spirit he lies; quite stops*
> *Mercy with insult; dares, and drops,*
> *Like a scorch'd fly, that spins in vain*
> *Upon the axis of its pain,*
> *Then takes its doom, to limp and crawl,*
> *Blind and forgot, from fall to fall."*

Let me pause for a moment to say that I believe this thought, of the possibility of death—if calmly realized, and steadily faced—would be one of the best possible tests as to our going to any scene of amusement being right or wrong. If the thought of sudden death acquires, for *you*, a special horror when imagined as happening in a *theatre*, then be very sure the theatre is harmful for *you*, however harmless it may be for others; and that *you* are incurring a deadly peril in going. Be sure the safest rule is that we should not dare to *live* in any scene in which we dare not *die*.

But, once realize what the true object *is* in life—that it is *not* pleasure, *not* knowledge, *not* even fame itself, "that last infirmity of noble minds"—but that it *is* the development of *character,* the rising to a higher, nobler, purer standard, the building-up of the perfect *Man*—and then, so long as we feel that this is going on, and will (we trust) go on for evermore, death has for us no terror; it is not a shadow, but a light; not an end, but a beginning!

One other matter may perhaps seem to call for apology—that I should have treated with such entire want of sympathy the British passion for "Sport", which no doubt has been in by-gone days, and is still, in some forms of it, an excellent school for hardihood and for coolness in moments of danger. But I am not entirely without sympathy for *genuine* "Sport": I can heartily admire the courage of the man who, with severe bodily toil, and at the risk of his life, hunts down some "man-eating" tiger: and I can heartily sympathize with him when he exults in the glorious excitement of the chase and the hand-to-hand struggle with the monster brought to bay. But I can but look with deep wonder and sorrow on the hunter who, at his ease and in safety, can find pleasure in what involves, for some defenceless creature, wild terror and a death of agony: deeper, if the hunter be one who has pledged himself to preach to men the Religion of universal Love: deepest of all, if it be one of those *"tender and delicate"* beings, whose very name serves as a symbol of Love—*"thy love to me was wonderful, passing the love of women"*—whose mission here is surely to help and comfort all that are in pain or sorrow!

> *"Farewell, farewell! but this I tell*
> *To thee, thou Wedding-Guest!*
> *He prayeth well, who loveth well*
> *Both man and bird and beast.*
>
> *He prayeth best, who loveth best*
> *All things both great and small;*
> *For the dear God who loveth us,*
> *He made and loveth all."*

A beggar's palace

CHAPTER 1

Less Bread! More Taxes!

—AND then all the people cheered again, and one man, who was more excited that the rest, flung his hat high into the air, and shouted (as well as I could make out) "Who roar for the Sub-Warden?" *Everybody* roared, but whether it was for the Sub-Warden, or not, did not clearly appear: some were shouting "Bread!" and some "Taxes!", but no one seemed to know what it was they really wanted.

All this I saw from the open window of the Warden's breakfast-saloon, looking across the shoulder of the Lord Chancellor, who had sprung to his feet the moment the shouting began, almost as if he had been expecting it, and had rushed to the window which commanded the best view of the market-place.

"What *can* it all mean?" he kept repeating to himself, as, with his hands clasped behind him, and his gown floating in the air, he paced rapidly up and down the room. "I never heard such shouting before—and at this time of the morning, too! And with such unanimity! Doesn't it strike *you* as very remarkable?"

I represented, modestly, that to *my* ears it appeared that they were shouting for different things, but the Chancellor would not listen to my suggestion for a moment. "They all shout the same words, I assure you!" he said: then, leaning well out of the window, he whispered to a man who was standing close underneath, "Keep 'em together, ca'n't you? The Warden will be here directly. Give 'em the signal for the march up!" All this was evidently not meant for *my* ears, but I could scarcely help hearing it, considering that my chin was almost on the Chancellor's shoulder.

The "march up" was a very curious sight: a straggling procession of men, marching two and two, began from the other side of the market-place, and advanced in an irregular zig-zag fashion towards the Palace, wildly tacking from side to side, like a sailing vessel making way against an unfavourable wind—so that the head of the procession was often further from us at the end of one tack than it had been at the end of the previous one.

Yet it was evident that all was being done under orders, for I noticed that all eyes were fixed on the man who stood just under the window, and to whom the Chancellor was continually whispering. This man held his hat in one hand and a little green flag in the other: whenever he waved the flag the procession advanced a little nearer, when he dipped it they sidled a little farther off, and whenever he waved his hat they all raised a hoarse cheer. "Hoo-roah!" they cried, carefully keeping time with the hat as it bobbed up and down. "Hoo-roah! Noo! Consti! Tooshun! Less! Bread! More! Taxes!"

"That'll do, that'll do!" the Chancellor whispered. "Let 'em rest a bit till I give you the word. He's not here yet!" But at this moment the great folding-doors of the saloon were flung open, and he turned with a guilty start to receive His High Excellency. However it was only Bruno, and the Chancellor gave a little gasp of relieved anxiety.

"Morning!" said the little fellow, addressing the remark, in a general sort of way, to the Chancellor and the waiters. "Doos oo know where Sylvie is? I's looking for Sylvie!"

"She's with the Warden, I believe, y'reince!" the Chancellor replied with a low bow. There was, no doubt, a certain amount of absurdity in applying this title (which, as of course you see without my telling you, was nothing but "your Royal Highness" condensed into one syllable) to a small creature whose father was merely the Warden of Outland: still, large excuse must be made for a man who has passed several years at the Court of Fairyland, and had there acquired the almost impossible art of pronouncing five syllables as one.

But the bow was lost upon Bruno, who had run out of the room, even while the great feat of The Unpronounceable Monosyllable was being triumphantly performed.

Just then, a single voice in the distance was understood to shout "A speech from the Chancellor!" "Certainly, my friends!" the Chancellor replied with extraordinary promptitude. "You shall have a speech!" Here one of the waiters, who had been for some minutes busy making a queer-looking mixture of egg and sherry, respectfully presented it on a large silver salver. The Chancellor took it haughtily, drank it off thoughtfully, smiled benevolently on the happy waiter as he set down the empty glass, and began. To the best of my recollection this is what he said.

"Ahem! Ahem! Ahem! Fellow-sufferers, or rather suffering

fellows——" ("Don't call 'em names!" muttered the man under the window. "I didn't say *felons!*" the Chancellor explained.) "You may be sure that I always sympa——" ("'Ear, 'ear!" shouted the crowd, so loudly as quite to drown the orator's thin squeaky voice) "—that I always sympa——" he repeated. ("Don't simper quite so much!" said the man under the window. "It makes yer look a hidiot!" And, all this time, "'Ear, 'ear!" went rumbling round the market-place, like a peal of thunder.) "That I always *sympathize!*" yelled the Chancellor, the first moment there was silence. "But your *true* friend is the *Sub-Warden!* Day and night he is brooding on your wrongs—I should say your *rights*—that is to say your *wrongs*—no, I mean your *rights*——" ("Don't talk no more!"

growled the man under the window. "You're making a mess of it!") At
this moment the Sub-Warden entered the saloon. He was a thin man,
with a mean and crafty face, and a greenish-yellow complexion; and he
crossed the room very slowly, looking suspiciously about him as if he
thought there might be a savage dog hidden somewhere. "Bravo!" he
cried, patting the Chancellor on the back. "You did that speech very well
indeed. Why, you're a born orator, man!"

"Oh, that's nothing!" the Chancellor replied, modestly, with downcast
eyes. "Most orators are *born*, you know." The Sub-Warden thoughtfully
rubbed his chin. "Why, so they are!" he admitted. "I never considered it
in that light. Still, you did it very well. A word in your ear!"

The rest of their conversation was all in whispers: so, as I could hear
no more, I thought I would go and find Bruno.

I found the little fellow standing in the passage, and being addressed
by one of the men in livery, who stood before him, nearly bent double
from extreme respectfulness, with his hands hanging in front of him like
the fins of a fish. "His High Excellency", this respectful man was saying,
"is in his Study, y'reince!" (He didn't pronounce this quite so well as the
Chancellor.) Thither Bruno trotted, and I thought it well to follow him.

The Warden, a tall dignified man with a grave but very pleasant face,
was seated before a writing-table, which was covered with papers, and
holding on his knee one of the sweetest and loveliest little maidens it has
ever been my lot to see. She looked four or five years older than Bruno,
but she had the same rosy cheeks and sparkling eyes, and the same wealth
of curly brown hair. Her eager smiling face was turned upwards towards
her father's, and it was a pretty sight to see the mutual love with which
the two faces—one in the Spring of Life, the other in its late
Autumn—were gazing on each other.

"No, you've never seen him," the old man was saying: "you couldn't,
you know, he's been away so long—traveling from land to land, and
seeking for health, more years than you've been alive, little Sylvie!"

Here Bruno climbed upon his other knee, and a good deal of kissing,
on a rather complicated system, was the result.

"He only came back last night," said the Warden, when the kissing
was over: "he's been traveling post-haste, for the last thousand miles or
so, in order to be here on Sylvie's birthday. But he's a very early riser,
and I dare say he's in the Library already. Come with me and see him.
He's always kind to children. You'll be sure to like him."

"Has the Other Professor come too?" Bruno asked in an awe-struck
voice.

"Yes, they arrived together. The Other Professor is—well, you wo'n't like him quite so much, perhaps. He's a little more *dreamy*, you know."

"I wiss *Sylvie* was a little more dreamy," said Bruno.

"What *do* you mean, Bruno?" said Sylvie.

Bruno went on addressing his father. "She says she *ca'n't*, oo know. But I thinks it isn't *ca'n't*, it's *wo'n't*."

"Says she *ca'n't* dream!' the puzzled Warden repeated.

"She *do* say it," Bruno persisted. "When I says to her 'Let's stop lessons!', she says 'Oh, I ca'n't *dream* of letting oo stop yet!' "

"He always wants to stop lessons", Sylvie explained, "five minutes after we begin!"

"Five minutes' lessons a day!" said the Warden. "You wo'n't learn much at *that* rate, little man!"

"That's just what Sylvie says," Bruno rejoined. "She says I *wo'n't* learn my lessons. And I tells her, over and over, I *ca'n't* learn 'em. And what does oo think she says? She says 'It isn't *ca'n't*, it's *wo'n't!*' "

"Let's go and see the Professor," Warden said, wisely avoiding further discussion. The children got down off his knees, each secured a hand, and the happy trio set off for the Library—followed by me. I had come to the conclusion by this time that none of the party (except, for a few moments, the Lord Chancellor) was in the least able to see me.

"What's the matter with him?" Sylvie asked, walking with a little extra sedateness, by way of example to Bruno at the other side, who never ceased jumping up and down.

"What *was* the matter—but I hope he's all right now—was lumbago, and rheumatism, and that kind of thing. He's been curing *himself*, you know: he's a very learned doctor. Why, he's actually *invented* three new diseases, besides a new way of breaking your collar-bone!"

"Is it a nice way?" said Bruno.

"Well, hum, not *very*," the Warden said, as we entered the Library. "And here *is* the Professor. Good morning, Professor! Hope you're quite rested after your journey!"

A jolly-looking, fat little man, in a flowery dressing-gown, with a large book under each arm, came trotting in at the other end of the room, and was going straight across without taking any notice of the children. "I'm looking for Vol. Three," he said. "Do you happen to have seen it?"

"You don't see my *children*, Professor!" the Warden exclaimed, taking him by the shoulders and turning him round to face them.

The Professor laughed violently: then he gazed at them through his great spectacles, for a minutes or two, without speaking.

At last he addressed Bruno. "I hope you have had a good night, my child?"

Bruno looked puzzled. "I's had the same night *oo've* had," he replied. "There's only been *one* night since yesterday!"

It was the Professor's turn to look puzzled now. He took off his spectacles, and rubbed them with his handkerchief. Then he gazed at them again. Then he turned to the Warden. "Are they bound?" he enquired.

"No, we aren't," said Bruno, who thought himself quite able to answer *this* question.

The Professor shook his head sadly. "Not even half-bound?"

"Why *would* we be half-bound?" said Bruno. "We're not prisoners!"

But the Professor had forgotten all about them by this time, and was speaking to the Warden again. "You'll be glad to hear", he was saying, "that the Barometer's beginning to move——"

"Well, which way?" said the Warden—adding to the children, "Not that *I* care, you know. Only *he* thinks it affects the weather. He's a wonderfully clever man, you know. Sometimes he says things that only the Other Professor can understand. Sometimes he says things that *nobody* can understand! Which way is it, Professor? Up or down?"

"Neither!" said the Professor, gently clapping his hands. "It's going sideways—if I may so express myself."

"And what kind of weather does *that* produce?" said the Warden. "Listen children! Now you'll hear something worth knowing!"

"Horizontal weather," said the professor, and made straight for the door, very nearly trampling on Bruno, who had only just time to get out of his way.

"*Isn't* he learned?" the Warden said, looking after him with admiring eyes. "Positively he runs over with learning!"

"But he needn't run over *me*!" said Bruno.

The Professor was back in a moment: he had changed his dressing-gown for a frock-coat, and had put on a pair of very strange-looking boots, the tops of which were open umbrellas. "I thought you'd like to see them," he said. "*These* are the boots for horizontal weather!"

"But what's the use of wearing umbrellas round one's knees?"

"In *ordinary* rain," the Professor admitted, "they would *not* be of much use. But if ever it rained *horizontally*, you know, they would be invaluable—simply invaluable!"

"Take the Professor to the breakfast-saloon, children," said the Warden. "And tell them not to wait for me. I had breakfast early, as I've some business to attend to." The children seized the Professor's hands, as familiarly as if they had known him for years, and hurried him away. I followed respectfully behind.

CHAPTER 2

L'Amie Inconnue

As we entered the breakfast saloon, the Professor was saying "—and he had breakfast by himself, early: so he begged you wouldn't wait for him, my Lady. This way, my Lady," he added, "this way!" And then, with (as it seemed to me) most superfluous politeness, he flung open the door of my compartment, and ushered in "—a young and lovely lady!" I muttered to myself with some bitterness. "And this is, of course, the opening scene of Vol. I. *She* is the Heroine. And *I* am one of those subordinate characters that only turn up when needed for the development of her destiny, and whose final appearance is outside the church, waiting to greet the Happy Pair!"

"Yes, my lady, change at Fayfield," were the next words I heard (oh that too obsequious Guard!), "next station but one." And the door closed, and the lady settled down into her corner, and the monotonous throb of the engine (making one feel as if the train were some gigantic monster, whose very circulation we could feel) proclaimed that we were once more speeding on our way. "The lady had a perfectly formed nose," I caught myself saying to myself, "hazel eyes, and lips——" and here it occurred to me that to see, for myself, what "the lady" was really like, would be more satisfactory than much speculation.

I looked round cautiously, and—was entirely disappointed of my hope. The veil, which shrouded her whole face, was too thick for me to see more than the glitter of bright eyes and hazy outline of what *might* be a lovely oval face, but might also, unfortunately, be an equally *un*lovely one. I closed my eyes again, saying to myself "—couldn't have a better chance for an experiment in Telepathy! I'll *think out* her face and afterwards test the portrait with the original."

At first, no result at all crowned my efforts, though I "divided my swift mind", now hither, now thither, in a way that I felt sure would have made Æneas green with envy: but the dimly-seen oval remained as provokingly blank as ever—a mere Ellipse, as if in some mathematical diagram, without even the Foci that might be made to do duty as a nose and a mouth. Gradually, however, the conviction came upon me that I could, by a certain concentration of thought, *think the veil away*, and so get a glimpse of the mysterious face—as to which the two questions, "is she pretty?" and "is she plain?", still hung suspended, in my mind, in beautiful equipoise.

Success was partial—and fitful—still there *was* a result: ever and anon, the veil seemed to vanish, in a sudden flash of light: but, before I could fully realize the face, all was dark again. In each such glimpse, the face seemed to grow more childish and more innocent: and, when I had at last *thought* the veil entirely away, it was, unmistakeably, the sweet face of little Sylvie!

"So, either I've been dreaming about Sylvie," I said to myself, "and this is the reality. Or else I've really been with Sylvie, and this is a dream! Is Life itself a dream, I wonder?"

To occupy the time, I got out the letter which had caused me to take this sudden railway-journey from my London home down to a strange fishing-town on the North coast, and read it over again:

"Dear old Friend,

"I'm sure it will be as great a pleasure to me, as it can possibly be to you, to meet once more after so many years: and of course I shall be ready to give you all the benefit of such medical skill as I have: only, you know, one mustn't violate professional etiquette! And you are already in the hands of a first-rate London doctor, with whom it would be utter affectation for me to pretend to compete. (I make no doubt he is right in saying the heart is affected: all your symptoms point that way.) One thing, at any rate, I have already done in my doctorial capacity—secured you a bedroom on the ground-floor, so that you will not need to ascend the stairs at all.

"I shall expect you by last train on Friday, in accordance with your letter: and, till then, I shall say, in the words of the old song, 'Oh for Friday nicht! Friday's lang a-coming!'

"Yours always,

"ARTHUR FORESTER

"P.S. Do you believe in Fate?"

This Postscript puzzled me sorely. "He is far too sensible a man", I thought, "to have become a Fatalist. And yet what else can he mean by it?" And, as I folded up the letter and put it away, I inadvertently repeated the words aloud. "Do you believe in Fate?"

The fair "Incognita" turned her head quickly at the sudden question. "No, I don't!" she said with a smile. "Do you?"

"I—I didn't mean to ask the question!" I stammered, a little taken aback at having begun a conversation in so unconventional a fashion.

The lady's smile became a laugh—not a mocking laugh, but the laugh of a happy child who is perfectly at her ease. "Didn't you?" she said. "Then it was a case of what you Doctors call 'unconscious cerebration'?"

"I am no Doctor," I replied. "Do I look so like one? Or what makes you think it?"

She pointed to the book I had been reading, which was so lying that its title, "Diseases of the Heart", was plainly visible.

"One needn't be a *Doctor*", I said, "to take an interest in medical books. There s another class of readers, who are yet more deeply interested——"

"You mean the *Patients*?" she interrupted, while a look of tender pity gave new sweetness to her face. "But", with an evident wish to avoid a possibly painful topic, "one needn't be *either*, to take an interest in books of *Science*. Which contain the greatest amount of Science, do you think, the books, or the minds?"

"Rather a profound question for a lady!" I said to myself, holding, with the conceit so natural to Man, that Woman's intellect is essentially shallow. And I considered a minute before replying. "If you mean *living* minds, I don't think it's possible to decide. There is so much *written* Science that no living person has ever *read*: and there is so much *thought-out* Science that hasn't yet been *written*. But, if you mean the whole human race, then I think the *minds* have it: everything, recorded in *books*, must have once been in some *mind*, you know."

"Isn't that rather like one of the Rules in Algebra?" my Lady enquired. ("*Algebra* too!" I thought with increasing wonder.) "I mean, if we consider thoughts as *factors*, may we not say that the Least Common

Multiple of all the *minds* contains that of all the books; but not the other way?"

"Certainly we may!" I replied, delighted with the illustration. "And what a grand thing it would be", I went on dreamily, thinking aloud rather than talking, "if we could only *apply* that Rule to books! You know, in finding the Least Common Multiple, we strike out a quantity wherever it occurs, except in the term where it is raised to its highest power. So we should have to erase every recorded thought, except in the sentence where it is expressed with the greatest intensity."

My Lady laughed merrily. "*Some* books would be reduced to blank paper, I'm afraid!" she said.

"They would. Most libraries would be terribly diminished in *bulk*. But just think what they would gain in *quality*!"

"When will it be done?" she eagerly asked. "If there's any chance of it in *my* time, I think I'll leave off reading, and wait for it!"

"Well, perhaps in another thousand years or so———"

"Then there's no use waiting!" said my Lady. "Let's sit down. Uggug, my pet, come and sit by me!"

"Anywhere but by *me*!" growled the Sub-Warden. "The little wretch always manages to upset his coffee!"

I guessed at once (as perhaps the reader will also have guessed, if, like myself, he is *very* clever at drawing conclusions) that my Lady was the Sub-Warden's wife, and that Uggug (a hideous fat boy, about the same age as Sylvie, with the expression of a prize-pig) was their son. Sylvie and Bruno, with the Lord Chancellor, made up a party of seven.

"And you actually got a plunge-bath every morning?" said the Sub-Warden, seemingly in continuation of a conversation with the Professor. "Even at the little roadside-inns?"

"Oh, certainly, certainly!" the Professor replied with a smile on his jolly face. "Allow me to explain. It is, in fact, a very simple problem in Hydrodynamics. (That means a combination of Water and Strength.) If we take a plunge-bath, and a man of great strength (such as myself) about to plunge into it, we have a perfect example of this science. I am bound to admit", the Professor continued, in a lower tone and with downcast eyes, "that we need a man of *remarkable* strength. He must be able to spring from the floor to about twice his own height, gradually turning over as he rises, so as to come down again head first."

"Why, you need a *flea*, not a *man*!" exclaimed the Sub-Warde

"Pardon me," said the Professor. "This particular kind of bat adapted for a flea. Let us suppose", he continued, folding his table into a graceful festoon, "that this represents what is perhaps *the n

A portable plunge-bath

of this Age—the Active Tourist's Portable Bath. You may describe it briefly, if you like," looking at the Chancellor, "by the letters A.T.P.B."

The Chancellor, much disconcerted at finding everybody looking at him, could only murmur, in a shy whisper, "Precisely so!"

"One great advantage of this plunge-bath", continued the Professor, "is that it requires only half-a-gallon of water——"

"I don't call it a *plunge*-bath", His Sub-Excellency remarked, "unless your Active Tourist goes *right under!*"

"But he *does* go right under," the old man gently replied. "The A.T. hangs up the P.B. on a nail—*thus*. He then empties the water-jug into it—places the empty jug below the bag—leaps into the air—descends head-first into the bag—the water rises round him to the top of the bag—and there you are!" he triumphantly concluded. "The A.T. is as much under water as if he'd gone a mile or two down into the Atlantic!"

"And he's drowned, let us say, in about four minutes——"

"By no means!" the Professor answered with a proud smile. "After about a minute, he quietly turns a tap at the lower end of the P.B.—all the water runs back into the jug—and there you are again!"

"But how in the world is he to get *out* of the bag again?"

"*That*, I take it," said the Professor, "is the most beautiful part of the whole invention. All the way up the P.B. inside, are loops for the thumbs; so it's something like going up-stairs, only perhaps less comfortable; and, by the time the A.T. has risen out of the bag, all but his head, he's sure to topple over, one way or the other—the Law of Gravity secures *that*. And there he is on the floor again!"

"A little bruised, perhaps?"

"Well, yes, a little bruised; but *having had his plunge-bath*: that's the great thing."

"Wonderful! It's almost beyond belief!" murmured the Sub-Warden. The Professor took it as a compliment, and bowed with a gratified smile.

"*Quite* beyond belief!" my Lady added—meaning, no doubt, to be more complimentary still. The Professor bowed, but he didn't smile *this* time.

"I can assure you", he said earnestly, "that, *provided the bath was made*, I used it every morning. I certainly *ordered* it—*that* I am clear about—my only doubt is, whether the man ever finished making it. It's difficult to remember, after so many years——"

At this moment the door, very slowly and creakingly, began to open, and Sylvie and Bruno jumped up, and ran to meet the well-known footstep.

CHAPTER 3

Birthday-Presents

"IT'S my brother!" the Sub-Warden exclaimed, in a warning whisper. "Speak out and be quick about it!"

The appeal was evidently addressed to the Lord Chancellor, who instantly replied, in a shrill monotone, like a little boy repeating the alphabet, "As I was remarking, your Sub-Excellency, this portentous movement——"

"You began too soon!" the other interrupted, scarcely able to restrain himself to a whisper, so great was his excitement. "He couldn't have heard you. Begin again!"

"As I was remarking," chanted the obedient Lord Chancellor, "this portentous movement has already assumed the dimensions of a Revolution!"

"And what *are* the dimensions of a Revolution?" The voice was genial and mellow, and the face of the tall dignified old man, who had just entered the room, leading Sylvie by the hand, and with Bruno riding triumphantly on his shoulder, was too noble and gentle to have scared a less guilty man: but the Lord Chancellor turned pale instantly, and could hardly articulate the words "The dimensions—your—your High Excellency? I—I—scarcely comprehend!"

"Well, the length, breadth, and thickness, if you like it better!" And the old man smiled, half-contemptuously.

The Lord Chancellor recovered himself with a great effort, and pointed to the open window. "If your High Excellency will listen for a moment to the shouts of the exasperated populace——" ("of the exasperated populace!" the Sub-Warden repeated in a louder tone, as the Lord Chancellor, being in a state of abject terror, had dropped almost into a whisper) "—you will understand what it is they want."

And at that moment there surged into the room a hoarse confused cry, in which the only clearly audible words were "Less—bread—More—

taxes!" The old man laughed heartily. "What in the world——" he was beginning: but the Chancellor heard him not. "Some mistake!" he muttered, hurrying to the window, from which he shortly returned with an air of relief. "*Now* listen!" he exclaimed, holding up his hand impressively. And now the words came quite distinctly, and with the regularity of the ticking of a clock, "More—bread—Less—taxes!"

"More bread!" the Warden repeated in astonishment. "Why, the new Government Bakery was opened only last week, and I gave orders to sell the bread at cost-price during the present scarcity! What *can* they expect more?"

"The Bakery's closed, y'reince!" the Chancellor said, more loudly and clearly than he had spoken yet. He was emboldened by the consciousness that *here*, at least, he had evidence to produce: and he placed in the Warden's hands a few printed notices, that were lying ready, with some open ledgers, on a side-table.

"Yes, yes, *I* see!" the Warden muttered, glancing carelessly through them. "Order countermanded by my brother, and supposed to be *my* doing! Rather sharp practice! It's all right!" he added in a louder tone. "My name is signed to it: so I take it on myself. But what do you mean by 'Less Taxes'? How *can* they be less? I abolished the last of them a month ago!"

"It's been put on again, y'reince, and by y'reince's own orders!" and other printed notices were submitted for inspection.

The Warden, whilst looking them over, glanced once or twice at the Sub-Warden, who had seated himself before one of the open ledgers, and was quite absorbed in adding it up; but he merely repeated "It's all right. I accept it as my doing."

"And they do say", the Chancellor went on sheepishly—looking much more like a convicted thief than an Officer of State, "that a change of Government, by the abolition of the Sub-Warden—I mean," he hastily added, on seeing the Warden's look of astonishment, "the abolition of the *office* of Sub-Warden, and giving the present holder the right to act as *Vice*-Warden whenever the Warden is absent—would appease all this seedling discontent. I mean," he added, glancing at a paper he held in his hand, "all this *seething* discontent!"

"For fifteen years", put in a deep but very harsh voice, "my husband has been acting as Sub-Warden. It is too long! It is much too long!" My Lady was a vast creature at all times: but, when she frowned and folded her arms, as now, she looked more gigantic than ever, and made one try to fancy what a haystack would look like, if out of temper.

"He would distinguish himself as a Vice!" my Lady proceeded, being far too stupid to see the double meaning of her words. "There has been no such Vice in Outland for many a long year, as he would be!"

"What course would *you* suggest, Sister?" the Warden mildly enquired.

My Lady stamped, which was undignified: and snorted, which was ungraceful. "This is no *jesting* matter!" she bellowed.

"I will consult my brother," said the Warden. "Brother!"

"—and seven makes a hundred and ninety-four, which is sixteen and twopence," the Sub-Warden replied. "Put down two and carry sixteen."

The Chancellor raised his hands and eyebrows, lost in admiration. "*Such* a man of business!" he murmured.

"Brother, could I have a word with you in my Study?" the Warden said in a louder tone. The Sub-Warden rose with alacrity, and the two left the room together.

My Lady turned to the Professor, who had uncovered the urn, and was taking its temperature with his pocket-thermometer. "Professor!" she began, so loudly and suddenly that even Uggug, who had gone to sleep in his chair, left off snoring and opened one eye. The Professor pocketed his thermometer in a moment, clasped his hands, and put his head on one side with a meek smile.

"You were teaching my son before breakfast, I believe?" my Lady loftily remarked. "I hope he strikes you as having talent?"

"Oh, very much so indeed, my Lady!" the Professor hastily replied, unconsciously rubbing his ear, while some painful recollection seemed to cross his mind. "I was very forcibly struck by His Magnificence, I assure you!"

"He is a charming boy!" my Lady exclaimed. "Even his snores are more musical than those of other boys!"

If that *were* so, the Professor seemed to think, the snores of *other* boys must be something too awful to be endured: but he was a cautious man, and he said nothing.

"And he's so clever!" my Lady continued "No one will enjoy your Lecture more—by the way, have you fixed the time for it yet? You've never given one, you know: and it was promised years ago, before you——"

"Yes, yes, my Lady, *I* know! Perhaps next Tuesday—or Tuesday week——"

"That will do very well," said my Lady, graciously. "Of course you will let the Other Professor lecture as well?"

"I think *not*, my Lady," the Professor said with some hesitation. "You see, he always stands with his back to the audience. It does very well for *reciting*; but for *lecturing*——"

"You are quite right," said my Lady. "And, now I come to think of it, there would hardly be time for more than *one* Lecture. And it will go off all the better, if we begin with a Banquet, and a Fancy-dress Ball——"

"It will indeed!" the Professor cried, with enthusiasm.

"I shall come as a Grass-hopper," my Lady calmly proceeded. "What shall *you* come as, Professor?"

The Professor smiled feebly. "I shall come as—as early as I can, my Lady!"

"You mustn't come in before the doors are opened," said my Lady.

"I ca'n't," said the Professor. "Excuse me a moment. As this is Lady Sylvie's birthday, I would like to——" and he rushed away.

Bruno began feeling in his pockets, looking more and more melancholy as he did so: then he put his thumb in his mouth, and considered for a minute: then he quietly left the room.

He had hardly done so before the Professor was back again, quite out of breath. "Wishing you many happy returns of the day, my dear child!" he went on, addressing the smiling little girl, who had run to meet him. "Allow me to give you a birthday-present. It's a second-hand pin-cushion, my dear. And it only cost fourpence-halfpenny!"

"Thank you, it's *very* pretty!" And Sylvie rewarded the old man with a hearty kiss.

"And the *pins* they gave me for nothing!" the Professor added in high glee. "Fifteen of em, and only *one* bent!"

"I'll make the bent one into a *hook*!" said Sylvie. "To catch Bruno with, when he runs away from his lessons!"

"You ca'n't guess what *my* present is!" said Uggug, who had taken the butter-dish from the table, and was standing behind her, with a wicked leer on his face.

"No, I ca'n't guess," Sylvie said without looking up. She was still examining the Professor's pin-cushion.

"It's *this*!" cried the bad boy, exultingly, as he emptied the dish over her, and then, with a grin of delight at his own cleverness, looked round for applause.

Sylvie coloured crimson, as she shook off the butter from her frock: but she kept her lips tight shut, and walked away to the window, where she stood looking out and trying to recover her temper.

Uggug's triumph was a very short one: the Sub-Warden had returned, just in time to be a witness of his dear child's playfulness, and in another moment a skilfully applied box on the ear had changed his grin of delight into a howl of pain.

"My darling!" cried his mother, enfolding him in her fat arms. "Did they box his ears for nothing? A precious pet!"

"It's not for *nothing!*" growled the angry father. "Are you aware, Madam, that *I* pay the house-bills, out of a fixed annual sum? The loss of all that wasted butter falls on *me!* Do you hear, Madam!"

"Hold your tongue, Sir!" My Lady spoke very quietly—almost in a whisper. But there was something in her *look* which silenced him. "Don't you see it was only a *joke*? And a very clever one, too! He only meant that he loved nobody *but* her! And instead of being pleased with the compliment, the spiteful little thing has gone away in a huff!"

The Sub-Warden was a very good hand at changing a subject. He walked across to the window. "My dear," he said, "is that a *pig* that I see down below, rooting about among your flower-beds?"

"A *pig!*" shrieked my Lady, rushing madly to the window, and almost pushing her husband out, in her anxiety to see for herself. "Whose pig is it? How did it get in? Where's that crazy Gardener gone?"

At this moment Bruno re-entered the room, and passing Uggug (who was blubbering his loudest, in the hope of attracting notice) as if he was quite used to that sort of thing, he ran up to Sylvie and threw his arms round her. "I went to my toy-cupboard", he said with a very sorrowful face, "to see if there were *somefin* fit for a present for oo! And there isn't *nuffin!* They's *all* broken, every one! And I haven't got *no* money left, to buy oo a birthday-present! And I ca'n't give oo nuffin but *this!*" ("*This*" was a very earnest hug and a kiss.)

"Oh, thank you, darling!" cried Sylvie. "I like *your* present best of all!" (But if so, why did she give it back so quickly?)

His Sub-Excellency turned and patted the two children on the head with his long lean hands. "Go away, dears!" he said. "There's business to talk over."

Sylvie and Bruno went away hand in hand: but, on reaching the door, Sylvie came back again and went up to Uggug timidly. "I don't mind about the butter," she said, "and I—I'm sorry he hurt you!" And she tried to shake hands with the little ruffian: but Uggug only blubbered louder, and wouldn't make friends. Sylvie left the room with a sigh.

The Sub-Warden glared angrily at his weeping son. "Leave the room, Sirrah!" he said, as loud as he dared. His wife was still leaning out of the window, and kept repeating "I *ca'n't* see that pig! Where *is* it?"

"It's moved to the right—now it's gone a little to the left," said the Sub-Warden: but he had his back to the window, and was making signals to the Lord Chancellor, pointing to Uggug and the door, with many a cunning nod and wink.

The Chancellor caught his meaning at last, and crossing the room, took that interesting child by the ear—the next moment he and Uggug were out of the room, and the door shut behind them: but not before one piercing yell had rung through the room, and reached the ears of the fond mother.

"What *is* that hideous noise?" she fiercely asked, turning upon her startled husband.

"It's some hyæna—or other," replied the Sub-Warden, looking vaguely up to the ceiling, as if that was where they usually were to be found. "Let us to business, my dear. Here comes the Warden." And he picked up from the floor a wandering scrap of manuscript, on which I just caught the words "after which Election duly holden the said Sibimet and Tabikat his wife may at their pleasure assume Imperial——" before, with a guilty look, he crumpled it up in his hand.

CHAPTER 4

A Cunning Conspiracy

THE Warden entered at this moment: and close behind him came the Lord Chancellor, a little flushed and out of breath, and adjusting his wig, which appeared to have been dragged partly off his head.

"But where is my precious child?" my Lady enquired, as the four took their seats at the small side-table devoted to ledgers and bundles and bills.

"He left the room a few minutes ago—with the Lord Chancellor," the Sub-Warden briefly explained.

"Ah!" said my Lady, graciously smiling on that high official. "Your Lordship has a very *taking* way with children! I doubt if any one could *gain the ear* of my darling Uggug so quickly as *you* can!" For an entirely stupid woman, my Lady's remarks were curiously full of meaning, of which she herself was wholly unconscious.

The Chancellor bowed, but with a very uneasy air. "I think the Warden was about to speak," he remarked, evidently anxious to change the subject.

But my Lady would not be checked. "He is a clever boy," she continued with enthusiasm, "but he needs a man like your Lordship to *draw him out!*"

The Chancellor bit his lip, and was silent. He evidently feared that, stupid as she looked, she understood what she said *this* time, and was having a joke at his expense. He might have spared himself all anxiety: whatever accidental meaning her *words* might have, she *herself* never meant anything at all.

"It is all settled!" the Warden announced, wasting no time over preliminaries. "The Sub-Wardenship is abolished, and my brother is appointed to act as Vice-Warden whenever I am absent. So, as I am going abroad for a while, he will enter on his new duties at once."

"And there will really be a Vice after all?" my Lady enquired.

"I hope so!" the Warden smilingly replied.

My Lady looked much pleased, and tried to clap her hands: but you might as well have knocked two feather-beds together, for any noise it made. "When my husband is Vice", she said, "it will be the same as if we had a *hundred* Vices!"

"Hear, hear!" cried the Sub-Warden.

"You seem to think it very remarkable", my Lady remarked with some severity, "that your wife should speak the truth!"

"No, not *remarkable* at all!" her husband anxiously explained. "*Nothing* is remarkable that *you* say, sweet one!"

My Lady smiled approval of the sentiment, and went on. "And am I Vice-Wardeness?"

"If you choose to use that title," said the Warden: "but 'Your Excellency' will be the proper style of address. And I trust that both '*His* Excellency' and '*Her* Excellency' will observe the Agreement I have drawn up. The provision I am *most* anxious about is this." He unrolled a large parchment scroll, and read aloud the words " '*item*, that we will be kind to the poor'. The Chancellor worded it for me," he added, glancing at that great Functionary. "I suppose, now, that word '*item*' has some deep legal meaning?"

"Undoubtedly!" replied the Chancellor, as articulately as he could with a pen between his lips. He was nervously rolling and unrolling several other scrolls, and making room among them for the one the Warden had just handed to him. "These are merely the rough copies," he explained: "and, as soon as I have put in the final corrections——" making a great commotion among the different parchments, "—a semi-colon or two that I have accidentally omitted——" here he darted about, pen in hand, from one part of the scroll to another, spreading sheets of blotting-paper over his corrections, "all will be ready for signing."

"Should it not be read out, first?" my Lady enquired.

"No need, no need!" the Sub-Warden and the Chancellor exclaimed at the same moment, with feverish eagerness.

"No need at all," the Warden gently assented. "Your husband and I have gone through it together. It provides that he shall exercise the full authority of Warden, and shall have the disposal of the annual revenue attached to the office, until my return, or, failing that, until Bruno comes of age: and that he shall then hand over, to myself or to Bruno as the case may be, the Wardenship, the unspent revenue, and the contents of the Treasury, which are to be preserved, intact, under his guardianship."

All this time the Sub-Warden was busy, with the Chancellor's help, shifting the papers from side to side, and pointing out to the Warden the

'What a game!'

place where he was to sign. He then signed it himself, and my Lady and the Chancellor added their names as witnesses.

"Short partings are best," said the Warden. "All is ready for my journey. My children are waiting below to see me off." He gravely kissed my Lady, shook hands with his brother and the Chancellor, and left the room.

The three waited in silence till the sound of wheels announced that the Warden was out of hearing: then, to my surprise, they broke into peals of uncontrollable laughter.

"What a game, oh, what a game!" cried the Chancellor. And he and the Vice Warden joined hands, and skipped wildly about the room. My Lady was too dignified to skip, but she laughed like the neighing of a horse, and wave her handkerchief above her head: it was clear to her very limited understanding that *something* very clever had been done, but what it *was* she had yet to learn.

"You said I should hear all about it when the Warden had gone," she remarked, as soon as she could make herself heard.

"And so you shall, Tabby!" her husband graciously replied, as he removed the blotting paper, and showed the two parchments lying side by side. "This is the one he read but didn't sign: and this is the one he signed but didn't read! You see it was all covered up, except the place for signing the names——"

"Yes, yes!" my Lady interrupted eagerly, and began comparing the two Agreements. " '*Item*, that he shall exercise the authority of Warden, in the Warden's absence.' Why, that's been changed into 'shall be absolute governor for life, with the title of Emperor, if elected to that office by the people.' What! Are you *Emperor,* darling?"

"Not yet, dear," the Vice-Warden replied. "It wo'n't do to let this paper be seen, just at present. All in good time."

My Lady nodded, and read on. " '*Item*, that we will be kind to the poor.' Why, that's omitted altogether!"

"Course it is!" said her husband. "*We're* not going to bother about the wretches!"

"*Good*," said my Lady, with emphasis, and read on again. " '*Item*, that the contents of the Treasury be preserved intact.' Why, that's altered into 'shall be at the absolute disposal of the Vice-Warden'! Well, Sibby, that *was* a clever trick! *All* the Jewels, only think! May I go and put them on directly?"

"Well, not *just* yet, Lovey," her husband uneasily replied "You see the public mind isn't quite ripe for it yet. We must feel our way. Of course we'll have the coach-and-four out, at once. And I'll take the title of Emperor, as soon as we can safely hold an Election. But they'll hardly stand our using the *Jewels*, as long as they know the Warden's alive. We must spread a report of his death. A little Conspiracy——"

"A Conspiracy!" cried the delighted lady, clapping her hands. "Of all things, I *do* like a Conspiracy! It's so interesting!"

The Vice-Warden and the Chancellor interchanged a wink or two. "Let her conspire to her heart's content!" the cunning Chancellor whispered. "It'll do no harm!"

"And when will the Conspiracy——"

"Hist!" her husband hastily interrupted her, as the door opened, and Sylvie and Bruno came in, with their arms twined lovingly round each other—Bruno sobbing convulsively, with his face hidden on his sister's shoulder, and Sylvie more grave and quiet, but with tears streaming down her cheeks.

"Mustn't cry like that!" the Vice-Warden said sharply, but without any effect on the weeping children. "Cheer 'em up a bit!" he hinted to my Lady.

"*Cake!*" my Lady muttered to herself with great decision, crossing the room and opening a cupboard, from which she presently returned with two slices of plum-cake. "Eat, and don't cry!" were her short and simple orders: and the poor children sat down side by side, but seemed in no mood for eating.

For the second time the door opened—or rather was *burst* open, this time, as Uggug rushed violently into the room, shouting "that old Beggar's come again!"

"He's not to have any food——" the Vice-Warden was beginning, but the Chancellor interrupted him. "It's all right," he said, in a low voice: "the servants have their orders."

"He's just under here," said Uggug, who had gone to the window, and was looking down into the courtyard.

"Where, my darling?" said his fond mother, flinging her arms round the neck of the little monster. All of us (except Sylvie and Bruno, who took no notice of what was going on) followed her to the window. The old Beggar looked up at us with hungry eyes. "Only a crust of bread, your Highness!" he pleaded. He was a fine old man, but looked sadly ill and worn. "A crust of bread is what I crave!" he repeated. "A single crust and a little water!"

"Here's some water, drink this!" Uggug bellowed, emptying a jug of water over his head.

"Well done, my boy!" cried the Vice-Warden. "That's the way to settle such folk!"

"Clever boy!" the Wardeness chimed in. "*Hasn't* he good spirits?"

"Take a stick to him!" shouted the Vice-Warden, as the old Beggar shook the water from his ragged cloak, and again gazed meekly upwards.

"Take a red-hot poker to him!" my Lady again chimed in.

Possibly there was no red-hot poker handy: but some *sticks* were forthcoming in a moment, and threatening faces surrounded the poor old wanderer, who waved them back with quiet dignity. "No need to break my old bones," he said. "I am going. Not even a crust!"

"Poor, *poor* old man!" exclaimed a little voice at my side, half choked with sobs. Bruno was at the window, trying to throw out his slice of plum-cake, but Sylvie held him back.

"He *shall* have my cake!" Bruno cried passionately struggling out of Sylvie's arms.

"Yes, yes, darling!" Sylvie gently pleaded. "But don't *throw* it out! He's gone away, don't you see? Let's go after him." And she led him out of the room, unnoticed by the rest of the party, who were wholly absorbed in watching the old Beggar.

The Conspirators returned to their seats, and continued their conversation in an undertone, so as not to be heard by Uggug, who was still standing at the window.

"By the way, there was something about Bruno succeeding to the Wardenship," said my Lady. "How does *that* stand in the new Agreement?"

The Chancellor chuckled. "Just the same, word for word," he said, "with *one* exception, my Lady. Instead of 'Bruno', I've taken the liberty to put in——" he dropped his voice to a whisper, "—to put in 'Uggug', you know!"

"Uggug, indeed!" I exclaimed, in a burst of indignation I could no longer control. To bring out even that one word seemed a gigantic effort: but, the cry once uttered, all effort ceased at once: a sudden gust swept away the whole scene, and I found myself sitting up, staring at the young lady in the opposite corner of the carriage, who had now thrown back her veil, and was looking at me with an expression of amused surprise.

CHAPTER 5

A Beggar's Palace

THAT I had said *something*, in the act of waking, I felt sure: the hoarse stifled cry was still ringing in my ears, even if the startled look of my fellow-traveler had not been evidence enough: but what could I possibly say by way of apology?

"I hope I didn't frighten you?" I stammered out at last. "I have no idea what I said. I was dreaming."

"You said '*Uggug indeed!*' " the young lady replied, with quivering lips that *would* curve themselves into a smile, in spite of all her efforts to look grave. "At least—you didn't *say* it—you *shouted* it!"

"I'm very sorry," was all I could say, feeling very penitent and helpless. "She *has* Sylvie's eyes!" I thought to myself, half-doubting whether, even now, I were fairly awake. "And that sweet look of innocent wonder is all Sylvie's, too. But Sylvie *hasn't* got that calm resolute mouth—nor that far-away look of dreamy sadness, like one that has had some deep sorrow, very long ago——" And the thick-coming fancies almost prevented my hearing the lady's next words.

"If you had had a 'Shilling Dreadful' in your hand," she proceeded, "something about Ghosts—or Dynamite—or Midnight Murder—one could understand it: those things aren't worth the shilling, unless they give one a Nightmare. But really— with only a *medical treatise*, you know——" and she glanced, with a pretty shrug of contempt, at the book over which I had fallen asleep.

Her friendliness, and utter unreserve, took me aback for a moment; yet there was no touch of forwardness, or boldness, about the child—for child, almost, she seemed to be: I guessed her at scarcely over twenty—all was the innocent frankness of some angelic visitant, new to the ways of earth and the conventionalisms—or, if you will, the barbarisms—of Society. "Even so", I mused, "will *Sylvie* look and speak, in another ten years."

"You don't care for Ghosts, then," I ventured to suggest, "unless they are really terrifying?"

"Quite so," the lady assented. "The regular Railway-Ghosts—I mean the Ghosts of ordinary Railway-literature—are very poor affairs. I feel inclined to say, with Alexander Selkirk, 'Their tameness is shocking to me'! And they never do any Midnight Murders. They couln't 'welter in gore', to save their lives!"

" 'Weltering in gore' is a very expressive phase, certainly. Can it be done in *any* fluid, I wonder?"

"I think *not*," the lady readily replied—quite as if she had thought it out, long ago. "It has to be something *thick*. For instance, you might welter in bread-sauce. That, being *white*, would be more suitable for a Ghost, supposing it wished to welter!"

"You have a real good *terrifying* Ghost in that book?" I hinted.

"How *could* you guess?" she exclaimed with the most engaging frankness, and placed the volume in my hands. I opened it eagerly, with a not unpleasant thrill (like what a good ghost-story gives one) at the "uncanny" coincidence of my having so unexpectedly divined the subject of her studies.

It was a book of Domestic Cookery, open at the article "Bread Sauce".

I returned the book, looking, I suppose, a little blank, as the lady laughed merrily at my discomfiture. "It's far more exciting than some of the modern ghosts, I assure you! Now there was a Ghost last month—I don't mean a *real* Ghost in—in Supernature—but in a Magazine. It was a perfectly *flavourless* Ghost. It wouldn't have frightened a mouse! It wasn't a Ghost that one would even offer a chair to!"

"Three score years and ten, baldness, and spectacles, have their advantages after all!" I said to myself. "Instead of a bashful youth and maiden, gasping out monosyllables at awful intervals, here we have an old man and a child, quite at their ease, talking as if they had known each other for years! Then you think", I continued aloud, "that we ought *sometimes* to ask a Ghost to sit down? But have we any authority for it? In Shakespeare, for instance—there are plenty of ghosts *there*—does Shakespeare ever give the stage-direction 'hands chair to Ghost'?"

The lady looked puzzled and thoughtful for a moment: then she *almost* clapped her hands. "Yes, yes, he *does*!" she cried. "He makes Hamlet say 'Rest, rest, perturbed Spirit!' "

"And that, I suppose, means an easy-chair?"

"An American rocking-chair, I *think*——"

"Fayfield Junction, my Lady, change for Elveston!" the guard announced, flinging open the door of the carriage: and we soon found ourselves, with all our portable property around us, on the platform.

The accommodation, provided for passengers waiting at this Junction, was distinctly inadequate—a single wooden bench, apparently intended for three sitters only: and even this was already partially occupied by a very old man, in a smock frock, who sat, with rounded shoulders and drooping head, and with hands clasped on the top of his stick so as to make a sort of pillow for that wrinkled face with its look of patient weariness.

"Come, you be off!" the Station-master roughly accosted the poor old man. "You be off, and make way for your betters! This way, my Lady!" he added in a perfectly different tone. "If your Ladyship will take a seat, the train will be up in a few minutes." The cringing servility of his manner was due, no doubt, to the address legible on the pile of luggage, which announced their owner to be "Lady Muriel Orme, passenger to Elveston, *via* Fayfield Junction".

As I watched the old man slowly rise to his feet, and hobble a few paces down the platform, the lines came to my lips:

> *"From sackcloth couch the Monk arose,*
> *With toil his stiffen'd limbs he rear'd;*
> *A hundred years had flung their snows*
> *On his thin locks and floating beard."*

But the lady scarcely noticed the little incident. After one glance at the "banished man" who stood tremulously leaning on his stick, she turned to me. "This is *not* an American rocking-chair, by any means! Yet may I say," slightly changing her place, so as to make room for me beside her, "may I say, in Hamlet's words, 'Rest, rest——' " she broke off with a silvery laugh.

" '—perturbed Spirit!' " I finished the sentence for her. "Yes, that describes a railway-traveler *exactly*! And here is an instance of it," I added, as the tiny local train drew up alongside the platform, and the porters bustled about, opening carriage-doors—one of them helping the poor old man to hoist himself into a third-class carriage, while another of them obsequiously conducted the lady and myself into a first-class.

She paused, before following him, to watch the progress of the other passenger. "Poor old man!" she said. "How weak and ill he looks! It was a shame to let him be turned away like that. I'm very sorry——" At this moment it dawned on me that these words were not addressed to *me*, but that she was unconsciously thinking aloud. I moved away a few steps, and waited to follow her into the carriage, where I resumed the conversation.

'Come, you be off!'

"Shakespeare *must* have traveled by rail, if only in a dream: 'perturbed Spirit' is such a happy phrase."

" 'Perturbed' referring, no doubt," she rejoined, "to the sensational booklets, peculiar to the Rail. If Steam has done nothing else, it has at least added a whole new Species of English Literature!"

"No doubt of it," I echoed. "The true origin of all our medical books—and all our cookery-books——"

"No, no!" she broke in merrily. "I didn't mean *our* Literature! *We* are quite abnormal. But the booklets—the little thrilling romances, where the Murder comes at page fifteen, and the Wedding at page forty—surely *they* are due to Steam?"

"And when we travel by Electricity—if I may venture to develop your theory—we shall have leaflets instead of booklets, and the Murder and the Wedding will come on the same page."

"A development worthy of Darwin!" the lady exclaimed enthusiastically. "Only *you* reverse his theory. Instead of developing a mouse into an elephant, you would develop an elephant into a mouse!" But here we plunged into a tunnel, and I leaned back and closed my eyes for a moment, trying to recall a few of the incidents of my recent dream.

"I thought I saw——" I murmured sleepily: and then the phrase insisted on conjugating itself, and ran into "you thought you saw—he thought he saw——" and then it suddenly went off into a song:

> *"He thought he saw an Elephant,*
> *That practised on a fife:*
> *He looked again, and found it was*
> *A letter from his wife.*
> *'At length I realise', he said,*
> *'The bitterness of Life' "*

And what a wild being it was who sang these wild words! A Gardener he seemed to be—yet surely a mad one, by the way he brandished his rake—madder, by the way he broke, ever and anon, into a frantic jig—maddest of all, by the shriek in which he brought out the last words of the stanza!

It was so far a description of himself that he had the *feet* of an Elephant: but the rest of him was skin and bone: and the wisps of loose straw, that bristled all about him, suggested that he had been originally stuffed with it, and that nearly all the stuffing had come out.

Sylvie and Bruno waited patiently till the end of the first verse. Then Sylvie advanced alone (Bruno having suddenly turned shy) and timidly introduced herself with the words "Please, I'm Sylvie!"

"And who's that other thing?" said the Gardener.

"What thing?" said Sylvie, looking round. "Oh, that's Bruno. He's my brother."

"Was he your brother yesterday?" the Gardener anxiously enquired.

"Course I were!" cried Bruno, who had gradually crept nearer, and didn't at all like being talked about without having his share in the conversation.

"Ah, well!" the Gardener said with a kind of groan. "Things change so, here. Whenever I look again it's sure to be something different! Yet I does my duty! I gets up wriggle-early at five——"

"If I was *oo*," said Bruno, "I wouldn't wriggle so early. It's as bad as being a worm!" he added, in an undertone to Sylvie.

"But you shouldn't be lazy in the morning, Bruno," said Sylvie. "Remember, its the *early* bird that picks up the worm!"

"It may, if it likes!" Bruno said with a slight yawn. "I don't like eating worms, one bit. I always stop in bed till the early bird has picked them up!"

"I wonder you've the face to tell me such fibs!" cried the Gardener.

To which Bruno wisely replied, "Oo don't want a *face* to tell fibs wiz—only a *mouf*."

Sylvie discreetly changed the subject. "And did you plant all these flowers?" she said. "What a lovely garden you've made! Do you know, I'd like to live here *always!*"

"In the winter-nights——" the Gardener was beginning.

"But I'd nearly forgotten what we came about!" Sylvie interrupted. "Would you please let us through into the road? There's a poor old beggar just gone out—and he's very hungry—and Bruno wants to give him his cake, you know!"

"It's as much as my place is worth!" the Gardener muttered, taking a key from his pocket, and beginning to unlock a door in the garden-wall.

"How much *are* it wurf?" Bruno innocently enquired.

But the Gardener only grinned. "That's a secret!" he said. "Mind you come back quick!" he called after the children, as they passed out into the road. I had just time to follow them, before he shut the door again.

We hurried down the road, and very soon caught sight of the old Beggar, about a quarter of a mile ahead of us, and the children at once set off running to overtake him. Lightly and swiftly they skimmed over the ground, and I could not in the least understand how it was I kept up with them so easily. But the unsolved problem did not worry me so much

as at another time it might have done, there were so many other things
to attend to.

The old Beggar must have been very deaf, as he paid no attention
whatever to Bruno's eager shouting, but trudged wearily on, never pausing
until the child got in front of him and held up the slice of cake. The poor
little fellow was quite out of breath, and could only utter the one word
"Cake!"—not with the gloomy decision with which Her Excellency had
so lately pronounced it, but with a sweet childish timidity, looking up into
the old man's face with eyes that loved "all things both great and small".

The old man snatched it from him, and devoured it greedily, as some
hungry wild beast might have done, but never a word of thanks did he
give his little benefactor—only growled "More, more!" and glared at the
half-frightened children.

"There *is* no more!" Sylvie said with tears in her eyes. "I'd eaten mine.
It was a shame to let you be turned away like that. I'm very sorry——"

I lost the rest of the sentence, for my mind had recurred with a great
shock of surprise, to Lady Muriel Orme, who had so lately uttered these
very words of Sylvie's—yes, and in Sylvie's own voice, and with Sylvie's
gentle pleading eyes!

"Follow me!" were the next words I heard, as the old man waved his hand, with a dignified grace that ill suited his ragged dress, over a bush, that stood by the road side, which began instantly to sink into the earth. At another time I might have doubted the evidence of my eyes, or at least have felt some astonishment: but, in *this* strange scene, my whole being seemed absorbed in strong curiosity as to what would happen next.

When the bush had sunk quite out of our sight, marble steps were seen, leading downwards into darkness. The old man led the way, and we eagerly followed.

The staircase was so dark, at first, that I could only just see the forms of the children as, hand-in-hand, they groped their way down after their guide: but it got lighter every moment, with a strange silvery brightness, that seemed to exist in the air, as there were no lamps visible; and, when at last we reached a level floor, the room, we found ourselves in, was almost as light as day.

It was eight-sided, having in each angle a slender pillar, round which silken draperies were twined. The wall between the pillars was entirely covered, to the height of six or seven feet, with creepers, from which hung quantities of ripe fruit and of brilliant flowers, that almost hid the leaves. In another place, perchance, I might have wondered to see fruit and flowers growing together: here, my chief wonder was that neither fruit nor flowers were such as I had ever seen before. Higher up, each wall contained a circular window of coloured glass; and over all was an arched roof, that seemed to be spangled all over with jewels.

With hardly less wonder, I turned this way and that, trying to make out how in the world we had come in: for there was no door: and all the walls were thickly covered with the lovely creepers.

"We are safe here, my darlings!" said the old man, laying a hand on Sylvie's shoulder, and bending down to kiss her. Sylvie drew back hastily, with an offended air: but in another moment, with a glad cry of "Why, it's *Father*!", she had run into his arms.

"Father! Father!" Bruno repeated: and, while the happy children were being hugged and kissed, I could but rub my eyes and say "Where, then, are the rags gone to?"; for the old man was now dressed in royal robes that glittered with jewels and gold embroidery, and wore a circlet of gold around his head.

CHAPTER 6

The Magic Locket

"WHERE are we, father?" Sylvie whispered, with her arms twined closely around the old man's neck, and with her rosy cheek lovingly pressed to his.

"In Elfland, darling. It's one of the provinces of Fairyland."

"But I thought Elfland was *ever* so far from Outland: and we've come such a *tiny* little way!"

"You came by the Royal Road, sweet one. Only those of royal blood can travel along it: but *you've* been royal ever since I was made King of Elfland—that's nearly a month ago. They sent *two* ambassadors, to make sure that their invitation to me, to be their new King, should reach me. One was a Prince; so *he* was able to come by the Royal Road, and to come invisibly to all but me: the other was a Baron; so *he* had to come by the common road, and I dare say he hasn't even *arrived* yet."

"Then how far have we come?" Sylvie enquired.

"Just a thousand miles, sweet one, since the Gardener unlocked that door for you."

"A thousand miles!" Bruno repeated. "And may I eat one?"

"Eat a *mile*, little rogue?"

"No," said Bruno. "I mean may I eat one of that fruits?"

"Yes, child," said the father: "and then you'll find out what *Pleasure* is like—the Pleasure we all seek so madly, and enjoy so mournfully!"

Bruno ran eagerly to the wall, and picked a fruit that was *shaped* something like a banana, but had the *colour* of a strawberry.

He ate it with beaming looks, that became gradually more gloomy, and were very blank indeed by the time he had finished.

"It hasn't got no taste at all!" he complained. "I couldn't feel nuffin in my mouf! It's a—what's that hard word, Sylvie?"

"It was a *Phlizz*," Sylvie gravely replied. "Are they *all* like that, father?"

"They're all like that to *you*, darling, because you don't belong to Elfland—yet. But to *me* they are real."

Bruno looked puzzled. "I'll try anuvver kind of fruits!" he said, and jumped down off the King's knee. "There's some lovely striped ones, just like a rainbow!" And off he ran.

Meanwhile the Fairy-King and Sylvie were talking together, but in such low tones that I could not catch the words: so I followed Bruno, who was picking and eating other kinds of fruit, in the vain hope of finding *some* that had a taste. I tried to pick some myself—but it was like grasping air, and I soon gave up the attempt and returned to Sylvie.

"Look well at it, my darling," the old man was saying, "and tell me how you like it."

"It's just *lovely*," cried Sylvie delightedly. "Bruno, come and look!" And she held up, so that he might see the light through it, a heart-shaped Locket, apparently cut out of a single jewel, of a rich blue colour, with a slender gold chain attached to it.

"It are welly pretty," Bruno more soberly remarked: and he began spelling out some words inscribed on it. "All—will—love—Sylvie," he made them out at last. "And so they doos!" he cried, clasping his arms round her neck. "*Everybody* loves Sylvie!"

"But *we* love her best, don't we, Bruno?" said the old King, as he took possession of the Locket. "Now, Sylvie, look at *this*." And he showed her, lying on the palm of his hand, a Locket of a deep crimson colour, the same shape as the blue one, and, like it, attached to a slender golden chain.

"Lovelier and lovelier!" exclaimed Sylvie, clasping her hands in ecstasy. "Look, Bruno!"

"And there's words on this one, too," said Bruno. "Sylvie—will—love—all."

"Now you see the difference," said the old man: "different colours and different words. Choose one of them, darling. I'll give you whichever you like best."

Sylvie whispered the words, several times over, with a thoughtful smile, and then made her decision. "It's *very* nice to be loved," she said: "but it's nicer to love other people! May I have the red one, Father?"

The old man said nothing: but I could see his eyes fill with tears, as he bent his head and pressed his lips to her forehead in a long loving kiss. Then he undid the chain, and showed her how to fasten it round her neck, and to hide it away under the edge of her frock. "It's for you to *keep*, you know," he said in a low voice, "not for other people to *see*. You'll remember how to use it?"

"Yes, I'll remember," said Sylvie.

"And now, darlings, it's time for you to go back or they'll be missing you, and then that poor Gardener will get into trouble!"

Once more a feeling of wonder rose in my mind as to how in the world we were to *get* back again—since I took it for granted that wherever the children went, *I* was to go—but no shadow of doubt seemed to cross *their* minds, as they hugged and kissed him, murmuring, over and over again, "Good-bye, darling Father!" And then, suddenly and swiftly, the darkness of midnight seemed to close in upon us, and through the darkness harshly rang a strange wild song:

> *"He thought he saw a Buffalo*
> *Upon the chimney-piece:*
> *He looked again, and found it was*
> *His Sister's Husband's Niece.*
> *'Unless you leave this house', he said,*
> *'I'll send for the Police!' "*

"That was *me*!" he added, looking out at us, through the half-opened door, as we stood waiting in the road. "And that's what I'd have done —as sure as potatoes aren't radishes—if she hadn't have tooken herself off! But I always loves my *pay-rints* like anything."

"Who *are* oor *pay-rints*?" said Bruno.

"Them as pay *rint* for me, of course!" the Gardener replied. "You can come in now, if you like."

He flung the door open as he spoke, and we got out, a little dazzled and stupefied (at least *I* felt so) at the sudden transition from the half-darkness of the railway-carriage to the brilliantly-lighted platform of Elveston Station.

A footman, in a handsome livery came forward and respectfully touched his hat. "The carriage is here, my Lady," he said, taking from her the wraps and small articles she was carrying: and Lady Muriel, after shaking hands and bidding me "Good-night!" with a pleasant smile, followed him.

It was with a somewhat blank and lonely feeling that I betook myself to the van from which the luggage was being taken out: and, after giving directions to have my boxes sent after me, I made my way on foot to Arthur's lodgings, and soon lost my lonely feeling in the hearty welcome my old friend gave me, and the cosy warmth and cheerful light of the little sitting-room into which he led me.

"Little, as you see, but quite enough for us two. Now, take the easy-chair, old fellow, and let's have another look at you! well, you *do* look a bit pulled down!' and he put on a solemn professional air. "I prescribe Ozone, *quant. suff.* Social dissipation, *fiant pilulæ quam plurimæ:* to be taken, feasting, three times a day!"

"But, Doctor!" I remonstrated. "Society doesn't 'receive' three times a day!"

"That's all *you* know about it!" the young Doctor gaily replied. "At home, lawn-tennis, 3 P.M. At home, kettledrum, 5 P.M. At home, music (Elveston doesn't give dinners), 8 P.M. Carriages at 10. There you are!"

It sounded very pleasant, I was obliged to admit. "And I know some of the *lady*-society already," I added. "One of them came in the same carriage with me."

"What was she like? Then perhaps I can identify her."

"The *name* was Lady Muriel Orme. As to what she was *like*—well, *I* thought her very beautiful. Do you know her?"

"Yes—I do know her." And the grave Doctor coloured slightly as he added "Yes, I agree with you. She *is* beautiful."

"*I* quite lost my heart to her!" I went on mischievously. "We talked——"

"Have some supper!" Arthur interrupted with an air of relief, as the maid entered with the tray. And he steadily resisted all my attempts to return to the subject of Lady Muriel until the evening had almost worn itself away. Then, as we sat gazing into the fire, and conversation was lapsing into silence, he made a hurried confession.

"I hadn't meant to tell you anything about her", he said (naming no names, as if there were only one "she" in the world! "till you had seen more of her, and formed your own judgment of her: but somehow you surprised it out of me. And I've not breathed a word of it to any one else. But I can trust *you* with a secret, old friend! Yes! It's true of *me*, what I suppose *you* said in jest."

"In the merest jest, believe me!" I said earnestly. "Why, man, I'm three times her age! But if she's *your* choice, then I'm sure she's all that is good and—" "—and sweet," Arthur went on, "and pure, and self-denying, and true-hearted, and——" he broke off hastily, as if he could not trust himself to say more on a subject so sacred and so precious. Silence followed: and I leaned back drowsily in my easy-chair, filled with bright and beautiful imaginings of Arthur and his lady-love, and of all the peace and happiness in store for them.

I pictured them to myself walking together, lingeringly and lovingly, under arching trees, in a sweet garden of their own, and welcomed back by their faithful gardener, on their return from some brief excursion.

It seemed natural enough that the gardener should be filled with exuberant delight at the return of so gracious a master and mistress—and how strangely childlike they looked! I could have taken them for Sylvie and Bruno—less natural that he should show it by such wild dances, such crazy songs!

> *"He thought he saw a Rattlesnake*
> *That questioned him in Greek:*
> *He looked again, and found it was*
> *The Middle of Next Week.*
> *'The one thing I regret', he said,*
> *"Is that it cannot speak!'"*

—least natural of all that the Vice-Warden and "my Lady" should be standing close beside me, discussing an open letter, which had just been handed to him by the Professor, who stood, meekly waiting, a few yards off.

"If it were not for those two brats", I heard him mutter, glancing savagely at Sylvie and Bruno, who were courteously listening to the Gardener's song, "there would be no difficulty whatever."

"Let's hear that bit of the letter again," said my Lady. And the Vice-Warden read aloud:

"—and we therefore entreat you graciously to accept the Kingship, to which you have been unanimously elected by the Council of Elfland: and that you will allow your son Bruno—of whose goodness, cleverness, and beauty, reports have reached us—to be regarded as Heir-Apparent."

"But what's the difficulty?" said my Lady.

"Why, don't you see? The Ambassador, that brought this, is waiting in the house: and he's sure to see Sylvie and Bruno: and then, when he sees Uggug, and remembers all that about 'goodness, cleverness, and beauty.' why, he's sure to——"

"And *where* will you find a better boy than *Uggug*?" my Lady indignantly interrupted. "Or a wittier, or a lovelier?"

To all of which the Vice-Warden simply replied "Don't you be a great blethering goose! Our only chance is to keep those two brats out of sight. If *you* can manage *that*, you may leave the rest to *me*. *I'll* make him believe Uggug to be a model of cleverness and all that."

"We must change his name to Bruno, of course?" said my Lady.

The Vice-Warden rubbed his chin. 'Humph! No!" he said musingly. "Wouldn't do. The boy's such an utter idiot, he'd never learn to answer to it."

"*Idiot*, indeed!" cried my Lady. "He's no more an idiot than *I* am!"

"You're right, my dear," the Vice-Warden soothingly replied. "He isn't, indeed!"

My Lady was appeased. "Let's go in and receive the Ambassador," she said, and beckoned to the Professor. "Which room is he waiting in?" she inquired.

"In the Library, Madam."

"And *what* did you say his name was?" said the Vice-Warden.

The Professor referred to a card he held in his hand. "His Adiposity the Baron Doppelgeist."

"Why does he come with such a funny name?" said my Lady.

"He couldn't well change it on the journey," the Professor meekly replied, "because of the luggage."

"*You* go and receive him", my Lady said to the Vice-Warden, and *I'll* attend to the children."

CHAPTER 7

The Baron's Embassy

I WAS following the Vice-Warden, but, on second thoughts, went after my Lady, being curious to see how she would manage to keep the children out of sight.

I found her holding Sylvie's hand, and with her other hand stroking Bruno's hair in a most tender and motherly fashion: both children were looking bewildered and half-frightened.

"My own darlings," she was saying, "I've been planning a little treat for you! The Professor shall take you a long walk into the woods this beautiful evening: and you shall take a basket of food with you, and have a little picnic down by the river!"

Bruno jumped, and clapped his hands. "That *are* nice!" he cried. "Aren't it, Sylvie?"

Sylvie, who hadn't quite lost her surprised look, put up her mouth for a kiss. "Thank you *very* much," she said earnestly.

My Lady turned her head away to conceal the broad grin of triumph that spread over her vast face, like a ripple on a lake. "Little simpletons!" she muttered to herself, as she marched up to the house. I followed her in.

"Quite so, your Excellency," the Baron was saying as we entered the Library. "All the infantry were under *my* command." He turned, and was duly presented to my Lady.

"A *military* hero?" said my Lady. The fat little man simpered. "Well, yes," he replied, modestly casting down his eyes. "My ancestors were all famous for military genius."

My Lady smiled graciously. "It often runs in families," she remarked: "just as a love for pastry does."

The Baron looked slightly offended, and the Vice-Warden discreetly changed the subject. "Dinner will soon be ready," he said. "May I have the honour of conducting your Adiposity to the guest-chamber?"

"Certainly, certainly!" the Baron eagerly assented. "It would never do to keep *dinner* waiting!" And he almost trotted out of the room after the Vice-Warden.

He was back again so speedily that the Vice-Warden had barely time to explain to my Lady that her remark about "a love for pastry" was "unfortunate. You might have seen, with half an eye," he added, "that that's *his* line. Military genius, indeed! Pooh!"

"Dinner ready yet?" the Baron enquired, as he hurried into the room.

"Will be in a few minutes," the Vice-Warden replied. "Meanwhile, let's take a turn in the garden. You were telling me," he continued, as the trio left the house, "something about a great battle in which you had the command of the infantry——"

"True," said the Baron. "The enemy, as I was saying, far outnumbered us: but I marched my men right into the middle of—what's that?" the Military Hero exclaimed in agitated tones, drawing back behind the Vice-Warden, as a strange creature rushed wildly upon them, brandishing a spade.

"It's only the Gardener!" the Vice-Warden replied in an encouraging tone. "Quite harmless, I assure you. Hark, he's singing! It's his favourite amusement."

And once more those shrill discordant tones rang out:

> "He thought he saw a Banker's Clerk
> Descending from the bus:
> He looked again, and found it was
> A Hippopotamus:
> 'If this should stay to dine', he said,
> 'There wo'n't be much for us!' "

Throwing away the spade, he broke into a frantic jig, snapping his fingers, and repeating, again and again,

> "There wo'n't be much for us!
> There wo'n't be much for us!"

Once more the Baron looked slightly offended, but the Vice-Warden hastily explained that the song had no allusion to *him*, and in fact had no meaning at all. 'You didn't mean anything by it, now *did* you?" He appealed to the Gardener, who had finished his song, and stood, balancing himself on one leg, and looking at them, with his mouth open.

"I never means nothing," said the Gardener: and Uggug luckily came up at the moment, and gave the conversation a new turn.

"Allow me to present my son," said the Vice-Warden; adding, in a whisper, "one of the best and cleverest boys that ever lived! I'll contrive for you to see some of his cleverness. He knows everything that other boys *don't* know; and in archery, in fishing, in painting, and in music, his skill is—but you shall judge for yourself. You see that target over there? He shall shoot an arrow at it. Dear boy," he went on aloud, "his Adiposity would like to see you shoot. Bring his Highness' bow and arrows!"

Uggug looked very sulky as he received the bow and arrow, and prepared to shoot. Just as the arrow left the bow, the Vice-Warden trod heavily on the toe of the Baron, who yelled with the pain.

"Ten thousand pardons!" he exclaimed. "I stepped back in my excitement. See! It is a bull's-eye!"

The Baron gazed in astonishment. "He held the bow so awkwardly, it

seemed impossible!" he muttered. But there was no room for doubt: there was the arrow, right in the centre of the bull's-eye!

"The lake is close by," continued the Vice-Warden. "Bring his Highness' fishing-rod!" And Uggug most unwillingly held the rod, and dangled the fly over the water.

"A beetle on your arm!" cried my Lady, pinching the poor Baron's arm worse than if ten lobsters had seized it at once. "*That* kind is poisonous," she explained. "But *what* a pity! You missed seeing the fish pulled out!"

An enormous dead cod-fish was lying on the bank, with the hook in its mouth.

"I had always fancied", the Baron faltered, "that cod were *salt*-water fish?"

"Not in *this* country," said the Vice-Warden. "Shall we go in? Ask my son some question on the way—*any* subject you like!" And the sulky boy was violently shoved forwards to walk at the Baron's side.

"Could your Highness tell me", the Baron cautiously began, "how much seven times nine would come to?"

"Turn to the left!" cried the Vice-Warden, hastily stepping forwards to show the way—so hastily, that he ran against his unfortunate guest, who fell heavily on his face.

"*So* sorry!" my Lady exclaimed, as she and her husband helped him to his feet again. "My son was in the act of saying 'sixty-three' as you fell!"

The Baron said nothing: he was covered with dust, and seemed much hurt, both in body and mind. However, when they had got him into the house, and given him a good brushing, matters looked a little better.

Dinner was served in due course, and every fresh dish seemed to increase the good-humour of the Baron: but all efforts, to get him to express his opinion as to Uggug's cleverness, were in vain, until that interesting youth had left the room, and was seen from the open window, prowling about the lawn with a little basket, which he was filling with frogs.

"So fond of Natural History as he is, dear boy!" said the doting mother. "Now *do* tell us, Baron, what you think of him!"

"To be perfectly candid," said the cautious Baron, "I would like a *little* more evidence. I think you mentioned his skill in——"

"Music?" said the Vice-Warden. "Why, he's simply a prodigy! You shall hear him play the piano." And he walked to the window. "Ug—I mean my boy! Come in for a minute, *and bring the music-master with you*! To turn over the music for him," he added as an explanation.

Uggug, having filled his basket with frogs, had no objection to obey and soon appeared in the room, followed by a fierce-looking little man, who asked the Vice-Warden "Vot music vill you haf?"

"The Sonata that His Highness plays so charmingly," said the Vice-Warden.

"His Highness haf not——" the music-master began, but was sharply stopped by the Vice-Warden.

"Silence, Sir! Go and turn over the music for His Highness. My dear," (to the Wardeness) "will you show him what to do? And meanwhile, Baron, I'll just show you a most interesting map we have—of Outland, and Fairyland, and that sort of thing."

By the time my Lady had returned from explaining things to the music-master, the map had been hung up, and the Baron was already much bewildered by the Vice-Warden's habit of pointing to one place while he shouted out the name of another.

My Lady joining in, pointing out other places, and shouting other names, only made matters worse; and at last the Baron, in despair, took to pointing out places for himself, and feebly asked "Is that great yellow splotch *Fairyland*?"

"Yes, that's Fairyland," said the Vice-Warden: "and you might as well give him a hint," he muttered to my Lady, "about going back to-morrow. He eats like a shark! It would hardly do for *me* to mention it."

His wife caught the idea, and at once began giving hints of the most subtle and delicate kind. "Just see what a short way it is back to Fairyland! Why, if you started to-morrow morning, you'd get there in very little more than a week!"

The Baron looked incredulous. "It took me a full month to *come*," he said.

"But it's ever so much shorter, going *back*, you know!"

The Baron looked appealingly to the Vice-Warden, who chimed in readily. "You can go back *five* times, in the time it took you to come here *once* —if you start to-morrow morning!"

All this time the Sonata was pealing through the room. The Baron could not help admitting to himself that it was being magnificently played: but he tried in vain to get a glimpse of the youthful performer. Every time he had nearly succeeded in catching sight of him, either the Vice-Warden or his wife was sure to get in the way, pointing out some new place on the map, and deafening him with some new name.

He gave in at last, wished a hasty good-night, and left the room, while his host and hostess interchanged looks of triumph.

"Deftly done!" cried the Vice-Warden. "Craftily contrived! But what

The map of Fairyland

means all that tramping on the stairs?" He half-opened the door, looked out, and added in a tone of dismay, "The Baron's boxes are being carried down!"

"And what means all that rumbling of wheels?" cried my Lady. She peeped through the window curtains. "The Baron's carriage has come round!" she groaned.

At this moment the door opened: a fat, furious face looked in: a voice, hoarse with passion, thundered out the words "My room is full of frogs—I leave you!" and the door closed again.

And still the noble Sonata went pealing through the room: but it was *Arthur*'s masterly touch that roused the echoes, and thrilled my very soul with the tender music of the immortal "Sonata Pathetique": and it was not till the last note had died away that the tired but happy traveller could bring himself to utter the words "goodnight!" and to seek his much-needed pillow.

CHAPTER 8

A Ride on a Lion

THE next day glided away, pleasantly enough, partly in settling myself in my new quarters, and partly in strolling round the neighbourhood, under Arthur's guidance, and trying to form a general idea of Elveston and its inhabitants. When five o'clock arrived, Arthur proposed—without any embarrassment this time—to take me with him up to "the Hall", in order that I might make acquaintance with the Earl of Ainslie, who had taken it for the season, and renew acquaintance with his daughter Lady Muriel.

My first impressions of the gentle, dignified, and yet genial old man were entirely favourable: and the *real* satisfaction that showed itself on his daughter's face, as she met me with the words "this is indeed an unlooked-for pleasure!", was very soothing for whatever remains of personal vanity the failures and disappointments of many long years, and much buffeting with a rough world, had left in me.

Yet I noted, and was glad to note, evidence of a far deeper feeling than mere friendly regard, in her meeting with Arthur—though this was, as I gathered, an almost daily occurrence—and the conversation between them, in which the Earl and I were only occasional sharers, had an ease and a spontaneity rarely met with except between *very* old friends: and, as I knew that they had not known each other for a longer period than the summer which was now rounding into autumn, I felt certain that "Love", and Love alone, could explain the phenomenon.

"How convenient it would be", Lady Muriel laughingly remarked, *à propos* of my having insisted on saving her the trouble of carrying a cup of tea across the room to the Earl, "if cups of tea had no weight at all! Then perhaps ladies would *sometimes* be permitted to carry them for short distances!"

"One can easily imagine a situation", said Arthur, "where things would *necessarily* have no weight, relatively to each other, though each would have its usual weight, looked at by itself."

"Some desperate paradox!" said the Earl. "Tell us how it could be. We shall never guess it."

"Well, suppose this house, just as it is, placed a few billion miles above a planet, and with nothing else near enough to disturb it: of course it falls *to* the planet?"

The Earl nodded. "Of course—though it might take some centuries to do it."

"And is five-o'clock-tea to be going on all the while?" said Lady Muriel.

"That, and other things," said Arthur. "The inhabitants would live their lives, grow up and die, and still the house would be falling, falling, falling! But now as to the relative weight of things. Nothing can be *heavy*, you know, except by *trying* to fall, and being prevented from doing so. You all grant that?"

We all granted that.

"Well, now, if I take this book, and hold it out at arm's length, of course I feel its *weight*. It is trying to fall, and I prevent it. And, if I let go, it falls to the floor. But, if we were all falling together, it couldn't be trying to fall any quicker, you know: for, if I let go, what more could it do than fall? And, as my hand would be falling too—at the same rate—it would never leave it, for that would be to get ahead of it in the race. And it could never overtake the falling floor!"

"I see it clearly," said Lady Muriel. "But it makes one dizzy to think of such things! How *can* you make us do it?"

"There is a more curious idea yet," I ventured to say. "Suppose a cord fastened to the house, from below, and pulled down by some one on the planet. Then of course the *house* goes faster than its natural rate of falling: but the furniture—with our noble selves—would go on falling at their old pace, and would therefore be left behind."

"Practically, we should rise to the ceiling," said the Earl. "The inevitable result of which would be concussion of brain."

"To avoid that," said Arthur, "let us have the furniture fixed to the floor, and ourselves tied down to the furniture. Then the five-o'clock-tea could go on in peace."

"With one little drawback!" Lady Muriel gaily interrupted. "We should take the *cups* down with us: but what about the *tea*?"

"I had forgotten the *tea*," Arthur confessed. "*That*, no doubt, would rise to the ceiling—unless you chose to drink it on the way!"

"Which, I think, is *quite* nonsense enough for one while!" said the Earl. "What news does this gentleman bring us from the great world of London?"

This drew *me* into the conversation, which now took a more conventional tone. After a while, Arthur gave the signal for our departure, and in the cool of the evening we strolled down to the beach, enjoying the silence, broken only by the murmur of the sea and the far-away music of some fishermen's song, almost as much as our late pleasant talk.

We sat down among the rocks, by a little pool, so rich in animal, vegetable, and zoöphytic—or whatever is the right word—life, that I became entranced in the study of it, and, when Arthur proposed returning to our lodgings, I begged to be left there for a while, to watch and muse alone.

The fishermen's song grew ever nearer and clearer, as their boat stood in for the beach; and I would have gone down to see them land their cargo of fish, had not the microcosm at my feet stirred my curiosity yet more keenly.

One ancient crab, that was for ever shuffling frantically from side to side of the pool, had particularly fascinated me: there was a vacancy in its stare, and an aimless violence in its behaviour, that irresistibly recalled the Gardener who had befriended Sylvie and Bruno: and, as I gazed, I caught the concluding notes of the tune of his crazy song.

The silence that followed was broken by the sweet voice of Sylvie. "Would you please let us out into the road?"

"What! After that old beggar again?" the Gardener yelled, and began singing:

"He thought he saw a Kangaroo
That worked a coffee-mill:
He looked again, and found it was
A Vegetable-Pill.
'Were I to swallow this,' he said,
'I should be very ill!'"

"We don't want him to swallow *anything*," Sylvie explained. "He's not hungry. But we want to see him. So will you please——"

"Certainly!" the Gardener promptly replied. "I *always* please. Never displeases nobody. There you are!" And he flung the door open, and let us out upon the dusty high-road.

We soon found our way to the bush, which had so mysteriously sunk into the ground: and here Sylvie drew the Magic Locket from its hiding-place, turned it over with a thoughtful air, and at last appealed to Bruno in a rather helpless way. "What *was* it we had to do with it, Bruno? It's all gone out of my head!"

"Kiss it!" was Bruno"s invariable recipe in cases of doubt and difficulty. Sylvie kissed it, but no result followed.

"Rub it the wrong way," was Bruno's next suggestion.

"Which *is* the wrong way?" Sylvie most reasonably enquired. The obvious plan was to try *both* ways.

᛫ Rubbing from left to right had no visible effect whatever.

From right to left—"Oh, stop, Sylvie!" Bruno cried in sudden alarm. "Whatever *is* going to happen?"

For a number of trees, on the neighbouring hillside, were moving slowly upwards, in solemn procession: while a mild little brook, that had been rippling at our feet a moment before, began to swell, and foam, and hiss, and bubble, in a truly alarming fashion.

"Rub it some other way!" cried Bruno. "Try up-and-down! Quick!"

It was a happy thought. Up-and-down did it: and the landscape, which had been showing signs of mental aberration in various directions, returned to its normal condition of sobriety—with the exception of a small yellowish-brown mouse, which continued to run wildly up and down the road, lashing its tail like a little lion.

"Let's follow it," said Sylvie: and this also turned out a happy thought. The mouse at once settled down into a business-like jog-trot, with which we could easily keep pace. The only phenomenon, that gave me any uneasiness, was the rapid increase in the *size* of the little creature we were following, which became every moment more and more like a real lion.

Soon the transformation was complete: and a noble lion stood patiently waiting for us to come up with it. No thought of fear seemed to occur to the children, who patted and stroked it as if it had been a Shetland-pony.

"Help me up!" cried Bruno. And in another moment Sylvie had lifted him upon the broad back of the gentle beast, and seated herself behind him, pillion-fashion. Bruno took a good handful of mane in each hand, and made believe to guide this new kind of steed. "Gee-up!" seemed quite sufficient by way of *verbal* direction: the lion at once broke into an easy canter, and we soon found ourselves in the depths of the forest. I say "*we*", for I am certain that *I* accompanied them—though *how* I managed to keep up with a cantering lion I am wholly unable to explain. But I was certainly one of the party when we came upon an old beggar-man cutting sticks, at whose feet the lion made a profound obeisance, Sylvie and Bruno at the same moment dismounting, and leaping into the arms of their father.

"From bad to worse!" the old man said to himself, dreamily, when the children had finished their rather confused account of the Ambassador's visit, gathered no doubt from general report, as they had not seen him themselves. "From bad to worse! That is their destiny. I see it, but I cannot alter it. The selfishness of a mean and crafty man—the selfishness of an ambitious and silly woman—the selfishness of a spiteful and loveless

The mouse-lion

child—all tend one way, from bad to worse! And you, my darlings, must suffer it awhile, I fear. Yet, when things are at their worst, you can come to me. I can do but little as yet——"

Gathering up a handful of dust and scattering it in the air, he slowly and solemnly pronounced some words that sounded like a charm, the children looking on in awestruck silence:

> *"Let craft, ambition, spite,*
> *Be quenched in Reason's night,*
> *Till weakness turn to might,*
> *Till what is dark be light,*
> *Till what is wrong be right!"*

The cloud of dust spread itself out through the air, as if it were alive, forming curious shapes that were for ever changing into others.

"It makes letters! It makes words!" Bruno whispered, as he clung, half-frightened, to Sylvie. "Only I *ca'n't* make them out! Read them, Sylvie!"

"I'll try," Sylvie gravely replied. "Wait a minute—if only I could see that word——"

"I should be very ill!" a discordant voice yelled in our ears.

> *" 'Were I to swallow this', he said,*
> *'I should be very ill!' "*

CHAPTER 9

A Jester and a Bear

YES, we were in the garden once more: and, to escape that horrid discordant voice, we hurried indoors, and found ourselves in the library —Uggug blubbering, the Professor standing by with a bewildered air, and my Lady, with her arms clasped round her son's neck, repeating, over and over again, "and *did* they give him nasty lessons to learn? My own pretty pet!"

"What's all this noise about?" the Vice-Warden angrily enquired, as he strode into the room. "And who put the hat-stand here?" And he hung his hat up on Bruno, who was standing in the middle of the room, too much astonished by the sudden change of scene to make any attempt at removing it, though it came down to his shoulders, making him look something like a small candle with a large extinguisher over it.

The Professor mildly explained that His Highness had been graciously pleased to say he wouldn't do his lessons.

"Do your lessons this instant, you young cub!" thundered the Vice-Warden. "And take *this*!" and a resounding box on the ear made the unfortunate Professor reel across the room.

"Save me!" faltered the poor old man, as he sank, half-fainting, at my Lady's feet.

"Shave you? Of course I will!" my Lady replied, as she lifted him into a chair, and pinned an anti-macassar round his neck. "Where's the razor?"

The Vice-Warden meanwhile had got hold of Uggug, and was belabouring him with his umbrella. "Who left this loose nail in the floor?" he shouted. "Hammer it in, I say! Hammer it in!" Blow after blow fell on the writhing Uggug, till he dropped howling to the floor.

Then his father turned to the "shaving" scene which was being enacted, and roared with laughter. "Excuse me, dear, I ca'n't help it!" he said as soon as he could speak. "You *are* such an utter donkey! Kiss me, Tabby!"

And he flung his arms round the neck of the terrified Professor, who raised a wild shriek, but whether he received the threatened kiss or not I was unable to see, as Bruno, who had by this time released himself from his extinguisher, rushed headlong out of the room, followed by Sylvie; and I was so fearful of being left alone among all these crazy creatures that I hurried after them.

"We must go to Father!" Sylvie panted, as they ran down the garden. "I'm *sure* things are at their worst! I'll ask the Gardener to let us out again."

"But we ca'n't *walk* all the way!" Bruno whimpered. "How I *wiss* we had a coach-and-four, like Uncle!"

And, shrill and wild, rang through the air the familiar voice:

> *"He thought he saw a Coach-and-Four*
> *That stood beside his bed:*
> *He looked again, and found it was*
> *A Bear without a Head.*
> *'Poor thing,' he said, 'poor silly thing!*
> *It's waiting to be fed!' '"*

"No, I ca'n't let you out again!" he said, before the children could speak. "The Vice-Warden gave it me, he did, for letting you out last time! So be off with you!" And, turning away from them, he began digging frantically in the middle of a gravel-walk, singing, over and over again,

> *" 'Poor thing,' he said, 'poor silly thing!*
> *It's waiting to be fed' "*

but in a more musical tone than the shrill screech in which he had begun.

The music grew fuller and richer at every moment: other manly voices joined in the refrain: and soon I heard the heavy thud that told me the boat had touched the beach, and the harsh grating of the shingle as the men dragged it up. I roused myself, and, after lending them a hand in hauling up their boat, I lingered yet awhile to watch them disembark a goodly assortment of the hard-won "treasures of the deep".

When at last I reached our lodgings I was tired and sleepy, and glad enough to settle down again into the easy-chair, while Arthur hospitably went to his cupboard, to get me out some cake and wine, without which, he declared, he could not, as a doctor, permit my going to bed.

And how that cupboard-door *did* creak! It surely could not be *Arthur*, who was opening and shutting it so often, moving so restlessly about, and muttering like the soliloquy of a tragedy-queen!

No, it was a *female* voice. Also the figure—half-hidden by the cupboard-door—was a *female* figure, massive, and in flowing robes. Could it be the landlady? The door opened, and a strange man entered the room.

"What *is* that donkey doing?" he said to himself, pausing, aghast, on the threshold.

The lady, thus rudely referred to, was his wife. She had got one of the cupboards open, and stood with her back to him, smoothing down a sheet of brown paper on one of the shelves, and whispering to herself "So, so! Deftly done! Craftily contrived!"

Her loving husband stole behind her on tip-toe, and tapped her on the head. "Boh!" he playfully shouted at her ear. "Never tell me again I ca'n't say 'boh' to a goose!"

My Lady wrung her hands. "Discovered!" she groaned. "Yet no — he is one of us! Reveal it not, oh Man! Let it bide its time!"

"Reveal *what* not?" her husband testily replied, dragging out the sheet of brown paper. "What are you hiding here, my Lady? I insist upon knowing!"

My Lady cast down her eyes, and spoke in the littlest of little voices. "Don't make fun of it, Benjamin!" she pleaded. It's—it's—don't you understand? It's a DAGGER!"

"And what's *that* for?" sneered His Excellency. "We've only got to make people *think* he's dead! We haven't got to *kill* him! And made of tin, too!" he snarled, contemptuously bending the blade round his thumb. "Now, Madam, you'll be good enough to explain. First, what do you call me *Benjamin* for?"

"It's part of the Conspiracy, Love! One *must* have an alias, you know——"

"Oh, an *alias*, is it? Well! And next, what did you get this dagger for? Come, no evasions? You ca'n't deceive *me*!"

"I got it for—for—for——" the detected Conspirator stammered, trying her best to put on the assassin-expression that she had been practising at the looking-glass. "For——"

"For *what*, Madam!"

"Well, for eighteenpence, if you *must* know, dearest! That's what I got it for, on my——"

"Now *don't* say your Word and Honour!" groaned the other Conspirator. "Why, they aren't worth half the money, put together!"

"On my *birthday*," my Lady concluded in a meek whisper. "One *must* have a dagger, you know. It's part of the——"

"Oh, don't talk of Conspiracies!" her husband savagely interrupted, as he tossed the dagger into the cupboard. "You know about as much how to manage a Conspiracy as if you were a chicken. Why, the first thing is to get a disguise. Now, just look at this!"

And with pardonable pride he fitted on the cap and bells, and the rest of the Fool's dress, and winked at her, and put his tongue in his cheek. "Is *that* the sort of thing, now?" he demanded.

My Lady's eyes flashed with all a Conspirator's enthusiasm. "The very thing!" she exclaimed, clapping her hands. "You do look, oh, such a *perfect* Fool!"

The Fool smiled a doubtful smile. He was not quite clear whether it was a compliment or not, to express it so plainly. "You mean a Jester?

Yes, that's what I intended. And what do you think *your* disguise is to be?" And he proceeded to unfold the parcel, the lady watching him in rapture.

"Oh, how lovely!" she cried, when at last the dress was unfolded. "What a *splendid* disguise! An Esquimaux peasant-woman!"

"An Esquimaux peasant, indeed!" growled the other. "Here, put it on, and look at yourself in the glass. Why, it's a *Bear*, ca'n't you use your eyes?" He checked himself suddenly, as a harsh voice yelled through the room

> *"He looked again, and found it was*
> *A Bear without a Head!"*

But it was only the Gardener, singing under the open window. The Vice-Warden stole on tip-toe to the window. and closed it noiselessly, before he ventured to go on! "Yes, Lovey, a *Bear*: but not without a *head*, I hope, You're the Bear, and me the Keeper. And if any one knows us, they'll have sharp eyes, that's all!"

"I shall have to practise the steps a bit," my Lady said, looking out through the Bear's mouth: "one ca'n't help being rather human just at first, you know. And of course you'll say, 'Come up, Bruin!', won't you?"

"Yes, of course," replied the Keeper, laying hold of the chain, that hung from the Bear's collar, with one hand, while with the other he cracked a little whip. "Now go round the room in a sort of a dancing attitude. Very good, my dear, very good. Come up, Bruin! Come up, I say!"

He roared out the last words for the benefit of Uggug, who had just come into the room, and was now standing, with his hands spread out, and eyes and mouth wide open, the very picture of stupid amazement. "Oh, my!" was all he could gasp out.

The Keeper pretended to be adjusting the bear's collar, which gave him an opportunity of whispering, unheard by Uggug, "*my* fault, I'm afraid! Quite forgot to fasten the door. Plot's ruined if *he* finds it out! Keep it up a minute or two longer. Be savage!" Then, while seeming to pull it back with all his strength, he let it advance upon the scared boy: my Lady, with admirable presence of mind, kept up what she no doubt intended for a savage growl, though it was more like the purring of a cat: and Uggug backed out of the room with such haste that he tripped over the mat, and was heard to fall heavily outside—an accident to which even his doting mother paid no heed, in the excitement of the moment.

The Vice-Warden shut and bolted the door. "Off with the disguises!"

he panted. "There's not a moment to lose. He's sure to fetch the Professor, and we couldn't take *him* in, you know!" And in another minute the disguises were stowed away in the cupboard, the door unbolted, and the two Conspirators seated lovingly side-by-side on the sofa, earnestly discussing a book the Vice-Warden had hastily snatched off the table, which proved to be the City-Directory of the capital of Outland.

The door opened, very slowly and cautiously, and the Professor peeped in, Uggug's stupid face being just visible behind him.

"It is a beautiful arrangement!" the Vice-Warden was saying with enthusiasm. "You see, my precious one, that there are fifteen houses in Green Street, *before* you turn into West Street."

"*Fifteen* houses! Is it *possible*?" my Lady replied. "I thought it was fourteen!" And, so intent were they on this interesting question, that neither of them even looked up till the Professor, leading Uggug by the hand, stood close before them.

My Lady was the first to notice their approach. "Why, here's the Professor!" she exclaimed in her blandest tones. "And my precious child too! Are lessons over?"

"A strange thing has happened!" the Professor began in a trembling tone. "His Exalted Fatness" (this was one of Uggug's many titles) "tells me he has just seen, in this very room, a Dancing-Bear and a Court-Jester!"

The Vice-Warden and his wife shook with well-acted merriment.

"Not in *this* room, darling!" said the fond mother.

"We've been sitting here this hour or more, reading——here she referred to the book lying on her lap, "—reading the—the City-Directory."

"Let me feel your pulse, my boy!" said the anxious father. "Now put out your tongue. Ah, I thought so! He's a little feverish, Professor, and has had a bad dream. Put him to bed at once, and give him a cooling draught."

"I ain't been dreaming!" his Exalted Fatness remonstrated, as the Professor led him away.

"Bad grammar, Sir!" his father remarked with some sternness. "Kindly attend to *that* little matter, Professor, as soon as you have corrected the feverishness. And, by the way, Professor!" (The Professor left his distinguished pupil standing at the door, and meekly returned.) "There is a rumour afloat, that the people wish to elect an—in point of fact, an—you understand that I mean an——"

"Not *another Professor*!" the poor old man exclaimed in horror.

"No! Certainly not!" the Vice-Warden eagerly explained. "Merely an *Emperor*, you understand."

"An *Emperor*!" cried the astonished Professor, holding his head between his hands, as if he expected it to come to pieces with the shock. "What will the Warden——"

"Why, the *Warden* will most likely *be* the new Emperor!" my Lady explained. "Where could we find a better? Unless, perhaps——" she glanced at her husband.

"Where, indeed!" the Professor fervently responded, quite failing to take the hint.

The Vice-Warden resumed the thread of his discourse. "The reason I mentioned it, Professor, was to ask *you* to be so kind as to preside at the Election. You see it would make the thing *respectable*—no suspicion of anything underhand——"

"I fear I ca'n't, your Excellency!" the old man faltered. "What will the Warden——"

"True, true!" the Vice-Warden interrupted. "Your position, as Court-Professor, makes it awkward. I admit. Well, well! Then the Election shall be held without you."

"Better so, than if it were held *within* me!" the Professor murmured with a bewildered air, as if he hardly knew what he was saying. "Bed, I think your Highness said, and a cooling-draught?" And he wandered dreamily back to where Uggug sulkily awaited him.

I followed them out of the room, and down the passage, the Professor murmuring to himself, all the time, as a kind of aid to his feeble memory, "C, C, C; Couch, Cooling-Draught, Correct-Grammar", till, in turning a corner, he met Sylvie and Bruno, so suddenly that the startled Professor let go of his fat pupil, who instantly took to his heels.

CHAPTER 10

The Other Professor

"WE were looking for you!" cried Sylvie, in a tone of great relief. "We *do* want you so much, you ca'n't think!"

"What is it, dear children?" the Professor asked, beaming on them with a very different look from what Uggug ever got from him.

"We want you to speak to the Gardener for us," Sylvie said, as she and Bruno took the old man's hands and led him into the hall.

"He's ever so unkind!" Bruno mournfully added. "They's *all* unkind to us, now that Father's gone. The Lion were *much* nicer!"

"But you must explain to me, please," the Professor said with an anxious look, "*which* is the Lion, and *which* is the Gardener. It's *most* important not to get two such animals confused together. And one's very liable to do it in their case—both having mouths, you know——"

"Doos oo *always* confuses two animals together?" Bruno asked.

"Pretty often, I'm afraid," the Professor candidly confessed. "Now, for instance, there's the rabbit-hutch and the hall-clock." The Professor pointed them out. "One gets a little confused with *them*—both having doors, you know. Now, only yesterday—would you believe it?—I put some lettuces into the clock, and tried to wind up the rabbit!"

"Did the rabbit *go*, after oo wounded it up?" said Bruno.

The Professor clasped his hands on the top of his head, and groaned. "Go? I should think it *did* go! Why, it's *gone*! And where ever it's gone to—that's what I ca'n't find out! I've done my best—I've read all the article 'Rabbit' in the great dictionary—Come in!"

"Only the tailor, Sir, with your little bill," said a meek voice outside the door.

"Ah, well, I can soon settle *his* business," the Professor said to the children, "if you'll just wait a minute. How much is it, this year, my man?" The tailor had come in while he was speaking.

"Well, it's been a doubling so many years, you see," the tailor replied, a little gruffly, "and I think I'd like the money now. It's two thousand pound, it is!"

"Oh, that's nothing!" the Professor carelessly remarked, feeling in his pocket, as if he always carried at least *that* amount about with him. "But wouldn't you like to wait just another year, and make it *four* thousand? Just think how rich you'd be! Why, you might be a *King*, if you liked!"

"I don't know as I'd care about being a *King*," the man said thoughtfully. "But it *dew* sound a powerful sight o' money! Well, I think I'll wait——"

"Of course you will!" said the Professor. "There's good sense in *you*, I see. Good-day to you, my man!"

"Will you ever have to pay him that four thousand pounds?" Sylvie asked as the door closed on the departing creditor.

"*Never*, my child!" the Professor replied emphatically. "He'll go on doubling it, till he dies. You see it's *always* worth while waiting another year, to get twice as much money! And now what would you like to do, my little friends? Shall I take you to see the Other Professor? This would be an excellent opportunity for a visit," he said to himself, glancing at his watch: "he generally takes a short rest—of fourteen minutes and a half—about this time."

Bruno hastily went round to Sylvie, who was standing at the other side of the Professor, and put his hand into hers. "I *thinks* we'd like to go," he said doubtfully: "only please let's go all together. It's best to be on the safe side, oo know!"

"Why, you talk as if you were *Sylvie*!" exclaimed the Professor.

"I know I did," Bruno replied very humbly. "I quite forgotted I wasn't Sylvie. Only I fought he might be rarver fierce!"

The Professor laughed a jolly laugh. "Oh, he's quite tame!" he said. "He never bites, He's only a little—a little *dreamy*, you know." He took hold of Bruno's other hand, and led the children down a long passage I had never noticed before—not that there was anything remarkable in *that*: I was constantly coming on new rooms and passages in that mysterious Palace, and very seldom succeeded in finding the old ones again.

Near the end of the passage the Professor stopped. "This is his room," he said, pointing to the solid wall.

"We ca'n't get in through *there*!" Bruno exclaimed.

Sylvie said nothing, till she had carefully examined whether the wall opened anywhere. Then she laughed merrily. "You're playing us a trick, you dear old thing!" she said. "There's no *door* here!"

"There isn't any door to the room," said the Professor. "We shall have to climb in at the window."

The Other Professor

So we went into the garden, and soon found the window of the Other Professor's room. It was a ground-floor window, and stood invitingly open: the Professor first lifted the two children in, and then he and I climbed in after them.

The Other Professor was seated at a table, with a large book open before him, on which his forehead was resting: he had clasped his arms round the book, and was snoring heavily. "He usually reads like that", the Professor remarked, "when the book's very interesting: and then sometimes it's very difficult to get him to attend!"

This seemed to be one of the difficult times: the Professor lifted him up, once or twice, and shook him violently: but he always returned to his book the moment he was let go of, and showed by his heavy breathing that the book was as interesting as ever.

"How dreamy he is!" the Professor exclaimed. "He must have got to a *very* interesting part of the book!" And he rained quite a shower of thumps on the Other Professor's back, shouting "Hoy! Hoy!" all the time. "Isn't it *wonderful* that he should be so dreamy?" he said to Bruno.

"If he's always as *sleepy* as that," Bruno remarked, "a *course* he's dreamy!"

"But what are we to *do*?" said the Professor. "You see he's quite wrapped up in the book!"

"Suppose oo *shuts* the book?" Bruno suggested.

"That's it!" cried the delighted Professor. "Of course that'll do it!" And he shut up the book so quickly that he caught the Other Professor's nose between the leaves, and gave it a severe pinch.

The Other Professor instantly rose to his feet, and carried the book away to the end of the room, where he put it back in its place in the book-case. "I've been reading for eighteen hours and three-quarters," he said, "and now I shall rest for fourteen minutes and a half. Is the Lecture all ready?"

"Very nearly," the Professor humbly replied. "I shall ask you to give me a hint or two—there will be a few little difficulties——"

"And a Banquet, I think you said?"

"Oh, yes! The Banquet comes *first*, of course. People never enjoy Abstract Science, you know, when they're ravenous with hunger. And then there's the Fancy-Dress-Ball. Oh, there'll be lots of entertainment!"

"Where will the Ball come in?" said the Other Professor.

"I *think* it had better come at the beginning of the Banquet—it brings people together so nicely, you know."

"Yes, that's the right order. First the Meeting: then the Eating: then the Treating—for I'm sure any Lecture *you* give us will be a treat!" said the Other Professor, who had been standing with his back to us all this time, occupying himself in taking the books out, one by one, and turning them upside-down. An easel, with a blackboard on it, stood near him: and, every time that he turned a book upside-down, he made a mark on the board with a piece of chalk.

"And as to the 'Pig-Tale'—which *you* have so kindly promised to give us——" the Professor went on, thoughtfully rubbing his chin. "I think that had better come at the *end* of the Banquet: then people can listen to it quietly."

"Shall I *sing* it?" the Other Professor asked, with a smile of delight.

"If you *can*," the Professor replied, cautiously.

"Let me try," said the Other Professor, seating himself at the pianoforte. "For the sake of argument, let us assume that it begins on A flat." And he struck the note in question. "La, la, la! I think that's within an octave of it." He struck the note again, and appealed to Bruno, who was standing at his side. "Did I sing it like *that*, my child?"

"No, oo didn't," Bruno replied with great decision. "It were more like a duck."

"Single notes are apt to have that effect," the Other Professor said with a sigh. "Let me try a whole verse.

> *There was a Pig, that sat alone,*
> *   Beside a ruined Pump.*
> *By day and night he made his moan:*
> *It would have stirred a heart of stone*
> *To see him wring his hoofs and groan,*
> *   Because he could not jump.*

Would you call that a tune, Professor?" he asked, when he had finished.

The Professor considered a little. "Well," he said at last, "some of the notes are the same as others—and some are different—but I should hardly call it a *tune*."

"Let me try it a bit by myself," said the Other Professor. And he began touching the notes here and there, and humming to himself like an angry bluebottle.

"How do you like his singing?" the Professor asked the children in a low voice.

"It isn't very *beautiful*," Sylvie said, hesitatingly.

"It's very extremely *ugly*!" Bruno said, without any hesitation at all.

"All extremes are bad," the Professor said, very gravely. "For instance, Sobriety is a very good thing, when practised *in moderation*: but even Sobriety, when carried to an *extreme*, has its disadvantages."

"What are its disadvantages?" was the question that rose in my mind—and, as usual, Bruno asked it for me. "What *are* its lizard bandages?"

"Well, this is *one* of them," said the Professor. "When a man's tipsy (that's one extreme, you know), he sees one thing as two. But, when he's *extremely* sober (that's the other extreme), he sees two things as one. It's equally inconvenient, whichever happens."

"What does 'illconvenient' mean?" Bruno whispered to Sylvie.

"The difference between 'convenient' and 'inconvenient' is best explained by an example," said the Other Professor, who had overheard the question. "If you'll just think over any Poem that contains the two words—such as——"

The Professor put his hands over his ears, with a look of dismay. "If you once let him begin a *Poem*," he said to Sylvie, "he'll never leave off again! He never does!"

"Did he ever begin a Poem and not leave off again?" Sylvie enquired.

"Three times," said the Professor.

Bruno raised himself on tiptoe, till his lips were on a level with Sylvie's ear. "What became of them three Poems?" he whispered. "Is he saying them all now?"

"Hush!" said Sylvie. "The Other Professor is speaking!"

"I'll say it very quick," murmured the Other Professor, with downcast eyes, and melancholy voice, which contrasted oddly with his face, as he had forgotten to leave off smiling. ("At least it wasn't exactly a *smile*," as Sylvie said afterwards: "it looked as if his mouth was made that shape.")

"Go on then," said the Professor. "*What must be must be.*"

"Remember that!" Sylvie whispered to Bruno. "It's a very good rule for whenever you hurt yourself."

"And it's a very good rule for whenever I make a noise," said the saucy little fellow. "So *you* remember it too, Miss!"

"Whatever *do* you mean?" said Sylvie, trying to frown, a thing she never managed particularly well.

"Oftens and oftens," said Bruno, "haven't oo told me 'There mustn't be so much noise, Bruno!' when I've tolded oo 'There *must*!' Why, there isn't no rules at all about 'There mustn't'! But oo never believes *me*!"

"As if any one *could* believe *you*, you wicked wicked boy!" said Sylvie. The *words* were severe enough, but I am of opinion that, when you are really *anxious* to impress a criminal with a sense of his guilt, you ought not to pronounce the sentence with your lips *quite* close to his cheek—since a kiss at the end of it, however accidental, weakens the effect terribly.

CHAPTER 11

Peter and Paul

"As I was saying," the Other Professor resumed, "if you'll just think over any Poem, that contains the words—such as

> *'Peter is poor,' said noble Paul,*
> *'And I have always been his friend:*
> *And, though my means to give are small,*
> *At least I can afford to lend.*
> *How few, in this cold age of greed,*
> *Do good, except on selfish grounds!*
> *But I can feel for Peter's need,*
> *And I WILL LEND HIM FIFTY POUNDS!'*

> *How great was Peter's joy to find*
> *His friend in such a genial vein!*
> *How cheerfully the bond he signed,*
> *To pay the money back again!*
> *'We ca'n't, said Paul, 'be too precise:*
> *'Tis best to fix the very day:*
> *So, by a learned friend's advice,*
> *I've made it Noon, the Fourth of May.'*

> *'But this is April!' Peter said.*
> *'The First of April, as I think.*
> *Five little weeks will soon be fled:*
> *One scarcely will have time to wink!*
> *Give me a year to speculate—*
> *To buy and sell—to drive a trade—'*
> *Said Paul 'I cannot change the date.*
> *On May the Fourth it must be paid.'*

'Well, well!' said Peter, with a sigh.
   'Hand me the cash, and I will go.
I'll form a Joint-Stock Company,
   And turn an honest pound or so.'
'I'm grieved', said Paul, 'to seem unkind:
   The money shall of course be lent:
But, for a week or two, I find
   It will not be convenient.'

So, week by week, poor Peter came
    And turned in heaviness away;
For still the answer was the same,
    'I cannot manage it to-day.'
And now the April showers were dry—
    The five short weeks were nearly spent—
Yet still he got the old reply,
    'It is not quite convenient!'

The Fourth arrived, and punctual Paul
    Came, with his legal friend, at noon.
'I thought it best', said he, 'to call:
    One cannot settle things too soon.'
Poor Peter shuddered in despair:
    His flowing locks he wildly tore:
And very soon his yellow hair
    Was lying all about the floor.

The legal friend was standing by,
    With sudden pity half unmanned:
The tear-drop trembled in his eye,
    The signed agreement in his hand:
But when at length the legal soul
    Resumed its customary force,
'The Law', he said, 'we can't control:
    Pay, or the Law must take its course!'

Said Paul 'How bitterly I rue
    That fatal morning when I called!
Consider, Peter, what you do!
    You wo'n't be richer when you're bald!
Think you, by rending curls away,
    To make your difficulties less?
Forbear this violence, I pray:
    You do but add to my distress!'

'Not willingly would I inflict',
    Said Peter, 'on that noble heart
One needless pang. Yet why so strict?
    Is this to act a friendly part?
However legal it may be
    To pay what never has been lent,
This style of business seems to me
    Extremely inconvenient!

'No Nobleness of soul have I,
    Like some that in this Age are found!'
(Paul blushed in sheer humility,
    And cast his eyes upon the ground.)
'This debt will simply swallow all,
    And make my life a life of woe!'
'Nay, nay, my Peter!' answered Paul.
    'You must not rail on Fortune so!

'You have enough to eat and drink:
  You are respected in the world:
And at the barber's, as I think,
  You often get your whiskers curled.
Though Nobleness you ca'n't attain—
  To any very great extent—
The path of Honesty is plain,
However inconvenient!'

'*'Tis true*', said Peter, '*I'm alive:*
  I keep my station in the world:
Once in the week I just contrive
  To get my whiskers oiled and curled.
But my assets are very low:
  My little income's overspent:
To trench on capital, you know.
  Is always inconvenient!'

'*But pay your debts!*' cried honest Paul.
  '*My gentle Peter, pay your debts!*
What matter if it swallows all
  That you describe as your "assets"?
Already you're an hour behind:
  Yet Generosity is best.
It pinches me—but never mind!
  I WILL NOT CHARGE YOU INTEREST!'

'*How good! How great!*' poor Peter cried.
  '*Yet I must sell my Sunday wig—*
The scarf-pin that has been my pride—
  My grand piano—and my pig!'
Full soon his property took wings:
  And daily, as each treasure went,
He sighed to find the state of things
  Grow less and less convenient.

Weeks grew to months, and months to years:
  Peter was worn to skin and bone:
And once he even said, with tears,
  '*Remember, Paul, that promised Loan!*'
Said Paul 'I'll lend you, when I can,
  All the spare money I have got—
Ah, Peter, you're a happy man!
  Yours is an enviable lot!

'*I'm getting stout, as you may see:*
  It is but seldom I am well:
I cannot feel my ancient glee
  In listening to the dinner-bell:
But you, you gambol like a boy,
  Your figure is so spare and light:
The dinner-bell's a note of joy
  To such a healthy appetite!'

Said Peter 'I am well aware
  Mine is a state of happiness:
And yet how gladly could I spare
  Some of the comforts I possess!
What you call healthy appetite
  I feel as Hunger's savage tooth:
And, when no dinner is in sight,
  The dinner-bell's a sound of ruth!

'No scare-crow would accept this coat:
  Such boots as these you seldom see,
Ah, Paul, a single five-pound note
  Would make another man of me!'
Said Paul 'It fills me with surprise
  To hear you talk in such a tone:
I fear you scarcely realize
  The blessings that are all your own!

'You're safe from being overfed:
  You're sweetly picturesque in rags:
You never know the aching head
  That comes along with money-bags:
And you have time to cultivate
  That best of qualities, Content—
For which you'll find your present state
  Remarkably convenient!'

Said Peter 'Though I cannot sound
  The depths of such a man as you,
Yet in your character I've found
  An inconsistency or two.
You seem to have long years to spare
  When there's a promise to fulfil:
And yet how punctual you were
  In calling with that little bill!'

'One ca'n't be too deliberate',
  Said Paul, 'in parting with one's pelf.
With bills, as you correctly state,
  I'm punctuality itself.
A man may surely claim his dues:
  But, when there's money to be lent,
A man must be allowed to choose
  Such times as are convenient!'

It chanced one day, as Peter sat
  Gnawing a crust—his usual meal—
Paul bustled in to have a chat,
  And grasped his hand with friendly zeal
'I knew', said he, 'your frugal ways:
  So, that I might not wound your pride
By bringing strangers in to gaze,
  I've left my legal friend outside!

'You well remember, I am sure,
  When first your wealth began to go,
And people sneered at one so poor,
  I never used my Peter so!
And when you'd lost your little all,
  And found yourself a thing despised,
I need not ask you to recall
  How tenderly I sympathized!

'Then the advice I've poured on you,
  So full of wisdom and of wit:
All given gratis, though 'tis true
  I might have fairly charged for it!
But I refrain from mentioning
  Full many a deed I might relate—
For boasting is a kind of thing
  That I particularly hate.

'How vast the total sum appears
  Of all the kindnesses I've done,
From Childhood's half-forgotten years
  Down to that Loan of April One!
That Fifty Pounds! You little guessed
  How deep it drained my slender store:
But there's a heart within this breast,
  And I WILL LEND YOU FIFTY MORE!'

'Not so,' was Peter's mild reply,
  His cheeks all wet with grateful tears:
'No man recalls, so well as I,
  Your services in bygone years:
And this new offer, I admit,
  Is very very kindly meant—
Still, to avail myself of it
  Would not be quite convenient!'

"You'll see in a moment what the difference is between 'convenient' and 'inconvenient'. You quite understand it now, don't you?" he added, looking kindly at Bruno, who was sitting, at Sylvie's side, on the floor.

"Yes," said Bruno, very quietly. Such a short speech was very unusual, for him: but just then he seemed, I fancied, a little exhausted. In fact, he climbed up into Sylvie's lap as he spoke, and rested his head against her shoulder. "What a many verses it was!" he whispered.

CHAPTER 12

A Musical Gardener

THE Other Professor regarded him with some anxiety. "The smaller animal ought to go to bed *at once*," he said with an air of authority.

"Why *at once?*" said the Professor.

"Because he ca'n't go at twice," said the Other Professor.

The Professor gently clapped his hands. "Isn't he *wonderful!*" he said to Sylvie. "Nobody else could have thought of the reason, so quick. Why, *of course* he ca'n't go at twice! It would hurt him to be divided."

This remark woke up Bruno, suddenly and completely. "I don't want to be *divided*," he said decisively.

"It does very well on a *diagram*," said the Other Professor. "I could show it you in a minute, only the chalk's a little blunt."

"Take care!" Sylvie anxiously exclaimed, as he began, rather clumsily, to point it. "You'll cut your finger off, if you hold the knife so!"

"If oo cuts it off, will oo give it to *me*, please?" Bruno thoughtfully added.

"It's like this," said the Other Professor, hastily drawing a long line upon the black board, and marking the letters "*A*", "*B*", at the two ends, and "*C*" in the middle: "let me explain it to you. If *AB* were to be divided into two parts at *C*——"

"It would be drownded," Bruno pronounced confidently.

The Other Professor gasped. "*What* would be drownded?"

"Why the bumble-bee, of course!" said Bruno. "And the two bits would sink down in the sea!"

Here the Professor interfered, as the Other Professor was evidently too much puzzled to go on with his diagram.

"When I said it would *hurt* him, I was merely referring to the action of the nerves——"

The Other Professor brightened up in a moment. "The action of the nerves", he began eagerly, "is curiously slow in some people. I had a friend, once, that if you burnt him with a red-hot poker, it would take years and years before he felt it!"

"And if you only *pinched* him?" queried Sylvie.

"Then it would take ever so much longer, of course. In fact, I doubt if the man *himself* would ever feel it, at all. His grandchildren might."

"I wouldn't like to be the grandchild of a pinched grandfather, would *you*, Mister Sir?" Bruno whispered. "It might come just when you wanted to be happy!"

That would be awkward, I admitted, taking it quite as a matter of course that he had so suddenly caught sight of me. "But don't you *always* want to be happy, Bruno?"

"Not *always*," Bruno said thoughtfully. "Sometimes, when I's *too* happy, I wants to be a little miserable. Then I just tell Sylvie about it, oo know, and Sylvie sets me some lessons. Then it's all right."

"I'm sorry you don't like lessons," I said. "You should copy Sylvie. *She's* always as busy as the day is long!"

"Well, so am *I!*" said Bruno.

"No, no!" Sylvie corrected him. "*You're* as busy as they day is *short!*"

"Well, what's the difference?" Bruno asked. "Mister Sir, isn't the day as short as it's long? I mean, isn't it the *same* length?"

Never having considered the question in this light, I suggested that they had better ask the Professor; and they ran off in a moment to appeal to their old friend. The Professor left off polishing his spectacles to consider. "My dears," he said after a minute, "the day is the same length as anything that is the same length as *it*." And he resumed his never-ending task of polishing.

The children returned, slowly and thoughtfully, to report his answer. "*Isn't* he wise?" Sylvie asked in an awe-struck whisper. "If *I* was as wise as *that*, I should have a headache all day long, I *know* I should!"

"You appear to be talking to somebody—that isn't here," the Professor said, turning round to the children. "Who is it?"

Bruno looked puzzled. "I never talks to nobody when he isn't here!" he replied. "It isn't good manners. Oo should always wait till he comes, before oo talks to him!"

The Professor looked anxiously in my direction, and seemed to look through and through me without seeing me. "Then who are you talking to?" he said. "There isn't anybody here, you know, except the Other Professor—and *he* isn't here!" he added wildly, turning round and round like a teetotum. "Children! Help to look for him! Quick! He's got lost again!"

The children were on their feet in a moment.

"Where shall we look?" said Sylvie.

"Anywhere!" shouted the excited Professor. "Only be quick about it!" And he began trotting round and round the room, lifting up the chairs, and shaking them.

Bruno took a very small book out of the bookcase, opened it, and shook it in imitation of the Professor. "He isn't *here*," he said.

"He *ca'n't* be there, Bruno!" Sylvie said indignantly.

"Course he ca'n't!" said Bruno. "I should have shooked him out, if he'd been in there!"

"Has he ever been lost before?" Sylvie enquired, turning up a corner of the hearth-rug, and peeping under it.

"Once before," said the Professor: "he once lost himself in a wood——"

"And couldn't he find his-self again?" said Bruno. "Why didn't he shout? He'd be sure to hear his-self, 'cause he couldn't be far off, oo know."

"Let's try shouting," said the Professor.

"What shall we shout?" said Sylvie.

"On second thoughts, *don't* shout," the Professor replied. "The Vice-Warden might hear you. He's getting awfully strict!"

This reminded the poor children of all the troubles, about which they had come to their old friend. Bruno sat down on the floor and began crying. "He *is* so cruel!" he sobbed. "And he lets Uggug take away *all* my toys! And such horrid meals!"

"What did you have for dinner to-day?" said the Professor.

"A little piece of dead crow," was Bruno's mournful reply.

"He means rook-pie," Sylvie explained.

"It *were* a dead crow," Bruno persisted. "And there were a apple-pudding—and Uggug ate it all—and I got nuffin but a crust! And I asked for a orange—and—didn't get it!" And the poor little fellow buried his face in Sylvie's lap, who kept gently stroking his hair, as she went on. "It's all true, Professor dear! They *do* treat my darling Bruno very badly! And they're not kind to *me* either," she added in a lower tone, as if *that* were a thing of much less importance.

The Professor got out a large red silk handkerchief, and wiped his eyes. "I wish I could help you, dear children!" he said. "But what *can* I do?"

"We know the way to Fairyland—where Father's gone—quite well," said Sylvie: "if only the Gardener would let us out."

"Wo'n't he open the door for you?" said the Professor.

"Not for *us*," said Sylvie: "but I'm sure he would for *you*. Do come and ask him, Professor dear!"

"I'll come this minute!" said the Professor.

Bruno sat up and dried his eyes. "*Isn't* he kind, Mister Sir?"

"He is *indeed*," said I. But the Professor took no notice of my remark. He had put on a beautiful cap with a long tassel, and was selecting one of the Other Professor's walking sticks, from a stand in the corner of the room. "A thick stick in one's hand makes people respectful," he was saying to himself. "Come along, dear children!" And we all went out into the garden together.

"I shall address him, first of all," the Professor explained as we went along, "with a few playful remarks on the weather. I shall then question him about the Other Professor. This will have a double advantage. First, it will open the conversation (you ca'n't even drink a bottle of wine without opening it first): and secondly, if he's seen the Other Professor, we shall find him that way: and, if he hasn't we sha'n't."

On our way, we passed the target, at which Uggug had been made to shoot during the Ambassador's visit.

"See!" said the Professor, pointing out a hole in the middle of the bull's-eye. "His Imperial Fatness had only *one* shot at it; and he went in just *here!*"

Bruno carefully examined the hole. "Couldn't go in *there*," he whispered to me. "He are too *fat!*"

We had no sort of difficulty in *finding* the Gardener. Though he was hidden from us by some trees, that harsh voice of his served to direct us; and, as we drew nearer, the words of his song became more and more plainly audible:

> *"He thought he saw an Albatross*
> *That fluttered round the lamp:*
> *He looked again, and found it was*
> *A Penny-Postage-Stamp.*
> *'You'd best be getting home,' he said:*
> *'The nights are very damp!'"*

"Would it be afraid of catching cold?" said Bruno.

"If it got *very* damp", Sylvie suggested, "it might stick to something, you know."

"And *that* somefin would have to go by the post whatever it was!" Bruno eagerly exclaimed. "Suppose it was a cow! Wouldn't it be *dreadful* for the other things!"

"And all these things happened to *him*," said the Professor. "That's what makes the song so interesting."

"He must have had a very curious life," said Sylvie.

"You may say that!" the Professor heartily rejoined.

"Of course she may!" cried Bruno.

By this time we had come up to the Gardener, who was standing on one leg, as usual, and busily employed in watering a bed of flowers with an empty watering-can.

"It hasn't got no water in it!" Bruno explained to him, pulling his sleeve to attract his attention.

"It's lighter to hold," said the Gardener. "A lot of water in it makes one's arms ache." And he went on with his work, singing softly to himself

"The nights are very damp!"

"In digging things out of the ground—which you probably do now and then," the Professor began in a loud voice; "in making things into heaps—which no doubt you often do; and in kicking things about with one heel—which you seem never to leave off doing; have you ever happened to notice another Professor, something like me, but different?"

"Never!" shouted the Gardener, so loudly and violently that we all drew back in alarm. "There ain't such a thing!"

"We will try a less exciting topic," the Professor mildly remarked to the children. "You were asking——"

"We asked him to let us through the garden-door," said Sylvie: "but he wouldn't: but perhaps he would for *you!*"

The Professor put the request, very humbly and courteously.

"I wouldn't mind letting *you* out," said the Gardener. "But I mustn't open the door for *children*. D'you think I'd disobey the *Rules?* Not for one-and-sixpence!'

The Professor cautiously produced a couple of shillings.

"That'll do it!" the Gardener shouted, as he hurled the watering-can across the flower-bed, and produced a handful of keys—one large one, and a number of small ones.

"But look here, Professor dear!" whispered Sylvie. "He needn't open the door for *us*, at all. We can go out with *you*."

"True, dear child!" the Professor thankfully replied, as he replaced the coins in his pocket. "That saves two shillings!" And he took the children's hands, that they might all go out together when the door was opened. This, however, did not seem a very likely event, though the Gardener patiently tried all the small keys, over and over again.

At last the Professor ventured on a gentle suggestion. "Why not try the *large* one? I have often observed that a door unlocks *much* more nicely with its *own* key."

The very first trial of the large key proved a success: the Gardener opened the door, and held out his hand for the money.

The Professor shook his head. "You are acting by *Rule*", he explained, "in opening the door for *me*. And now it's open, we are going out by *Rule*—the Rule of *Three*."

The Gardener looked puzzled, and let us go out; but as he locked the door behind us, we heard him singing thoughtfully to himself:

> *"He thought he saw a Garden-Door*
> *That opened with a key:*
> *He looked again, and found it was*
> *A Double Rule of Three:*
> *'And all its mystery', he said,*
> *'Is clear as day to me!' "*

"I shall now return," said the Professor, when we had walked a few yards: "you see, it's impossible to read *here*, for all my books are in the house."

But the children still kept fast hold of his hands. "*Do* come with us!" Sylvie entreated with tears in her eyes.

"Well, well!" said the good-natured old man. "Perhaps I'll come after you, some day soon. But I *must* go back, *now*. You see I left off at a comma, and it's so awkward not knowing how the sentence finishes! Besides, you've got to go through Dogland first, and I'm always a little nervous about dogs. But it'll be quite easy to come, as soon as I've completed my new invention—for carrying one's-*self*, you know. It wants just a *little* more working out."

"Won't that be very tiring, to carry *yourself?*" Sylvie enquired.

"Well, no, my child. You see, whatever fatigue one incurs by *carrying*, one saves by *being carried! Good-bye, dears! Good-bye, Sir!"* he added to my intense surprise, giving my hand an affectionate squeeze.

"Good-bye, Professor!" I replied, but my voice sounded strange and far away, and the children took not the slightest notice of our farewell. Evidently they neither saw me nor heard me, as, with their arms lovingly twined round each other, they marched boldly on.

CHAPTER 13

A Visit to Dogland

"THERE'S a house, away there to the left," said Sylvie after we had walked what seemed to me about fifty miles. "Let's go and ask for a night's lodging."

"It looks a very comfable house," Bruno said, as we turned into the road leading up to it. "I doos hope the Dogs will be kind to us, I *is* so tired and hungry!"

A Mastiff, dressed in a scarlet collar, and carrying a musket, was pacing up and down, like a sentinel, in front of the entrance. He started, on catching sight of the children and came forwards to meet them, keeping his musket pointed straight at Bruno, who stood quite still, though he turned pale and kept tight hold of Sylvie's hand, while the Sentinel walked solemnly round and round them, and looked at them from all points of view.

"Oobooh, hooh boohooyah!" he growled at last. "Woobah yahwah oobooh! Bow wahbah woobooyah? Bow wow?" he asked Bruno, severely.

Of course *Bruno* understood all this, easily enough. All Fairies understand Doggee—that is, Dog-language. But, as *you* may find it a little
difficult, just at first, I had better put it into English for you. "Humans,
I verily believe! A couple of stray Humans! What Dog do you belong to?
What do you want?"

"We don't belong to a *Dog!*" Bruno began, in Doggee. ("Peoples *never*
belongs to Dogs!" he whispered to Sylvie.)

But Sylvie hastily checked him, for fear of hurting the Mastiff's feelings.
"Please, we want a little food, and a night's lodging—if there's room in
the house," she added timidly. Sylvie spoke Doggee very prettily: but I
think it's almost better, for *you*, to give the conversation in English.

"The *house*, indeed!" growled the Sentinel. "Have you never seen a
Palace in your life? Come along with me! His Majesty must settle what's
to be done with you."

They followed him through the entrance-hall, down a long passage,
and into a magnificent Saloon, around which were grouped dogs of all
sorts and sizes. Two splendid Blood-hounds were solemnly sitting up, one
on each side of the crown-bearer. Two or three Bull-dogs—whom I
guessed to be the Body-Guard of the King—were waiting in grim silence:
in fact the only voices at all plainly audible were those of two little dogs,

who had mounted a settee, and were holding a lively discussion that looked very like a quarrel.

"Lords and Ladies in Waiting, and various Court Officials," our guide gruffly remarked, as he led us in. Of *me* the Courtiers took no notice whatever: but Sylvie and Bruno were the subject of many inquisitive looks, and whispered remarks, of which I only distinctly caught *one*—made by a sly-looking Dachshund to his friend—"Bah wooh wahyah hoobah Oobooh, *hah* bah?" ("She's not such a bad-looking Human, *is* she?")

Leaving the new arrivals in the centre of the Saloon, the Sentinel advanced to a door, at the further end of it, which bore an inscription, painted on it in Doggee, "Royal Kennel—Scratch and Yell."

Before doing this, the Sentinel turned to the children, and said "Give me your names."

"We'd rather not!" Bruno exclaimed, pulling Sylvie away from the door. "We want them ourselves. Come back, Sylvie! Come quick!"

"Nonsense!" said Sylvie very decidedly: and gave their names in Doggee.

Then the Sentinel scratched violently at the door, and gave a yell that made Bruno shiver from head to foot.

"Hooyah wah!" said a deep voice inside. (That's Doggee for "Come in!")

"It's the King Himself!" the Mastiff whispered in an awestruck tone. "Take off your wigs, and lay them humbly at his paws." (What *we* should call "at his *feet*".)

Sylvie was just going to explain, very politely, that really they *couldn't* perform *that* ceremony, because their wigs wouldn't come off, when the door of the Royal Kennel opened, and an enormous Newfoundland Dog put his head out. "Bow wow?" was his first question.

"When His Majesty speaks to you", the Sentinel hastily whispered to Bruno, "you should prick up your ears!"

Bruno looked doubtfully at Sylvie. "I'd rather not, please," he said. "It would hurt."

"It doesn't hurt a bit!" the Sentinel said with some indignation. "Look! It's like this!" And he pricked up his ears like two railway signals.

Sylvie gently explained matters. "I'm afraid we ca'n't manage it," she said in a low voice. "I'm very sorry: but our ears haven't got the right——" she wanted to say "machinery" in Doggee: but she had forgotten the word, and could only think of "steam-engine".

The Sentinel repeated Sylvie's explanation to the King.

"Ca'n't prick up their ears without a steam-engine!" His Majesty exclaimed. "They *must* be curious creatures! I must have a look at them!"

The Dog-King

And he came out of his Kennel, and walked solemnly up to the children.

What was the amazement—not to say the horror—of the whole assembly, when Sylvie actually *patted His Majesty on the head*, while Bruno seized his long ears and pretended to tie them together under his chin!

The Sentinel groaned aloud: a beautiful Greyhound—who appeared to be one of the Ladies in Waiting—fainted away: and all the other Courtiers hastily drew back, and left plenty of room for the huge Newfoundland to spring upon the audacious strangers, and tear them limb from limb.

Only—he didn't. On the contrary His Majesty actually *smiled*—so far as a Dog *can* smile—and (the other Dogs couldn't believe their eyes, but it was true, all the same) His Majesty *wagged his tail!*

"Yah! Hooh hahwooh!" (that is "Well I never!") was the universal cry.

His Majesty looked round him severely, and gave a slight growl, which produced instant silence. "Conduct *my friends* to the banqueting-hall!" he said, laying such an emphasis on "*my friends*" that several of the dogs rolled over helplessly on their backs and began to lick Bruno's feet.

A procession was formed, but I only ventured to follow as far as the *door* of the banqueting-hall, so furious was the uproar of barking dogs within. So I sat down by the King, who seemed to have gone to sleep, and waited till the children returned to say good-night, when His Majesty got up and shook himself.

"Time for bed!" he said with a sleepy yawn. "The attendants will show you your room," he added, aside, to Sylvie and Bruno. "Bring lights!" And, with a dignified air, he held out his paw for them to kiss.

But the children were evidently not well practised in Court-manners. Sylvie simply stroked the great paw: Bruno hugged it: the Master of Ceremonies looked shocked.

All this time Dog-waiters, in splendid livery, were running up with lighted candles: but, as fast as they put them upon the table, other waiters ran away with them, so that there never seemed to be one for *me*, though the Master kept nudging me with his elbow, and repeating "I ca'n't let you sleep *here*! You're not in *bed*, you know!"

I made a great effort, and just succeeded in getting out the words "I know I'm not. I'm in an arm-chair."

"Well, forty winks will do you no harm," the Master said, and left me. I could scarcely hear his words: and no wonder: he was leaning over the side of a ship, that was miles away from the pier on which I stood. The ship passed over the horizon, and I sank back into the armchair.

The next thing I remember is that it was morning: breakfast was just over: Sylvie was lifting Bruno down from a high chair, and saying to a

Spaniel, who was regarding them with a most benevolent smile, "Yes, thank you, we've had a *very* nice breakfast. Haven't we, Bruno?"

"There was too many bones in the——" Bruno began, but Sylvie frowned at him, and laid her finger on her lips, for, at this moment, the travelers were waited on by a very dignified officer, the Head-Growler, whose duty it was, first to conduct them to the King to bid him farewell, and then to escort them to the boundary of Dogland. The great Newfoundland received them most affably, but instead of saying "good-bye", he startled the Head-Growler into giving three savage growls, by announcing that he would escort them himself.

"It is a most unusual proceeding, your Majesty!" the Head-Growler exclaimed, almost choking with vexation at being set aside, for he had put on his best Court-suit, made entirely of cat-skins, for the occasion.

"I shall escort them myself," His Majesty repeated, gently but firmly, laying aside the Royal robes, and changing his crown for a small coronet, "and you may stay at home."

"I *are* glad!" Bruno whispered to Sylvie, when they had got well out of hearing. "He were so *welly* cross!" And he not only patted their Royal escort, but even hugged him round the neck in the exuberance of his delight.

His Majesty calmly wagged the Royal tail. "It's quite a relief", he said, "getting away from that Palace now and then! Royal Dogs have a dull life of it, I can tell you! Would you mind" (this to Sylvie, in a low voice, and looking a little shy and embarrassed) "would you mind the trouble of just throwing that stick for me to fetch?"

Sylvie was too much astonished to do anything for a moment: it sounded such a monstrous impossibility that a *King* should wish to run after a stick. But *Bruno* was equal to the occasion, and with a glad shout of "Hi then! Fetch it, good Doggie!" he hurled it over a clump of bushes. The next moment the Monarch of Dogland had bounded over the bushes, and picked up the stick, and came galloping back to the children with it in his mouth. Bruno took it from him with great decision. "Beg for it!" he insisted; and His Majesty begged. "Paw!" commanded Sylvie; and His Majesty gave his paw. In short, the solemn ceremony of escorting the travelers to the boundaries of Dogland became one long uproarious game of play!

"But business is business!" the Dog-King said at last. "And I must go back to mine. I couldn't come any further," he added, consulting a dog-watch, which hung on a chain round his neck, "not even if there were a *Cat* in sight!"

They took an affectionate farewell of His Majesty, and trudged on.

"That *were* a dear dog!" Bruno exclaimed. "Has we to go far, Sylvie? I's tired!"

"Not much further, darling!" Sylvie gently replied. "Do you see that shining, just beyond those trees? I'm almost *sure* it's the gate of Fairyland! I know it's all golden—Father told me so—and so bright, so bright!" she went on dreamily.

"It dazzles!" said Bruno, shading his eyes with one little hand, while the other clung tightly to Sylvie's hand, as if he were half-alarmed at her strange manner.

For the child moved on as if walking in her sleep, her large eyes gazing into the far distance, and her breath coming and going in quick pantings of eager delight. I knew, by some mysterious mental light, that a great change was taking place in my sweet little friend (for such I loved to think her) and that she was passing from the condition of a mere Outland Sprite into the true Fairy-nature.

Upon Bruno the change came later: but it was completed in both before they reached the golden gate, through which I knew it would be impossible for *me* to follow. I could but stand outside, and take a last look at the two sweet children, ere they disappeared within, and the golden gate closed with a bang.

And with *such* a bang! "It never *will* shut like any other cupboard-door," Arthur explained. "There's something wrong with the hinge. However, here's the cake and wine. And you've had your forty winks. So you really *must* get off to bed, old man! You're fit for nothing else. Witness my hand, Arthur Forester, M.D."

By this time I was wide-awake again. "Not *quite* yet!" I pleaded. "Really I'm not sleepy now. And it isn't midnight yet."

"Well, I did want to say another word to you," Arthur replied in a relenting tone, as he supplied me with the supper he had prescribed. "Only I thought you were too sleepy for it to-night."

We took our midnight meal almost in silence; for an unusual nervousness seemed to have seized on my old friend.

"What kind of a night is it?" he asked, rising and undrawing the window-curtains, apparently to change the subject for a minute. I followed him to the window, and we stood together, looking out, in silence.

"When I first spoke to you about——" Arthur began, after a long and embarrassing silence, "that is, when we first talked about her—for I think it was *you* that introduced the subject—my own position in life forbade me to do more than worship her from a distance: and I was turning over plans for leaving this place finally, and settling somewhere out of all chance of meeting her again. That seemed to be my only chance of usefulness in life."

"Would that have been wise?" I said. "To leave yourself no hope at all?"

"There *was* no hope to leave," Arthur firmly replied, though his eyes glittered with tears as he gazed upwards into the midnight sky, from which one solitary star, the glorious "Vega", blazed out in fitful splendour through the driving clouds. "She was like that star to me—bright, beautiful, and pure, but out of reach, out of reach!"

He drew the curtains again, and we returned to our places by the fireside.

"What I wanted to tell you was this," he resumed. "I heard this evening from my solicitor. I can't go into the details of the business, but the upshot is that my worldly wealth is much more than I thought, and I am (or shall soon be) in a position to offer marriage, without imprudence, to any lady, even if she brought nothing. I doubt if there would be anything on *her* side: the Earl is poor, I believe. But I should have enough for both, even if health failed."

"I wish you all happiness in your married life!" I cried. "Shall you speak to the Earl to-morrow?"

"Not yet awhile," said Arthur. "He is very friendly, but I dare not think he means more than that, as yet. And as for—as for Lady Muriel, try as I may, I *cannot* read her feelings towards me. If there *is* love, she is hiding it! No, I must wait, I must wait!"

I did not like to press any further advice on my friend, whose judgment, I felt, was so much more sober and thoughtful than my own; and we parted without more words on the subject that had now absorbed his thoughts, nay, his very life.

The next morning a letter from *my* solicitor arrived, summoning me to town on important business.

CHAPTER 14

Fairy-Sylvie

FOR a full month the business, for which I had returned to London, detained me there; and even then it was only the urgent advice of my physician that induced me to leave it unfinished and pay another visit to Elveston.

Arthur had written once or twice during the month; but in none of his letters was there any mention of Lady Muriel. Still, I did not augur ill from his silence: to me it looked like the natural action of a lover, who, even while his heart was singing "She is mine", would fear to paint his happiness in the cold phrases of a written letter, but would wait to tell it by word of mouth. "Yes," I thought, "I am to hear his song of triumph from his own lips!"

The night I arrived we had much to say on other matters: and, tired with the journey, I went to bed early, leaving the happy secret still untold. Next day, however, as we chatted on over the remains of luncheon, I ventured to put the momentous question. "Well, old friend, you have told me nothing of Lady Muriel—nor when the happy day is to be?"

"The happy day", Arthur said, looking unexpectedly grave, "is yet in the dim future. We need to know—or, rather, *she* needs to know *me* better. I know *her* sweet nature, thoroughly, by this time. But I dare not speak till I am sure that my love is returned."

"Don't wait too long!" I said gaily. "Faint heart never won fair lady!"

"It *is* 'faint heart' perhaps. But really I *dare* not speak just yet."

"But meanwhile", I pleaded, "you are running a risk that perhaps you have not thought of. Some other man——"

"No," said Arthur firmly. "She is heart-whole: I am sure of that. Yet, if she loves another better than me, so be it! I will not spoil her happiness. The secret shall die with me. But she is my first—and my *only* love!"

"That is all very beautiful *sentiment*," I said, "but it is not *practical*. It is not like *you*.

> *He either fears his fate too much*
> *Or his desert is small,*
> *Who dares not put it to the touch,*
> *To win or lose it all."*

"I *dare* not ask the question whether there is another!" he said passionately. "It would break my heart to know it!"

"Yet is it wise to leave it unasked? You must not waste your life upon an 'if'!"

"I tell you I *dare* not!"

"May *I* find it out for you?" I asked, with the freedom of an old friend.

"No, no!" he replied with a pained look. "I entreat you to say nothing. Let it wait."

"As you please," I said: and judged it best to say no more just then. "But this evening", I thought, "I will call on the Earl. I may be able to *see* how the land lies, without so much as saying a word!"

It was a very hot afternoon—too hot to go for a walk or do anything—or else it wouldn't have happened, I believe.

In the first place, I want to know—dear Child who reads this!—why Fairies should always be teaching *us* to do our duty, and lecturing *us* when we go wrong, and we should never teach them anything? You can't mean to say that Fairies are never greedy, or selfish, or cross, or deceitful, because that would be nonsense, you know. Well then, don't you think they might be all the better for a little lecturing and punishing now and then?

I really don't see why it shouldn't be tried, and I'm almost sure that, if you could only catch a Fairy, and put it in the corner, and give it nothing but bread and water for a day or two, you'd find it quite an improved character—it would take down its conceit a little, at all events.

The next question is, what is the best time for seeing Fairies? I believe I can tell you all about that.

The first rule is, that it must be a *very* hot day—that we may consider as settled: and you must be just a *little* sleepy—but not too sleepy to keep your eyes open, mind. Well, and you ought to feel a little—what one may call "fairyish"—the Scotch call it "eerie", and perhaps that's a prettier word; if you don't know what it means, I'm afraid I can hardly explain it; you must wait till you meet a Fairy, and then you'll know.

And the last rule is that the crickets should not be chirping. I can't stop to explain that: you must take it on trust for the present.

So, if all these things happen together, you have a good chance of seeing a Fairy—or at least a much better chance than if they didn't.

The first thing I noticed, as I went lazily along through an open place in the wood, was a large Beetle lying struggling on its back, and I went down upon one knee to help the poor thing to its feet again. In some things, you know, you ca'n't be quite sure what an insect would like: for instance, I never could quite settle, supposing I were a moth, whether I would rather be kept out of the candle, or be allowed to fly straight in and get burnt—or again, supposing I were a spider, I'm not sure if I should be *quite* pleased to have my web torn down, and the fly let loose—but I feel quite certain that, if I were a beetle and had rolled over on my back, I should always be glad to be helped up again.

So, as I was saying, I had gone down upon one knee and was just reaching out a little stick to turn the Beetle over, when I saw a sight that made me draw back hastily and hold my breath, for fear of making any noise and frightening the little creature away.

Not that she looked as if she would be easily frightened: she seemed so good and gentle that I'm sure she would never expect that any one could wish to hurt her. She was only a few inches high, and was dressed in green, so that you really would hardly have noticed her among the long grass; and she was so delicate and graceful that she quite seemed to belong to the place, almost as if she were one of the flowers. I may tell you, besides, that she had no wings (I don't believe in Fairies with wings), and that she had quantities of long brown hair and large earnest brown eyes, and then I shall have done all I can to give you an idea of her.

Sylvie (I found out her name afterwards) had knelt down, just as I was doing, to help the Beetle; but it needed more than a little stick for *her* to get it on its legs again; it was as much as she could do, with both arms, to roll the heavy thing over; and all the while she was talking to it, half scolding and half comforting, as a nurse might do with a child that had fallen down.

"There, there! You needn't cry so much about it. You're not killed yet—though if you were, you couldn't cry, you know, and so it's a general rule against crying, my dear! And how did you come to tumble over? But I can see well enough how it was—I needn't ask you that—walking over sand-pits with your chin in the air, as usual. Of course if you go among sand-pits like that, you must expect to tumble. You should look."

The Beetle murmured something that sounded like "I *did* look," and Sylvie went on again.

"But I know you didn't! You never do! You always walk with your chin up—you're so dreadfully conceited. Well let's see how many legs are broken this time. Why, none of them, I declare! And what's the good of having six legs, my dear, if you can only kick them all about in the air when you tumble? Legs are meant to walk with, you know. Now don't begin putting out your wings yet; I've more to say. Go to the frog that lives behind that buttercup—give him my compliments—Sylvie's compliments—can you say 'compliments'?"

The Beetle tried, and, I suppose, succeeded.

"Yes, that's right. And tell him he's to give you some of that salve I left with him yesterday. And you'd better get him to rub it in for you. He's got rather cold hands, but you mustn't mind that."

I think the Beetle must have shuddered at this idea, for Sylvie went on in a graver tone. "Now you needn't pretend to be so particular as all that, as if you were too grand to be rubbed by a frog. The fact is, you ought to be very much obliged to him. Suppose you could get nobody but a toad to do it, how would you like *that?*"

There was a little pause, and then Sylvie added "Now you may go. Be a good beetle, and don't keep your chin in the air." And then began one of those performances of humming, and whizzing, and restless banging about, such as a beetle indulges in when it has decided to flying, but hasn't quite made up its mind which way to go. At last, in one of its awkward zig-zags, it managed to fly right into my face, and, by the time I had recovered from the shock, the little Fairy was gone.

I looked about in all directions for the little creature, but there was no trace of her—and my "eerie" feeling was quite gone off, and the crickets were chirping again merrily—so I knew she was really gone.

And now I've got time to tell you the rule about the crickets. They always leave off chirping when a Fairy goes by—because a Fairy's a kind of queen over them, I suppose—at all events it's a much grander thing than a cricket—so whenever you're walking out, and the crickets suddenly leave off chirping, you may be sure that they see a Fairy.

I walked on sadly enough, you may be sure. However, I comforted myself with thinking "It's been a very wonderful afternoon, so far. I'll just go quietly on and look about me, and I shouldn't wonder if I were to come across another Fairy somewhere."

Peering about in this way, I happened to notice a plant with rounded leaves, and with queer little holes cut in the middle of several of them. "Ah, the leafcutter bee!" I carelessly remarked—you know I am very learned in Natural History (for instance, I can always tell kittens from chickens at one glance)—and I was passing on, when a sudden thought made me stoop down and examine the leaves.

Then a little thrill of delight ran through me—for I noticed that the holes were all arranged so as to form letters; there were three leaves side by side, with "B", "R", and "U" marked on them, and after some search I found two more, which contained an "N" and an "O".

And then, all in a moment, a flash of inner light seemed to illumine a part of my life that had all but faded into oblivion—the strange visions I had experienced during my journey to Elveston: and with a thrill of delight I thought "Those visions are destined to be linked with my waking life!"

By this time the "eerie" feeling had come back again, and I suddenly observed that no crickets were chirping, so I felt quite sure that "Bruno" was somewhere very near.

And so indeed he was—so near that I had very nearly walked over him without seeing him; which would have been dreadful, always supposing that Fairies *can* be walked over—my own belief is that they are something of the nature of Will-o'-the-Wisps: and there's no walking over *them*.

Think of any pretty little boy you know, with rosy cheeks, large dark eyes, and tangled brown hair, and then fancy him made small enough to go comfortably into a coffee-cup, and you'll have a very fair idea of him.

"What's your name, little one?" I began, in as soft a voice as I could manage. And, by the way, why is it we always begin by asking little children their names? Is it because we fancy a name will help to make them a little bigger? You never thought of asking a real large man his name, now, did you? But, however that may be, I felt it quite necessary to know *his* name; so, as he didn't answer my question, I asked it again a little louder. "What's your name, my little man?"

"What's oors?" he said, without looking up.

I told him my name quite gently, for he was much too small to be angry with.

"Duke of Anything?" he asked, just looking at me for a moment, and then going on with his work.

"Not Duke at all," I said, a little ashamed of having to confess it.

"Oo're big enough to be two Dukes," said the little creature. "I suppose oo're Sir Something, then?"

"No," I said, feeling more and more ashamed. "I haven't got any title."

The Fairy seemed to think that in that case I really wasn't worth the trouble of talking to, for he quietly went on digging, and tearing the flowers to pieces.

After a few minutes I tried again. "*Please* tell me what your name is."

"Bruno," the little fellow answered, very readily. "Why didn't oo say 'please' before?"

"That's something like what we used to be taught in the nursery," I thought to myself, looking back through the long years (about a hundred of them, since you ask the question), to the time when I was a little child. And here an idea came into my head, and I asked him. "Aren't you one of the Fairies that teach children to be good?"

"Well, we have to do that sometimes," said Bruno, "and a dreadful bother it is." As he said this, he savagely tore a heartsease in two, and trampled on the pieces.

"What *are* you doing there, Bruno?" I said.

"Spoiling Sylvie's garden," was all the answer Bruno would give at first. But, as he went on tearing up the flowers, he muttered to himself "The nasty cross thing—wouldn't let me go and play this morning—said I must finish my lessons first—lessons, indeed! I'll vex her finely, though!"

"Oh, Bruno, you shouldn't do that!" I cried. "Don't you know that's revenge? And revenge is a wicked, cruel, dangerous thing!"

"River-edge?" said Bruno. "What a funny word! I suppose oo call it cruel and dangerous 'cause, if oo wented too far and tumbleded in, oo'd get drownded."

"No, not river-edge," I explained: "revenge" (saying the word very slowly). But I couldn't help thinking that Bruno's explanation did very well for either word.

"Oh!" said Bruno, opening his eyes very wide, but without trying to repeat the word.

"Come! Try to pronounce it, Bruno!" I said, cheerfully. "Re-venge, re-venge."

But Bruno only tossed his little head, and said he couldn't; that his mouth wasn't the right shape for words of that kind. And the more I laughed, the more sulky the little fellow got about it.

"Well, never mind, my little man!" I said. "Shall I help you with that job?"

"Yes, please," Bruno said, quite pacified. "Only I wiss I could think of somefin to vex her more than this. Oo don't know how hard it is to make her angry!"

"Now listen to me, Bruno, and I'll teach you quite a splendid kind of revenge!"

"Somefin that'll vex her finely?" he asked with gleaming eyes.

"Something that will vex her finely. First, we'll get up all the weeds in her garden. See, there are a good many at this end—quite hiding the flowers."

"But *that* won't vex her!" said Bruno.

"After that", I said, without noticing the remark, "we'll water this highest bed—up here. You see it's getting quite dry and dusty."

Bruno looked at me inquisitively, but he said nothing this time.

"Then after that," I went on, "the walks want sweeping a bit; and I think you might cut down that tall nettle—it's so close to the garden that it's quite in the way——"

"What *is* oo talking about?" Bruno impatiently interrupted me. "All that won't vex her a bit!"

"Won't it?" I said, innocently. "Then, after that, suppose we put in some of those coloured pebbles—just to mark the divisions between the different kinds of flowers, you know. That'll have a very pretty effect."

Bruno turned round and had another good stare at me. At last there came an odd little twinkle into his eyes, and he said, with quite a new meaning in his voice, "That'll do nicely. Let's put 'em in rows—all the red together, and all the blue together."

"That'll do capitally," I said; "and then—what kind of flowers does Sylvie like best?"

Bruno had to put his thumb in his mouth and consider a little before he could answer. "Violets," he said, at last.

"There's a beautiful bed of violets down by the brook——"

"Oh, let's fetch 'em!" cried Bruno, giving a little skip into the air.

"Here! Catch hold of my hand, and I'll help oo along. The grass is rather thick down that way."

I couldn't help laughing at his having so entirely forgotten what a big creature he was talking to. "No, not yet, Bruno," I said: "we must consider what's the right thing to do first. You see we've got quite a business before us."

"Yes, let's consider," said Bruno, putting his thumb into his mouth again, and sitting down upon a dead mouse.

"What do you keep that mouse for?" I said. "You should either bury it, or else throw it into the brook."

"Why, it's to measure with!" cried Bruno. "How ever would oo do a garden without one? We make each bed three mouses and a half long, and two mouses wide."

I stopped him, as he was dragging it off by the tail to show me how it was used, for I was half afraid the "eerie" feeling might go off before we had finished the garden, and in that case I should see no more of him or Sylvie. "I think the best way will be for *you* to weed the beds, while *I* sort out these pebbles, ready to mark the walks with."

"That's it!" cried Bruno. "And I'll tell oo about the caterpillars while we work."

"Ah, let's hear about the caterpillars," I said as I drew the pebbles together into a heap and began dividing them into colours.

And Bruno went on in a low, rapid tone, more as if he were talking to himself. "Yesterday I saw two little caterpillars, when I was sitting by the brook, just where oo go into the wood. They were quite green, and they had yellow eyes, and they didn't see *me*. And one of them had got a moth's wing to carry—a great brown moth's wing, oo know, all dry, with feathers. So he couldn't want it to eat, I should think—perhaps he meant to make a cloak for the winter?"

"Perhaps," I said, for Bruno had twisted up the last word into a sort of question, and was looking at me for an answer.

One word was quite enough for the little fellow, and he went on merrily. "Well, and so he didn't want the other caterpillar to see the moth's wing, oo know—so what must he do but try to carry it with all his left legs, and he tried to walk on the other set. Of course he toppled over after that."

"After what?" I said, catching at the last word, for, to tell the truth, I hadn't been attending much.

"He toppled over," Bruno repeated, very gravely, "and if *oo* ever saw a caterpillar topple over, oo'd know it's a welly serious thing, and not sit grinning like that—and I sha'n't tell oo no more!"

"Indeed and indeed, Bruno, I didn't mean to grin. See, I'm quite grave again now."

But Bruno only folded his arms, and said "Don't tell *me*. I see a little twinkle in one of oor eyes—just like the moon."

"Why do you think I'm like the moon, Bruno?" I asked.

"Oor face is large and round like the moon," Bruno answered, looking at me thoughtfully. "It doesn't shine quite so bright—but it's more cleaner."

I couldn't help smiling at this. "You know I sometimes wash *my* face, Bruno. The moon never does that."

"Oh, doosn't she though!" cried Bruno; and he leant forwards and added in a solemn whisper, "The moon's face gets dirtier and dirtier every night, till it's black all across. And then, when it's dirty all over—*so*—" (he passed his hand across his own rosy cheeks as he spoke) "then she washes it."

"Then it's all clean again, isn't it?"

"Not all in a moment," said Bruno. "What a deal of teaching oo wants! She washes it little by little—only she begins at the other edge, oo know."

By this time he was sitting quietly on the dead mouse with his arms folded, and the weeding wasn't getting on a bit: so I had to say "Work first, pleasure afterwards: no more talking till that bed's finished."

CHAPTER 15

Bruno's Revenge

AFTER that we had a few minutes of silence, while I sorted out the pebbles, and amused myself with watching Bruno's plan of gardening. It was quite a new plan to me: he always measured each bed before he weeded it, as if he was afraid the weeding would make it shrink; and once, when it came out longer than he wished, he set to work to thump the mouse with his little fist, crying out "There now! It's all gone wrong again! Why don't oo keep oor tail straight when I tell oo!"

"I'll tell oo what I'll do," Bruno said in a half-whisper, as we worked. "Oo like Fairies, don't oo?"

"Yes," I said: "of course I do, or I shouldn't have come here. I should have gone to some place where there are no Fairies."

Bruno laughed contemptuously. "Why, oo might as well say oo'd go to some place where there wasn't any air—supposing oo didn't like air!"

This was a rather difficult idea to grasp. I tried a change of subject. "You're nearly the first Fairy I ever saw. Have *you* ever seen any people besides me?"

"Plenty!" said Bruno. "We see 'em when we walk in the road."

"But they ca'n't see *you*. How is it they never tread on you?"

"Ca'n't *tread* on us," said Bruno, looking amused at my ignorance. "Why, suppose oo're walking, here—so—" (making little marks on the ground) "and suppose there's a Fairy—that's me—walking *here*. Very well then, oo put one foot here, and one foot here, and so oo doesn't tread on the Fairy."

This was all very well as an explanation, but it didn't convince me. "Why shouldn't I put one foot *on* the Fairy?" I asked.

"I don't know *why*," the little fellow said in a thoughtful tone. "But I know oo *wouldn't*. Nobody never walked on the top of a Fairy. Now I'll tell oo what I'll do, as oo're so fond of Fairies. I'll get oo an invitation to the Fairy-King's dinner-party. I know one of the head-waiters."

I couldn't help laughing at this idea. "Do the waiters invite the guests?" I asked.

"Oh, not *to sit down*!" Bruno said. "But to wait at table. Oo'd like that, wouldn't oo? To hand about plates, and so on."

"Well, but that's not so nice as sitting at the table, is it?"

"Of course it isn't," Bruno said, in a tone as if he rather pitied my ignorance; "but if oo're not even Sir Anything, oo ca'n't expect to be allowed to sit at the table, oo know."

I said, as meekly as I could, that I didn't expect it, but it was the only way of going to a dinner-party that I really enjoyed. And Bruno tossed his head, and said, in a rather offended tone, that I might do as I pleased—there were many he knew that would give their ears to go.

"Have you ever been yourself, Bruno?"

"They invited me once, last week," Bruno said, very gravely. "It was to wash up the soup-plates—no, the cheese-plates I mean—that was grand enough. And I waited at table. And I didn't hardly make only *one* mistake."

"What was it?" I said. "You needn't mind telling *me*."

"Only bringing scissors to cut the beef with," Bruno said carelessly. "But the grandest thing of all was, *I* fetched the King a glass of cider!"

"That *was* grand!" I said, biting my lip to keep myself from laughing.

"Wasn't it?" said Bruno, very earnestly. "Oo know it isn't every one that's had such an honour as *that!*"

This set me thinking of the various queer things we call "an honour" in this world, but which, after all, haven't a bit more honour in them than what Bruno enjoyed, when he took the King a glass of cider.

I don't know how long I might not have dreamed on in this way, if Bruno hadn't suddenly roused me. "Oh, come here quick!" he cried, in a state of the wildest excitement. "Catch hold of his other horn! I ca'n't hold him more than a minute!"

He was struggling desperately with a great snail, clinging to one of its horns, and nearly breaking his poor little back in his efforts to drag it over a blade of grass.

I saw we should have no more gardening if I let this sort of thing go on, so I quietly took the snail away, and put it on a bank where he couldn't reach it. "We'll hunt it afterwards, Bruno," I said, "if you really want to catch it. But what's the use of it when you've got it?"

"What's the use of a fox when oo've got it?" said Bruno. "I know oo big things hunt foxes."

I tried to think of some good reason why "big things" should hunt foxes, and he should not hunt snails, but none came into my head: so I said at last, "Well, I suppose one's as good as the other. I'll go snail-hunting myself some day."

"I should think oo wouldn't be so silly," said Bruno, "as to go snail-hunting by oorself. Why, oo'd never get the snail along, if oo hadn't somebody to hold on to his other horn!"

"Of course I sha'n't go *alone*," I said, quite gravely. "By the way, is that the best kind to hunt, or do you recommend the ones without shells?"

"Oh, no, we never hunt the ones without shells," Bruno said, with a little shudder at the thought of it. "They're always so cross about it; and then, if oo tumbles over them, they're ever so sticky!"

By this time we had nearly finished the garden. I had fetched some violets, and Bruno was just helping me to put in the last, when he suddenly stopped and said "I'm tired."

"Rest then," I said: "I can go on without you, quite well."

Bruno needed no second invitation: he at once began arranging the dead

mouse as a kind of sofa. "And I'll sing oo a little song," he said, as he rolled it about.

'Do," said I: "I like songs very much."

"Which song will oo choose?" Bruno said, as he dragged the mouse into a place where he could get a good view of me. " 'Ting, ting, ting' is the nicest."

There was no resisting such a strong hint as this: however, I pretended to think about it for a moment, and then said "Well, I like 'Ting, ting, ting' best of all."

"That shows oo're a good judge of music," Bruno said, with a pleased look. "How many hare-bells would oo like?" And he put his thumb into his mouth to help me to consider.

As there was only one cluster of hare-bells within easy reach, I said very gravely that I thought one would do *this* time, and I picked it and gave it to him. Bruno ran his hand once or twice up and down the flowers, like a musician trying an instrument, producing a most delicious delicate tinkling as he did so. I had never heard flower-music before—I don't think one can, unless one's in the "eerie" state—and I don't know quite how to give you an idea of what it was like, except by saying that it sounded like a peal of bells a thousand miles off. When he had satisfied himself that the flowers were in tune, he seated himself on the dead mouse (he never seemed really comfortable anywhere else), and, looking up at me with a merry twinkle in his eyes, he began. By the way, the tune was rather a curious one, and you might like to try it yourself, so here are the notes.

> *"Rise, oh, rise! The daylight dies:*
> *The owls are hooting, ting, ting, ting!*
> *Wake, oh, wake! Beside the lake*
> *The elves are fluting, ting, ting, ting!*
> *Welcoming our Fairy King,*
> *We sing, sing, sing."*

He sang the first four lines briskly and merrily, making the hare-bells chime in time with the music; but the last two he sang quite slowly and gently, and merely waved the flowers backwards and forwards. Then he left off to explain. "The Fairy-King is Oberon, and he lives across the lake—and sometimes he comes in a little boat—and we go and meet him—and then we sing this song, you know."

"And then you go and dine with him?" I said, mischievously.

"Oo shouldn't talk," Bruno hastily said: "it interrupts the song so."

I said I wouldn't do it again.

"I never talk myself when I'm singing," he went on very gravely: "so *oo* shouldn't either." Then he tuned the hare-bells once more, and sang:

> *"Hear, oh, hear! From far and near*
> *The music stealing, ting, ting, ting!*
> *Fairy bells adown the dells*
> *Are merrily pealing, ting, ting, ting!*
> *Welcoming our Fairy King,*
> *We ring, ring, ring.*
>
> *"See, oh, see! On every tree*
> *What lamps are shining, ting, ting, ting!*
> *They are eyes of fiery flies*
> *To light our dining, ting, ting, ting!*
> *Welcoming our Fairy King*
> *They swing, swing, swing.*

> *"Haste, oh, haste, to take and taste*
> *The dainties waiting, ting, ting, ting!*
> *Honey-dew is stored——"*

"Hush, Bruno!" I interrupted in a warning whisper. "She's coming!"

Bruno checked his song, and, as she slowly made her way through the long grass, he suddenly rushed out headlong at her like a little bull, shouting "Look the other way! Look the other way!"

"Which way?" Sylvie asked, in rather a frightened tone, as she looked round in all directions to see where the danger could be.

"*That* way!" said Bruno, carefully turning her round with her face to the wood. "Now, walk backwards—walk gently—don't be frightened: oo sha'n't trip!"

But Sylvie *did* trip notwithstanding: in fact he led her, in his hurry, across so many little sticks and stones, that it was really a wonder the poor child could keep on her feet at all. But he was far too much excited to think of what he was doing.

I silently pointed out to Bruno the best place to lead her to, so as to get a view of the whole garden at once: it was a little rising ground, about the height of a potato; and, when they had mounted it, I drew back into the shade, that Sylvie mightn't see me.

I heard Bruno cry out triumphantly "*Now* oo may look!" and then followed a clapping of hands, but it was all done by Bruno himself. Sylvie was silent—she only stood and gazed with her hands clasped together, and I was half afraid she didn't like it after all.

Bruno too was watching her anxiously, and when she jumped down off the mound, and began wandering up and down the little walks, he cautiously followed her about, evidently anxious that she should form her own opinion of it all, without any hint from him. And when at last she drew a long breath, and gave her verdict—in a hurried whisper, and without the slightest regard to grammar—"It's the loveliest thing as I never saw in all my life before!" the little fellow looked as well pleased as if it had been given by all the judges and juries in England put together.

"And did you really do it all by yourself, Bruno?" said Sylvie. "And all for me?"

"I was helped a bit," Bruno began, with a merry little laugh at her surprise. "We've been at it all the afternoon—I thought oo'd like——" and here the poor little fellow's lip began to quiver, and all in a moment he burst out crying, and running up to Sylvie he flung his arms passionately round her neck, and hid his face on her shoulder.

There was a little quiver in Sylvie's voice too, as she whispered "Why, what's the matter, darling?" and tried to lift up his head and kiss him.

But Bruno only clung to her, sobbing, and wouldn't be comforted till he had confessed. "I tried—to spoil oor garden—first—but I'll never—never——" and then came another burst of tears, which drowned the rest of the sentence. At last he got out the words "I liked—putting in the flowers—for *oo*, Sylvie—and I never was so happy before." And the rosy little face came up at last to be kissed, all wet with tears as it was.

Sylvie was crying too by this time, and she said nothing but "Bruno, dear!" and "*I* never was so happy before," though why these two children who had never been so happy before should both be crying was a mystery to *me*.

I felt very happy too, but of course I didn't cry: "big things" never do, you know—we leave all that to the Fairies. Only I think it must have been raining a little just then, for I found a drop or two on my cheeks.

After that they went through the whole garden again, flower by flower, as if it were a long sentence they were spelling out, with kisses for commas, and a great hug by way of a full-stop when they got to the end.

"Doos oo know, that was my river-edge, Sylvie?" Bruno solemnly began.

Sylvie laughed merrily. "What *do* you mean?" she said. And she pushed back her heavy brown hair with both hands, and looked at him with dancing eyes in which the big tear-drops were still glittering.

Bruno drew in a long breath, and made up his mouth for a great effort. "I mean re—venge," he said: "now oo under'tand." And he looked so happy and proud at having said the word right at last, that I quite envied him. I rather think Sylvie didn't "under'tand" at all; but she gave him a little kiss on each cheek, which seemed to do just as well.

So they wandered off lovingly together, in among the buttercups, each with an arm twined round the other, whispering and laughing as they went, and never so much as once looked back at poor me. Yes, once, just before I quite lost sight of them, Bruno half turned his head, and nodded me a saucy little good-bye over one shoulder. And that was all the thanks I got for *my* trouble. The very last thing I saw of them was this—Sylvie was stooping down with her arms round Bruno's neck, and saying coaxingly in his ear, "Do you know, Bruno, I've quite forgotten that hard word. Do say it once more. Come! Only this once, dear!"

But Bruno wouldn't try it again.

CHAPTER 16

A Changed Crocodile

THE Marvellous—the Mysterious—had quite passed out of my life for the moment: and the Common-place reigned supreme. I turned in the direction of the Earl's house, as it was now "the witching hour" of five, and I knew I should find them ready for a cup of tea and a quiet chat.

Lady Muriel and her father gave me a delightfully warm welcome. They were not of the folk we meet in fashionable drawing-rooms—who conceal all such feelings as they may chance to possess beneath the impenetrable mask of a conventional placidity. "The Man with the Iron Mask" was, no doubt, a rarity and a marvel in his own age: in modern London no one would turn his head to give him a second look! No, these were *real* people. When they *looked* pleased, it meant that they *were* pleased: and when Lady Muriel said, with a bright smile, "I'm *very* glad to see you again!" I knew that it was *true*.

Still I did not venture to disobey the injunctions—crazy as I felt them to be—of the love-sick young Doctor, by so much as alluding to his existence: and it was only after they had given me full details of a projected Picnic, to which they invited me, that Lady Muriel exclaimed, almost as an after-thought, "and *do*, if you can, bring Doctor Forester with you! I'm sure a day in the country would do him good. I'm afraid he studies too much——"

It was "on the tip of my tongue" to quote the words "His only books are woman's looks!" but I checked myself just in time—with something of the feeling of one who has crossed a street, and has been all but run over by a passing "Hansom".

"—and I think he has too lonely a life," she went on, with a gentle earnestness that left no room whatever to suspect a double meaning. '*Do* get him to come! And don't forget the day, Tuesday week. We can drive you over. It would be a pity to go by rail—there is so much pretty scenery on the road. And our open carriage just holds four."

"Oh, *I'll* persuade him to come!" I said with confidence—thinking "it would take all *my* powers of persuasion to keep him away!"

The Picnic was to take place in ten days: and though Arthur readily accepted the invitation I brought him, nothing that I could say would induce him to call—either with me or without me—on the Earl and his daughter in the meanwhile. No: he feared to "wear out his welcome", and, when at last the day for the expedition arrived, he was so childishly nervous and uneasy that I thought it best so to arrange our plans that we should go separately to the house—my intention being to arrive some time after him, so as to give him time to get over a meeting.

With this object I purposely made a considerable circuit on my way to the Hall (as we called the Earl's house): "and if I could only manage to lose my way a bit," I thought to myself, "that would suit me capitally!"

In this I succeeded better, and sooner, than I had ventured to hope for. The path through the wood had been made familiar to me, by many a solitary stroll, in my former visit to Elveston; and how I could have so suddenly and so entirely lost it—even though I *was* so engrossed in thinking of Arthur and his lady-love that I heeded little else—was a mystery to me. "And this open place," I said to myself, "seems to have some memory about it I cannot distinctly recall—surely it is the very spot where I saw those Fairy-Children! But I hope there are no snakes about!" I mused aloud, taking my seat on a fallen tree. "I certainly do *not* like snakes—and I don't suppose *Bruno* likes them, either!"

"No, he *doesn't* like them!" said a demure little voice at my side. "He's not *afraid* of them, you know. But he doesn't *like* them. He says they're too waggly!"

Words fail me to describe the beauty of the little group—couched on a patch of moss, on the trunk of the fallen tree, that met my eager gaze: Sylvie reclining with her elbow buried in the moss, and her rosy cheek resting in the palm of her hand, and Bruno stretched at her feet with his head in her lap.

"Too waggly?" was all I could say in so sudden an emergency.

"I'm not particular," Bruno said carelessly: "but I *do* like straight animals best——"

"But you like a dog when it wags its tail," Sylvie interrupted. "You *know* you do, Bruno!"

"But there's more of a dog, isn't there, Mister Sir?" Bruno appealed to me. "*You* wouldn't like to have a dog if it hadn't got nuffin but a head and a tail?"

I admitted that a dog of that kind would be uninteresting.

"There *isn't* such a dog as that," Sylvie thoughtfully remarked.

"But there *would* be," cried Bruno, "if the Professor shortened it up for us!"

"Shortened it up?" I said. "That's something new. How does he do it?"

"He's got a curious machine——" Sylvie was beginning to explain.

"A *welly* curious machine," Bruno broke in, not at all willing to have the story thus taken out of his mouth, "and if oo puts in—somefinoruvver—at *one* end, oo know—and he turns the handle—and it comes out at the uvver end, oh, ever so short!"

"As short as short!" Sylvie echoed.

"And one day—when we was in Outland, oo know—before we came to Fairlyland—me and Sylvie took him a big Crocodile. And he shortened it up for us. And it *did* look so funny! And it kept looking round, and saying 'wherever *is* the rest of me got to?' And then its eyes looked unhappy—"

"Not *both* its eyes," Sylvie interrupted.

"Course not!" said the little fellow. "Only the eye that *couldn't* see wherever the rest of it had got to. But the eye that *could* see wherever——"

"How short *was* the Crocodile?" I asked, as the story was getting a little complicated.

"Half as short again as when we caught it—*so* long," said Bruno, spreading out his arms to their full stretch.

I tried to calculate what this would come to, but it was too hard for me. Please make it out for me, dear Child who reads this!

"But you didn't leave the poor thing so short as that, did you?"

"Well, no. Sylvie and me took it back again and we got it stretched to—to—how much was it, Sylvie?"

"Two times and a half, and a little bit more," said Sylvie.

"It wouldn't like that better than the other way, I'm afraid?"

"Oh, but it did though!" Bruno put in eagerly. "It *were* proud of its new tail! Oo never saw a Crocodile so proud! Why it could go round and walk on the top of its tail, and along its back, all the way to its head!"

"Not *quite* all the way," said Sylvie. "It couldn't, you know."

"Ah, but it *did*, once!" Bruno cried triumphantly. "Oo weren't looking—but *I* watched it. And it walked on tipplety-toe, so as it wouldn't wake itself, 'cause it thought it were asleep. And it got both its paws on its tail. And it walked and it walked all the way along its back. And it walked and it walked on its forehead. And it walked a tiny little way down its nose! There now!"

This was a good deal worse than the last puzzle. Please, dear Child, help again!

"I don't believe no Crocodile never walked along its own forehead!" Sylvie cried, too much excited by the controversy to limit the number of her negatives.

"Oo don't know the *reason* why it did it!" Bruno scornfully retorted. "It had a welly good reason. I *heard* it say 'Why *shouldn't* I walk on my own forehead?' So a course it *did*, oo know!"

"If *that's* a good reason, Bruno," I said, "why shouldn't *you* get up that tree?"

"*Shall*, in a minute," said Bruno: "soon as we've done talking. Only two peoples *ca'n't* talk comfably togevver, when one's getting up a tree, and the other isn't!"

It appeared to me that a conversation would scarcely be "comfable" while trees were being climbed, even if *both* the "peoples" were doing it:

but it was evidently dangerous to oppose any theory of Bruno's; so I thought it best to let the question drop, and to ask for an account of the machine that made things *longer*.

This time Bruno was at a loss, and left it to Sylvie. "It's like a mangle," she said: "if things are put in, they get squoze———"

"Squeezeled!" Bruno interrupted.

"Yes," Sylvie accepted the correction, but did not attempt to pronounce the word, which was evidently new to her. "They get—like that—and they come out, oh, ever so long!"

"Once," Bruno began again, "Sylvie and me writed———"

"Wrote!" Sylvie whispered.

"Well, we *wroted* a Nursery-Song, and the Professor mangled it longer for us. It were '*There was a little Man, And he had a little gun, And the bullets———*' "

"I know the rest," I interrupted. "But would you say it *long*—I mean the way that it came out of the mangle?"

"We'll get the Professor to *sing* it for you," said Sylvie. "It would spoil it to *say* it."

"I would like to meet the Professor," I said. "And I would like to take you all with me, to see some friends of mine, that live near here. Would you like to come?"

"I don't think the *Professor* would like to come," said Sylvie. "He's *very* shy. But *we'd* like it very much. Only we'd better not come *this* size, you know."

The difficulty had occurred to me already: and I had felt that perhaps there *would* be a slight awkwardness in introducing two such tiny friends into Society. "What size will you be?" I enquired.

"We'd better come as—common *children*," Sylvie thoughtfully replied. "That's the easiest size to manage."

"Could you come to-day?" I said, thinking "then we could have you at the Picnic!"

Sylvie considered a little. "Not *to-day*," she replied. "We haven't got the things ready. We'll come on—Tuesday next, if you like. And now, *really*, Bruno, you must come and do your lessons."

"I *wiss* oo wouldn't say '*really* Bruno!' " the little fellow pleaded, with pouting lips that made him look prettier than ever. "It *always* shows there's something horrid coming! And I wo'n't kiss you, if you're so unkind."

"Ah, but you *have* kissed me!" Sylvie exclaimed in merry triumph.

"Well then, I'll *un*kiss you!" And he threw his arms round her neck for this novel, but apparently not *very* painful, operation.

"It's *very* like *kissing*!" Sylvie remarked, as soon as her lips were again free for speech.

"Oo don't know *nuffin* about it! It were just the *conkery*!" Bruno replied with much severity, as he marched away.

Sylvie turned her laughing face to me. "Shall we come on Tuesday?" she said.

"Very well," I said: "let it be Tuesday next. But where *is* the Professor? Did he come with you to Fairyland?"

"No," said Sylvie. "But he promised he'd come and see us, *some* day. He's getting his Lecture ready. So he has to stay at home."

"At home?" I said dreamily, not feeling quite sure what she had said.

"Yes, Sir. His Lordship and Lady Muriel *are* at home. Please to walk this way."

CHAPTER 17

The Three Badgers

STILL more dreamily I found myself following this imperious voice into a room where the Earl, his daughter, and Arthur, were seated. "So you're come *at last!*" said Lady Muriel, in a tone of playful reproach.

"I was delayed," I stammered. Though *what* it was that had delayed me I should have been puzzled to explain! Luckily no questions were asked.

The carriage was ordered round, the hamper, containing our contribution to the Picnic, was duly stowed away, and we set forth.

There was no need for *me* to maintain the conversation. Lady Muriel and Arthur were evidently on those most delightful of terms, where one has no need to check thought after thought, as it rises to the lips, with the fear "*this* will not be appreciated—*this* will give offence—*this* will sound too serious—this will sound flippant": like very old friends, in fullest sympathy, their talk rippled on.

"Why shouldn't we desert the Picnic and go in some other direction?" she suddenly suggested. "A party of four is surely self-sufficing? And as for *food*, our hamper——"

"Why *shouldn't* we? What a genuine *lady's* argument!" laughed Arthur. "A lady never knows on which side the *onus probandi*—the burden of proving—lies!"

"Do *men* always know?" she asked with a pretty assumption of meek docility.

"With *one* exception—the only one I can think of—Dr. Watts, who has asked the senseless question

> 'Why should I deprive my neighbour
> Of his goods against his will?'

Fancy *that* as an argument for Honesty! His position seems to be 'I'm only honest because I see no reason to steal.' And the *thief's* answer is of course complete and crushing. 'I deprive my neighbour of his goods because I want them myself. And I do it against his will because there's no chance of getting him to consent to it!' "

"I can give you one other exception," I said: "an argument I heard only to-day—and *not* by a lady. 'Why shouldn't I walk on my own forehead?' "

"What a curious subject for speculation!" said Lady Muriel, turning to me, with eyes brimming over with laughter. "May we know who propounded the question? And *did* he walk on his own forehead?"

"I ca'n't remember *who* it was said it!" I faltered. "Nor *where* I heard it!"

"Whoever it was, I hope we shall meet him at the Picnic!" said Lady Muriel. "It's a *far* more interesting question than '*Isn't* this a picturesque ruin?' '*Aren't* those autumn-tints lovely?' I shall have to answer those two questions *ten* times, at least, this afternoon!"

"That's one of the miseries of Society!" said Arthur. "Why ca'n't people let one enjoy the beauties of Nature without having to *say* so every minute? Why should Life be one long Catechism?"

"It's just as bad at a picture-gallery," the Earl remarked. "I went to the R.A. last May, with a conceited young artist: and he *did* torment me! I wouldn't have minded his criticizing the pictures *himself*: but *I* had to agree with him—or else to argue the point, which would have been worse!"

"It was *depreciatory* criticism, of course?" said Arthur.

"I don't see the 'of course' at all."

"Why, did you ever know a conceited man dare to *praise* a picture? The one thing he dreads (next to not being noticed) is *to be proved fallible!* If you once *praise* a picture, your character for *infallibility* hangs by a thread. Suppose it's a figure-picture, and you venture to say 'draws well'. Somebody measures it, and finds one of the proportions an eighth of an inch wrong. *You* are disposed of as a critic! 'Did you say he draws *well?*' your friends enquire sarcastically, while you hang your head and blush. No. The only *safe* course, if any one says 'draws well', is to shrug your shoulders. '*Draws* well?' you repeat thoughtfully. 'Draws *well?* Humph!' That's the way to become a great critic!"

Thus airily chatting, after a pleasant drive through a few miles of beautiful scenery, we reached the *rendezvous*—a ruined castle—where the rest of the picnic-party were already assembled. We spent an hour or two in sauntering about the ruins: gathering at last, by common consent, into a few random groups, seated on the side of a mound, which commanded a good view of the old castle and its surroundings.

The momentary silence, that ensued, was promptly taken possession of—or, more correctly, taken into custody—by a Voice; a voice so smooth, so monotonous, so sonorous, that one felt, with a shudder, that any other conversation was precluded, and that, unless some desperate remedy were adopted, we were fated to listen to a Lecture, of which no man could foresee the end!

The Speaker was a broadly-built man, whose large, flat, pale face was bounded on the North by a fringe of hair, on the East and West by a fringe of whisker, and on the South by a fringe of beard—the whole constituting a uniform halo of stubbly whitey-brown bristles. His features were so entirely destitute of expression that I could not help saying to myself—helplessly, as if in the clutches of a night-mare—"they are only penciled in: no final touches as yet!" And he had a way of ending every sentence with a sudden smile, which spread like a ripple over that vast blank surface, and was gone in a moment, leaving behind it such absolute solemnity that I felt impelled to murmur "it was not *he*: it was somebody else that smiled!"

"Do you observe?" (such was the phrase with which the wretch began each sentence) "Do you observe the way in which that broken arch, at the very top of the ruin, stands out against the clear sky? It is placed *exactly* right: and there is *exactly* enough of it. A little more, or a little less, and all would be utterly spoiled!"

"Oh gifted architect!" murmured Arthur, inaudibly to all but Lady Muriel and myself. "Foreseeing the exact effect his work would have, when in ruins, centuries after his death!"

"And do you observe, where those trees slope down the hill," (indicating them with a sweep of the hand, and with all the patronising air of the man who has himself arranged the landscape), "how the mists rising from the river fill up *exactly* those intervals where we *need* indistinctness, for artistic effect? Here, in the foreground, a few clear touches are not amiss: but a *back*-ground without mist, you know! It is simply barbarous! Yes, we *need* indistinctness!"

The orator looked so pointedly at *me* as he uttered these words, that I felt bound to reply, by murmuring something to the effect that I hardly felt the need *myself*—and that I enjoyed looking at a thing, better, when I could *see* it.

"Quite so!" the great man sharply took me up. "From *your* point of view, that is correctly put. But for any one who has a soul for *Art*, such a view is preposterous. *Nature* is one thing. *Art* is another. *Nature* shows us the world as it is. But *Art*—as a Latin author tells us—*Art*, you know—the words have escaped my memory——"

"*Ars est celare Naturam*," Arthur interposed with a delightful promptitude.

"Quite so!" the orator replied with an air of relief. "I thank you! *Ars est celare Naturam*—but that isn't it." And, for a few peaceful moments, the orator brooded, frowningly, over the quotation. The welcome opportunity was seized, and *another* voice struck into the silence.

"What a *lovely* old ruin it is!" cried a young lady in spectacles, the very embodiment of the March of Mind, looking at Lady Muriel, as the proper recipient of all really *original* remarks. "And *don't* you admire those autumn-tints on the trees? *I* do, *intensely!*"

Lady Muriel shot a meaning glance at me; but replied with admirable gravity. "Oh yes indeed, indeed! *So* true!"

"And isn't it strange", said the young lady, passing with startling suddenness from Sentiment to Science, "that the mere impact of certain coloured rays upon the Retina should give us such exquisite pleasure?"

"You have studied Physiology, then?" a certain young Doctor courteously enquired.

"Oh, *yes*! Isn't it a *sweet* Science?"

Arthur slightly smiled. "It seems a paradox, does it not," he went on, "that the image formed on the Retina should be inverted?"

"It *is* puzzling," she candidly admitted. "Why is it we do not *see* things upside-down?"

"You have never heard the Theory, then, that the *Brain* also is inverted?"

"No *indeed*! What a *beautiful* fact! But how is it *proved?*"

"*Thus*," replied Arthur, with all the gravity of ten Professors rolled into one. "What we call the *vertex* of the Brain is really its *base*: and what we call its *base* is really its *vertex*: it is simply a question of *nomenclature*."

This last polysyllable settled the matter. "How truly delightful!" the fair Scientist exclaimed with enthusiasm. "I shall ask our Physiological Lecturer why he never gave us that *exquisite* Theory!"

"I'd give something to be present when the question is asked!" Arthur whispered to me, as, at a signal from Lady Muriel, we moved on to where the hampers had been collected, and devoted ourselves to the more *substantial* business of the day.

We "waited" on ourselves, as the modern barbarism (combining two good things in such a way as to secure the discomforts of both and the advantages of neither) of having a picnic with servants to wait upon you, had not yet reached this out-of-the-way region—and of course the gentlemen did not even take their places until the ladies had been duly provided with all imaginable creature-comforts. Then I supplied myself with a plate of something solid and a glass of something fluid, and found a place next to Lady Muriel.

It had been left vacant—apparently, for Arthur, as a distinguished stranger: but he had turned shy, and had placed himself next to the young lady in spectacles, whose high rasping voice had already cast loose upon Society such ominous phrases as "Man is a bundle of Qualities!", "the Objective is only attainable through the Subjective!". Arthur was bearing it bravely: but several faces wore a look of alarm, and I thought it high time to start some less metaphysical topic.

"In my nursery days," I began, "when the weather didn't suit for an out-of-doors picnic, we were allowed to have a peculiar kind, that we enjoyed hugely. The table cloth was laid *under* the table, instead of upon it: we sat round it on the floor: and I believe we really enjoyed that extremely uncomfortable kind of dinner more than we ever did the orthodox arrangement!"

"I've no doubt of it," Lady Muriel replied. "There's nothing a well-regulated child hates so much as regularity. I believe a really healthy boy would thoroughly enjoy Greek Grammar—if only he might stand on his head to learn it! And your carpet-dinner certainly spared you *one* feature of a picnic, which is to me its chief drawback."

"The chance of a shower?" I suggested.

"No, the chance—or rather the certainty—of *live* things occurring in combination with one's food! *Spiders* are *my* bugbear. Now my father has *no* sympathy with that sentiment—*have* you, dear?" For the Earl had caught the word and turned to listen.

"To each his sufferings, all are men," he replied in the sweet sad tones that seemed natural to him: "each has his pet aversion."

"But you'll never guess *his*!" Lady Muriel said, with that delicate silvery laugh that was music to my ears.

I declined to attempt the impossible.

"He doesn't like *snakes*!" she said, in a stage whisper. "Now, isn't *that* an unreasonable aversion? Fancy not liking such a dear, coaxingly, *clingingly* affectionate creature as a snake!"

"Not like *snakes*!" I exclaimed. "Is such a thing possible?"

"No, he *doesn't* like them," she repeated with a pretty mock-gravity.

"He's not *afraid* of them, you know. But he doesn't *like* them. He says they're too waggly!"

I was more startled than I liked to show. There was something so *uncanny* in this echo of the very words I had so lately heard from that little forest-sprite, that it was only by a great effort I succeeded in saying, carelessly, "Let us banish so unpleasant a topic. Wo'n't you sing us something, Lady Muriel? I know you *do* sing without music."

"The only songs I know—without music—are *desperately* sentimental, I'm afraid! Are your tears all ready?"

"Quite ready! Quite ready!" came from all sides, and Lady Muriel—not being one of those lady-singers who thing it *de rigueur* to decline to sing till they have been petitioned three or four times, and have pleaded failure of memory, loss of voice, and other conclusive reasons for silence—began at once:

> *"There be three Badgers on a mossy stone,*
> *Beside a dark and covered way:*
> *Each dreams himself a monarch on his throne,*
> *And so they stay and stay—*
> *Though their old Father languishes alone,*
> *They stay, and stay, and stay.*

"There be three Herrings loitering around,
 Longing to share that mossy seat:
Each Herring tries to sing what she has found
 That makes Life seem so sweet.
Thus, with a grating and uncertain sound,
 They bleat, and bleat, and bleat.

"The Mother-Herring, on the salt sea-wave,
 Sought vainly for her absent ones:
The Father-Badger, writhing in a cave,
 Shrieked out 'Return, my sons!
You shall have buns', he shrieked, 'if you'll behave!
 Yea, buns, and buns, and buns!'

" 'I fear', said she, 'your sons have gone astray?
 My daughters left me while I slept.'
'Yes'm,' the Badger said: 'it's as you say.'
 'They should be better kept.'
Thus the poor parents talked the time away,
 And wept, and wept, and wept."

Here Bruno broke off suddenly. "The Herrings' Song wants anuvver tune, Sylvie," he said. "And I ca'n't sing it—not wizout oo plays it for me!"

Instantly Sylvie seated herself upon a tiny mushroom, that happened to grow in front of a daisy, as if it were the most ordinary musical instrument in the world, and played on the petals as if they were the notes of an organ. And such delicious *tiny* music it was! Such teeny-tiny music!

Bruno held his head on one side, and listened very gravely for a few moments until he had caught the melody. Then the sweet childish voice rang out once more:

> *"Oh, dear beyond our dearest dreams,*
> *Fairer than all that fairest seems!*
> *To feast the rosy hours away,*
> *To revel in a roundelay!*
> *How blest would be*
> *A life so free—*
> *Ipwergis-Pudding to consume,*
> *And drink the subtle Azzigoom!*
>
> *"And if, in other days and hours,*
> *Mid other fluffs and other flowers,*
> *The choice were given me how to dine—*
> *'Name what thou wilt: it shall be thine!'*
> *Oh, then I see*
> *The life for me—*
> *Ipwergis-Pudding to consume,*
> *And drink the subtle Azzigoom!"*

"Oo may leave off playing *now*, Sylvie. I can do the uvver tune much better wizout a compliment."

"He means 'without *accompaniment*,'" Sylvie whispered, smiling at my puzzled look: and she pretended to shut up the stops of the organ.

> *"The Badgers did not care to talk to Fish:*
> *They did not dote on Herrings' songs:*
> *They never had experienced the dish*
> *To which that name belongs:*
> *'And, oh, to pinch their tails', (this was their wish),*
> *'With tongs, yea, tongs, and tongs!'"*

I ought to mention that he marked the parenthesis, in the air, with his finger. It seemed to me a very good plan. You know there's no *sound* to represent it—any more than there is for a question.

'Those aged ones waxed gay'

Suppose you have said to your friend "You are better to-day," and that you want him to understand that you are asking him a *question*, what can be simpler than just to make a "?" in the air with your finger? He would understand you in a moment!

> " *'And are not these the Fish,' the Eldest sighed.*
> *'Whose Mother dwells beneath the foam?'*
> *'They are the Fish!' the Second one replied.*
> *'And they have left their home!'*
> *'Oh wicked Fish,' the Youngest Badger cried,*
> *'To roam, yeah, roam, and roam!'*

> "*Gently the Badgers trotted to the shore—*
> *The sandy shore that fringed the bay:*
> *Each in his mouth a living Herring bore—*
> *Those aged ones waxed gay:*
> *Clear rang their voices through the ocean's roar,*
> *'Hooray, hooray, hooray!'* "

"So they all got safe home again," Bruno said, after waiting a minute to see if *I* had anything to say: he evidently felt that *some* remark ought to be made. And I couldn't help wishing there were some such rule in Society, at the conclusion of a song—that the singer *herself* should say the right thing, and not leave it to the audience. Suppose a young lady has just been warbling ("with a grating and uncertain sound") Shelly's exquisite lyric "*I arise from dreams of thee*": how much nicer it would be, instead of *your* having to say "Oh, *thank* you, *thank* you!" for the young lady herself to remark, as she draws on her gloves, while the impassioned words "*Oh, press it to thine own, or it will break at last!*" are still ringing in your ears, "—but she wouldn't do it, you know. So it *did* break at last."

"And I *knew* it would!" she added quietly, as I started at the sudden crash of broken glass. "You've been holding it sideways for the last minute, and letting all the champagne run out! Were you asleep, I wonder? I'm *so* sorry my singing has such a narcotic effect!"

CHAPTER 18

Queer Street, Number Forty

LADY MURIEL was the speaker. And, for the moment, that was the only fact I could clearly realize. But how she came to be there—and how *I* came to be there—and how the glass of champagne came to be there—all these were questions which I felt it better to think out in silence, and not commit myself to any statement till I understood things a little more clearly.

"First accumulate a mass of Facts: and *then* construct a Theory." *That*, I believe, is the true Scientic Method. I sat up, rubbed my eyes, and began to accumulate Facts.

A smooth grassy slope, bounded, at the upper end, by venerable ruins half buried in ivy, at the lower, by a stream seen through arching trees—a dozen gaily-dressed people, seated in little groups here and there—some open hampers—the *débris* of a picnic—such were the *Facts* accumulated by the Scientific Researcher. And now, what deep, far-reaching *Theory* was he to construct from them? The Researcher found himself at fault. Yet stay! One Fact had escaped his notice. While all the rest were grouped in twos and in threes, *Arthur* was alone: while all tongues were talking, *his* was silent: while all faces were gay, *his* was gloomy and despondent. Here was a *Fact* indeed! The Researcher felt that a *Theory* must be constructed without delay.

Lady Muriel had just risen and left the party. Could *that* be the cause of his despondency? The Theory hardly rose to the dignity of a Working Hypothesis. Clearly more Facts were needed.

The Researcher looked round him once more: and now the Facts accumulated in such bewildering profusion, that the Theory was lost among them. For Lady Muriel had gone to meet a strange gentleman, just visible in the distance: and now she was returning with him, both of them talking eagerly and joyfully, like old friends who have been long parted: and now she was moving from group to group, introducing the new hero of the hour: and he, young, tall, and handsome, moved gracefully at her side, with the erect bearing and firm tread of a soldier. Verily, the Theory looked gloomy for Arthur! His eye caught mine, and he crossed to me.

"He is very handsome," I said.

"Abominably handsome!" muttered Arthur: then smiled at his own bitter words. "Lucky no one heard me but you!"

"Doctor Forester," said Lady Muriel, who had just joined us, "let me introduce to you my cousin Eric Lindon—*Captain* Lindon, I should say."

Arthur shook off his ill-temper instantly and completely, as he rose and gave the young soldier his hand. "I have heard of you," he said. "I'm very glad to make the acquaintance of Lady Muriel's cousin."

"Yes, that's all I'm dinstinguished for, *as yet!*" said Eric (so we soon got to call him) with a winning smile. "And I doubt", glancing at Lady Muriel, "if it even amounts to a good-conduct-badge! But it's something to begin with."

"You must come to my father, Eric," said Lady Muriel. "I think he's wandering among the ruins." And the pair moved on.

The gloomy look returned to Arthur's face: and I could see it was only to distract his thoughts that he took his place at the side of the metaphysical young lady, and resumed their interrupted discussion.

"Talking of Herbert Spencer," he began, "do you really find no *logical* difficulty in regarding Nature as a process of involution, passing from definite coherent homogeneity to indefinite incoherent heterogeneity?"

Amused as I was at the ingenious jumble he had made of Spencer's words, I kept as grave a face as I could.

"No *physical* difficulty," she confidently replied: "but I haven't studied *Logic* much. Would you *state* the difficulty?"

"Well," said Arthur, "do you accept it as self-evident? Is it as obvious, for instance, as that 'things that are greater than the same are greater than one another'?"

"To *my* mind," she modestly replied, "it seems *quite* as obvious. I grasp *both* truths by intuition. But *other* minds may need some logical—I forget the technical terms."

"For a *complete* logical argument", Arthur began with admirable solemnity, "we need two prim Misses——"

"Of course!" she interrupted. "I remember that word now. And they produce——?"

"A Delusion," said Arthur.

"Ye—es?" she said dubiously. "I don't seem to remember that so well. But what is the *whole* argument called?"

"A Sillygism."

"Ah, yes! I remember now. But I don't need a Sillygism, you know, to prove that mathematical axiom you mentioned."

"Nor to prove that 'all angles are equal', I suppose?"

"Why, of course not! One takes such a simple truth as that for granted!"

Here I ventured to interpose, and to offer her a plate of strawberries and cream. I felt really uneasy at the thought that she *might* detect the trick: and I contrived, unperceived by her, to shake my head reprovingly at the pseudo-philosopher. Equally unperceived by her, Arthur slightly raised his shoulders, and spread his hands abroad, as who should say "What else can I say to her?" and moved away leaving her to discuss her strawberries by "involution", or any other way she preferred.

By this time the carriages, that were to convey the revelers to their respective homes, had begun to assemble outside the Castle-grounds: and it became evident—now that Lady Muriel's cousin had joined our party—that the problem, how to convey five people to Elveston, with a carriage that would only hold four, must somehow be solved.

The Honourable Eric Lindon, who was at this moment walking up and down with Lady Muriel, might have solved it at once, no doubt, by announcing his intention of returning on foot. Of *this* solution there did not seem to be the very smallest probability.

The next best solution, it seemed to me, was that *I* should walk home: and this I at once proposed.

"You're sure you don't mind?" said the Earl. "I'm afraid the carriage wo'n't take us all, and I don't like to suggest to Eric to desert his cousin so soon."

"So far from minding it," I said, "I should prefer it. It will give me time to sketch this beautiful old ruin."

"I'll keep you company," Arthur suddenly said. And, in answer to what I suppose was a look of surprise on my face, he said in a low voice, "I *really* would rather. I shall be quite *de trop* in the carriage!"

"I think I'll walk too," said the Earl. "You'll have to be content with *Eric* as your escort," he added, to Lady Muriel, who had joined us while he was speaking.

"You must be as entertaining as Cerberus—'three gentlemen rolled into one'—" Lady Muriel said to her companion. "It will be a grand military exploit!"

"A sort of Forlorn Hope?" the Captain modestly suggested.

"You *do* pay pretty compliments!" laughed his fair cousin. "Good day to you, gentlemen three—or rather deserters three!" And the two young folk entered the carriage and were driven away.

"How long will your sketch take?" said Arthur.

"Well," I said, "I should like an hour for it. Don't you think you had better go without me? I'll return by train. I know there's one in about an hour's time."

"Perhaps that *would* be best," said the Earl. "The Station is quite close."

So I was left to my own devices, and soon found a comfortable seat, at the foot of a tree, from which I had a good view of the ruins.

"It is a very drowsy day," I said to myself, idly turning over the leaves of the sketch-book to find a blank page. "Why, I thought you were a mile off by this time!" For, to my surprise, the two walkers were back again.

"I came back to remind you", Arthur said, "that the trains go every ten minutes——"

"Nonsense!" I said. "It isn't the Metropolitan Railway!"

"It *is* the Metropolitan Railway," the Earl insisted. "This is a part of Kensington."

"Why do you talk with your eyes shut?" said Arthur. "Wake up!"

"I think it's the heat that makes me so drowsy," I said, hoping, but not feeling quite sure, that I was talking sense. "Am I awake now?"

"I think *not*," the Earl judicially pronounced. "What do *you* think, Doctor? He's only got one eye open!"

"And he's snoring like anything!" cried Bruno. "Do wake up, you dear old thing!" And he and Sylvie set to work, rolling the heavy head from side to side, as if its connection with the shoulders was a matter of no sort of importance.

And at last the Professor opened his eyes, and sat up, blinking at us with eyes of utter bewilderment. "Would you have the kindness to mention", he said, addressing me with his usual old-fashioned courtesy, "whereabouts we are just now—and *who* we are, beginning with me?"

I thought it best to begin with the children. "This is Sylvie, Sir; and *this* is Bruno."

"Ah, yes! I know *them* well enough!" the old man murmured. "It's *myself* I'm most anxious about. And perhaps you'll be good enough to mention, at the same time, how I got here?"

"A harder problem occurs to *me*," I ventured to say: "and that is, how you're to get back again."

"True, true!" the Professor replied. "That's *the* Problem, no doubt.

Viewed as a Problem, outside of oneself, it is a *most* interesting one. Viewed as a portion of one's own biography, it is, I must admit, very distressing!" He groaned, but instantly added, with a chuckle, "As to *myself*, I think you mentioned that I am———"

"Oo're the *Professor*!" Bruno shouted in his ear. "Didn't oo know *that*? Oo've come from *Outland*! And it's *ever* so far away from here!"

The Professor leapt to his feet with the agility of a boy. "Then there's no time to lose!" he exclaimed anxiously. "I'll just ask this guileless peasant, with his brace of buckets that contain (apparently) water, if he'll be so kind as to direct us. Guileless peasant!" he proceeded in a louder voice. "Would you tell us the way to Outland?"

The guileless peasant turned with a sheepish grin. "Hey?" was all he said.

"The—way—to—Outland!" the Professor repeated.

The guileless peasant set down his buckets and considered. "Ah, dunnot———"

"I ought to mention," the Professor hastily put in, "that whatever you say will be used in evidence against you."

The guileless peasant instantly resumed his buckets. "Then ah says nowt!" he answered briskly, and walked away at a great pace.

The children gazed sadly at the rapidly vanishing figure. "He goes very quick!" the Professor said with a sigh. "But I *know* that was the right thing to say. I've studied your English Laws. However, let's ask this next man that's coming. He is *not* guileless, and he is *not* a peasant—but I don't know that either point is of vital importance."

It was, in fact, the Honourable Eric Lindon, who had apparently fulfilled his task of escorting Lady Muriel home, and was now strolling leisurely up and down the road outside the house, enjoying a solitary cigar.

"Might I trouble you, Sir, to tell us the nearest way to Outland!" Oddity as he was, in outward appearance, the Professor was, in that essential nature which no outward disguise could conceal, a thorough gentleman.

And, as such, Eric Lindon accepted him instantly. He took the cigar from his mouth, and delicately shook off the ash, while he considered. "The name sounds strange to me," he said. "I doubt if I can help you."

"It is not *very* far from *Fairyland*," the Professor suggested.

Eric Lindon's eye-brows were slightly raised at these words, and an amused smile, which he courteously tried to repress, flitted across his handsome face. "A trifle *cracked*!" he muttered to himself. "But what a jolly old patriarch it is!" Then he turned to the children. "And ca'n't *you* help him, little folk?" he said, with a gentleness of tone that seemed to win their hearts at once. "Surely *you* know all about it?

> *'How many miles to Babylon?*
> *Three-score miles and ten.*
> *Can I get there by candlelight?*
> *Yes, and back again!'* "

To my surprise, Bruno ran forwards to him, as if he were some old friend of theirs, seized the disengaged hand and hung on to it with both of his own: and there stood this tall dignified officer in the middle of the road, gravely swinging a little boy to and fro, while Sylvie stood ready to push him, exactly as if a real swing had suddenly been provided for their pastime.

"We don't want to get to *Babylon*, oo know!" Bruno explained as he swung.

"And it isn't *candlelight*: it's *daylight!*" Sylvie added, giving the swing a push of extra vigour, which nearly took the whole machine off its balance.

By this time it was clear to me that Eric Lindon was quite unconscious of my presence. Even the Professor and the children seemed to have lost sight of me: and I stood in the midst of the group, as unconcernedly as a ghost, seeing but unseen.

"How perfectly isochronous!" the Professor exclaimed with enthusiasm. He had his watch in his hand, and was carefully counting Bruno's oscillations. "He measures time quite as accurately as a pendulum!"

"Yet even pendulums," the good-natured young soldier observed, as he carefully released his hand from Bruno's grasp, "are not a joy *for ever!* Come, that's enough for one bout, little man! Next time we meet, you shall have another. Meanwhile you'd better take this old gentleman to Queer Street, Number——"

"*We'll* find it!" cried Bruno eagerly, as they dragged the Professor away.

"We are much indebted to you!" the Professor said, looking over his shoulder.

"Don't mention it!" replied the officer, raising his hat as a parting salute.

"*What* number did you say!" the Professor called from the distance.

The officer made a trumpet of his two hands. "Forty!" he shouted in stentorian tones. "And not *piano*, by any means!" he added to himself. "It's a mad world, my masters, a mad world!" He lit another cigar, and strolled on towards his hotel.

"What a lovely evening!" I said, joining him as he passed me.

"Lovely indeed," he said. "Where did *you* come from? Dropped from the clouds?"

"I'm strolling your way," I said: and no further explanation seemed necessary.

"Have a cigar?"

"Thanks: I'm not a smoker."

"Is there a Lunatic Asylum near here?"

"Not that I know of."

"Thought there might be. Met a lunatic just now. Queer old fish as ever I saw!"

And so, in friendly chat, we took our homeward ways, and wished each other "good-night" at the door of his hotel.

Left to myself, I felt the "eerie" feeling rush over me again, and saw, standing at the door of Number Forty, and three figures I knew so well.

"Then it's the wrong house?" Bruno was saying.

"No, no! It's the right *house*," the Professor cheerfully replied: "but it's the wrong *street. That's* where we've made our mistake! Our best plan, now will be to——"

It was over. The street was empty. Commonplace life was around me, and the "eerie" feeling had fled.

CHAPTER 19

How to Make a Phlizz

THE week passed without any further communication with the "Hall", as Arthur was evidently fearful that we might "wear out our welcome"; but when, on Sunday morning, we were setting out for church, I gladly agreed to his proposal to go round and enquire after the Earl, who was said to be unwell.

Eric, who was strolling in the garden, gave us a good report of the invalid, who was still in bed, with Lady Muriel in attendance.

"Are you coming with us to church?" I enquired.

"Thanks, no," he courteously replied. "It's not—exactly in my line, you know. It's an excellent institution—for the *poor*. When I'm with my own folk, I go, just to set them an example. But I'm not known *here:* so I think I'll excuse myself sitting out a sermon. Country-preachers are always so dull!"

Arthur was silent till we were out of hearing. Then he said to himself, almost inaudibly, "*Where two or three are gathered together in my name, there am I in the midst of them.*"

"Yes," I assented: "no doubt that *is* the principle on which church-going rests."

"And when he *does* go," he continued (our thoughts ran so much together, that our conversation was often slightly elliptical), "I suppose he repeats the words '*I believe in the Communion of Saints*'?"

But by this time we had reached the little church, into which a goodly stream of worshippers, consisting mainly of fishermen and their families, was flowing.

The service would have been pronounced by any modern æsthetic religionist—or religious æsthete, which is it?—to be crude and cold: to me, coming fresh from the ever-advancing developments of a London church under a *soi-disant* "Catholic" Rector, it was unspeakably refreshing.

There was no theatrical procession of demure little choristers, trying their best not to simper under the admiring gaze of the congregation: the people's share in the service was taken by the people themselves, unaided, except that a few good voices, judiciously posted here and there among them, kept the singing from going too far astray.

There was no murdering of the noble music, contained in the Bible and the Liturgy, by its recital in a dead monotone, with no more expression than a mechanical talking-doll.

No, the prayers were *prayed*, the lessons were *read*, and—best of all—the sermon was *talked*; and I found myself repeating, as we left the church, the words of Jacob, when he *"awaked out of his sleep". " 'Surely the Lord is in this place! This is none other but the house of God, and 'this is the gate of heaven.' "*

"Yes," said Arthur, apparently in answer to my thoughts, "those 'high' services are fast becoming pure Formalism. More and more the people are beginning to regard them as 'performances', in which they only 'assist' in the French sense. And it is *specially* bad for the little boys. They'd be much less self-conscious as pantomime-fairies. With all that dressing-up, and stagy-entrances and exits, and being always *en evidence*, no wonder if they're eaten up with vanity, the blatant little coxcombs!"

When we passed the Hall on our return, we found the Earl and Lady Muriel sitting out in the garden. Eric had gone for a stroll.

We joined them, and the conversation soon turned on the sermon we had just heard, the subject of which was "selfishness'.

"What a change has come over our pulpits", Arthur remarked, "since the time when Paley gave that utterly selfish definition of virtue, '*the doing good to mankind, in obedience to the will of God, and for the sake of everlasting happiness*'!"

Lady Muriel looked at him enquiringly, but she seemed to have learned by intuition, what years of experience had taught *me*, that the way to elicit Arthur's deepest thoughts was neither to assent nor dissent, but simply to *listen*.

"At that time," he went on, "a great tidal wave of selfishness was sweeping over human thought. Right and Wrong had somehow been transformed into Gain and Loss, and Religion had become a sort of commercial transaction. We may be thankful that our preachers are beginning to take a nobler view of life."

"But is it not taught again and again in the *Bible?*" I ventured to ask.

"Not in the Bible, as a *whole*," said Arthur. "In the Old Testament, no doubt, rewards and punishments are constantly appealed to as motives for action. That teaching is best for *children*, and the Israelites seem to have been, mentally, *utter* children. We guide our children thus, at first: but we appeal, as soon as possible, to their innate sense of Right and Wrong: and, when *that* stage is safely past, we appeal to the highest motive of all, the desire for likeness to, and union with, the Supreme Good. I think you will find that to be the teaching of the Bible, *as a whole*, beginning with *'that thy days may be long in the land'*, and ending with *'be ye perfect, even as your Father which is in heaven is perfect'*."

We were silent for awhile, and then Arthur went off on another tack. "Look at the literature of Hymns, now. How cankered it is, through and through, with selfishness! There are few human compositions more utterly degraded than some modern Hymns!"

I quoted the stanza.

> *"Whatever, Lord, we lend to Thee,*
> *Repaid a thousandfold shall be,*
> *Then gladly will we give to Thee,*
> *Giver of all!"*

"Yes," he said grimly: "that is the typical stanza. And the very last charity-sermon I heard was infected with it. After giving many good reasons for charity, the preacher wound up with 'and, for all you give, you will be repaid a thousandfold!' Oh, the utter meanness of such a motive, to be put before men who *do* know what self-sacrifice is, who *can* appreciate generosity and heroism! Talk of Original *Sin!*" he went on with increasing bitterness. "Can you have a stronger proof of the Original Goodness there must be in this nation, than the fact that Religion has been preached to us, as a commercial speculation, for a century, and that we still believe in a God?"

"It couldn't have gone on so long", Lady Muriel musingly remarked, "if the Opposition hadn't been practically silenced—put under what the French call *la clôture*. Surely in any lecture-hall, or in private society, such teaching would soon have been hooted down?"

"I trust so," said Arthur: "and, though I don't want to see 'brawling in church' legalized, I must say that our preachers enjoy an *enormous* privilege—which they ill deserve, and which they misuse terribly. We put our man into a pulpit, and we virtually tell him 'Now, you may stand there and talk to us for half-an-hour. We wo'n't interrupt you by so much as a *word!* You shall have it all your own way!' And what does he give us in return? Shallow twaddle, that, if it were addressed to you over a dinner-table, you would think 'Does the man take me for a *fool?*'"

The return of Eric from his walk checked the tide of Arthur's eloquence, and, after a few minutes' talk on more conventional topics, we took our leave. Lady Muriel walked with us to the gate. "You have given me much to think about," she said earnestly, as she gave Arthur her hand. "I'm so

glad you came in!" And her words brought a real glow of pleasure into that pale worn face of his.

On the Tuesday, as Arthur did not seem equal to more walking, I took a long stroll by myself, having stipulated that he was not to give the *whole* day to his books, but was to meet me at the Hall at about tea-time. On my way back, I passed the Station just as the afternoon-train came in sight, and sauntered down the stairs to see it come in. But there was little to gratify my idle curiosity: and, when the train was empty, and the platform clear, I found it was about time to be moving on, if I meant to reach the Hall by five.

As I approached the end of the platform, from which a steep irregular wooden staircase conducted to the upper world, I noticed two passengers, who had evidently arrived by the train, but who, oddly enough, had entirely escaped my notice, though the arrivals had been so few. They were a young woman and a little girl: the former, so far as one could judge by appearances, was a nursemaid, or possibly a nursery-governess, in attendance on the child, whose refined face, even more than her dress, distinguished her as of a higher class than her companion.

The child's face was refined, but it was also a worn and sad one, and told a tale (or so I seemed to read it) of much illness and suffering, sweetly and patiently borne. She had a little crutch to help herself along with: and she was now standing, looking wistfully up the long staircase, and apparently waiting till she could muster courage to begin the toilsome ascent.

There are some things one *says* in life—as well as things one *does*—which come automatically, by *reflex action*, as the physiologists say (meaning, no doubt, action *without* reflection, just as *lucus* is said to be derived "*a non lucendo*"). Closing one's eyelids, when something seems to be flying into the eye, is one of those actions, and saying "May I carry the little girl up the stairs?" was another. It wasn't that any thought of offering help occurred to me, and that *then* I spoke: the first intimation I had, of being likely to make that offer, was the sound of my own voice, and the discovery that the offer had been made. The servant paused, doubtfully glancing from her charge to me, and then back again to the child. "Would you like it, dear?" she asked her. But no such doubt appeared to cross the child's mind: she lifted her arms eagerly to be taken up. "Please!" was all she said, while a faint smile flickered on the weary little face. I took her up with scrupulous care, and her little arm was at once clasped trustfully round my neck.

She was a *very* light weight—so light, in fact, that the ridiculous idea crossed my mind that it was rather easier going up, with her in my arms, than it would have been without her: and, when we reached the road above, with its cart-ruts and loose stones—all formidable obstacles for a lame child—I found that I had said "I'd better carry her over this rough place", before I had formed any *mental* connection between its roughness and my gentle little burden. "Indeed it's troubling you too much, Sir!" the maid exclaimed. "She can walk very well on the flat." But the arm, that was twined about my neck, clung just to say "She's no weight, really. I'll carry her a little further. I'm going your way."

The nurse raised no further objection: and the next speaker was a ragged little boy, with bare feet, and a broom over his shoulder, who ran across the road, and pretended to sweep the perfectly dry road in front of us. "Give us a 'ap'ny!" the little urchin pleaded, with a broad grin on his dirty face.

"*Don't* give him a 'ap'ny!" said the little lady in my arms. The *words* sounded harsh: but the *tone* was gentleness itself. "He's an *idle* little boy!" And she laughed a laugh of such silvery sweetness as I had never yet heard from any lips but Sylvie's. To my astonishment, the boy actually *joined* in the laugh, as if there were some subtle sympathy between them, as he ran away down the road and vanished through a gap in the hedge.

But he was back in a few moments, having discarded his broom and provided himself, from some mysterious source, with an exquisite bouquet of flowers. "Buy a posy, buy a posy! Only a 'ap'ny!" he chanted, with the melancholy drawl of a professional beggar.

"*Don't* buy it!" was Her Majesty's edict as she looked down, with a lofty scorn that seemed curiously mixed with tender interest, on the ragged creature at her feet.

But this time I turned rebel, and ignored the royal commands. Such lovely flowers, and of forms so entirely new to me, were not to be abandoned at the bidding of any little maid, however imperious. I bought the bouquet: and the little boy, after popping the halfpenny into his mouth, turned head-over-heels, as if to ascertain whether the human mouth is really adapted to serve as a money-box.

With wonder, that increased every moment, I turned over the flowers, and examined them one by one: there was not a single one among them that I could remember having ever seen before. At last I turned to the nursemaid. "Do these flowers grow wild about here? I never saw——" but the speech died away on my lips. The nursemaid had vanished!

"You can put me down, *now*, if you like," Sylvie quietly remarked.

I obeyed in silence, and could only ask myself "Is this a *dream*?", on finding Sylvie and Bruno walking one on either side of me, and clinging to my hands with the ready confidence of childhood.

"You're larger than when I saw you last!" I began. "Really I think we ought to be introduced again! There's so much of you that I never met before, you know."

"Very well!" Sylvie merrily replied. "This is *Bruno*. It doesn't take long. He's only got one name!"

"There's *another* name to me!" Bruno protested, with a reproachful look at the Mistress of the Ceremonies. "And it's—'*Esquire*'!"

"Oh, of course. I forgot," said Sylvie. "Bruno—*Esquire*!"

"And did you come here to meet *me*, my children?" I enquired.

"You know I *said* we'd come on Tuesday," Sylvie explained. "Are we the proper size for common children?"

"Quite the right size for *children*," I replied, (adding mentally "though not *common* children, by any means!") "But what became of the nursemaid?"

"It are *gone*!" Bruno solemnly replied.

"Then it wasn't solid, like Sylvie and you?"

"No. Oo couldn't *touch* it, oo know. If oo walked *at* it, oo'd go right froo!"

"I quite expected you'd find it out, once," said Sylvie. "Bruno ran it against a telegraph post, by accident. And it went in two halves. But you were looking the other way."

I felt that I had indeed missed an opportunity: to witness such an event as a nursemaid going "in two halves" does not occur twice in a life-time!

"When did oo guess it were Sylvie?" Bruno enquired.

"I didn't guess it, till it *was* Sylvie," I said. "But how did you manage the nursemaid?"

"*Bruno* managed it," said Sylvie. "It's called a Phlizz."

"And how do you make a Phlizz, Bruno?"

"The Professor teached me how," said Bruno. "First oo takes a lot of air——"

"Oh, *Bruno*!" Sylvie interposed. "The Professor said you weren't to tell!"

"But who did her *voice*?" I asked.

"Indeed it's troubling you too much, Sir! She can walk very well on the flat."

Bruno laughed merrily as I turned hastily from side to side, looking in

all directions for the speaker. "That were *me*!" he gleefully proclaimed, in his own voice.

"She can indeed walk very well on the flat," I said. "And I think *I* was the Flat."

By this time we were near the Hall. "This is where my friends live," I said. "Will you come in and have some tea with them?"

Bruno gave a little jump of joy: and Sylvie said "Yes, please. You'd like some tea, Bruno, wouldn't you? He hasn't tasted *tea*", she explained to me, "since we left Outland."

"And *that* weren't *good* tea!" said Bruno. "It were so *welly* weak!"

CHAPTER 20

Light Come, Light Go

LADY MURIEL'S smile of welcome could not *quite* conceal the look of surprise with which she regarded my new companions.

I presented them in due form. "This is *Sylvie*, Lady Muriel. And this is *Bruno*."

"Any surname?" she enquired, her eyes twinkling with fun.

"No," I said gravely. "No surname."

"She laughed, evidently thinking I said it in fun; and stooped to kiss the children—a salute to which *Bruno* submitted with reluctance: *Sylvie* returned it with interest.

While she and Arthur (who had arrived before me) supplied the children with tea and cake, I tried to engage the Earl in conversation: but he was restless and *distrait*, and we made little progress. At last, by a sudden question, he betrayed the cause of his disquiet.

"*Would* you let me look at those flowers you have in your hand?"

"Willingly!" I said, handing him the bouquet. Botany was, I knew, a favourite study of his: and these flowers were to me so entirely new and mysterious, that I was really curious to see what a botanist would say of them.

They did *not* diminish his disquiet. On the contrary, he became every moment more excited as he turned them over. "*These* are all from Central India!" he said, laying aside part of the bouquet. "They are rare, even there: and I have never seen them in any other part of the world. *These* two are Mexican.—*This* one——" (He rose hastily and carried it to the window, to examine it in a better light, the flush of excitement mounting to his very forehead) "—is, I am nearly sure—but I have a book of Indian Botany here——" He took a volume from the book-shelves, and turned the leaves with trembling fingers. "Yes! Compare it with this picture! It is the exact duplicate! This is the flower of the Upas-tree, which usually grows only in the depths of forests; and the flower fades so quickly after being plucked, that it is scarcely possible to keep its form or colour even so far as the outskirts of the forest! Yet this is in full bloom! *Where* did you get these flowers?" he added with breathless eagerness.

I glanced at Sylvie, who, gravely and silently, laid her finger on her lips, then beckoned to Bruno to follow her, and ran out into the garden; and I found myself in the position of a defendant whose two most important witnesses have been suddenly taken away. "Let me give you the flowers!" I stammered out at last, quite "at my wit's end" as to how to get out of the difficulty. "You know much more about them than I do!"

"I accept them most gratefully! But you have not yet told me——" the Earl was beginning, when we were interrupted, to my great relief, by the arrival of Eric Lindon.

To *Arthur*, however, the newcomer was, I saw clearly, anything but welcome. His face clouded over: he drew a little back from the circle, and took no further part in the conversation, which was wholly maintained, for some minutes, by Lady Muriel and her lively cousin, who were discussing some new music that had just arrived from London.

"Do just try this one!" he pleaded. "The music looks easy to sing at sight, and the song's quite appropriate to the occasion."

"Then I suppose it's

> *'Five o'clock tea!*
> *Ever to thee*
> *Faithful I'll be,*
> *Five o'clock tea!'* "

laughed Lady Muriel, as she sat down to the piano, and lightly struck a few random chords.

"Not quite: and yet it *is* a kind of 'ever to thee faithfull I'll be!' It's a pair of hapless lovers: *he* crosses the briny deep: and *she* is left lamenting."

"That is *indeed* appropriate!" she replied mockingly, as he placed the song before her. "And am *I* to do the lamenting? And who for, if you please?"

She played the air once or twice through, first in quick, and finally in slow, time; and then gave us the whole song with as much graceful ease as if she had been familiar with it all her life:

> *"He steps so lightly to the land,*
> *All in his manly pride:*
> *He kissed her cheek, he pressed her hand,*
> *Yet still she glanced aside.*

'Too gay he seems,' she darkly dreams,
'Too gallant and too gay
To think of me—poor simple me—
When he is far away!'

'I bring my Love this goodly pearl
Across the seas,' he said:
'A gem to deck the dearest girl
That ever sailor wed!'
She clasps it tight: her eyes are bright:
Her throbbing heart would say
'He thought of me—he thought of me—
When he was far away!'

The ship has sailed into the West:
Her ocean-bird is flown:
A dull dead pain is in her breast,
And she is weak and lone:
Yet there's a smile upon her face,
A smile that seems to say
'He'll think of me—he'll think of me—
When he is far away!

'Though waters wide between us glide,
Our lives are warm and near:
No distance parts two faithful hearts—
Two hearts that love so dear:
And I will trust my sailor-lad,
For ever and a day,
To think of me—to think of me—
When he is far away!' "

The look of displeasure, which had begun to come over Arthur's face when the young Captain spoke of Love so lightly, faded away as the song proceeded, and he listened with evident delight. But his face darkened again when Eric demurely remarked "Don't you think 'my *soldier*-lad' would have fitted the tune just as well?"

"Why, so it would!" Lady Muriel gaily retorted. "Soldiers, sailors, tinkers, tailors, what a lot of words would fit in! I think 'my *tinker*-lad' sounds best. Don't *you*?"

To spare my friend further pain, I rose to go, just as the Earl was beginning to repeat his particularly embarrassing question about the flowers.

"You have not yet——"

"Yes, I've *had* some tea, thank you!" I hastily interrupted him. "And now we really *must* be going. Good evening, Lady Muriel!" And we made our adieux, and escaped, while the Earl was still absorbed in examining the mysterious bouquet.

Lady Muriel accompanied us to the door. "You *couldn't* have given my father a more acceptable present!" she said, warmly. "He is so passionately fond of Botany. I'm afraid *I* know nothing of the *theory* of it, but I keep his *Hortus Siccus* in order. I must get some sheets of blotting-paper, and dry these new treasures for him before they begin to fade."

"*That* wo'n't be no good at all!" said Bruno, who was waiting for us in the garden.

"Why wo'n't it?" said I. "You know I *had* to give the flowers, to stop questions."

"Yes, it ca'n't be helped," said Sylvie: "but they *will* be sorry when they find them gone!"

"But how will they go?"

"Well, I don't know *how*. But they *will* go. The nosegay was only a *Phlizz*, you know. Bruno made it up."

These last words were in a whisper, as she evidently did not wish Arthur to hear. But of this there seemed to be little risk: he hardly seemed to notice the children, but paced on, silent and abstracted; and when, at the entrance to the wood, they bid us a hasty farewell and ran off, he seemed to wake out of a day-dream.

The bouquet vanished, as Sylvie had predicted; and when, a day or two afterwards, Arthur and I once more visited the Hall, we found the Earl and his daughter, with the old housekeeper, out in the garden, examining the fastenings of the drawing-room window.

"We are holding an Inquest," Lady Muriel said, advancing to meet us: "and we admit you, as Accessories before the Fact, to tell us all you know about those flowers."

"The Accessories before the Fact decline to answer *any* questions," I gravely replied. "And they reserve their defence."

"Well then, turn Queen's Evidence, please! The flowers have disappeared in the night," she went on, turning to Arthur, "and we are *quite* sure no one in the house has meddled with them. Somebody must have entered by the window——"

"But the fastenings have not been tampered with," said the Earl.

"It must have been while you were dining, my Lady," said the housekeeper.

"That was it," said the Earl. "The thief must have seen you bring the flowers", turning to me, "and have noticed that you did *not* take them away. And he must have known their great value—they are simply *priceless!*" he exclaimed, in sudden excitement.

"And you never told us how you got them!" said Lady Muriel.

"Some day," I stammered, "I may be free to tell you. Just now, would you excuse me?"

The Earl looked disappointed, but kindly said "Very well, we will ask no questions".

"But we consider you a *very* bad Queen's Evidence," Lady Muriel added playfully, as we entered the arbour. "We pronounce you to be an accomplice: and we sentence you to solitary confinement, and to be fed on bread and—butter. Do you take sugar?"

"It is disquieting, certainly," she resumed, when all "creature-comforts" had been duly supplied, "to find that the house has been entered by a thief—in this out-of-the-way place. If only the flowers had been *eatables*, one might have suspected a thief of quite another shape——"

"You mean that universal explanation for all mysterious disappearances, 'the *cat* did it'?" said Arthur.

"Yes," she replied. "What a convenient thing it would be if all thieves had the same shape! It's so confusing to have some of them quadrupeds and others bipeds!"

"It has occurred to me", said Arthur, "as a curious problem in Teleology—the Science of Final Causes," he added, in answer to an enquiring look from Lady Muriel.

"And a Final Cause is——?"

"Well, suppose we say—the last of a series of connected events—each of the series being the cause of the next—for whose sake the first event takes place."

"But the last event is practically an *effect* of the first, isn't it? And yet you call it a *cause* of it!"

Arthur pondered a moment. "The words are rather confusing, I grant you," he said. "Will this do? The last event is an effect of the first: but the *necessity* for that event is a cause of the *necessity* for the first."

"That seems clear enough," said Lady Muriel. "Now let us have the problem."

"It's merely this. What object can we imagine in the arrangement by which each different size (roughly speaking) of living creatures has its special shape? For instance, the human race has one kind of

Five o'clock tea

shape—bipeds. Another set, ranging from the lion to the mouse, are quadrupeds. Go down a step or two further, and you come to insects with six legs—hexapods—a beautiful name, is it not? But beauty, in our sense of the word, seems to diminish as we go down: the creature becomes more—I won't say 'ugly' of any of God's creatures—more uncouth. And, when we take the microscope, and go a few steps lower still, we come upon animalculæ, terribly uncouth, and with a terrible number of legs!"

"The other alternative," said the Earl, "would be a *diminuendo* series of repetitions of the same type. Never mind the monotony of it: let's see how it would work in other ways. Begin with the race of men, and the creatures they require: let us say horses, cattle, sheep, and dogs—we don't exactly require frogs and spiders, do we, Muriel?"

Lady Muriel shuddered perceptibly: it was evidently a painful subject. "We can dispense with *them*," she said gravely.

"Well, then we'll have a second race of men, half-a-yard high——"

"—who would have *one* source of exquisite enjoyment, not possessed by ordinary men!" Arthur interrupted.

"*What* source?" said the Earl.

"Why, the grandeur of scenery! Surely the grandeur of a mountain, to *me*, depends on its *size*, relative to me? Double the height of the mountain, and of course it's twice as grand. Halve *my* height, and you produce the same effect."

"Happy, happy, happy Small!" Lady Muriel murmured rapturously. "None but the Short, none but the Short, none but the Short enjoy the Tall!"

"But let me go on," said the Earl. "We'll have a third race of men, five inches high; a fourth race, an inch high——"

"They couldn't eat common beef and mutton, I'm sure!" Lady Muriel interrupted.

"True, my child, I was forgetting. Each set must have its own cattle and sheep."

"And its own vegetation," I added. "What could a cow, an inch high, do with grass that waved far above its head?"

"That is true. We must have a pasture within a pasture, so to speak. The common grass would serve our inch-high cows as a green forest of palms, while round the root of each tall stem would stretch a tiny carpet of microscopic grass. Yes, I think our scheme will work fairly well. And it would be very interesting, coming into contact with the races below us. What sweet little things the inch-high bull-dogs would be! I doubt if even *Muriel* would run away from one of them!"

"Don't you think we ought to have a *crescendo* series, as well?" said Lady Muriel. "Only fancy being a hundred yards high! One could use an elephant as a paper-weight, and a crocodile as a pair of scissors!"

"And would you have races of different sizes communicate with one another?" I enquired. "Would they make war on one another, for instance, or enter into treaties?"

"*War* we must exclude, I think. When you could crush a whole nation with one blow of your fist, you couldn't conduct war on equal terms. But anything, involving a collision of *minds* only, would be possible in our ideal world—for of course we must allow mental powers to all, irrespective of size. Perhaps the fairest rule would be that, the *smaller* the race, the *greater* should be its intellectual development!"

"Do you mean to say", said Lady Muriel, "that these manikins of an inch high are to *argue* with me?"

"Surely, surely!" said the Earl. "An argument doesn't depend for its logical force on the *size* of the creature that utters it!"

She tossed her head indignantly. "I would *not* argue with any man less than six inches high!" she cried. "I'd make him *work*!"

"What at?" said Arthur, listening to all this nonsense with an amused smile.

"*Embroidery!*" she readily replied. "What *lovely* embroidery they would do!"

"Yet, if they did it wrong," I said, "you couldn't *argue* the question. I don't know *why:* but I agree that it couldn't be done."

"The reason is," said Lady Muriel, "one couldn't sacrifice one's *dignity* so far."

"Of course one couldn't!" echoed Arthur. "Any more than one could argue with a potato. It would be altogether—excuse the ancient pun—*infra dig!*"

"I doubt it," said I. "Even a pun doesn't *quite* convince me."

"Well, if that is *not* the reason," said Lady Muriel, "what reason would you give?"

I tried hard to understand the meaning of this question: but the persistent humming of the bees confused me, and there was a drowsiness in the air that made every thought stop and go to sleep before it had got well thought out: so all I could say was "That must depend on the *weight* of the potato".

I felt the remark was not so sensible as I should have like it to be. But Lady Muriel seemed to take it quite as a matter of course. "In that case——" she began, but suddenly started, and turned away to listen. "Don't you hear him?" she said. "He's crying. We must go to him, somehow."

And I said to myself "That's very strange! I quite thought it was *Lady Muriel* talking to me. Why, it's *Sylvie* all the while!" And I made another great effort to say something that should have some meaning it it. "Is it about the potato?"

CHAPTER 21

Through the Ivory Door

"I DON'T know," said Sylvie. "Hush! I must think. I could go to him, by myself, well enough. But I want *you* to come too."

"Let me go with you," I pleaded. "I can walk as fast as *you* can, I'm sure."

Sylvie laughed merrily. "What nonsense!" she cried. "Why, you ca'n't walk a bit! You're lying quite flat on your back! You don't understand these things."

"I can walk as well as *you* can," I repeated. And I tried my best to walk a few steps: but the ground slipped away backwards, quite as fast as I could walk, so that I made no progress at all. Sylvie laughed again.

"There, I told you so! You've no idea how funny you look, moving your feet about in the air,, as if you were walking! Wait a bit. I'll ask the Professor what we'd better do." And she knocked at his study-door.

The door opened, and the Professor looked out. "What's that crying I heard just now?" he asked. "Is it a human animal?"

"It's a boy," Sylvie said.

"I'm afraid you've been teasing him?"

"No, *indeed* I haven't!" Sylvie said, very earnestly. "I *never* tease him!"

"Well, I must ask the Other Professor about it." He went back into the study, and we heard him whispering "small human animal—says she hasn't been teasing him—the kind that's called Boy——"

"Ask her *which* Boy," said a new voice. The Professor came out again. "*Which* Boy is it that you haven't been teasing?"

Sylvie looked at me with twinkling eyes. "You dear old thing!" she exclaimed, standing on tip-toe to kiss him, while he gravely stooped to receive the salute. "How you *do* puzzle me! Why, there are *several* boys I haven't been teasing!"

The Professor returned to his friend: and this time the voice said "Tell her to bring them here—*all* of them!"

"I ca'n't, and I wo'n't!" Sylvie exclaimed, the moment he reappeared. "It's *Bruno* that's crying: and he's my brother: and, please, we *both* want to go: he ca'n't walk, you know: he's—he's *dreaming*, you know" (this in a whisper, for fear of hurting my feelings). "*Do* let's go through the Ivory Door!"

'I'll ask him," said the Professor, disappearing again. He returned directly. "He says you may. Follow me, and walk on tip-toe."

The difficulty with me would have been, just then, *not* to walk on tip-toe. It seemed very hard to reach down far enough to just touch the floor, as Sylvie led me through the study.

The Professor went before us to unlock the Ivory Door. I had just time to glance at the Other Professor, who was sitting reading, with his back to us, before the Professor showed us out through the door, and locked it behind us. Bruno was standing with his hands over his face, crying bitterly.

"What's the matter, darling?" said Sylvie, with her arms round his neck.

"Hurted mine self *welly* much!" sobbed the poor little fellow.

"I'm *so* sorry, darling! How ever *did* you manage to hurt yourself so?"

"Course I managed it!" said Bruno, laughing through his tears. "Does oo think nobody else but *oo* ca'n't manage things?"

Matters were looking distinctly brighter, now Bruno had begun to argue. "Come, let's hear all about it!" I said.

"My foot took it into its head to slip——" Bruno began.

"A foot hasn't got a head!" Sylvie put in, but all in vain.

"I slipted down the bank. And I tripted over a stone. And the stone hurted my foot! and I trod on a Bee. And the Bee stinged my finger!"

Poor Bruno sobbed again. The complete list of woes was too much for his feelings. "And it knewed I didn't *mean* to trod on it!" he added, as the climax.

"That Bee should be ashamed of itself!" I said severely, and Sylvie hugged and kissed the wounded hero till all tears were dried.

"My finger's quite unstung now!" said Bruno. "Why doos there be stones? Mister Sir, doos oo know?"

"They're good for *something*," I said: "even if we don't know *what*. What's the good of *dandelions*, now?"

"Dindledums?" said Bruno. "Oh, they're ever so pretty! And stones aren't pretty, one bit. Would oo like some dindledums, Mister Sir?"

"Bruno!" Sylvie murmured reproachfully. "You mustn't say 'Mister' and 'Sir' both at once! Remember what I told you!"

"You telled·me I were to say 'Mister' when I spoked *about* him, and I were to say 'Sir' when I spoked *to* him!"

"Well, you're not doing *both*, you know."

"Ah, but I *is* doing bofe, Miss Praticular!" Bruno exclaimed triumphantly. "I wishted to speak *about* the Gemplun—and I wishted to speak *to* the Gemplun. So a course I said 'Mister Sir'!"

"That's all right, Bruno," I said.

"*Course* it's all right!" said Bruno. "Sylvie just knows nuffin at all!"

"There never *was* an impertinenter boy!" said Sylvie, frowning till her bright eyes were nearly invisible.

"And there never was an ignoranter girl!" retorted Bruno. "Come along and pick some dindledums. *That's all she's fit for!*" he added in a very loud whisper to me.

"But why do you say 'Dindledums', Bruno? *Dandelions* is the right word."

"It's because he jumps about so," Sylvie said, laughing.

"Yes, that's it," Bruno assented. "Sylvie tells me the words, and then, when I jump about, they get shooken up in my head—till they're all froth!"

I expressed myself as perfectly satisfied with this explanation. "But aren't you going to pick me any dindledums, after all?"

"Course we will!" cried Bruno. "Come along, Sylvie!" And the happy children raced away, bounding over the turf with the fleetness and grace of young antelopes.

"Then you didn't find your way back to Outland?" I said to the Professor.

"Oh yes, I did!" he replied, "We never got to Queer Street; but I found another way. I've been backwards and forwards several times since then. I had to be present at the Election, you know, as the author of the new Money-Act. The Emperor was so kind as to wish that *I* should have the credit of it. 'Let come what come may,' (I remember the very words of the Imperial Speech) 'if it *should* turn out that the Warden *is* alive, *you* will bear witness that the change in the coinage is the *Professor's* doing, not *mine!*' I never was so glorified in my life, before!" Tears trickled down his cheeks at the recollection, which apparently was not *wholly* a pleasant one.

"Is the Warden supposed to be *dead*?"

"Well, it's *supposed* so: but, mind you, *I* don't believe it! The evidence is *very* weak—mere hear-say. A wandering Jester, with a Dancing-Bear (they found their way into the Palace, one day) has been telling people he comes from Fairyland, and that the Warden died there. *I* wanted the Vice-Warden to question him, but most unluckily, he and my Lady were always out walking when the Jester came round. Yes, the Warden's supposed to be dead!" And more tears trickled down the old man's cheeks.

"But what is the new Money-Act?"

The Professor brightened up again. "The Emperor started the thing," he said. "He wanted to make everybody in Outland twice as rich as he was before—just to make the new Government popular. Only there wasn't nearly enough money in the Treasury to do it. So *I* suggested that he might do it by doubling the value of every coin and bank-note in Outland. It's the simplest thing possible. I wonder nobody ever thought of it before! And you never saw such universal joy. The shops are full from morning to night. Everybody's buying everything!"

"And how was the glorifying done?"

A sudden gloom overcast the Professor's jolly face. "They did it as I went home after the Election," he mournfully replied. "It was kindly meant—but I didn't like it! They waved flags all round me till I was nearly blind: and they rang bells till I was nearly deaf: and they strewed the road so thick with flowers that I lost my way!" And the poor old man sighed deeply.

"How far is it to Outland?" I asked, to change the subject.

"About five days' march. But one *must* go back—occasionally. You see, as Court-Professor, I have to be *always* in attendance on Prince Uggug. The Empress would be *very* angry if I left him, even for an hour."

"But surely, every time you come here, you are absent ten days, at least?"

"Oh, more than that!" the Professor exclaimed. "A fortnight, sometimes. But of course I keep a memorandum of the exact time when I started, so that I can put the Court-time back to the very moment!"

"Excuse me," I said. "I don't understand."

Silently the Professor drew from his pocket a square gold watch, with six or eight hands, and held it out for my inspection. "This", he began, "is an Outlandish Watch——"

"So I should have thought."

"—which has the peculiar property that, instead of *its* going with the *time*, the *time* goes with *it*. I trust you understand me now?"

"Hardly," I said.

"Permit me to explain. So long as it is let alone, it takes its own course. Time has *no* effect upon it."

"I have known such watches," I remarked.

"It *goes*, of course, at the usual rate. Only the time has to go *with* it. Hence, if I move the hands, I change the time. To move them *forwards*, in *advance* of the true time, is impossible: but I can move them as much as a month *backwards*—that is the limit. And then you have the events all over again—with any alterations experience may suggest."

"*What* a blessing such a watch would be", I thought, "in real life! To be able to unsay some heedless word—to undo some reckless deed! Might I see the thing done?"

"With pleasure!" said the good natured Professor. "When I move *this* hand back to *here*", pointing out the place, "History goes back fifteen minutes!"

Trembling with excitement, I watched him push the hand round as he described.

"Hurted mine self *welly* much!"

Shrilly and suddenly the words rang in my ears, and, more startled than I cared to show, I turned to look for the speaker.

Yes! There was Bruno, standing with the tears running down his cheeks, just as I had seen him a quarter of an hour ago; and there was Sylvie with her arms round his neck!

I had not the heart to make the dear little fellow go through his troubles a second time, so hastily begged the Professor to push the hands round into their former position. In a moment Sylvie and Bruno were gone again, and I could just see them in the far distance, picking "dindledums".

"Wonderful, indeed!" I exclaimed.

"It has another property, yet more wonderful," said the Professor. "You see this little peg? That is called the 'Reversal Peg'. If you push it in, the events of the next hour happen in the reverse order. Do not try it now. I will lend you the Watch for a few days, and you can amuse yourself with experiments."

"Thank you very much!" I said as he gave me the Watch. "I'll take the greatest care of it—why, here are the children again!"

"We could only but find *six* dindledums," said Bruno, putting them into my hands, " 'cause Sylvie said it were time to go back. And here's a big blackberry for *ooself*! We couldn't only find but *two*!"

"Thank you: it's *very* nice," I said. "And I suppose *you* ate the other, Bruno?"

"No, I didn't," Bruno said, carelessly. "*Aren't* they pretty dindledums, Mister Sir?"

"Yes, very: but what makes you limp so, my child?"

"Mine foot's come *hurted* again!" Bruno mournfully replied. And he sat down on the ground, and began nursing it.

The Professor held his head between his hands—an attitude that I knew indicated distraction of mind. "Better rest a minute," he said. "It may be better then—or it may be worse. If only I had some of my medicines here! I'm Court-Physician, you know," he added, aside to me.

"Shall I go and get you some blackberries, darling?" Sylvie whispered, with her arms round his neck; and she kissed away a tear that was trickling down his cheek.

Bruno brightened up in a moment. "That *are* a good plan!" he exclaimed. "I thinks my foot would come *quite* unhurted, if I eated a blackberry—two or three blackberries—six or seven blackberries——"

Sylvie got up hastily. "I'd better go", she said, aside to me, "before he gets into the double figures!"

"Let me come and help you," I said. "I can reach higher up than you can."

"Yes, please," said Sylvie, putting her hand into mine: and we walked off together.

"Bruno *loves* blackberries," she said, as we paced slowly along by a tall hedge, that looked a promising place for them, "and it was so *sweet* of him to make me eat the only one!"

"Oh, it was *you* that ate it, then? Bruno didn't seem to like to tell me about it."

"No; I saw that," said Sylvie. "He's always afraid of being praised. But he *made* me eat it, really! I would much rather he—oh, what's that?" And she clung to my hand, half-frightened, as we came in sight of a hare, lying on its side with legs stretched out, just in the entrance to the wood.

"It's a *hare*, my child. Perhaps it's asleep."

"No, it isn't asleep," Sylvie said, timidly going nearer to look at it· "it's eyes are open. Is it—is it——" her voice dropped to an awe-struck whisper, "is it *dead*, do you think?"

"Yes, it's quite dead," I said, after stooping to examine it. "Poor thing! I think it's been hunted to death. I know the harriers were out yesterday. But they haven't touched it. Perhaps they caught sight of another, and left it to die of fright and exhaustion."

"Hunted to *death*?" Sylvie repeated to herself, very slowly and sadly. "I thought hunting was a thing they *played* at—like a game. Bruno and I hunt snails: but we never hurt them when we catch them!"

"Sweet angel!" I thought. "How am I to get the idea of *Sport* into your innocent mind?" And as we stood, hand-in-hand, looking down at the dead hare, I tried to put the thing into such words as she could understand. "You know what fierce wild-beasts lions and tigers are?" Sylvie nodded. "Well, in some countries men *have* to kill them, to save their own lives, you know."

"Yes," said Sylvie: "if one tried to kill *me*, Bruno would kill *it*—if he could."

"Well, and so the men—the hunters—get to enjoy it, you know: the running, and the fighting, and the shouting, and the danger."

"Yes," said Sylvie. "Bruno likes danger."

"Well, but, in *this* country, there aren't any lions and tigers, loose: so they hunt other creatures, you see." I hoped, but in vain, that this would satisfy her, and that she would ask no more questions.

"They hunt *foxes*," Sylvie said, thoughtfully. "And I think they *kill* them, too. Foxes are very fierce. I daresay men don't love them. Are hares fierce?"

"No," I said, "A hare is a sweet, gentle, timid animal—almost as gentle as a lamb."

"But, if men *love* hares, why—why———" Her voice quivered, and her sweet eyes were brimming over with tears.

"I'm afraid they *don't* love them, dear child."

"All *children* love them," Sylvie said. "All *ladies* love them."

"I'm afraid even *ladies* go to hunt them sometimes."

Sylvie shuddered. "Oh, no, not *ladies*!" she earnestly pleaded. "Not Lady Muriel!"

"No, *she* never does, I'm sure—but this is too sad a sight for *you*, dear. Let's try and find some———"

But Sylvie was not satisfied yet. In a hushed, solemn tone, with bowed head and clasped hands, she put her final question. "Does GOD love hares?"

"Yes!" I said. "I'm *sure* He does! He loves every living thing. Even sinful *men*. How much more the animals, that cannot sin!"

'I don't know what 'sin' means," said Sylvie. And I didn't try to explain it.

"Come, my child," I said, trying to lead her away. "Wish good-bye to the poor hare, and come and look for blackberries."

"Good-bye, poor hare!" Sylvie obediently repeated, looking over her shoulder at it as we turned away. And then, all in a moment, her self-command gave way. Pulling her hand out of mine, she ran back to where the dead hare was lying, and flung herself down at its side in such an agony of grief as I could hardly have believed possible in so young a child.

"Oh, my darling, my darling!" she moaned over and over again. "And GOD meant your life to be so beautiful!"

Sometimes, but always keeping her face hidden on the ground, she would reach out one little hand, to stroke the poor dead thing, and then once more bury her face in her hands, and sob as if her heart would break.

I was afraid she would really make herself ill: still I thought it best to let her weep away the first sharp agony of grief: and, after a few minutes, the sobbing gradually ceased, and Sylvie rose to her feet, and looked calmly at me, though tears were still streaming down her cheeks.

I did not dare to speak again, just yet; but simply held out my hand to her, that we might quit the melancholy spot.

"Yes, I'll come now," she said. Very reverently she kneeled down, and kissed the dead hare; then rose and gave me her hand, and we moved on in silence.

A child's sorrow is violent, but short; and it was almost in her usual voice that she said, after a minute, "Oh, stop, stop! Here are some *lovely* blackberries!"

We filled our hands with fruit, and returned in all haste to where the Professor and Bruno were seated on a bank, awaiting our return.

Just before we came within hearing-distance, Sylvie checked me. "Please don't tell *Bruno* about the hare!" she said.

"Very well, my child! But why not?"

Tears again glittered in those sweet eyes, and she turned her head away, so that I could scarcely hear her reply. "He's—he's very *fond* of gentle creatures, you know. And he'd—he'd be so sorry! I don't want him to be made sorry."

"And *your* agony of sorrow is to count for nothing, then, sweet, unselfish child!" I thought to myself. But no more was said till we had reached our friends; and Bruno was far too much engrossed, in the feast we had brought him, to take any notice of Sylvie's unusually grave manner.

"I'm afraid it's getting rather late, Professor?" I said.

"Yes, indeed," said the Professor. "I must take you all through the Ivory Door again. You've stayed your full time."

"Mightn't we stay a *little* longer!" pleaded Sylvie.

"Just *one* minute!" added Bruno.

But the Professor was unyielding. "It's a great privilege, coming through at all," he said. "We must go now." And we followed him obediently to the Ivory Door, which he threw open, and signed to me to go through first.

"You're coming too, aren't you?" I said to Sylvie.

"Yes," she said: "but you wo'n't see us after you've gone through."

"But suppose I wait for you outside?" I asked, as I stepped through the doorway.

"In that case," said Sylvie, "I think the potato would be *quite* justified in asking *your* weight. I can quite imagine a really *super* kidney-potato declining to argue with any one under *fifteen stone*!"

With a great effort I recovered the thread of my thoughts. "We lapse very quickly into nonsense!" I said.

CHAPTER 22

Crossing the Line

"LET us lapse back again," said Lady Muriel. "Take another cup of tea? I hope *that's* sound common sense?"

"And all that strange adventure", I thought, "has occupied the space of a single comma in Lady Muriel's speech! A single comma, for which grammarians tell us to 'count *one*'!" (I felt no doubt that the Professor had kindly put back the time for me, to the exact point at which I had gone to sleep.)

When a few minutes afterwards, we left the house, Arthur's first remark was certainly a strange one. "We've been there just *twenty minutes*," he said, "and I've done nothing but listen to you and Lady Muriel talking: and yet, somehow, I feel exactly as if *I* had been talking with her for an *hour* at least!"

And so he *had* been, I felt no doubt: only, as the time had been put back to the beginning of the *tête-à-tête* he referred to, the whole of it had passed into oblivion, if not into nothingness! But I valued my own reputation for sanity too highly to venture on explaining to *him* what had happened.

For some cause, which I could not at the moment divine, Arthur was unusually grave and silent during our walk home. It could not be connected with Eric Lindon, I thought, as he had for some days been away in London: so that, having Lady Muriel almost "all to himself"—for *I* was only too glad to hear those two conversing, to have any wish to intrude any remarks of my own—he *ought*, theoretically, to have been specially radiant and contented with life. "Can he have heard any bad news?" I said to myself. And, almost as if he had read my thoughts, he spoke.

"He will be here by the last train," he said, in the tone of one who is continuing a conversation rather than beginning one.

"Captain Lindon, do you mean?"

"Yes—Captain Lindon," said Arthur: "I said 'he', because I fancied we were talking about him. The Earl told me he comes to-night, though *to-morrow* is the day when he will know about the Commission that he's hoping for. I wonder he doesn't stay another day to hear the result, if he's really so anxious about it as the Earl believes he is."

"He can have a telegram sent after him," I said: "but it's not very soldier-like, running away from possible bad news!"

"He's a very good fellow," said Arthur: "but I confess it would be good news for *me*, if he got his Commission, and his Marching Orders all at once! I wish him all happiness—with *one* exception. Good night!" (We had reached home by this time.) "I'm not good company to-night—better be alone."

It was much the same, next day. Arthur declared he wasn't fit for Society, and I had to set forth alone for an afternoon-stroll. I took the road to the Station, and, at the point where the road from the "Hall" joined it, I paused, seeing my friends in the distance, seemingly bound for the same goal.

"Will you join us?" the Earl said, after I had exchanged greetings with him, and Lady Muriel, and Captain Lindon. "This restless young man is expecting a telegram, and we are going to the Station to meet it."

"There is also a restless young woman in the case," Lady Muriel added.

"That goes without saying, my child," said her father. "Women are *always* restless!"

"For generous appreciation of all one's *best* qualities," his daughter impressively remarked, "there's nothing to compare with a father, is there, Eric?"

"Cousins are not 'in it'," said Eric: and then somehow the conversation lapsed into two duologues, the younger folk taking the lead, and the two old men following with less eager steps.

"And when are we to see your little friends again?" said the Earl. "They are singularly attractive children."

"I shall be delighted to bring them, when I can," I said. "But I don't know, myself, when I am likely to see them again."

"I'm not going to question you," said the Earl: "but there's no harm in mentioning that Muriel is simply tormented with curiosity! We know most of the people about here, and she has been vainly trying to guess what house they can possibly be staying at."

"Some day I may be able to enlighten her: but just at present——"

"Thanks. She must bear it as best she can. *I* tell her it's a grand opportunity for practising *patience*. But she hardly sees it from that point of view. Why, there *are* the children!"

So indeed they were: waiting (for *us*, apparently) at a stile, which they could not have climbed over more than a few moments, as Lady Muriel and her cousin had passed it without seeing them. On catching sight of us, Bruno ran to meet us, and to exhibit to us, with much pride, the handle of a clasp-knife—the blade having been broken off—which he had picked up in the road.

"And what shall you use it for, Bruno?" I said.

'Don't know," Bruno carelessly replied: "must think."

"A child's first view of life", the Earl remarked, with that sweet sad smile of his, "is that it is a period to be spent in accumulating portable property. That view gets modified as the years glide away." And he held out his hand to Sylvie, who had placed herself by me, looking a little shy of him.

But the gentle old man was not one with whom any child, human or fairy, could be shy for long; and she had very soon deserted my hand for his—Bruno alone remaining faithful to his first friend. We overtook the other couple just as they reached the Station, and both Lady Muriel and Eric greeted the children as old friends—the latter with the words "So you got to Babylon by candlelight, after all?"

"Yes, and back again!" cried Bruno.

Lady Muriel looked from one to the other in blank astonishment. "What, *you* know them, Eric?" she exclaimed. "This mystery grows deeper every day!"

"Then we must be somewhere in the Third Act," said Eric. "You don't expect the mystery to be cleared up till the Fifth Act, do you?"

"But it's such a *long* drama!" was the plaintive reply. "We *must* have got to the Fifth Act by this time!"

"*Third* Act, I assure you," said the young soldier mercilessly. "Scene, a railway-platform. Lights down. Enter Prince (in disguise, of course) and faithful Attendant. *This* is the Prince——" (taking Bruno's hand) "and here stands his humble Servant! What is your Royal Highness's next command?" And he made a most courtier-like low bow to his puzzled little friend.

"Oo're *not* a Servant!" Bruno scornfully exclaimed. "Oo're a *Gemplun!*"

"*Servant*, I assure your Royal Highness!" Eric respectfully insisted. "Allow me to mention to your Royal Highness my various situations—past, present, and future."

"What did oo begin wiz?" Bruno asked, beginning to enter into the jest. "Was oo a shoe-black?"

"Lower than that, your Royal Highness! Years ago, I offered myself as a *Slave*—as a '*Confidential* Slave', I think it's called?" he asked, turning to Lady Muriel.

But Lady Muriel heard him not: something had gone wrong with her glove, which entirely engrossed her attention.

"Did oo get the place?" said Bruno.

"Sad to say, your Royal Highness, I did *not*! So I had to take a situation as—as *Waiter*, which I have now held for some years—haven't I?" He again glanced at Lady Muriel.

"Sylvie dear, *do* help me to button this glove!" Lady Muriel whispered, hastily stooping down, and failing to hear the question.

"And what will oo be *next*?" said Bruno.

"My next place will, I hope, be that of *Groom*. And after that——"

"Don't puzzle the child so!" Lady Muriel interrupted. "What nonsense you talk!"

"—after that," Eric persisted, "I hope to obtain the situation of *Housekeeper*, which—*Fourth Act*!" he proclaimed, with a sudden change of tone. "Lights turned up. Red lights. Green lights. Distant rumble heard. Enter a passenger-train!"

And in another minute the train drew up alongside of the platform, and a stream of passengers began to flow out from the booking office and waiting-rooms.

"Did you ever make *real* life into a drama?" said the Earl. "Now just try. I've often amused myself that way. Consider this platform as our stage. Good entrances and exits on *both* sides, you see. Capital background scene: real engine moving up and down. All this bustle, and people passing to and fro, must have been most carefully rehearsed! How naturally they do it! With never a glance at the audience! And every grouping is quite fresh, you see. No repetition!"

It really was admirable, as soon as I began to enter into it from this point of view. Even a porter passing, with a barrow piled with luggage, seemed so realistic that one was tempted to applaud. He was followed by an angry mother, with hot red face, dragging along two screaming children, and calling, to some one behind, "John! Come on!" Enter, John, very meek, very silent, and loaded with parcels. And he was followed, in his turn, by a frightened little nursemaid, carrying a fat baby, also screaming. All the children screamed.

"Capital byplay!" said the old man aside. "Did you notice the nurse-maid's look of terror? It was simply *perfect!*"

"You have struck quite a new vein," I said. "To most of us Life and its pleasures seem like a mine that is nearly worked out."

"Worked out!" exclaimed the Earl. "For any one with true dramatic instincts, it is only the Overture that is ended! The real treat has yet to begin. You go to a theatre, and pay your ten shillings for a stall, and what do you get for your money? Perhaps it's a dialogue between a couple of farmers—unnatural in their overdone caricature of farmers' dress—more unnatural in their constrained attitudes and gestures—most unnatural in their attempts at ease and geniality in their talk. Go instead and take a seat in a third-class railway-carriage, and you'll get the same dialogue done *to the life*! Front-seats—no orchestra to block the view—and nothing to pay!"

"Which reminds me," said Eric. "There is nothing to pay on receiving a telegram! Shall we enquire for one?" And he and Lady Muriel strolled off in the direction of the Telegraph-Office.

"I wonder if Shakespeare had that thought in his mind", I said, "when he wrote 'All the world's a stage'?"

The old man sighed. "And so it is," he said, "look at it as you will. Life is indeed a drama; a drama with but few *encores*—and no *bouquets!*" he added dreamily. "We spend one half of it in regretting the things we did in the other half!"

"And the secret of *enjoying* it", he continued, resuming his cheerful tone, "is *intensity!*"

"But not in the modern æsthetic sense, I presume? Like the young lady, in Punch, who begins a conversation with 'Are you *intense?*' "

"By no means!" replied the Earl. "What I mean is intensity of *thought*—a concentrated *attention*. We lose half the pleasure we might have in Life, by not really *attending*. Take any instance you like: it doesn't matter *how* trivial the pleasure may be—the principle is the same. Suppose *A* and *B* are reading the same second-rate circulating-library novel. *A* never troubles himself to master the relationships of the characters, on which perhaps all the interest of the story depends: he 'skips' over all the descriptions of scenery, and every passage that looks rather dull: he doesn't half attend to the passages he does read: he goes on reading—merely from want of resolution to find another occupation—for hours after he ought to have put the book aside: and reaches the 'FINIS' in a state of utter weariness and depression! *B* puts his whole soul *into* the thing—on the principle that 'whatever is worth doing is worth doing *well*': he masters the genealogies: he calls up pictures before his 'mind's eye' as he reads about the scenery: best of all, he resolutely shuts the book at the end of some chapter, while his interest is yet at its keenest, and turns to other subjects; so that, when next he allows himself an hour at it, it is like a hungry man sitting down to dinner: and, when the book is finished, he returns to the work of his daily life like 'a giant refreshed'!"

"But suppose the book were really *rubbish*—nothing to repay attention?"

"Well, suppose it," said the Earl. "My theory meets *that* case, I assure you! *A* never finds out that it *is* rubbish, but maunders on to the end, trying to believe he's enjoying himself. *B* quietly shuts the book, when he's read a dozen pages, walks off to the Library, and changes it for a better! I have yet *another* theory for adding to the enjoyment of Life—that is, if I have not exhausted your patience? I'm afraid you find me a very garrulous old man."

"No indeed!" I exclaimed earnestly. And indeed I felt as if one *could* not easily tire of the sweet sadness of that gentle voice.

"It is, that we should learn to take our pleasures *quickly*, and our pains *slowly*."

"But why? I should have put it the other way, myself."

"By taking *artificial* pain—which can be as trivial as you please—*slowly*, the result is that, when *real* pain comes, however severe, all you need do is to let it go at its *ordinary* pace, and it's over in a moment!"

"Very true," I said, "but how about the *pleasure*?"

"Why, by taking it quick, you can get so much more into life. It takes *you* three hours and a half to hear and enjoy an opera. Suppose *I* can take it in, and enjoy it, in half-an-hour. Why, I can enjoy *seven* operas, while you are listening to *one*!"

"Always supposing you have an orchestra capable of *playing* them," I said. "And that orchestra has yet to be found!"

The old man smiled. "I have heard an air played," he said, "and by no means a short one—played right through, variations and all, in three seconds!"

"When? and how?" I asked eagerly, with a half-notion that I was dreaming again.

"It was done by a little musical-box," he quietly replied. "After it had been wound up, the regulator, or something, broke, and it ran down, as I said, in about three seconds. But it *must* have played all the notes, you know!"

"Did you *enjoy* it?" I asked with all the severity of a cross-examining barrister.

"No, I didn't!" he candidly confessed. "But then, you know, I hadn't been trained to that kind of music!"

"I should much like to *try* your plan," I said, and, as Sylvie and Bruno happened to run up to us at the moment, I left them to keep the Earl company, and strolled along the platform, making each person and event play its part in an *extempore* drama for my especial benefit. "What, is the Earl tired of you already?" I said, as the children ran past me.

"No!" Sylvie replied with great emphasis. "He wants the evening-paper. So Bruno's going to be a little newsboy!"

"Mind you charge a good price for it!" I called after them.

Returning up the platform, I came upon Sylvie alone.

"Well, child," I said, "where's your little news-boy? Couldn't he get you an evening-paper?"

"He went to get one at the book-stall at the other side," said Sylvie; "and he's coming across the line with it—oh, Bruno, you ought to cross by the bridge!" for the distant thud, thud, of the Express was already audible. Suddenly a look of horror came over her face. "Oh, he's fallen down on the rails!" she cried, and darted past me at a speed that quite defied the hasty effort I made to stop her.

But the wheezy old Station-Master happened to be close behind me: he wasn't good for much, poor old man, but he was good for this; and, before I could turn round, he had the child clasped in his arms, saved from the certain death she was rushing to. So intent was I in watching this scene, that I hardly saw a flying figure in a light grey suit, who shot across from the back of the platform, and was on the line in another second. So far as one could take note of time in such a moment of horror, he had about ten clear seconds, before the Express would be upon him, in which to cross the rails and to pick up Bruno. Whether he did so or not it was quite impossible to guess: the next thing one knew was that the Express had passed, and that, whether for life or death, all was over. When the cloud of dust had cleared away, and the line was once more visible, we saw with thankful hearts that the child and his deliverer were safe.

"All right!" Eric called to us cheerfully, as he recrossed the line. "He's more frightened than hurt!"

He lifted the little fellow up into Lady Muriel's arms, and mounted the platform as gaily as if nothing had happened: but he was as pale as death, and leaned heavily on the arm I hastily offered him, fearing he was about

to faint. "I'll just—sit down a moment——" he said dreamily: "—where's Sylvie?"

Sylvie ran to him, and flung her arms round his neck, sobbing as if her heart would break. "Don't do that, my darling!" Eric murmured, with a strange look in his eyes. "Nothing to cry about now, you know. But you very nearly got yourself killed for nothing!"

"For Bruno!" the little maiden sobbed. "And he would have done it for me. Wouldn't you, Bruno?"

"Course I would!" Bruno said, looking round with a bewildered air.

Lady Muriel kissed him in silence as she put him down out of her arms. Then she beckoned Sylvie to come and take his hand, and signed to the children to go back to where the Earl was seated. "Tell him," she whispered with quivering lips, "tell him—all is well!" Then she turned to the hero of the day. "I thought it was *death*," she said. "Thank God, you are safe! Did you see how near it was?"

"I saw there was just time," Eric said lightly. "A soldier must learn to carry his life in his hand, you know. I'm all right now. Shall we go to the telegraph-office again? I daresay it's come by this time."

I went to join the Earl and the children, and we waited—almost in silence, for no one seemed inclined to talk, and Bruno was half-asleep on Sylvie's lap—till the others joined us. No telegram had come.

"I'll take a stroll with the children," I said, feeling that we were a little *de trop*, "and I'll look in, in the course of the evening."

"We must go back into the wood, now," Sylvie said, as soon as we were out of hearing. "We ca'n't stay this size any longer."

"Then you will be quite tiny Fairies, again, next time we meet?"

"Yes," said Sylvie: "but we'll be children again some day—if you'll let us. Bruno's very anxious to see Lady Muriel again."

"She are *welly* nice," said Bruno.

"I shall be very glad to take you to see her again," I said. "Hadn't I better give you back the Professor's Watch? It'll be too large for you to carry when you're Fairies, you know."

Bruno laughed merrily. I was glad to see he had quite recovered from the terrible scene he had gone through. "Oh, no, it wo'n't!" he said. "When *we* go small, *it'll* go small!"

"And then it'll go straight to the Professor," Sylvie added, "and you wo'n't be able to use it any more: so you'd better use it all you can, *now*. We *must* go small when the sun sets. Good-bye!"

"Good-bye!" cried Bruno. But their voices sounded very far away, and, when I looked round, both children had disappeared.

"And it wants only two hours to sunset!" I said as I strolled on. "I must make the best of my time!"

CHAPTER 23

An Outlandish Watch

As I entered the little town, I came upon two of the fishermen's wives interchanging that last word "which never was the last": and it occurred to me, as an experiment with the Magic Watch, to wait till the little scene was over, and then to "encore" it.

"Well, good night t'ye! And ye winna forget to send us word when your Martha writes?"

"Nay, ah winna forget. An' if she isn't suited, she can but coom back. Good night t'ye!"

A casual observer might have thought "and there ends the dialogue!" That casual observer would have been mistaken.

"Ah, she'll like 'em, I war'n' ye! *They'll* not treat her bad, yer may depend. They're varry canny fowk. Good night!"

"Ay, they *are* that! Good night!"

"Goodnight! And ye'll send us word if she writes?"

"Aye, ah will', yer may depend! Good night t'ye!"

And at last they parted. I waited till they were some twenty yards apart, and then put the Watch a minute back. The instantaneous change was startling: the two figures seemed to flash back into their former places.

"—isn't suited, she can but coom back. Good night t'ye!" one of them was saying: and so the whole dialogue was repeated, and, when they had parted for the second time, I let them go their several ways, and strolled on through the town.

"But the real usefulness of this magic power", I thought, "would be to undo some harm, some painful event, some accident—" I had not long to wait for an opportunity of testing *this* property also of the Magic Watch, for, even as the thought passed through my mind, the accident I was imagining occurred. A light cart was standing at the door of the "Great Millinery Depôt" of Elveston, laden with card-board packing-cases, which the driver was carrying into the shop, one by one. One of the cases had fallen into the street. but it scarcely seemed worth while to step forward and pick it up, as the man would be back again in a moment. Yet, in that moment, a young man riding a bicycle came sharp round the corner of the street and, in trying to avoid running over the box, upset his machine, and was thrown headlong against the wheel of the spring-cart. The driver ran out to his assistance, and he and I together raised the unfortunate cyclist and carried him into the shop. His head was cut and bleeding; and one knee seemed to be badly injured; and it was speedily settled that he had better be conveyed at once to the only Surgery in the place. I helped them in emptying the cart, and placing in it some pillows for the wounded man to rest on; and it was only when the driver had mounted to his place, and was starting for the Surgery, that I bethought me of the strange power I possessed of undoing all this harm.

"Now is my time!" I said to myself, as I moved back the hand of the Watch, and saw, almost without surprise this time, all things restored to the places they had occupied at the critical moment when I had first noticed the fallen packing-case.

Instantly I stepped out into the street, picked up the box, and replaced it in the cart: in the next moment the bicycle had spun round the corner, passed the cart without let or hindrance, and soon vanished in the distance, in a cloud of dust.

"Delightful power of magic!" I thought. "How much of human suffering I have—not only relieved, but actually annihilated!" And, in a glow of conscious virtue, I stood watching the unloading of the cart, still holding the Magic Watch open in my hand, as I was curious to see what would happen when we again reached the exact time at which I had put back the hand.

The result was one that, if only I had considered the thing carefully, I might have foreseen; as the hand of the Watch touched the mark, the spring-cart—which had driven off, and was by this time half-way down the street, was back again at the door, and in the act of starting, while—oh woe for the golden dream of world-wide benevolence that had dazzled my dreaming fancy!—the wounded youth was once more reclining on the heap of pillows, his pale face set rigidly in the hard lines that told of pain resolutely endured.

"Oh mocking Magic Watch!" I said to myself, as I passed out of the little town, and took the seaward road that led to my lodgings. "The good I fancied I could do is vanished like a dream: the evil of this troublesome world is the only abiding reality!"

And now I must record an experience so strange, that I think it only fair, before beginning to relate it, to release my much-enduring reader from any obligation he may feel to believe this part of my story. *I* would not have believed it, I freely confess, if I had not seen it with my own eyes: then why should I expect it of my reader, who, quite possibly, has never seen anything of the sort?

I was passing a pretty little villa, which stood rather back from the road, in its own grounds, with bright flower-beds in front—creepers wandering over the walls and hanging in festoons about the bow-windows—an easy-chair forgotten on the lawn, with a newspaper lying near it—a small pug-dog "couchant" before it, resolved to guard the treasure even at the sacrifice of life—and a front-door standing invitingly half-open. "Here is my chance", I thought, "for testing the reverse action of the Magic Watch!" I pressed the "reversal-peg" and walked in. In *another* house, the entrance of a stranger might cause surprise—perhaps anger, even going so far as to expel the said stranger with violence: but *here*, I knew, nothing of the sort could happen. The *ordinary* course of events—first, to think nothing about me; then, hearing my footsteps to look up and see me; and then to wonder what business I had there—would be reversed by the action of my Watch. They would *first* wonder who I was, *then* see me, then look down, and think no more about me. And as to being expelled with violence, *that* event would necessarily come *first* in this case. "So, if I can once get *in*," I said to myself, "all risk of *expulsion* will be over!"

The pug-dog sat up, as a precautionary measure, as I passed; but, as I took no notice of the treasure he was guarding, he let me go by without even one remonstrant bark. "He that takes my life," he seemed to be saying, wheezily, to himself, "takes trash: But he that takes the *Daily Telegraph*——!" But this awful contingency I did not face.

The party in the drawing-room—I had walked straight in, you understand, without ringing the bell, or giving any notice of my approach—consisted of four laughing rosy children, of ages from about fourteen down to ten, who were, apparently, all coming towards the door (I found they were really walking *backwards*), while their mother, seated by the fire with some needle-work on her lap, was saying, just as I entered the room, "Now, girls, you may get your things on for a walk."

To my utter astonishment—for I was not yet accustomed to the action of the Watch—"all smiles ceased" (as Browning says) on the four pretty faces, and they all got out pieces of needle-work, and sat down. No one noticed *me* in the least, as I quietly took a chair and sat down to watch them.

When the needle-work had been unfolded, and they were all ready to begin, their mother said "Come, *that's* done, at last! You may fold up your work, girls." But the children took no notice whatever of the remark; on the contrary, they set to work at once sewing—if that is the proper word to describe an operation such as *I* had never before witnessed. Each of them threaded her needle with a short end of thread attached to the work, which was instantly pulled by an invisible force through the stuff, dragging the needle after it: the nimble fingers of the little sempstress caught it at the other side, but only to lose it again the next moment. And so the work went on, steadily undoing itself, and the neatly-stitched little dresses, or whatever they were, steadily falling to pieces. Now and then one of the children would pause, as the recovered thread became inconveniently long, wind it on a bobbin, and start again with another short end.

At last all the work was picked to pieces and put away, and the lady led the way into the next room, walking backwards, and making the insane remark "Not yet, dear: we *must* get the sewing done first." After which, I was not surprised to see the children skipping backwards after her, exclaiming "Oh, mother, it *is* such a lovely day for a walk!"

In the dining-room, the table had only dirty plates and empty dishes on it. However the party—with the addition of a gentleman, as good-natured, and as rosy, as the children—seated themselves at it very contentedly.

You have seen people eating cherry-tart, and every now and then cautiously conveying a cherry-stone from their lips to their plates? Well, something like that went on all through this ghastly—or shall we say "ghostly"?—banquet. An empty fork is raised to the lips; there it received a neatly-cut piece of mutton, and swiftly conveys it to the plate, where it instantly attaches itself to the mutton already there. Soon one of the plates, furnished with a complete slice of mutton and two potatoes, was handed up to the presiding gentleman, who quietly replaced the slice on the joint, and the potatoes in the dish.

Their conversation was, if possible, more bewildering than their mode of dining. It began by the youngest girl suddenly, and without provocation, addressing her eldest sister. "Oh, you *wicked* story-teller!" she said.

I expected a sharp reply from the sister; but, instead of this, she turned laughingly to her father, and said, in a very loud stage-whisper, "To be a bride!"

The father, in order to do *his* part in a converstion that seemed only fit for lunatics, replied "Whisper it to me, dear."

But she *didn't* whisper (these children never did anything they were told): she said, quite loud, "Of course not! Everybody knows what *Dolly* wants!"

And little Dolly shrugged her shoulders, and said, with a pretty pettishness, "Now, Father, you're not to tease! You know I don't want to be bride's-maid to *anybody*!"

"And Dolly's to be the fourth," was her father's idiotic reply.

Here Number Three put in her oar. "Oh, it *is* settled, Mother dear, really and truly! Mary told us all about it. It's to be next Tuesday four weeks—and three of her cousins are coming to be bride's-maids—and——"

"*She* doesn't forget it Minnie!" the Mother laughingly replied. "I do wish they'd get it settled! I don't like long engagements."

And Minnie wound up the conversation—if so chaotic a series of remarks deserves the name—with "Only think! We passed the Cedars this morning, just exactly as Mary Davenant was standing at the gate, wishing good-bye to Mister—I forget his name. Of course we looked the other way."

By this time I was so hopelessly confused that I gave up listening, and followed the dinner down into the kitchen.

But to you, O hypercritical reader, resolute to believe no item of this weird adventaure, what need to tell how the mutton was placed on the spit, and slowly unroasted—how the potatoes were wrapped in their skins, and handed over to the gardener to be buried—how, when the mutton had at length attained to rawness, the fire, which had gradually changed from red-heat to a mere blaze, died down so suddenly that the cook had only just time to catch its last flicker on the end of a match—or how the maid, having taken the mutton off the spit, carried it (backwards, of course) out of the house, to meet the butcher, who was coming (also backwards) down the road?

The longer I thought over this strange adventure, the more hopelessly tangled the mystery became: and it was a real relief to meet Arthur in the road, and get him to go with me up to the Hall, to learn what news the telegraph had brought. I told him, as we went, what had happened at the Station, but as to my further adventures I thought it best, for the present, to say nothing.

The Earl was sitting alone when we entered. "I am glad you are come in to keep me company," he said. "Muriel is gone to bed—the excitement of that terrible scene was too much for her—and Eric has gone to the hotel to pack his things, to start for London by the early train."

"Then the telegram has come!" I said.

"Did you not hear? Oh, I had forgotten: it came in after you left the Station. Yes, it's all right: Eric has got his commission; and, now that he has arranged matters with Muriel, he has business in town that must be seen to at once."

"What arrangement do you mean?" I asked with a sinking heart, as the thought of Arthur's crushed hopes came to my mind. "Do you mean that they are *engaged*?"

"They have been engaged—in a sense—for two years," the old man gently replied: "that is, he has had my promise to consent to it, so soon as he could secure a permanent and settled line in life. I could never be happy with my child married to a man without an object to live for—without even an object to die for!"

"I hope they will be happy," a strange voice said. The speaker was evidently in the room, but I had not heard the door open, and I looked around in some astonishment. The Earl seemed to share my surprise. "Who spoke?" he exclaimed.

"It was I," said Arthur, looking at us with a worn, haggard face, and eyes from which the light of life seemed suddenly to have faded. "And let me wish *you* joy also, dear friend," he added, looking sadly at the Earl, and speaking in the same hollow tones that had startled us so much.

"Thank you," the old man said, simply and heartily.

A silence followed: then I rose, feeling sure that Arthur would wish to be alone, and bade our gentle host "Good night": Arthur took his hand, but said nothing: nor did he speak again, as we went home, till we were in the house and had lit our bed-room candles. Then he said, more to himself than to me, "*The heart knoweth its own bitterness.* I never understood those words till now."

The next few days passed wearily enough. I felt no inclination to call again, by myself, at the Hall; still less to propose that Arthur should go with me: it seemed better to wait till Time—that gentle healer of our bitterest sorrows—should have helped him to recover from the first shock of the disappointment that had blighted his life.

Business, however, soon demanded my presence in town; and I had to announce to Arthur that I must leave him for a while. "But I hope to run down again in a month," I added. "I would stay now, if I could. I don't think it's good for you to be alone."

"No, I ca'n't face solitude, *here*, for long," said Arthur. "But don't think about *me*. I have made up my mind to accept a post in India, that has been offered me. Out there, I suppose I shall find something to live for; I ca'n't see *anything* at present. '*This life of mine I guard, as God's high gift, from scathe and wrong, Not greatly care to lose!*' "

"Yes," I said: "your name-sake bore as heavy a blow, and lived through it."

"A far heavier one than *mine*," said Arthur. "The woman *he* loved proved false. There is no such cloud as *that* on my memory of—of——" He left the name unuttered and went on hurriedly. "But *you* will return, will you not?"

"Yes, I shall come back for a short time."

"Do," said Arthur: "and you shall write and tell me of our friends. I'll send you my address when I'm settled down."

CHAPTER 24

The Frogs' Birthday-Treat

AND so it came to pass that, just a week after the day when my Fairy-friends first appeared as Children, I found myself taking a farewell-stroll through the wood, in the hope of meeting them once more. I had but to stretch myself on the smooth turf, and the "eerie" feeling was on me in a moment.

"Put oor ear *welly* low down," said Bruno. "and I'll tell oo a secret! It's the Frogs' Birthday-Treat—and we've lost the Baby!"

"*What* Baby?" I said, quite bewildered by this complicated piece of news.

"The *Queen's* Baby, a course!" said Bruno. "Titania's Baby. And we's *welly* sorry. Sylvie, she's—oh so sorry!"

"*How* sorry is she?" I asked, mischievously.

"Three-quarters of a yard," Bruno replied with perfect solemnity. "And *I'm* a little sorry too," he added, shutting his eyes so as not to see that he was smiling.

"And what are you doing about the Baby?"

"Well, the *soldiers* are all looking for it—up and down—everywhere."

"The *soldiers*?" I exclaimed.

"Yes, a course!" said Bruno. "When there's no fighting to be done, the soldiers doos any little odd jobs, oo know."

I was amused at the idea of its being a "little odd job" to find the Royal Baby. "But how did you come to lose it?" I asked.

"We put it in a flower," Sylvie, who had just joined us, explained with her eyes full of tears. "Only we ca'n't remember *which*!"

"She says *us* put it in a flower," Bruno interrupted, " 'cause she doesn't want *I* to get punished. But it were really *me* what put it there. *Sylvie* were picking Dindledums."

"You shouldn't say '*us* put it in a flower'," Sylvie very gravely remarked.

"Well, *hus*, then," said Bruno. "I never *can* remember those horrid H's!"

"Let me help you to look for it," I said. So Sylvie and I made a "voyage of discovery" among all the flowers; but there was no Baby to be seen.

"What's become of Bruno?" I said, when we had completed our tour.

"He's down in the ditch there," said Sylvie, "amusing a young Frog."

I went down on my hands and knees to look for him, for I felt very curious to know how young Frogs *ought* to be amused. After a minute's search, I found him sitting at the edge of the ditch, by the side of the little Frog, and looking rather disconsolate.

"How are you getting on, Bruno?" I said, nodding to him as he looked up.

"Ca'n't amuse it no more," Bruno answered, very dolefully, " 'cause it wo'n't say what it would like to do next! I've showed it all the duck-weeds—and a live caddisworm—but it wo'n't say nuffin! What—would oo—like?" he shouted into the ear of the Frog: but the little creature sat quite still, and took no notice of him. "It's deaf, I think!" Bruno said, turning away with a sigh. "And it's time to get the Theatre ready."

"Who are the audience to be?"

"Only but Frogs," said Bruno. "But they haven't comed yet. They wants to be drove up, like sheep."

"Would it save time", I suggested, "if *I* were to walk round with Sylvie, to drive up the Frogs, while *you* get the Theatre ready?"

"That *are* a good plan!" cried Bruno. "But where *are* Sylvie?"

"I'm here!" said Sylvie, peeping over the edge of the bank. "I was just watching two Frogs that were having a race."

"Which won it?" Bruno eagerly inquired.

Sylvie was puzzled. "He *does* ask such hard questions!" she confided to me.

"And what's to happen in the Theatre?" I asked.

"First they have their Birthday-Feast," Sylvie said: "then Bruno does some Bits of Shakespeare; then he tells them a Story."

"I should think the Frogs like the Feast best. Don't they?"

"Well, there's generally very few of them that get any. They *will* keep their mouths shut so tight! And it's just as well they *do*," she added, "because Bruno likes to cook it himself: and he cooks *very* queerly. Now they're all in. Would you just help me to put them with their heads the right way?"

We soon managed this part of the business, though the Frogs kept up a most discontented croaking all the time.

"What *are* they saying?" I asked Sylvie.

"They're saying 'Fork! Fork!' It's very silly of them! You're not going to *have* forks!" she announced with some severity. "Those that want any Feast have just got to open their mouths, and Bruno'll put some of it in!"

At this moment Bruno appeared, wearing a little white apron to show that he was a Cook, and carrying a tureen full of very queer-looking soup. I watched very carefully as he moved about among the Frogs; but I could not see that *any* of them opened their mouths to be fed—except one very young one, and I'm nearly sure it did it accidentally, in yawning. However, Bruno instantly put a large spoonful of soup into its mouth, and the poor little thing coughed violently for some time.

So Sylvie and I had to share the soup between us, and to *pretend* to enjoy it, for it certainly was *very* queerly cooked.

I only ventured to take *one* spoonful of it ("Sylvie's Summer-Soup," Bruno said it was), and must candidly confess that it was not *at all* nice; and I could not feel surprised that so many guests had kept their mouths shut up tight.

"What's the soup *made* of, Bruno?" said Sylvie, who had put a spoonful of it to her lips, and was making a wry face over it.

And Bruno's answer was anything but encouraging. "Bits of things!"

The entertainment was to conclude with "Bits of Shakespeare", as Sylvie expressed it, which were all to be done by Bruno, Sylvie being fully engaged in making the Frogs keep their heads towards the stage: after which Bruno was to appear in his real character, and tell them a Story of his own invention.

"Will the Story have a Moral to it?" I asked Sylvie, while Bruno was away behind the hedge, dressing for the first "Bit".

"I *think* so," Sylvie replied doubtfully. "There generally *is* a Moral, only he puts it in too soon."

"And will he *say* all the Bits of Shakespeare?"

"No, he'll only *act* them," said Sylvie. "He knows hardly any of the words. When I see what he's dressed like, I've to tell the Frogs what character it is. They're always in such a hurry to guess! Don't you hear them all saying 'What? What?'" And so indeed they were: it had only sounded like croaking, till Sylvie explained it, but I could now make out the "Wawt? Wawt?" quite distinctly.

"But why do they try to guess it before they see it?"

"I don't know," Sylvie said: "but they always *do*. Sometimes they begin guessing weeks and weeks before the day!"

(So now, when you hear the Frogs croaking in a particularly melancholy way, you may be sure they're trying to guess Bruno's next Shakespeare "Bit". Isn't *that* interesting?)

However, the chorus of guessing was cut short by Bruno, who suddenly rushed on from behind the scenes, and took a flying leap down among the Frogs, to re-arrange them.

For the oldest and fattest Frog—who had never been properly arranged so that he could see the stage, and so had no idea what was going on—was getting restless, and had upset several of the Frogs, and turned others round with their heads the wrong way. And it was no good at all, Bruno said, to do a "Bit" of Shakespeare when there was nobody to look at it (you see he didn't count *me* as anybody). So he set to work with a stick, stirring them up, very much as you would stir up tea in a cup, till most of them had at least *one* great stupid eye gazing at the stage.

"*Oo* must come and sit among them, Sylvie," he said in despair, "I've put these two side-by-side, with their noses the same way, ever so many times, but they *do* squarrel so!"

So Sylvie took her place as "Mistress of the Ceremonies", and Bruno vanished again behind the scenes, to dress for the first "Bit".

"Hamlet!" was suddenly proclaimed, in the clear sweet tones I knew so well. The croaking all ceased in a moment, and I turned to the stage, in some curiosity to see what Bruno's ideas were as to the behaviour of Shakespeare's great Character.

According to this eminent interpreter of the Drama, Hamlet wore a short black cloak (which he chiefly used for muffling up his face, as if he suffered a good deal from toothache), and turned out his toes very much as he walked. "To be or not to be!" Hamlet remarked in a cheerful tone, and then turned head-over-heels several times, his cloak dropping off in the performance.

I felt a little disappointed: Bruno's conception of the part seemed so wanting in dignity. "Wo'n't he say any more of the speech?" I whispered to Sylvie.

"I *think* not," Sylvie whispered in reply. "He generally turns head-over-heels when he doesn't know any more words."

Bruno had meanwhile settled the question by disappearing from the stage; and the Frogs instantly began inquiring the name of the next Character.

"You'll know directly!" cried Sylvie, as she adjusted two or three young Frogs that had struggled round with their backs to the stage. "Macbeth!" she added, as Bruno re-appeared.

Macbeth had something twisted round him, that went over one shoulder and under the other arm, and was meant, I believe, for a Scotch plaid. He had a thorn in his hand, which he held out at arm's length, as if he were a little afraid of it. "Is this a *dagger?*" Macbeth inquired, in a puzzled sort of tone: and instantly a chorus of "Thorn! Thorn!" arose from the Frogs (I had quite learned to understand their croaking by this time).

"It's a *dagger!*" Sylvie proclaimed in a peremptory tone. "Hold your tongues!" and the croaking ceased at once.

Shakespeare has not told us, so far as I know, that Macbeth had any such eccentric habit as turning head-over-heels in private life: but Bruno evidently considered it quite an essential part of the character, and left the stage in a series of somersaults. However, he was back again in a few moments, having tucked under his chin the end of a tuft of wool (probably left on the thorn by a wandering sheep), which made a magnificent beard, that reached nearly down to his feet.

"Shylock!" Sylvie proclaimed. "No, I beg your pardon!" she hastily corrected herself, "King Lear! I hadn't noticed the crown." (Bruno had very cleverly provided one, which fitted him exactly, by cutting out the centre of a dandelion to make room for his head.)

King Lear folded his arms (to the imminent peril of his beard) and said, in a mild explanatory tone, "Ay, every *inch* a king!" and then paused, as if to consider how this could best be proved. And here, with all possible defence to Bruno as a Shakespearean critic, I *must* express my opinion that the poet did *not* mean his three great tragic heroes to be so strangely alike in their personal habits; nor do I believe that he would have accepted the faculty of turning head-over-heels as any proof at all of royal descent. Yet it appeared that King Lear, after deep meditation, could think of no other argument by which to prove his kingship: and, as this was the last of the "Bits" of Shakespeare ("We never do more than *three*," Sylvie explained in a whisper), Bruno gave the audience quite a long series of somersaults before he finally retired, leaving the enraptured Frogs all crying out "More! More!" which I suppose was their way of encoring a performance. But Bruno wouldn't appear again, till the proper time came for telling the Story.

When he appeared at last in his *real* character, I noticed a remarkable change in his behaviour. He tried no more somersaults. It was clearly his opinion that, however suitable the habit of turning head-over-heels might be to such petty individuals as Hamlet and King Lear, it would never do for *Bruno* to sacrifice his dignity to such an extent. But it was equally clear that he did not feel entirely at his ease, standing all alone on the

The Frogs' birthday-treat

stage, with no costume to disguise him; and though he began, several times, "There were a Mouse—", he kept glancing up and down, and on all sides, as if in search of more comfortable quarters from which to tell the story. Standing on one side of the stage, and partly overshadowing it, was a tall fox-glove, which seemed, as the evening breeze gently swayed it hither and thither, to offer exactly the sort of accommodation that the orator desired. Having once decided on his quarters, it needed only a second or two for him to run up the stem like a tiny squirrel, and to seat himself astride on the topmost bend, where the fairybells clustered most clearly, and from whence he could look down on his audience from such a height that all shyness vanished, and he began his Story merrily.

"Once there were a Mouse and a Crocodile and a Man and a Goat and a Lion." I had never heard the "dramatis personæ" tumbled into a story with such profusion and in such reckless haste; and it fairly took my breath away. Even Sylvie gave a little gasp, and allowed three of the Frogs, who seemed to be getting tired of the entertainment, to hop away into the ditch, without attempting to stop them.

"And the Mouse found a Shoe, and it thought it were a Mouse-trap. So it got right in, and it stayed in ever so long."

"Why did it *stay* in?" said Sylvie. Her function seemed to be much the same as that of the Chorus in a Greek Play: she had to encourage the orator, and draw him out, by a series of intelligent questions.

" 'Cause it thought it couldn't get out again," Bruno explained. "It were a clever mouse. It knew it couldn't get out of traps!"

"But why did it go in at all?" said Sylvie.

"—and it jamp, and it jamp," Bruno proceeded, ignoring this question, "and at last it got right out again. And it looked at the mark in the Shoe. And the Man's name were in it. So it knew it wasn't its own Shoe."

"Had it thought it *was*?" said Sylvie.

"Why, didn't I tell oo it thought it was a *Mouse-trap*?" the indignant orator replied. "Please, Mister Sir, will oo make Sylvie attend?" Sylvie was silenced, and was all attention: in fact, she and I were most of the audience now, as the Frogs kept hopping away, and there were very few of them left.

"So the mouse gave the Man his Shoe. And the Man were welly glad, 'cause he hadn't got but one Shoe, and he were hopping to get the other."

Here I ventured on a question. "Do you mean 'hopping', or 'hoping'?"

"Bofe," said Bruno. "And the Man took the Goat out of the Sack." ("We haven't heard of the *sack* before," I said. "Now you wo'n't hear of it again," said Bruno.) "And he said to the Goat, 'Oo will walk about here till I comes back.' And he went and he tumbled into a deep hole. And the Goat walked round and round. And it walked under the Tree. And it wug its tail. And it looked up in the Tree. And it sang a sad little Song. Oo never heard such a sad little Song!"

"Can you sing it, Bruno?" I asked.

"Iss, I can," Bruno readily replied. "And I sa'n't. It would make Sylvie cry——"

"It wouldn't!" Sylvie interrupted in great indignation. "And I don't believe the Goat sang it at all!"

"It did, though!" said Bruno. "It singed it right froo. I *sawed* it singing with its long beard——"

"It couldn't sing with its *beard*," I said, hoping to puzzle the little fellow: "a beard isn't a *voice*."

"Well then, *oo* couldn't walk with Sylvie!" Bruno cried triumphantly. "Sylvie isn't a *foot*!"

I thought I had better follow Sylvie's example, and be silent for a while. Bruno was too sharp for us.

"And when it had singed all the Song, it ran away—for to get along to look for the Man, oo know. And the Crocodile got along after it—for to bite it, oo know. And the Mouse got along after the Crocodile."

"Wasn't the Crocodile *running*?" Sylvie enquired. She appealed to me. "Crocodiles do run, don't they?"

I suggested "crawling" as the proper word.

"He wasn't running," said Bruno, "and he wasn't crawling. He went struggling along like a portmanteau. And he held his chin ever so high in the air——"

"What did he do *that* for?" said Sylvie.

" 'Cause he hadn't got a toofache!" said Bruno. "Ca'n't oo make out *nuffin* wizout I 'splain it? Why, if he'd had a toofache, a course he'd have held his head down—like this—and he'd have put a lot of warm blankets round it!"

"If he'd *had* any blankets," Sylvie argued.

"Course he *had* blankets!" retorted her brother. "Doos oo think Crocodiles goes walks wizout blankets? And he frowned with his eyebrows. And the Goat was welly flightened at his eyebrows!"

"I'd never be afraid of *eyebrows*!" exclaimed Sylvie.

"I should think oo *would*, though, if they'd got a Crocodile fastened to them, like these had! And so the Man jamp, and he jamp, and at last he got right out of the hole."

Sylvia gave another little gasp: this rapid dodging about among the characters of the Story had taken away her breath.

"And he runned away—for to look for the Goat, oo know. And he heard the Lion grunting——"

"Lions don't grunt," said Sylvie.

"This one did," said Bruno. "And its mouth were like a large cupboard. And it had plenty of room in its mouth. And the Lion runned after the Man—for to eat him, oo know. And the Mouse runned after the Lion."

"But the Mouse was running after the *Crocodile*," I said: "he couldn't run after *both*!"

Bruno sighed over the density of his audience, but explained very patiently. "He *did* runned after *bofe:* 'cause they went the same way! And first he caught the Crocodile, and then he didn't catch the Lion. And when he'd caught the Crocodile, what doos oo think he did—'cause he'd got pincers in his pocket?"

"I ca'n't guess," said Sylvie.

"Nobody couldn't guess it!" Bruno cried in high glee. "Why, he wrenched out that Crocodile's toof!"

"*Which* tooth?" I ventured to ask.

But Bruno was not to be puzzled. "The toof he were going to bite the Goat with, a course!"

"He couldn't be sure about that," I argued, "unless he wrenched out *all* its teeth."

Bruno laughed merrily, and half sang, as he swung himself backwards and forwards, "He did—wrenched—out—*all* its teef!"

"Why did the Crocodile wait to have them wrenched out?" said Sylvie.

"It had to wait," said Bruno.

I ventured on another question. "But what became of the Man who said 'You may wait here till I come Back'?"

"He didn't say 'Oo *May*'," Bruno explained. "He said, 'Oo *will*.' Just like Sylvie says to me 'Oo will do oor lessons till twelve o'clock.' Oh, I *wiss*," he added with a little sigh, "I *wiss* Sylvie would say 'Oo *may* do oor lessons'!"

This was a dangerous subject for discussion, Sylvie seemed to think. She returned to the Story. "But what became of the Man?"

"Well, the Lion springed at him. But it came so slow, it were three weeks in the air——"

"Did the Man wait for it all that time?" I said.

"Course he didn't!" Bruno replied, gliding head-first down the stem of the fox-glove, for the Story was evidently close to its end. "He sold his

house, and he packed up his things, while the Lion were coming. And he went and he lived in another town. So the Lion ate the wrong man."

This was evidently the Moral: so Sylvie made her final proclamation to the Frogs. "The Story's finished! And whatever is to be *learned* from it," she added, aside to me, "I'm sure *I* don't know!"

I did not feel *quite* clear about it myself, so made no suggestion: but the Frogs seemed quite content, Moral or no Moral, and merely raised a husky chorus of "Off! Off!" as they hopped away.

CHAPTER 25

Looking Eastward

"IT'S just a week," I said, three days later, to Arthur, "since we heard of Lady Muriel's engagement. I think *I* ought to call, at any rate, and offer my congratulations. Wo'n't you come with me?"

A pained expression passed over his face. "When must you leave us?" he asked.

"By the first train on Monday."

"Well—yes, I *will* come with you. It would seem strange and unfriendly if I didn't. But this is only Friday. Give me till Sunday afternoon. I shall be stronger then."

Shading his eyes with one hand, as if half-ashamed of the tears that were coursing down his cheeks, he held the other out to me. It trembled as I clasped it.

I tried to frame some words of sympathy; but they seemed poor and cold, and I left them unspoken. "Good night!" was all I said.

"Good night, dear friend!" he replied. There was a manly vigour in his tone that convinced me he was wrestling with, and triumphing over, the great sorrow that had so nearly wrecked his life—and that, on the stepping-stone of his dead self, he would surely rise to higher things!

There was no chance, I was glad to think, as we set out on Sunday afternoon, of meeting *Eric* at the Hall, as he had returned to town the day after his engagement was announced. *His* presence might have disturbed the calm—the almost unnatural calm—with which Arthur met the woman who had won his heart, and murmured the few graceful words of sympathy that the occasion demanded.

Lady Muriel was perfectly radiant with happiness; sadness could not live in the light of such a smile: and even Arthur brightened under it, and, when she remarked "You see I'm watering my flowers, though it *is* the Sabbath-Day," his voice had almost its old ring of cheerfulness as he replied "Even on the Sabbath-Day works of mercy are allowed. But this *isn't* the Sabbath-Day. The Sabbath-Day has ceased to exist."

"I know it's not *Saturday*," Lady Muriel replied: 'but isn't Sunday often called 'the Christian Sabbath'?"

"It is so called, I think, in recognition of the *spirit* of the Jewish institution, that one day in seven should be a day of *rest*. But I hold that Christians are freed from the *literal* observance of the Fourth Commandment."

"Then where is our *authority* for Sunday observance?"

"We have, first, the fact that the seventh day was 'sanctified', when God rested from the work of Creation. That is binding on us as *Theists*. Secondly, we have the fact that 'the Lord's Day' is a *Christian* institution. That is binding on us as *Christians*."

"And your practical rules would be——?"

"First, as Theists, to keep it *holy* in some special way, and to make it, so far as is reasonably possible, a day of *rest*. Secondly, as *Christians*, to attend public worship."

"And what of *amusements*?"

"I would say of them, as of all kinds of *work*, whatever is innocent on a week-day, is innocent on Sunday, provided it does not interfere with the duties of the day."

"Then you would allow children to *play* on Sunday?"

"Certainly I should. Why make the day irksome to their restless natures?"

"I have a letter somewhere," said Lady Muriel, "from an old friend, describing the way in which Sunday was kept in her younger days. I will fetch it for you."

"I had a similar description, *vivâ voce*, years ago," Arthur said when she had left us, "from a little girl. It was really touching to hear the melancholy tone in which she said 'On Sunday I mustn't play with my doll! On Sunday I mustn't run on the sands! On Sunday I mustn't dig in the garden!' Poor child! She had indeed abundant cause for hating Sunday!"

"Here is the letter," said Lady Muriel, returning. "Let me read you a piece of it."

"When, as a child, I first opened my eyes on a Sunday-morning, a feeling of dismal anticipation, which began at least on the Friday, culminated. I knew what was before me, and my wish, if not my word, was 'Would God it were evening!' It was no day of rest, but a day of texts, of catechisms (Watts'), of tracts about converted swearers, godly char-women, and edifying deaths of sinners saved.

"Up with the lark, hymns and portions of Scripture had to be learned by heart till 8 o'clock, when there were family-prayers, then breakfast, which I was never able to enjoy, partly from the fast already undergone, and partly from the outlook I dreaded.

"At 9 came Sunday-School; and it made me indignant to be put into the class with the village-children, as well as alarmed lest, by some mistake of mine, I should be put below them.

"The Church-Service was a veritable Wilderness of Zin. I wandered in it, pitching the tabernacle of my thoughts on the lining of the square family-pew, the fidgets of my small brothers, and the horror of knowing that, on the Monday, I should have to write out, from memory, jottings of the rambling disconnected extempore sermon, which might have any text but its own, and to stand or fall by the result.

"This was followed by a cold dinner at 1 (servants to have *no* work), Sunday-School again from 2 to 4, and Evening-Service at 6. The intervals were perhaps the greatest trial of all, from the efforts I had to make, to be less than usually sinful, by reading books and sermons as barren as the Dead Sea. There was but one rosy spot, in the distance, all that day; and that was 'bed-time', which never could come too early!"

"Such teaching was well meant, no doubt," said Arthur; "but it must have driven many of its victims into deserting the Church-Services altogether."

"I'm afraid *I* was a deserter this morning," she gravely said. "I had to write to Eric. Would you—would you mind my telling you something he said about *prayer*? It had never struck me in that light before."

"In what light?" said Arthur.

"Why, that all Nature goes by fixed, regular laws—Science has proved *that*. So that asking God to *do* anything (except of course praying for *spiritual* blessings) is to expect a miracle: and we've no right to do *that*. I've not put it as well as *he* did: but that was the outcome of it, and it has confused me. Please tell me what you can say in answer to it."

"I don't propose to discuss *Captain Lindon's* difficulties," Arthur gravely replied; "specially as he is not present. But, if it is *your* difficulty," (his voice unconsciously took a tender tone) "then I will speak."

"It *is* my difficulty," she said anxiously.

"Then I will begin by asking 'Why did you except *spiritual* blessings?' Is not your mind a part of Nature?"

"Yes, but Free-Will comes in there—I can *choose* this or that; and God can influence my choice."

"Then you are not a Fatalist?"

"Oh, no!" she earnestly exclaimed.

"Thank God!" Arthur said to himself, but in so low a whisper that only *I* heard it. "You grant then that I can, by an act of free choice, move this cup," suiting the action to the word, "*this* way or *that* way?"

"Yes, I grant it."

"Well, let us see how far the result is produced by fixed laws. The *cup* moves because certain mechanical forces are impressed on it by my *hand*. My *hand* moves because certain forces—electric, magnetic, or whatever 'nerve-force' may prove to be—are impressed on it by my *brain*. This nerve-force, stored in the brain, would probably be traceable, if Science were complete, to chemical forces supplied to the brain by the blood, and ultimately derived from the food I eat and the air I breathe."

"But would not that be Fatalism? Where would Free-Will come in?"

"In *choice* of nerves," replied Arthur. "The nerve-force in the brain may flow just as naturally down one nerve as down another. We need something more than a fixed Law of Nature to settle *which* nerve shall carry it. That 'something' is Free-Will."

Her eyes sparkled. "I see what you mean!" she exclaimed. "Human Free-Will is an exception to the system of fixed Law. Eric said something like that. And then I think he pointed out that God can only influence Nature by influencing Human Wills. So that we *might* reasonably pray '*give us this day our daily bread*', because many of the causes that produce bread are under Man's control. But to pray for rain, or fine weather, would be as unreasonable as—" she checked herself, as if fearful of saying something irreverent.

In a hushed, low tone, that trembled with emotion, and with the solemnity of one in the presence of death, Arthur slowly replied "*Shall he that contendeth with the Almighty instruct him?* Shall we, 'the swarm that in the noon-tide beam were born,' feeling in ourselves the power to direct, this way or that, the forces of Nature—of *Nature*, of which we form so trivial a part—shall we, in our boundless arrogance, in our pitiful conceit, *deny* that power to the Ancient of Days? Saying, to our Creator, 'Thus far and no further. Thou madest, but thou canst not rule!'?"

Lady Muriel had covered her face in her hands, and did not look up. She only murmured "Thanks, thanks!" again and again.

We rose to go. Arthur said, with evident effort, "One word more. If you would *know* the power of Prayer—in anything and everything that Man can need—*try* it. *Ask, and it shall be given you.* I—*have* tried it. I *know* that God answers prayer!"

Our walk home was a silent one, till we had nearly reached the lodgings: then Arthur murmured—and it was almost an echo of my own thoughts—"*What knowest thou, O wife, whether thou shalt save thy husband?*"

The subject was not touched on again. We sat on, talking, while hour after hour, of this our last night together, glided away unnoticed. He had much to tell me about India, and the new life he was going to, and the *work* he hoped to do. And his great generous soul seemed so filled with noble ambition as to have no space left for any vain regret or selfish repining.

"Come, it is nearly morning!" Arthur said at last, rising and leading the way upstairs. "The sun will be rising in a few minutes; and, though I *have* basely defrauded you of your last chance of a night's rest here, I'm sure you'll forgive me: for I really *couldn't* bring myself to say 'Good night' sooner. And God knows whether you'll ever see me again, or hear of me!"

"*Hear* of you I am certain I shall!" I warmly responded, and quoted the concluding lines of that strange poem "Waring":

> *"Oh, never star*
> *Was lost here, but it rose afar!*
> *Look East, where whole new thousands are!*
> *In Vishnu-land what Avatar?"*

"Aye, look Eastward!" Arthur eagerly replied, pausing at the stair-case window, which commanded a fine view of the sea and the eastward horizon. "The West is the fitting tomb for all the sorrow and the sighing, all the errors and the follies of the Past: for all its withered Hopes and all its buried Loves! From the East comes new strength, new ambition, new Hope, new Life, new Love! Look Eastward! Aye, look Eastward!"

His last words were still ringing in my ears as I entered my room, and undrew the window-curtains, just in time to see the sun burst in glory from his ocean-prison, and clothe the world in the light of a new day.

"So may it be for him, and me, and all of us!" I mused. "All that is evil, and dead, and hopeless, fading with the Night that is past! All that is good, and living, and hopeful, rising with the dawn of Day!

"Fading, with the Night, the chilly mists, and the noxious vapours, and the heavy shadows, and the wailing gusts, and the owl's melancholy hootings: rising, with the Day, the darting shafts of light, and the wholesome morning breeze, and the warmth of a dawning life, and the mad music of the lark! Look Eastward!

"Fading, with the Night, the clouds of ignorance, and the deadly blight of sin, and the silent tears of sorrow: and ever rising, higher, higher, with

the Day, the radiant dawn of knowledge, and the sweet breath of purity, and the throb of a world's ecstasy! Look Eastward!

"Fading, with the Night, the memory of a dead love, and the withered leaves of a blighted hope, and the sickly repinings and moody regrets that numb the best energies of the soul: and rising, broadening, rolling upward like a living flood, the manly resolve, and the dauntless will, and the heavenward gaze of faith—*the substance of things hoped for, the evidence of things not seen*!

"Look Eastward! Aye, look Eastward!"

❧ IV ❧

Sylvie and Bruno Concluded

with forty-six illustrations by
Harry Furniss

Dreams, that elude the Maker's frenzied grasp—
Hands, stark and still, on a dead Mother's breast,
Which nevermore shall render clasp for clasp,
Or deftly soothe a weeping Child to rest—
In suchlike forms me listeth to portray
My Tale, here ended. Thou delicious Fay—
The guardian of a Sprite that lives to tease thee—
Loving in earnest, chiding but in play
The merry mocking Bruno! Who, that sees thee,
Can fail to love thee, Darling, even as I?—
My sweetest Sylvie we must say "Good-bye!"

Preface

LET me here express my sincere gratitude to the many Reviewers who have noticed, whether favourably or unfavourably, the previous Volume. Their unfavourable remarks were, most probably, well-deserved; the favourable ones less probably so. Both kinds have no doubt served to make the book known, and have helped the reading Public to form their opinions of it. Let me also here assure them that it is not from any want of respect for their criticisms, that I have carefully forborne from reading *any* of them. I am strongly of opinion that an author had far better *not* read any reviews of his books: the unfavourable ones are almost certain to make him cross, and the favourable ones conceited; and *neither* of these results is desirable.

Criticisms have, however, reached me from private sources, to some of which I propose to offer a reply.

One such critic complains that Arthur's strictures, on sermons and on choristers, are too severe. Let me say, in reply, that I do *not* hold myself responsible for *any* of the opinions expressed by the characters in my book. They are simply opinions which, it seemed to me, might probably be held by the persons into whose mouths I put them, and which were worth consideration.

Other critics have objected to certain innovations in spelling, such as "ca'n't", "wo'n't", "traveler". In reply, I can only plead my firm conviction that the popular usage is *wrong*. As to "ca'n't", it will not be disputed that, in all *other* words ending in "n't", these letters are an abbreviation of "not"; and it is surely absurd to suppose that, in this solitary instance, "not" is represented by " 't"! In fact "can't" is the *proper* abbreviation for "can it", just as "is't" is for "is it". Again, in "wo'n't", the first apostrophe is needed, because the word "would" is here *abridged* into "wo": but I hold it proper to spell "don't" with only *one apostrophe, because the word "do" is here complete.* As to such words as "traveler", I hold the correct principle to be, to *double* the consonant when the accent falls on that syllable; otherwise to leave it *single*. This rule is observed in most cases (e.g. we double the "r" in "preferred", but leave it single in "offered"), so that I am only extending, to other cases, an existing rule. I admit, however, that I do not spell "parallel", as the rule would have it; but here we are constrained, by the etymology, to insert the double "l".

In the Preface to Vol. I. were two puzzles, on which my readers might exercise their ingenuity. One was, to detect the 3 lines of "padding", which I had found it necessary to supply in the passage extending from the middle of p. 262 to the middle of p. 264. They are the 23rd, 24th and 25th lines of p. 263. The other puzzle was, to determine which (if any) of the 8 stanzas of the Gardener's Song (see pp. 277, 283, 285, 288, 296, 302, 327, 328) were adapted to the context, and which (if any) had the context adapted to them. The last of them is the only one that was adapted to the context, the "Garden-Door that opened with a key" having been substituted for some creature (a Cormorant, I think) "that nestled in a tree". At pp. 283, 296, and 327, the context was adapted to the stanza. At p. 288, neither stanza nor context was altered: the connection between them was simply a piece of good luck.

In the Preface to Vol. I., at pp. 239, 240, I gave an account of the making-up of the story of "Sylvie and Bruno". A few more details may perhaps be acceptable to my Readers.

It was in 1873, as I *now* believe, that the idea first occurred to me that a little fairy-tale (written, in 1867, for "Aunt Judy's Magazine", under the title "Bruno's Revenge") might serve as the nucleus of a longer story. This I surmise, from having found the original draft of the last paragraph of Vol. II., dated 1873. So that this paragraph has been waiting 20 years for its chance of emerging into print—more than twice the period so cautiously recommended by Horace for "repressing" one's literary efforts!

It was in February, 1885, that I entered into negotiations, with Mr. Harry Furniss, for illustrating the book. Most of the substance of *both* Volumes was then in existence in manuscript: and my original intention was to publish the *whole* story at once. In September, 1885, I received from Mr. Furniss the first set of drawings—the four which illustrate "Peter and Paul": in November, 1886, I received the second set—the three which illustrate the Professor's song about the "little man" who had "a little gun": and in January, 1887, I received the third set—the four which illustrate the "Pig-Tale".

So we went on, illustrating first one bit of the story, and then another, without any idea of sequence. And it was not till March, 1889, that, having calculated the number of pages the story would occupy, I decided on dividing it into *two* portions, and publishing it half at a time. This necessitated the writing of a *sort* of conclusion for the first Volume: and *most* of my Readers, I fancy, regarded this as the *actual* conclusion, when that Volume appeared in December, 1889. At any rate, among all the letters I received about it, there was only *one* which expressed *any* suspicion that it was not a *final* conclusion. This letter was from a child. She wrote "we were so glad, when we came to the end of the book, to find that there was no ending-up, for that shows us that you are going to write a sequel."

It may interest some of my Readers to know the *theory* on which this story is constructed. It is an attempt to show what might *possibly* happen, supposing that Fairies really existed; and that they were sometimes visible to us, and we to them; and that they were sometimes able to assume human form: and supposing, also, that human beings might sometimes become conscious of what goes on in the Fairy-world—by actual transference of their immaterial essence, such as we meet with in "Esoteric Buddhism".

I have supposed a Human being to be capable of various physical states, with varying degrees of consciousness, as follows:

(*a*) the ordinary state, with no consciousness of the presence of Fairies;

(*b*) the "eerie" state, in which, while conscious of actual surroundings, he is *also* conscious of the presence of Fairies;

(*c*) a form of trance, in which, while *un*conscious of actual surroundings, and apparently asleep, he (i.e. his immaterial essence) migrates to other scenes, in the actual world, or in Fairyland, and is conscious of the presence of Fairies.

I have also supposed a Fairy to be capable of migrating from Fairyland into the actual world, and of assuming, at pleasure, a Human form; and also to be capable of various psychical states, viz.

(*a*) the ordinary state, with no consciousness of the presence of Human beings;

(*b*) a sort of "eerie" state, in which he is conscious, if in the actual world, of the presence of actual Human beings; if in Fairyland, of the presence of the immaterial essences of Human beings.

I will here tabulate the passages, in both Volumes, where abnormal states occur.

Vol. I.	Historian's Locality and	State.	Other Characters.
pp. 247–254	In train	*c*	Chancellor (*b*) p. 247.
260–272	do.	*c*	
277–284	do.	*c*	
285–293	At lodgings..........	*c*	
295–302	On beach	*c*	
302–335	At lodgings..........	*c*	S. and B. (*b*) pp. 324–326.
			Professor (*b*) p. 329.
339–351	In wood	*b*	Bruno (*b*) pp. 342–351.
353–357	In wood, sleep-walking	*c*	S. and B. (*b*).
365–367	Among ruins	*c*	do. (*b*).
371, 372	do. dreaming	*a*	
372–374	do. sleep-walking	*c*	S. B. and Professor in Human form.
375...	In street............	*b*	
379–386	At station, &c........	*b*	S. and B. (*b*).
391–409	In garden	*c*	S. B. and Professor (*b*).
403–409	On road, &c.	*a*	S. and B. in Human form.
410–415	In street, &c.	*a*	
417–427	In wood	*b*	S. and B. (*b*).
Vol. II.			
pp. 450–457	In garden	*b*	S. and B. (*b*).
469–471	On road	*b*	do. (*b*).
472–484	do.	*b*	do. in Human form.
484–491	do.	*b*	do. (*b*).
516–543	In drawing-room	*a*	do. in Human form.
544–559	do.	*c*	do. (*b*).
567–572	In smoking-room.....	*c*	do. (*b*).
587–589	In wood	*b*	do. (*a*); Lady Muriel (*b*).
590–607	At lodgings..........	*c*	
611–635	do.	*c*	
639–end.	do.	*b*	

In the Preface to Vol. I., at pp. 239 and 240, I gave an account of the *origination* of some of the ideas embodied in the book. A few more such details may perhaps interest my Readers:

I. p. 344. The very peculiar use, here made of a dead mouse, comes from real life. I once found two very small boys, in a garden, playing a microscopic game of "Single-Wicket". The bat was, I think, about the size of a tablespoon; and the utmost distance attained by the ball, in its most daring flights, was some 4 or 5 yards. The *exact* length was of course a matter of *supreme* importance; and it was always carefully measured out (the batsman and the bowler amicably sharing the toil) with a dead mouse!

I. p. 369. The two quasi-mathematical Axioms, quoted by Arthur at p. 369-70 of Vol. I. ("Things that are greater than the same are greater than one another", and "All angles are equal") were actually enunciated, in all seriousness, by undergraduates at a University situated not 100 miles from Ely.

II. p. 452. Bruno's remark ("I can, if I like, &c.") was actually made by a little boy.

II. p. 454. So also was his remark ("I know what it *doesn't* spell"). And his remark ("I just twiddled my eyes, &c.") I heard from the lips of a little girl, who had just solved a puzzle I had set her.

II. p. 474. Bruno's soliloquy ("For its father, &c.") was actually spoken by a little girl, looking out of the window of a railway-carriage.

II. p. 510. The remark, made by a guest at the dinner-party, when asking for a dish of fruit ("I've been wishing for them, &c.") I heard made by the great Poet-Laureate, whose loss the whole reading-world has so lately had to deplore.

II. p. 521. Bruno's speech, on the subject of the age of "Mein Herr", embodies the reply of a little girl to the question "Is your grandmother an *old* lady?" "I don't know if she's an *old* lady," said this cautious young person; "she's *eighty-three*."

II. p. 540. The speech about "Obstruction" is no mere creature of my imagination! It is copied *verbatim* from the columns of the Standard, and was spoken by Sir William Harcourt, who was, at the time, a member of the "Opposition", at the "National Liberal Club", on July the 16th, 1890.

II. p. 599. The Professor's remark, about a dog's tail, that "it doesn't bite at *that* end", was actually made by a child, when warned of the danger he was incurring by pulling the dog's tail.

II. p. 623. The dialogue between Sylvie and Bruno, which occupies lines 14 to 19, is a *verbatim* report (merely substituting "cake" for "penny") of a dialogue overheard between two children.

One story in this Volume—"Bruno's Picnic"—I can vouch for as suitable for telling to children, having tested it again and again; and, whether my audience has been a dozen little girls in a village-school, or some thirty or forty in a London drawing-room, or a hundred in a High School, I have always found them earnestly attentive, and keenly appreciative of such fun as the story supplied.

May I take this opportunity of calling attention to what I flatter myself was a successful piece of name-coining, at p. 265 of Vol. I. Does not the name "Sibimet" fairly embody the character of the Sub-Warden? The gentle Reader has no doubt observed what s singularly useless article in a house a brazen trumpet is, if you simply leave it lying about, and never blow it!

Readers of the first Volume, who have amused themselves by trying to solve the two puzzles propounded at page 240 of the Preface, may perhaps like to exercise their ingenuity in discovering which (if any) of the following parallelisms were intentional, and which (if any) accidental.

"Little Birds".   Events, and Persons.

      Stanza 1. Banquet.
                2. Chancellor.
                3. Empress and Spinach (II. 597).
                4. Warden's Return.
                5. Professor's Lecture (II. 601).
                6. Other Professor's Song (I. 312).
                7. Petting of Uggug.
                8. Baron Doppelgeist.
                9. Jester and Bear (I. 305). Little Foxes.
             10. Bruno's Dinner-Bell; Little Foxes.

I will publish the answer to this puzzle in the Preface to a little book of "Original Games and Puzzles", now in course of preparation.

I have reserved, for the last, one or two rather more serious topics.

I had intended, in this Preface, to discuss more fully, than I had done in the previous Volume, the "Morality of Sport", with special reference to letters I have received from lovers of Sport, in which they point out the many great advantages which men get from it, and try to prove that the suffering, which it inflicts on animals, is too trivial to be regarded.

But, when I came to think the subject out, and to arrange the whole of the arguments "pro" and "con", I found it much too large for treatment here. Some day, I hope to publish an essay on this subject. At present, I will content myself with stating the net result I have arrived at.

It is, that God has given to Man an absolute right to take the *lives* of other animals, for *any* reasonable cause, such as the supply of food: but that He has *not* given to Man the right to inflict *pain*, unless when necessary: that mere pleasure, or advantage, does not constitute such a necessity: and, consequently, that pain, inflicted for the purposes of *Sport*, is cruel, and therefore wrong. But I find it a far more complex question than I had supposed; and that the "case", on the side of the Sportsman, is a much stronger one than I had supposed. So, for the present, I say no more about it.

Objections have been raised to the severe language I have put into the mouth of "Arthur", at p. 377, on the subject of "Sermons", and at pp. 376, 377, on the subjects of Choral Services and "Choristers".

I have already protested against the assumption that I am ready to endorse the opinions of characters in my story. But, in these two instances, I admit that I am much in sympathy with "Arthur". In my opinion, far too many sermons are expected from our preachers; and, as a consequence, a great many are preached, which are not worth listening to; and, as a consequence of *that*, we are very apt *not* to listen. The reader of this paragraph probably heard a sermon last Sunday morning? Well, let him, if he can, name the text, and state how the preacher treated it!

Then, as to "Choristers", and all the other accessories—of music, vestments, processions, &c.—which have come, along with them, into fashion—while freely admitting that the "Ritual" movement was sorely needed, and that it has effected a vast improvement in our Church-Services, which had become dead and dry to the last degree, I hold that, like many other desirable movements, it has gone too far in the opposite direction, and has introduced many new dangers.

For the Congregation this new movement involves the danger of learning to think that the Services are done *for* them; and that their bodily *presence* is all they need contribute. And, for Clergy and Congregation alike, it involves the danger of regarding these elaborate Services as *ends in themselves*, and of forgetting that they are simply *means*, and the very hollowest of mockeries, unless they bear fruit in our *lives*.

For the Choristers it seems to involve the danger of self-conceit, as described at p. 376 (N.B. "stagy-entrances" is a misprint for "stage-entrances"), the danger of regarding those parts of the Service, where their help is not required, as not worth attending to, the danger of coming to regard the Service as a mere outward form—a series of postures to be assumed, and of words to be said or sung, while the *thoughts* are elsewhere—and the danger of "familiarity" breeding "contempt" for sacred things.

Let me illustrate these last two forms of danger, from my own experience. Not long ago, I attended a Cathedral-Service, and was placed immediately behind a row of men, members of the Choir; and I could not help noticing that they treated the *Lessons* as a part of the Service to which they needed not to give *any* attention, and as affording them a convenient opportunity for arranging music-books, &c., &c. Also I have frequently seen a row of little choristers, after marching in procession to their places, kneel down, as if about to pray, and rise from their knees after a minute spent in looking about them, it being but too evident that the attitude was a mere mockery. Surely it is very dangerous, for these children, to thus accustom them to *pretend* to pray? As an instance of irreverent treatment of holy things, I will mention a custom, which no doubt many of my readers have noticed in Churches where the Clergy and Choir enter in procession, viz. that, at the end of the private devotions, which are carried on in the vestry, and which are of course inaudible to the Congregation, the final "Amen" is *shouted*, loud enough to be heard all through the Church. This serves as a signal, to the Congregation, to prepare to rise when the procession appears: and it admits of no dispute that it is for this purpose that it is thus shouted. When we remember to Whom that "Amen" is *really* addressed, and consider that it is here *used* for the same purpose as one of the Church-bells, we must surely admit that it is a piece of gross irreverence? To *me* it is much as if I were to see a Bible used as a footstool.

As an instance of the dangers, for the Clergy themselves, introduced by this new movement, let me mention the fact that according to *my* experience, Clergymen of this school are *specially* apt to retail comic anecdotes, in which the most sacred names and words—sometimes actual texts from the Bible—are used as themes for jesting. Many such things are repeated as having been originally said by *children*, whose utter ignorance of evil must no doubt acquit *them*, in the sight of God, of all blame; but it must be otherwise for those who *consciously* use such innocent utterances as material for their unholy mirth.

Let me add, however, *most* earnestly, that I fully believe that this profanity is, in many cases, *un*conscious: the "environment" (as I have tried to explain at pp. 503, 504) makes all the difference between man and man; and I rejoice to think that many of these profane stories—which *I* find so painful to listen to, and should feel it a sin to repeat—give to *their* ears no pain, and to *their* consciences no shock; and that *they* can utter, not less sincerely than myself, the two prayers, "*Hallowed be Thy Name*," and "*from hardness of heart, and contempt of Thy Word and Commandment, Good Lord, deliver us!*" To which I would desire to add, for their sake and for my own, Keble's beautiful petition, "*help us, this and every day, To live more nearly as we pray!*" It is, in fact, for its *consequences*—for the grave dangers, both to speaker and to hearer, which it involves—rather than for what it is *in itself*, that I mourn over this clerical habit of profanity in social talk. To the *believing* hearer it brings the danger of loss of reverence for holy things, by the mere act of listening to, and enjoying, such jests; and also the temptation to retail them for the amusement of others. To the *unbelieving* hearer it brings a welcome confirmation of his theory that religion is a fable, in the spectacle of its accredited champions thus betraying their trust. And to the speaker himself it must surely bring the danger of *loss of faith*. For surely such jests, if uttered with no consciousness of harm, must necessarily be also uttered with no consciousness, at the moment, of the *reality* of God, as a *living being*, who hears all we say. And he, who allows himself the habit of thus uttering holy words, with no thought of their meaning, is but too likely to find that, for him, God has become a myth, and heaven a poetic fancy—that, for him, the light of life is gone, and that he is at heart an atheist, lost in *"a darkness that may be felt"*.

There is, I fear, at the present time, an increasing tendency to irreverent treatment of the name of God and of subjects connected with religion. Some of our theatres are helping this downward movement by the gross caricatures of clergymen which they put upon the stage: some of our clergy are themselves helping it, by showing that they can lay aside the spirit of reverence, along with their surplices, and can treat as jests, when *outside* their churches, names and things to which they pay an almost superstitious veneration when *inside*: the "Salvation Army" has, I fear, with the best intentions, done much to help it, by the coarse familiarity with which they treat holy things: and surely every one, who desires to *live* in the spirit of the prayer *"Hallowed be Thy Name"*, ought to do what he can, however little that may be, to check it. So I have gladly taken this unique opportunity, however unfit the topic may seem for the Preface to a book of this kind, to express some thoughts which have weighed on my mind for a long time. I did not expect, when I wrote the Preface to Vol. I, that it would be read to any appreciable extent: but I rejoice to believe, from evidence that has reached me, that it *has* been read by many, and to hope that this Preface will also be so: and I think that, among them, some will be found ready to sympathize with the views I have put forwards, and ready to help, with their prayers and their example, the revival, in Society, of the waning spirit of reverence.

A Fairy-duet

CHAPTER 1

Bruno's Lessons

During the next month or two my solitary town-life seemed, by contrast, unusually dull and tedious. I missed the pleasant friends I had left behind at Elveston—the genial interchange of thought—the sympathy which gave to one's ideas a new and vivid reality: but, perhaps more than all, I missed the companionship of the two Fairies—or Dream-Children, for I had not yet solved the problem as to who or what they were—whose sweet playfulness had shed a magic radiance over my life.

In office-hours—which I suppose reduce most men to the mental condition of a coffee-mill or a mangle—time sped along much as usual: it was in the pauses of life, the desolate hours when books and newspapers palled on the sated appetite, and when, thrown back upon one's own dreary musings, one strove—all in vain—to people the vacant air with the dear faces of absent friends, that the real bitterness of solitude made itself felt.

One evening, feeling my life a little more wearisome than usual, I strolled down to my Club, not so much with the hope of meeting any friend there, for London was now "out of town", as with the feeling that here, at least, I should hear "sweet words of human speech", and come into contact with human thought.

However, almost the first face I saw there *was* that of a friend. Eric Lindon was lounging, with rather a "bored" expression of face, over a newspaper; and we fell into conversation with a mutual satisfaction which neither of us tried to conceal.

After a while I ventured to introduce what was just then the main subject of my thoughts. "And so the Doctor" (a name we had adopted by a tacit agreement, as a convenient compromise between the formality of "Doctor Forester" and the intimacy—to which Eric Lindon hardly seemed entitled—of "Arthur") "has gone abroad by this time, I suppose? Can you give me his present address?"

"He is still at Elveston—I believe," was the reply. "But I have not been there since I last met you."

I did not know which part of this intelligence to wonder at most. "And might I ask—if it isn't taking too much of a liberty—when your wedding-bells are to—or perhaps they *have* rung, already?"

"No," said Eric, in a steady voice, which betrayed scarcely a trace of emotion: "*that* engagement is at an end. I am still 'Benedick the *un*married man'."

After this, the thick-coming fancies—all radiant with new possibilities of happiness for Arthur—were far too bewildering to admit of any further conversation, and I was only too glad to avail myself of the first decent excuse, that offered itself, for retiring into silence.

The next day I wrote to Arthur, with as much of a reprimand for his long silence as I could bring myself to put into words, begging him to tell me how the world went with him.

Needs must that three or four days—possibly more—should elapse before I could receive his reply; and never had I known days drag their slow length along with a more tedious indolence.

To while away the time, I strolled, one afternoon, into Kensington Gardens, and, wandering aimlessly along any path that presented itself, I soom became aware that I had somehow strayed into one that was wholly new to me. Still, my elfish experiences seemed to have so completely faded out of my life that nothing was further from my thoughts than the idea of again meeting my fairy-friends, when I chanced to notice a small creature, moving among the grass that fringed the path, that did not seem to be an insect, or a frog, or any other living thing that I could think of. Cautiously kneeling down, and making an *ex tempore* cage of my two hands, I imprisoned the little wanderer, and felt a sudden thrill of surprise and delight on discovering that my prisoner was no other than *Bruno* himself!

Bruno took the matter *very* coolly, and, when I had replaced him on the ground, where he would be within easy conversational distance, he began talking, just as if it were only a few minutes since last we had met.

"Doos oo know what the *Rule* is", he enquired, "when oo catches a Fairy, withouten its having tolded oo where it was?" (Bruno's notions of English Grammar had certainly *not* improved since our last meeting.)

"No," I said. "I didn't know there was any Rule about it."

"I *think* oo've got a right to *eat* me," said the little fellow looking up into my face with a winning smile. "But I'm not pruffickly sure. Oo'd better not do it wizout asking."

It did indeed seem reasonable not to take so irrevocable a step as *that*, without due enquiry. "I'll certainly *ask* about it first," I said. "Besides, I don't know yet whether you would be *worth* eating!"

"I guess I'm *deliciously* good to eat," Bruno remarked in a satisfied tone, as if it were something to be rather proud of.

"And what are you doing here, Bruno?"

"*That's* not my name!" said my cunning little friend. "Don't oo know my name's 'Oh Bruno!'? That's what Sylvie always calls me, when I says mine lessons."

"Well then, what are you doing here, oh Bruno?"

"Doing mine lessons, a-course!" With that roguish twinkle in his eye, that always came when he knew he was talking nonsense.

"Oh, *that's* the way you do your lessons, is it? And do you remember them well?"

"Always can 'member *mine* lessons," said Bruno. "It's *Sylvie's* lessons that's so *dreffully* hard to 'member!" He frowned, as if in agonies of thought, and tapped his forehead with his knuckles. "I *ca'n't* think enough to understand them!" he said despairingly. "It wants *double* thinking, I believe!"

"But where's Sylvie gone?"

"That's just what *I* want to know!" said Bruno disconsolately. "What ever's the good of setting me lessons, when she isn't here to 'splain the hard bits?"

"*I'll* find her for you!" I volunteered; and, getting up, I wandered round the tree under whose shade I had been reclining, looking on all sides for Sylvie. In another minute I *again* noticed some strange thing moving among the grass, and, kneeling down, was immediately confronted with Sylvie's innocent face, lighted up with a joyful surprise at seeing me, and was accosted, in the sweet voice I knew so well, with what seemed to be the *end* of a sentence whose beginning I had failed to catch.

"—and I think he ought to have *finished* them by this time. So I'm going back to him. Will you come too? It's only just round at the other side of this tree."

It was but a few steps for *me*; but it was a great many for Sylvie; and I had to be very careful to walk slowly, in order not to leave the little creature so far behind as to lose sight of her.

To find Bruno's *lessons* was easy enough: they appeared to be neatly written out on large smooth ivy-leaves, which were scattered in some confusion over a little patch of ground where the grass had been worn away; but the pale student, who ought by rights to have been bending over them, was nowhere to be seen: we looked in all directions, for some time in vain; but at last Sylvie's sharp eyes detected him, swinging on a tendril of ivy, and Sylvie's stern voice commanded his instant return to *terra firma* and to the business of Life.

"Pleasure first and business afterwards" seemed to be the motto of these tiny folk, so many hugs and kisses had to be interchanged before anything else could be done.

"Now, Bruno," Sylvie said reproachfully, "didn't I tell you you were to go on with your lessons, unless you heard to the contrary?"

"But I *did* heard to the contrary!" Bruno insisted, with a mischievous twinkle in his eye.

"*What* did you hear, you wicked boy?"

"It were a sort of noise in the air," said Bruno: "a sort of a scrambling noise. Didn't *oo* hear it, Mister Sir?"

"Well, anyhow, you needn't go to *sleep* over them, you lazy-lazy!" For Bruno had curled himself up, on the largest "lesson", and was arranging another as a pillow.

"I *wasn't* asleep!" said Bruno, in a deeply-injured tone. "When I shuts mine eyes, it's to show that I'm *awake!*"

"Well, how much have you learned, then?"

"I've learned a little tiny bit," said Bruno, modestly, being evidently afraid of overstating his achievement. "*Ca'n't* learn no more!"

"Oh Bruno! You know you *can*, if you like."

"Course I can, if I *like*," the pale student replied; "but I ca'n't if I *don't* like!"

Sylvie had a way—which I could not too highly admire—of evading Bruno's logical perplexities by suddenly striking into a new line of thought; and this masterly stratagem she now adopted.

"Well, I must say *one* thing——"

"Did oo know, Mister Sir," Bruno thoughtfully remarked, "that Sylvie ca'n't count? Whenever she says 'I must say *one* thing', I *know* quite well she'll say *two* things! And she always doos."

"Two heads are better than one, Bruno," I said, but with no very distinct idea as to what I meant by it.

"I shouldn't mind having two *heads*," Bruno said softly to himself:

"One head to eat mine dinner, and one head to argue wiz Sylvie—doos oo think oo'd look prettier if oo'd got *two* heads, Mister Sir?"

The case did not, I assured him, admit of a doubt.

"The reason why Sylvie's so cross——" Bruno went on very seriously, almost sadly.

Sylvie's eyes grew large and round with surprise at this new line of enquiry—her rosy face being perfectly radiant with good humour. But she said nothing.

"Wouldn't it be better to tell me after the lessons are over?" I suggested.

"Very well," Bruno said with a resigned air: "only she wo'n't be cross then."

"There's only three lessons to do," said Sylvie. "Spelling, and Geography, and Singing."

"Not *Arithmetic*?" I said.

"No, he hasn't a head for Arithmetic——"

"Course I haven't!" said Bruno. "Mine head's for *hair*. I haven't got a *lot* of heads!'

"—and he ca'n't learn his Multiplication-table——"

"I like *History* ever so much better," Bruno remarked. "Oo has to *repeat* that Muddlecome table——"

"Well, and you have to repeat——"

"No, oo hasn't!" Bruno interrupted. "History repeats itself. The Professor said so!"

Sylvie was arranging some letters on a board—E—V—I—L. "Now, Bruno," she said, "what does *that spell*?"

Bruno looked at it, in solemn silence, for a minute. "I know what it *doesn't* spell!" he said at last.

"That's no good," said Sylvie. "What *does* it spell?"

Bruno took another look at the mysterious letters. "Why, it's 'LIVE', backwards!" he exclaimed. (I thought it was, indeed.)

"How *did* you manage to see that?" said Sylvie.

"I just twiddled my eyes," said Bruno, "and then I saw it directly. Now may I sing the King-fisher Song?"

"Geography next," said Sylvie. "Don't you know the Rules?"

"I think there oughtn't to be such a lot of Rules, Sylvie! I thinks——"

"Yes, there *ought* to be such a lot of Rules, you wicked, wicked boy! And how dare you *think* at all about it? And shut up that mouth directly!"

So, as "that mouth" didn't seem inclined to shut up of itself, Sylvie shut it for him—with both hands—and sealed it with a kiss, just as you would fasten up a letter.

"Now that Bruno is fastened up from talking," she went on, turning to me, "I'll show you the Map he does his lessons on."

And there it was, a large Map of the World, spread out on the ground. It was so large that Bruno had to crawl about on it, to point out the places named in the "King-fisher Lesson".

"When a King-fisher sees a Lady-bird flying away, he says '*Ceylon*, if you *Candia*!' and when he catches it he says 'Come to *Media*! And if you're *Hungary* or thirsty, I'll give you some *Nubia*!' When he takes it in his claws, he says '*Europe*!' When he puts it into his beak, he says '*India*!' When he's swallowed it, he says '*Eton*!' That's all."

"That's *quite* perfect," said Sylvie. "Now, you may sing the King-fisher Song."

"Will *oo* sing the chorus?" Bruno said to me.

I was just beginning to say "I'm afraid I don't know the *words*", when Sylvie silently turned the map over, and I found the words were all written on the back. In one respect it was a *very* peculiar song: the chorus to each verse came in the *middle*, instead of at the *end* of it. However, the tune was so easy that I soon picked it up, and managed the chorus as well, perhaps, as it is possible for *one* person to manage such a thing. It was in vain that I signed to Sylvie to help me: she only smiled sweetly and shook her head.

> *"King Fisher courted Lady Bird—*
>
> **Sing Beans, sing Bones, sing Butterflies!**
> *'Find me my match,' he said,*
> *'With such a noble head—*
> *With such a beard, as white as curd—*
> *With such expressive eyes!'*
>
> *" 'Yet pins have heads,' said Lady Bird—*
>
> **Sing Prunes, sing Prawns, sing Primrose-Hill!**
> *'And, where you stick them in,*
> *They stay, and thus a pin*
> *Is very much to be preferred*
> *To one that's never still!'*
>
> *" 'Oysters have beards,' said Lady Bird—*
>
> **Sing Flies, sing Frogs, sing Fiddle-strings!**
> *'I love them, for I know*
> *They never chatter so:*
> *They would not say one single word—*
> *Not if you crowned them Kings!'*
>
> *" 'Needles have eyes,' said Lady Bird—*
>
> **Sing Cats, sing Corks, sing Cowslip-tea!**
> *'And they are sharp—just what*
> *Your Majesty is* not:
> *So get you gone—'tis too absurd*
> *To come a-courting me!' "*

"So he went away," Bruno added as a kind of postscript, when the last note of the song had died away, "Just like he always did."

"Oh, my *dear* Bruno!" Sylvie exclaimed, with her hands over her ears. "You shouldn't say 'like': you should say '*what*'."

To which Bruno replied, doggedly, "I only says 'what!' when oo doosn't speak loud, so as I can hear oo."

"Where did he go to?" I asked, hoping to prevent an argument.

"He went more far than he'd never been before," said Bruno.

"You should never say 'more far'," Sylvie corrected him: "you should say '*farther*'."

"Then *oo* shouldn't say 'more broth', when we're at dinner," Bruno retorted: "oo should say '*brother*'!"

This time Sylvie evaded an argument by turning away, and beginning to roll up the Map. "Lessons are over!" she proclaimed in her sweetest tones.

"And has there been no *crying* over them?" I enquired. "Little boys *always* cry over their lessons, don't they?"

"I never cries after twelve o'clock," said Bruno: " 'cause then it's getting so near to dinner-time."

"Sometimes, in the morning," Sylvie said in a low voice; "when it's Geography-day, and when he's been disobe——"

"*What* a fellow you are to talk, Sylvie!" Bruno hastily interposed. "Doos oo think the world was *made* for oo to talk in?"

"Why, where would you *have* me talk, then?" Sylvie said, evidently quite ready for an argument.

But Bruno answered resolutely. "I'm not going to argue about it, 'cause it's getting late, and there wo'n't be time—but oo's as 'ong as ever oo can be!" And he rubbed the back of his hand across his eyes, in which tears were beginning to glitter.

Sylvie's eyes filled with tears in a moment. "I didn't mean it, Bruno, *darling*!" she whispered; and the rest of the argument was lost "amid the tangles of Neæra's hair", while the two disputants hugged and kissed each other.

But this new form of argument was brought to a sudden end by a flash of lightning, which was closely followed by a peal of thunder, and by a torrent of rain-drops, which came hissing and spitting, almost like live creatures, through the leaves of the tree that sheltered us. "Why, it's raining cats and dogs!" I said.

"And all the *dogs* has come down *first*," said Bruno: "There's nothing but *cats* coming down now!"

In another minute the pattering ceased, as suddenly as it had begun. I stepped out from under the tree, and found that the storm was over; but I looked in vain, on my return, for my tiny companions. They had vanished with the storm, and there was nothing for it but to make the best of my way home.

On the table lay, awaiting my return, an envelope of that peculiar yellow tint which always announces a telegram, and which must be, in the memories of so many of us, inseparably linked with some great and sudden sorrow—something that has cast a shadow, never in this world to be wholly lifted off, on the brightness of Life. No doubt. it has *also* heralded—for many of us—some sudden news of joy; but this, I think, is less common: human life seems, on the whole, to contain more of sorrow than of joy. And yet the world goes on. Who knows why?

This time, however, there was no shock of sorrow to be faced: in fact, the few words it contained ("Could not bring myself to write. Come soon. Always welcome. A letter follows this. Arthur.") seemed so like Arthur himself speaking, that it gave me quite a thrill of pleasure, and I at once began the preparations needed for the journey.

CHAPTER 2

Love's Curfew

"FAYFIELD Junction! Change for Elveston!"

What subtle memory could there be, linked to these commonplace words, that caused such a flood of happy thoughts to fill my brain? I dismounted from the carriage in a state of joyful excitement for. which I could not at first account. True, I had taken this very journey, and at the same hour of the day, six months ago; but many things had happened since then, and an old man's memory has but a slender hold on recent events: I sought "the missing link" in vain. Suddenly I caught sight of a bench—the only one provided on the cheerless platform—with a lady seated on it, and the whole forgotten scene flashed upon me as vividly as if it were happening over again.

"Yes," I thought. "This bare platform is, for me, rich with the memory of a dear friend! She was sitting on that very bench, and invited me to share it, with some quotation from Shakespeare—I forget what. I'll try the Earl's plan for the Dramatization of Life, and fancy that figure to be Lady Muriel; and I wo'n't undeceive myself too soon!"

So I strolled along the platform, resolutely "making-believe" (as children say) that the casual passenger, seated on that bench, was the Lady Muriel I remembered so well. She was facing away from me, which aided the elaborate cheatery I was practising on myself: but, though I was careful, in passing the spot, to look the other way, in order to prolong the pleasant illusion, it was inevitable that, when I turned to walk back again, I should see who it was. It was Lady Muriel herself!

The whole scene now returned vividly to my memory; and, to make this repetition of it stranger still, there was the same old man, whom I remembered seeing so roughly ordered off, by the Station-Master, to make room for his titled passenger. The same, but "with a difference": no longer tottering feebly along the platform, but actually seated at Lady Muriel's side, and in conversation with her! "Yes, put it in your purse," she was saying, "and remember you're to spend it all for *Minnie*. And mind you bring her something nice, that'll do her real good! And give her my love!" So intent was she on saying these words, that, although the sound of my footstep had made her lift her head and look at me, she did not at first recognize me.

I raised my hat as I approached, and then there flashed across her face a genuine look of joy, which so exactly recalled the sweet face of Sylvie, when last we met in Kensington Gardens, that I felt quite bewildered.

Rather than disturb the poor old man at her side, she rose from her seat, and joined me in my walk up and down the platform, and for a

minute or two our conversation was as utterly trivial and commonplace as if we were merely two casual guests in a London drawing-room. Each of us seemed to shrink, just at first, from touching on the deeper interests which linked our lives together.

The Elveston train had drawn up at the platform, while we talked; and, in obedience to the Station-Master's obsequious hint of "This way, my Lady! Time's up!", we were making the best of our way towards the end which contained the sole first-class carriage, and were just passing the now-empty bench, when Lady Muriel noticed, lying on it, the purse in which her gift had just been so carefully bestowed, the owner of which, all unconscious of his loss, was being helped into a carriage at the other end of the train. She pounced on it instantly. "Poor old man!" she cried. "He mustn't go off, and think he's lost it!"

"Let *me* run with it! I can go quicker than you!" I said. But she was already half-way down the platform, flying ("running" is much too mundane a word for such fairy-like motion) at a pace that left all possible efforts of *mine* hopelessly in the rear.

She was back again before I had well completed my audacious boast of speed in running, and was saying, quite demurely, as we entered our carriage, "and you really think *you* could have done it quicker?"

"No, indeed!" I replied. "I plead 'Guilty' of gross exaggeration, and throw myself on the mercy of the Court!"

"The Court will overlook it—for this once!" Then her manner suddenly changed from playfulness to an anxious gravity.

"You are not looking your best!" she said with an anxious glance. "In fact, I think you look *more* of an invalid than when you left us. I very much doubt if London agrees with you?"

"It *may* be the London air," I said, "or it may be the hard work—or my rather lonely life: anyhow, I've *not* been feeling very well, lately. But Elveston will soon set me up again. Arthur's prescription—he's my doctor, you know, and I heard from him this morning—is 'plenty of ozone, and new milk, and *pleasant society*'!"

"Pleasant society?" said Lady Muriel, with a pretty make-believe of considering the question. "Well, really I don't know where we can find *that* for you! We have so few neighbours. But new milk we *can* manage. Do get it of my old friend Mrs. Hunter, up there, on the hill-side. You may rely upon the *quality*. And her little Bessie comes to school every day, and passes your lodgings. So it would be very easy to send it."

"I'll follow your advice with pleasure," I said; "and I'll go and arrange about it to-morrow. I know Arthur will want a walk."

"You'll find it quite an easy walk—under three miles, I think."

"Well, now that we've settled that point, let me retort your own remark upon yourself. I don't think *you're* looking quite your best!"

"I daresay not," she replied in a low voice; and a sudden shadow seemed to overspread her face. "I've had some troubles lately. It's a matter about which I've been long wishing to consult you, but I couldn't easily write about it. I'm *so* glad to have this opportunity!"

"Do you think", she began again, after a minute's silence, and with a visible embarrassment of manner most unusual in her, "that a promise, deliberately and solemnly given, is *always* binding—except, of course, where its fulfilment would involve some actual *sin*?"

"I ca'n't think of any other exception at this moment," I said. "That branch of casuistry is usually, I believe, treated as a question of truth and untruth——"

"Surely that *is* the principle?" she eagerly interrupted. "I always thought the Bible-teaching about it consisted of such texts '*lie not one to another*'?"

"I have thought about that point," I replied; "and it seems to me that the essence of *lying* is the intention of *deceiving*. If you give a promise, fully *intending* to fulfil it, you are certainly acting truthfully *then*; and, if you afterwards break it, that does not involve any *deception*. I cannot call it *untruthful*."

Another pause of silence ensued. Lady Muriel's face was hard to read: she looked pleased, I thought, but also puzzled; and I felt curious to know whether her question had, as I began to suspect, some bearing on the breaking off of her engagement with Captain (now Major) Lindon.

"You have relieved me from a great fear," she said; "but the thing is of course *wrong*, somehow. What texts would *you* quote, to prove it wrong?"

"Any that enforce the payment of *debts*. If *A* promises something to *B*, *B* has a claim upon *A*. And *A*'s sin, if he breaks his promise, seems to me more analogous to *stealing* than to *lying*."

"It's a new way of looking at it—to me," she said; "but it seems a *true* way, also. However, I wo'n't deal in generalities, with an old friend like you! For we *are* old friends, somehow. Do you know, I think we *began* as old friends?" she said with a playfulness of tone that ill accorded with the tears that glistened in her eyes.

"Thank you very much for saying so," I replied. "I like to think of you as an *old* friend," ("—though you don't look it!" would have been the almost necessary sequence, with any other lady; but she and I seemed to have long passed out of the time when compliments, or any such trivialities, were possible).

Here the train paused at a station, where two or three passengers entered the carriage; so no more was said till we had reached our journey's end.

On our arrival at Elveston she readily adopted my suggestion that we should walk up together; so, as soon as our luggage had been duly taken charge of—hers by the servant who met her at the station, and mine by one of the porters—we set out together along the familiar lanes, now linked in my memory with so many delightful associations. Lady Muriel at once recommenced the conversation at the point where it had been interrupted.

"You knew of my engagement to my cousin Eric. Did you also hear——"

"Yes," I interrupted, anxious to spare her the pain of giving any details. "I heard it had all come to an end."

"I would like to tell you how it happened," she said; "as that is the very point I want your advice about. I had long realized that we were not in sympathy in religious belief. His ideas of Christianity are very shadowy; and even as to the existence of a God he lives in a sort of dreamland. But it has not affected his life! I feel sure, now, that the most absolute Atheist *may* be leading, though walking blindfold, a pure and noble life. And if you knew half the good deeds——" she broke off suddenly, and turned away her head.

"I entirely agree with you," I said. "And have we not our Saviour's own promise that such a life shall surely lead to the light?"

"Yes, I know it," she said in a broken voice, still keeping her head turned away. "And so I told him. He said he would believe, for *my* sake, if he could. And he wished for *my* sake, he could see things as I did. But that is all wrong!" she went on passionately. "God *cannot* approve such low motives as that! Still it was not *I* that broke it off. I knew he loved me; and I had *promised*; and——"

"Then it was *he* that broke it off?"

"He released me unconditionally." She faced me again now, having quite recovered her usual calmness of manner.

"Then what difficulty remains?"

"It is *this*, that I don't believe he did it of his own free will. Now, supposing he did it *against* his will, merely to satisfy my scruples, would not his claim on me remain just as strong as ever? And would not my promise be as binding as ever? My father says 'no'; but I ca'n't help fearing he is biased by his love for me. And I've asked no one else. I have many friends—friends for the bright sunny weather; not friends for the clouds and storms of life; not *old* friends like you!"

"Let me think a little," I said: and for some minutes we walked on in silence, while, pained to the heart at seeing the bitter trial that had come upon this pure and gentle soul, I strove in vain to see my way through the tangled skein of conflicting motives.

"If she loves him truly", (I seemed at last to grasp the clue to the problem) "is not *that*, for her the voice of God? May she not hope that she is sent to him, even as Ananias was sent to Saul in his blindness, that he may receive his sight?" Once more I seemed to hear Arthur whispering *"What knowest thou, O wife, whether thou shalt save thy husband?"* and I broke the silence with the words "If you still love him truly——"

"I do *not!*" she hastily interrupted. "At least—not in *that* way. I *believe* I loved him when I promised; but I was very young: it is hard to know. But, whatever the feeling was, it is dead *now*. The motive on *his* side is Love: on *mine* it is—Duty!"

Again there was a long silence. The whole skein of thought was tangled worse than ever. This time *she* broke the silence. "Don't misunderstand me!" she said. "When I said my heart was not *his*, I did not mean it was any one else's! At present I feel bound to *him*; and, till I know I am absolutely free, in the sight of God, to love any other than him, I'll never even *think* of any one else— in *that* way, I mean. I would die sooner!" I had never imagined my gentle friend capable of such passionate utterances.

I ventured on no further remark until we had nearly arrived at the Hall-gate; but, the longer I reflected, the clearer it became to me that no call of Duty demanded the sacrifice—possibly of the happiness of a life—which she seemed ready to make. I tried to make this clear to *her* also, adding some warnings on the dangers that surely awaited a union in which mutual love was wanting. "The only argument for it, worth considering," I said in conclusion, "seems to be his supposed *reluctance* in releasing you from your promise. I have tried to give to that argument its *full* weight, and my conclusion is that it does *not* affect the rights of the case, or invalidate the release he has given you. My belief is that you are *entirely* free to act as *now* seems right."

"I am *very* grateful to you," she said earnestly. "Believe it, please! I ca'n't put it into proper words!" and the subject was dropped by mutual consent: and I only learned, long afterwards, that our discussion had really served to dispel the doubts that had harassed her so long.

We parted at the Hall-gate, and I found Arthur eagerly awaiting my arrival; and, before we parted for the night, I had heard the whole story—how he had put off his journey from day to day, feeling that he *could* not go away from the place till his fate had been irrevocably settled by the wedding taking place: how the preparations for the wedding, and the excitement in the neighbourhood, had suddenly come to an end, and he had learned (from Major Lindon, who called to wish him good-bye) that the engagement had been broken off by mutual consent: how he had instantly abandoned all his plans for going abroad, and had decided to stay on at Elveston, for a year or two at any rate, till his newly-awakened hopes should prove true or false; and how, since that memorable day, he had avoided all meetings with Lady Muriel, fearing to betray his feelings before he had had any sufficient evidence as to how she regarded him. "But it is nearly six weeks since all that happened," he said in conclusion, "and we can meet in the ordinary way, now, with no need for any painful allusions. I would have written to tell you all this: only I kept hoping from day to day that—that there would be *more* to tell!"

"And how should there be *more*, you foolish fellow," I fondly urged, "if you never even go near her? Do you expect the offer to come from *her*?"

Arthur was betrayed into a smile. "No," he said, "I hardly expect *that*. But I'm a desperate coward. There's no doubt about it!"

"And what *reasons* have you heard of for breaking off the engagement?"

"A good many," Arthur replied, and proceeded to count them on his fingers. "First, it was found that she was dying of—something; so *he* broke it off. Then it was found that *he* was dying of—some other thing; so *she* broke it off. Then the Major turned out to be a confirmed gamester; so the *Earl* broke it off. Then the Earl insulted him; so the *Major* broke it off. It got a good deal broken off, all things considered!"

"You have all this on the very best authority, of course?"

"Oh, certainly! And communicated in the strictest confidence! Whatever defects Elveston society suffers from, *want of information* isn't one of them!"

"Nor *reticence*, either, it seems. But, seriously, do you know the real reason?"

"No, I'm quite in the dark."

I did not feel that I had any right to enlighten him; so I changed the subject, to the less engrossing one of "new milk", and we agreed that I should walk over, next day, to Hunter's farm, Arthur undertaking to set me part of the way, after which he had to return to keep a business engagement.

CHAPTER 3

Streaks of Dawn

NEXT day proved warm and sunny, and we started early, to enjoy the luxury of a good long chat before he would be obliged to leave me.

"This neighbourhood has more than its due proportion of the *very* poor," I remarked, as we passed a group of hovels, too dilapidated to deserve the name of "cottages".

"But the few rich", Arthur replied, "give more than their due proportion of help in charity. So the balance is kept."

"I suppose the *Earl* does a good deal?"

"He *gives* liberally; but he has not the health or strength to do more. Lady Muriel does more in the way of school-teaching and cottage-visiting than she would like me to reveal."

"Then *she*, at least, is not one of the 'idle mouths' one so often meets with among the upper classes. I have sometimes thought they would have a hard time of it, if suddenly called on to give their *raison d'être*, and to show cause why they should be allowed to live any longer!"

"The whole subject", said Arthur, "of what we may call 'idle mouths' (I mean persons who absorb some of the material *wealth* of a community—in the form of food, clothes, and so on—without contributing its equivalent in the form of productive *labour*) is a complicated one, no doubt. I've tried to think it out. And it seemed to me that the simplest form of the problem, to start with, is a community without *money*, who buy and sell by *barter* only; and it makes it yet simpler to suppose the food and other things to be capable of *keeping* for many years without spoiling."

"Yours is an excellent plan," I said. "What is your solution of the problem?"

"The commonest type of 'idle mouths' ", said Arthur, "is no doubt due to money being left by parents to their own children. So I imagined a man—either exceptionally clever, or exceptionally strong and industrious—who had contributed so much valuable labour to the needs of the community that its equivalent, in clothes, etc., was (say) five times as much as he needed for himself. We cannot deny his *absolute* right to give the superfluous wealth as he chooses. So, if he leaves *four* children behind him (say two sons and two daughters), with enough of all the necessaries of life to last them a life-time, I cannot see that the *community* is in any way wronged if they choose to do nothing in life but to 'eat, drink, and be merry'. Most certainly, the community could not fairly say, in reference to *them, 'if a man will not work, neither let him eat.'* Their reply would be crushing. 'The labour has already been *done*, which is a fair equivalent for the food we are eating; and you have had the benefit of it. On what principle of justice can you demand *two* quotas of work for *one* quota of food?' "

"Yet surely", I said, "there is something wrong *somewhere*, if these four people are well able to do useful work, and if that work is actually *needed* by the community, and they elect to sit idle?"

"I think there *is*," said Arthur: "but it seems to me to arise from a Law of God—that every one shall do as much as he can to help others—and not from any *rights*, on the part of the community, to exact labour as an equivalent for food that has already been fairly earned."

"I suppose the *second* form of the problem is where the 'idle mouths' possess *money* instead of *material* wealth?"

"Yes," replied Arthur: "and I think the simplest case is that of *paper*-money. *Gold* is itself a form of material wealth; but a bank-note is merely a *promise* to hand over so much *material* wealth when called upon to do so. The father of these four 'idle mouths', had done (let us say) five thousand pounds' worth of useful work for the community. In return for this, the community had given him what amounted to a written promise to hand over, whenever called upon to do so, five thousand pounds' worth of food, etc. Then, if he only uses *one* thousand pounds' worth himself, and leaves the rest of the notes to his children, surely they have a full right to *present* these written promises, and to say 'hand over the food, for which the equivalent labour has been already done'. Now I think *this* case well worth stating, publicly and clearly. I should like to drive it into the heads of those Socialists who are priming our ignorant paupers with such sentiments as 'Look at them bloated haristocrats! Doing not a stroke o' work for theirselves, and living on the sweat of *our brows*!' I should like to *force* them to see that the *money*, which those 'haristocrats' are spending, represents so much labour *already* done for the community, and whose equivalent, in *material* wealth, is *due from the community*."

"Might not the Socialists reply 'Much of this money does not represent *honest* labour *at all*. If you could trace it back, from owner to owner, though you might begin with several legitimate steps, such as gifts, or bequeathing by will, or 'value received', you would soon reach an owner who had no moral right to it but had got it by fraud or other crimes; and of course his successors in the line would have no better right to it than *he* had.' "

"No doubt, no doubt," Arthur replied. "But surely that involves the logical fallacy of *proving too much*? It is *quite* as applicable to *material* wealth, as it is to *money*. If we once begin to go back beyond the fact that the *present* owner of certain property came by it honestly, and to ask whether any previous owner, in past ages, got it by fraud, would *any* property be secure?"

After a minute's thought, I felt obliged to admit the truth of this.

"My general conclusion," Arthur continued, "from the mere standpoint of human *rights*, man against man, was this—that if some wealthy 'idle mouth', who has come by his money in a lawful way, even though not one atom of the labour it represents has been his own doing, chooses to spend it on his own needs, without contributing any labour to the community from whom he buys his food and clothes, that community had no *right* to interfere with him. But it's quite another thing, when we come to consider the *divine* law. Measured by *that* standard, such a man is undoubtedly doing wrong, if he fails to use, for the good of those in need, the strength or the skill, that God has given him. That strength and skill do *not* belong to the community, to be paid to *them* as a *debt*: they do *not* belong to the man *himself*, to be used for his *own* enjoyment: they *do* belong to God, to be used according to *His* will; and we are not left in doubt as to what this will is. '*Do good, and lend, hoping for nothing again.*' "

"Anyhow," I said, "an 'idle mouth' very often gives away a great deal in charity."

"In *so-called* 'charity'," he corrected me. "Excuse me if I seem to speak *un*charitably. I would not dream of *applying* the term to any *individual*. But I would say, *generally*, that a man who gratifies every fancy that occurs to him—denying himself in *nothing*—and merely gives to the poor some part, or even *all*, of his *superfluous* wealth, is only deceiving himself if he calls it *charity*."

"But, even in giving away *superfluous* wealth, he *may* be denying himself the miser's pleasure in hoarding?"

"I grant you that, gladly," said Arthur. "Given that he *has* that morbid craving, he is doing a good deed in restraining it."

"But, even in spending on *himself*", I persisted, "our typical rich man often does good, by employing people who would otherwise be out of work: and that is often better than pauperizing them by *giving* the money."

"I'm glad you've said that!" said Arthur. "I would not like to quit the subject without exposing the *two* fallacies of that statement—which have gone so long uncontradicted that Society now accepts it as an axiom!"

"What are they?" I said. "I don't even see *one*, myself."

"One is merely the fallacy of *ambiguity*—the assumption that '*doing good*' (that is, benefiting somebody) is necessarily *a good thing to do* (that is, a *right* thing). The other is the assumption that, if one of two specified acts is *better* than another, it is necessarily a *good* act in itself. I should like to call this the fallacy of *comparison*—meaning that it assumes that what is *comparatively* good is therefore *positively* good."

"Then what is *your* test of a good act?"

"That it shall be *our best*," Arthur confidently replied. "And even *then* '*we are unprofitable servants*'. But let me illustrate the two fallacies. Nothing illustrates a fallacy so well as an extreme case, which fairly comes under it. Suppose I find two children drowning in a pond. I rush in, and save one of the children, and then walk away, leaving the other to drown. Clearly I have '*done good*', in saving a child's life? But—— Again, supposing I meet an inoffensive stranger, and knock him down and walk on. Clearly that is '*better*' than if I had proceeded to jump upon him and break his ribs? But——"

"Those 'buts' are quite unanswerable," I said. "But I should like an instance from *real* life."

"Well, let us take one of those abominations of modern Society, a Charity-Bazaar. It's an interesting question to think out—how much of the money, that reaches the object in view, is *genuine* charity; and whether even *that* is spent in the *best* way. But the subject needs regular classification, and analysis, to understand it properly."

"I should be glad to *have* it analysed," I said: "it has often puzzled me."

"Well, if I am really not boring you. Let us suppose our Charity-Bazaar to have been organized to aid the funds of some Hospital: and that A, B, C *give* their services in making articles to sell, and in acting as salesmen, while X, Y, Z buy the articles, and the money so paid goes to the Hospital.

"There are two distinct species of such Bazaars: one, where the payment exacted is merely the *market-value* of the goods supplied, that is, exactly what you would have to pay at a shop: the other, where *fancy-prices* are asked. We must take these separately.

"First, the 'market-value' case. Here A, B, C are exactly in the same position as ordinary shopkeepers; the only difference being that they give the proceeds to the Hospital. Practically, they are *giving their skilled labour* for the benefit of the Hospital. This seems to me to be genuine charity. And I don't see how they could use it better. But X, Y, Z are exactly in the same position as any ordinary purchasers of goods. To talk of 'charity' in connection with *their* share of the business, is sheer nonsense. Yet they are very likely to do so.

"Secondly, the case of 'fancy-prices'. Here I think the simplest plan is to divide the payment into two parts, the 'market-value' and the excess over that. The 'market-value' part is on the same footing as in the first case: the *excess* is all we have to consider. Well, A, B, C do not *earn* it; so we may put *them* out of the question: it is a *gift*, from X, Y, Z, to the hospital. And my opinion is that it is not given in the best way: far better buy what they choose to *buy*, and give what they choose to *give*, as two *separate* transactions: then there is *some* chance that their motive in giving may be real charity, instead of a mixed motive—half charity, half self-pleasing. 'The trail of the serpent is over it all.' And *therefore* it is that I hold all such spurious 'Charities' in *utter* abomination!" He ended with unusual energy, and savagely beheaded, with his stick, a tall thistle at the road-side, behind which I was startled to see Sylvie and Bruno standing. I caught at his arm, but too late to stop him. Whether the stick reached them, or not, I could not feel sure: at any rate they took not the smallest notice of it, but smiled gaily, and nodded to me: and I saw at once that they were only visible to *me*: the "eerie" influence had not reached to *Arthur*.

"Why did you try to save it?" he said. "*That's* not the wheedling Secretary of a Charity-Bazaar! I only wish it were!" he added grimly.

"Does oo know, that stick went right froo my head!" said Bruno. (They had run round to me by this time, and each had secured a hand.) "Just under my chin! I *are* glad I aren't a thistle!"

"Well, we've threshed *that* subject out, anyhow!" Arthur resumed. 'I'm afraid I've been talking too much, for *your* patience and for my strength. I must be turning soon. This is about the end of my tether."

> *"Take, O boatman, thrice thy fee;*
> *Take, I give it willingly;*
> *For, invisible to thee,*
> *Spirits twain have crossed with me!"*

I quoted, involuntarily.

"For utterly inappropriate and irrelevant quotations," laughed Arthur, "you are 'ekalled by few, and excelled by none'!" And we strolled on.

As we passed the head of the lane that led down to the beach, I noticed a single figure moving slowly along it, seawards. She was a good way off, and had her back to us: but it was Lady Muriel, unmistakably. Knowing that Arthur had not seen her, as he had been looking, in the other direction, at a gathering rain-cloud, I made no remark, but tried to think of some plausible pretext for sending him back by the sea.

The opportunity instantly presented itself. "I'm getting tired," he said. "I don't think it would be prudent to go further. I had better turn here."

I turned with him, for a few steps, and as we again approached the head of the lane, I said, as carelessly as I could, "Don't go back by the

road. It's too hot and dusty. Down this lane, and along the beach, is nearly as short; and you'll get a breeze off the sea."

"Yes, I think I will," Arthur began; but at that moment we came into sight of Lady Muriel, and he checked himself. "No, it's too far round. Yet it certainly *would* be cooler——" He stood, hesitating, looking first one way and then the other—a melancholy picture of utter infirmity of purpose!

How long this humiliating scene would have continued, if *I* had been the only external influence, it is impossible to say; for at this moment Sylvie, with a swift decision worthy of Napoleon himself, took the matter into her own hands. "You go and drive *her*, up this way," she said to Bruno. "I'll get *him* along!" And she took hold of the stick that Arthur was carrying, and gently pulled him down the lane.

He was totally unconscious that any will but his own was acting on the stick, and appeared to think it had taken a horizontal position simply because he was pointing with it. "Are not those *orchises* under the hedge there?" he said. "I think that decides me. I'll gather some as I go along."

Meanwhile Bruno had run on behind Lady Muriel, and, with much jumping about and shouting (shouts audible to no one but Sylvie and myself), much as if he were driving sheep, he managed to turn her round and make her walk, with eyes demurely cast upon the ground, in our direction.

The victory was ours! And, since it was evident that the lovers, thus urged together, *must* meet in another minute, I turned and walked on, hoping that Sylvie and Bruno would follow my example, as I felt sure that the fewer the spectators the better it would be for Arthur and his good angel.

"And what sort of meeting was it?" I wondered, as I paced dreamily on.

CHAPTER 4

The Dog-King

"THEY shooked hands," said Bruno, who was trotting at my side, in answer to the unspoken question.

"And they looked *ever* so pleased!" Sylvie added from the other side.

"Well, we must get on, now, as quick as we can," I said. "If only I knew the best way to Hunter's farm!"

"They'll be sure to know in this cottage," said Sylvie.

"Yes, I suppose they will. Bruno, would you run in and ask?"

Sylvie stopped him, laughingly, as he ran off. "Wait a minute," she said. "I must make you *visible* first, you know."

"And *audible* too, I suppose?" I said, as she took the jewel, that hung round her neck, and waved it over his head, and touched his eyes and lips with it.

"Yes," said Sylvie: "and *once*, do you know, I made him *audible*, and forgot to make him *visible*! And he went to buy some sweeties in a shop. And the man *was* so frightened! A voice seemed to come out of the air, 'Please, I want two ounces of barley-sugar drops!' And a shilling came *bang* down upon the counter! And the man said 'I ca'n't *see* you!' And Bruno said 'It doosn't sinnify seeing *me*, so long as oo can see the *shilling*!' But the man said he never sold barley-sugar drops to people he couldn't *see*. So we had to—*Now*, Bruno, you're ready!" And away he trotted.

Sylvie spent the time, while we were waiting for him, in making *herself* visible also. "It's rather awkward, you know," she explained to me, "when we meet people, and they can see *one* of us, and ca'n't see the *other*!"

In a minute or two Bruno returned, looking rather disconsolate. "He'd got friends with him, and he were *cross*!" he said. "He asked me who I were. And I said 'I'm Bruno: who is *these* peoples?' And he said 'One's my half-brother, and t'other's my half-sister: and I don't want no more company! Go along with yer!' And I said 'I ca'n't go along *wizout* mine

self!' And I said 'Oo shouldn't have *bits* of peoples lying about like that!
It's welly untidy!' And he said 'Oh, don't talk to *me*!' And he pushted me
outside! And he shutted the door!''

"And you never asked where Hunter's farm was?" queried Sylvie.

"Hadn't room for any questions," said Bruno. "The room were so
crowded."

"Three people *couldn't* crowd a room," said Sylvie.

"They *did*, though," Bruno persisted. "*He* crowded it most. He's such
a welly *thick* man—so as oo couldn't knock him down."

I failed to see the drift of Bruno's argument. "Surely *anybody* could
be knocked down," I said: "thick or thin wouldn't matter."

"Oo couldn't knock *him* down," said Bruno. "He's more wide than he's
high: so, when he's lying down he's more higher than when he's standing:
so a-course oo couldn't knock him *down!*"

"Here's another cottage," I said: "*I'll* ask the way, *this* time."

There was no need to go in, this time, as the woman was standing in
the doorway, with a baby in her arms, talking to a respectably dressed
man—a farmer, as I guessed—who seemed to be on his way to the town.

"—and when there's *drink* to be had," he was saying, "he's just the
worst o' the lot, is your Willie. So they tell me. He gets fairly mad wi' it!"

"I'd have given 'em the lie to their faces, a twelve-month back!" the
woman said in a broken voice. "But a' canna noo! A' canna noo!" She
checked herself on catching sight of us, and hastily retreated into the
house, shutting the door after her.

"Perhaps you can tell me where Hunter's farm is?" I said to the man,
as he turned away from the house.

"I can *that*, Sir!" He replied with a smile. "I'm John Hunter hissel, at
your sarvice. It's nobbut half a mile further—the only house in sight,
when you get round bend o' the road yonder. You'll find my good woman
within, if so be you've business wi' *her*. Or mebbe I'll do as well?"

"Thanks," I said. "I want to order some milk. Perhaps I had better
arrange it with your wife?"

"Aye," said the man. "*She* minds all *that*. Good day t'ye, Master—and
to your bonnie childer, as well!" And he trudged on.

"He should have said '*child*', not '*childer*'," said Bruno. "Sylvie's not
a *childer*!"

"He meant *both* of us," said Sylvie.

"No, he didn't!" Bruno persisted. " 'cause he said 'bonnie', oo know!"

"Well, at any rate he *looked* at us both," Sylvie maintained.

"Well, then he *must* have seen we're not *both* bonnie!" Bruno retorted.

"A-*course* I'm much uglier than *oo*! Didn't he mean *Sylvie*, Mister Sir?" he shouted over his shoulder, as he ran off.

But there was no use in replying, as he had already vanished round the bend of the road. When we overtook him he was climbing a gate, and was gazing earnestly into the field, where a horse, a cow, and a kid were browsing amicably together. "For its father, a *Horse*," he murmured to himself. "For its mother, a *Cow*. For their dear little child, a *little* Goat, is the most curiousest thing I ever seen in my world!"

'Bruno's World!" I pondered. "Yes, I suppose every child has a world of his own—and every man, too, for the matter of that. I wonder if *that*'s the cause for all the misunderstanding there is in in Life?"

"That *must* be Hunter's farm!" said Sylvie, pointing to a house on the brow of the hill, led up to by a cart-road. "There's no other farm in sight, *this* way; and you *said* we must be nearly there by this time."

I had *thought* it, while Bruno was climbing the gate, but I couldn't remember having *said* it. However, Sylvie was evidently in the right. "Get down, Bruno," I said, "and open the gate for us."

"It's a good thing we's with oo, *isn't* it, Mister Sir?" said Bruno, as we entered the field. "That big dog might have bited oo, if oo'd been alone! Oo needn't be *flightened* of it!" he whispered, clinging tight to my hand to encourage me. "It aren't fierce!"

"Fierce!" Sylvie scornfully echoed, as the dog—a magnificent New-foundland—that had come galloping down the field to meet us, began curveting round us, in gambols full of graceful beauty, and welcoming us with short joyful barks. "Fierce! Why, it's as gentle as a lamb! It's—why, Bruno, don't you know? It's——"

"So it *are*!" cried Bruno, rushing forwards and throwing his arms round its neck. "Oh, you *dear* dog!" And it seemed as if the two children would never have done hugging and stroking it.

"And how *ever* did he get *here*?" said Bruno. "Ask him, Sylvie. I doosn't know how."

And then began an eager talk in Doggee, which of course was lost upon *me*; and I could only *guess*, when the beautiful creature, with a sly glance at me, whispered something in Sylvie's ear, that *I* was now the subject of conversation. Sylvie looked round laughingly.

"He asked me who you are," she explained. "And I said '*He's our friend*'. And he said 'What's his name?' And I said 'It's *Mister Sir*'. And he said 'Bosh!' "

"What is 'Bosh!' in Doggee," I enquired.

"It's the same as in English," said Sylvie. "Only, when a *dog* says it,

it's a sort of whisper, that's half a *cough* and half a *bark*. Nero, say
'*Bosh!*' "

And Nero, who had now begun gamboling round us again, said "*Bosh!*"
several times; and I found that Sylvie's description of the sound was
perfectly accurate.

"I wonder what's behind this long wall?" I said, as we walked on.

"It's the *Orchard*," Sylvie replied, after a consultation with Nero. "See,
there's a boy getting down off the wall, at that far corner. And now he's
running away across the field. I do believe he's been stealing the apples!"

Bruno set off after him, but returned to us in a few moments, as he had
evidently no chance of overtaking the young rascal.

"I couldn't catch him!" he said. "I wiss I'd started a little sooner. His
pockets *was* full of apples!"

The Dog-King looked up at Sylvie, and said something in Doggee.

"Why, of *course* you can!" Sylvie exclaimed. "How stupid not to think
of it! *Nero*'ll hold him for us, Bruno! But I'd better make him invisible,
first." And she hastily got out the Magic Jewel, and began waving it over
Nero's head, and down along his back.

"That'll do!" cried Bruno, impatiently. "After him, good Doggie!"

"Oh, Bruno!" Sylvie exclaimed reproachfully. "You shouldn't have sent
him off so quick! I hadn't done the tail!"

Meanwhile Nero was coursing like a greyhound down the field: so at
least I concluded from all *I* could see of him—the long feathery tail,
which floated like a meteor through the air—and in a very few seconds
he had come up with the little thief.

"He's got him safe, by one foot!" cried Sylvie, who was eagerly watching
the chase. "Now there's no hurry, Bruno!"

So we walked, quite leisurely, down the field, to where the frightened
lad stood. A more curious sight I had seldom seen, in all my "eerie"
experiences. Every bit of him was in violent action, except the left foot,
which was apparently glued to the ground—there being nothing visibly
holding it: while, at some little distance, the long feathery tail was waving
gracefully from side to side, showing that Nero, at least, regarded the
whole affair as nothing but a magnificent game of play.

"What's the matter with you?" I said, as gravely as I could.

"Got the crahmp in me ahnkle!" the thief groaned in reply. "An' me
fut's gone to sleep!" And he began to blubber aloud.

"Now, look here!" Bruno said in a commanding tone, getting in front
of him. "Oo've got to give up those apples!"

The lad glanced at me, but didn't seem to reckon *my* interference as

A royal thief-taker

worth anything. Then he glanced at Sylvie: *she* clearly didn't count for very much, either. Then he took courage. "It'll take a better man than any of *yer* to get 'em!" he retorted defiantly.

Sylvie stooped and patted the invisible Nero. "A *little* tighter!" she whispered. And a sharp yell from the ragged boy showed how promptly the Dog-King had taken the hint.

"What's the matter *now*?" I said. "Is your ankle worse?"

"And it'll get worse, and worse, and worse," Bruno solemnly assured him, "till oo gives up those apples!"

Apparently the thief was convinced of this at last, and he sulkily began emptying his pockets of the apples. The children watched from a little distance, Bruno dancing with delight at every fresh yell extracted from Nero's terrified prisoner.

"That's all," the boy said at last.

"It *isn't* all!" cried Bruno. "There's three more in that pocket!"

Another hint from Sylvie to the Dog-King—another sharp yell from the thief, now convicted of lying also—and the remaining three apples were surrendered.

"Let him go, please," Sylvie said in Doggee, and the lad limped away at a great pace, stooping now and then to rub the ailing ankle in fear, seemingly, that the "crahmp" might attack it again.

Bruno ran back, with his booty, to the orchard wall, and pitched the apples over it one by one. "I's welly afraid *some* of them's gone under the wrong trees!" he panted, on overtaking us again.

"The *wrong* trees!" laughed Sylvie. "Trees *ca'n't* do wrong! There's no such things as *wrong* trees!"

"Then there's no such things as *right* trees, neither!" cried Bruno. And Sylvie gave up the point.

"Wait a minute, please!" she said to me. "I must make Nero *visible*, you know!"

"No, *please* don't!" cried Bruno, who had by this time mounted on the Royal back, and was twisting the Royal hair into a bridle. "It'll be *such* fun to have him like this!"

"Well, it *does* look funny," Sylvie admitted, and led the way to the farm-house, where the farmer's wife stood, evidently much perplexed at the weird procession now approaching her. "It's summat gone wrong wi' my spectacles, I doubt!" she murmured, as she took them off, and began diligently rubbing them with a corner of her apron.

Meanwhile Sylvie had hastily pulled Bruno down from his steed, and

'Summat wrong wi' my spectacles'

SWAIN sc

had just time to make His Majesty wholly visible before the spectacles were resumed.

All was natural, now; but the good woman still looked a little uneasy about it. "My eyesight's getting bad," she said, "but I see you *now*, my darlings! You'll give me a kiss, won't you?"

Bruno got behind me, in a moment: however Sylvie put up *her* face, to be kissed, as representative of *both*, and we all went in together.

CHAPTER 5

Matilda Jane

"COME to me, my little gentleman," said our hostess, lifting Bruno into her lap, "and tell me everything."

"I ca'n't," said Bruno. "There wouldn't be time. Besides, I don't know everything."

The good woman looked a little puzzled, and turned to Sylvie for help. "Does he like *riding*?" she asked.

"Yes, I *think* so," Sylvie gently replied. "He's just had a ride on *Nero*."

"Ah, Nero's a grand dog, isn't he? Were you ever outside a *horse*, my little man?"

"*Always!*" Bruno said with great decision. "Never was *inside* one. Was *oo*?"

Here I thought it well to interpose, and to mention the business on which we had come, and so relieved her, for a few minutes, from Bruno's perplexing questions.

"And those dear children will like a bit of cake, *I'll* warrant!" said the farmer's hospitable wife, when the business was concluded, as she opened her cupboard, and brought out a cake. "And don't you waste the crust, little gentleman!" she added, as she handed a good slice of it to Bruno. "You know what the poetry-book says about wilful waste?"

"No, I don't," said Bruno. "What *doos* he say about it?"

"Tell him, Bessie!" And the mother looked down, proudly and lovingly, on a rosy little maiden, who had just crept shyly into the room, and was leaning against her knee. "What's that your poetry-book says about wilful waste?"

"*For wilful waste makes woeful want,*" Bessie recited, in an almost inaudible whisper: "*and you may live to say 'How much I wish I had the crust that then I threw away!'*"

"Now try if *you* can say it, my dear! *For wilful——*"

"For *wifful*—sumfinoruvver——" Bruno began, readily enough; and then there came a dead pause. "Ca'n't remember no more!"

"Well, what do you *learn* from it, then? You can tell us *that*, at any rate?"

Bruno ate a little more cake, and considered: but the moral did not seem to him to be a very obvious one.

"Always to——" Sylvie prompted him in a whisper.

"Always to——" Bruno softly repeated: and then, with sudden inspiration, "always to look where it goes to!"

"Where *what* goes to, darling?"

"Why the *crust*, a course!" said Bruno. "Then, if I lived to say "*How much I wiss I had the crust——*' (and all that), I'd know where I frew it to!"

This new interpretation quite puzzled the good woman. She returned to the subject of "Bessie". "Wouldn't you like to see Bessie's doll, my dears! Bessie, take the little lady and gentleman to see Matilda Jane!"

Bessie's shyness thawed away in a moment. "Matilda Jane has just woke up," she stated, confidentially, to Sylvie. "Won't you help me on with her frock? Them strings *is* such a bother to tie!"

"I can tie *strings*," we heard, in Sylvie's gentle voice, as the two little girls left the room together. Bruno ignored the whole proceeding, and strolled to the window, quite with the air of a fashionable gentleman. Little girls, and dolls, were not at all in his line.

And forthwith the fond mother proceeded to tell me (as what mother is not ready to do?) of all Bessie's virtues (and vices too, for the matter of that) and of the many fearful maladies which, notwithstanding those ruddy cheeks and that plump little figure, had nearly, time and again, swept her from the face of the earth.

When the full stream of loving memories had nearly run itself out, I began to question her about the working men of that neighbourhood, and specially the "Willie," whom we had heard of at his cottage. "He was a good fellow once," said my kind hostess: "but it's the drink has ruined him! Not that I'd rob them of the drink—it's good for the most of them—but there's some as is too weak to stand agin' temptations: it's a thousand pities, for *them*, as they ever built the Golden Lion at the corner there!"

"The Golden Lion?" I repeated.

"It's the new Public," my hostess explained. "And it stands right in the way, and handy for the workmen, as they come back from the brickfields, as it might be to-day, with their week's wages. A deal of money gets wasted that way. And some of 'em gets drunk."

"If only they could have it in their own houses——" I mused, hardly knowing I had said the words out loud.

"That's it!" she eagerly exclaimed. It was evidently a solution, of the problem, that she had already thought out. "If only you could manage, so's each man to have his own little barrel in his own house—there'd hardly be a drunken man in the length and breadth of the land!"

And then I told her the old story—about a certain cottager who bought himself a little barrel of beer, and installed his wife as bar-keeper: and how, every time he wanted his mug of beer, he regularly paid her over the counter for it: and how she never would let him go on "tick", and was a perfectly inflexible bar-keeper in never letting him have more than his proper allowance: and how, every time the barrel needed refilling, she had plenty to do it with, and something over for her money-box: and how, at the end of the year, he not only found himself in first-rate health and spirits, with that undefinable but quite unmistakable air which always distinguishes the sober man from the one who takes "a drop too much", but had quite a box full of money, all saved out of his own pence!

"If only they'd all do like that!" said the good woman, wiping her eyes, which were overflowing with kindly sympathy. "Drink hadn't need to be the curse it is to some——"

"Only a *curse*", I said, "when it is used wrongly. Any of God's gifts may be turned into a curse, unless we use it wisely. But we must be getting home. Would you call the little girls? Matilda Jane has seen enough of company, for *one* day, I'm sure!"

"I'll find 'em in a minute," said my hostess, as she rose to leave the room. "Maybe that young gentleman saw which way they went?"

"Where are they, Bruno?" I said.

"They ain't in the field," was Bruno's rather evasive reply, " 'cause there's nothing but *pigs* there, and Sylvie isn't a pig. Now don't interrupt me any more, 'cause I'm telling a story to this fly; and it wo'n't attend!"

"They're among the apples, I'll warrant 'em!" said the Farmer's wife. So we left Bruno to finish his story, and went out into the orchard, where we soon came upon the children, walking sedately side by side, Sylvie carrying the doll, while little Bess carefully shaded its face, with a large cabbage-leaf for a parasol.

As soon as they caught sight of us, little Bess dropped her cabbage-leaf and came running to meet us, Sylvie following more slowly, as her precious charge evidently needed great care and attention.

"I'm its Mamma, and Sylvie's the Head-Nurse," Bessie explained: "and Sylvie's taught me ever such a pretty song, for me to sing to Matilda Jane!"

"Let's hear it once more, Sylvie," I said, delighted at getting the chance I had long wished for, of hearing her sing. But Sylvie turned shy and frightened in a moment. "No, *please not!*" she said, in an earnest "aside" to me. "Bessie knows it quite perfect now. Bessie can sing it!"

"Aye, aye! Let Bessie sing it!" said the proud mother. "Bessie has a bonny voice of her own," (this again was an "aside" to me) "though I say it as shouldn't!"

Bessie was only too happy to accept the "encore". So the plump little Mamma sat down at our feet, with her hideous daughter reclining stiffly across her lap (it was one of a kind that wo'n't sit down, under *any* amount of persuasion), and, with a face simply beaming with delight, began the lullaby, in a shout that *ought* to have frightened the poor baby into fits. The Head-Nurse crouched down behind her, keeping herself respectfully in the background, with her hands on the shoulders of her little mistress, so as to be ready to act as Prompter, if required, and to supply "*each gap in faithless memory void*".

The shout, with which she began, proved to be only a momentary effort. After a very few notes, Bessie toned down, and sang on in a small but very sweet voice. At first her great black eyes were fixed on her mother, but soon her gaze wandered upwards, among the apples, and she seemed to have quite forgotten that she had any other audience than her Baby, and her Head-Nurse, who once or twice supplied, almost inaudibly, the right note, when the singer was getting a little "flat".

> "Matilda Jane, you never look
> At any toy or picture-book:
> I show you pretty things in vain––
> You must be blind, Matilda Jane!

> "I ask you riddles, tell you tales,
> But all our conversation fails:
> You never answer me again—
> I fear you're dumb, Matilda Jane!

"Matilda, darling, when I call,
You never seem to hear at all:
I shout with all my might and main—
But you're so deaf, Matilda Jane!

"Matilda Jane, you needn't mind:
For, though you're deaf, and dumb, and blind,
There's some one loves you, it is plain—
And that is me, Matilda Jane!"

She sang three of the verses in a rather perfunctory style, but the last stanza evidently excited the little maiden. Her voice rose, ever clearer and louder: she had a rapt look on her face, as if suddenly inspired, and, as she sang the last few words, she clasped to her heart the inattentive Matilda Jane.

"Kiss it now!" prompted the Head-Nurse. And in a moment the simpering meaningless face of the Baby was covered with a shower of passionate kisses.

"What a bonny song!" cried the Farmer's wife. "Who made the words, dearie?"

"I—I think I'll look for Bruno," Sylvie said demurely, and left us hastily. The curious child seemed always afraid of being praised, or even noticed.

"Sylvie planned the words," Bessie informed us, proud of her superior information: "and Bruno planned the music—and *I* sang it!" (this last circumstance, by the way, we did not need to be told).

So we followed Sylvie, and all entered the parlour together. Bruno was still standing at the window, with his elbows on the sill. He had, apparently, finished the story that he was telling to the fly, and had found a new occupation. "Don't imperrupt!" he said as we came in. "I'm counting the Pigs in the field!"

"How many are there?" I enquired.

"About a thousand and four," said Bruno.

"You mean 'about a thousand'," Sylvie corrected him. "There's no good saying '*and four*': you *ca'n't* be sure about the four!"

"And you're as wrong as ever!" Bruno exclaimed triumphantly. "It's just the *four* I *can* be sure about; 'cause they're here, grubbling under the window! It's the *thousand* I isn't pruffickly sure about!"

"But some of them have gone into the sty," Sylvie said, leaning over him to look out of the window.

"Yes," said Bruno; "but they went so slowly and so fewly, I didn't care to count *them*."

"We must be going, children," I said. "Wish Bessie good-bye." Sylvie flung her arms round the little maiden's neck, and kissed her: but Bruno stood aloof, looking unusually shy. ("I never kiss *nobody* but Sylvie!" he explained to me afterwards.) The Farmer's wife showed us out: and we were soon on our way back to Elveston.

"And that's the new public-house that we were talking about, I suppose?" I said, as we came in sight of a long low building, with the words "THE GOLDEN LION" over the door.

"Yes, that's it," said Sylvie. "I wonder if *her* Willie's inside? Run in, Bruno, and see if he's there."

I interposed, feeling that Bruno was, in a sort of way, in *my* care. "That's not a place to send a child into." For already the revellers were getting noisy: and a wild discord of singing, shouting, and meaningless laughter came to us through the open windows.

"They wo'n't *see* him, you know," Sylvie explained. "Wait a minute, Bruno!" She clasped the jewel, that always hung round her neck, between the palms of her hands, and muttered a few words to herself. What they were I could not at all make out, but some mysterious change seemed instantly to pass over us. My feet seemed to me no longer to press the ground, and the dream-like feeling came upon me, that I was suddenly endowed with the power of floating in the air. I could still just *see* the children: but their forms were shadowy and unsubstantial, and their voices sounded as if they came from some distant place and time, they were so unreal. However, I offered no further opposition to Bruno's going into the house. He was back again in a few moments. "No, he isn't come yet," he said. "They're talking about him inside, and saying how drunk he was last week."

While he was speaking, one of the men lounged out through the door, a pipe in one hand and a mug of beer in the other, and crossed to where we were standing, so as to get a better view along the road. Two or three others leaned out through the open window, each holding his mug of beer, with red faces and sleepy eyes. "Canst see him, lad?" one of them asked.

"I dunnot know," the man said, taking a step forwards, which brought us nearly face to face. Sylvie hastily pulled me out of his way. "Thanks, child," I said. "I had forgotten he couldn't see us. What would have happened if I had stayed in his way?"

"I don't know," Sylvie said gravely. "It wouldn't matter to *us*; but *you* may be different." She said this in her usual voice, but the man took no sort of notice, though she was standing close in front of him, and looking up into his face as she spoke.

"He's coming now!" cried Bruno, pointing down the road.

"He be a-coomin noo!" echoed the man, stretching out his arm exactly over Bruno's head, and pointing with his pipe.

"Then *chorus* agin!" was shouted out by one of the red-faced men in the window: and forthwith a dozen voices yelled, to a harsh discordant melody, the refrain:

> *"There's him, an' yo', an' me,*
> *Roarin' laddies!*
> *We loves a bit o' spree,*
> *Roarin' laddies we,*
> *Roarin' laddies*
> *Roarin' laddies!"*

The man lounged back again to the house, joining lustily in the chorus as he went: so that only the children and I were in the road when "Willie" came up.

CHAPTER 6

Willie's Wife

HE made for the door of the public-house, but the children intercepted him. Sylvie clung to one arm; while Bruno, on the opposite side, was pushing him with all his strength, and many inarticulate cries of "Gee-up! Gee-back! Woah then!" which he had picked up from the waggoners.

"Willie" took not the least notice of them: he was simply conscious that *something* had checked him: and, for want of any other way of accounting for it, he seemed to regard it as his own act.

"I wunnut coom in," he said: "not to-day."

"A mug o' beer wunnut hurt 'ee!" his friends shouted in chorus. "*Two* mugs wunnut hurt 'ee! Nor a dozen mugs!"

"Nay," said Willie. "I'm agoan whoam."

"What, withouten thy drink, Willie man?" shouted the others. But "Willie man" would have no more discussion, and turned doggedly away, the children keeping one on each side of him, to guard him against any change in his sudden resolution.

For a while he walked on stoutly enough, keeping his hands in his pockets, and softly whistling a tune, in time to his heavy tread: his success, in appearing entirely at his ease, was *almost* complete; but a careful observer would have noted that he had forgotten the second part of the air, and that, when it broke down, he instantly began it again, being too nervous to think of another, and too restless to endure silence.

It was not the old fear that possessed him now—the old fear that had been his dreary companion every Saturday night he could remember as he had reeled along, steadying himself against gates and garden-palings, and when the shrill reproaches of his wife had seemed to his dazed brain only the echo of a yet more piercing voice within the intolerable wail of a hopeless remorse: it was a wholly new fear that had come to him now: life had taken on itself a new set of colours, and was lighted up with a new and dazzling radiance, and he did not see, as yet, how his home-life,

and his wife and child, would fit into the new order of things: the very novelty of it all was, to his simple mind, a perplexity and an overwhelming terror.

And now the tune died into sudden silence on the trembling lips, as he turned a sharp corner, and came in sight of his own cottage, where his wife stood, leaning with folded arms on the wicket-gate, and looking up the road with a pale face, that had in it no glimmer of the light of hope—only the heavy shadow of a deep stony despair.

Willie's wife

"Fine an' early, lad! Fine an' early!" the words might have been words of welcoming, but oh, the bitterness of the tone in which she said it! "What brings thee from thy merry mates, and all the fiddling and the jigging? Pockets empty, I doubt? Or thou'st come, mebbe, for to see thy little one die? The bairnie's clemmed, and I've nor bite nor sup to gie her. But what does *thou* care?" She flung the gate open, and met him with blazing eyes of fury.

The man said no word. Slowly, and with downcast eyes, he passed into the house, while she, half terrified at his strange silence, followed him in without another word; and it was not till he had sunk into a chair, with his arms crossed on the table and with drooping head, that she found her voice again.

It seemed entirely natural for us to go in with them: at another time one would have asked leave for this, but I felt, I knew not why, that we were in some mysterious way invisible, and as free to come and to go as disembodied spirits.

The child in the cradle woke up, and raised a piteous cry, which in a moment brought the children to its side: Bruno rocked the cradle, while Sylvie tenderly replaced the little head on the pillow from which it had slipped. But the mother took no heed of the cry, nor yet of the satisfied "coo" that it set up when Sylvie had made it happy again: she only stood gazing at her husband, and vainly trying, with white quivering lips (I believe she thought he was mad), to speak in the old tones of shrill upbraiding that he knew so well.

"And thou'st spent all thy wages—I'll swear thou hast—on the devil's own drink—and thou'st been and made thysen a beast again—as thou allus dost——"

"Hasna!" the man muttered, his voice hardly rising above a whisper, as he slowly emptied his pockets on the table. "There's th' wage, Missus, every penny on't."

The woman gasped and put one hand to her heart, as if under some great shock of surprise. "Then *how*'s thee gotten th' drink?"

"*Hasna* gotten it," he answered her, in a tone more sad than sullen. "I hanna touched a drop this blessed day. No!" he cried aloud, bringing his clenched fist heavily down upon the table, and looking up at her with gleaming eyes, "nor I'll never touch another drop o' the cursed drink—till I die—so help me God my Maker!" His voice, which had suddenly risen to a hoarse shout, dropped again as suddenly: and once more he bowed his head, and buried his face in his folded arms.

The woman had dropped upon her knees by the cradle, while he was speaking. She neither looked at him nor seemed to hear him. With hands clasped above her head, she rocked herself wildly to and fro. "Oh my God! Oh my God!" was all she said, over and over again.

Sylvie and Bruno gently unclasped her hands and drew them down—till she had an arm round each of them, though she took no notice of them, but knelt on with eyes gazing upwards, and lips that moved as if in silent thanksgiving. The man kept his face hidden, and uttered no sound: but one could *see* the sobs that shook him from head to foot.

After a while he raised his head—his face all wet with tears. "Polly!" he said softly; and then, louder, "Old Poll!"

Then she rose from her knees and came to him, with a dazed look, as if she were walking in her sleep. "Who was it called me old Poll?" she asked: her voice took on it a tender playfulness: her eyes sparkled; and the rosy light of Youth flushed her pale cheeks, till she looked more like a happy girl of seventeen than a worn woman of forty. "Was that my own lad, my Willie, a-waiting for me at the stile?"

His face too was transformed, in the same magic light, to the likeness of a bashful boy: and boy and girl they seemed, as he wound an arm about her, and drew her to his side, while with the other hand he thrust from him the heap of money, as though it were something hateful to the touch. "Tak it, lass," he said, "tak it all! An' fetch us summat to eat: but get a sup o' milk, first, for t' bairn."

"My *little* bairn!" she murmured as she gathered up the coins. "My own little lassie!" Then she moved to the door, and was passing out, but a sudden thought seemed to arrest her: she hastily returned—first to kneel down and kiss the sleeping child, and then to throw herself into her husband's arms and be strained to his heart. The next moment she was on her way, taking with her a jug that hung on a peg near the door: we followed close behind.

We had not gone far before we came in sight of a swinging sign-board bearing the word "DAIRY" on it, and here she went in, welcomed by a little curly white dog, who, not being under the "eerie" influence, saw the children, and received them with the most effusive affection. When I got inside, the dairyman was in the act of taking the money. "Is't for thysen, Missus, or for t' bairn?" he asked, when he had filled the jug, pausing with it in his hand.

"For t' *bairn*!" she said, almost reproachfully. "Think'st tha I'd touch a drop *mysen*, while as *she* hadna got her fill?"

"All right, Missus," the man replied, turning away with the jug in his hand. "Let's just mak sure it's good measure." He went back among his shelves of milk-bowls, carefully keeping his back towards her while he emptied a little measure of cream into the jug, muttering to himself "mebbe it'll hearten her up a bit, the little lassie!"

The woman never noticed the kind deed, but took back the jug with a simple "Good evening, Master," and went her way: but the children had been more observant, and, as we followed her out, Bruno remarked "That were *welly* kind: and I loves that man: and if I was welly rich I'd give him a hundred pounds—and a bun. That little grummeling dog doosn't know its business!" He referred to the dairyman's little dog, who had apparently quite forgotten the affectionate welcome he had given us on our arrival, and was now following at a respectful distance, doing his best to "*speed the parting guest*" with a shower of little shrill barks, that seemed to tread on one another's heels.

"What *is* a dog's business?" laughed Sylvie. "Dogs ca'n't keep shops and give change!"

"Sisters' businesses *isn't* to laugh at their brothers," Bruno replied with perfect gravity. "And dogs' businesses is to *bark*—not like that: it should finish one bark before it begins another: and it should—Oh Sylvie, there's some dindledums!"

And in another moment the happy children were flying across the common, racing for the patch of dandelions.

While I stood watching them, a strange dreamy feeling came upon me: a railway-platform seemed to take the place of the green sward, and, instead of the light figure of Sylvie bounding along, I seemed to see the flying form of Lady Muriel; but whether Bruno had also undergone a transformation, and had become the old man whom she was running to overtake, I was unable to judge, so instantaneously did the feeling come and go.

When I re-entered the little sitting-room which I shared with Arthur, he was standing with his back to me, looking out of the open window, and evidently had not heard me enter. A cup of tea, apparently just tasted and pushed aside, stood on the table, on the opposite side of which was a letter, just begun, with the pen lying across it: an open book lay on the sofa: the London paper occupied the easy chair; and on the little table which stood by it, I noticed an unlighted cigar and an open box of cigar-lights: all things betokened that the Doctor, usually so methodical and so self-contained, had been trying every form of occupation, and could settle to none!

"This is very unlike *you*, Doctor!" I was beginning, but checked myself, as he turned at the sound of my voice, in sheer amazement at the wonderful change that had taken place in his appearance. Never had I seen a face so radiant with happiness, or eyes that sparkled with such unearthly light! "Even thus", I thought, "must the herald-angel have looked, who brought to the shepherds, watching over their flocks by night, that sweet message of *'peace on earth, good-will to men'*!"

"Yes, dear friend!" he said, as if in answer to the question that I suppose he read in my face. "It is true! It is true!"

No need to ask *what* was true. "God bless you both!" I said, as I felt the happy tears brimming to my eyes. "You were made for each other!"

"Yes," he said, simply, "I believe we were. And *what* a change it makes in one's Life! This isn't the same world! That isn't the sky I saw yesterday! Those clouds—I never saw such clouds in all my life before! They look like troops of hovering angels!"

To *me* they looked very ordinary clouds indeed: but then I had not fed *"on honeydew, And drunk the milk of Paradise"*!

"She wants to see you—at once," he continued, descending suddenly to the things of earth. "She says *that* is the *one* drop yet wanting in her cup of happiness!"

"I'll go at once," I said, as I turned to leave the room. "Wo'n't you come with me?"

"No, Sir!" said the Doctor, with a sudden effort—which proved an utter failure—to resume his professional manner. "Do I *look* like coming with you? Have you never heard that two is company, and——"

"Yes," I said, "I *have* heard it: and I'm painfully aware that *I* am *Number Three*! But, *when* shall we three meet again?"

"*When the hurly-burly's done!*" he answered with a happy laugh, such as I had not heard from him for many a year.

CHAPTER 7

Mein Herr

So I went on my lonely way, and, on reaching the Hall, I found Lady
Muriel standing at the garden-gate waiting for me.

"No need to *give* you joy, or to *wish* you joy?" I began.

"None *whatever*!" she replied, with the joyous laugh of a child. "We
give people what they haven't got: we *wish* for something that is yet to
come. For me, it's all *here*! It's all *mine*! Dear friend," she suddenly broke
off, "do you think Heaven ever begins on *Earth*, for any of us?"

"For *some*," I said. "For some, perhaps, who are simple and childlike.
You know he said 'of such is the Kingdom of Heaven'."

Lady Muriel clasped her hands, and gazed up into the cloudless sky,
with a look I had often seen in Sylvie's eyes. "I feel as if it had begun for
me," she almost whispered. "I feel as if *I* were one of the happy children,
whom He bid them bring near to Him, though the people would have
kept them back. Yes, He has seen me in the throng. He has read the
wistful longing in my eyes. He has beckoned me to Him. They have *had*
to make way for me. He has taken me up in His arms. He has put His
hands upon me and blessed me!" She paused, breathless in her perfect
happiness.

"Yes," I said. "I think He has!"

"You must come and speak to my father," she went on, as we stood
side by side at the gate, looking down the shady lane. But, even as she
said the words, the "eerie" sensation came over me like a flood: I saw the
dear old Professor approaching us, and also saw, what was stranger still,
that he was visible to *Lady Muriel*!

What was to be done? Had the fairy-life been merged in the real life?
Or was Lady Muriel "eerie" also, and thus able to enter into the fairy-
world along with me? The words were on my lips ("I see an old friend
of mine in the lane: if you don't know him, may I introduce him to you?")
when the strangest thing of all happened: Lady Muriel spoke.

"I see an old friend of mine in the lane," she said: "if you don't know him, may I introduce him to you?"

I seemed to wake out of a dream: for the "eerie" feeling was still strong upon me, and the figure outside seemed to be changing at every moment, like one of the shapes in a kaleidoscope: now he was the *Professor*, and now he was somebody else! By the time he had reached the gate, he certainly was somebody else: and I felt that the proper course was for *Lady Muriel*, not for *me*, to introduce him. She greeted him kindly, and, opening the gate, admitted the venerable old man—a German, obviously—who looked about him with dazed eyes, as if *he*, too, had but just awaked from a dream!

No, it was certainly *not* the Professor! My old friend *could* not have grown that magnificent beard since last we met: moreover, he would have recognised *me*, for I was certain that *I* had not changed much in the time.

As it was, he simply looked at me vaguely, and took off his hat in response to Lady Muriel's words "Let me introduce Mein Herr to you"; while in the words, spoken in a strong German accent, "proud to make your acquaintance, Sir!" I could detect no trace of an idea that we had ever met before.

Lady Muriel led us to the well-known shady nook, where preparations for afternoon-tea had already been made, and, while she went in to look for the Earl, we seated ourselves in two easy-chairs, and "Mein Herr" took up Lady Muriel's work, and examined it through his large spectacles (one of the adjuncts that made him so provokingly like the Professor). "Hemming pocket-handkerchiefs?" he said, musingly. "So *that* is what the English miladies occupy themselves with, is it?"

"It is the one accomplishment", I said, "in which Man has never yet rivalled Woman!"

Here Lady Muriel returned with her father; and, after he had exchanged some friendly words with "Mein Herr", and we had all been supplied with the needful "creature-comforts", the newcomer returned to the suggestive subject of Pocket-handkerchiefs.

"You have heard of Fortunatus's Purse, Miladi? Ah, so! Would you be surprised to hear that, with three of these leetle hankerchiefs, you shall make the Purse of Fortunatus, quite soon, quite easily?"

"Shall I indeed?" Lady Muriel eagerly replied, as she took a heap of them into her lap, and threaded her needle. "*Please* tell me how, Mein Herr! I'll make one before I touch another drop of tea!"

"You shall first," said Mein Herr, possessing himself of two of the handkerchiefs, spreading one upon the other, and holding them up by two corners, "you shall first join together these upper corners, the right to the right, the left to the left; and the opening between them shall be the *mouth of the Purse*."

A very few stitches sufficed to carry out *this* direction. "Now, if I sew the other three edges together", she suggested, "the bag is complete?"

"Not so, Miladi: the *lower* edges shall *first* be joined—ah, not so!" (as she was beginning to sew them together). "Turn one of them over, and join the *right* lower corner of the one to the *left* lower corner of the other, and sew the lower edges together in what you would call *the wrong way*."

"*I* see!" said Lady Muriel, as she deftly executed the order. "And a very twisted, uncomfortable, uncanny-looking bag it makes! But the *moral* is a lovely one. Unlimited wealth can only be attained by doing things *in the wrong way!* And how are we to join up these mysterious—no, I mean *this* mysterious opening?" (twisting the thing round and round with a puzzled air). "Yes, it *is* one opening. I thought it was *two*, at first."

"You have seen the puzzle of the Paper Ring?" Mein Herr said, addressing the Earl. "Where you take a slip of paper, and join its ends together, first twisting one, so as to join the *upper* corner of *one* end to the *lower* corner of the *other*?"

"I saw one made, only yesterday," the Earl replied. "Muriel, my child, were you not making one, to amuse those children you had to tea?"

"Yes, I know that Puzzle," said Lady Muriel. "The Ring has only *one* surface, and only *one* edge, It's very mysterious!"

"The *bag* is just like that, isn't it?" I suggested. "Is not the *outer* surface of one side of it continuous with the *inner* surface of the other side?"

"So it is!" she exclaimed. "Only it *isn't* a bag, just yet. How shall we fill up this opening, Mein Herr?"

"Thus!" said the old man impressively, taking the bag from her, and rising to his feet in the excitement of the explanation. "The edge of the opening consists of *four* handkerchief edges, and you can trace it continuously, round and round the opening: down the right edge of *one* handkerchief, up the left edge of the *other*, and then down the left edge of the *one*, and up the right edge of the *other!*"

"So you can!" Lady Muriel murmured thoughtfully, leaning her head on her hand, and earnestly watching the old man. "And that *proves* it to be only *one* opening!"

She looked so strangely like a child, puzzling over a difficult lesson, and Mein Herr had become, for the moment, so strangely like the old Professor, that I felt utterly bewildered: the "eerie" feeling was on me in its full

force, and I felt almost *impelled* to say "Do you understand it, Sylvie?" However I checked myself by a great effort, and let the dream (if indeed it *was* a dream) go on to its end.

"Now, this *third* handkerchief", Mein Herr proceeded, "has *also* four edges, which you can trace continuously round and round: all you need do is to join its four edges to the four edges of the opening. The Purse is then complete, and its outer surface———"

"*I* see!" Lady Muriel eagerly interrupted. "Its *outer* surface will be continuous with its *inner* surface! But it will take time. I'll sew it up after tea." She laid aside the bag, and resumed her cup of tea. "But why do you call it Fortunatus's Purse, Mein Herr?"

The dear old man beamed upon her, with a jolly smile, looking more exactly like the Professor than ever. "Don't you see, my child—I should say Miladi? Whatever is *inside* that Purse, is *outside* it; and whatever is *outside* it, is *inside* it. So you have all the wealth of the world in that leetle Purse!"

His pupil clapped her hands, in unrestrained delight. "I'll certainly sew the third handkerchief in—*some* time," she said: "but I wo'n't take up your time by trying it now. Tell us some more wonderful things, please!" And her face and her voice so *exactly* recalled Sylvie, that I could not help glancing round, half-expecting to see *Bruno* also!

Mein Herr began thoughtfully balancing his spoon on the edge of his teacup, while he pondered over this request. "Something wonderful—like Fortunatus's Purse? *That* will give you—when it is made—wealth beyond your wildest dreams: but it will not give you *Time!*"

A pause of silence ensued—utilized by Lady Muriel for the very practical purpose of refilling the teacups.

"In *your* country", Mein Herr began with a startling abruptness, "what becomes of all the wasted Time?"

Lady Muriel looked grave. "Who can tell?" she half-whispered to herself. "All one knows is that it is gone—past recall!"

"Well, in *my*—I mean in a country *I* have visited", said the old man, "they store it up: and it comes in *very* useful, years afterwards! For example, suppose you have a long tedious evening before you: nobody to talk to: nothing you care to do: and yet hours too soon to go to bed. How do *you* behave then?"

"I get *very* cross," she frankly admitted: "and I want to throw things about the room!"

"When that happens to—to the people I have visited, they never act *so*. By a short and simple process—which I cannot explain to you—they store up the useless hours: and, on some *other* occasion, when they happen to *need* extra time, they get them out again."

The Earl was listening with a slightly incredulous smile. "Why cannot you *explain* the process?" he enquired.

Mein Herr was ready with a quite unanswerable reason. "Because you have no *words*, in *your* language, to convey the ideas which are needed. I could explain it in—in—but you would not understand it!"

"No indeed!" said Lady Muriel, graciously dispensing with the *name* of the unknown language. "I never learnt it—at least, not to speak it *fluently*, you know. *Please* tell us some more wonderful things!"

"They run their railway-trains without any engines—nothing is needed but machinery to *stop* them with. Is *that* wonderful enough, Miladi?"

"But where does the *force* come from?" I ventured to ask.

Mein Herr turned quickly round, to look at the new speaker. Then he took off his spectacles, and polished them, and looked at me again, in evident bewilderment. I could see he was thinking—as indeed *I* was also—that we *must* have met before.

"They use the force of *gravity*," he said. "It is a force known also in *your* country, I believe?"

"But that would need a railway going *down-hill*," the Earl remarked. "You ca'n't have *all* your railways going down-hill?"

"They *all* do", said Mein Herr.

"Not from *both* ends?"

"From *both* ends."

"Then I give it up!" said the Earl.

"Can you explain the process?" said Lady Muriel. "Without using that language, that I ca'n't speak fluently?"

"Easily," said Mein Herr. "Each railway is in a long tunnel, perfectly straight: so of course the *middle* of it is nearer the centre of the globe than the two ends: so every train runs half-way *down-hill*, and that gives it force enough to run the *other* half *up*-hill."

"Thank you. I understand that perfectly," said Lady Muriel. "But the velocity, in the *middle* of the tunnel, must be something *fearful!*"

Mein Herr was evidently much gratified at the intelligent interest Lady Muriel took in his remarks. At every moment the old man seemed to grow more chatty and more fluent. "You would like to know our methods of *driving*?" he smilingly enquired. "To us, a run-away horse is of no import at all!"

Lady Muriel slightly shuddered. "To *us* it is a very real danger," she said.

"That is because your carriage is wholly *behind* your horse. Your horse runs. Your carriage follows. Perhaps your horse has the bit in his teeth. Who shall stop him? You fly, ever faster and faster! Finally comes the inevitable upset!"

"But suppose *your* horse manages to get the bit in his teeth?"

"No matter! We would not concern ourselves. Our horse is harnessed in the very centre of our carriage. Two wheels are in front of him, and two behind. To the roof is attached one end of a broad belt. This goes under the horse's body, and the other end is attached to a leetle—what you call a 'windlass', I think. The horse takes the bit in his teeth. He runs away. We are flying at ten miles an hour! We turn our little windlass, five turns, six turns, seven turns, and—poof! Our horse is off the ground! *Now* let him gallop in the air as much as he pleases: our *carriage* stands still. We sit round him, and watch him till he is tired. Then we let him down. Our horse is glad, very much glad, when his feet once more touch the ground!"

"Capital!" said the Earl, who had been listening attentively. "Are there any other peculiarities in your carriages?"

"In the *wheels*, sometimes, my Lord. For your health, *you* go to sea: to be pitched, to be rolled, occasionally to be drowned. *We* do all that on land: we are pitched, as you: we are rolled, as you; but *drowned*, no! There is no water!"

"What are the wheels like, then?"

"They are *oval*, my Lord. Therefore the carriages rise and fall."

"Yes, and pitch the carriage backwards and forwards: but how do they make it *roll*?"

"They do not match, my Lord. The *end* of one wheel answers to the side of the opposite wheel. So first one side of the carriage rises, then the other. And it pitches all the while. Ah, you must be a good sailor, to drive in our boat-carriages!"

"I can easily believe it," said the Earl.

Mein Herr rose to his feet. "I must leave you now, Miladi," he said, consulting his watch. "I have another engagement."

"I only wish we had stored up some extra time!" Lady Muriel said, as she shook hands with him. "Then we could have kept you a little longer!"

"In *that* case I would gladly stay," replied Mein Herr. "As it is—I fear I must say goodbye!"

"Where did you first meet him?" I asked Lady Muriel, when Mein Herr had left us. "And where does he live? And what is his real name?"

"We first—met—him——" she musingly replied, "really, I ca'n't remember *where*! And I've no idea where he lives! And I've no idea where he lives! And I never heard any other name! It's very curious. It never occurred to me before to consider what a mystery he is!"

"I hope we shall meet again," I said: "he interests me very much."

"He will be at our farewell-party, this day fortnight," said the Earl. "Of course you will come? Muriel is anxious to gather all our friends around us once more, before we leave the place."

And then he explained to me—as Lady Muriel had left us together—that he was so anxious to get his daughter away from a place full of so many painful memories connected with the now-cancelled engagement with Major Lindon, that they had arranged to have the wedding in a month's time, after which Arthur and his wife were to go on a foreign tour.

"Don't forget Tuesday week!" he said as we shook hands at parting. "I only wish you could bring with you those charming children, that you introduced to us in the summer. Talk of the mystery of Mein Herr! That's *nothing* to the mystery that seems to attend *them*! I shall never forget those marvellous flowers!"

"I will bring them if I possibly can," I said. But how to *fulfil* such a promise, I mused to myself on my way back to our lodgings, was a problem entirely beyond my skill!

CHAPTER 8

In a Shady Place

THE ten days glided swiftly away: and, the day before the great party was to take place, Arthur proposed that we should stroll down to the Hall, in time for afternoon-tea.

"Hadn't you better go *alone*?" I suggested. "Surely *I* shall be very much *de trop*?"

"Well, it'll be a kind of *experiment*," he said. "*Fiat experimentum in corpore vili!*" he added, with a graceful bow of mock politeness towards the unfortunate victim. "You see I shall have to bear the sight, to-morrow night, of my lady-love making herself agreeable to everybody except the right person, and I shall bear the agony all the better if we have a dress-rehearsal beforehand!"

"*My* part in the play being, apparently, that of the sample *wrong* person?"

"Well, no," Arthur said musingly, as we set forth: "there's no such part in a regular company. 'Heavy Father'? *That* wo'n't do: that's filled already. 'Singing Chambermaid'? Well, the 'First Lady' doubles *that* part. 'Comic Old Man'? You're not comic enough. After all, I'm afraid there's no part for you but the 'Well-dressed Villain': only", with a critical side-glance, "I'm a *leetle* uncertain about the dress!"

We found Lady Muriel alone, the Earl having gone out to make a call, and at once resumed old terms of intimacy, in the shady arbour where the tea-things seemed to be always waiting. The only novelty in the arrangements (one which Lady Muriel seemed to regard as *entirely* a matter of course), was that two of the chairs were placed *quite* close together, side by side. Strange to say, *I* was not invited to occupy *either* of them! ·

"We have been arranging, as we came along, about letter-writing," Arthur began. "He will want to know how we're enjoying our Swiss tour: and of course we must pretend we *are*?"

"Of course," she meekly assented.

"And the skeleton-in-the-cupboard——" I suggested.

"—is always a difficulty", she quickly put in, "when you're travelling about, and when there are no cupboards in the hotels. However, *ours* is a *very* portable one; and will be neatly packed, in a nice leather case——"

"But please don't think about *writing*", I said, "when you've anything more attractive on hand. I delight in *reading* letters, but I know well how tiring it is to *write* them."

"It *is*, sometimes," Arthur assented. "For instance, when you're very shy of the person you have to write to."

"Does that show itself in the *letter*?" Lady Muriel enquired. "Of course, when I hear any one *talking*—*you*, for instance—I can see how *desperately* shy he is! But can you see that in a *letter*?"

"Well, of course, when you hear any one talk *fluently*—*you*, for instance—you can see how desperately *un*-shy she is—not to say saucy! But the shyest and most intermittent talker must *seem* fluent in letter-writing. He may have taken half-an-hour to *compose* his second sentence; but there it is, close after the first!"

"Then letters don't express all that they *might* express?"

"That's merely because our system of letter-writing is incomplete. A shy writer *ought* to be able to show that he is so. Why shouldn't he make *pauses* in writing, just as he would do in speaking? He might leave blank spaces—say half a page at a time. And a *very* shy girl—if there *is* such a thing—might write a sentence on the *first* sheet of her letter—then put in a couple of blank sheets—then a sentence on the *fourth* sheet: and so on."

"I quite foresee that *we*—I mean this clever little boy and myself—" Lady Muriel said to me, evidently with the kind wish to bring me into the conversation, "—are going to become famous—of course all our inventions are common property now—for a new Code of Rules for Letter-writing! Please invent some more, little boy!"

"Well, another thing *greatly* needed, little girl, is some way of expressing that we *don't* mean anything."

"Explain yourself, little boy! Surely *you* can find no difficulty in expressing a *total* absence of meaning?"

"I mean that you should be able, when you *don't* mean a thing to be taken seriously, to express that wish. For human nature is so constituted that whatever you write seriously is taken as a joke, and whatever you mean as a joke is taken seriously! At any rate, it is so in writing to a *lady*!"

"Ah! you're not used to writing to ladies!" Lady Muriel remarked, leaning back in her chair, and gazing thoughtfully into the sky. "You should try."

"Very good," said Arthur. "How many ladies may I begin writing to? As many as I can count on the fingers of both hands?"

"As many as you can count on the *thumbs* of *one* hand!" his lady-love replied with much severity. "What a *very* naughty little boy he is! *Isn't* he?" (with an appealing glance at me).

"He's a little fractious," I said. "Perhaps he's cutting a tooth." While to myself I said "How *exactly* like Sylvie talking to Bruno!"

"He wants his tea." (The naughty little boy volunteered the information.) "He's getting very tired, at the mere *prospect* of the great party to-morrow!"

"Then he shall have a good rest before-hand!" she soothingly replied. "The tea isn't made yet. Come, little boy, lean well back in your chair, and think about nothing—or about *me*, whichever you prefer!"

"All the same, all the same!" Arthur sleepily murmured, watching her with loving eyes, as she moved her chair away to the tea table, and began to make the tea. "Then he'll wait for his tea, like a good patient little boy!"

"Shall I bring you the London Papers?" said Lady Muriel. "I saw them lying on the table as I came out, but my father said there was nothing in them, except that horrid murder-trial." (Society was just then enjoying its daily thrill of excitement in studying the details of a specially sensational murder in a thieves' den in the East of London.)

"I have no appetite for horrors," Arthur replied. "But I hope we have learned the lesson they should teach us—though we are very apt to read it backwards!"

"You speak in riddles," said Lady Muriel. "Please explain yourself. See now," suiting the action to the word, "I am sitting at your feet, just as if you were a second Gamaliel! Thanks, no." (This was to me, who had risen to bring her chair back to its former place.) "Pray don't disturb yourself. This tree and the grass make a very nice easy-chair. *What* is the lesson that one always reads wrong?"

Arthur was silent for a minute. "I would like to be clear what it *is* I mean," he said, slowly and thoughtfully, "before I say anything to *you*—because you *think* about it."

Anything approaching to a compliment was so unusual an utterance for Arthur, that it brought a flush of pleasure to her cheek, as she replied "It is *you*, that give me the ideas to think about."

"One's first thought", Arthur proceeded, "in reading anything specially vile or barbarous, as done by a fellow-creature, is apt to be that we see a new depth of Sin revealed *beneath* us: and we seem to gaze down into that abyss from some higher ground, far apart from it."

"I think I understand you now. You mean that one ought to think—not 'God, I thank Thee that I am not as other men are'—but 'God, be merciful to me also, who might be, but for Thy grace, a sinner as vile as he!' "

"No," said Arthur. "I mean a great deal more than that."

She looked up quickly, but checked herself, and waited in silence.

"One must begin further back, I think. Think of some other man, the same age as this poor wretch. Look back to the time when they both began life—before they had sense enough to know Right from Wrong. *Then*, at any rate, they were equal in God's sight?"

She nodded assent.

"We have, then, two distinct epochs at which we may contemplate the two men whose lives we are comparing. At the first epoch they are, so far as moral responsibility is concerned, on precisely the same footing: they are alike incapable of doing right or wrong. At the second epoch the one man—I am taking an extreme case, for contrast—has won the esteem

and love of all around him: his character is stainless, and his name will be held in honour hereafter: the other man's history is one unvaried record of crime, and his life is at last forfeited to the outraged laws of his country. Now what have been the causes, in each case, of each man's condition being what it is at the second epoch? They are of two kinds—one acting from within, the other from without. These two kinds need to be discussed separately—that is, if I have not already tired you with my prosing?"

"On the contrary," said Lady Muriel, "it is a special delight to me to have a question discussed in this way—analysed and arranged so that one can understand it. Some books, that profess to argue out a question, are to me intolerably wearisome, simply because the ideas are all arranged haphazard—a sort of 'first come, first served'."

"You are very encouraging," Arthur replied, with a pleased look. "The causes, acting from *within*, which make a man's character what it is at any given moment, are his successive acts of volition—that is, his acts of choosing whether he will do this or that."

"We are to assume the existence of Free-Will?" I said, in order to have that point made quite clear.

"If not," was the quiet reply, "*cadit quaestio:* and I have no more to say."

"We *will* assume it!" the rest of the audience—the majority, I may say, looking at it from Arthur's point of view—imperiously proclaimed. The orator proceeded.

"The causes, acting from *without*, are his surroundings—what Mr. Herbert Spencer calls his 'environment'. Now the point I want to make clear is this, that a man is responsible for his act of choosing, but *not* responsible for his environment. Hence, if these two men make, on some given occasion, when they are exposed to equal temptation, equal efforts to resist and to choose the right, their condition, in the sight of God, must be the same. If He is pleased in the one case, so will He be in the other; if displeased in the one case, so also in the other."

"That is so, no doubt: I see it quite clearly," Lady Muriel put in.

"And yet, owing to their different environments, the one may win a great victory over the temptation, while the other falls into some black abyss of crime."

"But surely you would not say those men were equally guilty in the sight of God?"

"Either that", said Arthur, "or else I must give up my belief in God's perfect justice. But let me put one more case, which will show my meaning even more forcibly. Let the one man be in a high social position—the other, say, a common thief. Let the one be tempted to some trivial act of unfair dealing—something which he can do with the absolute certainty that it will never be discovered—something which he can with perfect ease forbear from doing—and which he distinctly knows to be a sin. Let the other be tempted to some terrible crime—as men would consider it—but under an almost overwhelming pressure of motives—of course not *quite* overwhelming, as that would destroy all responsibility. Now, in this case, let the second man make a *greater* effort at resistance than the first. Also suppose *both* to fall under the temptation—I say that the second man is, in God's sight, *less* guilty than the other."

Lady Muriel drew a long breath. "It upsets all one's ideas of Right and Wrong—just at first! Why, in that dreadful murder-trial, you would say, I suppose, that it was possible that the least guilty man in the Court was the murderer, and that possibly the judge who tried him, by yielding to the temptation of making one unfair remark, had committed a crime outweighing the criminal's whole career!"

"Certainly I should," Arthur firmly replied. "It sounds like a paradox, I admit. But just think what a grievous sin it must be, in God's sight, to yield to some very slight temptation, which we could have resisted with perfect ease, and to do it deliberately, and in the full light of God's Law. What penance can atone for a sin like *that*?"

"I ca'n't reject your theory," I said. "But how it seems to widen the possible area of Sin in the world!"

"Is that so?" Lady Muriel anxiously enquired.

"Oh, not so, not so!" was the eager reply. "To me it seems to clear away much of the cloud that hangs over the world's history. When this view first made itself clear to me, I remember walking out into the fields, repeating to myself that like of Tennyson '*There seemed no room for sense of wrong!*'" The thought, that perhaps the real guilt of the human race was infinitely less than I fancied it—that the millions, whom I had thought of as sunk in hopeless depths of sin, were perhaps, in God's sight, scarcely sinning at all—was more sweet than words can tell! Life seemed more bright and beautiful, when once that thought had come! '*A livelier emerald twinkles in the grass, A purer sapphire melts into the sea!*' " His voice trembled as he concluded, and the tears stood in his eyes.

Lady Muriel shaded her face with her hand, and was silent for a minute. "It is a beautiful thought," she said, looking up at last. "Thank you—Arthur, for putting it into my head!"

The Earl returned in time to join us at tea, and to give us the very unwelcome tidings that a fever had broken out in the little harbour-town

506 SYLVIE AND BRUNO CONCLUDED

that lay below us—a fever of so malignant a type that, though it had only appeared a day or two ago, there were already more than a dozen down in it, two or three of whom were reported to be in imminent danger.

In answer to the eager questions of Arthur—who of course took a deep scientific interest in the matter—he could give very few *technical* details, though he had met the local doctor. It appeared, however, that it was an almost *new* disease—at least in *this* century, though it *might* prove to be identical with the "Plague" recorded in History—*very* infectious, and frightfully rapid in its action. "It will not, however, prevent our party tomorrow," he said in conclusion. "None of the guests belong to the infected district, which is, as you know, exclusively peopled by fishermen: so you may come with out any fear."

Arthur was very silent, all the way back, and, on reaching our lodgings, immediately plunged into medical studies, connected with the alarming malady of whose arrival he had just heard.

CHAPTER 9

The Farewell-Party

ON the following day, Arthur and I reached the Hall in good time, as only a few of the guests—it was to be a party of eighteen—had as yet arrived; and these were talking with the Earl, leaving us the opportunity of a few words apart with our hostess.

"Who is that *very* learned-looking man with the large spectacles?" Arthur enquired. "I haven't met him here before, have I?"

"No, he's a new friend of ours," said Lady Muriel: "a German, I believe. He *is* such a dear old thing! And quite the most learned man I ever met—with *one* exception, of course!" she added humbly, as Arthur drew himself up with an air of offended dignity.

"And the young lady in blue, just beyond him, talking to that foreign-looking man. Is *she* learned, too?"

"I don't know," said Lady Muriel. "But I'm told she's a wonderful piano-forte-player. I hope you'll hear her tonight. I asked that foreigner to take her in, because *he's* very musical, too. He's a French Count, I believe; and he sings *splendidly!*"

"Science—music—singing—you have indeed got a complete party!" said Arthur. "I feel quite a privileged person, meeting all these stars. I *do* love music!"

"But the party isn't *quite* complete!" said Lady Muriel. "You haven't brought us those two beautiful children," she went on, turning to me. "He brought them here to tea, you know, one day last summer," again addressing Arthur: "and they *are* such darlings!"

"They are, *indeed*," I assented.

"But why haven't you brought them with you? You promised my father you *would*."

"I'm very sorry," I said; "but really it was impossible to bring them with me." Here I most certainly *meant* to conclude the sentence: and it was with a feeling of utter amazement, which I cannot adequately describe, that I heard myself *going on speaking*. "—but they are to join me here in the course of the evening" were the words, uttered in *my* voice, and seeming to come from *my* lips.

"I'm *so* glad!" Lady Muriel joyfully replied. "I *shall* enjoy introducing them to some of my friends here! When do you expect them?"

I took refuge in silence. The only *honest* reply would have been "That was not *my* remark. *I* didn't say it, and *it isn't true!*" But I had not the moral courage to make such a confession. The character of a "lunatic" is not, I believe, very difficult to *acquire*: but it is amazingly difficult to *get rid of*: and it seemed quite certain that any such speech as *that* would *quite* justify the issue of a write "*de lunatico inquirendo*".

Lady Muriel evidently thought I had failed to hear her question, and turned to Arthur with a remark on some other subject; and I had time to recover from my shock of surprise—or to awake out of my momentary "eerie" condition, whichever it was.

When things around me seemed once more to be real, Arthur was saying "I'm afraid there's no help for it: they *must* be finite in number."

"I should be sorry to have to believe it," said Lady Muriel. "Yet, when one comes to think of it, there *are* no new melodies, now-a-days. What people talk of as 'the last new song' always recalls to *me* some tune I've known as a child!"

"The day must come—if the world lasts long enough——" said Arthur, "when every possible tune will have been composed—every possible pun perpetrated——" (Lady Muriel wrung her hands, like a tragedy-queen) "and, worse than that, every possible *book* written! For the number of *words* is finite."

"It'll make very little difference to the *authors*," I suggested. "Instead of saying '*what* book shall I write?' an author will ask himself '*which* book shall I write?' A mere verbal distinction!"

Lady Muriel gave me an approving smile. "But *lunatics* would always write new books, surely?" she went on. "They *couldn't* write the sane books over again!"

"True," said Arthur. "But their books would come to an end, also. The number of lunatic *books* is as finite as the number of lunatics."

"And *that* number is becoming greater every year," said a pompous man, whom I recognized as the self-appointed showman on the day of the picnic.

"So they say," replied Arthur. "And, when ninety per cent. of us are lunatics," (he seemed to be in a wildly nonsensical mood) "the asylums will be put to their proper use."

"And that is——?" the pompous man gravely enquired.

"*To shelter the sane!*" said Arthur. "*We* shall bar ourselves in. The lunatics will have it all their own way, *outside*. They'll do it a little queerly, no doubt. Railway-collisions will be always happening: steamers always blowing up: most of the towns will be burnt down: most of the ships sunk——"

"And most of the men *killed*!" murmured the pompous man, who was evidently hopelessly bewildered.

"Certainly," Arthur assented. "Till at last there will be *fewer* lunatics than sane men. Then *we* come out: *they* go in: and things return to their normal condition!"

The pompous man frowned darkly, and bit his lip, and folded his arms, vainly trying to think it out. "He is *jesting*!" he muttered to himself at last, in a tone of withering contempt, as he stalked away.

By this time the other guests had arrived; and dinner was announced. Arthur of course took down Lady Muriel: and *I* was pleased to find myself seated at her other side, with a severe-looking old lady (whom I had not met before, and whose name I had, as is usual in introductions, entirely failed to catch, merely gathering that it sounded like a compound-name) as my partner for the banquet.

She appeared, however, to be acquainted with Arthur, and confided to me in a low voice her opinion that he was "a very argumentative young man". Arthur, for his part, seemed well inclined to show himself worthy of the character she had given him, and, hearing her say "I never take wine with my soup!" (this was *not* a confidence to me, but was launched upon Society, as a matter of general interest), he at once challenged a combat by asking her "*when* would you say that property *commence* in a plate of soup?"

"This is *my* soup," she sternly replied: "and what is before you is *yours*."

"No doubt," said Arthur: "but *when* did I begin to own it? Up to the moment of its being put into the plate, it was the property of our host: while being offered round the table, it was, let us say, held in trust by the waiter: did it become mine when I accepted it? Or when it was placed before me? Or when I took the first spoonful?"

"He is a *very* argumentative young man!" was all the old lady would say: but she said it audibly, this time, feeling that Society had a right to know it.

Arthur smiled mischievously. "I shouldn't mind betting you a shilling", he said, "that the Eminent Barrister next you" (It certainly *is* possible to say words so as to make them begin with capitals!) "ca'n't answer me!"

"I *never* bet," she sternly replied.

"Not even sixpenny points at *whist*?"

"*Never!*" she repeated. "*Whist* is innocent enough: but whist played for *money*!" She shuddered.

Arthur became serious again. "I'm afraid I ca'n't take that view," he said. "I consider that the introduction of small stakes for card-playing was one of the most *moral* acts Society ever did, *as* Society."

"How was it so?" said Lady Muriel.

"Because it took Cards, once for all, out of the category of games at which *cheating* is possible. Look at the way Croquet is demoralizing Society. Ladies are beginning to cheat at it, terribly: and, if they're found out, they only laugh, and call it fun. But when there's *money* at stake, that is out of the question. The swindler is *not* accepted as a wit. When a man sits down to cards, and cheats his friends out of their money, he doesn't get much *fun* out of it—unless he thinks it fun to be kicked down stairs!"

"If all gentlemen thought as badly of ladies as *you* do," my neighbour remarked with some bitterness, "there would be very few—very few——". She seemed doubtful how to end her sentence, but at last took "honey-moons" as a safe word.

"On the contrary," said Arthur, the mischievous smile returning to his face, "if only people would adopt *my* theory, the number of honeymoons—quite of a new kind—would be greatly increased!"

"May we hear about this new kind of honeymoon?" said Lady Muriel.

"Let *X* be the gentleman," Arthur began, in a slightly raised voice, as he now found himself with an audience of *six*, including "Mein Herr", who was seated at the other side of my polynomial partner. "Let *X* be the gentleman, and *Y* the lady to whom he thinks of proposing. He applies for an Experimental Honeymoon. It is granted. Forthwith the young couple—accompanied by the great-aunt of *Y*, to act as chaperone—start for a month's tour, during which they have many a moonlight-walk, and many a *tête-à-tête* conversation, and each can form a more correct estimate of the other's character, in four *weeks*, than would have been possible in as many *years*, when meeting under the ordinary restrictions of Society. And it is only after their *return* that *X* finally decides whether he will, or will not, put the momentous question to *Y*!"

"In nine cases out of ten", the pompous man proclaimed, "he would decide to break it off!"

"Then, in nine cases out of ten," Arthur rejoined, "an unsuitable match would be prevented, and *both* parties saved from misery!"

"The only really *unsuitable* matches", the old lady remarked, "are those made without sufficient *Money*. Love may come *afterwards*. Money is needed *to begin with*!"

This remark was cast loose upon Society, as a sort of general challenge; and, as such, it was at once accepted by several of those within hearing: *Money* became the keynote of the conversation for some time: and a fitful echo of it was again heard, when the dessert had been placed upon the table, the servants had left the room, and the Earl had started the wine in its welcome progress round the table.

"I'm very glad to see you keep up the old customs," I said to Lady Muriel as I filled her glass. "It's really delightful to experience, once more, the peaceful feeling that comes over one when the waiters have left the room—when one can converse without feeling of being overheard, and without having dishes constantly thrust over one's shoulder. How much more sociable it is to be able to pour out the wine for the ladies, and to hand the dishes to those who wish for them!"

"In that case, kindly send those peaches down here," said a fat red-faced man, who was seated beyond our pompous friend. "I've been wishing for them—diagonally—for some time!"

"Yes, it *is* a ghastly innovation", Lady Muriel replied, "letting the waiters carry round the wine at dessert. For one thing, they *always* take it the wrong way round—which of course brings bad luck to *everybody* present!"

"Better go the *wrong* way than not go *at all!*" said our host. "Would you kindly help yourself?" (This was to the fat red-faced man.) "You are not a teetotaler, I think?"

"Indeed but I *am!*" he replied, as he pushed on the bottles. "Nearly twice as much money is spent in England on *Drink*, as on any other article of food. Read this card." (What faddist ever goes about without a pocketful of the appropriate literature?) "The stripes of different colours represent the amounts spent on various articles of food. Look at the highest three. Money spent on butter and on cheese, thirty-five millions: on bread, seventy millions: on *intoxicating liquors*, one hundred and thirty-six millions! If I had my way, I would close every public-house in the land! Look at that card, and read the motto. *That's where all the money goes to!*"

"Have you seen the *Anti-Teetotal Card*?" Arthur innocently enquired.

"No, Sir, I have not!" the orator savagely replied. "What is it like?"

"Almost exactly like this one. The coloured stripes are the same. Only, instead of the words 'Money spent on', it has 'Incomes derived from sale of'; and, instead of 'That's where all the money goes to', its motto is *'That's where all the money comes from!'* "

The red-faced man scowled, but evidently considered Arthur beneath his notice. So Lady Muriel took up the cudgels. "Do you hold the theory", she enquired, "that people can preach teetotalism more effectually by being teetotalers themselves?"

"Certainly I do!" replied the red-faced man. "Now, here is a case in point," unfolding a newspaper-cutting: "let me read you this letter from a teetotaler. *To the Editor. Sir, I was once a moderate drinker, and knew a man who drank to excess. I went to him. 'Give up this drink,' I said. 'It will ruin your health!' 'You drink,' he said: 'why shouldn't I?' 'Yes,' I said, 'but I know when to leave off.' He turned away from me. 'You drink in your way,' he said: 'let me drink in mine. Be off!' Then I saw that, to do any good with him, I must forswear drink. From that hour I haven't touched a drop!*"

"There! What do you say to *that*?" He looked round triumphantly, while the cutting was handed round for inspection.

"How very curious!" exclaimed Arthur when it had reached him. "Did you happen to see a letter, last week, about early rising? It was strangely like this one."

The red-faced man's curiosity was roused. "Where did it appear?" he asked.

"Let me read it to you," said Arthur. He took some papers from his pocket, opened one of them, and read as follows. *To the Editor. Sir, I was once a moderate sleeper, and knew a man who slept to excess. I pleaded with him. 'Give up this lying in bed,' I said. 'It will ruin your health!' 'You go to bed,' he said: 'why shouldn't I?' 'Yes,' I said, 'but I know when to get up in the morning.' He turned away from me. 'You sleep in your way,' he said: 'let me sleep in mine. Be off!' Then I saw that to do any good with him, I must forswear sleep. From that hour I haven't been to bed!"*

Arthur folded and pocketed his paper, and passed on the newspaper-cutting. None of us dared to laugh, the red-faced man was evidently so angry. "Your parallel doesn't run on all fours!" he snarled.

"*Moderate* drinkers never do so!" Arthur quietly replied. Even the stern old lady laughed at this.

"But it needs many other things to make a *perfect* dinner!" said Lady Muriel, evidently anxious to change the subject. "Mein Herr! What is *your* idea of a perfect dinner party?"

The old man looked around smilingly, and his gigantic spectacles seemed more gigantic than ever. "A *perfect* dinner-party?" he repeated. "First, it must be presided over by our present hostess!"

"That of *course!*" she gaily interposed. "But what *else* Mein Herr?"

"I can but tell you what I have seen," said Mein Herr, "in mine own—in the country I have traveled in."

He paused for a full minute, and gazed steadily at the ceiling—with so dreamy an expression on his face, that I feared he was going off into a reverie, which seemed to be his normal state. However, after a minute, he suddenly began again.

"That which chiefly causes the failure of a dinner-party, is the running-short—not of meat, nor yet of drink, but of *conversation.*"

"In an *English* dinner-party", I remarked, "I have never known *small-talk* run short!"

"Pardon me," Mein Herr respectfully replied, "I did not say 'small-talk'. I said 'conversation'. All such topics as the weather, or politics, or local gossip, are unknown among us. They are either vapid or controversial. What we need for *conversation* is a topic of *interest* and of *novelty*. To secure these things we have tried various plans—Moving-Pictures, Wild-Creatures, Moving-Guests, and a Revolving-Humorist. But this last is only adapted to *small* parties."

"Let us have it in four separate Chapters, please!" said Lady Muriel, who was evidently deeply interested—as, indeed, most of the party were, by this time: and, all down the table, talk had ceased, and heads were leaning forwards, eager to catch fragments of Mein Herr's oration.

"Chapter One! Moving-Pictures!" was proclaimed in the silvery voice of our hostess.

"The dining-table is shaped like a circular ring," Mein Herr began, in low dreamy tones, which, however, were perfectly audible in the silence. "The guests are seated at the inner side as well as the outer, having ascended to their places by a winding-staircase, from the room below. Along the middle of the table runs a little railway; and there is an endless train of trucks, worked round by machinery; and on each truck there are two pictures, leaning back to back. The train makes two circuits during dinner; and, when it has been *once* round, the waiters turn the pictures round in each truck, making them face the other way. Thus *every* guest sees *every* picture!"

He paused, and the silence seemed deader than ever. Lady Muriel looked aghast. "Really, if this goes on," she exclaimed, "I shall have to drop a pin! Oh, it's *my* fault, is it?" (In answer to an appealing look from Mein Herr.) "I was forgetting my duty. Chapter Two! Wild-Creatures!"

"We found the Moving-Pictures a *little* monotonous," said Mein Herr. "People didn't care to talk Art through a whole dinner; so we tried Wild-Creatures. Among the flowers, which we laid (just as *you* do) about the table, were to be seen, here a mouse, there a beetle; here a spider" (Lady Muriel shuddered), "there a wasp; here a toad, there a snake"; ("Father!" said Lady Muriel, plaintively. "Did you hear *that*?"); "so we had plenty to talk about!"

"And when you got stung——" the old lady began.

"They were all chained-up, dear Madam!"

And the old lady gave a satisfied nod.

There was no silence to follow, *this* time. "Third Chapter!" Lady Muriel proclaimed at once. "Moving-Guests!"

"Even the Wild-Creatures proved monotonous," the orator proceeded. "So we left the guests to choose their own subjects; and, to avoid monotony, we changed *them*. We made the table of *two* rings; and the inner ring moved slowly round, all the time, along with the floor in the middle and the inner row of guests. Thus *every* inner guest was brought face-to-face with *every* outer guest. It was a little confusing, sometimes, to have to *begin* a story to one friend and *finish* it to another; but *every* plan has its faults, you know."

"Fourth Chapter!" Lady Muriel hastened to announce. "The Revolving-Humorist!"

"For a *small* party we found it an excellent plan to have a round table, with a hole cut in the middle large enough to hold *one* guest. Here we placed our *best* talker. He revolved slowly, facing every other guest in turn: and he told lively anecdotes the whole time!"

"I shouldn't like it!" murmured the pompous man. "It would make me giddy, revolving like that! I should decline to——" here it appeared to dawn upon him that perhaps the assumption he was making was not warranted by the circumstances: he took a hasty gulp of wine, and choked himself.

But Mein Herr had relapsed into reverie, and made no further remark. Lady Muriel gave the signal, and the ladies left the room.

CHAPTER 10

Jabbering and Jam

WHEN the last lady had disappeared, and the Earl, taking his place at the head of the table, had issued the military order "Gentlemen! Close up the ranks, if you please!" and when, in obedience to his command, we had gathered ourselves compactly round him, the pompous man gave a deep sigh of relief, filled his glass to the brim, pushed on the wine, and began one of his favourite orations. "They are charming, no doubt! Charming, but very frivolous. They drag us down, so to speak, to a lower level. They——"

"Do not all pronouns require antecedent *nouns?*" the Earl gently enquired.

"Pardon me," said the pompous man, with lofty condescension. "I had overlooked the noun. The ladies. We regret their absence. Yet we console ourselves. *Thought is free.* With them, we are limited to *trivial* topics—Art, Literature, Politics, and so forth. One can bear to discuss *such* paltry matters with a lady. But no man, in his senses——" (he looked sternly round the table, as if defying contradiction) "—ever yet discussed *WINE* with a lady!" He sipped his glass of port, leaned back in his chair, and slowly raised it up to his eye, so as to look through it at the lamp. "The vintage, my Lord?" he enquired, glancing at his host.

The Earl named the date.

"So I had supposed. But one likes to be certain. The *tint* is, perhaps, slightly pale. But the *body* is unquestionable. And as for the *bouquet*——"

Ah, that magic Bouquet! How vividly that magic word recalled the scene! The little beggar boy turning his somersault in the road—the sweet little crippled maiden in my arms—the mysterious evanescent nurse-maid—all rushed tumultuously into my mind, like the creatures of a dream: and through this mental haze there still boomed on, like the tolling of a bell, the solemn voice of the great connoisseur of *WINE*!

Even *his* utterances had taken on themselves a strange and dream-like form. "No," he resumed—and *why* is it, I pause to ask, that, in taking up the broken thread of a dialogue, one *always* begins with this cheerless monosyllable? After much anxious thought, I have come to the conclusion that the object in view is the same as that of the schoolboy, when the sum he is working has got into a hopeless muddle, and when in despair he takes the sponge, washes it all out, and begins again. Just in the same way the bewildered orator, by the simple process of denying *everything* that has been hitherto asserted, makes a clean sweep of the whole discussion, and can "start fair" with a fresh theory. "No," he resumed: "there's nothing like cherry-jam, after all. That's what *I* say!"

"Not for *all* qualities!" an eager little man shrilly interposed. "For *richness* of general tone I don't say that it *has* a rival. But for *delicacy* of modulation—for what one may call the '*harmonics*' of flavour—give *me* good old *raspberry*-jam!"

"Allow me one word!" The fat red-faced man, quite hoarse with excitement, broke into the dialogue. "It's too important a question to be settled by Amateurs! I can give you the views of a *Professional*—perhaps the most experienced jam-taster now living. Why, I've known him fix the age of strawberry-jam, to a *day*—and we all know what a difficult jam it is to give a date to—on a single tasting! Well, I put to him the *very* question you are discussing. His words were '*cherry*-jam is best, for mere *chiaroscuro* of flavour; *raspberry*-jam lends itself best to those resolved discords that linger so lovingly on the tongue: but, for rapturous *utterness* of saccharine perfection, it's *apricot-jam first and the rest nowhere!*' That was well put, *wasn't it*?"

"Consummately put!" shrieked the eager little man.

"I know your friend well," said the pompous man. "As a jam-taster, he has no rival! Yet I scarcely think——"

But here the discussion became general: and his words were lost in a confused medley of names, every guest sounding the praises of his own favourite jam. At length, through the din, our host's voice made itself heard. "Let us join the ladies!" These words seemed to recall me to waking life; and I felt sure that, for the last few minutes, I had relapsed into the "eerie" state.

"A strange dream!" I said to myself as we trooped upstairs. "Grown men discussing, as seriously as if they were matters of life and death, the hopelessly trivial details or mere *delicacies*, that appeal to no higher human function than the nerves of the tongue and palate! What a humiliating spectacle such a discussion would be in waking life!"

When, on our way to the drawing-room, I received from the housekeeper my little friends, clad in the daintiest of evening costumes, and looking, in the flush of expectant delight, more radiantly beautiful than I had ever seen them before. I felt no shock of surprise, but accepted the fact with the same unreasoning apathy with which one meets the events of a dream, and was merely conscious of a vague anxiety as to how they would acquit themselves in so novel a scene—forgetting that Court-life in Outland was as good training as they could need for Society in the more substantial world.

It would be best, I thought, to introduce them as soon as possible to some good-natured lady-guest, and I selected the young lady whose piano-forte-playing had been so much talked of. "I am sure you like children," I said. "May I introduce two little friends of mine? This is Sylvie—and this is Bruno."

The young lady kissed Sylvie very graciously. She would have done the same for *Bruno*, but he hastily drew back out of reach. "Their faces are new to me," she said. "Where do you come from, my dear?"

I had not anticipated so inconvenient a question; and, fearing that it might embarrass Sylvie, I answered for her. "They come from some distance. They are only here just for this one evening."

"How far have you come, dear?" the young lady persisted.

Sylvie looked puzzled. "A mile or two, I *think*," she said doubtfully.

"A mile or *three*," said Bruno.

"You shouldn't say 'a mile or *three*'," Sylvie corrected him.

The young lady nodded approval. "Sylvie's quite right. It isn't usual to say 'a mile or *three*'."

"It would be usual—if we said it often enough," said Bruno.

It was the young lady's turn to look puzzled now. "He's very quick, for his age!" she murmured. "You're not more than seven, are you, dear?" she added aloud.

"I'm not so many as *that*," said Bruno. "I'm *one*. Sylvie's *one*. Sylvie and me is *two*. *Sylvie* taught me to count."

"Oh, I wasn't *counting* you, you know!" the young lady laughingly replied.

"Hasn't oo *learnt* to count?" said Bruno.

The young lady bit her lip. "Dear! What embarrassing questions he *does* ask!" she said in a half-audible "aside".

"Bruno, you shouldn't!" Sylvie said reprovingly.

"Shouldn't *what*?" said Bruno.

"You shouldn't ask—that sort of questions."

"*What* sort of questions?" Bruno mischievously persisted.

"What *she* told you not," Sylvie replied, with a shy glance at the young lady, and losing all sense of grammar in her confusion.

"Oo ca'n't pronounce it!" Bruno triumphantly cried. And he turned to the young lady, for sympathy in his victory. "I *knewed* she couldn't pronounce 'umbrellasting'!"

The young lady thought it best to return to the arithmetical problem. "When I asked if you were *seven*, you know, I didn't mean 'how many *children*?' I meant 'how many *years*——' "

"Only got *two* ears," said Bruno. "Nobody's got *seven* ears."

"And you belong to this little girl?" the young lady continued, skilfully evading the anatomical problem.

"No I doosn't belong to *her*!" said Bruno. "Sylvie belongs to *me*!" And he clasped his arms round her as he added "She are my very mine!"

"And, do you know," said the young lady, "I've a little sister at home, exactly like *your* sister? I'm sure they'd love each other."

"They'd be very extremely useful to each other," Bruno said, thoughtfully. "And they wouldn't want no looking-glasses to brush their hair wiz."

"Why not, my child?"

"Why, each one would do for the other one's looking-glass a-course!" cried Bruno.

But here Lady Muriel, who had been standing by, listening to this bewildering dialogue, interrupted it to ask if the young lady would favour us with some music; and the children followed their new friend to the piano.

Arthur came and sat down by me. "If rumour speaks truly," he whispered, "we are to have a real treat!" And then, amid a breathless silence, the performance began.

She was one of those players whom Society talks of as "brilliant", and she dashed into the loveliest of Haydn's Symphonies in a style that was clearly the outcome of years of patient study under the best masters. At first it seemed to be the perfection of piano-forte-playing; but in a few minutes I began to ask myself, wearily, "*What* is it that is wanting? *Why* does one get no pleasure from it?"

Then I set myself to listen intently to every note; and the mystery explained itself. There *was* an almost perfect mechanical *correctness*—and there was nothing else! False notes, of course, did not occur: she knew the piece too well for *that*; but there was just enough irregularity of *time* to betray that the player had no real "ear" for music—just enough inarticulateness in the more elaborate passages to show that she did not think her audience worth taking real pains for—just enough mechanical monotony of accent to take all *soul* out of the heavenly modulations she was profaning—in short, it was simply irritating; and, when she had rattled off the finale and had struck the final chord as if, the instrument being now done with, it didn't matter how many wires she broke, I could not even *affect* to join in the stereotyped "Oh, *thank* you!" which was chorused around me.

Lady Muriel joined us for a moment. "Isn't it *beautiful*?" she whispered to Arthur, with a mischievous smile.

"No, it isn't!" said Arthur. But the gentle sweetness of his face quite neutralized the apparent rudeness of the reply.

"Such execution, you know!" she persisted.

"That's what she *deserves*," Arthur doggedly replied: "but people are so prejudiced against capital——"

"Now you're beginning to talk nonsense!" Lady Muriel cried. "But you *do* like Music, don't you? You said so just now."

"Do I like *Music*?" the Doctor repeated softly to himself. "My dear Lady Muriel, there is Music and Music. Your question is painfully vague. You might as well ask 'Do you like *People*?'"

Lady Muriel bit her lip, frowned, and stamped with one tiny foot. As a dramatic representation of ill-temper, it was distinctly *not* a success. However, it took in *one* of her audience, and Bruno hastened to interpose, as peacemaker in a rising quarrel, with the remark "*I* likes Peoples!"

Arthur laid a loving hand on the little curly head. "What? *All* Peoples?" he enquired.

"Not *all* Peoples," Bruno explained. "Only but Sylvie—and Lady Muriel—and him——" (pointing to the Earl) "and oo—and oo!"

"You shouldn't point at people," said Sylvie. "It's very rude."

"In Bruno's World," I said, "there are only *four* People—worth mentioning!"

"In Bruno's World!" Lady Muriel repeated thoughtfully. "A bright and flowery world. Where the grass is always green, where the breezes always blow softly, and the rain-clouds never gather; where there are no wild beasts, and no deserts——"

"There *must* be deserts," Arthur decisively remarked. "At least if it was *my* ideal world."

"But what possible use is there in a *desert*?" said Lady Muriel. "*Surely* you would have no wilderness in your ideal world?"

Arthur smiled. "But indeed I *would*!" he said. "A wilderness would be more necessary than a railway; and *far* more conducive to general happiness than church-bells!"

"But what would you use it for?"

"*To practise music in,*" he replied. "All the young ladies, that have no ear for music, but insist on learning it, should be conveyed, every morning, two or three miles into the wilderness. There each would find a comfortable room provided for her, and also a cheap second-hand piano-forte, on which she might play for hours, without adding one needless pang to the sum of human misery!"

Lady Muriel glanced round in alarm, lest these barbarous sentiments should be overheard. But the fair musician was at a safe distance. "At any rate you must allow that she's a sweet girl?" she resumed.

"Oh, certainly. As sweet as *eau sucrée*, if you choose—and nearly as interesting!"

"You are incorrigible!" said Lady Muriel, and turned to me. "I hope you found Mrs. Mills an interesting companion?"

"Oh, *that's* her name, is it?" I said. "I fancied there was *more* of it."

"So there is: and it will be 'at your proper peril' (whatever that may mean) if you ever presume to address her as 'Mrs. Mills'. She is 'Mrs. Ernest—Atkinson—Mills'!"

"She is one of those would-be grandees," said Arthur, "who think that, by tacking on to their surname all their spare Christian-names, with hyphens between, they can give it an aristocratic flavour. As if it wasn't trouble enough to remember *one* surname!"

By this time the room was getting crowded, as the guests, invited for the evening-party, were beginning to arrive, and Lady Muriel had to devote herself to the task of welcoming them, which she did with the sweetest grace imaginable. Sylvie and Bruno stood by her, deeply interested in the process.

"I hope you like my friends?" she said to them. "Specially my dear old friend, Mein Herr (What's become of him, I wonder? Oh, there he is!), that old gentleman in spectacles, with a long beard!"

"He's a grand old gentleman!" Sylvie said, gazing admiringly at "Mein Herr", who had settled down in a corner, from which his mild eyes beamed on us through a gigantic pair of spectacles. "And what a lovely beard!"

"What does he call his-self?" Bruno whispered.

"He calls himself 'Mein Herr'," Sylvie whispered in reply.

Bruno shook his head impatiently. "That's what he calls his *hair*, not his *self*, oo silly!" He appealed to me. "What doos he call his *self*, Mister Sir?"

"That's the only name *I* know of," I said. "But he looks very lonely. Don't you pity his grey hairs?"

"I pities his *self*," said Bruno, still harping on the misnomer; "but I doosn't pity his *hair*, one bit. His *hair* ca'n't feel!"

"We met him this afternoon," said Sylvie. "We'd been to see Nero, and we'd had *such* fun with him, making him invisible again! And we saw that nice old gentleman as we came back."

"Well, let's go and talk to him, and cheer him up a little," I said: "and perhaps we shall find out what he calls himself."

CHAPTER 11

The Man in the Moon

THE children came willingly. With one of them on each side of me, I approached the corner occupied by "Mein Herr". "You don't object to *children*, I hope?" I began.

"Crabbed age and youth cannot live together!" the old man cheerfully replied, with a most genial smile. "Now take a good look at me, my children! You would guess me to be an *old* man, wouldn't you?"

At first sight, though his face had reminded me so mysteriously of "the Professor", he had seemed to be decidedly a *younger* man: but, when I

came to look into the wonderful depth of those large dreamy eyes, I felt, with a strange sense of awe, that he was incalculably *older:* he seemed to gaze at us out of some by-gone age, centuries away.

"I don't know if oo're an *old* man," Bruno answered, as the children, won over by the gentle voice, crept a little closer to him. "I thinks oo're *eighty-three*."

"He is very exact!" said Mein Herr.

"Is he anything like right?" I said.

"There are reasons," Mein Herr gently replied, "reasons which I am not at liberty to explain, for not mentioning *definitely* any Persons, Places, or Dates. One remark only I will permit myself to make—that the period of life, between the ages of a hundred-and-sixty-five and a hundred-and-seventy-five, is a specially *safe* one."

"How do you make that out?" I said.

"Thus. You would consider swimming to be a very safe amusement, if you scarcely ever heard of any one dying of it. Am I not right in thinking that you never heard of any one dying between those two ages?"

"I see what you mean," I said: "but I'm afraid you ca'n't prove *swimming* to be safe, on the same principle. It is no uncommon thing to hear of some one being *drowned*."

"In *my* country," said Mein Herr. "no one is *ever* drowned."

"Is there no water deep enough?"

"Plenty! But we ca'n't *sink*. We are all *lighter than water*. Let me explain," he added, seeing my look of surprise. "Suppose you desire a race of *pigeons* of a particular shape or colour, do you not select, from year to year, those that are nearest to the shape or colour you want, and keep those, and part with the others?"

"We do," I replied. "We call it 'Artificial Selection'."

"Exactly so," said Mein Herr. "Well, *we* have practised that for some centuries—constantly selecting the *lighest* people: so that, now, *everybody* is lighter than water."

"Then you never can be drowned at *sea*?"

"Never! It is only on the *land*—for instance, when attending a play in a theatre—that we are in such a danger."

"How can that happen at a *theatre*?"

"Our theatres are all *underground*. Large tanks of water are placed above. If a fire breaks out, the taps are turned, and in one minute the theatre is flooded, up to the very roof! Thus the fire is extinguished."

"*And* the audience, I presume?"

"That is a minor matter," Mein Herr carelessly replied. "But they have the comfort of knowing that, whether drowned or not, they are all *lighter than water*. We have not yet reached the standard of making people lighter than *air*: but we are *aiming* at it; and, in another thousand years or so——"

"What doos oo do wiz the peoples that's too heavy?" Bruno solemnly enquired.

"We have applied the same process," Mein Herr continued, not noticing Bruno's question, "to many other purposes. We have gone on selecting *walking-sticks*—always keeping those that walked *best*—till we have obtained some, that can walk by themselves! We have gone on selecting *cotton-wool*, till we have got some lighter than air! You've no idea what a useful material it is! We call it 'Imponderal'."

"What do you use it for?"

"Well, chiefly for *packing* articles, to go by Parcel-Post. It makes them weigh *less than nothing*, you know."

"And how do the Post Office people know what you have to pay?"

"That's the beauty of the new system!" Mein Herr cried exultingly.

"They pay *us*: we don't pay *them*! I've often got as much as five shillings for sending a parcel."

"But doesn't your Government object?"

"Well, they *do* object a little. They say it comes so expensive, in the long run. But the thing's as clear as daylight, by their own rules. If I send a parcel, that weighs a pound *more* than nothing, I *pay* three-pence: so, of course, if it weighs a pound *less* than nothing, I ought to *receive* three-pence."

"It is *indeed* a useful article!" I said.

"Yet even 'Imponderal' has its disadvantages," he resumed. "I bought some, a few days ago, and put it into my *hat*, to carry it home, and the hat simply floated away!"

"Had oo some of that funny stuff in oor hat *to-day*?" Bruno enquired. "Sylvie and me saw oo in the road, and oor hat were ever so high up! Weren't it, Sylvie?"

"No, that was quite another thing," said Mein Herr. "There was a drop or two of rain falling: so I put my hat on the top of my stick—as an umbrella, you know. As I came along the road", he continued, turning to me, "I was overtaken by——"

"—a shower of rain?" said Bruno.

"Well, it *looked* more like the tail of a dog," Mein Herr replied. "It was the most curious thing! Something rubbed affectionately against my knee. And I looked down. And I could see *nothing*! Only, about a yard off, there was a dog's tail, wagging, all by itself!"

"Oh, *Sylvie*!" Bruno murmured reproachfully. "Oo didn't finish making him visible!"

"I'm *so* sorry!" Sylvie said, looking very penitent. "I meant to rub it along his back, but we were in such a hurry. We'll go and finish him to-morrow. Poor thing! Perhaps he'll get no supper to-night!"

"*Course* he won't!" said Bruno. "Nobody never gives bones to a dog's tail!"

Mein Herr looked from one to the other in blank astonishment. "I do not understand you," he said. "I had lost my way, and I was consulting a pocket-map, and somehow I had dropped one of my gloves, and this invisible *Something*, that had rubbed against my knee, actually brought it back to me!"

"Course he did!" said Bruno. "He's *welly* fond of fetching things."

Mein Herr looked so thoroughly bewildered that I thought it best to change the subject. "What a useful thing a pocket-map is!" I remarked.

"That's another thing we've learned from *your* Nation," said Mein Herr, "map-making. But we've carried it much further than *you*. What do you consider the *largest* map that would be really useful?"

'About six inches to the mile."

"Only *six inches*!" exclaimed Mein Herr. "We very soon got to six *yards* to the mile. Then we tried a *hundred* yards to the mile. And then came the grandest idea of all! We actually made a map of the country, on the scale of *a mile to the mile*!"

"Have you used it much?" I enquired.

"It has never been spread out, yet," said Mein Herr: "the farmers objected: they said it would cover the whole country, and shut out the sunlight! So we now use the country itself, as its own map, and I assure you it does nearly as well. Now let me ask you *another* question. What is the smallest *world* you would care to inhabit?"

"*I* know!" cried Bruno, who was listening intently. "I'd like a little teeny-tiny world, just big enough for Sylvie and me!"

"Then you would have to stand on opposite side of it," said Mein Herr. "And so you would never see your sister *at all*!"

"And I'd have no *lessons*," said Bruno.

"You don't mean to say you've been trying experiments in *that* direction!" I said.

"Well, not *experiments* exactly. We do not profess to *construct* planets. But a scientific friend of mine, who has made several balloon-voyages, assures me he has visited a planet so small that he could walk right round it in twenty minutes! There had been a great battle, just before his visit, which had ended rather oddly: the vanquished army ran away at full speed, and in a very few minutes found themselves face-to-face with the victorious army, who were marching home again, and who were so frightened at finding themselves between *two* armies, that they surrendered at once! Of course that lost them the battle, though, as a matter of fact they had killed *all* the soldiers on the other side."

"Killed soldiers *ca'n't* run away," Bruno thoughtfully remarked.

" 'Killed' is a technical word," replied Mein Herr. "In the little planet I speak of, the bullets were made of soft black stuff, which marked everything it touched. So, after a battle, all you had to do was to count how many soldiers on each side were 'killed'—that means 'marked on the *back*', for marks in *front* didn't count."

"Then you couldn't 'kill' any, unless they ran away?" I said.

"My scientific friend found out a better plan than *that*. He pointed out that, if only the bullets were sent *the other way round the world*, they would hit the enemy in the *back*. After that, the *worst* marksmen were considered the *best* soldiers; and *the very worst of all* always got First Prize."

"And how did you decide which was *the very worst of all*?"

"Easily. The *best* possible shooting is, you know, to hit what is exactly in *front* of you: so of course the *worst* possible is to hit what is exactly *behind* you."

"They were strange people in that little planet!" I said.

"They were indeed! Perhaps their method of *government* was the strangest of all. In *this* planet, I am told, a Nation consists of a number of Subjects, and one King: but, in the little planet I speak of, it consisted of a number of *Kings*, and one *Subject*!"

"You say you are 'told' what happens in *this* planet," I said. "May I venture to guess that you yourself are a visitor from some *other* planet?"

Bruno clapped his hands in his excitement. "Is oo the Man-in-the-Moon?" he cried.

Mein Herr looked uneasy. "I am *not* in the Moon, my child," he said evasively. "To return to what I was saying. I think *that* method of government ought to answer *well*. You see, the Kings would be sure to make Laws contradicting each other: so the Subject could never be punished, because, *whatever* he did he'd be obeying *some* Law."

"And, whatever he did, he'd be *dis*obeying *some* Law!" cried Bruno. "So he'd *always* be punished!"

Lady Muriel was passing at the moment, and caught the last word. "Nobody's going to be punished *here*!" she said, taking Bruno in her arms. "This is Liberty-Hall! Would you lend me the children for a minute?"

"The children desert us, you see," I said to Mein Herr, as she carried them off: "so we old folk must keep each other company!"

The old man sighed. "Ah, well! We're old folk *now*; and yet I was a child myself, once—at least I fancy so."

It *did* seem rather unlikely fancy, I could not help owning to myself—looking at the shaggy white hair, and the long beard—that he could *ever* have been a child. "You are fond of young people?" I said.

"Young *men*," he replied. "Not of *children* exactly. I used to teach young men—many a year ago—in my dear old University!"

"I didn't quite catch its *name*?" I hinted.

"I did not name it," the old man replied mildly. "Nor would you know the name if I did. Strange tales I could tell you of all the changes I have witnessed there! But it would weary you, I fear."

"No, *indeed*!" I said. "Pray go on. What kind of changes?"

But the old man seemed to be more in a humour for questions than for answers. "Tell me," he said, laying his hand impressively on my arm, "tell me something. For I am a stranger in your land.and I know little of *your* modes of education: yet something tells me *we* are further on than *you* in the eternal cycle of change—and that many a theory *we* have tried and found to fail, *you* also will try, with a wilder enthusiasm: you will find to fail, with a bitterer despair!"

It was strange to see how, as he talked, and his words flowed more and more freely, with a certain rhythmic eloquence, his features seemed to glow with an inner light, and the whole man seemed to be transformed, as if he had grown fifty years younger in a moment of time.

CHAPTER 12

Fairy-Music

THE silence that ensued was broken by the voice of the musical young lady, who had seated herself near us, and was conversing with one of the newly-arrived guests. "Well!" she said in a tone of scornful surprise. "We *are* to have something new in the way of music, it appears!"

I looked round for an explanation, and was nearly as much astonished as the speaker herself: it was *Sylvie* whom Lady Muriel was leading to the piano!

"Do try it, my darling!" she was saying. "I'm sure you can play very nicely!"

Sylvie looked round at me, with tears in her eyes. I tried to give her an encouraging smile, but it was evidently a great strain on the nerves of a child so wholly unused to be made an exhibition of, and she was frightened and unhappy. Yet here came out the perfect sweetness of her disposition: I could see that she was resolved to forget herself, and do her best to give pleasure to Lady Muriel and her friends. She seated herself at the instrument, and began instantly. Time and expression, so far as one could judge, were perfect: but her touch was one of such extraordinary lightness that it was at first scarcely possible, through the hum of conversation which still continued, to catch a note of what she was playing.

But in a minute the hum had died away into absolute silence, and we all sat, entranced and breathless, to listen to such heavenly music as none then present could ever forget.

Hardly touching the notes at first, she played a sort of introduction in a minor key—like an embodied twilight; one felt as though the lights were growing dim, and a mist were creeping through the room. Then there flashed through the gathering gloom the first few notes of a melody so lovely, so delicate, that one held one's breath, fearful to lose a single note of it. Ever and again the music dropped into the pathetic minor key with which it had begun, and, each time that the melody forced its way, so to speak, through the enshrouding gloom into the light of day, it was more entrancing, more magically sweet. Under the airy touch of the child, the instrument actually seemed to *warble*, like a bird. "*Rise up, my love, my fair one,*" it seemed to sing, "*and come away! For lo, the winter is past, the rain is over and gone; the flowers appear on the earth; the time of the singing of birds is come!*" One could fancy one heard the tinkle of the last few drops, shaken from the trees by a passing gust—that one saw the first glittering rays of the sun, breaking through the clouds.

The Count hurried across the room in great excitement. "I *cannot* remember myself", he exclaimed, "of the name of this so charming an air! It is of an opera, most surely. Yet not even will the *opera* remind his name to me! What you call him, dear child?"

Sylvie looked round at him with a rapt expression of face. She had ceased playing, but her fingers still wandered fitfully over the keys. All fear and shyness had quite passed away now, and nothing remained but the pure joy of the music that had thrilled our hearts.

"The title of it!" the Count repeated impatiently. "How call you the opera?"

"I don't know what an opera *is*," Sylvie half-whispered.

"How, then, call you the *air*?"

"I don't know any name for it," Sylvie replied, as she rose from the instrument.

"But this is marvellous!" exclaimed the Count, following the child, and addressing himself to me, as if I were the proprietor of this musical prodigy, and so *must* know the origin of her music. "You have heard her

play this, sooner—I would say 'before this occasion'? How call you the air?"

I shook my head; but was saved from more questions by Lady Muriel, who came up to petition the Count for a song.

The Count spread out his hands apologetically, and ducked his head. "But, Milady, I have already respected—I would say prospected—all your songs; and there shall be none fitted to my voice! They are not for basso voices!"

"Wo'n't you look at them again?" Lady Muriel implored.

"Let's help him!" Bruno whispered to Sylvie. "Let's get him—*you* know!"

Sylvie nodded. "Shall *we* look for a song for you?" she said sweetly to the Count.

"Mais *oui*!" the little man exclaimed.

"Of course we may!" said Bruno, while, each taking a hand of the delighted Count, they led him to the music-stand.

"There is still hope!" said Lady Muriel over her shoulder, as she followed them.

I turned to "Mein Herr", hoping to resume our interrupted conversation. "You were remarking——" I began: but at this moment Sylvie came to call Bruno, who had returned to my side, looking unusually serious. "*Do* come, Bruno!" she entreated. "You know we've nearly found it!" Then, in a whisper, "The locket's in my *hand*, now. I couldn't get it out while they were looking!"

But Bruno drew back. "The man called me names," he said with dignity.

"What names?" I enquired with some curiosity.

"I asked him", said Bruno, "which sort of song he liked. And he said '*A* song of *a* man, not of *a* lady'. And I said 'Shall Sylvie and me find you the song of Mister Tottles?' And he said 'Wait, eel!' And I'm *not* an eel, oo know!"

"I'm *sure* he didn't mean it!" Sylvie said earnestly. "It's something French—you know he ca'n't talk English so well as——"

Bruno relented visibly. "Course he knows no better, if he's Flench! Flenchmen *never* can speak English so goodly as *us*!" And Sylvie led him away, a willing captive.

"Nice children!" said the old man, taking off his spectacles and rubbing them carefully. Then he put them on again, and watched with an approving smile, while the children tossed over the heap of music, and we just caught Sylvie's reproving words, "We're *not* making hay, Bruno!"

"This has been a long interruption to our conversation," I said. "Pray let us go on!"

"Willingly!" replied the gentle old man. "I was much interested in what you——" He paused a moment, and passed his hand uneasily across his brow. "One forgets," he murmured. "What was I saying? Oh! Something you were to tell me. Yes. Which of your teachers do you value the most highly, those whose words are easily understood, or those who puzzle you at every turn?"

I feel obliged to admit that we generally admired most the teachers we couldn't quite understand.

"Just so," said Mein Herr. "That's the way it begins. Well, *we* were at that stage some eighty years ago—or was it ninety? Our favourite teacher got more obscure every year; and every year we admired him more—just as *your* Art-fanciers call *mist* the fairest feature in a landscape, and admire a view with frantic delight when they can see nothing! Now I'll tell you how it ended. It was Moral Philosophy that our idol lectured on. Well, his pupils couldn't make head or tail of it, but they got it all by heart; and, when Examination-time came, they wrote it down; and the Examiners said 'Beautiful! (What depth!)' "

"But what good was it to the young men *afterwards*?"

"Why, don't you see?" replied Mein Herr. "*They* became teachers in their turn, and *they* said all these things over again; and *their* pupils wrote it all down; and the Examiners accepted it; and nobody had the ghost of an idea what it all meant!"

"And how did it end?"

"It ended this way. We woke up one fine day, and found there was no one in the place that knew *anything* about Moral Philosophy. So we abolished it, teachers, classes, examiners, and all. And if any one wanted to learn anything about it, he had to make it out for himself; and after another twenty years or so there were several men that really knew something about it! Now tell me another thing. How long do you teach a youth before you examine him, in your Universities?"

I told him, three or four years.

"Just so, just what *we* did!" he exclaimed. "We taught 'em a bit, and, just as they were beginning to take it in, we took it all out again! We pumped our wells dry before they were a quarter full—we stripped our orchards while the apples were still in blossom—we applied the severe logic of arithmetic to our chickens, while peacefully slumbering in their shells! Doubtless it's the early bird that picks up the worm—but if the bird gets up so outrageously early that the worm is still deep underground, what *then* is its chance of a breakfast?"

Not much, I admitted.

"Now see how that works!" he went on eagerly. "If you want to pump your wells so soon—and I suppose you tell me that is what you *must* do?"

"We must," I said. "In an over-crowded country like this, nothing but Competitive Examinations——"

Mein Herr threw up his hands wildly. "What, *again*?" he cried. "I thought it was dead, fifty years ago! Oh this Upas tree of Competitive Examinations! Beneath whose deadly shade all the original genius, all the exhaustive research, all the untiring life-long diligence by which our fore-fathers have so advanced human knowledge, must slowly but surely wither away, and give place to a system of Cookery, in which the human mind is a sausage, and all we ask is, how much indigestible stuff can be crammed into it!"

Always after these bursts of eloquence, he seemed to forget himself for a moment, and only to hold on to the thread of thought by some single word. "Yes, *crammed*," he repeated. "We went through all that stage of the disease—had it bad, I warrant you! Of course, as the Examination was all in all, we tried to put in just what was wanted—and the *great* thing to aim at was, that the Candidate should know absolutely *nothing* beyond the needs of the Examination! I don't say it was ever *quite* achieved: but one of my own pupils (pardon an old man's egotism) came very near it. After the Examination, he mentioned to me the few facts which he knew but had *not* been able to bring in, and I can assure you they were trivial, Sir, absolutely trivial!"

I feebly expressed my surprise and delight.

The old man bowed, with a gratified smile, and proceeded. "At that time, no one had hit on the much more rational plan of watching for the individual scintillations of genius, and rewarding them as they occurred. As it was, we made our unfortunate pupil into a Leyden-jar, charged him up to the eyelids—then applied the knob of a Competitive Examination, and drew off one magnificent spark, which very often cracked the jar! What mattered *that*? We labeled it 'First Class Spark', and put it away on the shelf."

"But the more rational system——?" I suggested.

"Ah, yes! *that* came next. Instead of giving the whole reward of learning in one lump, we used to pay for every good answer as it occurred. How well I remember lecturing in those days, with a heap of small coins at my elbow! It was 'A *very* good answer, Mr. Jones!' (that meant a shilling, mostly). 'Bravo, Mr. Robinson!' (that meant half-a-crown). Now I'll tell you how *that* worked. Not one single fact would any of them take in, without a fee! And when a clever boy came up from school, he got paid more for learning than we got paid for teaching him! Then came the wildest craze of all."

"What, *another* craze?" I said.

"It's the last one," said the old man. "I must have tired you out with my long story. Each College wanted to get the clever boys: so we adopted a system which we had heard was very popular in England: the Colleges competed against each other, and the boys let themselves out to the highest bidder! What geese we were! Why, they were bound to come to the University *somehow*. We needn't have paid 'em! And all our money went in getting clever boys to come to one College rather than another! The competition was so keen, that at last mere money-payments were not enough. Any College, that wished to secure some specially clever young man, had to waylay him at the station, and hunt him through the streets. The first who touched him was allowed to have him."

"That hunting-down of the scholars, as they arrived, must have been a curious business," I said. "Could you give me some idea of what it was like?"

"Willingly!" said the old man. "I will describe to you the very last Hunt that took place, before that form of Sport (for it was actually reckoned among the *Sports* of the day: we called it 'Cub-Hunting') was finally abandoned. I witnessed it myself, as I happened to be passing by at the moment, and was what we called 'in at the death'. I can see it now!" he went on in an excited tone, gazing into vacancy with those large dreamy eyes of his "It seems like yesterday; and yet it happened——" He checked himself hastily, and the remaining words died away into a whisper.

"*How* many years ago did you say?" I asked, much interested in the prospect of at last learning *some* definite fact in his history.

"*Many* years ago," he replied. "The scene at the Railway-Station had been (so they told me) one of wild excitement. Eight or nine Heads of Colleges had assembled at the gates (no one was allowed inside), and the Station-Master had drawn a line on the pavement, and insisted on their all standing behind it. The gates were flung open! The young man darted through them, and fled like lightning down the street, while the Heads of

Colleges actually *yelled* with excitement on catching sight of him! The Proctor gave the word, in the old statutory form, *'Semel! Bis! Ter! Currite!'*, and the Hunt began! Oh, it was a fine sight, believe me! At the first corner he dropped his Greek Lexicon: further on, his railway-rug: then various small articles: then his umbrella: lastly, what I suppose he prized most, his hand-bag; but the game was up: the spherical Principal of—of——"

"Of *which* College?" I said.

"—of *one* of the Colleges", he resumed, "had put into operation the Theory—his own discovery—of Accelerated Velocity, and captured him just opposite to where I stood. I shall never forget that wild breathless struggle! But it was soon over. Once in those great bony hands, escape was impossible!"

"May I ask why you speak of him as the *'spherical'* Principal?" I said.

"The epithet referred to his *shape*, which was a perfect *sphere*. You

are aware that a bullet, another instance of a perfect sphere, when falling in a perfectly straight line, moves with Accelerated Velocity?"

I bowed assent.

"Well, my spherical friend (as I am proud to call him) set himself to investigate the *causes* of this. He found them to be *three*. One; that it is a perfect *sphere*. Two; that it moves in a *straight line*. Three; that its direction is *not upwards*. When these three conditions are fulfilled, you get Accelerated Velocity."

"Hardly," I said: "if you will excuse my differing from you. Suppose we apply the theory to *horizontal* motion. It a bullet is fired *horizontally*, it——"

"——it does *not* move in a *straight line*," he quietly finished my sentence for me.

"I yield the point," I said. "What did your friend do next?"

"The next thing was to apply the theory, as you rightly suggest, to *horizontal* motion. But the moving body, ever tending to *fall*, needs *constant support*, if it is to move in a true horizontal line. 'What, then,' he asked himself, 'will give *constant support to a moving body*?' And his answer was '*Human legs*!' *That* was the discovery that immortalized his name!"

"His name being——?" I suggested.

"I had not mentioned it," was the gentle reply of my most unsatisfactory informant. "His next step was an obvious one. He took to a diet of suet-dumplings, until his body had become a perfect sphere. *Then* he went out for his first experimental run—which nearly cost him his life!"

"How was *that*?"

"Well, you see, he had no idea of the *tremendous* new Force in Nature that he was calling into play. He began too fast. In a very few minutes he found himself moving at a hundred miles an hour! And, if he had not had the presence of mind to charge into the middle of a haystack (which he scattered to the four winds) there can be no doubt that he would have left the Planet he belonged to, and gone right away into Space!"

"And how came that to be the *last* of the Cub-Hunts?" I enquired.

"Well, you see, it led to a rather scandalous dispute between two of the Colleges. *Another* Principal had laid his hand on the young one, so nearly at the same moment as the *spherical* one, that there was no knowing which had touched him first. The dispute got into print, and did us no credit, and, in short, Cub-Hunts came to an end. Now I'll tell you what cured us of that wild craze of ours, the bidding against each other, for the clever scholars, just as if they were articles to be sold by auction! Just when the craze had reached its highest points, and when one of the Colleges had actually advertised a Scholarship of one thousand pounds *per annum*, one of our tourists brought us the manuscript of an old African legend—I happen to have a copy of it in my pocket. Shall I translate it for you?"

"Pray go on," I said, though I felt I was getting *very* sleepy.

CHAPTER 13

What Tottles Meant

MEIN HERR unrolled the manuscript, but, to my great surprise, instead of *reading* it, he began to *sing* it, in a rich mellow voice that seemed to ring through the room.

> *"One thousand pounds per annum*
> *Is not so bad a figure, come!"*
> *Cried Tottles. "And I tell you, flat,*
> *A man may marry well on that!*
> *To say 'the Husband needs the Wife'*
> *Is not the way to represent it.*
> *The crowning joy of Woman's life*
> *Is* Man!" *said Tottles (and he meant it).*

> *The blissful Honey-moon is past:*
> *The Pair have settled down at last:*
> *Mamma-in-law their home will share,*
> *And make their happiness her care.*
> *"Your income is an ample one:*
> *Go it, my children!" (And they went it).*
> *"I rayther think this kind of fun*
> *Wo'n't last!" said Tottles (and he meant it).*

They took a little country-box—
A box at Covent Garden also:
They lived a life of double-knocks,
Acquaintances began to call so:
Their London house was much the same
(It took three hundred, clear, to rent it):
"Life is a very jolly game!"
Cried happy Tottles (and he meant it).

"Contented with a frugal lot"
(He always used that phrase at Gunter's),
He bought a handy little yacht—
A dozen serviceable hunters—
The fishing of a Highland Loch—
A sailing-boat to circumvent it—
"The sounding of that Gaelic 'och'
Beats me!" said Tottles (and he meant it).

Here, with one of those convulsive starts that wake one up in the very act of dropping off to sleep, I became conscious that the deep musical tones that thrilled me did *not* belong to Mein Herr, but to the French Count. The old man was still conning the manuscript.

"I *beg* your pardon for keeping you waiting!" he said. "I was just making sure that I knew the English for all the words. I am quite ready now." And he read me the following Legend:

"In a city that stands in the very centre of Africa, and is rarely visited by the casual tourist, the people had always bought eggs—a daily necessary in a climate where egg-flip was the usual diet—from a Merchant who came to their gates once a week. And the people always bid wildly against each other: so there was quite a lively auction every time the Merchant came, and the last egg in his basket used to fetch the value of two or three camels, or thereabouts. And eggs got dearer every week. And still they drank their egg-flip, and wondered where all their money went to.

"And there came a day when they put their heads together. And they understood what donkeys they had been.

"And next day, when the Merchant came, only *one* Man went forth. And he said 'Oh, thou of the hook-nose and the goggle-eyes, thou of the measureless beard, how much for that lot of eggs?'

"And the Merchant answered him 'I *could* let thee have that lot at ten thousand piastres the dozen'.

"And the Man chuckled inwardly, and said '*Ten* piastres the dozen I offer thee, and no more, oh descendant of a distinguished grandfather!'

"And the Merchant stroked his beard, and said 'Hum! I will await the coming of thy friends.' So he waited. And the Man waited with him. And they waited both together."

"The manuscript breaks off here," said Mein Herr, as he rolled it up again; "but it was enough to open our eyes. We saw what simpletons we had been—buying our Scholars much as those ignorant savages bought their eggs—and the ruinous system was abandoned. If only we could have abandoned, along with it, all the *other* fashions we had borrowed from you, instead of carrying them to their logical results! But it was not to be.

What ruined my country, and drove me from my home, was the introduction—into the *Army*, of all places—of your theory of Political Dichotomy!"

"Shall I trouble you too much," I said, "if I ask you to explain what you mean by 'the Theory of Political Dichotomy'?"

"No trouble at all!" was Mein Herr's most courteous reply. "I quite enjoy talking, when I get so good a listener. What started the thing, with us, was the report brought to us, by one of our most eminent statesmen, who had stayed some time in England, of the way affairs were managed there. It was a political necessity (so he assured us, and we believed him, though we had never discovered it till that moment) that there should be *two* Parties, in every affair and on every subject. In *Politics*, the two Parties, which you had found it necessary to institute, were called, he told us, 'Whigs' and 'Tories'."

"That must have been some time ago?" I remarked.

"It *was* some time ago," he admitted. "And this was the way the affairs of the British Nation were managed. (You will correct me if I misrepresent it. I do but repeat what our traveler told us.) These two Parties—which were in chronic hostility to each other—took turns in conducting the Government; and the Party, that happened *not* to be in power, was called the 'Opposition', I believe?"

"That is the right name," I said. "There have always been, so long as we have had a Parliament at all, *two* Parties, one 'in', and one 'out'."

"Well, the function of the 'Ins' (if I may so call them) was to do the best they could for the national welfare—in such things as making war or peace, commercial treaties, and so forth?"

"Undoubtedly," I said.

"And the function of the 'Outs' was (so our traveler assured us, though we were very incredulous at first) to *prevent* the 'Ins' from succeeding in any of these things?"

'To *criticize* and to *amend* their proceedings," I corrected him. "It would be *unpatriotic* to *hinder* the Government in doing what was for the good of the Nation! We have always held a *Patriot* to be the greatest of heroes, and an *unpatriotic* spirit to be one of the worst of human ills!"

"Excuse me for a moment," the old gentleman courteously replied, taking out his pocket-book. "I have a few memoranda here, of a correspondence I had with our tourist, and, if you will allow me, I'll just refresh my memory—although I quite agree with you—it is, as you say, one of the worst of human ills———" And, here Mein Herr began singing again.

But oh, the worst of human ills
(Poor Tottles found) are "little bills"!
And, with no balance in the Bank
What wonder that his spirits sank?
Still, as the money flowed away,
He wondered how on earth she spent it.
"You cost me twenty pounds a day,
At least!" cried Tottles (and he meant it).

She sighed. "Those Drawing Rooms, you know!
I really never thought about it:
Mamma declared we ought to go—
We should be Nobodies without it.
That diamond-circlet for my brow—
I quite believed that she had sent it,
Until the Bill came in just now——'
"Viper!" cried Tottles (and he meant it).

Poor Mrs. T. could bear no more,
But fainted flat upon the floor.
Mamma-in-law, with anguish wild,
Seeks, all in vain, to rouse her child.
"Quick! Take this box of smelling-salts!
Don't scold her, James, or you'll repent it,
She's a dear girl, with all her faults——"
"She is!" groaned Tottles (and he meant it).

"I was a donkey", Tottles cried,
"To choose your daughter for my bride!
'Twas you that bid us cut a dash!
'Tis you have brought us to this smash!
You don't suggest one single thing
That can in any way prevent it——
"Then what's the use of arguing?"
"Shut up!" cried Tottles (and he meant it).

Once more I started into wakefulness, and realized that Mein Herr was not the singer. He was still consulting his memoranda.

"It is exactly what my friend told me," he resumed, after conning over various papers. " '*Unpatriotic*' is the very word I had used, in writing to him, and '*hinder*' is the very word he used in his reply! Allow me to read you a portion of his letter:

" 'I can assure you,' he writes, 'that, unpatriotic as you may think it, the recognized function of the 'Opposition' is to hinder in every manner not forbidden by the Law, the action of the Government. This process is called 'Legitimate Obstruction': and the greatest triumph the 'Opposition' can ever enjoy, is when they are able to point out that, owing to their 'Obstruction', the Government have failed in everything they have tried to do for the good of the Nation!' "

"Your friend has not put it *quite* correctly," I said. "The Opposition would no doubt be glad to point out that the Government had failed *through their own fault* but *not* that they had failed on account of *Obstruction*!"

"You think so?' he gently replied. "Allow me now to read to you this newspaper-cutting, which my friend enclosed in his letter. It is part of the report of a public speech, made by a Statesman who was at the time a member of the 'Opposition':

" 'At the close of the Session, he thought they had no reason to be discontented with the fortunes of the campaign. They had routed the enemy at every point. But the pursuit must be continued. They had only to follow up a disordered and dispirited foe.' "

"Now to what portion of your national history would you guess that the speaker was referring?"

"Really, the number of *successful* wars we have waged during the last century", I replied, with a glow of British pride, "is *far* too great for me to guess, with any chance of success, *which* it was we were then engaged in. However. I will name '*India*' as the most probable. The Mutiny was no doubt, all but crushed, at the time that speech was made. What a fine, manly, *patriotic* speech it must have been!" I exclaimed in an outburst of enthusiasm.

"You think so?" he replied, in a tone of gentle pity. "Yet my friend tells me that the '*disordered and dispirited foe*' simply meant the States-men who happened to be in power at the moment; that the '*pursuit*' simply meant 'Obstruction'; and that the words '*they had routed the enemy*' simply meant that the 'Opposition' had succeeded in hindering the Government from doing any of the work which the Nation had empowered them to do!"

I thought it best to say nothing.

"It seemed queer to *us*, just at first," he resumed, after courteously waiting a minute for me to speak: "but, when once we had mastered the idea, our respect for your Nation was so great that we carried it into every department of life! It was '*the beginning of the end*' with us. My country never held up its head again!" And the poor old gentleman sighed deeply.

"Let us change the subject," I said. 'Do not distress yourself, I beg!"

"No, no!" he said, with an effort to recover himself. "I had rather finish my story! The next step (after reducing our Government to impotence, and putting a stop to all useful legislation, which did not take us long to do) was to introduce what we called 'the glorious British Principle of Dichotomy' into *Agriculture*. We persuaded many of the well-to-do farmers to divide their staff of labourers into two Parties, and to set them one against the other. They were called, like our political Parties, the 'Ins' and the 'Outs': the business of the 'Ins' was to do as much of ploughing, sowing, or whatever might be needed, as they could manage in a day, and at night they were paid according to the amount they had *done*: the business of the 'Outs' was to hinder them, and *they* were paid for the amount they had *hindered*. The farmers found they had to pay only *half* as much wages as they did before, and they didn't observe that the amount of work done was only a *quarter* as much as was done before: so they took it up quite enthusiastically, *at first*."

"And *afterwards*——?" I enquired.

"Well, *afterwards* they didn't like it quite so well. In a very short time, things settled down into a regular routine. No work *at all* was done. So the 'Ins' got no wages, and the 'Outs' got full pay. And the farmers never discovered, till most of them were ruined, that the rascals had agreed to manage it so, and had shared the pay between them! While the thing lasted, there were funny sights to be seen! Why, I've often watched a ploughman, with two horses harnessed to the plough, doing his best to get it *forwards*; while the opposition-ploughman, with three donkeys harnessed at the *other* end, was doing *his* best to get it *backwards*! And the plough never moving an inch, *either* way!"

"But *we* never did anything like *that*!" I exclaimed.

"Simply because you were less *logical* than we were," replied Mein Herr. "There is *sometimes* an advantage in being a donk—Excuse me! No *personal* allusion intended. All this happened *long ago*, you know!"

"Did the Dichotomy-Principle succeed in *any* direction?" I enquired.

'In *none*," Mein Herr candidly confessed. 'It had a *very* short trial in *Commerce*. The shop-keepers *wouldn't* take it up, after once trying the plan of having half the attendants busy in folding up and carrying away the goods which the other half were trying to spread out upon the counters. They said the Public didn't like it!"

"I don't wonder at it," I remarked.

"Well, we tried 'the British Principle' for some years. And the end of it all was——" His voice suddenly dropped, almost to a whisper; and large tears began to roll down his cheeks. "—the end was that we got involved in a war; and there was a great battle, in which we far out-numbered the enemy. But what could one expect, when only *half* of our soldiers were fighting, and the other half pulling them back? It ended in a crushing defeat—an utter rout. This caused a Revolution; and most of the Government were banished. I myself was accused of Treason, for having so strongly advocated 'the British Principle'. My property was all forfeited, and—and—I was driven into exile! 'Now the mischief's done,' they said, 'perhaps you'll kindly leave the country?' It nearly broke my heart, but I had to go!"

The melancholy tone became a wail: the wail became a chant: the chant became a song—though whether it was *Mein Herr* was singing, this time, or somebody else, I could not feel certain.

> *"And, now the mischief's done, perhaps*
> *You'll kindly go and pack your traps?*
> *Since* two *(your daughter and your son)*
> *Are Company, but* three *are none.*
> *A course of saving we'll begin:*
> *When change is needed,* I'll *invent it.*
> *Don't think to put* your *finger in*
> This *pie!" cried Tottles (and he meant it).*

The music seemed to die away. Mein Herr was again speaking in his ordinary voice. "Now tell me one thing more," he said. "Am I right in thinking that in *your* Universities, though a man may reside some thirty or forty years, you examine him, once for all, at the end of the first three or four?'

"That is so, undoubtedly," I admitted.

"Practically, then, you examine a man at the *beginning* of his career!' the old man said to himself rather than to me. "And what guarantee have you that he *retains* the knowledge for which you have rewarded him—beforehand, as *we* should say?"

"None," I admitted, feeling a little puzzled at the drift of his remarks. "How do *you* secure that object?"

"By examining him at the *end* of his thirty or forty years—not at the beginning," he gently replied. "On an average, the knowledge then found is about one-fifth of what it was at first—the process of forgetting going on at a very steady uniform rate—and he, who forgets *least*, gets *most* honour, and most rewards."

"Then you give him the money when he needs it no longer? And you make him live most of his life on *nothing*!"

"Hardly that. He gives his orders to the tradesmen: they supply him, for forty, sometimes fifty years, at their own risk: then he gets his Fellowship—which pays him in *one* year as much as *your* Fellowships pay in fifty—and then he can easily pay all his bills, with interest."

"But suppose he fails to get his Fellowship? That must occasionally happen."

"That occasionally happens." It was Mein Herr's turn, now, to make admissions.

"And what becomes of the tradesmen?"

"They calculate accordingly. When a man appears to be getting alarmingly ignorant, or stupid, they will sometimes refuse to supply him any longer. You have no idea with what enthusiasm a man will begin to rub up his forgotten sciences or languages, when his butcher has cut off the supply of beef and mutton!"

"And who are the Examiners?"

"The young men who have just come, brimming over with knowledge. You would think it a curious sight," he went on, "to see mere boys examining such old men. I have known a man set to examine his own grandfather. It was a little painful for both of them, no doubt. The old gentleman was as bald as a coot——"

"How bald would that be?" I've no idea why I asked this question. I felt I was getting foolish.

CHAPTER 14

Bruno's Picnic

"As *bald* as bald," was the bewildering reply. "Now, Bruno, I'll tell you a story."

"And I'll tell *oo* a story," said Bruno, beginning in a great hurry for fear of Sylvie getting the start of him: "once there were a Mouse—a little tiny Mouse—such a tiny little Mouse! Oo never saw such a tiny Mouse——"

"Did nothing ever happen to it, Bruno?" I asked. "Haven't you anything more to tell us, besides its being so tiny?"

"Nothing never happened to it," Bruno solemnly replied.

"Why did nothing never happen to it?" said Sylvie, who was sitting, with her head on Bruno's shoulder, patiently waiting for a chance of beginning *her* story.

"It were too tiny," Bruno explained.

"*That's* no reason!" I said. "However tiny it was, things might happen to it."

Bruno looked pityingly at me, as if he thought me very stupid. "It were too tiny," he repeated. "If anything happened to it, it would die—it were so *very* tiny!"

"Really that's enough about its being tiny!" Sylvie put in. "Haven't you invented any more about it?"

"Haven't invented no more yet."

"Well, then, you shouldn't begin a story till you've invented more! Now be quiet, there's a good boy, and listen to *my* story."

And Bruno, having quite exhausted all his inventive faculty, by beginning in too great a hurry, quietly resigned himself to listening. "Tell about the other Bruno, please," he said coaxingly.

Sylvie put her arms round his neck, and began:—

"The wind was whispering among the trees," ("That wasn't good

manners!" Bruno interrupted. "Never mind about manners," said Sylvie)
"and it was evening—a nice moony evening, and the Owls were
hooting——"

"Pretend they weren't Owls!" Bruno pleaded, stroking her cheek with
his fat little hand. "I don't like Owls. Owls have such great big eyes.
Pretend they were Chickens!"

"Are you afraid of their great big eyes, Bruno?" I said.

"Aren't 'fraid of nothing," Bruno answered in as careless a tone as he
could manage: "they're ugly with their great big eyes. I think if they
cried, the tears would be as big—oh, as big as the moon!" And he laughed
merrily. "Doos Owls cry ever, Mister Sir?"

"Owls cry never," I said gravely, trying to copy Bruno's way of speaking:
"they've got nothing to be sorry for, you know."

"Oh, but they have!" Bruno exclaimed. "They're ever so sorry, 'cause
they killed the poor little Mouses!"

"But they're not sorry when they're *hungry*, I suppose?"

"Oo don't know nothing about Owls!" Bruno scornfully remarked.
"When they're hungry, they're very, *very* sorry they killed the little
Mouses, 'cause if they *hadn't* killed them there'd be sumfin for supper,
oo know!"

Bruno was evidently getting into a dangerously inventive state of mind,
so Sylvie broke in with "Now I'm going on with the story. So the
Owls—the Chickens, I mean—were looking to see if they could find a
nice fat Mouse for their supper——'

"Pretend it was a nice 'abbit!" said Bruno.

"But it *wasn't* a nice habit, to kill Mouses," Sylvie argued. "I ca'n't
pretend *that*!"

"I didn't say 'habit', oo silly fellow!" Bruno replied with a merry twinkle
in his eyes. " 'abbits—that runs about in the fields!"

"Rabbit? Well it can be a Rabbit, if you like. But you mustn't alter my
story so much, Bruno. A Chicken *couldn't* eat a Rabbit!"

"But it might have wished to see if it could try to eat it."

"Well, it wished to see if it could try—oh, really, Bruno, that's nonsense!
I shall go back to the Owls."

"Well, then, pretend they hadn't great eyes!"

"And they saw a little boy," Sylvie went on, disdaining to make any
further corrections. "And he asked them to tell him a story. And the
Owls hooted and flew away——' ("Oo shouldn't say *flewed*; oo should
say *flied*," Bruno whispered. But Sylvie wouldn't hear.) "And he met a
Lion. And he asked the Lion to tell him a story. And the Lion said 'yes',

it would. And, while the Lion was telling him the story, it nibbled some of his head off——"

"Don't say 'nibbled'!" Bruno entreated. "Only little things nibble—little thin sharp things, with edges——"

"Well, then, it *'nubbled'*," said Sylvie. "And when it had nubbled *all* his head off, he went away, and he never said 'thank you'!"

"That were very rude," said Bruno. "If he couldn't speak, he might have nodded—no, he couldn't nod. Well, he might have shaked *hands* with the Lion!"

"Oh, I'd forgotten that part!" said Sylvie. "He *did* shake hands with it. He came back again, you know, and he thanked the Lion very much, for telling him the story."

"Then his head had growed up again?" said Bruno.

"Oh yes, it grew up in a minute. And the Lion begged pardon, and said it wouldn't nubble off little boys' heads—not never no more!"

Bruno looked much pleased at this change of events. "Now that are a *really* nice story!" he said. "*Aren't* it a nice story, Mister Sir?"

"Very," I said. "I would like to hear another story about that Boy."

"So would *I*," said Bruno, stroking Sylvie's cheek again. "*Please* tell about Bruno's Picnic; and don't talk about *nubbly* Lions!"

"I wo'n't, if it frightens you," said Sylvie.

"*Flightens* me!" Bruno exclaimed indignantly. "It isn't *that*! It's 'cause 'nubbly' 's such a grumbly word to say—when one person's got her head on another person's shoulder. When she talks like that," he exclaimed to me, 'the talking goes down bofe sides of my face—all the way to my chin—and it *doos* tickle so! It's enough to make a beard grow, that it is!"

He said this with great severity, but it was evidently meant for a joke: so Sylvie laughed—a delicious musical little laugh, and laid her soft cheek on the top of her brother's curly head, as if it were a pillow, while she went on with the story. "So this Boy——"

"But it wasn't *me*, oo know!" Bruno interrupted. "And oo needn't try to look as if it was, Mister Sir!"

I represented, respectfully, that I was trying to look as if it wasn't.

"—he was a middling good Boy——"

"He were a *welly* good Boy!" Bruno corrected her. "And he never did nothing he wasn't told to do——"

"*That* doesn't make a good Boy!" Sylvie said contemptuously.

"That *do* make a good Boy!" Bruno insisted.

Sylvie gave up the point. "Well, he was a *very* good Boy, and he always kept his promises, and he had a big cupboard——'

"—for to keep all his promises in!" cried Bruno.

"If he kept *all* his promises," Sylvie said, with a mischievous look in her eyes, "he wasn't like *some* Boys I know of!"

"He had to put *salt* with them, a-course," Bruno said gravely: "oo ca'n't keep promises when there isn't any salt. And he kept his birthday on the second shelf."

"How long did he keep his birthday?" I asked. "I never can keep *mine* more than twenty-four hours."

"Why, a birthday *stays* that long by itself!" cried Bruno. "Oo doosn't know how to keep birthdays! This Boy kept *his* a whole year!"

"And then the next birthday would begin," said Sylvie. "So it would be his birthday *always*."

"So it were," said Bruno. "Doos *oo* have treats on *oor* birthday, Mister Sir?"

"Sometimes," I said.

"When oo're *good*, I suppose?"

"Why, it *is* a sort of treat, being good, isn't it?" I said.

"A sort of *treat*!" Bruno repeated. "It's a sort of *punishment*, *I* think!"

"Oh, Bruno!" Sylvie interrupted, almost sadly. "How *can* you?"

"Well, but it *is*," Bruno persisted. "Why, look here, Mister Sir! *This* is being good!" And he sat bolt upright, and put on an absurdly solemn face. "First oo must sit up as straight as pokers——"

"—as *a* poker," Sylvie corrected him.

"—as straight as *pokers*," Bruno firmly repeated. "Then oo must clasp oor hands—*so*. Then—'Why hasn't 'oo brushed oor hair? Go and brush it *toreckly*!' Then—'Oh, Bruno, oo mustn't dog's-ear the daisies!' Did oo learn *oor* spelling wiz daisies, Mister Sir?"

"I want to hear about that Boy's *Birthday*," I said.

Bruno returned to the story instantly. "Well, so this Boy said 'Now it's my Birthday!' And so—I'm tired!" he suddenly broke off, laying his head in Sylvie's lap. "Sylvie knows it best. Sylvie's grown-upper than me. Go on, Sylvie!"

Sylvie patiently took up the thread of the story again. "So he said 'Now it's my Birthday. Whatever shall I do to keep my Birthday?' All *good* little Boys—" (Sylvie turned away from Bruno, and made a great pretence of whispering to *me*) "—all *good* little Boys—Boys that learn their lessons quite perfect—they always keep their birthdays you know. So of course *this* little Boy kept *his* Birthday."

"Oo may call him Bruno, if oo like," the little fellow carelessly remarked. "It weren't *me*, but it makes it more interesting."

"So Bruno said to himself 'The properest thing to do is to have a Picnic, all by myself, on the top of the hill. And I'll take some Milk and some Bread, and some Apples: and first and foremost, I want some *Milk*!' So, first and foremost, Bruno took a milk-pail——"

"And he went and milkted the Cow!" Bruno put in.

"Yes," said Sylvie, meekly accepting the new verb. "And the Cow said 'Moo! What are you going to do with all that Milk?' And Bruno said 'Please'm, I want it for my Picnic.' And the Cow said 'Moo! But I hope you wo'n't *boil* any of it?' And Bruno said 'No, *indeed* I wo'n't! New Milk's so nice and so warm, it wants no boiling!' "

"It doesn't want no boiling," Bruno offered as an amended version.

"So Bruno put the Milk in a bottle. And then Bruno said 'Now I want some Bread!' So he went to the Oven, and he took out a delicious new Loaf. And the Oven——".

"—ever so light and so puffy!" Bruno impatiently corrected her. "Oo shouldn't leave out so many words!"

Sylvie humbly apologized. "—a delicious new Loaf, ever so light and so puffy. And the Oven said——" Here Sylvie made a long pause. "Really I don't know *what* an Oven begins with, when it wants to speak!'

Both children looked appealingly at me; but I could only say, helplessly, "I haven't the least idea! *I* never heard an Oven speak!"

For a minute or two we all sat silent; and then Bruno said, very softly, "Oven begins wiz 'O'."

"*Good* little boy!" Sylvie exclaimed. "He does his spelling *very* nicely. *He's cleverer than he knows!* " she added, aside, to *me*. "So the Oven said 'O! What are you going to do with all that Bread?' And Bruno said 'Please—' Is an Oven 'Sir' or ' 'm', would you say?" She looked to me for a reply.

"*Both*, I think," seemed to me the safest thing to say.

Sylvie adopted the suggestion instantly. "So Bruno said 'Please, Sirm, I want it for my Picnic.' And the Oven said 'O! But I hope you wo'n't *toast* any of it?' And Bruno said, 'No, *indeed* I wo'n't! New Bread's so light and so puffy, it wants no toasting!' "

"It never doesn't want no toasting," said Bruno. "I *wiss* oo wouldn't say it so short!"

"So Bruno put the Bread in the hamper. Then Bruno said 'Now I want some Apples!' So he took the hamper, and he went to the Apple-Tree, and he picked some lovely ripe Apples. And the Apple-Tree said——" Here followed another long pause.

Bruno adopted his favourite expedient of tapping his forehead; while Sylvie gazed earnestly upwards, as if she hoped for some suggestion from the birds, who were singing merrily among the branches overhead. But no result followed.

"What *does* an Apple-Tree begin with, when it wants to speak?" Sylvie murmured despairingly, to the irresponsive birds.

At last, taking a leaf out of Bruno's book, I ventured on a remark. "Doesn't 'Apple-Tree' always begin with Eh!'?"

"Why, of *course* it does! How *clever* of you!" Sylvie cried delightedly.

Bruno jumped up, and patted me on the head. I tried not to feel conceited.

"So the Apple-Tree said 'Eh! What are you going to do with all those Apples?' and Bruno said 'Please, Sir, I want them for my Picnic.' And the Apple-Tree said 'Eh! But I hope you wo'n't *bake* any of them?' And Bruno said 'No, *indeed* I wo'n't! Ripe Apples are so nice and so sweet, they want no baking!' "

"They never doesn't——" Bruno was beginning, but Sylvie corrected herself before he could get the words out.

" 'They never doesn't nohow want no baking.' So Bruno put the Apples in the hamper, along with the Bread, and the bottle of Milk. And he set off to have a Picnic, on the top of the hill, all by himself——"

"He wasn't greedy, oo know, to have it all by himself," Bruno said, patting me on the cheek to call my attention; " 'cause he hadn't got no brothers and sisters."

"It was very sad to have no *sisters*, wasn't it?" I said.

"Well, I don't know," Bruno said thoughtfully; " 'cause he hadn't no lessons to do. So he didn't mind."

Sylvie went on. "So, as he was walking along the road, he heard behind him such a curious sort of noise—a sort of a Thump! Thump! Thump! 'Whatever *is* that?' said Bruno. 'Oh, I know!' said Bruno. 'Why, it's only my Watch a-ticking!' "

"*Were* it his Watch a-ticking?" Bruno asked me, with eyes that fairly sparkled with mischievous delight.

"No doubt of it!" I replied. And Bruno laughed exultingly.

"Then Bruno thought a little harder. And he said "No! it *ca'n't* be my Watch a-ticking; because I haven't *got* a Watch!' "

Bruno peered up anxiously into my face, to see how I took it. I hung my head, and put a thumb into my mouth, to the evident delight of the little fellow.

"So Bruno went a little further along the road. And then he heard it again, that queer noise—Thump! Thump! Thump! 'Whatever *is* that?' said Bruno. 'Oh, I know!' said Bruno. 'Why, it's only the Carpenter a-mending my Wheelbarrow!' "

"*Were* it the Carpenter a-mending his Wheelbarrow?" Bruno asked me.

I brightened up, and said "It *must* have been!" in a tone of absolute conviction.

Bruno threw his arms round Sylvie's neck. "Sylvie!" he said, in a perfectly audible whisper. "He says it *must* have been!"

"Then Bruno thought a little harder. And he said 'No! It *ca'n't* be the Carpenter a-mending my Wheelbarrow, because I haven't *got* a Wheelbarrow!' "

This time I hid my face in my hands, quite unable to meet Bruno's look of triumph.

"So Bruno went a little further along the road. And then he heard that queer noise again—Thump! Thump! Thump! So he thought he'd look round, *this* time, just to *see* what it was. And what should it be but a great Lion!"

"A great big Lion," Bruno corrected her.

"A great big Lion. And Bruno was ever so frightened, and he ran——"

"No, he wasn't *flightened* a bit!" Bruno interrupted. (He was evidently anxious for the reputation of his name-sake.) "He runned away to get a good look at the Lion; 'cause he wanted to see if it were the same Lion what used to nubble little Boys' heads off; and he wanted to know how big it was!"

"Well, he ran away, to get a good look at the Lion. And the Lion trotted slowly after him. And the Lion called after him, in a very gentle voice, 'Little Boy, little Boy! You needn't be afraid of *me!* I'm a very *gentle* old Lion now. I *never* nubble little Boys' heads off, as I used to do.' And so Bruno said 'Don't you *really*, Sir? Then what do you live on?' And the Lion——"

"Oo *see* he weren't a bit flightened!" Bruno said to me, patting my cheek again. " 'cause he remembered to call it 'Sir', oo know."

I said that no doubt that was the *real* test whether a person was frightened or not.

"And the Lion said 'Oh, I live on bread-and-butter, and cherries, and marmalade, and plum-cake—' "

"—and *apples!*" Bruno put in.

"Yes, 'and apples'. And Bruno said 'Wo'n't you come with me to my

Picnic?' And the Lion said 'Oh, I should like it *very much indeed!*' And
Bruno and the Lion went away together." Sylvie stopped suddenly.

"Is that *all*?" I asked, despondingly.

"Not *quite* all," Sylvie slily replied "There's a sentence or two more.
Isn't there, Bruno?"

"Yes," with a carelessness that was evidently put on: "just a sentence
or two more."

"And, as they were walking along, they looked over a hedge, and who
should they see but a little black Lamb! And the Lamb was ever so
frightened. And it ran——"

"It were *really* flightened!" Bruno put in.

"It ran away. And Bruno ran after it. And he called 'Little Lamb! You
needn't be afraid of *this* Lion! It *never* kills things! It lives on cherries,
and marmalade—' "

"—and *apples*!" said Bruno. 'Oo *always* forgets the apples!"

"And Bruno said 'Wo'n't you come with us to my Picnic?' And the
Lamb said 'Oh, I should like it *very much indeed*, if my Ma will let me!'
And Bruno said 'Let's go and ask your Ma!' And they went to the old
Sheep. And Bruno said 'Please, may your little Lamb come to my Picnic?'
And the Sheep said 'Yes, if it's learnt all its lessons.' And the Lamb said
'Oh yes, Ma! I've learnt *all* my lessons!' "

"Pretend it hadn't any lessons!" Bruno earnestly pleaded.

"Oh, that would never do!" said Sylvie. "I ca'n't leave out all about the
lessons! And the old Sheep said 'Do you know your A B C yet? Have you
learnt A?' And the Lamb said 'Oh yes, Ma! I went to the A-field, and I
helped them to make A!' 'Very good, my child! And have you learnt B?'
'Oh yes, Ma! I went to the B-hive, and the B gave me some honey!' 'Very
good, my child! And have you learnt C?' 'Oh yes, Ma! I went to the C-
side, and I saw the ships sailing on the C!' 'Very good, my child! You may
go to Bruno's Picnic.' "

"So they set off. And Bruno walked in the middle, so that the Lamb
mightn't see the Lion——"

"It were *flightened*," Bruno explained.

"Yes, and it trembled so; and it got paler and paler; and, before they'd
got to the top of the hill, it was a *white* little Lamb—as white as snow!"

"But *Bruno* weren't flightened!" said the owner of that name. "So *he*
staid black!"

"No, he *didn't* stay black! He staid *pink*!" laughed Sylvie. "I shouldn't
kiss you like this, you know, if you were *black*!"

"Oo'd *have* to!" Bruno said with great decision. "Besides, Bruno wasn't

Bruno, oo know—I mean, Bruno wasn't *me*—I mean—don't talk nonsense, Sylvie!"

"I wo'n't do it again!" Sylvie said very humbly. "And so, as they went along, the Lion said 'Oh, I'll tell you what I used to do when I was a young Lion. I used to hide behind trees, to watch for little Boys.' " (Bruno cuddled a little closer to her.) " 'And, if a little thin scraggy Boy came by, why, I used to let him go. But, if a little fat juicy——' "

Bruno could bear no more. "Pretend he wasn't juicy!" he pleaded, half-sobbing.

"Nonsense, Bruno!" Sylvie briskly replied. "It'll be done in a moment! '—if a little fat juicy Boy came by, why, I used to spring out and gobble him up! Oh, you've no *idea* what a delicious thing it is—a little juicy

Boy!' And Bruno said 'Oh, if you please, Sir, *don't* talk about eating little boys! It makes me so *shivery*!' "

The real Bruno shivered, in sympathy with the hero.

"And the Lion said 'Oh, well, we wo'n't talk about it, then! I'll tell you what happened on my wedding-day——' "

"I like *this* part better," said Bruno, patting my cheek to keep me awake.

" 'There was, oh, such a lovely wedding-breakfast! At *one* end of the table there was a large plum-pudding. And at the other end there was a nice roasted *Lamb*! Oh, you've no *idea* what a delicious thing it is—a nice roasted Lamb!' And the Lamb said 'Oh, if you please, Sir, *don't* talk about eating Lambs! It makes me so *shivery*!' And the Lion said 'Oh, well, we wo'n't talk about it, then!' "

CHAPTER 15

The Little Foxes

"So, when they got to the top of the hill, Bruno opened the hamper: and he took out the Bread, and the Apples, and the Milk: and they ate, and they drank. And when they'd finished the Milk, and eaten half the Bread and half the Apples, the Lamb said 'Oh, my paws is so sticky! I want to wash my paws!' And the Lion said 'Well, go down the hill, and wash them in the brook, yonder. We'll wait for you!' "

"It never comed back!" Bruno solemnly whispered to me.

But Sylvie overheard him. "You're not to whisper, Bruno! It spoils the story! And when the Lamb had been gone a long time, the Lion said to Bruno 'Do go and see after that silly little Lamb! It must·have lost its way.' And Bruno went down the hill. And when he got to the brook, he saw the Lamb sitting on the bank: and who should be sitting by it but an old Fox!"

'Enter the Lion'

"Don't know who *should* be sitting by it," Bruno said thoughtfully to himself. "A old Fox *were* sitting by it."

"And the old Fox were saying," Sylvie went on, for once conceding the grammatical point. "'Yes, my dear, you'll be ever so happy with us, if you'll only come and see us! I've got three little Foxes there, and we do love little Lambs so dearly!' And the Lamb said 'But you never *eat* them, do you, Sir?' And the Fox said 'Oh, no! What, *eat* a Lamb? We never *dream* of doing such a thing!' So the Lamb said 'Then I'll come with you.' And off they went, hand in hand."

"That Fox were welly extremely wicked, *weren't* it?" said Bruno.

"No, no!" said Sylvie, rather shocked at such violent language. "It wasn't quite so bad as that!"

"Well, I mean, it wasn't nice," the little fellow corrected himself.

"And so Bruno went back to the Lion. 'Oh, come quick!' he said. 'The Fox has taken the Lamb to his house with him! I'm *sure* he means to eat it!' And the Lion said 'I'll come as quick as ever I can!' And they trotted down the hill."

"Do oo think he caught the Fox, Mister Sir?" said Bruno. I shook my head, not liking to speak: and Sylvie went on.

"And when they got to the house, Bruno looked in at the window. And there he saw the three little Foxes sitting round the table, with their clean pinafores on, and spoons in their hands——"

"Spoons in their hands!" Bruno repeated in an ecstasy of delight.

"And the Fox had got a great big knife—all ready to kill the poor little Lamb——" ("Oo needn't be flightened, Mister Sir!" Bruno put in, in a hasty whisper.)

"And just as he was going to do it, Bruno heard a great ROAR——" (The real Bruno put his hand into mine, and held tight), "and the Lion came *bang* through the door, and the next moment it had bitten off the old Fox's head! And Bruno jumped in at the window, and went leaping round the room, and crying out 'Hooray! Hooray! The old Fox is dead! The old Fox is dead!'"

Bruno got up in some excitement. "May I do it now?" he enquired.

Sylvie was quite decided on this point. "Wait till afterwards," she said. "The speeches come next, don't you know? You always love the speeches, *don't* you?"

"Yes, I doos," said Bruno: and sat down again.

"The Lion's speech. 'Now, you silly little Lamb, go home to your mother, and never listen to old Foxes again. And be very good and obedient.'"

"The Lamb's speech. 'Oh, indeed, Sir, I will, Sir!' and the Lamb went away." ("But *oo* needn't go away!" Bruno explained. "It's quite the nicest part—what's coming now!" Sylvie smiled. She liked having an appreciative audience.)

"The Lion's speech to Bruno. 'Now, Bruno, take those little Foxes home with you, and teach them to be good obedient little Foxes! Not like that wicked old thing there, that's got no head!' " ("That hasn't go no head," Bruno repeated.)

"Bruno's speech to the Lion. 'Oh, indeed, Sir, I will, Sir!' And the Lion went away." ("It gets betterer and betterer, now," Bruno whispered to me, "right away to the end!")

"Bruno's speech to the little Foxes. 'Now, little Foxes, you're going to have your first lesson in being good. I'm going to put you into the hamper, along with the Apples and the Bread: and you're not to eat the Apples: and you're not to eat the Bread: and you're not to eat *anything*—till we get to my house: and then you'll have your supper.' "

"The little Foxes' speech to Bruno. The little Foxes said nothing.

"So Bruno put the Apples into the hamper—and the little Foxes—and the Bread—" ("They had picnicked all the Milk," Bruno explained in a whisper) "—and he set off to go to his house." ("We're getting near the end now," said Bruno.)

"And, when he had got a little way, he thought he would look into the hamper, and see how the little Foxes were getting on."

"So he opened the door——" said Bruno.

"Oh, Bruno!" Sylvie exclaimed, "*you're* not telling the story! So he opened the door, and behold, there were no Apples! So Bruno said 'Eldest little Fox, have *you* been eating the Apples?' And the eldest little Fox said 'No no no!' " (It is impossible to give the tone in which Sylvie repeated this rapid little 'No no no!' The nearest I can come to it is to say that it was much as if a young and excited duck had tried to quack the words. It was too quick for a quack, and yet too harsh to be anything else.) "Then he said 'Second little Fox, have *you* been eating the Apples?' And the second little Fox said 'No no no!' Then he said 'Youngest little Fox, have *you* been eating the Apples?' And the youngest little Fox *tried* to say 'No no no!' but its mouth was so full, it couldn't, and it only said 'Wauch! Wauch! Wauch!' And Bruno looked into its mouth. And its mouth was full of Apples! And Bruno shook his head, and he said 'Oh dear, oh dear! What bad creatures these Foxes are!' "

Bruno was listening intently: and, when Sylvie paused to take breath, he could only just gasp out the words "About the Bread?"

"Yes," said Sylvie, "the Bread comes next. So he shut the door again; and he went a little further; and then he thought he'd just peep in once more. And behold, there was no Bread!" ("What do 'behold' *mean*?" said Bruno. "Hush!" said Sylvie.) "And he said 'Eldest little Fox, have *you* been eating the Bread?' And the eldest little Fox said 'No no no!' 'Second little Fox, have *you* been eating the Bread?' And the second little Fox only said 'Wauch! Wauch! Wauch!' And Bruno looked into its mouth, and its mouth was full of Bread!" ("It might have chokeded it," said Bruno.) "So he said 'Oh dear, oh dear! What *shall* I do with these Foxes?' And he went a little further." ("Now comes the most interesting part," Bruno whispered.)

"And when Bruno opened the hamper again, what do you think he saw?" ("Only *two* Foxes!" Bruno cried in a great hurry.) "You shouldn't tell it so quick. However, he *did* see only *two* Foxes. And he said 'Eldest little Fox, have you been eating the youngest little Fox?' And the eldest little Fox said 'No no no!' 'Second little Fox, have *you* been eating the youngest little Fox?' And the second little Fox did its very best to say 'No no no!' but it could only say 'Weuchk! Weuchk! Weuchk!' And when Bruno looked into its mouth, it was half full of Bread, and half full of Fox!" (Bruno said nothing in the pause this time. He was beginning to pant a little, as he knew the crisis was coming.)

"And when he'd got nearly home, he looked once more into the hamper, and he saw——"

"Only——" Bruno began, but a generous thought struck him, and he looked at me. "*Oo* may say it, *this* time, Mister Sir!" he whispered. It was a noble offer, but I wouldn't rob him of the treat. "Go on, Bruno," I said, "you say it much the best." "Only—but—*one*—Fox!" Bruno said with great solemnity.

" 'Eldest little Fox,' " Sylvie said, dropping the narrative-form in her eagerness, " 'you've been *so* good that I can hardly believe *you've* been disobedient: but I'm *afraid* you've been eating your little sister?' And the eldest little Fox said 'Whihuauch! Whihuauch!' and then it choked. And Bruno looked into its mouth, and it *was* full!" (Sylvie paused to take breath, and Bruno lay back among the daisies, and looked at me triumphantly. "Isn't it *grand*, Mister Sir?" said he. I tried hard to assume a critical tone. "It's grand," I said: "but it frightens one so!" "Oo may sit a little closer to *me*, if oo like," said Bruno.)

"And so Bruno went home: and took the hamper into the kitchen, and opened it. And he saw——" Sylvie looked at *me*, this time, as if she thought I had been rather neglected and ought to be allowed *one* guess, at any rate.

"He ca'n't guess!" Bruno cried eagerly. "I 'fraid I *must* tell him! There weren't—*nuffin* in the hamper!" I shivered in terror, and Bruno clapped his hands with delight. "He *is* flightened, Sylvie! Tell the rest!"

"So Bruno said 'Eldest little Fox, have you been eating *yourself*, you wicked little Fox?' And the eldest little Fox said 'Whihuauch!' And then Bruno saw there was only its *mouth* in the hamper! So he took the mouth, and he opened it, and shook, and shook! And at last he shook the little Fox out of its own mouth! And then he said 'Open your mouth again, you wicked little thing!' And he shook, and shook! And he shook out the second little Fox! And he said 'Now open *your* mouth!' And he shook and shook! And he shook out the youngest little Fox, and all the Apples, and all the Bread!

"And then Bruno stood the little Foxes up against the wall: and he made them a little speech. 'Now, little Foxes, you've begun very wickedly—and you'll have to be punished. First you'll go up to the nursery, and wash your faces, and put on clean pinafores. Then you'll hear the bell ring for supper. Then you'll come down: and *you wo'n't have any supper*: but you'll have a good *whipping*! Then you'll go to bed. Then in the morning you'll hear the bell ring for breakfast. *But you wo'n't have any breakfast*! You'll have a good *whipping*! Then you'll have your lessons. And, perhaps, if you're *very* good, when dinnertime comes, you'll have a little dinner, and no more whipping!' " ("How *very* kind he was!" I whispered to Bruno. "*Middling* kind," Bruno corrected me gravely.)

"So the little Foxes ran up to the nursery. And soon Bruno went into the hall, and rang the big bell. 'Tingle, tingle, tingle! Supper, supper, supper!' Down came the little Foxes, in such a hurry for their supper! Clean pinafores! Spoons in their hands! And, when they got into the dining-room, there was ever such a white table-cloth on the table! But there was nothing on it but a big whip. And they had *such* a whipping!" (I put my handkerchief to my eyes, and Bruno hastily climbed upon my knee and stroked my face. "Only *one* more whipping, Mister Sir!" he whispered. "Don't cry more than oo ca'n't help!")

"And the next morning early, Bruno rang the big bell again. 'Tingle, tingle, tingle! Breakfast, breakfast, breakfast!' Down came the little Foxes! Clean pinafores! Spoons in their hands! No breakfast! Only the big whip! Then came lessons," Sylvie hurried on, for I still had my handkerchief to my eyes. "And the little Foxes were ever so good! And they learned their lessons backwards, and forwards, and upside-down. And at last Bruno rang the big bell again. 'Tingle, tingle, tingle! Dinner, dinner, dinner!' And when the little Foxes came down——" ("Had they clean pinafores on?" Bruno enquired. "Of course!" said Sylvie. "And spoons?" "Why, you *know* they had!" "Couldn't be *certain*," said Bruno.) "—they came as slow as slow! And they said 'Oh! There'll be no dinner! There'll only be the big whip!' But, when they got into the room, they saw the most *lovely* dinner!" ("Buns?" cried Bruno, clapping his hands.) "Buns, and cake, and——" ("—and jam?" said Bruno.) "Yes, jam—and soup—and——" ("—and *sugar plums*!" Bruno put in once more; and Sylvie seemed satisfied.)

"And ever after that, they *were* such good little Foxes! They did their lessons as good as gold—and they never did what Bruno told them not to—and they never ate each other any more—and *they never ate themselves*!"

The story came to an end so suddenly, it almost took my breath away; however I did my best to make a pretty speech of thanks. "I'm sure it's very—very—very much so, I'm sure!" I seemed to hear myself say.

CHAPTER 16

Beyond These Voices

"I DIDN'T quite catch what you said!" were the next words that reached my ear, but certainly *not* in the voice either of Sylvie or of Bruno, whom I could just see, through the crowd of guests, standing by the piano, and listening to the Count's song. Mein Herr was the speaker. "I didn't quite catch what you said!" he repeated. "But I've no doubt you take *my* view of it. Thank you *very* much for your kind attention. There is only but *one* verse left to be sung!" These last words were not in the gentle voice of Mein Herr, but in the deep bass of the French Count. And, in the silence that followed, the final stanza of "Tottles" rang through the room.

> *See now this couple settled down*
> *In quiet lodgings, out of town:*
> *Submissively the tearful wife*
> *Accepts a plain and humble life:*
> *Yet begs one boon on bended knee:*
> *"My ducky-darling, don't resent it!*
> *Mamma might come for two or three——"*
> *"NEVER!" yelled Tottles. And he meant it.*

The conclusion of the song was followed by quite a chorus of thanks and compliments from all parts of the room, which the gratified singer responded to by bowing low in all directions. "It is to me a great privilege", he said to Lady Muriel, 'to have met with this so marvellous a song. The accompaniment to him is so strange, so mysterious: it is as if a new music were to be invented! I will play him once again so as that to show you what I mean." He returned to the piano, but the song had vanished.

The bewildered singer searched through the heap of music lying on an adjoining table, but it was not there, either. Lady Muriel helped in the search: others soon joined: the excitement grew. "What *can* have become of it?" exclaimed Lady Muriel. Nobody knew: one thing only was certain, that no one had been near the piano since the Count had sung the last verse of the song.

"Nevare mind him!" he said, most good-naturedly. "I shall give it you with memory alone!" He sat down, and began vaguely fingering the notes; but nothing resembling the tune came out. Then he, too, grew excited. "But what oddness! How much of singularity! That I might lose, not the words alone, but the tune also—that is quite curious, I suppose?"

We all supposed it, heartily.

"It was that sweet little boy, who found it for me," the Count suggested. 'Quite perhaps *he* is the thief?"

"Of course he is!" cried Lady Muriel. "Bruno! Where are you, my darling?"

But no Bruno replied: it seemed that the two children had vanished as suddenly, and as mysteriously, as the song.

"They are playing us a trick?" Lady Muriel gaily exclaimed. "This is only an *ex tempore* game of Hide-and-Seek! That little Bruno is an embodied Mischief!"

The suggestion was a welcome one to most of us, for some of the guests

were beginning to look decidedly uneasy. A general search was set on foot with much enthusiasm: curtains were thrown back and shaken, cupboards opened, and ottomans turned over; but the number of possible hiding-places proved to be strictly limited; and the search came to an end almost as soon as it had begun.

"They must have run out, while we were wrapped up in the song," Lady Muriel said, addressing herself to the Count, who seemed more agitated than the others; "and no doubt they've found their way back to the house-keeper's room."

"Not by *this* door!" was the earnest protest of a knot of two or three gentlemen, who had been grouped round the door (one of them actually leaning against it) for the last half-hour, as they declared. "*This* door has not been opened since the song began!"

An uncomfortable silence followed this announcement. Lady Muriel ventured no further conjectures, but quietly examined the fastenings of the windows, which opened as doors. They all proved to be well fastened, *inside.*

Not yet at the end of her resources, Lady Muriel rang the bell. "Ask the housekeeper to step here," she said, "and to bring the children's walking-things with her."

"I've brought them, my Lady," said the obsequious housekeeper, entering after another minute of silence. "I thought the young lady would have come to my room to put on her boots. Here's your boots, my love!" she added cheerfully, looking in all directions for the children. There was no answer, and she turned to Lady Muriel with a puzzled smile. "Have the little darlings hid themselves?"

"I don't see them, just now," Lady Muriel replied, rather evasively. "You can leave their things here, Wilson. *I'll* dress them, when they're ready to go."

The two little hats, and Sylvie's walking-jacket, were handed round among the ladies, with many exclamations of delight. There certainly was a sort of witchery of beauty about them. Even the little boots did not miss their share of favourable criticism. "Such natty little things!" the musical young lady exclaimed, almost fondling them as she spoke. "And what tiny tiny feet they must have!"

Finally, the things were piled together on the centre-ottoman, and the guests, despairing of seeing the children again, began to wish good-night and leave the house.

There were only some eight or nine left—to whom the Count was explaining, for the twentieth time, how he had had his eye on the children during the last verse of the song; how he had then glanced round the room, to see what effect "de great chest-note" had had upon his audience; and how, when he looked back again, they had both disappeared—when exclamations of dismay began to be heard on all sides, the Count hastily bringing his story to an end to join in the outcry.

The walking-things had all disappeared!

After the utter failure of the search for the *children*, there was a very half-hearted search made for their *apparel*. The remaining guests seemed only too glad to get away, leaving only the Count and our four selves.

The Count sank into an easy-chair, and panted a little.

"Who then *are* these dear children, I pray you?" he said. "Why come they, why go they, in this so little ordinary a fashion? That the music should make itself vanish—that the hats, the boots, should make themselves to vanish—how is it, I pray you?"

"I've no idea where they are!" was all I could say, on finding myself appealed to, by general consent, for an explanation.

The Count seemed about to ask further questions, but checked himself.

"The hour makes himself to become late," he said. "I wish to you a very good night, my Lady. I betake myself to my bed—to dream—if that indeed I be not dreaming now!" And he hastily left the room.

"Stay awhile, stay awhile!" said the Earl, as I was about to follow the Count. "*You* are not a guest, you know! Arthur's friend is at *home* here!"

"Thanks!" I said, as with true English instincts, we drew our chairs together round the fire-place, though no fire was burning—Lady Muriel having taken the heap of music on her knee, to have one more search for the strangely-vanished song.

"Don't you sometimes feel a wild longing", she said, addressing herself to me, "to have something more to do with your hands, while you talk, than just holding a cigar, and now and then knocking off the ash? Oh, I know all that you're going to say!" (This was to Arthur, who appeared about to interrupt her.) "The Majesty of Thought supersedes the work of the fingers. A Man's severe thinking, *plus* the shaking-off a cigar-ash, comes to the same total as a Woman's trivial fancies, *plus* the most elaborate embroidery. *That's* your sentiment, isn't it, only better expressed?"

Arthur looked into the radiant, mischievous face, with a grave and very tender smile. "Yes," he said resignedly: "that is my sentiment, exactly."

"Rest of body, and activity of mind," I put in. "Some writer tells us *that* is the acme of human happiness."

"Plenty of *bodily* rest, at any rate!" Lady Muriel replied, glancing at the three recumbent figures around her. "But what you call activity of *mind*——"

"—is the privilege of young Physicians *only*," said the Earl. "We old men have no claim to be active. *What can an old man do but die?*"

"A good many other things, I should *hope*," Arthur said earnestly.

"Well, maybe. Still you have the advantage of me in many ways, dear boy! Not only that *your* day is dawning while *mine* is setting, but your *interest* in Life—somehow I ca'n't help envying you *that*. It will be many a year before you lose your hold of *that*."

"Yet surely many human interests *survive* human Life?" I said.

"Many do, no doubt. And *some* forms of Science; but only *some*, I think. Mathematics, for instance: *that* seems to possess an endless interest: one ca'n't imagine *any* form of Life, or *any* race of intelligent beings, where Mathematical truth would lose its meaning. But I fear *Medicine* stands on a different footing. Suppose you discover a remedy for some disease hitherto supposed to be incurable. Well, it is delightful for the moment, no doubt—full of interest—perhaps it brings you fame and fortune. But what then? Look on, a few years, into a life where disease has no existence. What is your discovery worth, *then*? Milton makes Jove promise too much. '*Of so much fame in heaven expect thy meed.*' Poor comfort when one's 'fame' concerns matters that will have ceased to have a meaning!"

"At any rate one wouldn't care to make any *fresh* medical discoveries," said Arthur. "I see no help for *that*—though I shall be sorry to give up my favourite studies. Still, medicine, disease, pain, sorrow, sin—I fear they're all linked together. Banish sin, and you banish them all!"

"*Military* science is a yet stronger instance," said the Earl. "Without sin, *war* would surely be impossible. Still any mind, that has had in this life any keen interest, not in *itself* sinful, will surely find itself *some* congenial line of work hereafter. Wellington may have no more *battles* to fight—and yet—

> '*We doubt not that, for one so true,*
> *There must be other, nobler work to do,*
> *Than when he fought at Waterloo,*
> *And Victor he must ever be!'* "

He lingered over the beautiful words, as if he loved them: and his voice, like distant music, died away into silence.

After a minute or two he began again. "If I'm not wearying you, I would like to tell you an idea of the future Life which has haunted me for years, like a sort of waking nightmare—I ca'n't reason myself out of it."

"Pray do," Arthur and I replied, almost in a breath. Lady Muriel put aside the heap of music, and folded her hands together.

"The one idea", the Earl resumed, "that has seemed to me to overshadow all the rest, is that of *Eternity*—involving, as it seems to do, the necessary *exhaustion* of all subjects of human interest. Take Pure Mathematics, for instance—a Science independent of our present surroundings. I have studied it, myself, a little. Take the subject of circles and ellipses—what we call 'curves of the second degree'. In a future Life, it would only be a question of so many years (or *hundreds* of years, if you like), for a man to work out *all* their properties. Then he *might* go to curves of the third degree. Say *that* took ten times as long (you see we have *unlimited* time to deal with). I can hardly imagine his *interest* in the subject holding out even for those; and, though there is no limit to the *degree* of the curves he might study, yet surely the time, needed to exhaust *all* the novelty and interest of the subject, would be absolutely *finite*? And so of all other branches of Science. And, when I transport myself, in thought, through some thousands or millions of years, and fancy myself possessed of as much Science as one created reason can carry, I ask myself 'What then? With nothing more to learn, can one rest content on *knowledge*, for the eternity yet to be lived through?' It has been a very wearying thought to me. I have sometimes fancied one *might*, in that event, say 'It is better *not* to be', and pray for personal *annihilation*—the Nirvana of the Buddhists."

"But that is only half the picture," I said. "Besides working for *oneself*, may there not be the helping of *others*?"

"Surely, surely!" Lady Muriel exclaimed in a tone of relief, looking at her father with sparkling eyes.

"Yes," said the Earl, "so long as there *were* any others needing help. But, given ages and ages more, surely all created reasons would at length reach the same dead level of *satiety*. And *then* what is there to look forward to?"

"I know that weary feeling," said the Young Doctor. "I have gone through it all, more than once. Now let me tell you how I have put it to myself. I have imagined a little child, playing with toys on his nursery-floor, and yet able to *reason*, and to look on, thirty years ahead. Might he not say to himself 'By that time I shall have had enough of bricks and ninepins. How weary Life will be!' Yet, if we look forward through those thirty years, we find him a great statesman, full of interests and joys far more intense than his baby-life could give—joys wholly inconceivable to his baby-mind—joys such as no baby-language could in the faintest degree describe. Now, may not our life, a million years hence, have the same relation, to our life now, that the man's life has to the child's? And, just as one might try, all in vain, to express to that child, in the language of bricks and ninepins, the meaning of 'politics', so perhaps all those descriptions of Heaven, with its music, and its feasts, and its streets of gold, may be only attempts to describe, in *our* words, things for which we *really* have no words at all. Don't you think that, in *your* picture of another life, you are in fact transplanting that child into political life, without making any allowance for his growing up?"

"I think I understand you," said the Earl. "The music of Heaven *may* be something beyond our powers of thought. Yet the music of Earth is sweet! Muriel, my child, sing us something before we go to bed!"

"Do," said Arthur, as he rose and lit the candles on the cottage-piano, lately banished from the drawing-room to make room for a "semi-grand". "There is a song here, that I have never heard you sing.

> *'Hail to thee, blithe spirit!*
> *Bird thou never wert,*
> *That from Heaven, or near it,*
> *Pourest thy full heart!'* "

he read from the page he had spread open before her.

"And our little life here", the Earl went on, "is, to that grand time, like a child's summer-day! One gets tired as night draws on," he added, with a touch of sadness in his voice, "and one gets to long for bed! For those welcome words 'Come, child, 'tis bed-time!' "

CHAPTER 17

To the Rescue!

"It *isn't* bed-time!" said a sleepy little voice. "The owls hasn't gone to bed, and I s'a'n't go to sleep wizout oo sings to me!"

"Oh, Bruno!" cried Sylvie. "Don't you know the owls have only just got up? But the *frogs* have gone to bed, ages ago.'

"Well, *I* aren't a frog," said Bruno.

"What shall I sing?" said Sylvie, skilfully avoiding the argument.

"Ask Mister Sir," Bruno lazily replied, clasping his hands behind his curly head, and lying back on his fernleaf, till it almost bent over with his weight. "This aren't a comfable leaf, Sylvie. Find me a comfabler— please!" he added, as an after-thought, in obedience to a warning finger held up by Sylvie. "I doosn't like being feet-upwards!"

It was a pretty sight to see—the motherly way in which the fairy-child gathered up her little brother in her arms, and laid him on a stronger leaf. She gave it just a touch to set it rocking, and it went on vigorously by itself, as if it contained some hidden machinery. It certainly wasn't the wind, for the evening-breeze had quite died away again, and not a leaf was stirring over our heads.

"Why does that one leaf rock so, without the others?" I asked Sylvie. She only smiled sweetly and shook her head. "I don't know *why*," she said. "It always does, if it's got a fairy-child on it. It *has* to, you know."

"And can people see the leaf rock, who ca'n't see the Fairy on it?"

"Why, of course!" cried Sylvie. "A leaf's a leaf, and everybody can see it; but Bruno's Bruno, and they ca'n't see *him*, unless they're eerie, like you."

Then I understood how it was that one sometimes sees—going through the woods in a still evening—one fernleaf rocking steadily on, all by itself. Haven't you ever seen that? Try if you can see the fairy-sleeper on it, next time; but don't *pick* the leaf, whatever you do; let the little one sleep on!

But all this time Bruno was getting sleepier and sleepier. "Sing, sing!" he murmured fretfully, Sylvie looked to me for instructions. "What shall it be?" she said.

"Could you sing him the nursery-song you once told me of?" I suggested. "The one that had been put through the mind-mangle, you know. '*The little man that had a little gun*,' I think it was."

"Why, that are one of the *Professor's* songs!" cried Bruno. "I likes the little man; and I likes the way they spinned him—like a teetle-totle-tum." And he turned a loving look on the gentle old man who was sitting at the other side of his leaf-bed, and who instantly began to sing, accompanying himself on his Outlandish guitar, while the snail, on which he sat, waved its horns in time to the music.

> *In stature the Manlet was dwarfish—*
> *No burly big Blunderbore he:*
> *And he wearily gazed on the crawfish*
> *His Wifelet had dressed for his tea.*
> *"Now reach me, sweet Atom, my gunlet,*
> *And hurl the old shoelet for luck:*
> *Let me hie to the bank of the runlet,*
> *And shoot thee a Duck!"*

She has reached him his minikin gunlet:
  She has hurled the old shoelet for luck:
She is busily baking a bunlet,
  To welcome him home with his Duck.
On he speeds, never wasting a wordlet,
  Though thoughtlets cling; closely as wax,
To the spot where the beautiful birdlet
        So quietly quacks.

Where the Lobsterlet lurks, and the Crablet
  So slowly and sleepily crawls:
Where the Dolphin's at home, and the Dablet
  Pays long ceremonious calls:
Where the Grublet is sought by the Froglet:
  Where the Frog is pursued by the Duck:
Where the Ducklet is chased by the Doglet—
        So runs the world's luck!

He has loaded with bullet and powder:
  His footfall is noiseless as air:
But the Voices grow louder and louder,
  And bellow, and bluster, and blare.
They bristle before him and after,
  They flutter above and below,
Shrill shriekings of lubberly laughter,
        Weird wailings of woe!

They echo without him, within him:
  They thrill through his whiskers and beard:
Like a teetotum seeming to spin him,
  With sneers never hitherto sneered.
"Avengement," they cry, "on our Foelet!
  Let the Manikin weep for our wrongs!
Let us drench him, from toplet to toelet,
        With Nursery-Songs!

"He shall muse upon 'Hey! Diddle! Diddle!'
  On the Cow that surmounted the Moon:
He shall rave of the Cat and the Fiddle,
  And the Dish that eloped with the Spoon:
And his soul shall be sad for the Spider,
  When Miss Muffet was sipping her whey,
That so tenderly sat down beside her,
        And scared her away!

"The music of Midsummer-madness
  Shall sting him with many a bite,
Till, in rapture of rollicking sadness,
  He shall groan with a gloomy delight:
He shall swathe him, like mists of the morning,
  In platitudes luscious and limp,
Such as deck, with a deathless adorning,
        The Song of the Shrimp!

"When the Ducklet's dark doom is decided,
   We will trundle him home in a trice:
And the banquet, so plainly provided,
   Shall round into rose-buds and rice:
In a blaze of pragmatic invention
   He shall wrestle with Fate, and shall reign:
But he has not a friend fit to mention,
     So hit him again!"

He has shot it, the delicate darling!
   And the Voices have ceased from their strife:
Not a whisper of sneering or snarling,
   As he carries it home to his wife:
Then, cheerily champing the bunlet
   His spouse was so skilful to bake,
He hies him once more to the runlet,
     To fetch her the Drake!

"He's sound asleep now," said Sylvie, carefully tucking in the edge of a violet-leaf, which she had been spreading over him as a sort of blanket: "good night!"

"Good night!" I echoed.

"You may well say 'good night'!" laughed Lady Muriel, rising and shutting up the piano as she spoke. "When you've been nid—nid—nodding all the time I've been singing for your benefit! What was it all about, now?" she demanded imperiously.

"Something about a duck?" I hazarded. "Well, a bird of some kind?" I corrected myself, perceiving at once that *that* guess was wrong, at any rate.

"*Something about a bird of some kind!*" Lady Muriel repeated, with as much withering scorn as her sweet face was capable of conveying. "And that's the way he speaks of Shelley's Sky-Lark, is it? When the Poet particularly says '*Hail to thee, blithe spirit! Bird thou never wert!*' "

She led the way to the smoking-room, where, ignoring all the usages of Society and all the instincts of Chivalry, the three Lords of the Creation reposed at their ease in low rocking-chairs, and permitted the one lady who was present to glide gracefully about among us, supplying our wants in the form of cooling drinks, cigarettes, and lights. Nay, it was only *one* of the three who had the chivalry to go beyond the common-place "thank you", and to quote the Poet's exquisite description of how Geraint, when waited on by Enid, was moved

> *"To stoop and kiss the tender little thumb*
> *That crossed the platter as she laid it down,"*

and to suit the action to the word—an audacious liberty for which, I feel bound to report, he was *not* duly reprimanded.

As no topic of conversation seemed to occur to any one, and as we were, all four, on those delightful terms with one another (the only terms, I think, on which any friendship, that deserves the name of *intimacy*, can be maintained) which involve no sort of necessity for *speaking* for mere speaking's sake, we sat in silence for some minutes.

At length I broke the silence by asking "Is there any fresh news from the harbour about the Fever?"

"None since this morning," the Earl said, looking very grave. "But that was alarming enough. The Fever is spreading fast: the London doctor has taken fright and left the place, and the only one now available isn't a regular doctor at all: he is apothecary, and doctor, and dentist, and I don't know what other trades, all in one. It's a bad outlook for those poor fishermen—and a worse one for all the women and children."

"How many are there of them altogether?" Arthur asked.

"There were nearly one hundred, a week ago," said the Earl: "but there have been twenty or thirty deaths since then."

"And what religious ministrations are there to be had?"

"There are three brave men down there," the Earl replied, his voice trembling with emotion, "gallant heroes as ever won the Victoria Cross! I am certain that no one of the three will ever leave the place merely to save his own life. There's the Curate: his wife is with him: they have no children. Then there's the Roman Catholic Priest. And there's the Wesleyan Minister. They go amongst their own flocks mostly; but I'm told that those who are dying like to have *any* of the three with them. How slight the barriers seem to be that part Christian from Christian, when one has to deal with the great facts of Life and the reality of Death!"

"So it must be, and so it should be——" Arthur was beginning, when the front-door bell rang, suddenly and violently.

We heard the front-door hastily opened, and voices outside: then a knock at the door of the smoking-room, and the old house-keeper appeared, looking a little scared.

"Two persons, my Lord, to speak with Dr. Forester."

Arthur stepped outside at once, and we heard his cheery "Well, my men?" but the answer was less audible, the only words I could distinctly catch being "ten since morning, and two more just——"

"But there *is* a doctor there?" we heard Arthur say: and a deep voice, that we had not heard before, replied "Dead, Sir. Died three hours ago."

Lady Muriel shuddered, and hid her face in her hands: but at this moment the front-door was quietly closed, and we heard no more.

For a few minutes we sat quite silent: then the Earl left the room, and soon returned to tell us that Arthur had gone away with the two fishermen, leaving word that he would be back in about an hour. And, true enough, at the end of that interval—during which very little was said, none of us seeming to have the heart to talk—the front-door once more creaked on its rusty hinges, and a step was heard in the passage, hardly to be recognized as Arthur's, so slow and uncertain was it, like a blind man feeling his way.

He came in, and stood before Lady Muriel, resting one hand heavily on the table, and with a strange look in his eyes, as if he were walking in his sleep.

"Muriel—my love——" he paused, and his lips quivered: but after a minute he went on more steadily. "Muriel—my darling—they—*want* me—down in the harbour."

"*Must* you go?" she pleaded, rising and laying her hands on his shoulders, and looking up into his face with her great eyes brimming over with tears. "Must *you* go, Arthur? It may mean—death!"

He met her gaze without flinching. "It *does* mean death," he said, in a husky whisper: "but—darling—I am *called*. And even my life itself——" His voice failed him, and he said no more.

For a minute she stood quite silent, looking upwards with a helpless gaze, as if even prayer were now useless, while her features worked and quivered with the great agony she was enduring. Then a sudden inspiration seemed to come upon her and light up her face with a strange sweet smile. "*Your* life?" she repeated. "It is not *yours* to give!"

Arthur had recovered himself by this time, and could reply quite firmly, "That is true," he said. "It is not *mine* to give. It is *yours*, now, my—wife that is to be! And you—do *you* forbid me to go? Will you not spare me, my own beloved one?"

Still clinging to him, she laid her head softly on his breast. She had never done such a thing in my presence before, and I knew how deeply she must be moved. "I *will* spare you", she said, calmly and quietly, "to God."

"And to God's poor," he whispered.

"And to God's poor," she added. "When must it be, sweet love?"

"To-morrow morning," he replied. "And I have much to do before then."

And then he told us how he had spent his hour of absence. He had been to the Vicarage, and had arranged for the wedding to take place at eight the next morning (there was no legal obstacle, as he had, some time before this, obtained a Special Licence) in the little church we knew so well. "My old friend here", indicating me, "will act as 'Best Man', I know: your father will be there to give you away: and—and—you will dispense with bride's-maids, my darling?"

She nodded: no words came.

"And then I can go with a willing heart—to do God's work—knowing that we are *one*—and that we are together in *spirit*, though not in bodily presence—and are most of all together when we pray! Our *prayers* will go up together——"

"Yes, yes!" sobbed Lady Muriel. "But you must not stay longer now,

my darling! Go home and take some rest. You will need all your strength to-morrow——"

'Well, I will go," said Arthur. "We will be here in good time to-morrow. Good night, my own own darling!"

I followed his example, and we two left the house together. As we walked back to our lodgings, Arthur sighed deeply once or twice, and seemed about to speak—but no words came, till we had entered the house, and had lit our candles, and were at our bedroom-doors. Then Arthur said "Good night, old fellow! God bless you!"

"God bless you!" I echoed from the very depths of my heart.

We were back again at the Hall by eight in the morning, and found Lady Muriel and the Earl, and the old Vicar, waiting for us. It was a strangely sad and silent party that walked up to the little church and back; and I could not help feeling that it was much more like a funeral than a wedding: to Lady Muriel it *was* in fact, a funeral rather than a wedding, so heavily did the presentiment weigh upon her (as she told us afterwards) that her newly-won husband was going forth to his death.

Then we had breakfast; and, all too soon, the vehicle was at the door, which was to convey Arthur, first to his lodgings, to pick up the things he was taking with him, and then as far towards the death-stricken hamlet as it was considered safe to go. One or two of the fishermen were to meet him on the road, to carry his things the rest of the way.

"And are you quite sure you are taking all that you will need?" Lady Muriel asked.

"All that I shall need as a *doctor*, certainly. And my own personal needs are few: I shall not even take any of my own wardrobe—there is a fisherman's suit, ready-made, that is waiting for me at my lodgings. I shall only take my watch, and a few books, and—stay—there *is* one book I should like to add, a pocket-Testament—to use at the bedsides of the sick and dying——"

"Take mine!" said Lady Muriel: and she ran upstairs to fetch it. "It has nothing written in it but 'Muriel'," she said as she returned with it: "shall I inscribe——"

"No, my own one," said Arthur, taking it from her. "What *could* you inscribe better than that? Could any human name mark it more clearly as my own individual property? Are *you* not mine? Are you not," (with all the old playfulness of manner) "as Bruno would say, 'my *very mine*'?"

He bade a long and loving adieu to the Earl and to me, and left the room, accompanied only by his wife, who was bearing up bravely, and was—*outwardly*, at least—less overcome than her old father. We waited in the room a minute or two, till the sounds of wheels had told us that Arthur had driven away; and even then we waited still, for the step of Lady Muriel, going upstairs to her room, to die away in the distance. Her step, usually so light and joyous, now sounded slow and weary, like one who plods on under a load of hopeless misery; and I felt almost as hopeless, and almost as wretched as she. "Are we four destined *ever* to meet again, on this side the grave?" I asked myself, as I walked to my home. And the tolling of a distant bell seemed to answer me, "No! No! No!"

CHAPTER 18

A Newspaper-Cutting

EXTRACT FROM THE "FAYFIELD CHRONICLE"

Our readers will have followed with painful interest, the accounts we have from time to time published of the terrible epidemic which has, during the last two months, carried off most of the inhabitants of the little fishing-harbour adjoining the village of Elveston. The last survivors, numbering twenty-three only, out of a population which, three short months ago, exceeded one hundred and twenty, were removed on Wednesday last, under the authority of the Local Board, and safely lodged in the County Hospital: and the place is now veritably "a city of the dead", without a single human voice to break its silence.

The rescuing party consisted of six sturdy fellows—fishermen from the neighbourhood—directed by the resident Physician of the Hospital, who came over for that purpose, heading a train of hospital-ambulances. The six men had been selected—from a much larger number who had volunteered for this peaceful "forlorn hope"—for their strength and robust health, as the expedition was considered to be, even now, when the malady has expended its chief force, not unattended with danger.

Every precaution that science could suggest, against the risk of infection, was adopted: and the sufferers were tenderly carried on litters, one by one, up the steep hill, and placed in the ambulances which, each provided with a hospital nurse, were waiting on the level road. The fifteen miles, to the Hospital, were done at a walking-pace, as some of the patients were in too prostrate a condition to bear jolting, and the journey occupied the whole afternoon.

The twenty-three patients consist of nine men, six women, and eight children. It has not been found possible to identify them all, as some of the children—left with no surviving relatives—are infants: and two men and one woman are not yet able to make rational replies, the brain-powers being entirely in abeyance. Among a more well-to-do race, there would no doubt have been names marked on the clothes; but here no such evidence is forthcoming.

Besides the poor fishermen and their families, there were but five persons to be accounted for: and it was ascertained, beyond a doubt, that all five are numbered with the dead. It is a melancholy pleasure to place on record the names of these genuine martyrs—than whom none, surely, are more worthy to be entered on the glory-roll of England's heroes! They are as follows:

The Rev. James Burgess, M.A., and Emma his wife. He was the Curate at the Harbour, not thirty years old, and had been married only two years. A written record was found in their house, of the dates of their deaths.

Next to theirs we will place the honoured named of Dr. Arthur Forester, who, on the death of the local physician, nobly faced the imminent peril of death, rather than leave these poor folk uncared for in their last extremity. No record of his name, or of the date of his death, was found: but the corpse was easily identified, although dressed in the ordinary fisherman's suit (which he was known to have adopted when he went down there), by a copy of the New Testament, the gift of his wife, which was found, placed next his heart, with his hands crossed over it. It was not thought prudent to remove the body, for burial elsewhere: and accordingly it was at once committed to the ground, along with four others found in different houses, with all due reverence. His wife, whose maiden name was Lady Muriel Orme, had been married to him on the very morning on which he undertook his self-sacrificing mission.

Next we record the Rev. Walter Saunders, Wesleyan Minister. His death is believed to have taken place two or three weeks ago, as the words "Died October 5" were found written on the wall of the room which he is known to have occupied—the house being shut up, and apparently not having been entered for some time.

Last—though not a whit behind the other four in glorious self-denial and devotion to duty—let us record the name of Father Francis, a young Jesuit Priest who had been only a few months in the place. He had not been dead many hours when the exploring party came upon the body, which was identified, beyond the possibility of doubt, by the dress, and the crucifix which was, like the young Doctor's Testament, clasped closely to his heart.

Since reaching the hospital, two of the men and one of the children have died. Hope is entertained for all the others: though there are two or three cases where the vital powers seem to be so entirely exhausted that it is but "hoping against hope" to regard ultimate recovery as even possible.

CHAPTER 19

A Fairy-Duet

THE year—what an eventful year it had been for me!—was drawing to a close, and the brief wintry day hardly gave light enough to recognize the old familiar objects, bound up with so many happy memories, as the train glided round the last bend into the station, and the hoarse cry of "Elveston! Elveston!" resounded along the platform.

It was sad to return to the place, and to feel that I should never again see the glad smile of welcome, that had awaited me here so few months ago. "And yet, if I were to find him here," I muttered, as in solitary state I followed the porter, who was wheeling my luggage on a barrow, "and if he *were* to *'strike a sudden hand in mine, And ask a thousand things of home,'* I should not—no, *'I should not feel it to be strange'*!"

Having given directions to have my luggage taken to my old lodgings, I strolled off alone, to pay a visit, before settling down in my own quarters, to my dear old friends—for such I indeed felt them to be, though it was barely half a year since first we met—the Earl and his widowed daughter.

The shortest way, as I well remembered, was to cross through the churchyard. I pushed open the little wicket-gate and slowly took my way among the solemn memorials of the quiet dead, thinking of the many who had, during the past year, disappeared from the place, and had gone to "join the majority". A very few steps brought me in sight of the object of my search. Lady Muriel, dressed in the deepest mourning, her face hidden by a long crape veil, was kneeling before a little marble cross, round which she was fastening a wreath of flowers.

The cross stood on a piece of level turf, unbroken by any mound, and I knew that it was simply a memorial-cross, for one whose dust reposed elsewhere, even before reading the simple inscription:

In loving Memory of
ARTHUR FORESTER, M.D.

whose mortal remains lie buried by the sea:
whose spirit has returned to God who gave it.

"GREATER LOVE HATH NO MAN THAN THIS, THAT
A MAN LAY DOWN HIS LIFE FOR HIS FRIENDS."

She threw back her veil on seeing me approach, and came forwards to meet me, with a quiet smile, and far more self-possessed than I could have expected.

"It is quite like old times, seeing *you* here again!" she said, in tones of genuine pleasure. "Have you been to see my father?"

"No," I said: "I was on my way there, and came through here as the shortest way. I hope he is well, and you also?"

"Thanks, we are both quite well. And you? Are you any better yet?"

"Not much better, I fear: but no worse, I am thankful to say."

"Let us sit here awhile, and have a quiet chat," she said. The calmness—almost indifference—of her manner quite took me by surprise. I little guessed what a fierce restraint she was putting upon herself.

"One can be so quiet here," she resumed. "I come here every—every day."

"It is very peaceful," I said.

"You got my letter?"

"Yes, but I delayed writing. It is so hard to say—on *paper*——"

"I know. It was kind of you. You were with us when we saw the last of——" She paused a moment, and went on more hurriedly. "I went down to the harbour several times, but no one knows which of those vast graves it is. However, they showed me the house he died in: that was some comfort. I stood in the very room where—where——" She struggled in vain to go on. The flood-gates had given way at last, and the outburst of grief was the most terrible I had ever witnessed. Totally regardless of my presence, she flung herself down on the turf, burying her face in the grass, and with her hands clasped round the little marble cross. "Oh, my

darling, my darling!" she sobbed. "And God meant your life to be so
beautiful!"

I was startled to hear, thus repeated by Lady Muriel, the very words
of the darling child whom I had seen weeping so bitterly over the dead
hare. Had some mysterious influence passed, from that sweet fairy-spirit,
ere she went back to Fairyland, into the human spirit that loved her so
dearly? The idea seemed too wild for belief. And yet, are there not "*more
things in heaven and earth than are dreamt of in our philosophy*"?

"God *meant* it to be beautiful," I whispered, "and surely it *was*
beautiful? God's purpose never fails!" I dared say no more, but rose and
left her. At the entrance-gate to the Earl's house I waited, leaning on the
gate and watching the sun set, revolving many memories—some happy,
some sorrowful—until Lady Muriel joined me.

She was quite calm again now. "Do come in," she said. "My father will
be so pleased to see you!"

The old man rose from his chair, with a smile, to welcome me; but his self-command was far less than his daughter's, and the tears coursed down his face as he grasped both my hands in his, and pressed them warmly.

My heart was too full to speak; and we all sat silent for a minute or two. Then Lady Muriel rang the bell for tea. "You *do* take five o'clock tea, I know!" she said to me, with the sweet playfulness of manner I remembered so well, "even though you *ca'n't* work your wicked will on the Law of Gravity, and make the teacups descend into Infinite Space, a little faster than the tea!"

This remark gave the tone to our conversation. By a tacit mutual consent, we avoided, during this our first meeting after her great sorrow, the painful topics that filled our thoughts, and talked like light-hearted children who had never known a care.

"Did you ever ask yourself the question," Lady Muriel began, *à propos* of nothing, "what is the *chief* advantage of being a Man instead of a Dog?"

"No, indeed," I said: "but I think there are advantages on the *Dog's* side of the question as well."

"No doubt," she replied, with that pretty mock-gravity that became her so well: "but, on *Man's* side, the chief advantage seems to me to consist in *having pockets*! It was borne in upon me—upon *us*, I should say; for my father and I were returning from a walk—only yesterday. We met a dog carrying home a bone. What it wanted it for, I've no idea: certainly there was no *meat* on it——"

A strange sensation came over me, that I had heard all this, or something exactly like it, before: and I almost expected her next words to be "perhaps he meant to make a cloak for the winter?" However what she really said was "and my father tried to account for it by some wretched joke about *pro bono publico*. Well, the dog laid down the bone—*not* in disgust with the pun, which would have shown it to be a dog of taste—but simply to rest its jaws, poor thing! I *did* pity it so! Won't you join my *Charitable Association for supplying dogs with pockets*? How would *you* like to have to carry your walking-stick in your mouth?"

Ignoring the difficult question as to the *raison d'être* of a walking-stick, supposing one had no *hands*, I mentioned a curious instance, I had once witnessed, of reasoning by a dog. A gentleman, with a lady, and child, and a large dog, were down at the end of a pier on which I was walking. To amuse his child, I suppose, the gentleman put down on the ground his umbrella and the lady's parasol, and then led the way to the other end of the pier, from which he sent the dog back for the deserted articles. I was watching with some curiosity. The dog came racing back to where I stood, but found an unexpected difficulty in picking up the things it had come for. With the umbrella in its mouth, its jaws were so far apart that it could get no firm grip on the parasol. After two or three failures, it paused and considered the matter.

Then it put down the umbrella and began with the parasol. Of course that didn't open its jaws nearly so wide, and it was able to get a good hold of the umbrella, and galloped off in triumph. One couldn't doubt that it had gone through a real train of logical thought.

"I entirely agree with you," said Lady Muriel: "but don't orthodox writers condemn that view, as putting Man on the level of the lower animals? Don't they draw a sharp boundary-line between Reason and Instinct?"

"That certainly *was* the orthodox view, a generation ago," said the Earl. "The truth of Religion seemed ready to stand or fall with the assertion that Man was the only reasoning animal. But that is at an end now. Man can still claim *certain* monopolies—for instance, such a use of *language* as enables us to utilize the work of many, by 'division of labour'. But the belief, that we have a monopoly of *Reason*, has long been swept away. Yet no catastrophe has followed. As some old poet says, '*God is where he was*'."

"Most religious believers would *now* agree with Bishop Butler," said I, "and not reject a line of argument, even if it led straight to the conclusion that animals have some kind of *soul*, which survives their bodily death."

"I *would* like to know *that* to be true!" Lady Muriel exclaimed. "If only for the sake of the poor horses. Sometimes I've thought that, if anything *could* make me cease to believe in a God of perfect justice, it would be the sufferings of horses—without guilt to deserve it, and without any compensation!"

"It is only part of the great Riddle," said the Earl, "why innocent beings *ever* suffer. It *is* a great strain on Faith—but not a *breaking* strain, I think."

"The sufferings of *horses*", I said, "are chiefly caused by *Man's* cruelty. So *that* is merely one of the many instances of Sin causing suffering to others than the Sinner himself. But don't you find a greater difficulty in sufferings inflicted by animals upon each other? For instance, a cat playing with a mouse. Assuming it to have no *moral* responsibility, isn't that a greater mystery than a man over-driving a horse?"

"I think it *is*," said Lady Muriel, looking a mute appeal to her father.

"What right have we to make that assumption?" said the Earl. "*Many* of our religious difficulties are merely deductions from unwarranted assumptions. The wisest answer to most of them, is, I think, '*behold, we know not anything*'?"

"You mentioned 'division of labour', just now," I said. "Surely it is carried to a wonderful perfection in a hive of bees?"

"So wonderful—so entirely super-human—" said the Earl, "and so entirely inconsistent with the intelligence they show in other ways—that I feel no doubt at all that it is *pure* Instinct, and *not*, as some hold, a very high order of Reason. Look at the utter stupidity of a bee, trying to find its way out of an open window! It *doesn't* try, in any reasonable sense of the word: it simply bangs itself about! We should call a puppy *imbecile*, that behaved so. And yet we are asked to believe that its intellectual level is above Sir Isaac Newton!"

"Then you hold that *pure* Instinct contains no *Reason* at all?"

"On the contrary," said the Earl, "I hold that the work of a bee-hive involves Reason of the *highest* order. But none of it is done by the *Bee*. *God* has reasoned it all out, and has put into the mind of the Bee the *conclusions*, only, of the reasoning process."

"But how do their minds come to work *together*?" I asked.

"What right have we to assume that they *have* minds?"

"Special pleading, special pleading!" Lady Muriel cried, in a most unfilial tone of triumph. "Why, you yourself said, just now, 'the mind of the Bee'!"

"But I did *not* say '*minds*', my child," the Earl gently replied. "It has occurred to me, as the most probable solution of the 'Bee'-mystery, that a swarm of Bees *have only one mind among them*. We often see one mind animating a most complex collection of limbs and organs, *when joined together*. How do we know that any material connection is necessary? May not mere neighbourhood be enough? If so, a swarm of bees is simply a single animal whose many limbs are not quite close together!"

"It is a bewildering thought," I said, "and needs a night's rest to grasp it properly. Reason and Instinct *both* tell me I ought to go home. So, good-night!"

"I'll 'set' you part of the way," said Lady Muriel. "I've had no walk to-day. It will do me good, and I have more to say to you. Shall we go through the wood? It will be pleasanter than over the common, even though it *is* getting a little dark."

We turned aside into the shade of interlacing boughs, which formed an architecture of almost perfect symmetry, grouped into lovely groined arches, or running out, far as the eye could follow, into endless aisles, and chancels, and naves, like some ghostly cathedral, fashioned out of the dream of a moon-struck poet.

"Always, in this wood," she began after a pause (silence seemed natural in this dim solitude), "I begin thinking of Fairies! May I ask you a question?" she added hesitatingly. "Do you believe in Fairies?"

The momentary impulse was so strong to tell her of my experiences in this very wood, that I had to make a real effort to keep back the words that rushed to my lips. "If you mean, by 'believe', 'believe in their *possible* existence', I say 'Yes'. For their *actual existence*, of course, one would need *evidence*."

"You were saying, the other day", she went on, "that you would accept *anything*, on good evidence, that was not à *priori* impossible. And I think you named *Ghosts* as an instance of a *provable* phenomenon. Would *Fairies* be another instance?"

"Yes, I think so." And again it was hard to check the wish to say more: but I was not yet sure of a sympathetic listener.

"And have you any theory as to what sort of place they would occupy in Creation? Do tell me what you think about them! Would they, for instance (supposing such beings to exist), would they have any moral responsibility? I mean" (and the light bantering tone suddenly changed to one of deep seriousness) "would they be capable of *sin*?"

"They can reason—on a lower level, perhaps, than men and women—never rising, I think, above the faculties of a child; and they have a moral sense, most surely. Such a being, without *free will*, would be an absurdity. So I am driven to the conclusion that they *are* capable of sin."

"You believe in them?" she cried delightedly, with a sudden motion as if about to clap her hands. "Now tell me, have you any reason for it?"

And still I strove to keep back the revelation I felt sure was coming. "I believe that there is *life* everywhere—not *material* only, not merely what is palpable to our senses—but immaterial and invisible as well. We believe in our own immaterial essence—call it 'soul', or 'spirit', or what you will. Why should not other similar essences exist around us, *not* linked on to a visible and *material* body? Did not God make this swarm of happy insects, to dance in this sunbeam for one hour of bliss, for no other object, that we can imagine, than to swell the sum of conscious happiness? And where shall we dare to draw the line, and say 'He has made all these and no more'?"

"Yes, yes!" she assented, watching me with sparkling eyes. "But these are only reasons for not *denying*. You have more reasons than this, have you not?"

"Well, yes," I said, feeling I might safely tell all now. "And I could not find a fitter time or place to say it. I have *seen* them—and in this very wood!"

Lady Muriel asked no more questions. Silently she paced at my side, with head bowed down and hands clasped tightly together. Only, as my tale went on, she drew a little short quick breath now and then, like a child panting with delight. And I told her what I had never yet breathed to any other listener, of my double life, and more than that (for *mine* might have been but a noonday-dream), of the double life of those two dear children.

And when I told her of Bruno's wild gambols, she laughed merrily; and when I spoke of Sylvie's sweetness and her utter unselfishness and trustful love, she drew a deep breath, like one who hears at last some precious tidings for which the heart has ached for a long while; and the happy tears chased one another down her cheeks.

"I have often longed to meet an angel," she whispered, so low that I could hardly catch the words. "I'm *so* glad I've seen Sylvie! My heart went out to the child the first moment that I saw her—Listen!" she broke off suddenly. "That's Sylvie singing! I'm sure of it! Don't you know her voice?"

"I have heard *Bruno* sing, more than once," I said: "but I never heard Sylvie."

"I have only heard her *once*," said Lady Muriel. "It was that day when you brought us those mysterious flowers. The children had run out into the garden; and I saw Eric coming in that way, and went to the window to meet him: and Sylvie was singing, under the trees, a song I had never heard before. The words were something like 'I think it is Love, I feel it is Love'. Her voice sounded far away, like a dream, but it was beautiful beyond all words—as sweet as an infant's first smile, or the first gleam of the white cliffs when one is coming *home* after weary years—a voice that seemed to fill one's whole being with peace and heavenly thoughts—Listen!" she cried, breaking off again in her excitement. "That *is* her voice, and that's the very song!"

I could distinguish no words, but there was a dreamy sense of music in the air that seemed to grow ever louder and louder, as if coming nearer to us. We stood quite silent, and in another minute the two children appeared, coming straight towards us through an arched opening among the trees. Each had an arm round the other, and the setting sun shed a golden halo round their heads, like what one sees in pictures of saints.

They were looking in our direction, but evidently did not see us, and I soon made out that Lady Muriel had for once passed into a condition familiar to *me*, that we were both of us "eerie", and that, though we could see the children so plainly, we were quite invisible to *them*.

The song ceased just as they came into sight: but, to my delight, Bruno instantly said "Let's sing it all again, Sylvie! It *did* sound so pretty!" And Sylvie replied "Very well. It's *you* to begin, you know."

So Bruno began, in the sweet childish treble I knew so well:

> *"Say, what is the spell, when her fledgelings are cheeping,*
> *   That lures the bird home to her nest?*
> *Or wakes the tired mother, whose infant is weeping,*
> *   To cuddle and croon it to rest?*
> *What's the magic that charms the glad babe in her arms,*
> *   Till it cooes with the voice of the dove?"*

And now ensued quite the strangest of all the strange experiences that marked the wonderful year whose history I am writing—the experience of *first* hearing Sylvie's voice in song. Her part was a very short one—only a few words—and she sang it timidly, and very low indeed, scarcely audibly, but the *sweetness* of her voice was simply indescribable; I have never heard any earthly music like it.

> *" 'Tis a secret, and so let us whisper it low——*
> *And the name of the secret is Love!"*

On me the first effect of her voice was a sudden sharp pang that seemed to pierce through one's very heart. (I had felt such a pang only once before in my life, and it had been from *seeing* what, at the moment, realized one's idea of perfect beauty—it was in a London exhibition, where, in making my way through a crowd, I suddenly met, face to face, a child of quite unearthly beauty.) Then came a rush of burning tears to the eyes, as though one could weep one's soul away for pure delight. And lastly there fell on me a sense of awe that was almost terror—some such feeling as Moses must have had when he heard the words "*Put off thy shoes from off thy feet, for the place whereon thou standest is holy ground*". The figures of the children became vague and shadowy, like glimmering meteors: while their voices rang together in exquisite harmony as they sang:

> *"For I think it is Love,*
> *For I feel it is Love,*
> *For I'm sure it is nothing but Love!"*

By this time I could see them clearly once more. Bruno again sang by himself:

> *"Say, whence is the voice that, when anger is burning,*
> *Bids the whirl of the tempest to cease?*
> *That stirs the vexed soul with an aching—a yearning*
> *For the brotherly hand-grip of peace?*
> *Whence the music that fills all our being—that thrills*
> *Around us, beneath, and above?"*

Sylvie sang more courageously, this time: the words seemed to carry her away, out of herself:

> *" 'Tis a secret: none knows how it comes, how it goes:*
> *But the name of the secret is Love!"*

And clear and strong the chorus rang out:

> *"For I think it is Love,*
> *For I feel it is Love,*
> *For I'm sure it is nothing but Love!"*

Once more we heard Bruno's delicate little voice alone:

> *"Say whose is the skill that paints valley and hill,*
> *Like a picture so fair to the sight?*
> *That flecks the green meadow with sunshine and shadow,*
> *Till the little lambs leap with delight?"*

And again uprose that silvery voice, whose angelic sweetness I could hardly bear:

> *" 'Tis a secret untold to hearts cruel and cold,*
> *Though 'tis sung, by the angels above,*
> *In notes that ring clear for the ears that can hear——*
> *And the name of the secret is Love!"*

And then Bruno joined in again with

> *"For I think it is Love,*
> *For I feel it is Love,*
> *For I'm sure it is nothing but Love!"*

"That *are* pretty!" the little fellow exclaimed, as the children passed us—so closely that we drew back a little to make room for them, and it seemed we had only to reach out a hand to touch them: but this we did not attempt.

"No use to try and stop them!" I said, as they passed away into the shadows. "Why, they could not even *see* us!"

"No use at all," Lady Muriel echoed with a sigh. "One would *like* to meet them again, in living form! But I feel, somehow, *that* can never be. They have passed out of *our* lives!" She sighed again; and no more was said, till we came out into the main road, at a point near my lodgings.

"Well, I will leave you here," she said. "I want to get back before dark: and I have a cottage-friend to visit, first. Good night, dear friend! Let us see you soon—and often!" she added, with an affectionate warmth that went to my very heart. *"For those are few we hold as dear!"*

"Good night!" I answered. "Tennyson said that of a worthier friend than me."

"Tennyson didn't know what he was talking about!" she saucily rejoined, with a touch of her old childish gaiety, and we parted.

CHAPTER 20

Gammon and Spinach

My landlady's welcome had an extra heartiness about it: and though, with a rare delicacy of feeling, she made no direct allusion to the friend whose companionship had done so much to brighten life for me, I felt sure that it was a kindly sympathy with my solitary state that made her so specially anxious to do all she could think of to ensure my comfort, and make me feel at home.

The lonely evening seemed long and tedious: yet I lingered on, watching the dying fire, and letting Fancy mould the red embers into the forms and faces belonging to bygone scenes. Now it seemed to be Bruno's roguish smile that sparkled for a moment, and died away: now it was Sylvie's rosy cheek: and now the Professor's jolly round face, beaming with delight. "You're welcome, my little ones!" he seemed to say. And then the red coal, which for the moment embodied the dear old Professor, began to wax dim, and with its dying lustre the words seemed to die away into silence. I seized the poker, and with an artful touch or two revived the

waning glow, while Fancy—no coy minstrel she—sang me once again the
magic strain I loved to hear.

"You're welcome, little ones!" the cheery voice repeated. "I told them
you were coming. Your rooms are all ready for you. And the Emperor
and the Empress—well, I think they're rather pleased than otherwise! In
fact, Her Highness said 'I hope they'll be in time for the Banquet!' Those
were her very words, I assure you!"

"Will Uggug be at the Banquet?" Bruno asked. And both children
looked uneasy at the dismal suggestion.

"Why, of course he will!" chuckled the Professor. "Why, it's his
birthday, don't you know? And his health will be drunk, and all that sort
of thing. What would the Banquet be without *him*?"

"Ever so much nicer," said Bruno. But he said it in a *very* low voice,
and nobody but Sylvie heard him.

The Professor chuckled again. "It'll be a jolly Banquet, now *you've*
come, my little man! I *am* so glad to see you again!"

"I 'fraid we've been very long in coming," Bruno politely remarked.

"Well, yes," the Professor assented. "However, you're very short, now
you're come: that's *some* comfort." And he went on to enumerate the
plans for the day. "The Lecture comes first," he said. "*That* the Empress
insists on. She says people will eat so much at the Banquet, they'll be too
sleepy to attend to the Lecture afterwards—and perhaps she's right.
There'll just be a little *refreshment*, when the people first arrive—as a
kind of surprise for the Empress, you know. Ever since she's been—well,
not *quite so* clever as she once was—we've found it desirable to concoct
little surprises for her. *Then* comes the Lecture——"

"What? The Lecture you were getting ready—ever so long ago?"
Sylvie enquired.

"Yes—that's the one," the Professor rather reluctantly admitted. "It
has taken a goodish time to prepare. I've got so many other things to
attend to. For instance, I'm Court-Physician. I have to keep all the Royal
Servants in good health—and that reminds me!" he cried, ringing the bell
in a great hurry. "This is Medicine-Day! We only give Medicine once a
week. If we were to begin giving it every day, the bottles would *soon* be
empty!"

"But if they were ill on the *other* days?" Sylvie suggested.

"What, ill on the wrong *day*!" exclaimed the Professor. "Oh, that
would never do! A Servant would be dismissed *at once*, who was ill on the
wrong day! This is the Medicine for *to-day*," he went on, taking down a
large jug from a shelf. "I mixed it, myself, first thing this morning. Taste

it!" he said, holding out the jug to Bruno. "Dip in your finger, and taste it!"

Bruno did so, and made such an excruciatingly wry face that Sylvie exclaimed in alarm, "Oh, Bruno, you mustn't!"

"It's welly extremely nasty!" Bruno said, as his face resumed its natural shape.

"Nasty?" said the Professor. "Why, of *course* it is! What would Medicine be, if it wasn't *nasty*?"

"Nice," said Bruno.

"I was going to say——" the Professor faltered, rather taken aback by the promptness of Bruno's reply, "——that *that* would never do! Medicine *has* to be nasty, you know. Be good enough to take this jug, down into the Servants' Hall," he said to the footman who answered the bell: "and tell them it's their Medicine for *to-day*."

'Which of them is to drink it?" the footman asked, as he carried off the jug.

"Oh, I've not settled *that* yet!" the Professor briskly replied. "I'll come and settle that, soon. Tell them not to begin, on any account, till I come! It's really *wonderful*", he said, turning to the children, "the success I've had in curing Diseases! Here are some of my memoranda." He took down from the shelf a heap of little bits of paper, pinned together in twos and threes. "Just look at *this* set, now. '*Under-Cook Number Thirteen recovered from Common Fever—Febris Communis.*' And now see what's pinned to it. '*Gave Under-Cook Number Thirteen a Double Dose of Medicine.*' *That's* something to be proud of, *isn't* it?"

"But which happened *first*?" said Sylvie, looking very much puzzled.

The Professor examined the papers carefully. "They are not *dated*, I find," he said with a slightly dejected air: "so I fear I ca'n't tell you. But they *both* happened: there's no doubt of *that*. The *Medicine's* the great thing, you know. The *Diseases* are much less important. You can keep a *Medicine*, for years and years: but nobody ever wants to keep a *Disease*! By the way, come and look at the platform. The Gardener asked me to come and see if it would do. We may as well go before it gets dark."

"We'd like to, very much!" Sylvie replied. "Come, Bruno, put on your hat. Don't keep the dear Professor waiting!"

"Ca'n't find my hat!" the little fellow sadly replied. "I were rolling it about. And it's rolled itself away!"

"Maybe it's rolled in *there*," Sylvie suggested, pointing to a dark recess, the door of which stood half open: and Bruno ran in to look. After a minute he came slowly out again, looking very grave, and carefully shut the cupboard door after him.

"It aren't in there," he said, with such unusual solemnity, that Sylvie's curiosity was aroused.

"What *is* in there, Bruno?"

"There's cobwebs—and two spiders——" Bruno thoughtfully replied, checking off the catalogue on his fingers, "——and the cover of a picture-book—and a tortoise—and a dish of nuts—and an old man."

"An old man!" cried the Professor, trotting across the room in great excitement. "Why, it must be the Other Professor, that's been lost for ever so long!"

He opened the door of the cupboard wide: and there he was, the Other Professor, sitting in a chair, with a book on his knee, and in the act of

helping himself to a nut from a dish, which he had taken down off a shelf just within his reach. He looked around at us, but said nothing till he had cracked and eaten the nut. Then he asked the old question "Is the Lecture all ready?"

"It'll begin in an hour," the Professor said, evading the question. "First, we must have something to surprise the Empress. And then comes the Banquet——"

"The Banquet!" cried the Other Professor, springing up, and filling the room with a cloud of dust. Then I'd better go and—and brush myself a little. What a state I'm in!"

"He *does* want brushing!" the Professor said, with a critical air. "Here's your hat, little man! I had put it on by mistake. I'd quite forgotten I had *one* on, already. Let's go and look at the platform."

"And there's that nice old Gardener singing still!" Bruno exclaimed in delight, as we went out into the garden. "I do believe he's been singing that very song ever since we went away!"

"Why, of course he has!" replied the Professor. "It wouldn't be the thing to leave off, you know."

"Wouldn't be *what* thing?" said Bruno: but the Professor thought it best not to hear the question. "What are you doing with that hedgehog?" he shouted at the Gardener, whom they found standing upon one foot, singing softly to himself, and rolling a hedgehog up and down with the other foot.

"Well, I wanted fur to know what hedgehogs lives on: so I be a-keeping this here hedgehog—fur to see if it eats potatoes——"

"Much better keep a potato," said the Professor; "and see if hedgehogs eat it!"

"That be the roight way, sure-ly!" the delighted Gardener exclaimed. "Be you come to see the platform?"

"Aye, aye!" the Professor cheerily replied. "And the children have come back, you see!"

The Gardener looked round at them with a grin. Then he led the way to the Pavilion; and as he went he sang:

> *"He looked again, and found it was*
> *A Double Rule of Three:*
> *'And all its Mystery', he said,*
> *'Is clear as day to me!'"*

"You've been *months* over that song," said the Professor. "Isn't it finished yet?"

"There be only one verse more," the Gardener sadly replied. And, with tears streaming down his cheeks, he sang the last verse:

> "He thought he saw an Argument
> That proved he was the Pope:
> He looked again, and found it was
> A Bar of Mottled Soap.
> 'A fact so dread', he faintly said,
> 'Extinguishes all hope!'"

Choking with sobs, the Gardener hastily stepped on a few yards ahead of the party, to conceal his emotion.

"Did *he* see the Bar of Mottled Soap?" Sylvie enquired, as we followed.

"Oh, certainly!" said the Professor. "That song is his own history, you know."

Tears of an ever-ready sympathy glittered in Bruno's eyes. "I's *welly* sorry he isn't the Pope!" he said. "Aren't *you* sorry, Sylvie?"

"Well—I hardly know," Sylvie replied in the vaguest manner. "Would it make him any happier?" she asked the Professor.

"It wouldn't make the *Pope* any happier," said the Professor. "Isn't the platform *lovely*?" he asked, as we entered the Pavilion.

"I've put an extra beam under it!" said the Gardener, patting it affectionately as he spoke. "And now it's that strong, as—as a mad elephant might dance upon it!"

"Thank you *very* much!" the Professor heartily rejoined. "I don't know that we shall exactly require—but it's convenient to know." And he led the children upon the platform, to explain the arrangements to them. "Here are three seats, you see, for the Emperor and the Empress and Prince Uggug. But there must be two more chairs here!" he said, looking down at the Gardener. "One for Lady Sylvie, and one for the smaller animal!"

"And may I help in the Lecture?" said Bruno. "I can do some conjuring tricks."

"Well, it's not exactly a *conjuring* lecture," the Professor said, as he arranged some curious-looking machines on the table. "However, what can you do? Did you ever go through a table, for instance?"

"Often!" said Bruno. "*Haven't* I, Sylvie?"

The Professor was evidently surprised, though he tried not to show it. "This must be looked into," he muttered to himself, taking out a note-book. "And first—what kind of table?"

"Tell him!" Bruno whispered to Sylvie, putting his arms round her neck.

"Tell him yourself," said Sylvie.

"Ca'n't," said Bruno. "It's a *bony* word."

"Nonsense!" laughed Sylvie. "You can say it well enough, if you only try. Come!"

"Muddle——" said Bruno. "That's a bit of it."

"*What* does he say?" cried the bewildered Professor.

"He means the multiplication-table," Sylvie explained.

The Professor looked annoyed, and shut up his note-book again. "Oh, that's *quite* another thing," he said.

"It are ever so many other things," said Bruno. "*Aren't* it, Sylvie?"

A loud blast of trumpets interrupted this conversation. "Why, the entertainment has *begun!*" the Professor exclaimed, as he hurried the children into the Reception-Saloon. "I had no idea it was so late!"

A small table, containing cake and wine, stood in a corner of the Saloon; and here we found the Emperor and Empress waiting for us. The rest of the Saloon had been cleared of furniture, to make room for the guests. I was much struck by the great change a few months had made in the faces of the Imperial Pair. A vacant stare was now the *Emperor's* usual expression; while over the face of the *Empress* there flitted, ever and anon, a meaningless smile.

"So you're come at last!" the Emperor sulkily remarked, as the Professor and the children took their places. It was evident that he was *very* much out of temper: and we were not long in learning the cause of this. He did not consider the preparations, made for the Imperial party, to be such as suited their rank. "A common mahogany table!" he growled, pointing to it contemptuously with his thumb. "Why wasn't it made of gold, I should like to know?"

"It would have taken a very long——" the Professor began, but the Emperor cut the sentence short.

"Then the cake! Ordinary plum! Why wasn't it made of—of——" He broke off again. "Then the wine! Merely old Madeira! Why wasn't it——? Then this chair! That's worst of all. Why wasn't it a throne? One *might* excuse the other omissions, but I *ca'n't* get over the chair!"

"What *I* ca'n't get over", said the Empress, in eager sympathy with her angry husband, "is the *table!*"

"Pooh!" said the Emperor.

"It is much to be regretted!" the Professor mildly replied, as soon as he had a chance of speaking. After a moment's thought he strengthened the remark. "*Everything*," he said addressing Society in general, "is *very much* to be regretted!"

A murmur of "Hear, hear!" rose from the crowded Saloon.

There was a rather awkward pause: The Professor evidently didn't know how to begin. The Empress leant forwards, and whispered to him. "A few jokes, you know, Professor—just to put people at their ease!"

"True, true, Madam!" the Professor meekly replied. "This little boy——"

"*Please* don't make any jokes about me!" Bruno exclaimed, his eyes filling with tears.

"I wo'n't if you'd rather I didn't," said the kind-hearted Professor. "It was only something about a Ship's Buoy: a harmless pun—but it doesn't matter." Here he turned to the crowd and addressed them in a loud voice. "Learn your A's!" he shouted. "Your B's! Your C's! and your D's! *Then* you'll be at your ease!"

There was a roar of laughter from all the assembly, and then a great deal of confused whispering. "*What* was it he said? Something about bees, I fancy——"

The Empress smiled in her meaningless way, and fanned herself. The poor Professor looked at her timidly: he was clearly at his wits' end again, and hoping for another hint. The Empress whispered again.

"Some spinach, you know, Professor, as a surprise."

The Professor beckoned to the Head-Cook, and said something to him in a low voice. Then the Head-Cook left the room, followed by all the other cooks.

"It's difficult to get things started," the Professor remarked to Bruno. "When once we get started, it'll go on all right, you'll see."

"If oo want to startle people", said Bruno, "oo should put live frogs on their backs."

Here the cooks all came in again, in a procession, the Head-Cook coming last and carrying something, which the others tried to hide by waving flags all round it. "Nothing but flags, Your Imperial Highness! Nothing but flags!" he kept repeating, as he set it before her. Then all the flags were dropped in a moment, as the Head-Cook raised the cover from an enormous dish.

"What is it?" the Empress said faintly, as she put her spy-glass to her eye. "Why, it's *Spinach*, I declare!"

"Her Imperial Highness is surprised," the Professor explained to the

'Her Imperial Highness is surprised!'

attendants: and some of them clapped their hands. The Head-Cook made a low bow, and in doing so dropped a spoon on the table, as if by accident, just within reach of the Empress, who looked the other way and pretended not to see it.

"I *am* surprised!" the Empress said to Bruno "Aren't you?"

"Not a bit," said Bruno. "I heard——" but Sylvie put her hand over his mouth, and spoke for him. "He's rather tired, I think. He wants the Lecture to begin."

"I want the *supper* to begin," Bruno corrected her.

The Empress took up the spoon in an absent manner, and tried to balance it across the back of her hand, and in doing this she dropped it into the dish: and, when she took it out again, it was full of spinach. "How curious!" she said, and put it into her mouth. "It tastes just like *real* spinach! I thought it was an imitation—but I do believe it's real!" And she took another spoonful.

"It wo'n't be real much longer," said Bruno.

But the Empress had had enough spinach by this time, and somehow—I failed to notice the exact process—we all found ourselves in the Pavilion, and the Professor in the act of beginning the long-expected Lecture.

CHAPTER 21

The Professor's Lecture

"IN SCIENCE—in fact, in most things—it is usually best *to begin at the beginning*. In *some* things, of course, it's better to begin at the *other* end. For instance, if you wanted to paint a dog green, it *might* be best to begin with the *tail*, as it doesn't bite at *that* end. And so——"

"May *I* help oo?" Bruno interrupted.

"Help me do *what*?" said the puzzled Professor, looking up for a moment, but keeping his finger on the book he was reading from, so as not to lose his place.

"To paint a dog green!" cried Bruno. "Oo can begin wiz its *mouf*, and I'll——"

"No, no!" said the Professor. "We haven't got to the *Experiments* yet. And so", returning to his note-book, "I'll give you the Axioms of Science. After that I shall exhibit some Specimens. Then I shall explain a Process or two. And I shall conclude with a few Experiments. An *Axiom*, you know, is a thing that you accept without contradiction. For instance, if I were to say 'Here we are!', that would be accepted without any contradiction, and it's a nice sort of remark to *begin* a conversation with. So it would be an *Axiom*. Or again, supposing I were to say, 'Here we are not!', *that* would be——"

"——a fib!" cried Bruno.

"Oh, *Bruno*!" said Sylvie in a warning whisper. "Of course it would be an *Axiom*, if the Professor said it!"

"——that would be accepted, if people were civil," continued the Professor; "so it would be *another* Axiom."

"It *might* be an Axeldum," Bruno said: "but it wouldn't be *true*!"

"Ignorance of Axioms", the Lecturer continued, "is a great drawback in life. It wastes so much time to have to say them over and over again. For instance, take the Axiom, '*Nothing is greater than itself*'; that is, '*Nothing can contain itself.*' How often you hear people say, 'He was so excited, he was quite unable to contain himself.' Why *of course* he was unable! The *excitement* had nothing to do with it!"

"I say, look here, you know!" said the Emperor, who was getting a little restless. "How many Axioms are you going to give us? At *this* rate, was sha'n't get to the *Experiments* till to-morrow-week!"

"Oh, sooner than *that*, I assure you!" the Professor replied, looking up in alarm. "There are only," (he referred to his notes again) "only *two* more, that are really *necessary*."

"Read 'em out, and get on to the *Specimens*," grumbled the Emperor.

"The *First* Axiom", the Professor read out in a great hurry, "consists of these words, '*Whatever is, is.*' And the Second consists of *these* words, '*Whatever isn't, isn't.*' We will now go on to the *Specimens*. The first tray contains Crystals and other Things." He drew it towards him, and again referred to his notebook. "Some of the labels—owing to insufficient adhesion——" Here he stopped again, and carefully examined the page with his eye-glass. "I ca'n't read the rest of the sentence," he said at last, "but it *means* that the labels have come loose, and the Things have got mixed——"

"Let *me* stick 'em on again!" cried Bruno eagerly, and began licking them, like postage-stamps, and dabbing them down upon the *Crystals* and the other Things. But the Professor hastily moved the tray out of his reach. "They *might* get fixed to the *wrong* Specimens, you know!" he said.

"Oo shouldn't have any *wrong* peppermints in the tray!" Bruno boldly replied. "*Should* he, Sylvie?"

But Sylvie only shook her head.

The Professor heard him not. He had taken up one of the bottles, and was carefully reading the label through his eye-glass. "Our first Specimen——" he announced, as he placed the bottle in front of the other Things, "is—that is, it is called——" here he took it up, and examined the label again, as if he thought it might have changed since he last saw it, "is called Aqua Pura—common water—the fluid that cheers—"

"Hip! Hip! Hip!" the Head-Cook began enthusiastically.

"—but *not* inebriates!" the Professor went on quickly, but only just in time to check the "Hooroar!" which was beginning.

"Our second Specimen", he went on, carefully opening a small jar, "is—" here he removed the lid, and a large beetle instantly darted out, and with an angry buzz went straight out of the Pavilion, "—is—or rather, I should say," looking sadly into the empty jar, "it *was*—a curious kind of Blue Beetle. Did anyone happen to remark—as it went past—three blue spots under each wing?"

Nobody had remarked them.

"Ah, well!" the Professor said with a sigh. "It's a pity. Unless you remark that kind of thing *at the moment*, it's very apt to get overlooked! The *next* Specimen, at any rate, will not fly away! It is—in short, or perhaps, more correctly, at *length*—an *Elephant*. You will observe——"
Here he beckoned to the Gardener to come up on the platform, and with his help began putting together what looked like an enormous dog-kennel, with short tubes projecting out of it on both sides.

"But we've seen *Elephants* before," the Emperor grumbled.

"Yes, but not through a *Megaloscope*!" the Professor eagerly replied. "You know you ca'n't see a *Flea*, properly, without a *magnifying*-glass—what we call a *Microscope*. Well, just in the same way, you ca'n't see an *Elephant*, properly without a *minimifying*-glass. There's one in each of these little tubes. And *this* is a *Megaloscope*! The Gardener will now bring in the next Specimen. Please open *both* curtains, down at the end there, and make way for the Elephant!"

There was a general rush to the sides of the Pavilion, and all eyes were turned to the open end, watching for the return of the Gardener, who had gone away singing "*He thought he saw an Elephant That practised on a Fife!*" There was silence for a minute: and then his harsh voice was heard again in the distance. "*He looked again*—come up then! *He looked again, and found it was*—woa back! *and found it was A letter from his*—make way there! He's a-coming!"

And in marched or waddled—it is hard to say which is the right word—an Elephant, on its hind-legs, and playing on an enormous fife which it held with its fore-feet.

The Professor hastily threw open a large door at the end of the Megaloscope, and the huge animal, at a signal from the Gardener, dropped the fife, and obediently trotted into the machine, the door of which was at once shut by the Professor. "The Specimen is now ready for observation!" he proclaimed. "It is exactly the size of the common Mouse—*Mus Communis!* "

There was a general rush to the tubes, and the spectators watched with delight the minikin creature, as it playfully coiled its trunk round the Professor's extended finger, finally taking its stand upon the palm of his hand, while he carefully lifted it out, and carried it off to exhibit to the Imperial party.

"Isn't it a *darling*?" cried Bruno. "May I stroke it, please? I'll touch it *welly* gently!"

The Empress inspected it solemnly with her eye-glass. "It is very small," she said in a deep voice. "Smaller than elephants usually are, I believe?"

The Professor gave a start of delighted surprise. "Why, that's *true*!" he murmured to himself. Then louder, turning to the audience, "Her Imperial Highness has made a remark which is perfectly sensible!" And a wild cheer arose from that vast multitude.

"The next Specimen", the Professor proclaimed, after carefully placing the little elephant in the tray, among the Crystals and other things, "is a *Flea*, which we will enlarge for the purposes of observation." Taking a small pill-box from the tray, he advanced to the Megaloscope, and reversed all the tubes. "The Specimen is ready!" he cried, with his eye at one of the tubes, while he carefully emptied the pill-box through a little hole at the side. "It is now the size of the Common Horse—*Equus Communis!*"

There was another general rush, to look through the tubes, and the Pavilion rang with shouts of delight, through which the Professor's anxious tones could scarcely be heard. "Keep the door of the Microscope *shut*!" he cried. "If the creature were to escape, *this size*, it would——" But the

mischief was done. The door had swung open, and in another moment the Monster had got out, and was trampling down the terrified, shrieking spectators.

But the Professor's presence of mind did not desert him. "Undraw those curtains!" he shouted. It was done. The Monster gathered its legs together, and in one tremendous bound vanished into the sky.

"Where *is* it?" said the Emperor, rubbing his eyes.

"In the next Province, I fancy," the Professor replied. "That jump would take it at *least* five miles! The next thing is to explain a Process or two. But I find there is hardly room enough to operate—the smaller animal is rather in my way——"

"Who does he mean?" Bruno whispered to Sylvie.

"He means *you!*" Sylvie whispered back. "Hush!"

"Be kind enough to move—angularly—to *this* corner," the Professor said, addressing himself to Bruno.

Bruno hastily moved his chair in the direction indicated. "Did I move angrily enough?" he inquired. But the Professor was once more absorbed in his Lecture, which he was reading from his note-book.

"I will now explain the process of—the name is blotted, I'm sorry to say. It will be illustrated by a number of—of——" here he examined the pages for some time, and at last said "It seems to be either 'Experiments' or 'Specimens'——"

"Let it be *Experiments*," said the Emperor. "We've seen plenty of *Specimens*."

"Certainly, certainly!" the Professor assented. "We will have some Experiments."

"May *I* do them?" Bruno eagerly asked.

"Oh dear no!" The Professor looked dismayed. "I really don't know what would happen if *you* did them!"

"Nor nobody doosn't know what'll happen if *oo* doos them!" Bruno retorted.

"Our First Experiment requires a Machine. It has two knobs—only *two*—you can count them, if you like."

The Head-Cook stepped forwards, counted them, and retired satisfied.

"Now you *might* press those two knobs together—but that's not the way to do it. Or you *might* turn the Machine upside-down—but *that's* not the way to do it!"

"What *are* the way to do it?" said Bruno, who was listening very attentively.

The Professor smiled benignantly. "Ah, yes!" he said, in a voice like the heading of a chapter. "The Way To Do It! Permit me!" and in a moment he had whisked Bruno upon the table. "I divide my subject", he began, "into three parts——"

"I think I'll get down!" Bruno whispered to Sylvie. "It aren't nice to be divided!"

"He hasn't got a knife, silly boy!" Sylvie whispered in reply. "Stand still! You'll break all the bottles!"

"The first part is to take hold of the knobs," putting them into Bruno's hands. "The second part is——" Here he turned the handle, and, with a loud "Oh!", Bruno dropped both the knobs, and began rubbing his elbows.

The Professor chuckled in delight. "It had a sensible effect. *Hadn't* it?" he enquired.

"No, it hadn't a *sensible* effect!" Bruno said indignantly. "It were very silly indeed. It jingled my elbows, and it banged my back, and it crinkled my hair, and it buzzed among my bones!"

"I'm sure it *didn't*!" said Sylvie. "You're only inventing!"

"Oo doesn't know nuffin about it!" Bruno replied. "Oo wasn't there to see. Nobody ca'n't go among my bones. There isn't room!"

"Our Second Experiment", the Professor announced, as Bruno returned to his place, still thoughtfully rubbing his elbows, "is the production of that seldom-seen-but-greatly-to-be-admired phenomenon, Black Light! You have seen White Light, Red Light, Green Light, and so on: but never, till this wonderful day, have any eyes but mine seen *Black Light!* This box", carefully lifting it upon the table, and covering it with a heap of blankets, "is quite full of it. The way I made it was this—I took a lighted candle into a dark cupboard and shut the door. Of course the cupboard was then full of *Yellow* Light. Then I took a bottle of Black ink, and poured it over the candle: and, to my delight, every atom of the Yellow Light turned *Black!* That was indeed the proudest moment of my life! Then I filled a box with it. And now—would anyone like to get under the blankets and see it?"

Dead silence followed this appeal: but at last Bruno said "*I'll* get under, if it won't jingle my elbows."

Satisfied on this point, Bruno crawled under the blankets, and, after a minute or two, crawled out again, very hot and dusty, and with his hair in the wildest confusion.

"What did you see in the box?" Sylvie eagerly enquired.

"I saw *nuffin!*" Bruno sadly replied. "It were too dark!"

"He has described the appearance of the thing exactly!" the Professor exclaimed with enthusiasm. "Black Light, and Nothing, look so extremely alike, at first sight, that I don't wonder he failed to distinguish them! We will now proceed to the Third Experiment."

The Professor came down, and led the way to where a post had been driven firmly into the ground. To one side of the post was fastened a chain, with an iron weight hooked on to the end of it, and from the other side projected a piece of whalebone, with a ring at the end of it. "This is a *most* interesting Experiment!" the Professor announced. "It will need *time*, I'm afraid: but that is a trifling disadvantage. Now observe. If I were to unhook this weight, and let go, it would fall to the ground. You do not deny *that?*"

Nobody denied it.

"And in the same way, if I were to bend this piece of whalebone round the post—thus—and put the ring over this hook—thus—it stays bent: but, if I unhook it, it straightens itself again. You do not deny *that?*"

Again, nobody denied it.

"Well, now, suppose we left things just as they are, for a long time. The force of the *whalebone* would get exhausted, you know, and it would

stay bent, even when you unhooked it. Now, *why* shouldn't the same thing happen with the *weight*? The *whalebone* gets so used to being bent, that it ca'n't *straighten* itself any more. Why shouldn't the *weight* get so used to being held up, that it ca'n't *fall* any more? That's what *I* want to know!"

"That's what *we* want to know!" echoed the crowd.

"How long must we wait?" grumbled the Emperor.

The Professor looked at his watch. "Well, I *think* a thousand years will do to *begin* with," he said. "Then we will cautiously unhook the weight: and, if it *still* shows (as perhaps it will) a *slight* tendency to fall, we will hook it on to the chain again, and leave it for *another* thousand years."

Here the Empress experienced one of those flashes of Common Sense which were the surprise of all around her. "Meanwhile there'll be time for another Experiment," she said.

"There will *indeed*!" cried the delighted Professor. "Let us return to the platform, and proceed to the *Fourth* Experiment!"

"For this concluding Experiment, I will take a certain Alkali, or Acid—I

forget which. Now you'll see what will happen when I mix it with Some—"
here he took up a bottle, and looked at it doubtfully, "—when I mix it
with—with Something——"

Here the Emperor interrupted. "What's the *name* of the stuff?" he
asked.

"I don't remember the *name*," said the Professor: "and the label has
come off." He emptied it quickly into the other bottle, and, with a
tremendous bang, both bottles flew to pieces, upsetting all the machines,
and filling the Pavilion with thick black smoke. I sprang to my feet in
terror, and—and found myself standing before my solitary hearth, where
the poker, dropping at last from the hand of the sleeper, had knocked
over the tongs and the shovel, and had upset the kettle, filling the air with
clouds of steam. With a weary sigh, I betook myself to bed.

CHAPTER 22

The Banquet

"*Heaviness may endure for a night: but joy cometh in the morning.*" The
next day found me quite another being. Even the memories of my lost
friend and companion were sunny as the genial weather that smiled
around me. I did not venture to trouble Lady Muriel, or her father, with
another call so soon: but took a walk into the country, and only turned
homewards when the low sunbeams warned me that day would soon be
over.

On my way home, I passed the cottage where the old man lived, whose
face always recalled to me the day when I first met Lady Muriel; and I
glanced in as I passed, half-curious to see if he were still living there.

Yes: the old man was still alive. He was sitting out in the porch, looking just as he did when I first saw him at Fayfield Junction—it seemed only a few days ago!

"Good evening!" I said, pausing.

"Good evening, Maister!" he cheerfully responded. "Wo'n't ee step in?"

I stepped in, and took a seat on the bench in the porch. "I'm glad to see you looking so hearty," I began. "Last time, I remember, I chanced to pass just as Lady Muriel was coming away from the house. Does she still come to see you?"

"Ees," he answered slowly. "She has na forgotten me. I don't lose her bonny face for many days together. Well I mind the very first time she come, after we'd met at Railway Station. She told me as she come to mak' amends. Dear child! Only think o' that! To mak' amends!"

"To make amends for what?" I enquired. "What could *she* have done to need it?"

"Well, it were loike this, you see? We were both on us a-waiting fur t' train at t' Junction. And I had setten mysen down upat t' bench. And Station-Maister, *he* comes and he orders me off—fur t' mak' room for her Ladyship, you understand?"

"I remember it all," I said. "I was there myself that day."

"*Was* you, now? Well, an' she axes my pardon fur 't. Think o' that, now! *My* Pardon! An owd ne'er-do-weel like me! Ah! She's been here many a time, sin' then. Why, she were in here only yestere'en, as it were, a-sittin', as it might be, where you're a-sitting now, an' lookin' sweeter and kinder nor an angel! An' she says 'You've not got your Minnie, now,' she says, 'to fettle for ye.' Minnie was my grand-daughter, Sir, as lived wi' me. She died, a matter of two months ago—or it may be three. She was a bonny lass—and a good lass, too. Eh, but life has been rare an' lonely without her!"

He covered his face in his hands: and I waited a minute or two, in silence, for him to recover himself.

"So she says, 'Just tak' *me* fur your Minnie!' she says. 'Didna Minnie mak' your tea fur you?' says she. 'Ay,' says I. An' she mak's the tea. 'An' didna Minnie light your pipe?' says she. 'Ay', says I. An' she lights the pipe for me. 'An' didna Minnie set out your tea in t' porch?' An' I says 'My dear,' I says, 'I'm thinking you're Minnie hersen!' An' she cries a bit. We both on us cries a bit——"

Again I kept silence for a while.

"An' while I smokes my pipe, she sits an' talks to me—as loving an' as pleasant! I'll be bound I thowt it were Minnie come again! An' when she gets up to go, I says 'Winnot ye shak' hands wi' me?' says I. An' she says 'Na,' she says: 'a cannot *shak' hands* wi' thee!" she says."

'I'm sorry she said *that*," I put in, thinking it was the only instance I had ever known of pride of rank showing itself in Lady Muriel.

"Bless you, it werena *pride*!" said the old man, reading my thoughts. "She says '*Your* Minnie never *shook hands* wi' you!' she says. 'An' *I'm* your Minnie now,' she says. An' she just puts her dear arms about my neck—and she kisses me on t' cheek—an' may God in Heaven bless her!" And here the poor old man broke down entirely, and could say no more.

The Other Professor's fall

"God bless her!" I echoed. "And good night to you!" I pressed his hand, and left him. "Lady Muriel," I said softly to myself as I went homewards, "truly you know how to 'mak' amends'!"

Seated once more by my lonely fireside, I tried to recall the strange vision of the night before, and to conjure up the face of the dear old Professor among the blazing coals. "That black one—with just a touch of red—would suit him well," I thought. "After such a catastrophe, it would be sure to be covered with black stains—and he would say:

"The result of *that* combination—you may have noticed?—was an *Explosion*! Shall I repeat the Experiment?"

"No, no! Don't trouble yourself!" was the general cry. And we all trooped off, in hot haste, to the Banqueting-Hall, where the feast had already begun.

No time was lost in helping the dishes, and very speedily every guest found his plate filled with good things.

"I have always maintained the principle," the Professor began, "That it is a good rule to take some food—occasionally. The great advantage of dinner-parties——" he broke off suddenly. "Why, actually here's the Other Professor!" he cried. "And there's no place left for him!"

The Other Professor came in reading a large book, which he held close to his eyes. One result of his not looking where he was going was that he tripped up, as he crossed the Saloon, flew up into the air, and fell heavily on his face in the middle of the table.

"*What* a pity!" cried the kind-hearted Professor, as he helped him up.

"It wouldn't be *me*, if I didn't trip," said the Other Professor.

The Professor looked much shocked. "Almost *anything* would be better than *that*!" he exclaimed. "It never does", he added, aside to Bruno, "to be anybody else, does it?"

To which Bruno gravely replied "I's got nuffin on my plate."

The Professor hastily put on his spectacles to make sure that the *facts* were all right, to begin with: then he turned his jolly round face upon the unfortunate owner of the empty plate. "And what would you like next, my little man?"

"Well," Bruno said, a little doubtfully, "I think I'll take some plum-pudding, please—while I think of it."

"Oh, Bruno!" (This was a whisper from Sylvie.) "It isn't good manners to ask for a dish before it comes!"

And Bruno whispered back "But I might forget to ask for some, when it comes, oo know—I *do* forget things, sometimes," he added, seeing Sylvie about to whisper more.

And *this* assertion Sylvie did not venture to contradict.

Meanwhile a chair had been placed for the Other Professor, between the Empress and Sylvie. Sylvie found him a rather uninteresting neighbour: in fact, she couldn't afterwards remember that he had made more than *one* remark to her during the whole banquet, and that was "What a comfort a Dictionary is!" (She told Bruno, afterwards, that she had been too much afraid of him to say more than "Yes, Sir" in reply: and that had been the end of their conversation. On which Bruno expressed a very decided opinion that *that* wasn't worth calling a "conversation" at all. "Oo should have asked him a riddle!" he added triumphantly. "Why, *I* asked the Professor *three* riddles! One was that one you asked me in the morning, 'How many pennies is there in two shillings?' and another was——" "Oh, Bruno!" Sylvie interrupted. "*That* wasn't a riddle!" "It *were!*" Bruno fiercely replied.)

By this time a waiter had supplied Bruno with a plateful of *something*, which drove the plum-pudding out of his head.

"Another advantage of dinner-parties", the Professor cheerfully explained, for the benefit of anyone that would listen, "is that it helps you to *see* your friends. If you want to *see* a man, offer him something to eat. It's the same rule with a mouse."

"This Cat's very kind to the Mouses," Bruno said, stooping to stroke a remarkably fat specimen of the race, that had just waddled into the room, and was rubbing itself affectionately against the leg of his chair. "Please, Sylvie, pour some milk in your saucer. Pussie's ever so thirsty!"

"Why do you want *my* saucer?" Sylvie. "You've got one yourself!"

"Yes, I know," said Bruno: "but I wanted *mine* for to give it some *more* milk in."

Sylvie looked unconvinced: however it seemed quite impossible for her *ever* to refuse what her brother asked: so she quietly filled her saucer with milk, and handed it to Bruno, who got down off his chair to administer it to the cat.

"The room's very hot, with all this crowd," the Professor said to Sylvie. "I wonder why they don't put some lumps of ice in the grate? You fill it with lumps of coal in the winter, you know, and you sit around it and enjoy the warmth. How jolly it would be to fill it now with lumps of ice, and sit round and enjoy the coolth!"

Hot as it was, Sylvie shivered a little at the idea. "It's very cold *outside*," she said. "My feet got almost frozen to-day."

"That's the *shoemaker's* fault!" the Professor cheerfully replied. "How often I've explained to him that he *ought* to make boots with little iron frames under the soles, to hold lamps! But he never *thinks*. No one would suffer from cold, if only they would *think* of those little things. I always use hot ink, myself, in the winter. Very few people ever think of *that*! Yet how simple it is!"

"Yes, it's very simple," Sylvie said politely. "Has the cat had enough?" This was to Bruno, who had brought back the saucer only half-emptied.

But Bruno did not hear the question. "There's somebody scratching at the door and wanting to come in," he said. And he scrambled down off his chair, and went and cautiously peeped out through the door-way.

"Who was it wanted to come in?" Sylvie asked, as he returned to his place.

"It were a Mouse," said Bruno. "And it peepted in. And it saw the Cat. And it said 'I'll come in another day.' And I said 'Oo needn't be flightened. The Cat's *welly* kind to Mouses.' And it said 'But I's got some imporkant business what I *must* attend to.' And it said 'I'll call again to-morrow.' And it said 'Give my love to the Cat.' "

"What a fat cat it is!" said the Lord Chancellor, leaning across the Professor to address his small neighbour. "It's quite a wonder!"

"It was awfully fat when it camed in," said Bruno: "so it would be more wonderfuller if it got thin all in a minute."

"And that was the 'reason, I suppose," the Lord Chancellor suggested, "why you didn't give it the rest of the milk?"

"No," said Bruno. "It was a betterer reason. I tooked the saucer up 'cause it were so discontented!"

"It doesn't look so to *me*," said the Lord Chancellor. "What made you think it was discontented?"

"'Cause it grumbled in its throat."

"Oh, Bruno!" cried Sylvie. "Why, that's the way cats show they're *pleased*!"

Bruno looked doubtful. "It's not a good way," he objected. "Oo wouldn't say *I* were pleased, if I made that noise in my throat!"

"What a singular boy!" the Lord Chancellor whispered to himself: but Bruno had caught the words.

"What do it mean to say '*a singular* boy'?" he whispered to Sylvie.

"It means *one* boy," Sylvie whispered in return. "And *plural* means two or three."

"Then I's welly glad I *is* a singular boy!" Bruno said with great emphasis. "It would be *horrid* to be two or three boys! P'raps they wouldn't play with me!"

"Why *should* they?" said the Other Professor, suddenly waking up out of a deep reverie. "They might be asleep, you know."

"Couldn't, if *I* was awake," Bruno said cunningly.

"Oh, but they might indeed!" the Other Professor protested. "Boys don't all go to sleep at once, you know. So these boys—but who are you talking about?"

"He *never* remembers to ask that first!" the Professor whispered to the children.

"Why, the rest of *me*, a-course!" Bruno exclaimed triumphantly. "Supposing I was two or three boys!"

The Other Professor sighed, and seemed to be sinking back into his reverie; but suddenly brightened up again, and addressed the Professor. "There's nothing more to be done *now*, is there?"

"Well, there's the dinner to finish," the Professor said with a bewildered smile: "and the heat to bear. I hope you'll enjoy the dinner—such as it is; and that you wo'n't mind the heat—such as it isn't."

The sentence *sounded* well, but somehow I couldn't quite understand it; and the Other Professor seemed to be no better off. "Such as it isn't *what*?" he peevishly enquired.

"It isn't as hot as it might be," the Professor replied, catching at the first idea that came to hand.

"Ah, I see what you mean *now*!" the Other Professor graciously remarked. "It's very badly expressed, but I quite see it *now*! Thirteen minutes and a half ago," he went on, looking first at Bruno and then at his watch as he spoke, "you said 'this Cat's very kind to the Mouses.' It must be a singular animal!"

"So it *are*," said Bruno, after carefully examining the Cat, to make sure how many there were of it.

"But how do you know it's kind to the Mouses—or, more correctly speaking, the *Mice*?"

" 'Cause it *plays* with the Mouses," said Bruno; "for to amuse them, oo know."

"But that is just what I *don't* know," the Other Professor rejoined. "My belief is, it plays with them to *kill* them!"

"Oh, that's quite a *accident*!" Bruno began, so eagerly, that it was evident he had already propounded this very difficulty to the Cat. "It 'splained all that to me, while it were drinking the milk. It said 'I teaches the Mouses new games: the Mouses likes it ever so much.' It said 'Sometimes little accidents happens: sometimes the Mouses kills theirselves.' It said 'I's always *welly* sorry, when the Mouses kills theirselves.' It said——"

"If it was so *very* sorry," Sylvie said, rather disdainfully, "it wouldn't *eat* the Mouses after they'd killed themselves!"

But this difficulty, also, had evidently not been lost sight of in the exhaustive ethical discussion just concluded. "It said——" (the orator constantly omitted, as superfluous, his own share in the dialogue, and merely gave us the replies of the Cat) "It said 'Dead Mouses *never* objecks to be eaten.' It said 'There's no use wasting good Mouses.' It said 'Wifful——' sumfinoruvver. It said 'And oo may live to say "How much I wiss I had the Mouse that then I frew away!"' It said——"

"It hadn't *time* to say such a lot of things!" Sylvie interrupted indignantly.

"Oo doesn't know how Cats speaks!" Bruno rejoined contemptuously. "Cats speaks *welly* quick!"

CHAPTER 23

The Pig-Tale

BY this time the appetites of the guests seemed to be nearly satisfied, and even *Bruno* had the resolution to say, when the Professor offered him a fourth slice of plum-pudding, "I thinks three helpings is enough!"

Suddenly the Professor started as if he had been electrified. "Why, I had nearly forgotten the most important part of the entertainment! The Other Professor is to recite a Tale of a Pig—I mean a Pig-Tale," he corrected himself. "It has Introductory Verses at the beginning, and at the end."

"It ca'n't have Introductory Versus at the *end*, can it?" said Sylvie.

"Wait till you hear it," said the Professor: "then you'll see. I'm not sure it hasn't some in the *middle*, as well." Here he rose to his feet, and there was an instant silence through the Banqueting-Hall: they evidently expected a speech.

"Ladies, and gentlemen," the Professor began, "the Other Professor is so kind as to recite a Poem. The title of it is 'The Pig-Tale'. He never recited it before!" (General cheering among the guests.) "He will never recite it again!" (Frantic excitement, and wild cheering all down the hall, the Professor himself mounting the table in hot haste, to lead the cheering, and waving his spectacles in one hand and a spoon in the other.)

Then the Other Professor got up, and began:

> *Little Birds are dining*
> *Warily and well,*
> *Hid in mossy cell:*
> *Hid, I say, by waiters*
> *Gorgeous in their gaiters—*
> *I've a Tale to tell.*

Little Birds are feeding
 Justices with jam,
  Rich in frizzled ham:
Rich, I say, in oysters
Haunting shady cloisters—
  That is what I am.

Little Birds are teaching
 Tigresses to smile,
  Innocent of guile:
Smile, I say, not smirkle—
Mouth a semicircle,
  That's the proper style.

Little Birds are sleeping
 All among the pins,
  Where the loser wins:
Where, I say, he sneezes
When and how he pleases—
  So the Tale begins.

There was a Pig that sat alone
  Beside a ruined Pump:
By day and night he made his moan—
It would have stirred a heart of stone
To see him wring his hoofs and groan,
  Because he could not jump.

A certain Camel heard him shout—
  A Camel with a hump.
"Oh, is it Grief, or is it Gout?
What is this bellowing about?"
That Pig replied, with quivering snout,
  "Because I cannot jump!"

That Camel scanned him, dreamy-eyed.
  "Methinks you are too plump.
I never knew a Pig so wide—
That wobbled so from side to side—
Who could, however much he tried,
  Do such a thing as jump!

"Yet mark those trees, two miles away,
  All clustered in a clump:
If you could trot there twice a day,
Nor ever pause for rest or play,
In the far future—Who can say?—
  You may be fit to jump."

That Camel passed, and left him there,
  Beside the ruined Pump.
Oh, horrid was that Pig's despair!
His shrieks of anguish filled the air.
He wrung his hoofs, he rent his hair,
  Because he could not jump.

There was a Frog that wandered by—
  A sleek and shining lump:
Inspected him with fishy eye,
And said "O Pig, what makes you cry?"
And bitter was that Pig's reply,
  "Because I cannot jump!"

That Frog he grinned a grin of glee,
  And hit his chest a thump.
"O Pig," he said, "be ruled by me,
And you shall see what you shall see.
This minute, for a trifling fee,
  I'll teach you how to jump!

"You may be faint from many a fall,
  And bruised by many a bump:
But, if you persevere through all,
And practise first on something small,
Concluding with a ten-foot wall,
  You'll find that you can jump!"

That Pig looked up with joyful start:
  "Oh Frog, you are a trump!
Your words have healed my inward smart—
Come, name your fee and do your part:
Bring comfort to a broken heart,
  By teaching me to jump!"

"My fee shall be a mutton-chop,
  My goal this ruined Pump.
Observe with what an airy flop
I plant myself upon the top!
Now bend your knees and take a hop,
  For that's the way to jump!"

Uprose that Pig, and rushed, full whack,
  Against the ruined Pump:
Rolled over like an empty sack,
And settled down upon his back,
While all his bones at once went "Crack!"
  It was a fatal jump.

When the Other Professor had recited this Verse, he went across to the fire-place, and put his head up the chimney. In doing this, he lost his balance, and fell head-first into the empty grate, and got so firmly fixed there that it was some time before he could be dragged out again.

Bruno had had time to say "I thought he wanted to see how many peoples was up the chimbley."

And Sylvie had said "*Chimney*—not chimbley."

And Bruno had said "Don't talk 'ubbish!"

All this, while the Other Professor was being extracted.

"You must have blacked your face!" the Empress said anxiously. "Let me send for some soap?"

"Thanks, no," said the Other Professor, keeping his face turned away. "Black's quite a respectable colour. Besides, soap would be no use without water——"

Keeping his back well turned away from the audience, he went on with the Introductory Verses:

Little Birds are writing
Interesting books,
To be read by cooks:
Read, I say, not roasted—
Letterpress, when toasted,
Loses its good looks.

Little Birds are playing
Bagpipes on the shore,
Where the tourists snore:
"Thanks!" they cry. "'Tis thrilling!
Take, oh take this shilling!
Let us have no more!"

Little Birds are bathing
Crocodiles in cream,
Like a happy dream:
Like, but not so lasting—
Crocodiles, when fasting,
Are not all they seem!

That Camel passed, as Day grew dim
  Around the ruined Pump.
"O broken heart! O broken limb!
It needs", that Camel said to him,
"Something more fairy-like and slim,
  To execute a jump!"

That Pig lay still as any stone,
  And could not stir a stump:
Nor ever, if the truth were known,
Was he again observed to moan,
Nor ever wring his hoofs and groan,
  Because he could not jump.

That Frog made no remark, for he
Was dismal as a dump:
He knew the consequence must be
That he would never get his fee—
And still he sits, in miserie,
Upon that ruined Pump!

"It's a miserable story!" said Bruno. "It begins miserably, and it ends miserablier. I think I shall cry. Sylvie, please lend me your handkerchief."

"I haven't got it with me," Sylvie whispered.

"Then I wo'n't cry," said Bruno manfully.

"There are more Introductory Verses to come," said the Other Professor, "but I'm hungry." He sat down, cut a large slice of cake, put it on Bruno's plate, and gazed at his own empty plate in astonishment.

"Where did you get that cake?" Sylvie whispered to Bruno.

"He gived it me," said Bruno.

"But you shouldn't ask for things! You *know* you shouldn't!"

"I didn't ask," said Bruno, taking a fresh mouthful: "he *gived* it me."

Sylvie considered this for a moment: then she saw her way out of it. "Well, then, ask him to give *me* some!"

"You seem to enjoy that cake?" the Professor remarked.

"Doos that mean 'munch'?" Bruno whispered to Sylvie.

Sylvie nodded. "It means 'to munch' and 'to *like* to munch'."

Bruno smiled at the Professor. "I *doos* enjoy it," he said.

The Other Professor caught the word. "And I hope you're enjoying *yourself*, little Man?" he enquired.

Bruno's look of horror quite startled him. "No, *indeed* I aren't!" he said.

The Other Professor looked thoroughly puzzled. "Well, well!" he said. "Try some cowslip wine!" And he filled a glass and handed it to Bruno. "Drink this, my dear, and you'll be quite another man!"

"Who shall I be?" said Bruno, pausing in the act of putting it to his lips.

"Don't ask so many questions!" Sylvie interposed, anxious to save the poor old man from further bewilderment. "Suppose we get the Professor to tell us a story."

Bruno adopted the idea with enthusiasm. "*Please* do!" he cried eagerly. "Sumfin about tigers—and bumble-bees—and robin-redbreasts, oo knows!"

"Why should you always have *live* things in stories?" said the Professor. "Why don't you have events, or circumstances?"

"Oh, *please* invent a story like that!" cried Bruno.

The Professor began fluently enough. "Once a coincidence was taking a walk with a little accident, and they met an explanation—a *very* old explanation—so old that it was quite doubled up, and looked more like a conundrum——" he broke off suddenly.

"*Please* go on!" both children exclaimed.

The Professor made a candid confession. "It's a very difficult sort to invent, I find. Suppose Bruno tells one, first."

Bruno was only too happy to adopt the suggestion.

"Once there were a Pig, and a Accordion, and two jars of Orange-marmalade——"

"The *dramatis personæ*," murmured the Professor. "Well, what then?"

"So, when the Pig played on the Accordion," Bruno went on, "one of the Jars of Orange-marmalade didn't like the tune, and the other Jar of Orange-marmalade did like the tune—I *know* I shall get confused among those Jars of Orange-marmalade, Sylvie!" he whispered anxiously.

"I will now recite the other Introductory Verses," said the Other Professor.

Little Birds are choking
 Baronets with bun,
 Taught to fire a gun:
Taught, I say, to splinter
Salmon in the winter—
 Merely for the fun.

Little Birds are hiding
 Crimes in carpet-bags,
 Blessed by happy stags:
Blessed, I say, though beaten—
Since our friends are eaten
 When the memory flags.

Little Birds are tasting
 Gratitude and gold,
 Pale with sudden cold:
Pale, I say, and wrinkled—
When the bells have tinkled,
 And the Tale is told.

"The next thing to be done", the Professor cheerfully remarked to the Lord Chancellor, as soon as the applause, caused by the recital of the Pig-Tale, had come to an end, "is to drink the Emperor's health, is it not?"

"Undoubtedly!" the Lord Chancellor replied with much solemnity, as he rose to his feet to give the necessary directions for the ceremony. "Fill your glasses!" he thundered. All did so, instantly. "Drink the Emperor's health!" A general gurgling resounded all through the Hall. "Three cheers for the Emperor!" The faintest possible sound followed *this* announcement: and the Chancellor, with admirable presence of mind, instantly proclaimed "A speech from the Emperor!"

The Emperor had begun his speech almost before the words were uttered. "However unwilling to be Emperor—since you all wish me to be Emperor—you know how badly the late Warden managed things—with such enthusiasm as you have shown—he persecuted you—he taxed you too heavily—you know who is fittest man to be Emperor—my brother had no sense——"

How long this curious speech might have lasted it is impossible to say, for just at this moment a hurricane shook the palace to its foundations, bursting open the windows, extinguishing some of the lamps, and filling the air with clouds of dust, which took strange shapes in the air, and seemed to form words.

But the storm subsided as suddenly as it had risen—the casements swung into their places again: the dust vanished: all was as it had been a minute ago—with the exception of the Emperor and Empress, over whom had come a wondrous change. The vacant stare, the meaningless smile, had passed away: all could see that these two strange beings had returned to their senses.

The Emperor continued his speech as if there had been no interruption. "And we have behaved—my wife and I—like two arrant Knaves. We deserve no better name. When my brother went away, you lost the best Warden you ever had. And I've been doing my best, wretched hypocrite that I am, to cheat you into making me an Emperor. Me! One that has hardly got the wits to be a shoe-black!"

The Lord Chancellor wrung his hands in despair. "He is mad, good people!" he was beginning. But both speeches stopped suddenly—and, in the dead silence that followed, a knocking was heard at the outer door.

"What is it?" was the general cry. People began running in and out. The excitement increased every moment. The Lord Chancellor, forgetting all the rules of Court-ceremony, ran full speed down the hall, and in a minute returned, pale and gasping for breath.

CHAPTER 24

The Beggar's Return

"YOUR Imperial Highnesses!" he began. "It's the old Beggar again! Shall we set the dogs at him?"

"Bring him here!" said the Emperor.

The Chancellor could scarcely believe his ears. "*Here*, your Imperial Highness? Did I rightly understand——"

"Bring him here!" the Emperor thundered once more. The Chancellor tottered down the hall—and in another minute the crowd divided, and the poor old Beggar was seen entering the Banqueting-Hall.

He was indeed a pitiable object: the rags, that hung about him, were all splashed with mud: his white hair and his long beard were tossed about in wild disorder. Yet he walked upright, with a stately tread, as if used to command: and—strangest sight of all—Sylvie and Bruno came with him, clinging to his hands, and gazing at him with looks of silent love.

Men looked eagerly to see how the Emperor would receive the bold intruder. Would he hurl him from the steps of the daïs? But no. To their utter astonishment, the Emperor knelt as the beggar approached, and with bowed head murmured "Forgive us!"

"Forgive us!" the Empress, kneeling at her husband's side, meekly repeated.

The Outcast smiled. "Rise up!" he said. "I forgive you!" And men saw with wonder that a change had passed over the old beggar, even as he spoke. What had seemed, but now, to be vile rags and splashes of mud, were seen to be in truth kingly trappings, broidered with gold, and sparkling with gems. All knew him now, and bent low before the Elder Brother, the true Warden.

"Brother mine, and Sister mine!" the Warden began, in a clear voice that was heard all through that vast hall. "I come not to disturb you. Rule on, as Emperor, and rule wisely. For I am chosen King of Elfland. To-morrow I return there, taking nought from thence, save only—save

only——" his voice trembled, and with a look of ineffable tenderness, he laid his hands in silence on the heads of the two little ones who clung around him.

But he recovered himself in a moment, and beckoned to the Emperor to resume his place at the table. The company seated themselves again—room being found for the Elfin-King between his two children—and the Lord Chancellor rose once more, to propose the next toast.

"The next toast—the hero of the day—why, he isn't here!" he broke off in wild confusion.

Good gracious! Everybody had forgotten Prince Uggug!

"He was told of the Banquet, of course?" said the Emperor.

"Undoubtedly!" replied the Chancellor. "*That* would be the duty of the Gold Stick in Waiting."

"Let the Gold Stick come forwards!" the Emperor gravely said.

The Gold Stick came forwards. "I attended on His Imperial Fatness," was the statement made by the trembling official. "I told him of the Lecture and the Banquet——."

"What followed!" said the Emperor: for the unhappy man seemed almost too frightened to go on.

"His Imperial Fatness was graciously pleased to be sulky. His Imperial Fatness was graciously pleased to box my ears. His Imperial Fatness was graciously pleased to say 'I don't care!' "

" 'Don't-care' came to a bad end," Sylvie whispered to Bruno. "I'm not sure, but I *believe* he was hanged."

The Professor overheard her. "*That* result", he blandly remarked, "was merely a case of mistaken identity."

Both children looked puzzled.

"Permit me to explain. 'Don't-care' and 'Care' were twin-brothers. 'Care', you know, killed the Cat. And they caught 'Don't-care' by mistake, and hanged him instead. And so 'Care' is alive still. But he's very unhappy without his brother. That's why they say 'Begone, dull Care!' "

"Thank you!" Sylvie said, heartily. "It's very extremely interesting. Why, it seems to explain *everything*!"

"Well, not quite *everything*," the Professor modestly rejoined. "There are two or three scientific difficulties—"

"What was your general impression as to His Imperial Fatness?" the Emperor asked the Gold Stick.

"My impression was that His Imperial Fatness was getting more——"

"More *what*?"

All listened breathlessly for the next word.

"More PRICKLY!"

"He must be sent for *at once*!" the Emperor exclaimed. And the Gold Stick went off like a shot. The Elfin-King sadly shook his head. "No use, no use!" he murmured to himself. "Loveless, loveless!"

Pale, trembling, speechless, the Gold Stick came slowly back again.

"Well?" said the Emperor. "Why does not the Prince appear?"

"One can easily guess," said the Professor. "His Imperial Fatness is, without doubt, a little preoccupied."

Bruno turned a look of solemn enquiry on his old friend. "What do that word mean?"

But the Professor took no notice of the question. He was eagerly listening to the Gold Stick's reply.

"Please your Highness! His Imperial Fatness is——" Not a word more could he utter.

'Porcupine!'

The Empress rose in an agony of alarm. "Let us go to him!" she cried. And there was a general rush for the door.

Bruno slipped off his chair in a moment. "May we go too?" he eagerly asked. But the King did not hear the question, as the Professor was speaking to him. "*Preoccupied*, your Majesty!" he was saying. "That is what he is, no doubt!"

"May we go and see him?" Bruno repeated. The King nodded assent, and the children ran off. In a minute or two they returned, slowly and gravely. "Well?" said the King. "What's the matter with the Prince?"

"He's—what *you* said," Bruno replied looking at the Professor. "That hard word." And he looked to Sylvie for assistance.

"Porcupine," said Sylvie.

"No, no!" the Professor corrected her. " '*Pre-occupied*,' you mean."

"No, it's *porcupine*," persisted Sylvie. "Not that other word at all. And please will you come? The house is all in an uproar." ("And oo'd better bring an uproar-glass wiz oo!" added Bruno.)

We got up in great haste, and followed the children upstairs. No one took the least notice of *me*, but I wasn't at all surprised at this, as I had long realized that I was quite invisible to them all—even to Sylvie and Bruno.

All along the gallery, that led to the Prince's apartment, an excited crowd was surging to and fro, and the Babel of voices was deafening: against the door of the room three strong men were leaning, vainly trying to shut it—for some great animal inside was constantly bursting it half open, and we had a glimpse, before the men could push it back again, of the head of a furious wild beast, with great fiery eyes and gnashing teeth. Its voice was a sort of mixture—there was the roaring of a lion, and the bellowing of a bull, and now and then a scream like a gigantic parrot. "There is no judging by the voice!" the Professor cried in great excitement. "What is it?" he shouted to the men at the door. And a general chorus of voices answered him "Porcupine! Prince Uggug has turned into a Porcupine!"

"A new Specimen!" exclaimed the delighted Professor. "Pray let me go in. It should be labeled at once!"

But the strong men only pushed him back. "Label it, indeed! Do you want to be eaten up?" they cried.

"Never mind about Specimens, Professor!" said the Emperor, pushing his way through the crowd. "Tell us how to keep him safe!"

"A large cage!" the Professor promptly replied. "Bring a large cage," he said to the people generally, "with strong bars of steel, and a portcullis made to go up and down like a mouse-trap! Does anyone happen to have such a thing about him?"

It didn't sound a likely sort of thing for anyone to have about him; however, they brought him one directly: curiously enough, there happened to be one standing in the gallery.

"Put it facing the opening of the door, and draw up the portcullis!" This was done in a moment.

"Blankets now!" cried the Professor. "This is a most interesting Experiment!"

There happened to be a pile of blankets close by: and the Professor had hardly said the word, when they were all unfolded and held up like curtains all around. The Profesor rapidly arranged them in two rows, so as to make a dark passage, leading straight from the door to the mouth of the cage.

"Now fling the door open!" This did not need to be done: the three men had only to leap out of the way, and the fearful monster flung the door open for itself, and, with a yell like the whistle of a steam-engine, rushed into the cage.

"Down with the portcullis!" No sooner said than done: and all breathed freely once more, on seeing the Porcupine safely caged.

The Professor rubbed his hands in childish delight. "The Experiment has succeeded!" he proclaimed. "All that is needed now is to feed it three times a day, on chopped carrots and——"

"Never mind about its food, just now!" the Emperor interrupted. "Let us return to the Banquet. Brother, will you lead the way?" And the old man, attended by his children, headed the procession down stairs. "See the fate of a loveless life!" he said to Bruno, as they returned to their places. To which Bruno made reply, "I always loved Sylvie, so I'll never get prickly like that!"

"He *is* prickly, certainly," said the Professor, who had caught the last words, "but we must remember that, however porcupiny, he is royal still! After this feast is over, I'm going to take a little present to Prince Uggug—just to soothe him, you know: it isn't pleasant living in a cage."

"What'll you give him for a birthday-present?" Bruno enquired.

"A small saucer of chopped carrots," replied the Professor. "In giving birthday-presents, *my* motto is—cheapness! I should think I save forty pounds a year by giving—oh, *what* a twinge of pain!"

"My old enemy!" groaned the Professor, "Lumbago—rheumatism—that sort of thing. I think I'll go and lie down a bit." And he hobbled out of the Saloon, watched by the pitying eyes of the two children.

"He'll be better soon!" the Elfin-King said cheerily. "Brother!" turning to the Emperor, "I have some business to arrange with you to-night. The Empress will take care of the children." And the two Brothers went away together, arm-in-arm.

The Empress found the children rather sad company. They could talk of nothing but "the dear Professor", and "what a pity he's so ill", till at last she made the welcome proposal "Let's go and see him!"

The children eagerly grasped the hands she offered them: and we went off to the Professor's study, and found him lying on the sofa, covered up with blankets, and reading a little manuscript-book. "Notes on Vol. Three!" he murmured, looking up at us. And there, on a table near him, lay the book he was seeking when first I saw him.

"And how are you now, Professor?" the Empress asked, bending over the invalid.

The Professor looked up, and smiled feebly. "As devoted to your Imperial Highness as ever!" he said in a weak voice. "All of me, that is not Lumbago, is Loyalty!"

"A sweet sentiment!" the Empress exclaimed with tears in her eyes. "You seldom hear anything so beautiful as that—even in a Valentine!"

"We must take you to stay at the seaside," Sylvie said, tenderly. "It'll do you ever so much good! And the Sea's so grand!"

"But a Mountain's grander!" said Bruno.

"What is there grand about the Sea?" said the Professor. "Why, you could put it all into a teacup!"

"*Some* of it," Sylvie corrected him.

"Well, you'd only want a certain number of teacups to hold it *all*. And *then* where's the grandeur? Then as to a Mountain—why, you could carry it all away in a wheelbarrow, in a certain number of years!"

"It wouldn't look grand—the bits of it in the wheelbarrow," Sylvie candidly admitted.

"But when oo put it together again——" Bruno began.

"When you're older," said the Professor, "you'll know that you *ca'n't* put Mountains together again so easily! One lives and one learns, you know!"

"But it needn't be the *same* one, need it?" said Bruno. "Wo'n't it do, if *I* live, and if *Sylvie* learns?"

"I *ca'n't* learn without living!" said Sylvie.

"But I *can* live without learning!" Bruno retorted. "Oo just try me!"

"What I meant, was—" the Professor began, looking much puzzled, "—was—that you don't know *everything*, you know."

"But I *do* know everything I know!" persisted the little fellow. "I know ever so many things! Everything, 'cept the things I *don't* know. And Sylvie knows all the rest."

The Professor sighed, and gave it up. "Do you know what a Boojum is?"

"*I* know!" cried Bruno. "It's the thing what wrenches people out of their boots!"

"He means 'bootjack'," Sylvie explained in a whisper.

"You ca'n't wrench people out of *boots*," the Professor mildly observed.

Bruno laughed saucily. "Oo *can*, though! Unless they're *welly* tight in."

"Once upon a time there was a Boojum——" the Professor began, but stopped suddenly. "I forget the rest of the Fable," he said. "And there was a lesson to be learned from it. I'm afraid I forget *that* too."

"*I'll* tell oo a Fable!" Bruno began in a great hurry. "Once there were a Locust, and a Magpie, and a Engine-driver. And the Lesson is, to learn to get up early——"

"It isn't a bit interesting!" Sylvie said contemptuously. "You shouldn't put the Lesson so soon."

"When did you invent that Fable?" said the Professor. "Last week?"

"No!" said Bruno. "A deal shorter ago than that, Guess again!"

"I ca'n't guess," said the Professor. "How long ago?"

"Why, it isn't invented yet!" Bruno exclaimed triumphantly. "But I *have* invented a lovely one! Shall I say it?"

"If you've *finished* inventing it," said Sylvie. "And let the Lesson be 'to try again'!"

"No," said Bruno with great decision. "The Lesson are '*not* to try again'!" "Once there were a lovely china man, what stood on the chimbley-piece. And he stood, and he stood. And one day he tumbleded off, and he didn't hurt his self one bit. Only he *would* try again. And the next time he tumbleded off, he hurted his self welly much, and breaked off ever so much varnish."

"But how did he come back on the chimney-piece after his first tumble?" said the Empress. (It was the first sensible question she had asked in all her life.)

"*I* put him there!" cried Bruno.

"Then I'm afraid you know something about his tumbling," said the Professor. "Perhaps you pushed him?"

To which Bruno replied, very seriously, "Didn't pushed him *much*—he were a *lovely* china man," he added hastily, evidently very anxious to change the subject.

"Come, my children!" said the Elfin-King, who had just entered the

room. "We must have a little chat together, before you go to bed." And he was leading them away, but at the door they let go his hands, and ran back again to wish the Professor good night.

"Good night, Professor, good night!" And Bruno solemnly shook hands with the old man, who gazed at him with a loving smile, while Sylvie bent down to press her sweet lips upon his forehead.

"Good night, little ones!" said the Professor. "You may leave me now—to ruminate. I'm as jolly as the day is long, except when it's necessary to ruminate on some very difficult subject. All of me," he murmured sleepily as we left the room, "all of me, that isn't *Bonhommie*, is Rumination!"

"*What* did he say, Bruno?" Sylvie enquired, as soon as we were safely out of hearing.

"I *think* he said 'All of me that isn't Bone-disease is Rheumatism.' Whatever *are* that knocking, Sylvie?"

Sylvie stopped, and listened anxiously. It sounded like some one kicking at a door, "I *hope* it isn't that Porcupine breaking loose!" she exclaimed.

"Let's go on!" Bruno said hastily. "There's nuffin to wait for, oo know!"

CHAPTER 25

Life Out of Death

THE sound of kicking, or knocking, grew louder every moment: and at last a door opened somewhere near us. "Did you say 'come in!' Sir?" my landlady asked timidly.

"Oh yes, come in!" I replied. "What's the matter?"

"A note has just been left for you, Sir, by the baker's boy. He said he was passing the Hall, and they asked him to come round and leave it here."

The note contained five words only. "Please come at once. Muriel."

A sudden terror seemed to chill my very heart. "The Earl is ill!" I said to myself. "Dying, perhaps!" And I hastily prepared to leave the house.

"No bad news, Sir, I hope?" my landlady said, as she saw me out. "The boy said as some one had arrived unexpectedly——"

"I hope that is it!" I said. But my feelings were those of fear rather than of hope: though, on entering the house, I was somewhat reassured by finding luggage lying in the entrance, bearing the initials "E. L."

"It's only Eric Lindon after all!" I thought, half relieved and half annoyed. "Surely she need not have sent for me for *that*!"

Lady Muriel met me in the passage. Her eyes were gleaming—but it was the excitement of joy, rather than of grief. "I have a surprise for you!" she whispered.

"You mean that Eric Lindon is here?" I said, vainly trying to disguise the involuntarily bitterness of my tone. " '*The funeral baked meats did coldly furnish forth the marriage-tables*,' " I could not help repeating to myself. How cruelly I was misjudging her!

"No, no!" she eagerly replied. "At least—Eric *is* here. But——" her voice quivered, "but there is *another*!"

No need for further question. I eagerly followed her in. There on the bed, he lay—pale and worn—the mere shadow of his old self—my old friend come back again from the dead!

"Arthur!" I exclaimed. I could not say another word.

"Yes, back again, old boy!" he murmured, smiling as I grasped his hand. "*He*", indicating Eric, who stood near, "saved my life—*He* brought me back. Next to God, we must thank *him*, Muriel, my wife!"

Silently I shook hands with Eric, and with the Earl: and with one consent we moved into the shaded side of the room, where we could talk without disturbing the invalid, who lay, silent and happy, holding his wife's hand in his, and watching her with eyes that shone with the deep steady light of Love.

"He has been delirious till to-day," Eric explained in a low voice: "and even to-day he has been wandering more than once. But the sight of *her* has been new life to him." And then he went on to tell us, in would-be careless tones—I knew how he hated any display of feeling—how he had insisted on going back to the plague-stricken town, to bring away a man whom the doctor had abandoned as dying, but who *might*, he fancied, recover if brought to the hospital: how he had seen nothing in the wasted features to remind him of Arthur, and only recognized him when he visited the hospital a month after: how the doctor had forbidden him to announce the discovery, saying that any shock to the over-taxed brain might kill him at once: how he had stayed on at the hospital, and nursed the sick man by night and day—all this with the studied indifference of one who is relating the common-place acts of some chance acquaintance!

"And this was his *rival*!" I thought. "The man who had won from him the heart of the woman he loved!"

"The sun is setting," said Lady Muriel, rising and leading the way to the open window. "Just look at the western sky? What lovely crimson tints! We shall have a glorious day to-morrow——" We had followed her across the room, and were standing in a little group, talking in low tones in the gathering gloom, when we were startled by the voice of the sick man, murmuring words too indistinct for the ear to catch.

"He is wandering again," Lady Muriel whispered, and returned to the bedside. We drew a little nearer also: but no, this had none of the incoherence of delirium. "*What reward shall I give unto the Lord*", the tremulous lips were saying, "*for all the benefits that He hath done unto me? I will receive the cup of salvation, and call—and call——*" but here the poor weakened memory failed, and the feeble voice died into silence.

His wife knelt down at the bedside, raised one of his arms, and drew

'His wife knelt down at his side'

it across her own, fondly kissing the thin white hand that lay so listlessly in her loving grasp. It seemed to me a good opportunity for stealing away without making her go through any form of parting: so, nodding to the Earl and Eric, I silently left the room. Eric followed me down the stairs, and out into the night.

"Is it Life or Death?" I asked him, as soon as we were far enough from the house for me to speak in ordinary tones.

"It is *Life*!" he replied with eager emphasis. "The doctors are quite agreed as to *that*. All he needs now, they say, is rest, and perfect quiet, and good nursing. He's quite sure to get rest and quiet, here: and, as for the nursing, why, I think it's just *possible*——" (he tried hard to make his trembling voice assume a playful tone) "he may even get fairly well nursed, in his present quarters!"

"I'm sure of it!" I said. "Thank you so much for coming out to tell me!" And, thinking he had now said all he had come to say, I held out my hand to bid him good night. He grasped it warmly, and added, turning his face away as he spoke, "By the way, there is one other thing I wanted to say. I thought you'd like to know that—that I'm not—not in the mind I was in when last we met. It isn't—that I can accept Christian belief—at least, not yet. But all this came about so strangely. And she had prayed, you know. And I had prayed. And—and" his voice broke, and I could only just catch the concluding words, "*there is a God that answers prayer! I know it for certain now.*" He wrung my hand once more, and left me suddenly. Never before had I seen him so deeply moved.

So, in the gathering twilight, I paced slowly homewards, in a tumultuous whirl of happy thoughts: my heart seemed full, and running over, with joy and thankfulness: all that I had so fervently longed for, and prayed for, seemed now to have come to pass. And, though I reproached myself, bitterly, for the unworthy suspicion I had for one moment harboured against the true-hearted Lady Muriel, I took comfort in knowing it had been but a passing thought.

Not Bruno himself could have mounted the stairs with so buoyant a step, as I felt my way up in the dark, not pausing to strike a light in the entry, as I knew I had left the lamp burning in my sitting-room.

But it was no common *lamplight* into which I now stepped, with a strange, new, dreamy sensation of some subtle witchery that had come over the place. Light, richer and more golden than any lamp could give, flooded the room, streaming in from a window I had somehow never noticed before, and lighting up a group of three shadowy figures, that grew momently more distinct—a grave old man in royal robes, leaning back in an easy chair, and two children, a girl and a boy, standing at his side.

"Have you the Jewel still, my child?" the old man was saying.

"Oh, *yes!*" Sylvie exclaimed with unusual eagerness. "Do you think I'd *ever* lose it or forget it?" She undid the ribbon round her neck, as she spoke, and laid the Jewel in her father's hand.

Bruno looked at it admiringly. "What a lovely brightness!" he said. "It's just like a little red star! May I take it in my hand?"

Sylvie nodded: and Bruno carried it off to the window, and held it aloft against the sky, whose deepening blue was already spangled with stars. Soon he came running back in some excitement. "Sylvie! Look here!" he cried. "I can see right through it when I hold it up to the sky. And it isn't red a bit: it's, oh such a lovely blue! And the words are all different! Do look at it!"

Sylvie was quite excited, too, by this time; and the two children eagerly held up the Jewel to the light, and spelled out the legend between them, "ALL WILL LOVE SYLVIE."

"Why, this is the *other* Jewel!" cried Bruno. "Don't you remember, Sylvie? The one you *didn't* choose!"

Sylvie took it from him, with a puzzled look, and held it, now up to the light, now down. "It's blue, *one* way," she said softly to herself, "and it's red the *other* way! Why, I thought there were *two* of them—Father!" she suddenly exclaimed, laying the Jewel once more in his hand, "I do believe it was the *same* Jewel all the time!"

"Then you choosed it from *itself*," Bruno thoughtfully remarked. "Father, *could* Sylvie choose a thing from itself?"

"Yes, my own one," the old man replied to Sylvie, not noticing Bruno's embarrassing question, "it *was* the same Jewel—but you chose quite right." And he fastened the ribbon round her neck again.

"SYLVIE WILL LOVE ALL—ALL WILL LOVE SYLVIE." Bruno murmured, raising himself on tiptoe to kiss the "little red star". "And, when you look *at* it, it's red and fierce like the sun—and, when you look *through* it, it's gentle and blue like the sky!"

"God's own sky," Sylvie said, dreamily.

"God's own sky," the little fellow repeated, as they stood, lovingly clinging together, and looking out into the night. "But oh, Sylvie, what makes the sky such a *darling* blue?"

Sylvie's sweet lips shaped themselves to reply, but her voice sounded faint and very far away. The vision was fast slipping from my eager gaze:

but it seemed to me, in that last bewildering moment, that not Sylvie but an angel was looking out through those trustful brown eyes, and that not Sylvie's but an angel's voice was whispering

"IT IS LOVE."

V

A Tangled Tale

with six illustrations by
Arthur B. Frost

TO MY PUPIL

Beloved Pupil! Tamed by thee,
    Addish-, Subtrac-, Multiplica-tion,
Division, Fractions, Rule of Three,
    Attest thy deft manipulation!

Then onward! Let the voice of Fame
    From Age to Age repeat thy story,
Till thou hast won thyself a name
    Exceeding even Euclid's glory.

Preface

THIS Tale originally appeared as a serial in *The Monthly Packet* beginning in April 1880. The writer's intention was to embody in each Knot (like the medicine so dexterously, but ineffectually, concealed in the jam of our early childhood) one or more mathematical questions—in Arithmetic, Algebra, or Geometry, as the case might be—for the amusement, and possible edification, of the fair readers of that magazine.

L. C.

December 1885.

"At a pace of six miles in the hour"

A Tangled Tale

KNOT I

Excelsior

Goblin, lead them up and down

THE ruddy glow of sunset was already fading into the sombre shadows of night, when two travelers might have been observed swiftly—at a pace of six miles in the hour—descending the rugged side of a mountain; the younger bounding from crag to crag with the agility of a fawn, while his companion, whose aged limbs seemed ill at east in the heavy chain armour habitually worn by tourists in that district, toiled on painfully at his side.

As is always the case under such circumstances, the younger knight was the first to break the silence.

"A goodly pace, I trow!" he exclaimed. "We sped not thus in the ascent!"

"Goodly, indeed!" the other echoed with a groan. "We clomb it but at three miles in the hour."

"And on the dead level our pace is——?" the younger suggested; for he was weak in statistics, and left all such details to his aged companion.

"Four miles in the hour," the other wearily replied. "Not an ounce more," he added, with that love of metaphor so common in old age, "and not a farthing less!"

" 'Twas three hours past high noon when we left our hostelry," the young man said, musingly. "We shall scarce be back by supper-time. Perchance mine host will roundly deny us all food!"

"He will chide our tardy return," was the grave reply, "and such a rebuke will be meet."

"A brave conceit!" cried the other, with a merry laugh. "And should we bid him bring us yet another course, I trow his answer will be tart!"

"We shall but get our deserts," sighed the elder knight, who had never seen a joke in his life, and was somewhat displeased at his companion's untimely levity. " 'Twill be nine of the clock", he added in an undertone, "by the time we regain our hostelry. Full many a mile shall we have plodded this day!"

"How many? How many?" cried the eager youth, ever athirst for knowledge.

The old man was silent.

"Tell me", he answered, after a moment's thought, "what time it was when we stood together on yonder peak. Not exact to the minute!" he added hastily, reading a protest in the young man's face. "An thy guess be within one poor half-hour of the mark, 'tis all I ask of thy mother's son! Then will I tell thee, true to the last inch, how far we shall have trudged betwixt three and nine of the clock."

A groan was the young man's only reply; while his convulsed features and the deep wrinkles that chased each other across his manly brow, revealed the abyss of arithmetical agony into which one chance question had plunged him.

KNOT 2

Eligible Apartments

> *Straight down the crooked lane,*
> *And all round the square.*

"LET'S ask Balbus about it," said Hugh.

"All right," said Lambert.

"*He* can guess it," said Hugh.

"Rather," said Lambert.

No more words were needed: the two brothers understood each other perfectly.

Balbus was waiting for them at the hotel: the journey down had tired him, he said: so his two pupils had been the round of the place, in search of lodgings, without the old tutor who had been their inseparable companion from their childhood. They had named him after the hero of their Latin exercise-book, which overflowed with anecdotes of that versatile genius—anecdotes whose vagueness in detail was more than compensated by their sensational brilliance. "Balbus has overcome all his enemies" had been marked by their tutor, in the margin of the book, "Successful Bravery." In this way he had tried to extract a moral from every anecdote about Balbus—sometimes one of warning, as in, "Balbus had borrowed a healthy dragon," against which he had written, "Rashness in Speculation"—sometimes of encouragement, as in the words, "Influence of Sympathy in United Action," which stood opposite to the anecdote, "Balbus was assisting his mother-in-law to convince the dragon"—and sometimes it dwindled down to a single word, such as "Prudence", which was all he could extract from the touching record that "Balbus, having scorched the tail of the dragon, went away". His pupils liked the short morals best, as it left them more room for marginal illustrations, and in this instance they required all the space they could get to exhibit the rapidity of the hero's departure.

Their report of the state of things was discouraging. That most fashionable of watering-places, Little Mendip, was "chock-full" (as the boys expressed it) from end to end. But in one Square they had seen no less than four cards, in different houses, all announcing in flaming capitals "ELIGIBLE APARTMENTS." "So there's plenty of choice, after all, you see," said spokesman Hugh in conclusion.

"That doesn't follow from the data," said Balbus, as he rose from the easy-chair, where he had been dozing over *The Little Mendip Gazette*. "They may be all single rooms. However, we may as well see them. I shall be glad to stretch my legs a bit."

An unprejudiced bystander might have objected that the operation was needless, and that this long lank creature would have been all the better with even shorter legs: but no such thought occurred to his loving pupils. One on each side, they did their best to keep up with his gigantic strides, while Hugh repeated the sentence in their father's letter, just received from abroad, over which he and Lambert had been puzzling. "He says a friend of his, the Governor of—*what* was that name again, Lambert?" ("Kgovjni," said Lambert). "Well, yes. The Governor of—what-you-may-call-it—wants to give a *very* small dinner-party, and he means to ask his father's brother-in-law, his brother's father-in-law, his father-in-law's brother, and his brother-in-law's father: and we're to guess how many guests there will be."

There was an anxious pause. "*How* large did he say the pudding was to be?" Balbus said at last. "Take its cubical contents, divide by the cubical contents of what each man can eat, and the quotient——"

"He didn't say anything about pudding," said Hugh, "—and here's the Square," as they turned a corner and came into sight of the "eligible apartments".

"It *is* a Square!" was Balbus's first cry of delight, as he gazed around him. "Beautiful! Beau-ti-ful! Equilateral! *And* rectangular!"

The boys looked round with less enthusiasm. "Number Nine is the first with a card," said prosaic Lambert; but Balbus would not so soon awake from his dream of beauty.

"See, boys!" he cried. "Twenty doors on a side! What symmetry! Each side divided into twenty-one equal parts! It's delicious!"

"Shall I knock, or ring?" said Hugh, looking in some perplexity at a square brass plate which bore the simple inscription, "RING ALSO."

"Both," said Balbus. "That's an Ellipsis, my boy. Did you never see an Ellipsis before?"

"I couldn't hardly read it," said Hugh evasively. "It's no good having an Ellipsis, if they don't keep it clean."

"Which there is *one* room, gentlemen," said the smiling landlady. "And a sweet room too! As snug a little backroom——"

"We will see it," said Balbus gloomily, as they followed her in. "I knew how it would be! One room in each house! No view, I suppose?"

"Which indeed there *is*, gentlemen!" the landlady indignantly protested, as she drew up the blind, and indicated the back-garden.

"Cabbages, I perceive," said Balbus. "Well, they're green, at any rate."

"Which the greens at the shops," their hostess explained, "are by no means dependable upon. Here you has them on the premises, *and* of the best."

"Does the window open?" was always Balbus's first question in testing a lodging: and, "Does the chimney smoke?" his second. Satisfied on all points, he secured the refusal of the room, and they moved on to Number Twenty-five.

This landlady was grave and stern. "I've nobbut one room left," she told them: "and it gives on the back-gyardin."

"But there are cabbages?" Balbus suggested.

The landlady visibly relented. "There is, sir," she said: "and good ones, though I say it as shouldn't. We ca'n't rely on the shops for greens. So we grows them ourselves."

"Balbus was assisting his mother-in-law to convince the dragon."

"A singular advantage," said Balbus; and, after the usual questions, they went on to Fifty-two.

"And I'd gladly accommodate you all, if I could," was the greeting that met them. "We are but mortal" ("Irrelevant!" muttered Balbus), "and I've let all my rooms but one."

"Which one is a back-room, I perceive," said Balbus: "and looking out on—on cabbages, I presume?"

"Yes, indeed, sir!" said their hostess. "Whatever *other* folks may do, *we* grows our own. For the shops——"

"An excellent arrangement!" Balbus interrupted. "Then one can really depend on their being good. Does the window open?"

The usual questions were answered satisfactorily: but this time Hugh added one of his own invention—"Does the cat scratch?"

The landlady looked round suspiciously, as if to make sure the cat was not listening. "I will not deceive you, gentlemen," she said. "It *do* scratch, but not without you pulls its whiskers! It'll never do it", she repeated slowly, with a visible effort to recall the exact words of some written agreement between herself and the cat, "without you pulls its whiskers!"

"Much may be excused in a cat so treated," said Balbus, as they left the house and crossed to Number Seventy-three, leaving the landlady curtseying on the doorstep, and still murmuring to herself her parting words, as if they were a form of blessing, "—not without you pulls its whiskers!"

At Number Seventy-three they found only a small shy girl to show the house, who said "yes'm" in answer to all questions.

"The usual room," said Balbus, as they marched in "the usual back-garden, the usual cabbages. I suppose you can't get them good at the shops?"

"Yes'm," said the girl.

"Well, you may tell your mistress we will take the room, and that her plan of growing her own cabbages is simply *admirable!*"

"Yes'm," said the girl, as she showed them out.

"One day-room and three bedrooms," said Balbus, as they returned to the hotel. "We will take as our day-room the one that gives us the least walking to do to get to it."

"Must we walk from door to door, and count the steps?" said Lambert.

"No, no! Figure it out, my boys, figure it out!" Balbus gayly exclaimed, as he put pens, ink, and paper before his hapless pupils, and left the room.

"I say! It'll be a job!" said Hugh.

"Rather!" said Lambert.

Mad Mathesis

I waited for the train

"WELL, they call me so because I *am* a little mad, I suppose," she said, good-humouredly, in answer to Clara's cautiously worded question as to how she came by so strange a nickname. "You see, I never do what sane people are expected to do nowadays. I never wear long trains (talking of trains, that's the Charing Cross Metropolitan Station—I've something to tell you about *that*), and I never play lawn-tennis. I ca'n't cook an omelette. I ca'n't even set a broken limb! *There's* an ignoramus for you!"

Clara was her niece, and full twenty years her junior; in fact, she was still attending a High School—an institution of which Mad Mathesis spoke with undisguised aversion. "Let a woman be meek and lowly!" she would say. "None of your High Schools for me!" But it was vacation-time just now, and Clara was her guest, and Mad Mathesis was showing her the sights of that Eighth Wonder of the world—London.

"The Charing Cross Metropolitan Station!" she resumed, waving her hand towards the entrance as if she were introducing her niece to a friend. "The Bayswater and Birmingham Extension is just completed, and the trains now run round and round continuously—skirting the border of Wales, just touching at York, and so round by the east coast back to London. The way the trains run is *most* peculiar. The westerly ones go round in two hours; the easterly ones take three; but they always manage to start two trains from here, opposite ways, punctually every quarter of an hour."

"They part to meet again," said Clara, her eyes filling with tears at the romantic thought.

"No need to cry about it!" her aunt grimly remarked. "They don't meet on the same line of rails, you know. Talking of meeting, an idea strikes me!" she added, changing the subject with her usual abruptness. "Let's go opposite ways round, and see which can meet most trains. No need for a chaperon—ladies' saloon, you know. You shall go whichever way you like, and we'll have a bet about it!"

"I never make bets," Clara said very gravely. "Our excellent preceptress has often warned us——"

"You'd be none the worst if you did!" Mad Mathesis interrupted. "In fact, you'd be the better, I'm certain!"

"Neither does our excellent preceptress approve of puns," said Clara. "But we'll have a match, if you like. Let me choose my train," she added after a brief mental calculation, "and I'll engage to meet exactly half as many again as you do."

"Not if you count fair," Mad Mathesis bluntly interrupted. "Remember, we only count the trains we meet *on the way*. You mustn't count the one that starts as you start, nor the one that arrives as you arrive."

"That will only make the difference of *one* train," said Clara, as they turned and entered the station. "But I never travelled alone before. There'll be no one to help me to alight. However, I don't mind. Let's have a match."

A ragged little boy overheard her remark, and came running after her. "Buy a box of cigar-lights, Miss!" he pleaded, pulling her shawl to attract her attention. Clara stopped to explain.

"I never smoke cigars," she said in a meekly apologetic tone. "Our excellent preceptress——" But Mad Mathesis impatiently hurried her on, and the little boy was left gazing after her with round eyes of amazement.

The two ladies bought their tickets and moved slowly down the central platform, Mad Mathesis prattling on as usual—Clara silent, anxiously reconsidering the calculation on which she rested her hopes of winning the match.

"Mind where you go, dear!" cried her aunt, checking her just in time. "One step more, and you'd have been in that pail of cold water!"

"I know, I know," Clara said dreamily. "The pale, the cold, and the moony——"

"Take your places on the spring-boards!" shouted a porter.

"What are *they* for!" Clara asked in a terrified whisper.

"Merely to help us into the trains." The elder lady spoke with the nonchalance of one quite used to the process. "Very few people can get into a carriage without help in less than three seconds, and the trains only stop for one second." At this moment the whistle was heard, and two trains rushed into the station. A moment's pause, and they were gone again; but in that brief interval several hundred passengers had been shot into them, each flying straight to his place with the accuracy of a Minie bullet—while an equal number were showered out upon the side-platforms.

Three hours had passed away, and the two friends met again on the Charing Cross platform, and eagerly compared notes. Then Clara turned away with a sigh. To young impulsive hearts, like hers, disappointment is always a bitter pill. Mad Mathesis followed her, full of kindly sympathy.

"Try again, my love!" she said cheerily. "Let us vary the experiment. We will start as we did before, but not begin counting till our trains meet. When we see each other, we will say 'One!' and so count on till we come here again."

Clara brightened up. "I shall win *that*", she exclaimed eagerly, "if I may choose my train!"

Another shriek of engine whistles, another upheaving of spring-boards, another living avalanche plunging into two trains as they flashed by and the travelers were off again.

Each gazed eagerly from her carriage window, holding up her handkerchief as a signal to her friend. A rush and a roar. Two trains shot past each other in a tunnel, and two travelers leaned back in their corners with a sigh—or rather with *two* sighs—of relief "One!" Clara murmured to herself. "Won! It's a word of good omen. *This* time, at any rate, the victory will be mine!"

But *was* it?

KNOT 4

The Dead Reckoning

I did dream of money-bags to-night

NOONDAY on the open sea within a few degrees of the Equator is apt to be oppressively warm; and our two travelers were now airily clad in suits of dazzling white linen, having laid aside the chain-armour which they had found not only endurable in the cold mountain air they had lately been breathing, but a necessary precaution against the daggers of the banditti who infested the heights. Their holiday-trip was over, and they were now on their way home, in the monthly packet which plied between the two great ports of the island they had been exploring.

Along with their armour, the tourists had laid aside the antiquated speech it had pleased them to affect while in knightly disguise, and had returned to the ordinary style of two country gentlemen of the twentieth century.

Stretched on a pile of cushions, under the shade of a huge umbrella, they were lazily watching some native fishermen, who had come on board at the last landing-place, each carrying over his shoulder a small but heavy sack. A large weighing-machine, that had been used for cargo at the last port, stood on the deck; and round this the fishermen had gathered, and, with much unintelligible jabber, seemed to be weighing their sacks.

"More like sparrows in a tree than human talk, isn't it?" the elder tourist remarked to his son, who smiled feebly, but would not exert himself so far as to speak. The old man tried another listener.

"What have they got in those sacks, Captain?" he enquired, as that great being passed them in his never-ending parade to and fro on the deck.

The Captain paused in his march, and towered over the travelers—tall, grave, and serenely self-satisfied.

"Fishermen", he explained, "are often passengers in My ship. These five are from Mhruxi—the place we last touched at—and that's the way they carry their money. The money of this island is heavy, gentlemen, but it costs little, as you may guess. We buy it from them by weight—about five shillings a pound. I fancy a ten-pound note would buy all those sacks."

By this time the old man had closed his eyes—in order, no doubt, to concentrate his thoughts on these interesting facts; but the Captain failed to realize his motive, and with a grunt resumed his monotonous march.

Meanwhile the fishermen were getting so noisy over the weighing-machine that one of the sailors took the precaution of carrying off all the weights, leaving them to amuse themselves with such substitutes in the form of winch-handles, belaying-pins, etc., as they could find. This brought their excitement to a speedy end: they carefully hid their sacks in the folds of the jib that lay on the deck near the tourists, and strolled away.

When next the Captain's heavy footfall passed, the younger man roused himself to speak.

"*What* did you call the place those fellows came from, Captain?" he asked.

"Mhruxi, sir."

"And the one we are bound for?"

The Captain took a long breath, plunged into the word, and came out of it nobly. "They call it Kgovjni, sir."

"K—I give it up!" the young man faintly said.

He stretched out his hand for a glass of iced water which the compassionate steward had brought him a minute ago, and had set down, unluckily, just outside the shadow of the umbrella. It was scalding hot, and he decided not to drink it. The effort of making this resolution, coming close on the fatiguing conversation he had just gone through, was too much for him; he sank back among the cushions in silence.

His father courteously tried to make amends for his nonchalance.

"Whereabouts are we now, Captain?" said he. "Have you any idea?"

The Captain cast a pitying look on the ignorant landsman. "I could tell you that, sir," he said, in a tone of lofty condescension, "to an inch!"

"You don't say so!" the old man remarked, in a tone of languid surprise.

"And mean to," persisted the Captain. "Why, what do you suppose would become of My ship, if I were to lose My longitude and My latitude? Could *you* make anything of My Dead Reckoning?"

"Nobody could, I'm sure!" the other heartily rejoined.

But he had overdone it.

"It's *perfectly* intelligible", the Captain said, in an offended tone, "to anyone that understands such things." With these words he moved away, and began giving orders to the men, who were preparing to hoist the jib.

Our tourists watched the operation with such interest that neither of them remembered the five money-bags, which in another moment, as the wind filled out the jib, were whirled overboard and fell heavily into the sea.

But the poor fishermen had not so easily forgotten their property. In a moment they had rushed to the spot, and stood uttering cries of fury, and pointing, now to the sea, and now to the sailors who had caused the disaster.

The old man explained it to the Captain.

"Let us make it up among us," he added in conclusion. "Ten pounds will do it, I think you said?"

But the Captain put aside the suggestion with a wave of the hand.

"No, sir!" he said, in his grandest manner. "You will excuse Me, I am sure; but these are My passengers. The accident has happened on board My ship, and under My orders. It is for Me to make compensation." He turned to the angry fishermen. "Come here, my men!" he said, in the Mhruxian dialect. "Tell me the weight of each sack. I saw you weighing them just now."

Then ensued a perfect Babel of noise, as the five natives explained, all screaming together, how the sailors had carried off the weights, and they had done what they could with whatever came handy.

Two iron belaying-pins, three blocks, six holy stones, four winch-handles, and a large hammer, were now carefully weighed, the Captain superintending and noting the results. But the matter did not seem to be settled, even then: an angry discussion followed, in which the sailors and the five natives all joined: and at last the Captain approached our tourists with a disconcerted look, which he tried to conceal under a laugh.

"It's an absurd difficulty," he said. "Perhaps one of you gentlemen can suggest something. It seems they weighed the sacks two at a time!"

"If they didn't have five separate weighings, of course you ca'n't value them separately," the youth hastily decided.

"Let's hear all about it," was the old man's more cautious remark.

"They *did* have five separate weighings," the Captain said, "but—well, it beats *me* entirely!" he added, in a sudden burst of candour. "Here's the result: First and second sacks weighed twelve pounds; second and third, thirteen and a half; third and fourth, eleven and a half; fourth and fifth, eight; and then they say they had only the large hammer left, and it took *three* sacks to weigh it down—that's the first, third, and fifth—and *they* weighed sixteen pounds. There, gentlemen! Did you ever hear anything like *that*?"

The old man muttered under his breath, "If only my sister were here!" and looked helplessly at his son. His son looked at the five natives. The five natives looked at the Captain. The Captain looked at nobody: his eyes were cast down, and he seemed to be saying softly to himself, "Contemplate one another, gentlemen, if such be your good pleasure. *I* contemplate *Myself*!"

KNOT 5

Oughts and Crosses

Look here, upon this picture, and on this

"AND what made you choose the first train, Goosey?" said Mad Mathesis, as they got into the cab. "Couldn't you count better than *that*?"

"I took an extreme case," was the tearful reply. "Our excellent preceptress always says, 'When in doubt, my dears, take an extreme case.' And I *was* in doubt."

"Does it always succeed?" her aunt inquired.

Clara sighed. "Not *always*," she reluctantly admitted. "And I ca'n't make out why. One day she was telling the little girls—they make such a noise at tea, you know—'The more noise you make, the less jam you will have, and vice versa.' And I thought they wouldn't know what 'vice versa' meant: so I explained it to them. I said, 'If you make an infinite noise, you'll get no jam: and if you make no noise, you'll get an infinite lot of jam.' But our excellent preceptress said that wasn't a good instance. *Why* wasn't it?" she added plaintively.

Her aunt evaded the question. "One sees certain objections to it," she said. "But how did you work it with the Metropolitan trains? None of them go infinitely fast, I believe."

"I called them hares and tortoises," Clara said—a little timidly, for she dreaded being laughed at. "And I thought there couldn't be so many hares as tortoises on the Line: so I took an extreme case—one hare and an infinite number of tortoises."

"An extreme case, indeed," her aunt remarked with admirable gravity: "and a most dangerous state of things!"

"And I thought, if I went with a tortoise, there would be only *one* hare to meet: but if I went with the hare—you know there were *crowds* of tortoises!"

"It wasn't a bad idea," said the elder lady, as they left the cab, at the entrance of Burlington House. "You shall have another chance to-day. We'll have a match in marking pictures."

Clara brightened up. "I should like to try again, very much," she said. "I'll take more care this time. How are we to play?"

To this question Mad Mathesis made no reply: she was busy drawing lines down the margins of the catalogue. "See," she said after a minute, "I've drawn three columns against the names of the pictures in the long room, and I want you to fill them with oughts and crosses—crosses for good marks and oughts for bad. The first column is for choice of subject, and second for arrangement, the third for colouring. And these are the conditions of the match: You must give three crosses to two or three pictures. You must give two crosses to four or five——"

"Do you mean *only* two crosses?" said Clara. "Or may I count the three-cross pictures among the two-cross pictures?"

"Of course you may," said her aunt. "Anyone that has *three* eyes, may be said to have *two* eyes, I suppose?"

Clara followed her aunt's dreamy gaze across the crowded gallery, half-dreading to find that there was a three-eyed person in sight.

"And you must give one cross to nine or ten."

"And which wins the match?" Clara asked, as she carefully entered these conditions on a blank leaf in her catalogue.

"Whichever marks fewest pictures."

"But suppose we marked the same number?"

"Then whichever uses most marks."

Clara considered. "I don't think it's much of a match," she said. "I shall mark nine pictures, and give three crosses to three of them, two crosses to two more, and one cross each to all the rest."

"Will you, indeed?" said her aunt. "Wait till you've heard all the conditions, my impetuous child. You must give three oughts to one or two pictures, two oughts to three or four, and one ought to eight or nine. I don't want you to be *too* hard on the R.A.'s."

Clara quite gasped as she wrote down all these fresh conditions. "It's a great deal worse than Circulating Decimals!" she said. "But I'm determined to win, all the same!"

Her aunt smiled grimly. "We can begin *here*," she said, as they paused before a gigantic picture, which the catalogue informed them was the "Portrait of Lieutenant Brown, mounted on his favourite elephant".

"He looks awfully conceited!" said Clara. "I don't think he was the elephant's favourite Lieutenant. What a hideous picture it is! And it takes up room enough for twenty!"

"Mind what you say, my dear!" her aunt interposed. "It's by an R.A.!"

But Clara was quite reckless. "I don't care who it's by!" she cried. "And I shall give it three bad marks!"

Aunt and niece soon drifted away from each other in the crowd, and for the next half-hour Clara was hard at work, putting in marks and rubbing them out again, and hunting up and down for a suitable picture. This she found the hardest part of all. "I *ca'n't* find the one I want!" she exclaimed at last, almost crying with vexation.

"What is it you want to find, my dear?" The voice was strange to Clara, but so sweet and gentle that she felt attracted to the the owner of it, even before she had seen her; and when she turned, and met the smiling looks of two little old ladies, whose round dimpled faces, exactly alike, seemed never to have known a care, it was as much as she could do—as she confessed to Aunt Mattie afterwards—to keep herself from hugging them both. "I was looking for a picture", she said, "that has a good subject—and that's well arranged—but badly coloured."

The little old ladies glanced at each other in some alarm. "Calm yourself, my dear," said the one who had spoken first, "and try to remember which it was. What *was* the subject?"

"Was it an elephant, for instance?" the other sister suggested. They were still in sight of Lieutenant Brown.

"I don't know, indeed!" Clara impetuously replied. "You know it doesn't matter a bit what the subject *is*, so long as it's a good one!"

Once more the sisters exchanged looks of alarm, and one of them whispered something to the other, of which Clara caught only the one word "mad".

"They mean Aunt Mattie, of course," she said to herself—fancying, in her innocence, that London was like her native town, where everybody knew everybody else. "If you mean my aunt," she added aloud, "she's *there*—just three pictures beyond Lieutenant Brown."

"Ah, well! Then you'd better go to her, my dear!" her new friend said soothingly. "*She'll* find you the picture you want. Good-bye, dear!"

"Good-bye, dear!" echoed the other sister. "Mind you don't lose sight of your aunt!" And the pair trotted off into another room, leaving Clara rather perplexed at their manner.

"They're real darlings!" she soliloquized. "I wonder why they pity me so!" And she wandered on, murmuring to herself, "It must have two good marks, and——"

KNOT 6

Her Radiancy

One piecee thing that my have got,
Maskee[1] that thing my no can do.
You talkee you no sabey what?
Bamboo.

THEY landed, and were at once conducted to the Palace. About half-way they were met by the Governor, who welcomed them in English—a great relief to our travelers, whose guide could speak nothing but Kgovjnian.

"I don't half like the way they grin at us as we go by!" the old man whispered to his son. "And why do they say 'Bamboo' so often?"

"It alludes to a local custom," replied the Governor, who had overheard the question. "Such persons as happen in any way to displease Her Radiancy are usually beaten with rods."

The old man shuddered. "A most objectionable local custom!" he remarked with strong emphasis. "I wish we had never landed! Did you notice that black fellow, Norman, opening his great mouth at us? I verily believe he would like to eat us!"

Norman appealed to the Governor, who was walking at his other side. "Do they often eat distinguished strangers here?" he said, in as indifferent a tone as he could assume.

"Not often—not ever!" was the welcome reply. "They are not good for it. Pigs we eat, for they are fat. This old man is thin."

"And thankful to be so!" muttered the elder traveler. "Beaten we shall be without a doubt. It's a comfort to know it won't be Beaten without the B! My dear boy, just look at the peacocks!"

They were now walking between two unbroken lines of those gorgeous birds, each held in check, by means of a golden collar and chain, by a black slave, who stood well behind so as not to interrupt the view of the glittering tail, with its network of rustling feathers and its hundred eyes.

The Governor smiled proudly. "In your honour," he said, "Her Radiancy has ordered up ten thousand additional peacocks. She will, no doubt, decorate you, before you go, with the usual Star and Feathers."

"It'll be Star without the S!" faltered one of his hearers.

---

[1] "Maskee", in Pigeon-English, means "Without".

"Why do they say 'Bamboo!' so often?"

"Come, come! Don't lose heart!" said the other. "All this is full of charm for me."

"You are young, Norman," sighed his father; "young and light-hearted. For me, it is Charm without the C."

"The old one is sad," the Governor remarked with some anxiety. "He has, without doubt, effected some fearful crime?"

"But I haven't!" the poor old gentleman hastily exclaimed. "Tell him I haven't, Norman!"

"He has not, as yet," Norman gently explained. And the Governor repeated, in a satisfied tone, "Not as yet."

"Yours is a wondrous country!" the Governor resumed, after a pause. "Now here is a letter from a friend of mine, a merchant, in London. He and his brother went there a year ago, with a thousand pounds apiece; and on New Year's Day they had sixty thousand pounds between them!"

"How did they do it?" Norman eagerly exclaimed. Even the elder traveler looked excited.

The Governor handed him the open letter. "Anybody can do it, when once they know how," so ran this oracular document. 'We borrowed nought: we stole nought. We began the year with only a thousand pounds apiece: and last New Year's Day we had sixty thousand pounds between us—sixty thousand golden sovereigns!"

Norman looked grave and thoughtful as he handed back the letter. His father hazarded one guess. "Was it by gambling?"

"A Kgovjnian never gambles," said the Governor gravely, as he ushered them through the palace gates. They followed him in silence down a long passage, and soon found themselves in a lofty hall, lined entirely with peacocks' feathers. In the centre was a pile of crimson cushions, which almost concealed the figure of Her Radiancy—a plump little damsel, in a robe of green satin dotted with silver stars, whose pale round face lit up for a moment with a half-smile as the travelers bowed before her, and then relapsed into the exact expression of a wax doll, while she languidly murmured a word or two in the Kgovjnian dialect.

The Governor interpreted: "Her Radiancy welcomes you. She notes the Impenetrable Placidity of the old one, and the Imperceptible Acuteness of the youth."

Here the little potentate clapped her hands, and a troop of slaves instantly appeared, carrying trays of coffee and sweetmeats, which they offered to the guests, who had, at a signal from the Governor, seated themselves on the carpet.

"Sugar-plums!" muttered the old man. "One might as well be at a confectioner's! Ask for a penny bun, Norman!"

"Not so loud!" his son whispered. "Say something complimentary!" For the Governor was evidently expecting a speech.

"We thank Her Exalted Potency," the old man timidly began. "We bask in the light of her smile, which——"

"The words of old men are weak!" the Governor interrupted angrily. "Let the youth speak!"

"Tell her," cried Norman, in a wild burst of eloquence, "that, like two grasshoppers in a volcano, we are shrivelled up in the presence of Her Spangled Vehemence!"

"It is well," said the Governor, and translated this into Kgovjnian. "I am now to tell you", he proceeded, "what Her Radiancy requires of you before you go. The yearly competition for the post of Imperial Scarf-maker is just ended; you are the judges. You will take account of the rate of work, the lightness of the scarves, and their warmth. Usually the competitors differ in one point only. Thus, last year, Fifi and Gogo made the same number of scarves in the trial-week, and they were equally light; but Fifi's were twice as warm as Gogo's and she was pronounced twice as good. But this year, woe is me, who can judge it? Three competitors are here, and they differ in all points! While you settle their claims, you shall be lodged, Her Radiancy bids me say, free of expense—in the best dungeon, and abundantly fed on the best bread and water."

The old man groaned. "All is lost!" he wildly exclaimed. But Norman heeded him not: he had taken out his notebook, and was calmly jotting down the particulars.

"Three they be," the Governor proceeded. "Lolo, Mimi, and Zuzu. Lolo makes 5 scarves while Mimi makes 2; but Zuzu makes 4 while Lolo makes 3! Again, so fairy-like is Zuzu's handiwork, 5 of her scarves weigh no more than one of Lolo's; yet Mimi's is lighter still—5 of hers will but balance 3 of Zuzu's! And for warmth one of Mimi's is equal to 4 of Zuzu's; yet one of Lolo's is as warm as 3 of Mimi's!"

Here the little lady once more clapped her hands.

"It is our signal of dismissal!" the Governor hastily said. "Pay Her Radiancy your farewell compliments—and walk out backwards."

The walking part was all the elder tourist could manage. Norman simply said, "Tell Her Radiancy we are transfixed by the spectacle of Her Serene Brilliance, and bid an agonized farewell to her Condensed Milkiness!"

"Her Radiancy is pleased," the Governor reported, after duly trans-lating this. "She casts on you a glance from Her Imperial Eyes, and is confident that you will catch it!"

"That I warrant we shall!" the elder traveler moaned to himself distractedly.

Once more they bowed low, and then followed the Governor down a winding staircase to the Imperial Dungeon, which they found to be lined with coloured marble, lighted from the roof, and splendidly though not luxuriously furnished with a bench of polished malachite. "I trust you will not delay the calculation," the Governor said, ushering them in with much ceremony. "I have known great inconvenience—great and serious inconvenience—result to those unhappy ones who have delayed to execute the commands of Her Radiancy! And on this occasion she is resolute: she says the thing must and shall be done: and she has ordered up ten thousand additional bamboos!" With these words he left them, and they heard him lock and bar the door on the outside.

"I told you how it would end!" moaned the elder traveler, wringing his hands, and quite forgetting in his anguish that he had himself proposed the expedition, and had never predicted anything of the sort. "Oh, that we were well out of this miserable business!"

"Courage!" cried the younger cheerily. "*Hæc olim meminisse juvabit!* The end of all this will be glory!"

"Glory without the L!" was all the poor old man could say, as he rocked himself to and fro on the malachite bench. "Glory without the L!"

KNOT 7

Petty Cash

Base is the slave that pays

"AUNT MATTIE!"

"My child?"

"*Would* you mind writing it down at once? I shall be quite *certain* to forget it if you don't!"

"My dear, we really must wait till the cab stops. How can I possibly write anything in the midst of all this jolting?"

"But *really* I shall be forgetting it!"

Clara's voice took the plaintive tone that her aunt never knew how to resist, and with a sigh the old lady drew forth her ivory tablets and

prepared to record the amount that Clara had just spent at the confectioner's shop. Her expenditure was always made out of her aunt's purse,
but the poor girl knew, by bitter experience, that sooner or later "Mad
Mathesis" would expect an exact account of very penny that had gone,
and she waited, with ill-concealed impatience, while the old lady turned
the tablets over and over, till she had found the one headed "PETTY CASH".

"Here's the place," she said at last, "and here we have yesterday's
luncheon duly entered. *One glass lemonade* (Why ca'n't you drink water,
like me?), *three sandwiches* (They never put in half mustard enough. I
told the young woman so, to her face; and she tossed her head—like her
impudence!), *and seven biscuits. Total one-and-twopence.* Well, now for
today's?"

"One glass of lemonade——" Clara was beginning to say, when
suddenly the cab drew up, and a courteous railway-porter was handing
out the bewildered girl before she had had time to finish her sentence.

Her aunt pocketed the tablets instantly. "Business first," she said:
"petty cash—which is a form of pleasure, whatever *you* may
think—afterwards." And she proceeded to pay the driver, and to give
voluminous orders about the luggage, quite deaf to the entreaties of her
unhappy niece that she would enter the rest of the luncheon account.
"My dear, you really must cultivate a more capacious mind!" was all the
consolation she vouchsafed to the poor girl. "Are not the tablets of your
memory wide enough to contain the record of one single luncheon?"

"Not wide enough! Not half wide enough!" was the passionate reply.

The words came in aptly enough, but the voice was not that of Clara,
and both ladies turned in some surprise to see who it was that had so
suddenly struck into their conversation. A fat little old lady was standing
at the door of a cab, helping the driver to extricate what seemed an exact
duplicate of herself: it would have been no easy task to decide which was
the fatter or which looked the more good-humoured of the two sisters.

"I tell you the cab-door isn't half wide enough!" she repeated, as her
sister finally emerged, somewhat after the fashion of a pellet from a
pop-gun, and she turned to appeal to Clara. "Is it, dear?" she said, trying
hard to bring a frown into a face that dimpled all over with smiles.

"Some folks is too wide for 'em," growled the cab-driver.

"Don't provoke me, man!" cried the little old lady, in what she meant
for a tempest of fury. "Say another word and I'll put you into the County
Court, and sue you for a Habeas Corpus!" the cabman touched his hat,
and marched off, grinning.

"Nothing like a little Law to cow the ruffians, my dear!" she remarked

"I tell you the cab-door isn't half wide enough!"

confidentially to Clara. "You saw how he quailed when I mentioned the Habeas Corpus? Not that I've any idea what it means, but it sounds very grand, doesn't it?"

"It's very provoking," Clara replied, a little vaguely.

"Very!" the little old lady eagerly replied. "And we're very much provoked indeed. Aren't we, sister?"

"I never was so provoked in all my life!" the fatter sister assented radiantly.

By this time Clara had recognized her picture-gallery acquaintances, and, drawing her aunt aside, she hastily whispered her reminiscences. "I met them first in the Royal Academy—and they were very kind to me—and they were lunching at the next table to us, just now, you know—and they tried to help me to find the picture I wanted—and I'm sure they're dear old things!"

"Friends of yours, are they?" said Mad Mathesis. "Well I like their looks. You can be civil to them, while I get the tickets. But do try and arrange your ideas a little more chronologically!"

And so it came to pass that the four ladies found themselves seated side by side on the same bench waiting for the train, and chatting as if they had known one another for years.

"Now this I call quite a remarkable coincidence!" exclaimed the smaller and more talkative of the two sisters—the one whose legal knowledge had annihilated the cab-driver. "Not only that we should be waiting for the same train, and at the same station—*that* would be curious enough—but actually on the same day, and the same hour of the day! That's what strikes *me* so forcibly!" She glanced at the fatter and more silent sister, whose chief function in life seemed to be to support the family opinion, and who meekly responded:

"And me too, sister!"

"Those are not *independent* coincidences——" Mad Mathesis was just beginning, when Clara ventured to interpose.

"There's no jolting here," she pleaded meekly. "*Would* you mind writing it down now?"

Out came the ivory tablets once more. "What was it, then?" said her aunt.

"One glass of lemonade, one sandwich, one biscuit—Oh, dear me!" cried poor Clara, the historical tone suddenly changing to a wail of agony.

"Toothache?" said her aunt calmly, as she wrote down the items. The two sisters instantly opened their reticules and produced two different remedies for neuralgia, each marked "unequalled".

"It isn't that!" said poor Clara. "Thank you very much. It's only that I *ca'n't* remember how much I paid!"

"Well, try and make it out, then," said her aunt. "You've got yesterday's luncheon to help you, you know. And here's the luncheon we had the day before—the first day we went to that shop—*one glass lemonade, four sandwiches, ten biscuits. Total, one-and-fivepence.*" She handed the tablets to Clara, who gazed at them with eyes so dim with tears that she did not at first notice that she was holding them upside down.

The two sisters had been listening to all this with the deepest interest, and at this juncture the smaller one softly laid her hand on Clara's arm.

"Do you know, my dear," she said coaxingly, "my sister and I are in the very same predicament! Quite identically the very same predicament! Aren't we, sister?"

"Quite identically and absolutely the very——" began the fatter sister, but she was constructing her sentence on too large a scale, and the little one would not wait for her to finish it.

"Yes, my dear," she resumed; "we were lunching at the very same shop as you were—and we had two glasses of lemonade and three sandwiches and five biscuits—and neither of us has the least idea what we paid. Have we, sister?"

"Quite identically and absolutely——" murmured the other, who evidently considered that she was now a whole sentence in arrears, and that she ought to discharge one obligation before contracting any fresh liabilities; but the little lady broke in again, and she retired from the conversation a bankrupt.

"*Would* you make it out for us, my dear?" pleaded the little old lady.

"You can do Arithmetic, I trust?" her aunt said, a little anxiously, as Clara turned from one tablet to another, vainly trying to collect her thoughts. Her mind was a blank, and all human expression was rapidly fading out of her face.

A gloomy silence ensued.

KNOT 8

De Omnibus Rebus

This little pig went to market:
This little pig staid at home.

"BY Her Radiancy's express command," said the Governor, as he conducted the travelers, for the last time, from the Imperial presence, "I shall now have the ecstasy of escorting you as far as the outer gate of the Military Quarter, where the agony of parting—if indeed Nature can survive the shock—must be endured! From that gate grurmstipths start every quarter of an hour, both ways——"

"Would you mind repeating that word?" said Norman. "Grurm——?"

"Grurmstipths," the Governor repeated. "You call them omnibuses in England. They run both ways, and you can travel by one of them all the way down to the harbour."

The old man breathed a sigh of relief; four hours of courtly ceremony had wearied him, and he had been in constant terror lest something should call into use the ten thousand additional bamboos.

In another minute they were crossing a large quadrangle, paved with marble, and tastefully decorated with a pigsty in each corner. Soldiers, carrying pigs, were marching in all directions: and in the middle stood a gigantic officer giving orders in a voice of thunder, which made itself heard above all the uproar of the pigs.

"It is the Commander-in-Chief!" the Governor hurriedly whispered to his companions, who at once followed his example in prostrating themselves before the great man. The Commander gravely bowed in return. He was covered with gold lace from head to foot: his face wore an expression of deep misery: and he had a little black pig under each arm. Still the gallant fellow did his best, in the midst of the orders he was every moment issuing to his men, to bid a courteous farewell to the departing guests.

"Farewell, O old one!—carry these three to the South corner—and farewell to thee, thou young one—put this fat one on the top of the others in the Western sty—may your shadows never be less—woe is me, it is wrongly done! Empty out all the sties, and begin again!" And the soldier leant upon his sword, and wiped away a tear.

"He is in distress," the Governor explained as they left the court. "Her Radiancy has commanded him to place twenty-four pigs in those four sties, so that, as she goes round the court, she may always find the number in each sty nearer to ten than the number in the last."

"Does she call ten nearer to ten than nine is?" said Norman.

"Surely," said the Governor. "Her Radiancy would admit that ten is nearer to ten than nine is—and also nearer than eleven is."

"Then I think it can be done," said Norman.

The Governor shook his head. "The Commander has been transferring them in vain for four months," he said. "What hope remains? And Her Radiancy has ordered up ten thousand additional——"

"The pigs don't seem to enjoy being transferred," the old man hastily interrupted. He did not like the subject of bamboos.

"They are only *provisionally* transferred, you know," said the Governor. "In most cases they are immediately carried back again: so they need not mind it. And all is done with the greatest care, under the personal superintendence of the Commander-in-Chief."

"Of course she would only go *once* round?" said Norman.

"Alas no!" sighed their conductor. "Round and round. Round and round. These are Her Radiancy's own words. But oh, agony! Here is the outer gate, and we must part!" He sobbed as he shook hands with them, and the next moment was briskly walking away.

"He *might* have waited to see us off!" said the old man piteously.

"And he needn't have begun whistling the very *moment* he left us!" said the young one severely. "But look sharp—here are two what's-his-names in the act of starting!"

Unluckily, the sea-bound omnibus was full. "Never mind!" said Norman cheerily. "We'll walk on till the next one overtakes us."

They trudged on in silence, both thinking over the military problem, till they met an omnibus coming from the sea. The elder traveler took out his watch. "Just twelve minutes and a half since we started," he remarked in an absent manner. Suddenly the vacant face brightened; the old man had an idea. "My boy!" he shouted, bringing his hand down upon Norman's shoulder so suddenly as for a moment to transfer his centre of gravity beyond the base of support.

Thus taken off his guard, the young man wildly staggered forwards, and seemed about to plunge into space: but in another moment he had gracefully recovered himself. "Problem in Precession and Nutation," he remarked—in tones where filial respect only just managed to conceal a shade of annoyance. "What is it?" He hastily added, fearing his father might have been taken ill. "Will you have some brandy?"

"When will the next omnibus overtake us? When? When?" the old man cried, growing more excited every moment.

Norman looked gloomy. "Give me time," he said. "I must think it over." And once more the travelers passed on in silence—a silence only broken by the distant squeals of the unfortunate little pigs, who were still being provisionally transferred from sty to sty, under the personal superintendence of the Commander-in-Chief.

KNOT 9

A Serpent with Corners

Water, water, everywhere,
Nor any drop to drink.

"IT'LL just take one more pebble."

"Whatever *are* you doing with those buckets?"

The speakers were Hugh and Lambert. Place, the beach of Little Mendip. Time 1:30 P.M. Hugh was floating a bucket in another a size larger, and trying how many pebbles it would carry without sinking. Lambert was lying on his back, doing nothing.

For the next minute or two Hugh was silent, evidently deep in thought. Suddenly he started. "I say, look here, Lambert!" he cried.

"If it's alive, and slimy, and with legs, I don't care to," said Lambert.

"Didn't Balbus say this morning that, if a body is immersed in liquid it displaces as much liquid as is equal to its own bulk?" said Hugh.

"He said things of that sort," Lambert vaguely replied.

"Well, just look here a minute. Here's the little bucket almost quite immersed: so the water displaced ought to be just about the same bulk. And now just look at it!" He took out the little bucket as he spoke, and handed the big one to Lambert. "Why, there's hardly a teacupful! Do you mean to say *that* water is the same bulk as the little bucket?"

"Course it is," said Lambert.

"Well, look here again!" cried Hugh, triumphantly, as he poured the water from the big bucket into the little one. "Why, it doesn't half fill it!"

"That's *its* business," said Lambert. "If Balbus says it's the same bulk, why, it *is* the same bulk, you know."

"Well, I don't believe it," said Hugh.

"You needn't," said Lambert. "Besides, it's dinner-time. Come along."

They found Balbus waiting dinner for them, and to him Hugh at once propounded his difficulty.

"Let's get you helped first," said Balbus, briskly cutting away at the joint. "You know the old proverb, 'Mutton first, mechanics afterwards'?"

The boys did *not* know the proverb, but they accepted it in perfect good faith, as they did every piece of information, however startling, that came from so infallible an authority as their tutor. They ate on steadily in silence, and, when dinner was over, Hugh set out the usual array of pens, ink, and paper, while Balbus repeated to them the problem he had prepared for their afternoon's task.

"A friend of mine has a flower-garden—a very pretty one, though no great size——"

"How big is it?" said Hugh.

"That's what *you* have to find out!" Balbus gaily replied. "All *I* tell you is that it is oblong in shape—just half a yard longer than its width—and that a gravel-walk, one yard wide, begins at one corner and runs all round it."

"Joining into itself?" said Hugh.

"*Not* joining into itself, young man. Just before doing *that*, it turns a corner, and runs round the garden again, alongside of the first portion, and then inside that again, winding in and in, and each lap touching the last one, till it has used up the whole of the area."

"Like a serpent with corners?" said Lambert.

"Exactly so. And if you walk the whole length of it, to the last inch, keeping in the centre of the path, it's exactly two miles and half a furlong. Now, while you find out the length and breadth of the garden; I'll see if I can think out that sea-water puzzle."

"You said it was a flower-garden?" Hugh inquired, as Balbus was leaving the room.

"I did," said Balbus.

"Where do the flowers grow?" said Hugh. But Balbus thought it best not to hear the question. He left the boys to their problem, and, in the silence of his own room, set himself to unravel Hugh's mechanical paradox.

"To fix our thoughts," he murmured to himself, as, with hands deep-buried in his pockets, he paced up and down the room, "we will take a cylindrical glass jar, with a scale of inches marked up the side, and fill it with water up to the 10-inch mark: and we will assume that every inch depth of jar contains a pint of water. We will now take a solid cylinder,

"He remains steadfast and unmoved."

such that every inch of it is equal in bulk to *half* a pint of water, and plunge 4 inches of it into the water, so that the end of the cylinder comes down to the 6-inch mark. Well, that displaces 2 pints of water. What becomes of them? Why, if there were no more cylinder, they would lie comfortably on the top, and fill the jar up to the 12-inch mark. But unfortunately there *is* more cylinder, occupying half the space between the 10-inch and the 12-inch marks, so that only *one* pint of water can be accommodated there. What becomes of the other pint? Why, if there were no more cylinder, it would lie on the top, and fill the jar up to the 13-inch mark. But unfortunately—Shade of Newton!" he exclaimed, in sudden accents of terror. "When *does* the water stop rising?"

A bright idea struck him. "I'll write a little essay on it," he said.

Balbus's Essay

"When a solid is immersed in a liquid, it is well known that it displaces a portion of the liquid equal to itself in bulk, and that the level of the liquid rises just so much as it would rise if a quantity of liquid had been added to it, equal in bulk to the solid. Lardner says precisely the same process occurs when a solid is *partially* immersed: the quantity of liquid displaced, in this case, equalling the portion of the solid which is immersed, and the rise of the level being in proportion.

"Suppose a solid held above the surface of a liquid and partially immersed: a portion of the liquid is displaced, and the level of the liquid rises. But, by this rise of level, a little bit more of the solid is of course immersed, and so there is a new displacement of a second portion of the liquid, and a consequent rise of level. Again, this second rise of level causes a yet further immersion, and by consequence another displacement of liquid and another rise. It is self-evident that this process must continue till the entire solid is immersed, and that the liquid will then begin to immerse whatever holds the solid, which, being connected with it, must for the time be considered a part of it. If you hold a stick, six feet long, with its ends in a tumbler of water, and wait long enough, you must eventually be immersed. The question as to the source from which the water is supplied—which belongs to a high branch of mathematics, and is therefore beyond our present scope—does not apply to the sea. Let us therefore take the familiar instance of a man standing at the edge of the sea, at ebb-tide, with a solid in his hand, which he partially immerses: he remains steadfast and unmoved, and we all know that he must be drowned.

The multitudes who daily perish in this manner to attest a philosophical truth, and whose bodies the unreasoning wave casts sullenly upon our thankless shores, have a truer claim to be called the martyrs of science than a Galileo or a Kepler. To use Kossuth's eloquent phrase, they are the unnamed demigods of the nineteenth century."[1]

"There's a fallacy *somewhere*," he murmured drowsily, as he stretched his long legs upon the sofa. "I must think it over again." He closed his eyes, in order to concentrate his attention more perfectly, and for the next hour or so his slow and regular breathing bore witness to the careful deliberation with which he was investigating this new and perplexing view of the subject.

KNOT 10

Chelsea Buns

Yea, buns, and buns, and buns!

Old Song.

"How very, very sad!" exclaimed Clara; and the eyes of the gentle girl filled with tears as she spoke.

"Sad—but very curious when you come to look at it arithmetically," was her aunt's less romantic reply. "Some of them have lost an arm in their country's service, some a leg, some an ear, some an eye——"

"And some, perhaps, *all*!" Clara murmured dreamily, as they passed the long rows of weather-beaten heroes basking in the sun. "Did you notice that very old one, with a red face, who was drawing a map in the dust with his wooden leg, and all the others watching? I *think* it was a plan of a battle——"

"The Battle of Trafalgar, no doubt," her aunt interrupted briskly.

"Hardly that, I think," Clara ventured to say. "You see, in that case, he couldn't well be alive——"

"Couldn't well be alive!" the old lady contemptuously repeated. "He's as lively as you and me put together! Why, if drawing a map in the dust—with one's wooden leg—doesn't prove one to be alive, perhaps you'll kindly mention what *does* prove it!"

Clara did not see her way out of it. Logic had never been her forte.

[1] *Note by the writer.*—For the above essay I am indebted to a dear friend, now deceased.

"To return to the arithmetic," Mad Mathesis resumed—the eccentric old lady never let slip an opportunity of driving her niece into a calculation—"what percentage do you suppose must have lost all four—a leg, an arm, an eye, and an ear?"

"How *can* I tell?" gasped the terrified girl. She knew well what was coming.

"You ca'n't, of course, without data," her aunt replied: "but I'm just going to give you——"

"Give her a Chelsea bun, miss! That's what most young ladies like best!" The voice was rich and musical, and the speaker dexterously whipped back the snowy cloth that covered his basket, and disclosed a tempting array of the familiar square buns, joined together in rows, richly egged and browned, and glistening in the sun.

"No, sir! I shall give her nothing so indigestible! Be off!" The old lady waved her parasol threateningly: but nothing seemed to disturb the good humour of the jolly old man, who marched on, chanting his melodious refrain:

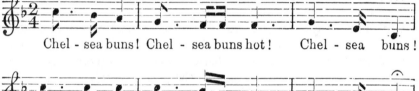

Chel - sea buns! Chel - sea buns hot! Chel - sea buns!

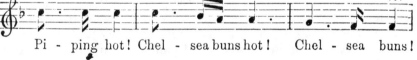

Pi - ping hot! Chel - sea buns hot! Chel - sea buns!

"Far too indigestible, my love!" said the old lady. "Percentages will agree with you ever so much better!"

Clara sighed, and there was a hungry look in her eyes as she watched the basket lessening in the distance; but she meekly listened to the relentless old lady, who at once proceeded to count off the data on her fingers.

"Say that 70 per cent have lost an eye—75 per cent an ear—80 per cent an arm—85 per cent a leg—that'll do it beautifully. Now, my dear, what percentage, *at least*, must have lost all four?"

No more conversation occurred—unless a smothered exclamation of, "Piping hot!" which escaped from Clara's lips as the basket vanished round a corner could be counted as such—until they reached the old Chelsea mansion, where Clara's father was then staying, with his three sons and their old tutor.

Balbus, Lambert, and Hugh had entered the house only a few minutes before them. They had been out walking, and Hugh had been propounding a difficulty which had reduced Lambert to the depths of gloom, and had even puzzled Balbus.

"It changes from Wednesday to Thursday at midnight, doesn't it?" Hugh had begun.

"Sometimes," said Balbus cautiously.

"Always," said Lambert decisively.

"*Sometimes*," Balbus gently insisted. "Six midnights out of seven, it changes to some other name."

"I meant, of course," Hugh corrected, "when it *does* change from Wednesday to Thursday, it does it at midnight—and *only* at midnight."

"Surely," said Balbus. Lambert was silent.

"Well, now, suppose it's midnight here in Chelsea. Then it's Wednesday *west* of Chelsea (say in Ireland or America), where midnight hasn't arrived yet: and it's Thursday *east* of Chelsea (say in Germany or Russia), where midnight has just passed by?"

"Surely," Balbus said again. Even Lambert nodded his time.

"But it isn't midnight anywhere else; so it ca'n't be changing from one day to another anywhere else. And yet, if Ireland and America and so on call it Wednesday, and Germany and Russia and so on call it Thursday, there *must* be some place—not Chelsea—that has different days on the two sides of it. And the worst of it is, the people *there* get their days in the wrong order: they've got Wednesday *east* of them, and Thursday *west*—just as if their day had changed from Thursday to Wednesday!"

"I've heard that puzzle before!" cried Lambert. "And I'll tell you the explanation. When a ship goes round the world from east to west, we know that it loses a day in its reckoning: so that when it gets home and calls its day Wednesday, it finds people here calling it Thursday, because we've had one more midnight than the ship has had. And when you go the other way round you gain a day."

"I know all that," said Hugh, in reply to this not very lucid explanation: "but it doesn't help me, because the ship hasn't proper days. One way round, you get more than twenty-four hours to the day, and the other way you get less: so of course the names get wrong: but people that live on in one place always get twenty-four hours to the day."

"I suppose there *is* such a place," Balbus said, meditatively, "though I never heard of it. And the people must find it queer, as Hugh says, to have the old day *east* of them, and the new one *west*: because, when midnight comes round to them, with the new day in front of it and the old one behind it, one doesn't see exactly what happens. I must think it over."

So they had entered the house in the state I have described—Balbus puzzled, and Lambert buried in gloomy thought.

"Yes, m'm, Master *is* at home, m'm," said the stately old butler. (N.B.—It is only a butler of experience who can manage a series of three M's together, without any interjacent vowels.) "And the *ole* party is a-waiting for you in the libery."

"I don't like his calling your father an *old* party," Mad Mathesis whispered to her niece, as they crossed the hall. And Clara had only just time to whisper in reply, "He meant the *whole* party," before they were ushered into the library, and the sight of the five solemn faces there assembled chilled her into silence.

Her father sat at the head of the table, and mutely signed to the ladies to take the two vacant chairs, one on each side of him. His three sons and Balbus completed the party. Writing materials had been arranged round the table, after the fashion of a ghostly banquet: the butler had evidently bestowed much thought on the grim device. Sheets of quarto paper, each flanked by a pen on one side and a pencil on the other, represented the plates—penwipers did duty for rolls of bread—while ink-bottles stood in the places usually occupied by wine-glasses. The *pièce de résistance* was a large green baize bag, which gave forth, as the old man restlessly lifted it from side to side, a charming jingle, as of innumerable golden guineas.

"Sister, daughter, sons—and Balbus——" the old man began, so nervously that Balbus put in a gentle "Hear, hear!" while Hugh drummed on the table with his fists. This disconcerted the unpractised orator. "Sister——" he began again, then paused a moment, moved the bag to the other side, and went on with a rush, "I mean—this being—a critical occasion—more or less—being the year when one of my sons comes of age——" he paused again in some confusion, having evidently got into the middle of his speech sooner than he intended: but it was too late to go back. "Hear, hear!" cried Balbus. "Quite so," said the old gentleman, recovering his self-possession a little: "when first I began this annual custom—my friend Balbus will correct me if I am wrong——" (Hugh whispered, "With a strap!" but nobody heard him except Lambert, who only frowned and shook his head at him "—this annual custom of giving each of my sons as many guineas as would represent his age—it was a critical time—so Balbus informed me—as the ages of two of you were together equal to that of the third—so on that occasion I made a speech——" He paused so long that Balbus thought it well to come to the rescue with the words, "It was a most——" but the old man checked him with a warning look: "yes, made a speech," he repeated. "A few years after that, Balbus pointed out—I say pointed out——" ("Hear,

hear!" cried Balbus. "Quite so," said the grateful old man.) "—that it was *another* critical occasion. The ages of two of you were together *double* that of the third. So I made another speech—another speech. And now again it's a critical occasion—so Balbus says—and I am making——" (here Mad Mathesis pointedly referred to her watch) "all the haste I can!" the old man cried, with wonderful presence of mind. "Indeed, sister, I'm coming to the point now! The number of years that have passed since that first occasion is just two-thirds of the numbers of guineas I then gave you. Now, my boys, calculate your ages from the data, and you shall have the money!"

"But we *know* our ages!" cried Hugh.

"Silence, sir!" thundered the old man, rising to his full height (he was exactly five-foot five) in his indignation. "I say you must use the data only! You mustn't even assume *which* it is that comes of age!" He clutched the bag as he spoke, and with tottering steps (it was about as much as he could do to carry it) he left the room.

"And *you* shall have a similar *cadeau*", the old lady whispered to her niece, "when you've calculated that percentage!" And she followed her brother.

Nothing could exceed the solemnity with which the old couple had risen from the table, and yet was it—was it a *grin* with which the father turned away from his unhappy sons? Could it be—could it be a *wink* with which the aunt abandoned her despairing niece? And were those—were those sounds of suppressed *chuckling* which floated into the room, just before Balbus (who had followed them out) closed the door? Surely not: and yet the butler told the cook—but no, that was merely idle gossip, and I will not repeat it.

The shades of evening granted their unuttered petition, and "closed not o'er" them (for the butler brought in the lamp): the same obliging shades left them a "lonely bark" (the wail of a dog, in the back-yard, baying the moon) for "a while": but neither "morn, alas", nor any other epoch, seemed likely to "restore" them—to that peace of mind which had once been theirs ere ever these problems had swooped upon them, and crushed them with a load of unfathomable mystery!

"It's hardly fair," muttered Hugh, "to give us such a jumble as this to work out!"

"Fair!" Clara echoed bitterly. "Well!"

And to all my readers I can but repeat the last words of gentle Clara:

FARE-WELL!

Appendix

"A knot," said Alice. "Oh, do let me help to undo it!"

ANSWERS TO KNOT I

Problem.—Two travelers spend from 3 o'clock till 9 in walking along a level road, up a hill, and home again: their pace on the level being 4 miles an hour, up hill 3, and down hill 6. Find the distance walked: also (within half an hour) time of reaching top of hill.

Answer.—24 miles: half-past 6.

Solution.—A level mile takes ¼ of an hour, up hill ⅓, down hill ⅙. Hence to go and return over the same mile, whether on the level or on the hillside, takes ½ an hour. Hence in 6 hours they went 12 miles out and 12 back. If the 12 miles out had been nearly all level, they would have taken a little over 3 hours; if nearly all up hill, a little under 4. Hence 3½ hours must be within ½ an hour of the time taken in reaching the peak; thus, as they started at 3, they got there within ½ an hour of ½ past 6.

Twenty-seven answers have come in. Of these, 9 are right, 16 partially right, and 2 wrong. The 16 give the *distance* correctly, but they have failed to grasp the fact that the top of the hill might have been reached at *any* moment between 6 o'clock and 7.

The two wrong answers are from GERTY VERNON and A NIHILIST. The former makes the distance "23 miles", while her revolutionary companion puts it at "27". GERTY VERNON says, "they had to go 4 miles along the plain, and got to the foot of the hill at 4 o'clock." They *might* have done so, I grant; but you have no ground for saying they *did* so. "It was 7½ miles to the top of the hill, and they reached that at ¼ before 7 o'clock." Here you go wrong in your arithmetic, and I must, however reluctantly, bid you farewell. 7½ miles, at 3 miles an hour, would *not* require 2¾ hours. A NIHILIST says, "Let x denote the whole number of miles; y the number of hours to hill-top; ∴ $3y$ = number of miles to hill-top, and $x - 3y$ = number of miles on the other side." You bewilder me. The other side of *what*? "Of the hill," you say. But then, how did they get home again? However, to accommodate your views we will build a new hostelry at the foot of the hill on the opposite side, and also assume (what I grant you is *possible*, though it is not *necessarily* true) that there was no level road at all. Even then you go wrong. You say:

$$"y = 6\,\frac{x - 3y}{6} \quad . \quad . \quad . \quad \text{(i)};$$

$$\frac{x}{4½} = 6 \qquad . \quad . \quad . \quad \text{(ii)}."$$

I grant you (i), but I deny (ii): it rests on the assumption that to go *part* of the time at 3 miles an hour, and the rest at 6 miles an hour, comes to the same result as going the *whole* time at 4½ miles an hour. But this would only be true if the "*part*" were in exact half, *i.e.* if they went up hill for 3 hours, and down hill for the other 3: which they certainly did *not* do.

The sixteen who are partially right, are AGNES BAILEY, F. K., FIFEE, G. E. B., H. P., KIT, M. E. T., MYSIE, A MOTHER'S SON, NAIRAM, A REDRUTHIAN, A SOCIALIST, SPEAR MAIDEN, T. B. C., VIS INERTIÆ, and YAK. Of these, F. K., FIFEE, T. B. C., and VIS INERTIÆ do not attempt the second part at all. F. K. and H. P. give no working. The rest make particular assumptions, such as that there was no level road—that there were 6 miles of level road—and so on, all leading to *particular* times being fixed for reaching the hill-top. The most curious assumption is that of AGNES BAILEY, who says, "Let x = number of hours occupied in ascent; then $\frac{x}{2}$ = hours occupied in descent; and $\frac{4x}{3}$ = hours occupied on the level." I suppose you were thinking of the relative *rates*, up hill and on the level; which we might express by saying that, if they went x miles up hill in a certain time, they would go $\frac{4x}{3}$ miles on the level *in the same time*. You have, in fact, assumed that they took *the same time* on the level that they took in ascending the hill. FIFEE assumed that, when the aged knight said they had gone "four miles in the hour" on the level, he meant that four miles was the *distance* gone, not merely the rate. This would have been—if FIFEE will excuse the slang expression—a "sell", ill-suited to the dignity of the hero.

And now, "descend, ye classic Nine!" who have solved the whole problem, and let me sing your praises. Your names are BLITHE, E. W., L. B., A MARLBOROUGH BOY, O. V. L., PUTNEY WALKER, ROSE, SEA-BREEZE, SIMPLE SUSAN, and MONEY-SPINNER. (These last two I count as one, as they send a joint answer.) ROSE and SIMPLE SUSAN and Co. do not actually state that the hill-top was reached sometime between 6 and 7, but, as they have clearly grasped the fact that a mile, ascended and descended, took the same time as two level miles, I mark them as "right". A MARLBOROUGH BOY and PUTNEY WALKER deserve honourable mention for their algebraic solutions, being the only two who have perceived that the question leads to *an indeterminate equation*. E. W. brings a charge of untruthfulness against the aged knight—a serious charge, for he was the very pink of chivalry! She says, "According to the data given, the time at the summit affords no clue to the total distance. It does not enable us to state precisely to an inch how much level and how much hill there was on the road." "Fair damsel," the aged knight replies, "—if, as I surmise, thy initials denote Early Womanhood—bethink thee that the word 'enable' is thine, not mine. I did but ask the time of reaching the hill-top as my *condition* for further parley. If *now* thou wilt not grant that I am a truth-loving man, then will I affirm that those same initials denote Envenomed Wickedness!"

Class List

I

A MARLBOROUGH BOY.   PUTNEY WALKER.

II

BLITHE.   ROSE.
E.W.   SEA-BREEZE.
L.B.   SIMPLE SUSAN.
O. V. L.   MONEY-SPINNER.

BLITHE has made so ingenious an addition to the problem, and SIMPLE SUSAN and Co. have solved it in such tuneful verse, that I record their answers in full. I have altered a word or two in BLITHE'S—which I trust she will excuse; it did not seem quite clear as it stood.

"Yet say," said the youth, as a gleam of inspiration lighted up the relaxing muscles of his quiescent features. "Stay. Methinks it matters little *when* we reached that summit, the crown of our toil. For in the space of time wherein we clambered up one mile and bounded down the same on our return, we could have trudged the *twain* on the level. We have plodded, then, four-and-twenty miles in these six mortal hours; for never a moment did we stop for catching of fleeting breath or for gazing on the scene around!"

"Very good," said the old man. "Twelve miles out and twelve miles in. And we reached the top sometime between six and seven of the clock. Now mark me! For every five minutes that had fled since six of the clock when we stood on yonder peak, so many miles had we toiled upwards on the dreary mountain side!"

The youth moaned and rushed into the hostel.

BLITHE.

> The elder and the younger knight
>   They sallied forth at three;
> How far they went on level ground
>   It matters not to me;
> What time they reached the foot of hill,
>   When they began to mount,
> Are problems which I hold to be
>   Of very small account.
>
> The moment that each waved his hat
>   Upon the topmost peak—
> To trivial query such as this
>   No answer will I seek.
> Yet can I tell the distance well
>   They must have travelled o'er:
> On hill and plain, 'twixt three and nine,
>   The miles were twenty-four.
>
> Four miles an hour their steady pace
>   Along the level track,
> Three when they climbed—but six when they
>   Came swiftly striding back
> Adown the hill; and little skill
>   It needs, methinks, to show,
> Up hill and down together told,
>   Four miles an hour they go.

For whether long or short the time
Upon the hill they spent,
Two thirds were passed in going up,
One third in the descent.
Two thirds at three, one third at six,
If rightly reckoned o'er,
Will make one whole at four—the tale
Is tangled now no more.

SIMPLE SUSAN.
MONEY SPINNER.

ANSWERS TO KNOT 2

§ 1. *The Dinner Party*

Problem.—The Governor of Kgovjni wants to give a very small dinner party, and invites his father's brother-in-law, his brother's father-in-law, his father-in-law's brother, and his brother-in-law's father. Find the number of guests.

Answer.—One.

In this genealogy, males are denoted by capitals, and females by small letters.

The Governor is E and his guest is C.

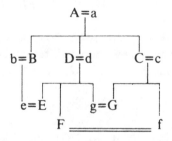

Ten answers have been received. Of these, one is wrong, GALANTHUS NIVALIS MAJOR, who insists on inviting *two* guests, one being the Governor's *wife's brother's father*. If she had taken his *sister's husband's father* instead, she would have found it possible to reduce the guests to *one*.

Of the nine who send right answers, SEA-BREEZE is the very faintest breath that ever bore the name! She simply states that the Governor's uncle might fulfil all the conditions "by intermarriages"! "Wind of the western sea", you have had a very narrow escape! Be thankful to appear in the Class List at all! Bog-Oak and Bradshaw of the Future use genealogies which require 16 people instead of 14, by inviting the Governor's *father's sister's husband* instead of his *father's wife's brother*. I cannot think this so good as one that requires only 14. Caius and Valentine deserve special mention as the only two who have supplied genealogies.

Class List

I

Bee.	M. M.	Old Cat.
Caius.	Matthew Matticks.	Valentine.

II

Bog-Oak.   Bradshaw of the Future.

III

Sea-Breeze

§ 2. *The Lodgings*

Problem.—A square has 20 doors on each side, which contains 21 equal parts. They are numbered all round, beginning at one corner. From which of the four, Nos. 9, 25, 52, 73, is the sum of distances, to the other three, least?

Answer.—From No. 9.

Let A be No. 9, B No. 25, C No. 52, and D No. 73.

Then $AB = \sqrt{(12^2 + 5^2)} = \sqrt{169} = 13$;
$\quad AC = 21$;
$\quad AD = \sqrt{(9^2 + 8^2)} = \sqrt{145} = 12 +$
$\qquad$ (N.B. *i.e.*, "between 12 and 13")
$\quad BC = \sqrt{(16^2 + 12^2)} = \sqrt{400} = 20$;
$\quad BD = \sqrt{(3^2 + 21^2)} = \sqrt{450} = 21 +$;
$\quad CD = \sqrt{(9^2 + 13^2)} = \sqrt{250} = 15 +$;

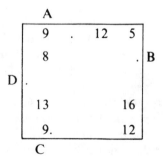

Hence from the sum of distances from A is between 46 and 47; from B, between 54 and 55; from C, between 56 and 57; from D, between 48 and 51. (Why not "between 48 and 49"? Make this out for yourselves.) Hence the sum is least for A.

Twenty-five solutions have been received. Of those, 15 must be marked "zero", 5 are partly right, and 5 right. Of the 15, I may dismiss ALPHABETICAL PHANTOM, BOG-OAK, DINAH MITE, FIFEE, GALANTHUS NIVALIS MAJOR (I fear the cold spring has blighted our SNOWDROP), GUY, H.M.S. PINAFORE, JANET, and VALENTINE with the simple remark that they insist on the unfortunate lodgers *keeping to the pavement*. (I used the words "crossed to Number Seventy-Three" for the special purpose of showing that *short cuts* were possible.) SEA-BREEZE does the same, and adds that "the result would be the same" even if they crossed the Square, but gives no proof of this. M. M. draws a diagram, and says that No. 9 is the house, "as the diagram shows". I cannot see *how* it does so. OLD CAT assumes that the house *must* be No. 9 or No. 73. She does not explain how she estimates the distances. BEE's arithmetic is faulty: she makes $\sqrt{169} + \sqrt{442} + \sqrt{130} = 741$. (I suppose you mean $\sqrt{742}$, which would be a little nearer the truth. But roots cannot be added in this manner. Do you think $\sqrt{9} + \sqrt{16}$ is 25, or even $\sqrt{25}$?) But AYR's state is more perilous still: she draws illogical conclusions with a frightful calmness. After pointing out (rightly) that AC is less than BD, she says, "therefore the nearest house to the other three must be A or C." And again, after pointing out (rightly) that B and D are both within the half-square containing A, she says, "therefore" AB + AD must be less than BC + CD. (There is no logical force in either "therefore". For the first, try Nos. 1, 21, 60, 70: this will make your premiss true, and your conclusion false. Similarly, for the second, try Nos. 1, 30, 51, 71.)

Of the five partly-right solutions, RAGS AND TATTERS and MAD HATTER (who send one answer between them) make No. 25 6 units from one corner instead of 5. CHEAM, E. R. D. L., and MEGGY MOTTS leave openings at the corners of the Square, which are not in the data: moreover CHEAM gives values for the distances without any hint that they are only *approximations*. CROPHI AND MOPHI make the bold and unfounded assumption that there were really 21 houses on each side, instead of 20 as stated by Balbus. "We may assume", they add, "that the doors of Nos. 21, 42, 63, 84, are invisible from the centre of the Square"! What is there, I wonder, that CROPHI AND MOPHI would *not* assume?

Of the five who are wholly right, I think BRADSHAW OF THE FUTURE, CAIUS, CLIFTON C., and MARTREB deserve special praise for their full *analytical* solutions. MATTHEW MATTICKS picks out No. 9, and proves it to be the right house in two ways, very neatly and ingeniously, but *why* he picks it out does not appear. It is an excellent *synthetical* proof, but lacks the analysis which the other four supply.

Class List

I

BRADSHAW OF THE FUTURE.
CAIUS.
CLIFTON C.
MARTREB.

II

MATTHEW MATTICKS.

III

CHEAM.	MEGGY POTTS.
CROPHI AND MOPHI.	⎰RAGS AND TATTERS.
E. R. D. L.	⎱MAD HATTER.

A remonstrance has reached me from SCRUTATOR on the subject of Knot I, which he declares was "no problem at all". "Two questions", he says, "are put. To solve one there is no data: the other answers itself." As to the first point, SCRUTATOR is mistaken; there *are* (not "is") data sufficient to answer the question. As to the other, it is interesting to know that the question "answers itself", and I am sure it does the question great credit: still I fear I cannot enter it on the list of winners, as this competition is only open to human beings.

ANSWERS TO KNOT 3

Problem.—(1) Two travelers, starting at the same time, went opposite ways round a circular railway. Trains start each way every 15 minutes, the easterly ones going round in 3 hours, the westerly in 2. How many trains did each meet on the way, not counting trains met at the terminus itself? (2) They went round, as before, each traveler counting as "one" the train containing the other traveler. How many did each meet?

Answers.—(1) 19. (2) The easterly traveler met 12; the other 8.

The trains one way took 180 minutes, the other way 120. Let us take the l.c.m., 360, and divide the railway into 360 units. The one set of trains went at the rate of 2 units a minute and at intervals of 30 units; the other at the rate of 3 units a minute and at intervals of 45 units. An easterly train starting has 45 units between it and the first train it will meet: it does ⅖ of this while the other does ⅗, and thus meets it at the end of 18 units, and so all the way round. A westerly train starting has 30 units between it and the first train it will meet: it does ⅗ of this while the other does ⅖, and thus meets it at the end of 18 units, and so all the way round. Hence if the railway be divided, by 19 posts, into 20 parts, each containing 18 units, trains meet at every post, and, in (1) each traveler passes 19 posts in going round, and so meets 19 trains. But, in (2), the easterly traveler only begins to count after traversing ⅖ of the journey, *i.e.* on reaching the 8th post, and so counts 12 posts: similarly, the other counts 8. They meet at the end of ⅖ of 3 hours, or ⅗ of 2 hours, *i.e.* 72 minutes.

Forty-five answers have been received. Of these, 12 are beyond the reach of discussion, as they give no working. I can but enumerate their names, ARDMORE, E. A., F. A. D., L. D., MATTHEW MATTICKS, M. E. T., POO-POO, and THE RED QUEEN are all wrong. BETA and ROWENA have got (1) right and (2) wrong. CHEEKY BOB and NAIRAM give the right answers, but it may perhaps make the one less cheeky, and induce the other to take a less inverted view of things, to be informed that, if this had been a competition for a prize, they would have got no marks. (N.B.—I have not ventured to put E.A.'s name in full as she only gave it provisionally, in case her answer should prove right.)

Of the 33 answers for which the working is given, 10 are wrong; 11 half-wrong and half-right; 3 right, except that they cherish the delusion that it was *Clara* who traveled in the easterly train—a point which the data do not enable us to settle; and 9 wholly right.

The 10 wrong answers are from Bo-Peep, Financier, I. W. T., Kate B., M. A. H., Q. Y. Z., Sea-Gull, Thistledown, Tom-Quad, and an unsigned one. Bo-Peep rightly says that the easterly traveler met all trains which started during the 3 hours of her trip, as well as all which started during the previous 2 hours, *i.e.* all which started at the commencements of 20 periods of 15 minutes each; and she is right in striking out the one she met at the moment of starting; but wrong in striking out the *last* train, for she did not meet this at the terminus, but 15 minutes before she got there. She makes the same mistake in (2). Financier thinks that any train, met for the second time, is not to be counted. I. W. T. finds, by a process which is not stated, that the travelers met at the end of 71 minutes and 26½ seconds. Kate B. thinks the trains which are met on starting and on arriving are *never* to be counted, even when met elsewhere. Q. Y. Z. tries a rather complex algebraic solution, and succeeds in finding the time of meeting correctly: all else is wrong. Sea-Gull seems to think that, in (1), the easterly train *stood still* for 3 hours; and says that, in (2) the travelers meet at the end of 71 minutes 40 seconds. Thistledown nobly confesses to having tried no calculation, but merely having drawn a picture of the railway and counted the trains; in (1) she counts wrong; in (2) she makes them meet in 75 minutes. Tom-Quad omits (1); in (2) he makes Clara count the train she met on her arrival. The unsigned one is also unintelligible; it states that the travelers go "¹⁄₂₄ more than the total distance to be traversed"! The "Clara" theory, already referred to, is adopted by 5 of these, *viz.*, Bo-Peep, Financier, Kate B., Tom-Quad, and the nameless writer.

The 11 half-right answers are from Bog-Oak, Bridget, Castor, Cheshire Cat, G. E. B., Guy, Mary, M. A. H., Old Maid, R. W., and Vendredi. All these adopt the "Clara" theory. Castor omits (1). Vendredi gets (1) right, but in (2) makes the same mistake as Bo-Peep. I notice in your solution a marvellous proportion-sum "300 miles : 2 hours :: one mile : 24 seconds." May I venture to advise your acquiring, as soon as possible, an utter disbelief in the possibility of a ratio existing between *miles* and *hours*? Do not be disheartened by your two friends' sarcastic remarks on your "roundabout ways". Their short method, of adding 12 and 8, has the slight disadvantage of bringing the answer wrong: even a "roundabout" method is better than *that*! M. A. H., in (2), makes the travelers count "one" *after* they met, not *when* they met. CHESHIRE CAT and OLD MAID get "20" as answer for (1), by forgetting to strike out the train met on arrival. The others all get "18" in various ways. BOG-OAK, GUY, and R. W. divide the trains which the westerly traveler has to meet into 2 sets, *viz.*, those already on the line, which they (rightly) make "11", and those which started during her 2 hours' journey (exclusive of train met on arrival), which they (wrongly) make "7"; and they make a similar mistake with the easterly train. BRIDGET (rightly) says that the westerly traveler met a train every 6 minutes for 2 hours, but (wrongly) makes the number "20"; it should be "21". G. E. B. adopts BO-PEEP'S method, but (wrongly) strikes out (for the easterly traveler) the train which started at the *commencement* of the previous 2 hours. MARY thinks a train met on arrival must not be counted, even when met on a *previous* occasion.

The 3 who are wholly right but for the unfortunate "Clara" theory, are F. LEE, G. S. C., and X. A. B.

And now "descend, ye classic ten!" who have solved the whole problem. Your names are AIX-LES-BAINS, ALGERNON BRAY (thanks for the friendly remark, which comes with a heart-warmth that not even the Atlantic could chill), ARVON, BRADSHAW OF THE FUTURE, FIFEE, H. L. R., J. L. O., OMEGA, S. S. G., and WAITING FOR THE TRAIN. Several of these have put Clara, provisionally, into the easterly train: but they seem to have understood that the data do not decide the point.

Class List

I

AIX-LES-BAINS.	H. L. R.
ALGERNON BRAY.	OMEGA.
BRADSHAW OF THE FUTURE.	S. S. G.
FIFEE.	WAITING FOR THE TRAIN.

II

ARVON.	J. L. O.

III

F. LEE.	G. S. C.	X. A. B.

ANSWERS TO KNOT 4

Problem.—There are 5 sacks of which Nos. 1, 2, weigh 12 lbs.; Nos. 2, 3, 13½ lbs.; Nos. 3, 4, 11½ lbs.; Nos. 4, 5, 8 lbs.; Nos. 1, 3, 5, 16 lbs. Required the weight of each sack.
Answer.—5½, 6½, 7, 4½, 3½.

The sum of all the weighings, 61 lbs, includes sack No. 3 *thrice* and each other *twice*. Deducting twice the sum of the 1st and 4th weighings, we get 21 lbs. for *thrice* No. 3, *i.e.* 7 lbs. for No. 3. Hence, the 2nd and 3rd weighings give 6½ lbs., 4½ lbs. for Nos. 2, 4; and hence again, the 1st and 4th weighings give 5½ lbs., 3½ lbs., for Nos. 1, 5.

Ninety-seven answers have been received. Of these, 15 are beyond the reach of discussion, as they give no working. I can but enumerate their names, and I take this opportunity of saying that this is the last time I shall put on record the names of competitors who give no sort of clue to the process by which their answers were obtained. In guessing a conundrum, or in catching a flea, we do not expect the breathless victor to give us afterwards, in cold blood, a history of the mental or muscular efforts by which he achieved his success; but a mathematical calculation is another thing. The names of this "mute inglorious" band are COMMON SENSE, D. E. R., DOUGLAS, E. L. ELLEN, I. M. T., J. M. C., JOSEPH, KNOT I, LUCY, MEEK, M. F. C., PYRAMUS, SHAH, VERITAS.

Of the eighty-two answers with which the working, or some approach to it, is supplied, one is wrong: seventeen have given solutions which are (from one cause or another) practically valueless: the remaining sixty-four I shall try to arrange in a Class List, according to the varying degrees of shortness and neatness to which they seem to have attained.

The solitary wrong answer is from NELL. To be thus "alone in a crowd" is a distinction—a painful one, no doubt, but still a distinction. I am sorry for you, my dear young lady, and I seem to hear your tearful exclamation, when you read these lines, "Ah! This is the knell of all my hopes!" Why, oh why, did you assume that the 4th and 5th bags weighed 4 lbs each? And why did you not test your answers? However, please try again: and please don't change your *nom-de-plume*: let us have NELL in the First Class next time!

The seventeen whose solutions are practically valueless are ARDMORE, A READY RECKONER, ARTHUR, BOG-LARK, BOG-OAK, BRIDGET, FIRST ATTEMPT, J. L. C., M. E. T., ROSE, ROWENA, SEA-BREEZE, SYLVIA, THISTLEDOWN, THREE-FIFTHS ASLEEP, VENDREDI and WINIFRED. BOG-LARK tries it by a sort of "rule of false", assuming experimentally that Nos. 1, 2, weigh 6 lbs each, and having thus produced 17½, instead of 16, as the weight of 1, 3, and 5, she removes "the superfluous pound and a half", but does not explain how she knows from which to take it. THREE-FIFTHS ASLEEP says that (when in that peculiar state) "it seemed perfectly clear" to her that, "3 out of the 5 sacks being weighed twice over, ⅗ of 45 = 27, must be the total weight of the 5 sacks." As to which I can only say, with the Captain, "it beats me entirely!" WINIFRED, on the plea that "one must have a starting-point", assumes (what I fear is a mere guess) that No. 1 weighed 5½ lbs. The rest all do it, wholly or partly, by guess-work.

The problem is of course (as any algebraist sees at once) a case of "simultaneous simple equations". It is, however, easily soluble by arithmetic only; and, when this is the case, I hold that it is bad workmanship to use the more complex method. I have not, this time, given more credit to arithmetical solutions; but in future problems I shall (other things being equal) give the highest marks to those who use the simplest machinery. I have put into class I those whose answers seemed specially short and neat, and into Class III those that seemed specially long or clumsy. Of the last set, A. C. M., FURZE-BUSH, JAMES, PARTRIDGE, R. W., and WAITING FOR THE TRAIN, have sent long wandering solutions, the substitutions have no definite method, but seeming to have been made to see what would come of it. CHILPOME and DUBLIN BOY omit some of the working. ARVON MARLBOROUGH BOY only finds the weight of *one* sack.

Class List

I

B. E. D.	NUMBER FIVE.
C. H.	PEDRO.
CONSTANCE JOHNSON.	R. E. X.
GREYSTEAD.	SEVEN OLD MEN.
GUY.	VIS INERTIÆ.
HOOPOE.	WILLY B.
J. F. A.	YAHOO.
M. A. H.	

II

AMERICAN SUBSCRIBER.
AN APRECIATIVE SCHOOL-MA'AM
AYR.
BRADSHAW OF THE FUTURE.
CHEAM.
C. M. G.
DINAH MITE.
DUCKWING.
E. C. M.
E. N. LOWRY.
ERA.
EUROCLYDON.
F. H .W.
FIFEE.
G. E. B.
HARLEQUIN.
HAWTHORN.
HOUGH GREEN.
J. A. B.
JACK TAR.

J. B. B.
KGOVJNI.
LAND LUBBER.
L. D.
MAGPIE.
MARY.
MHRUXI.
MINNIE.
MONEY SPINNER.
NAIRAM.
OLD CAT.
POLICHINELLE.
SIMPLE SUSAN.
S. S. G.
THISBE.
VERENA.
WAMBA.
WOLFE.
WYKEHAMICUS.
Y.M.A.H.

III

A. C. M.
ARVON MARLBOROUGH BOY.
CHILPOME.
DUBLIN BOY
FURZE-BUSH

JAMES.
PARTRIDGE.
R. W.
WAITING FOR THE TRAIN.

Problem.—To mark pictures, giving 3 X 's to 2 or 3, 2 to 4 or 5, and 1 to 9 or 10; also giving 3 o's to 1 or 2, 2 to 3 or 4, and 1 to 8 or 9; so as to mark the smallest possible number of pictures, and to give them the largest possible number of marks.

Answer.—10 pictures; 29 marks; arranged thus:

X	X	X	X	X	X	X	X	X	0
X	X	X	X	X		0	0	0	0
X	X	0	0	0	0	0	0	0	0

Solution.—By giving all the X 's possible, putting into brackets the optional ones, we get 10 pictures marked thus:

X	X	X	X	X	X	X	X	X	(X)
X	X	X	X	(X)					
X	X	(X)							

By then assigning 0's in the same way, beginning at the other end, we get 9 pictures marked thus:

							(0)	0	
						(0)	0	0	0
(0)	0	0	0	0	0	0	0	0	

All we have now to do is to run these two wedges as close together as they will go, so as to get the minimum number of pictures—erasing optional marks where by so doing we can run them closer, but otherwise letting them stand. There are 10 necessary marks in the 1st row, and in the 3rd; but only 7 in the 2nd. Hence we erase all optional marks in the 1st and 3rd rows, but let them stand in the 2nd.

Twenty-two answers have been received. Of these, 11 give no working, so, in accordance with what I announced in my last review of answers, I leave them unnamed, merely mentioning that 5 are right and 6 wrong.

Of the eleven answers with which some working is supplied, 3 are wrong. C. H. begins with the rash assertion that under the given conditions "the sum is impossible. For", he or she adds (these initialed correspondents are dismally vague beings to deal with: perhaps "it" would be a better pronoun), "10 is the least possible number of pictures" (granted) "therefore we must either give 2 × 's to 6, or 2 0's to 5". Why "must," O alphabetical phantom? It is nowhere ordained that every picture "must" have 3 marks! FIFEE sends a folio page of solution, which deserved a better fate: she offers three answers, in each of which 10 pictures are marked, with 30 marks; in one she gives 2 × 's to 6 pictures; in another to 7; in the third she gives 2 0's to 5; thus in every case ignoring the conditions. (I pause to remark that the condition "2 × 's to 4 or 5 pictures" can only mean "*either* to 4 *or else* to 5": if, as one competitor holds, it might mean *any* number not less than 4, the words "*or* 5" would be superfluous.) I. E. A. (I am happy to say that none of these bloodless phantoms appear this time in the class-list. Is it IDEA with the "D" left out?) gives 2 × 's to 6 pictures. She then takes me to task for using the word "ought" instead of "nought". No doubt, to one who thus rebels against the rules laid down for her guidance, the word must be distasteful. But does not I. E. A. remember the parallel of "adder"? That creature was originally "a nadder": then the two words took to bandying the poor "n" backwards and forwards like a shuttlecock, the final state of the game being "an adder". May not "a nought" have similarly become "an ought"? Anyhow, "oughts and crosses" is a very old game. I don't think I ever heard it called "noughts and crosses".

In the following Class List, I hope the solitary occupant of III will sheathe her claws when she hears how narrow an escape she has had of not being named at all. Her account of the process by which she got the answer is so meagre that, like the nursery tale of "Jack-a-Minory" (I trust I.E.A. will be merciful to the spelling), it is scarcely to be distinguished from "zero".

Class List

I

GUY.   OLD CAT.   SEA-BREEZE.

II

AYR.   F. LEE.
BRADSHAW OF THE FUTURE.   H. VERNON.

III

CAT.

Problem 1.—*A* and *B* began the year with only £1000 apiece. They borrowed nought; they stole nought. On the next New Year's day they had £60,000 between them. How did they do it?

Solution.—They went that day to the Bank of England *A* stood in front of it, while *B* went round and stood behind it.

Two answers have been received, both worthy of much honour. ADDLE-PATE makes them borrow "zero" and steal "zero", and uses both cyphers by putting them at the righthand end of the £1000, thus producing £100,000, which is well over the mark. But (or to express it in Latin) AT SPES INFRACTA has solved it even more ingeniously: with the first cypher she turns "1" of the £1000 into a "9", and adds the result to the original sum, thus getting £10,000: and in this, by means of the other "zero", she turns the"1" into a "6" thus hitting the exact £60,000.

Class List

I

AT SPES INFRACTA.

II

ADDLEPATE.

Problem 2.—*L* makes 5 scarves, while *M* makes 2: *Z* makes 4, while *L* makes 3. Five scarves of *Z's* weigh one of *L's*; 5 of *M's* weigh 3 of *Z's*. One of *M's* is as warm as 4 of *Z's* and one of *L's* as warm as 3 of *M's*. Which is best, giving equal weight in the result of rapidity of work, lightness, and warmth?

Answer.—The order is *M, L, Z.*

Solution.—As to rapidity (other things being constant), *L's* merit is to *M's* in the ratio of 5 to 2: *Z's* to *L's* in the ratio of 4 to 3. In order to get one set of 3 numbers fulfilling these conditions, it is perhaps simplest to take the one that occurs *twice* as unity, and reduce the others to fractions: this gives, for *L, M,* and *Z,* the marks 1, $\frac{2}{3}$, $\frac{4}{3}$. In estimating for *lightness,* we observe that the greater the weight, the less the merit, so that *Z's* merit is to *L's* as 5 to 1. Thus the marks for *lightness* are $\frac{1}{5}$, $\frac{5}{3}$, 1. And similarly, the marks for warmth are 3, 1, $\frac{1}{4}$. To get the total result, we must *multiply L's* 3 marks together, and do the same for *M* and for *Z.* The final numbers are $1 \times \frac{1}{5} \times 3$, $\frac{2}{5} \times \frac{5}{3} \times 1$, $\frac{4}{3} \times 1 \times \frac{1}{4}$; *i.e.* $\frac{3}{5}$, $\frac{2}{3}$, $\frac{1}{3}$; *i.e.* multiplying throughout by 15 (which will not alter the proportion), 9, 10, 5; showing the order of merit to be *M, L, Z.*

Twenty-nine answers have been received, of which five are right, and twenty-four wrong. These hapless ones have all (with three exceptions) fallen into the error of *adding* the proportional numbers together, for each candidate, instead of *multiplying. Why* the latter is right, rather than the former, is fully proved in textbooks, so I will not occupy space by stating it here: but it can be *illustrated* very easily by the case of length, breadth, and depth. Suppose *A* and *B* are rival diggers of rectangular tanks: the amount of work done is evidently measured by the number of *cubical feet* dug out. Let *A* dig a tank 10 feet long, 10 wide, 2 deep: let *B* dig one 6 feet long, 5 wide, 10 deep. The cubical contents are 200, 300; *i.e. B* is best digger in the ratio of 3 to 2. Now try marking for length, width, and depth, separately; giving a maximum mark of 10 to the best in each contest, and then *adding* the results!

Of the twenty-four malefactors, one gives no working, and so has no real claim to be named; but I break the rule for once, in deference to its success in Problem 1: he, she, or it, is ADDLEPATE. The other twenty-three may be divided into five groups.

First and worse are, I take it, those who put the rightful winner *last*; arranging them as "Lolo, Zuzu, Mimi". The names of these desperate wrong-doers are AYR, BRADSHAW OF THE FUTURE, FURZE-BUSH, and POLLUX (who sent a joint answer), GREYSTEAD, GUY, OLD HEN, and SIMPLE SUSAN. The latter was *once* best of all; the Old Hen has taken advantage of her simplicity, and beguiled her with the chaff which was the bane of her own chickenhood.

Secondly, I point the finger of scorn at those who have put the worst candidate at the top; arranging them as "Zuzu, Mimi, Lolo". They are GRÆCIA, M. M., OLD CAT, and R. E. X. " 'Tis Greece, but——"

The third set have avoided both these enormities, and have even succeeded in putting the worst last, their answer being "Lolo, Mimi, Zuzu". Their names are AYR (who also appears among the "quite too

too"), CLIFTON C., F. B., FIFEE, GRIG, JANET, and MRS. SAIREY GAMP. F. B. has not fallen into the common error; she *multiplies* together the proportionate number she gets, but in getting them she goes wrong, by reckoning warmth as a *de-merit*. Possibly she is "Freshly Burnt", or comes "From Bombay". JANET and MRS. SAIREY GAMP have also avoided this error: the method they have adopted is shrouded in mystery—I scarcely feel competent to criticise it. MRS. GAMP says, "If Zuzu makes 4 while Lolo makes 3, Zuzu makes 6 while Lolo makes 5 [bad reasoning], while Mimi makes 2." From this she concludes, "Therefore Zuzu excels in speed by 1" (*i.e.* when compared with Lolo? but what about Mimi?). She then compares the three kinds of excellence, measured on this mystic scale. JANET takes the statement that "Lolo makes 5 while Mimi makes 2", to prove that "Lolo makes 3 while Mimi makes 1 and Zuzu 4" (worse reasoning than MRS. GAMP'S), and thence concludes that "Zuzu excels in speed by ⅛"! JANET should have been ADELINE, "mystery of mysteries!"

The fourth set actually put Mimi at the top, arranging them as "Mimi, Zuzu, Lolo". They are MARQUIS AND CO., MARTREB, S. B. B. (first initial scarcely legible: *may* be meant for "J"), and STANZA.

The fifth set consists of AN ANCIENT FISH and CAMEL. These ill-assorted comrades, by dint of foot and fin, have scrambled into the right answer, but, as their method is wrong, of course it counts for nothing. Also AN ANCIENT FISH has very ancient and fishlike ideas as to *how* numbers represent merit: she says, "Lolo gains 2½ on Mimi." Two and a half *what*? Fish, fish, art thou in thy duty?

Of the five winners I put BALBUS and THE ELDER TRAVELLER slightly below the other three—BALBUS for defective reasoning, the other for scanty working. BALBUS gives two reasons for saying that *addition* of marks is *not* the right method, and then adds. "It follows that the decision must be made by *multiplying* the marks together". This is hardly more logical than to say, "This is not Spring: *therefore* it must be Autumn".

Class List

I

DINAH MITE.   E. B. D. L.   JORAM.

II

BALBUS.   THE ELDER TRAVELLER.

With regard to Knot 5, I beg to express to Vis Inertiæ and to any others, who, like her, understood the condition to be that *every* marked picture must have *three* marks, my sincere regret that the unfortunate phrase "*fill* the columns with oughts and crosses" should have caused them to waste so much time and trouble. I can only repeat that a *literal* interpretation of "fill" would seem to *me* to require that *every* picture in the gallery should be marked. Vis Inertiæ would have been in the First Class if she had sent in the solution she now offers.

ANSWERS TO KNOT 7

Problem.—Given that one glass of lemonade, 3 sandwiches, and 7 biscuits, cost 1*s*. 2*d*.; and that one glass of lemonade, 4 sandwiches, and 10 biscuits, cost 1*s*. 5*d*.: find the cost of (1) a glass of lemonade, a sandwich, and a biscuit; and (2) 2 glasses of lemonade, 3 sandwiches, and 5 biscuits.

Answer.—(1) 8*d*.; (2) 1*s*. 7*d*.

Solution.—This is best treated algebraically. Let x = the cost (in pence) of a glass of lemonade, y of a sandwich, and z of a biscuit. Then we have $x + 3y + 7z = 14$, and $x + 4y + 10z = 17$. And we require the values of $x + y + z$, and of $2x + 3y + 5z$. Now, from *two* equations only, we cannot find, *separately*, the values of *three* unknowns: certain *combinations* of them may, however, be found. Also, we know that we can, by the help of the given equations, eliminate 2 of the 3 unknowns from the quantity whose value is required, which will then contain one only. If, then, the required value is ascertainable at all, it can only be the third unknown vanishing of itself: otherwise the problem is impossible.

Let us then eliminate lemonade and sandwiches, and reduce everything to biscuits—a state of things even more depressing than "if all the world were apple-pie"—by subtracting the 1st equation from the 2nd, which eliminates lemonade, and gives $y + 3z = 3$, or $y = 3 - 3z$; and then substituting this value of y in the 1st, which gives $x - 2z = 5$, *i.e.* $x = 5 + 2z$. Now if we substitute these values of x, y in the quantities whose values are required, the first becomes $(5 + 2z) + (3 - 3z) + z$, *i.e.* 8: and the second becomes $2(5 + 2z) + 3(3 - 3z) + 5z$, *i.e.* 19. Hence the answers are (1) 8*d*., (2) 1*s*. 7*d*.

The above is a *universal* method: that is, it is absolutely certain either to produce the answer, or to prove that no answer is possible. The question may also be solved by combining the quantities whose values are given, so as to form those whose values are required. This is merely a matter of ingenuity and good luck: and as it *may* fail, even when the thing is possible, and is of no use in proving it *im*possible, I cannot rank this method as equal in value with the other. Even when it succeeds, it may prove a very tedious process. Suppose the 26 competitors who have sent in what I may call *accidental* solutions, had had a question to deal with where every number contained 8 or 10 digits! I suspect it would have been a case of "silvered is the raven hair" (see *Patience*) before any solution would have been hit on by the most ingenious of them.

Forty-five answers have come in, of which 44 give, I am happy to say, some sort of *working*, and therefore deserve to be mentioned by name, and have their virtues, or vices, as the case may be, discussed. Thirteen have made assumptions to which they have no right, and so cannot figure in the Class List, even though, in 10 of these 12 cases, the answer is right. Of the remaining 28, no less than 26 have sent in *accidental* solutions, and therefore fall short of the highest honours.

I will now discuss individual cases, taking the worst first, as my custom is.

FROGGY gives no working—at least this is all he gives: after starting the given equations, he says, "Therefore the difference, 1 sandwich + 3 biscuits, = 3*d*.": then follow the amounts of the unknown bills, with no further hint as to how he got them. FROGGY has had a *very* narrow escape of not being named at all!

Of those who are wrong, VIS INERTIÆ has sent in a piece of incorrect working. Peruse the horrid details, and shudder! She takes *x* (call it "*y*") as the cost of a sandwich, and concludes (rightly enough) that a biscuit will cost $\frac{3-y}{3}$. She then subtracts the second equation from the first, and deduces $3y + 7 \times \frac{3-y}{3} - 4y + 10 \times \frac{3-y}{3} = 3$. By making two mistakes in this line, she brings out $y = \frac{3}{2}$. Try it again, O VIS INERTIÆ! Away with INERTIÆ: infuse a little more VIS: and you will bring out the correct (though uninteresting) result, 0 = 0! This will show you that it is hopeless to try to coax anyone of these 3 unknowns to reveal its *separate* value. The other competitor who is wrong throughout, is either J. M. C. or T. M. C.: but whether he be a Juvenile Mis-Calculator or a True Mathematician Confused, he makes the answers 7*d*. and 1*s*. 5*d*. He assumes with Too Much Confidence that biscuits were ½*d*. each, and that Clara paid for 8, though she only ate 7!

We will now consider the 13 whose working is wrong, though the answer is right: and, not to measure their de-merits too exactly, I will take them in alphabetical order. ANITA finds (rightly) that "1 sandwich and 3 biscuits cost 3*d*." and proceeds, "therefore 1 sandwich = 1½*d*., 3 biscuits = 1½*d*., 1 lemonade = 6*d*." DINAH MITE begins like ANITA: and thence proves (rightly) that a biscuit costs less than 1*d*.: whence she concludes (wrongly) that it *must* cost ½*d*. F. C. W. is so beautifully resigned to the certainty of a verdict of "guilty", that I have hardly the heart to utter the word, without adding a "recommended to mercy owing to extenuating circumstances". But really, you know, where *are* the extenuating circumstances? She begins by assuming that lemonade is 4*d*. a glass, and sandwiches 3*d*. each (making with the 2 given equations, *four* conditions to be fulfilled by *three* miserable unknowns!) And, having (naturally) developed this into a contradiction, she then tries 5*d*. and 2*d*. with a similar result. (N.B.—*This* process might have been carried on through the whole of the Tertiary Period, without gratifying one single Megatherium.) She then, by a "happy thought", tries halfpenny biscuits, and so obtains a consistent result. This may be a good solution, viewing the problem as a conundrum: but it is *not* scientific. JANET identifies sandwiches with biscuits! "One sandwich + 3 biscuits" she makes equal to "4". Four *what*? MAYFAIR makes the astounding assertion that the equation, $s + 3b = 3$, "is evidently only satisfied by $s = \frac{3}{2}$, $b = \frac{1}{2}$"! OLD CAT believes that the assumption that a sandwich costs 1½*d*. is "the only way to avoid unmanageable fractions". But *why* avoid them? Is there not a certain glow of triumph in taming such a fraction? "Ladies and gentlemen, the fraction now before you is one that for years defied all efforts of a refining nature: it was, in a word, hopelessly vulgar. Treating it as a circulating decimal (the treadmill of fractions) only made matters worse. As a last resource, I reduced it to its lowest terms, and extracted its square root!" Joking apart, let me thank OLD CAT for some very kind words of sympathy, in reference to a correspondent (whose name I am happy to say I have now forgotten) who had found fault with me as a discourteous critic. O. V. L. is beyond my comprehension. He takes the given equations as (1) and (2): thence, by the process [(2)−(1)], deduces (rightly) equation (3), *viz.*, $s + 3b = 3$: and thence again, by the process [× 3] (a hopeless mystery), deduces $3s + 4b = 4$. I have nothing to say about it: I give it up. SEA BREEZE says, "It is immaterial to the answer" (why?) "in what proportion 3*d*. is divided between the sandwich and the

3 biscuits": so she assumes $s = 1\frac{1}{2}d.$, $b = \frac{1}{2}d.$ STANZA is one of a very irregular metre. At first she (like JANET) identifies sandwiches with biscuits. She then tries two assumptions ($s = 1$, $b = \frac{2}{3}$ and $s = \frac{1}{2}$, $b = \frac{5}{6}$,), and (naturally) ends in contradictions. Then she returns to the first assumption, and finds the three unknowns separately: *quod est absurdum.* STILETTO identifies sandwiches and biscuits, as "articles". Is the word ever used by confectioners? I fancied, "What is the next article, ma'am?" was limited to linendrapers. TWO SISTERS first assume that biscuits are 4 a penny, and then that they are 2 a penny, adding that "the answer will of course be the same in both cases". It is a dreamy remark, making one feel something like Macbeth grasping at the spectral dagger. "Is this a statement that I see before me?" If you were to say, "We both walked the same way this morning," and *I* were to say, "*One* of you walked the same way, but the other didn't," which of the three would be the most hopelessly confused? TURTLE PYATE (what *is* a Turtle Pyate, please?) and OLD CROW, who send a joint answer, and Y. Y., adopt the same method. Y. Y. gets the equation $s + 3b = 3$: and then says, "This must be apportioned in one of the three following ways." It *may* be, I grant you: but Y. Y. do you say "must"? I fear it is *possible* for Y. Y. to be *two* Y's. The other two conspirators are less positive; they say it "can" be so divided: but they add "either of the three prices being right"! This is bad grammar and bad arithmetic at once, O mysterious birds!

Of those who win honours, THE SHETLAND SNARK must have the Third Class all to himself. He has only answered half the question, viz. the amount of Clara's luncheon: the two little old ladies he pitilessly leaves in the midst of their "difficulty". I beg to assure him (with thanks for his friendly remarks) that entrance-fees and subscriptions are things unknown in that most economical of clubs, "The Knot-Untiers."

The authors of the 26 "accidental" solutions differ only in the number of steps they have taken between the data and the answers. In order to do them full justice I have arranged the second class in sections, according to the number of steps. The two Kings are fearfully deliberate! I suppose walking quick, or taking short cuts, is inconsistent with kingly dignity: but really, in reading THESEUS' solution, one almost fancied he was "marking time", and making no advance at all! The other King will, I hope, pardon me for having altered "Coal" into "Cole". King Coilus, or Coil, seems to have reigned soon after Arthur's time. Henry of Huntingdon identifies him with the King Coël who first built walls round Colchester, which was named after him. In the Chronicle of Robert of Gloucester we read:

Aftur Kyng Aruirag, of wam we habbeth y told,
Marius ys sone was kyng, quoynte mon & bold,
And ys sone was aftur hym, Coil was ys name,
Bothe it were quoynte men, & of noble fame.

BALBUS lays it down as a general principle that "in order to ascertain the cost of any one luncheon, it must come to the same amount upon two different assumptions". (*Query.* Should not "it" be "we"? Otherwise the *luncheon* is represented as wishing to ascertain its own cost!) He then makes two assumptions—one, that sandwiches cost nothing; the other, that biscuits cost nothing (either arrangement would lead to the shop being inconveniently crowded!)—and brings out the unknown luncheons as 8*d*. and 19*d*. on each assumption. He then concludes that this arrangement of results "shows that the answers are correct". Now I propose to disprove his general law by simply giving *one* instance of its failing. One instance is quite enough. In logical language, in order to disprove a "universal affirmative", it is enough to prove its contradictory, which is a "particular negative". (I must pause for digression on Logic, and especially on Ladies Logic. The universal affirmative, "Everybody says he's a duck," is crushed instantly by proving the particular negative, "Peter says he's a goose," which is equivalent to "Peter does *not* say he's a duck". And the universal negative, "Nobody calls on her," is well met by the particular affirmative, "*I* called yesterday." In short, either of two contradictories disproves the other: and the moral is that, since a particular proposition is much more easily proved than a universal one, it is the wisest course, in arguing with a lady, to limit one's *own* assertions to "particulars", and leave *her* to prove the "universal" contradictory, if she can. You will thus generally secure a *logical* victory: a *practical* victory is not to be hoped for, since she can always fall back upon the crushing remark, "*That* has nothing to do with it!"—a move for which man has not yet discovered any satisfactory answer. Now let us return to BALBUS.) Here is my "particular negative", on which to test his rule: Suppose the two recorded luncheons to have been "2 buns, one queen-cake, 2 sausage rolls, and a bottle of Zoëdone: total one-and-ninepence", and "one bun, 2 queen-cakes, a sausage-roll, and a bottle of Zoëdone: total one-and-fourpence". And suppose Clara's unknown luncheon to have been "3 buns, one queen-cake, one sausage-roll, and 2 bottles of Zoëdone": while the two little sisters had been indulging in "8 buns, 4 queen-cakes, 2 sausage-rolls, and 6 bottles of Zoëdone". (Poor souls, how thirsty they must have been!) If BALBUS will kindly try this by his principle of "two assumptions", first assuming that a bun is 1*d*. and a queen-cake 2*d*., and then that a bun is 3*d*. and a queen-cake 3*d*., he will bring out the other two luncheons, on each assumption, as "one-and-ninepence" and "four-and-tenpence" respectively, which harmony of results, he will say, "shows that the answers are correct." And yet, as a matter of fact, the buns were 2*d*. each, the queen-cakes 3*d*., the sausage-rolls 6*d*., and the Zoëdone 2*d*. a bottle: so that Clara's third luncheon had cost one-and-sevenpence, and her thirsty friends had spent four-and-fourpence!

Another remark of BALBUS I will quote and discuss: for I think it also may yield a moral for some of my readers. He says, "It is the same thing in substance whether in solving this problem we use words and call it arithmetic, or use letters and signs and call it algebra." Now this does not appear to me a correct description of the two methods: the arithmetical method is that of "synthesis" only: it goes from one known fact to another, till it reaches its goal: whereas the algebraical method is that of "analysis"; it begins with the goal, symbolically represented, and so goes backwards, dragging its veiled victim with it, till it has reached the full daylight of known facts, in which it can tear off the veil and say, "I know you!"

Take an illustration: Your house has been broken into and robbed, and you appeal to the policeman who was on duty that night. "Well, mum, I did see a chap getting out over your garden wall: but I was a good bit off, so I didn't chase him, like. I just cut down the short way to the 'Chequers', and who should I meet but Bill Sykes, coming full split round the corner. So I just ups and says, 'My lad, you're wanted.' That's all I says. And he says, 'I'll go along quiet, Bobby,' he says, 'without the darbies,' he says." There's your *Arithmetical* policeman. Now try the other method: "I seed somebody a-running, but he was well gone or ever *I* got nigh the place. So I just took a look round in the garden. And I noticed the footmarks, where the chap had come right across your flower-beds. They was big footmarks sure-ly. And I noticed as the left foot went down at the heel, ever so much deeper than the other. And I says to myself, 'The chap's been a big hulking chap: and he goes lame on his left foot'. And I rubs my hand on the wall where he got over, and there was soot on it, and no mistake. So I says to myself. 'Now where can I light on a big man, in the chimbley-sweep line, what's lame on one foot?' And I flashes up permiscuous: and I says, 'It's Bill Sykes!' says I." There is your *Algebraical* policeman—a higher intellectual type, to my thinking, than the other.

LITTLE JACK'S solution calls for a word of praise, as he has written out what really is an algebraical proof *in words*, without representing any of his facts as equations. If it is all his own, he will make a good algebraist in the time to come. I beg to thank Simple Susan for some kind words of sympathy, to the same effect as those received from Old Cat.

Hecla and Martreb are the only two who have used a method *certain* either to produce, or else to prove it impossible: so they must share between them the highest honours.

Class List

I

HECLA. MARTREB.

II

§ 1 (2 *steps*)
Adelaide.
Clifton C...
E. K. C.
Guy.
L'Inconnu.
Little Jack.
Nil Desperandum.
Simple Susan.
Yellow-Hammer.
Woolly One.

§ 2 (3 *steps*)
A. A.
A Christmas Carol.
Afternoon Tea.
An Appreciative School-ma'am.
Baby.
Balbus.
Bog-Oak.

§ 2 (3 *steps*)—continued
Wall-Flower.
The Red Queen.

§ 3 (4 *steps*)
Hawthorn.
Joram.
S. S. G.

§ 4 (5 *steps*)
A Stepney Coach.

§ 5 (6 *steps*)
Bay Laurel.
Bradshaw of the Future.

§ 6 (9 *steps*)
Old King Cole.

§ 7 (14 *steps*)
Theseus.

Answers to Correspondents

I have received several letters on the subjects of Knots 2 and 6, which lead me to think some further explanation desirable.

In Knot 2, I had intended the numbering of the houses to begin at one corner of the Square, and this was assumed by most, if not all, of the competitors. TROJANUS, however, says, "Assuming, in default of any information, that the street enters the square in the middle of each side, it may be supposed that the numbering begins at a street." But surely the other is the more natural assumption?

In Knot 6, the first Problem was, of course a mere *jeu de mots*, whose presence I thought excusable in a series of Problems whose aim is to entertain rather than to instruct: but it has not escaped the contemptuous criticisms of two of my correspondents, who seem to think that Apollo is in duty bound to keep his bow always on the stretch. Neither of them has guessed it: and this is true human nature. Only the other day—the 31st of September, to be quite exact—I met my old friend Brown, and gave him a riddle I had just heard. With one great effort of his colossal mind, Brown guessed it. "Right!" said I. "Ah," said he, "it's very neat—very neat. And it isn't an answer that would occur to everybody. Very neat indeed." A few yards farther on, I fell in with Smith, and to him I propounded the same riddle. He frowned over it for a minute, and then gave it up. Meekly I faltered out the answer. "A poor thing, sir!" Smith growled, as he turned away. "A very poor thing! I wonder you care to repeat such rubbish!" Yet Smith's mind is, if possible, even more colossal than Brown's.

The second Problem of Knot 6 is an example in ordinary Double Rule of Three, whose essential feature is that the result depends on the variation of several elements, which are so related to it that, if all but one be constant, it varies as that one: hence, if none be constant, it varies as their product. Thus, for example, the cubical contents of a rectangular tank vary as its length, if breadth and depth be constant, and so on; hence, if none be constant, it varies as the product of the length, breadth, and depth.

When the result is not thus connected with the varying elements, the problem ceases to be Rule of Three and often becomes one of great complexity.

To illustrate this, let us take two candidates for a prize, *A* and *B*, who are to compete in French, German, and Italian:

(*a*) Let it be known that the result is to depend on their *relative* knowledge of each subject, so that, whether their marks, for French, be "1, 2" or "100, 200", the result will be the same: and let it also be laid down that, if they get equal marks on 2 papers, the final marks are to have the same ratio as those of the 3rd paper. This is a case of ordinary Double Rule of Three. We multiply *A*'s 3 marks together, and do the same for *B*. Note that, if *A* gets a single "zero", his final mark is "zero", even if he gets full marks for 2 papers while *B* gets only one mark for each paper. This of course would be very unfair on *A*, though a correct solution under the given conditions.

(*b*) The result is to depend, as before, on *relative* knowledge; but French is to have twice as much weight as German or Italian. This is an unusual form of question. I should be inclined to say, "The resulting ratio is to be nearer to the French ratio than if we multiplied as in (*a*), and so much nearer that it would be necessary to use the other multipliers *twice* to produce the same result as in (*a*)": *e.g.*, if the French ratio were 9/10, and the others 4/9, 1/9, so that the ultimate ratio, by method (*a*), would be 3/45, I should multiply instead by 2/3, 1/3, giving the result, 1/5, which is nearer to 9/10 than if we had used method (*a*).

(*c*) The result is to depend on *actual* amount of knowledge of the 3 subjects collectively. Here we have to ask two questions: (1) What is to be the "unit" (*i.e.* "standard to measure by") in each subject? (2) Are these units to be of equal, or unequal, value? The usual "unit" is the knowledge shown by answering the whole paper correctly; calling this "100", all lower amounts are represented by numbers between "zero", and "100". Then, if these units are to be of equal value, we simply add *A*'s 3 marks together, and do the same for *B*.

(*d*) The conditions are the same as (*c*) but French is to have double weight. Here we simply double the French marks, and add as before.

(*e*) French is to have such weight that, if other marks be equal, the ultimate ratio is to be that of the French paper, so that a "zero" in this would swamp the candidate: but the other two results are to affect the result collectively, by the amount of knowledge shown, the two being reckoned of equal value. Here I should add *A*'s German and Italian marks together, and multiply by his French mark.

But I need not go on: the problem may evidently be set with many varying conditions, each requiring its own method of solution. The Problem in Knot 6 was meant to belong to variety (*a*), and to make this clear, I inserted the following passage:

"Usually the competitors differ in one point only. Thus, last year, Fifi and Gogo made the same number of scarves in the trial week, and they were equally light; but Fifi's were twice as warm as Gogo's, and she was pronounced twice as good."

What I have said will suffice, I hope, as an answer to BALBUS, who holds that (*a*) and (*c*) are the only possible varieties of the problem, and that to say, "We cannot use addition, therefore we must be intended to use multiplication," is no more logical than, from knowledge that one was not born in the night, to infer that he was born in the daytime; and also to FIFEE, who says, "I think a little more consideration will show you that our 'error of *adding* the proportional numbers together for each candidate instead of *multiplying*' is no error at all." Why, even if addition *had* been the right method to use, not one of the writers (I speak from memory) showed any consciousness of the necessity of fixing a "unit" for each subject. "No error at all"! They were positively steeped in error!

One correspondent (I do not name him, as the communication is not quite friendly in tone) writes thus: "I wish to add, very respectfully, that I think it would be in better taste if you were to abstain from the very trenchant expressions which you are accustomed to indulge in when criticising the answer. That such a tone must not be" ("be not"?) "agreeable to the persons concerned who have made mistakes may possibly have no great weight with you, but I hope that you will feel that it would be as well not to employ it, *unless you are quite certain of being correct yourself.*" The only instances the writer gives of the "trenchant expressions" are "hapless" and "malefactors". I beg to assure him (and any others who may need the assurance: I trust there are none) that all such words have been used in jest, and with no idea that they could possibly annoy any one, and that I sincerely regret any annoyance I may have thus inadvertently given. May I hope that in future they will recognize the distinction between severe language used in sober earnest, and the "words of unmeant bitterness", which Coleridge has alluded to in that lovely passage beginning, "A little child, a limber elf"? If the writer will refer to that passage, or to the Preface to *Fire, Famine, and Slaughter,* he will find the distinction, for which I plead, far better drawn out than I could hope to do in any words of mine.

The writer's insinuation that I care not how much annoyance I give to my readers I think it best to pass over in silence; but to his concluding remark I must entirely demur. I hold that to use language likely to annoy any of my correspondents would not be in the least justified by the plea that I was "quite certain of being correct". I trust that the knot-untiers and I are not on such terms as those!

I beg to thank G. B. for the offer of a puzzle—which, however, is too like the old one, "Make four 9's into 100."

ANSWERS TO KNOT 8

§ 1. *The Pigs*

Problem.—Place twenty-four pigs in four sties so that, as you go round and round, you may always find the number in each sty nearer to ten than the number in the last.

Answer.—Place 8 pigs in the first sty, 10 in the second, nothing in the third, and 6 in the fourth: 10 is nearer ten than 8; nothing is nearer ten than 10; 6 is nearer ten than nothing; and 8 is nearer ten than 6.

This problem is noticed by only two correspondents. BALBUS says, "It certainly cannot be solved mathematically, nor do I see how to solve it by any verbal quibble." NOLENS VOLENS makes Her Radiancy change the direction of going round; and even then is obliged to add, "the pig must be carried in front of her"!

§ 2. *The Grurmstipths*

Problem.—Omnibuses start from a certain point, both ways, every 15 minutes. A traveler, starting on foot along with one of them, meets one in 12½ minutes: when will he be overtaken by one?

Answer.—In 6¼ minutes.

Solution.—Let "*a*" be the distance an omnibus goes in 15 minutes, and "*x*" the distance from the starting-point to where the traveler is overtaken. Since the omnibus met is due at the starting-point in 2½ minutes, it goes in that time as far as the traveler walks in 12½, *i.e.*, it goes 5 times as fast. Now the overtaking omnibus is "*a*" behind the traveler when he starts, and therefore goes "*a* + *x*" while he goes "*x*".

Hence $a + x = 5x$; *i.e.* $4x = a$, and $x = \frac{a}{4}$. This distance would be traversed by an omnibus in $\frac{15}{4}$ minutes, and therefore by the traveler in $5 \times \frac{15}{4}$. Hence he is overtaken in 18¾ minutes after starting, *i.e.* in 6¼ minutes after meeting the omnibus.

Four answers have been received, of which two are wrong. DINAH MITE rightly states that the overtaking omnibus reached the point where they met the other omnibus 5 minutes after they left, but wrongly concludes that, going 5 times as fast, it would overtake them in another minute. The travelers are 5 minutes' walk ahead of the omnibus, and must walk ¼ of this distance farther before the omnibus overtakes them, which will be ⅕ of the distance traversed by the omnibus in the same time: this will require 1¼ minutes more. NOLENS VOLENS tries it by a process like "Achilles and the Tortoise". He rightly states that, when the overtaking omnibus leaves the gate, the travelers are ⅕ of "*a*" ahead, and that it will take the omnibus 3 minutes to traverse this distance: "during which time" the travelers, he tells us, go $\frac{1}{15}$ of "*a*" (this should be $\frac{1}{25}$). The travelers being now $\frac{1}{15}$ of "*a*" ahead, he concludes that the work remaining to be done is for the travelers to go $\frac{1}{60}$ of "*a*", while the omnibus goes $\frac{1}{12}$. The *principle* is correct, and might have been applied earlier.

Class List

I

BALBUS.   DELTA.

§ 1. *The Buckets*

Problem.—Lardner states that a solid, immersed in a fluid, displaces an amount equal to itself in bulk. How can this be true of a small bucket floating in a larger one?

Solution.—Lardner means, by "displaces", "occupies a space which might be filled with water without any change in the surroundings." If the portion of the floating bucket, which is above the water, could be annihilated, and the rest of it transformed into water, the surrounding water would not change its position: which agrees with Lardner's statement.

Five answers have been received, none of which explains the difficulty arising from the well-known fact that a floating body is the same weight as the displaced fluid. HECLA says that "Only that portion of the smaller bucket which descends below the original level of the water can be properly said to be immersed, and only an equal bulk of water is displaced." Hence, according to HECLA, a solid whose weight was equal to that of an equal bulk of water, would not float till the whole of it was below "the original level" of the water: but, as a matter of fact, it would float as soon as it was all under water. MAGPIE says the fallacy is "the assumption that one body can displace another from a place where it isn't", and that Lardner's assertion is incorrect, except when the containing vessel "was originally full to the brim". But the question of floating depends on the present state of things, not on past history. OLD KING COLE takes the same view as HECLA TYMPANUM and VINDEX assume that "displaced" means "raised above its original level", and merely explain how it comes to pass that the water, so raised, is less in bulk than the immersed portion of bucket, and thus land themselves—or rather set themselves floating—in the same boat as HECLA.

I regret that there is no Class List to publish for this Problem.

§ 2. *Balbus's Essay*

Problem.—Balbus states that if a certain solid be immersed in a certain vessel of water, the water will rise through a series of distances, two inches, one inch, half an inch, etc., which series has no end. He concludes that the water will rise without limit. Is this true?

Solution.—No. This series can never reach 4 inches, since, however many terms we take, we are always short of 4 inches by an amount equal to the last term taken.

Three answers have been received—but only two seem to me worthy of honours.

TYMPANUM says that the statement about the stick "is merely a blind, to which the old answer may well be applied, *solvitur ambulando*, or rather *mergendo*". I trust TYMPANUM will not test this in his own person, by taking the place of the man in Balbus's Essay! He would infallibly be drowned.

OLD KING COLE rightly points out that the series, 2, 1, etc., is a decreasing geometrical progression: while VINDEX rightly identifies the fallacy as that of "Achilles and the Tortoise".

Class List

I

OLD KING COLE.   VINDEX.

§ 3. *The Garden*

Problem.—An oblong garden, half a yard longer than wide, consists entirely of a gravel walk, spirally arranged, a yard wide and 3630 yards long. Find the dimensions of the garden.

Answers.—60, 60½.

Solution.—The number of yards and fractions of a yard traversed in walking along a straight piece of walk, is evidently the same as the number of square yards and fractions of a square yard contained in that piece of walk: and the distance traversed in passing through a square yard at a corner, is evidently a yard. Hence the area of the garden is 3630 square yards: *i.e.* if x be the width, $x(x + \frac{1}{2}) = 3630$. Solving this quadratic, we find $x = 60$. Hence the dimensions are 60, 60½.

Twelve answers have been received—seven right and five wrong.

C. G. L., NABOB, OLD CROW, and TYMPANUM assume that the number of yards in the length of the path is equal to the number of square yards in the garden. This is true, but should have been proved. But each is guilty of darker deeds. C. G. L.'s "working" consists of dividing 3630 by 60. Whence came this divisor, O Seigel? Divination? Or was it a dream? I fear this solution is worth noting. OLD CROW'S is shorter, and so (if possible) worth rather less. He says the answer "is at once seen to be 60 × 60½"! NABOB'S calculation is short, but "as rich as a NABOB" in error. He says that the square root of 3630, multiplied by 2, equals the length plus the breadth. That is $60 \cdot 25 \times 2 = 120½$. His first assertion is only true of a *square* garden. His second is irrelevant, since $60 \cdot 25$ is *not* the square root of 3630! Nay, Bob, this will *not* do! TYMPANUM says that, by extracting the square root of 3630, we get 60 yards with a remainder of 30/60, or half a yard, which we add so as to make the oblong 60 × 60½. This is very terrible: but worse remains behind. TYMPANUM proceeds thus: "But why should there be the half-yard at all? Because without it there would be no space at all for flowers. By means of it, we find reserved in the very centre a small plot of ground, two yards long by half a yard wide, the only space not occupied by walk." But Balbus expressly said that the walk "used up the whole of the area", O TYMPANUM! My tympa is exhausted: my brain is num! I can say no more.

HECLA indulges, again and again, in that most fatal of all habits in computation—the making *two* mistakes which cancel each other. She takes x as the width of the garden, in yards, and $x + \frac{1}{2}$ as its length, and makes her first "coil" the sum of $x - \frac{1}{2}, x - \frac{1}{2}, x - 1, x - 1$, *i.e.* $4x - 3$: but the fourth term should be $x - 1\frac{1}{2}$, so that her first coil is ½ a yard too long. Her second coil is the sum of $x - 2\frac{1}{2}, x - 2\frac{1}{2}, x - 3, x - 3$: here the first term should be $x - 2$ and the last $x - 3\frac{1}{2}$: these two mistakes cancel and this coil is therefore right. And the same thing is true of every other coil but the last, which needs an extra half-yard to reach the *end* of the path: and this exactly balances the mistake in the first coil. Thus the sum-total of the coils comes right though the working is all wrong.

Of the seven who are right, DINAH MITE, JANET, MAGPIE, and TAFFY make the same assumption as C. G. L. and Co. They then solve by a quadratic. MAGPIE also tries it by arithmetic progression, but fails to notice that the first and last "coils" have special values.

ALUMNUS ETONÆ attempts to prove what C. G. L. assumes by a particular instance, taking a garden 6 by 5½. He ought to have proved it generally: what is true of one number is not always true of others. OLD KING COLE solves it by an arithmetical progression. It is right, but too lengthy to be worth as much as a quadratic.

VINDEX proves it very neatly, by pointing out that a yard of walk measured along the middle represents a square yard of garden, "whether we consider the straight stretches of walk or the square yards at the angles, in which the middle line goes half a yard in one direction and then turns a right angle and goes half a yard in another direction."

Class List

I

VINDEX.

II

ALUMNUS ETONÆ.   OLD KING COLE.

III

DINAH MITE.   MAGPIE.
JANET.   TAFFY.

ANSWERS TO KNOT 10

§ 1. *The Chelsea Pensioners*

Problem.—If 70 per cent have lost an eye, 75 per cent an ear, 80 per cent an arm, 85 per cent a leg: what percentage, *at least*, must have lost all four?

Answer.—Ten.

Solution.—(I adopt that of POLAR STAR, as being better than my own.) Adding the wounds together, we get $70 + 75 + 80 + 85 = 310$, among 100 men; which gives 3 to each, and 4 to 10 men. Therefore the least percentage is 10.

Nineteen answers have been received. One is "5", but, as no working is given with it, it must, in accordance with the rule remain "a deed without a name". JANET makes it "35⁷⁄₁₀". I am sorry she has misunderstood the question, and has supposed that those who had lost an ear were 75 per cent *of those who had lost an eye*; and so on. Of course, on this supposition, the percentages must all be multiplied together. This she has done correctly, but I can give her no honours, as I do not think the question will fairly bear her interpretation. THREE SCORE AND TEN makes it "19⅜". Her solution has given me—I will not say "many anxious days and sleepless nights", for I wish to be strictly truthful, but—some trouble in making any sense at all of it. She makes the number of "pensioners wounded once" to be 310 ("per cent", I suppose!): dividing by 4, she gets 77½ as "average percentage": again dividing by 4, she gets 19⅜ as "percentage wounded four times". Does she suppose wounds of different kinds to "absorb" each other, so to speak? Then, no doubt, the data are equivalent to 77 pensioners with one wound each and a half-pensioner with a half-wound. And does she then suppose these concentrated wounds to be *transferable*, so that ¾ of these unfortunates can obtain perfect health by handing over their wounds to the remaining ¼? Granting these suppositions, her answer is right; or rather *if* the question had been, "A road is covered with one inch of gravel, along 77½ per cent of it. How much of it could be covered 4 inches deep with the same material?" her answer *would* have been right. But alas, that *wasn't* the question! DELTA makes some most amazing assumptions: "let every one who has not lost an eye have lost an ear," "let every one who has not lost both eyes and ears have lost an arm." Her ideas of a battlefield are grim indeed. Fancy a warrior who would continue fighting after losing both eyes, both ears, and both arms! This is a case which she (or "it"?) evidently considers *possible*.

Next come eight writers who have made the unwarrantable assumption that, because 70 per cent have lost any eye, *therefore* 30 per cent have *not* lost one, so that they have *both* eyes. This is illogical. If you give me a bag containing 100 sovereigns, and if in an hour I come to you (my face *not* beaming with gratitude nearly so much as when I received the bag) to say, "I am sorry to tell you that 70 of these sovereigns are bad," do I thereby guarantee the other 30 to be good? Perhaps I have not tested them yet. The sides of this illogical octagon are as follows, in alphabetical order: ALGERNON BRAY, DINAH MITE, G. S. C., JANE E., J. D. W., MAGPIE (who makes the delightful remark, "Therefore 90 per cent have two of something," recalling to one's memory that fortunate monarch with whom Xerxes was so much pleased that "he gave him ten of everything"!), S. S. G., and TOKIO.

BRADSHAW OF THE FUTURE and T. R. do the question in a piecemeal fashion—on the principle that the 70 per cent and the 75 per cent, though commenced at opposite ends of the 100, must overlap by *at least* 45 per cent; and so on. This is quite correct working, but not, I think, quite the best way of doing it.

The other five competitors will, I hope, feel themselves sufficiently glorified by being placed in the first class, without my composing a Triumphal Ode for each!

Class List

I

OLD CAT.	POLAR STAR.
OLD HEN.	SIMPLE SUSAN.
WHITE SUGAR.	

II

BRADSHAW OF THE FUTURE.	T. R.

III

ALGERNON BRAY.	J. D. W.
DINAH MITE.	MAGPIE.
G. S. C.	S. S. G.
JANE E.	TOKIO.

§ 2. *Change of Day*

I must postpone, *sine die*, the geographical problem—partly because I have not yet received the statistics I am hoping for, and partly because I am myself so entirely puzzled by it; and when an examiner is himself dimly hovering between a second class and a third, how is he to decide the position of others?

§ 3. *The Son's Ages*

Problem.—At first, two of the ages are together equal to the third. A few years afterwards, two of them are together double of the third, When the number of years since the first occasion is two-thirds of the sum of the ages on that occasion, one age is 21. What are the other two?

Answer.—15 and 18.

Solution.—Let the ages at first be x, y, $(x + y)$. Now, if $a + b = 2c$, then $(a - n) + (b - n) = 2(c - n)$, whatever be the value of n. Hence the second relationship, if *ever* true, was *always* true. Hence it was true at first. But it cannot be true that x and y are together double of $(x + y)$. Hence it must be true of $(x + y)$, together with x or y; and it does not matter which we take. We assume, then, $(x + y) + x = 2y$; *i.e.* $y = 2x$. Hence the three ages were, at first, x, $2x$, $3x$; and the number of years since that time is two-thirds of $6x$, *i.e.* is $4x$. Hence the present ages are $5x$, $6x$, $7x$. The ages are clearly *integers*, since this is only "the year when one of my sons comes of age". Hence $7x = 21$, $x = 3$, and the other ages are 15, 18.

Eighteen answers have been received. One of the writers merely asserts that the first occasion was 12 years ago, that the ages were then 9, 6, and 3; and that on the second occasion they were 14, 11, and 8! As a Roman father, I *ought* to withhold the name of the rash writer; but respect for age makes me break the rule: it is THREE SCORE AND TEN. JANE E. also asserts that the ages at first were 9, 6, 3: then she calculates the present ages, leaving the *second* occasion unnoticed. OLD HEN is nearly as bad; she "tried various numbers till I found one that fitted *all* the conditions"; but merely scratching up the earth, and pecking about, is *not* the way to solve a problem, O venerable bird! And close after OLD HEN prowls, with hungry eyes, OLD CAT, who calmly assumes, to begin with, that the son who comes of age is the *eldest*. Eat your bird, Puss, for you will get nothing from me!

There are yet two zeroes to dispose of. MINERVA assumes that, on *every* occasion, a son comes of age; and that it is only such a son who is "tipped with gold". Is it wise thus to interpret, "Now, my boys, calculate your ages, and you shall have the money"? BRADSHAW OF THE FUTURE says "let" the ages at first be 9, 6, 3, then assumes that the second occasion was 6 years afterwards, and on these baseless assumptions brings out the right answers. Guide *future* travelers, an thou wilt; thou art no Bradshaw for *this* Age!

Of those who win honours, the merely "honourable" are two. DINAH MITE ascertains (rightly) the relationship between the three ages at first, but then *assumes* one of them to be "6", thus making the rest of her solution tentative. M. F. C. does the algebra all right up to the conclusion that the present ages are $5z$, $6z$, and $7z$; it then assumes, without giving any reason, that $7z = 21$.

Of the more honourable, DELTA attempts a novelty—to discover *which* son comes of age by elimination: it assumes, successively, that it is the middle one, and that it is the youngest; and in each case it *apparently* brings out an absurdity. Still, as the proof contains the following bit of algebra: "$63 = 7x + 4y$: therefore $21 = x + 4/7$ of y," I trust it will admit that its proof is not *quite* conclusive. The rest of its work is good. MAGPIE betrays the deplorable tendency of her tribe—to appropriate any stray conclusion she comes across, without having any *strict* logical right to it. Assuming A, B, C, as the ages at first, and E as the number of the years that have elapsed since then, she finds (rightly) the 3 equations, $2A = B$, $C = B + A$, $D = 2B$. She then says, "Supposing that $A = 1$, then $B = 2$, $C = 3$, and $D = 4$. Therefore for A, B, C, D, four numbers are wanted which shall be to each other as 1:2:3:4." It is in the "therefore" that I detect the unconscientiousness of this bird. The conclusion *is* true, but this is only because the equations are "homogeneous" (*i.e.* having one "unknown" in each term), a fact which I strongly suspect had not been grasped—I beg pardon, clawed—by her. Were I to lay this little pitfall: "$A + 1 = B$, $B + 1 = C$; supposing $A = 1$, then $B = 2$, and $C = 3$.

Therefore for *A, B, C,* three numbers are wanted which shall be to one another as 1:2:3," would you not flutter down into it, O MAGPIE! as amiably as a Dove? SIMPLE SUSAN is anything but simple to *me*. After ascertaining that the 3 ages at first are as 3:2:1, she says, "Then, as two-thirds of their sum, added to one of them, =21, the sum cannot exceed 30, and consequently the highest cannot exceed 15." I suppose her (mental) argument is something like this: "Two-thirds of sum, +one age, =21, therefore sum, +3 halves of one age, =31½. But 3 halves of one age cannot be less than 1½ [here I perceive that SIMPLE SUSAN would on no account present a guinea to a newborn baby!]; hence the sum cannot exceed 30." This is ingenious, but her proof, after that, is (as she candidly admits) "clumsy and roundabout". She finds that there are 5 possible sets of ages, and eliminates four of them. Suppose that, instead of 5, there had been 5 million possible sets! Would SIMPLE SUSAN have courageously ordered in the necessary gallon of ink and ream of paper!

The solution sent in by C. R. is, like that of SIMPLE SUSAN, partly tentative, and so does not rise higher than being Clumsily Right.

Among those who have earned the highest honours, ALGERNON BRAY solves the problem quite correctly, but adds that there is nothing to exclude the supposition that all the ages were *fractional*. This would make the number of answers infinite. Let me meekly protest that I *never* intended my readers to devote the rest of their lives to writing out answers! E. M. RIX *points* out that, if fractional ages be admissible, any one of the three sons might be the one "come of age"; but she rightly rejects this supposition on the ground that it would make the problem indeterminate. WHITE SUGAR is the only one who has detected an oversight of mine: I had forgotten the possibility (which of course ought to be allowed for) that the son who came of age that *year*, need not have done so by that *day*, so that he *might* be only 20. This gives a second solution, *viz.*, 20, 24, 28. Well said, pure Crystal! Verily, thy "fair discourse hath been as sugar"!

Class List

I

ALGERNON BRAY.	S. S. G.
AN OLD FOGEY.	TOKIO.
E. M. RIX.	T. R.
G. S. C.	WHITE SUGAR.

II

C. R.   MAGPIE.

DELTA.   SIMPLE SUSAN.

III

DINAH MITE.   M. F. C.

I have received more than one remonstrance on my assertion, in the Chelsea Pensioner's problem, that it was illogical to assume, from the datum, "70 per cent have lost an eye," that 30 per cent have *not*. ALGERNON BRAY states, as a parallel case, "Suppose Tommy's father gives him 4 apples, and he eats one of them, how many has he left?" and says, "I think we are justified in answering, 3." I think so too. There is no "must" here, and data are evidently meant to fix the answer *exactly*: but, if the question were set me, "How many *must* he have left?" I should understand the data to be that his father gave him 4 *at least*, but *may* have given him more.

I take this opportunity of thanking those who have sent, along with their answers to the Tenth Knot, regrets that there are no more Knots to come, or petitions that I should recall my resolution to bring them to an end. I am most grateful for their kind words; but I think it wisest to end what, at best, was but a lame attempt. "The stretched metre of an antique song" is beyond my compass; and my puppets were neither distinctly *in* my life (like those I now address), nor yet (like Alice and the Mock Turtle) distinctly *out* of it. Yet let me at least fancy, as I lay down the pen, that I carry with me into my silent life, dear reader, a farewell smile from your unseen face, and a kindly farewell pressure from your unfelt hand! And so, good night! Parting is such sweet sorrow, that I shall say "good night!" till it be morrow.

VI

The Hunting of The Snark

an agony in eight fits

with nine illustrations by
Henry Holiday

INSCRIBED TO A DEAR CHILD:

IN MEMORY OF GOLDEN SUMMER HOURS

AND WHISPERS OF A SUMMER SEA

Girt with a boyish garb for boyish task,
  Eager she wields her spade: yet loves as well
Rest on a friendly knee, intent to ask
  The tale he loves to tell.

Rude spirits of the seething outer strife,
  Unmeet to read her pure and simple spright,
Deem, if you list, such hours a waste of life,
  Empty of all delight!

Chat on, sweet Maid, and rescue from annoy
  Hearts that by wiser talk are unbeguiled.
Ah, happy he who owns that tenderest joy,
  The heart-love of a child!

Away, fond thoughts, and vex my soul no more!
  Work claims my wakeful nights, my busy days
Albeit bright memories of that sunlit shore
  Yet haunt my dreaming gaze!

Preface

IF—and the thing is wildly possible—the charge of writing nonsense were ever brought against the author of this brief but instructive poem, it would be based, I feel convinced, on the line (in p. 738)

> "Then the bowsprit got mixed with the rudder sometimes:"

In view of this painful possibility, I will not (as I might) appeal indignantly to my other writings as a proof that I am incapable of such a deed: I will not (as I might) point to the strong moral purpose of this poem itself, to the arithmetical principles so cautiously inculcated in it, or to its noble teachings in Natural History—I will take the more prosaic course of simply explaining how it happened.

The Bellman, who was almost morbidly sensitive about appearances, used to have the bowsprit unshipped once or twice a week to be revarnished; and it more than once happened, when the time came for replacing it, that no one on board could remember which end of the ship it belonged to. They knew it was not of the slightest use to appeal to the Bellman about it—he would only refer to his Naval Code, and read out in pathetic tones Admiralty Instructions which none of them had ever been able to understand—so it generally ended in its being fastened on, anyhow, across the rudder. The helmsman[1] used to stand by with tears in his eyes: *he* knew it was all wrong, but alas! Rule 42 of the Code, "*No one shall speak to the Man at the Helm*," had been completed by the Bellman himself with the words "*and the Man at the Helm shall speak to no one.*" So remonstrance was impossible, and no steering could be done till the next varnishing day. During these bewildering intervals the ship usually sailed backwards.

---

[1] This office was usually undertaken by the Boots, who found in it a refuge from the Baker's constant complaints about the insufficient blacking of his three pairs of boots.

As this poem is to some extent connected with the lay of the Jabberwock, let me take this opportunity of answering a question that has often been asked me, how to pronounce "slithy toves". The "i" in "slithy" is long, as in "writhe"; and "toves" is pronounced so as to rhyme with "groves". Again, the first "o" in "borogoves" is pronounced like the "o" in "borrow". I have heard people try to give it the sound of the "o" in "worry". Such is Human Perversity.

This also seems a fitting occasion to notice the other hard words in that poem. Humpty-Dumpty's theory, of two meanings packed into one word like a portmanteau, seems to me the right explanation for all.

For instance, take the two words "fuming" and "furious". Make up your mind that you will say both words, but leave it unsettled which you will say first. Now open your mouth and speak. If your thoughts incline ever so little towards "fuming", you will say "fuming-furious"; if they turn, by even a hair's breadth, towards "furious", you will say "furious-fuming"; but if you have that rarest of gifts, a perfectly balanced mind, you will say "frumious".

Supposing that, when Pistol uttered the well-known words—

"Under which king, Bezonian? Speak or die!"

Justice Shallow had felt certain that it was either William or Richard, but had not been able to settle which; so that he could not possibly say either name before the other, can it be doubted that, rather than die, he would have gasped out "Rilchiam!"

"Supporting each man on the top of the tide"

The Hunting of the Snark

FIT THE FIRST

The Landing

"Just the place for a Snark!" the Bellman cried,
  As he landed his crew with care;
Supporting each man on the top of the tide
  By a finger entwined in his hair.

"Just the place for a Snark! I have said it twice:
  That alone should encourage the crew.
Just the place for a Snark! I have said it thrice:
  What I tell you three times is true."

The crew was complete: it included a Boots—
  A maker of Bonnets and Hoods—
A Barrister, brought to arrange their disputes—
  And a Broker, to value their goods.

A Billiard-marker, whose skill was immense,
  Might perhaps have won more than his share—
But a Banker, engaged at enormous expense,
  Had the whole of their cash in his care.

There was also a Beaver, that paced on the deck,
  Or would sit making lace in the bow:
And had often (the Bellman said) saved them from wreck
  Though none of the sailors knew how.

There was one who was famed for the number of things
 He forgot when he entered the ship:
His umbrella, his watch, all his jewels and rings,
 And the clothes he had bought for the trip.

He had forty-two boxes, all carefully packed,
 With his name painted clearly on each:
But, since he omitted to mention the fact,
 They were all left behind on the beach.

The loss of his clothes hardly mattered, because
 He had seven coats on when he came,
With three pair of boots—but the worst of it was,
 He had wholly forgotten his name.

He would answer to "Hi!" or to any loud cry,
 Such as "Fry me!" or "Fritter my wig!"
To "What-you-may-call-um!" or "What-was-his-name!"
 But especially "Thing-um-a-jig!"

While, for those who preferred a more forcible word,
 He had different names from these:
His intimate friends called him "Candle-ends",
 And his enemies "Toasted-cheese".

"His form is ungainly—his intellect small—"
 (So the Bellman would often remark)—
"But his courage is perfect! And that, after all,
 Is the thing that one needs with a Snark."

He would joke with hyænas, returning their stare
 With an impudent wag of the head:
And he once went a walk, paw-in-paw, with a bear,
 "Just to keep up its spirits," he said.

He came as a Baker: but owned, when too late—
 And it drove the poor Bellman half-mad—
He could only bake Bridecake—for which, I may state,
 No materials were to be had.

The last of the crew needs especial remark,
 Though he looked an incredible dunce:

"He had wholly forgotten his name"

"The Beaver kept looking the opposite way"

He had just one idea—but, that one being "Snark"
   The good Bellman engaged him at once.

He came as a Butcher: but gravely declared,
   When the ship had been sailing a week,
He could only kill Beavers. The Bellman looked scared,
   And was almost too frightened to speak:

But at length he explained, in a tremulous tone,
   There was only one Beaver on board;
And that was a tame one he had of his own,
   Whose death would be deeply deplored.

The Beaver, who happened to hear the remark,
   Protested, with tears in its eyes,
That not even the rapture of hunting the Snark
   Could atone for that dismal surprise!

It strongly advised that the Butcher should be
   Conveyed in a separate ship:
But the Bellman declared that would never agree
   With the plans he had made for the trip:

Navigation was always a difficult art,
   Though with only one ship and one bell:
And he feared he must really decline, for his part,
   Undertaking another as well.

The Beaver's best course was, no doubt, to procure
   A second-hand dagger-proof coat—
So the Baker advised it—and next, to insure
   Its life in some Office of note:

This the Baker suggested, and offered for hire
   (On moderate terms), or for sale,
Two excellent Policies, one Against Fire
   And one Against Damage From Hail.

Yet still, ever after that sorrowful day,
   Whenever the Butcher was by,
The Beaver kept looking the opposite way,
   And appeared unaccountably shy.

FIT THE SECOND

The Bellman's Speech

THE Bellman himself they all praised to the skies—
　　Such a carriage, such ease and such grace!
Such solemnity, too! One could see he was wise,
　　The moment one looked in his face!

He had bought a large map representing the sea,
　　Without the least vestige of land:
And the crew were much pleased when they found it to be
　　A map they could all understand.

"What's the good of Mercator's North Poles and Equators,
　　Tropics, Zones, and Meridian Lines?"
So the Bellman would cry: and the crew would reply
　　"They are merely conventional signs!

"Other maps are such shapes, with their islands and capes!
　　But we've got our brave Captain to thank"
(So the crew would protest) "that he's bought *us* the best—
　　A perfect and absolute blank!"

This was charming, no doubt: but they shortly found out
　　That the Captain they trusted so well
Had only one notion for crossing the ocean,
　　And that was to tingle his bell.

He was thoughtful and grave—but the orders he gave
　　Were enough to bewilder a crew.
When he cried "Steer to starboard, but keep her head larboard!"
　　What on earth was the helmsman to do?

Then the bowsprit got mixed with the rudder sometimes:
　　A thing, as the Bellman remarked,
That frequently happens in tropical climes,
　　When a vessel is, so to speak, "snarked".

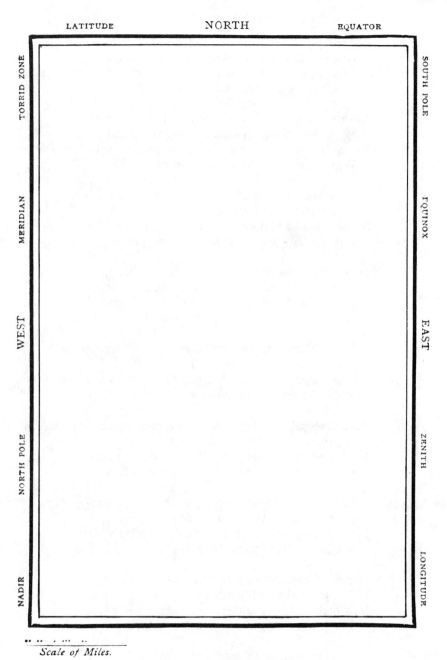

OCEAN-CHART.

But the principal failing occurred in the sailing,
   And the Bellman, perplexed and distressed,
Said he *had* hoped, at least, when the wind blew due East,
   That the ship would *not* travel due West!

But the danger was past—they had landed at last,
   With their boxes, portmanteaus, and bags:
Yet at first sight the crew were not pleased with the view
   Which consisted of chasms and crags.

The Bellman perceived that their spirits were low,
   And repeated in musical tone
Some jokes he had kept for a season of woe—
   But the crew would do nothing but groan.

He served out some grog with a liberal hand,
   And bade them sit down on the beach:
And they could not but own that their Captain looked grand,
   As he stood and delivered his speech.

"Friends, Romans, and countrymen, lend me your ears!"
   (They were all of them fond of quotations:
So they drank to his health, and they gave him three cheers,
   While he served out additional rations).

"We have sailed many months, we have sailed many weeks,
   (Four weeks to the month you may mark),
But never as yet ('tis your Captain who speaks)
   Have we caught the least glimpse of a Snark!

"We have sailed many weeks, we have sailed many days,
   (Seven days to the week I allow),
But a Snark, on the which we might lovingly gaze,
   We have never beheld till now!

"Come, listen, my men, while I tell you again
   The five unmistakable marks
By which you may know, wheresoever you go,
   The warranted genuine Snarks.

"Let us take them in order. The first is the taste,
   Which is meagre and hollow, but crisp:

Like a coat that is rather too tight in the waist,
  With a flavour of Will-o'-the-Wisp.

"Its habit of getting up late you'll agree
  That it carries too far, when I say
That it frequently breakfasts at five-o'clock tea,
  And dines on the following day.

"The third is its slowness in taking a jest.
  Should you happen to venture on one,
It will sigh like a thing that is deeply distressed:
  And it always looks grave at a pun.

"The fourth is its fondness for bathing-machines,
  Which it constantly carries about,
And believes that they add to the beauty of scenes—
  A sentiment open to doubt.

"The fifth is ambition. It next will be right
  To describe each particular batch:
Distinguishing those that have feathers, and bite,
  From those that have whiskers, and scratch.

"For, although common Snarks do no manner of harm,
  Yet I feel it my duty to say
Some are Boojums——" The Bellman broke off in alarm,
  For the Baker had fainted away.

FIT THE THIRD

The Baker's Tale

THEY roused him with muffins—they roused him with ice—
  They roused him with mustard and cress—
They roused him with jam and judicious advice—
  They set him conundrums to guess.

When at length he sat up and was able to speak,
  His sad story he offered to tell;

"But oh, beamish nephew, beware of the day"

And the Bellman cried "Silence! Not even a shriek!"
   And excitedly tingled his bell.

There was silence supreme! Not a shriek, not a scream,
   Scarcely even a howl or a groan,
As the man they called "Ho!" told his story of woe
   In an antediluvian tone.

"My father and mother were honest, though poor——"
   "Skip all that!" cried the Bellman in haste.
"If it once becomes dark, there's no chance of a Snark—
   We have hardly a minute to waste!"

"I skip forty years," said the Baker in tears,
   "And proceed without further remark
To the day when you took me aboard of your ship
   To help you in hunting the Snark.

"A dear uncle of mine (after whom I was named)
   Remarked, when I bade him farewell——"
"Oh, skip your dear uncle!" the Bellman exclaimed,
   As he angrily tingled his bell.

"He remarked to me then," said that mildest of men,
   " 'If your Snark be a Snark, that is right:
Fetch it home by all means—you may serve it with greens
   And it's handy for striking a light.

" 'You may seek it with thimbles—and seek it with care—
   You may hunt it with forks and hope;
You may threaten its life with a railway-share;
   You may charm it with smiles and soap——' "

("That's exactly the method," the Bellman bold
   In a hasty parenthesis cried,
"That's exactly the way I have always been told
   That the capture of Snarks should be tried!")

" 'But oh, beamish nephew, beware of the day,
   If your Snark be a Boojum! For then
You will softly and suddenly vanish away,
   And never be met with again!'

"It is this, it is this that oppresses my soul,
    When I think of my uncle's last words:
And my heart is like nothing so much as a bowl
    Brimming over with quivering curds!

"It is this, it is this——" "We have had that before!"
    The Bellman indignantly said.
And the Baker replied "Let me say it once more.
    It is this, it is this that I dread!

"I engage with the Snark—every night after dark—
    In a dreamy delirious fight:
I serve it with greens in those shadowy scenes,
    And I use it for striking a light:

"But if ever I meet with a Boojum, that day,
    In a moment (of this I am sure),
I shall softly and suddenly vanish away—
    And the notion I cannot endure!"

FIT THE FOURTH

The Hunting

THE Bellman looked uffish, and wrinkled his brow.
  "If only you'd spoken before!
It's excessively awkward to mention it now,
  With the Snark, so to speak, at the door!

"We should all of us grieve, as you well may believe,
  If you never were met with again—
But surely my man, when the voyage began,
  You might have suggested it then?

"It's excessively awkward to mention it now—
  As I think I've already remarked."
And the man they called "Hi!" replied, with a sigh,
  "I informed you the day we embarked.

"You may charge me with murder—or want of sense—
  (We are all of us weak at times):
But the slightest approach to a false pretence
  Was never among my crimes!

"I said it in Hebrew—I said it in Dutch—
  I said it in German and Greek:
But I wholly forgot (and it vexes me much)
  That English is what you speak!"

" 'Tis a pitiful tale," said the Bellman, whose face
  Had grown longer at every word:
"But, now that you've stated the whole of your case,
  More debate would be simply absurd.

"The rest of my speech" (he exclaimed to his men)
  "You shall hear when I've leisure to speak it.
But the Snark is at hand, let me tell you again!
  'Tis your glorious duty to seek it!

"To seek it with thimbles, to seek it with care;
  To pursue it with forks and hope;
To threaten its life with a railway-share;
  To charm it with smiles and soap!

"For the Snark's a peculiar creature, that wo'n't
  Be caught in a commonplace way.
Do all that you know, and try all that you don't:
  Not a chance must be wasted to-day!

"For England expects—I forbear to proceed:
  'Tis a maxim tremendous, but trite:
And you'd best be unpacking the things that you need
  To rig yourselves out for the fight."

Then the Banker endorsed a blank cheque (which he crossed),
  And changed his loose silver for notes:
The Baker with care combed his whiskers and hair,
  And shook the dust out of his coats:

The Boots and the Broker were sharpening a spade—
  Each working the grindstone in turn:
But the Beaver went on making lace, and displayed
  No interest in the concern:

Though the Barrister tried to appeal to its pride,
  And vainly proceeded to cite
A number of cases, in which making laces
  Had been proved an infringement of right.

The maker of Bonnets ferociously planned
  A novel arrangement of bows:
While the Billiard-marker with quivering hand
  Was chalking the tip of his nose.

But the Butcher turned nervous, and dressed himself fine,
  With yellow kid gloves and a ruff—
Said he felt it exactly like going to dine,
  Which the Bellman declared was all "stuff".

"Introduce me, now there's a good fellow," he said,
  "If we happen to meet it together!"

"To pursue it with forks and hope."

And the Bellman, sagaciously nodding his head,
Said "That must depend on the weather."

The Beaver went simply galumphing about,
At seeing the Butcher so shy:
And even the Baker, though stupid and stout,
Made an effort to wink with one eye.

"Be a man!" said the Bellman in wrath, as he heard
The Butcher beginning to sob.
"Should we meet with a Jubjub, that desperate bird,
We shall need all our strength for the job!"

FIT THE FIFTH

The Beaver's Lesson

THEY sought it with thimbles, they sought it with care;
They pursued it with forks and hope;
They threatened its life with a railway-share;
They charmed it with smiles and soap.

Then the Butcher contrived an ingenious plan
For making a separate sally;
And had fixed on a spot unfrequented by man,
A dismal and desolate valley.

But the very same plan to the Beaver occurred:
It had chosen the very same place:
Yet neither betrayed, by a sign or a word,
The disgust that appeared in his face.

Each thought he was thinking of nothing but "Snark"
And the glorious work of the day;
And each tried to pretend that he did not remark
That the other was going that way.

But the valley grew narrower and narrower still,
And the evening got darker and colder,

Till (merely from nervousness, not from good will)
   They marched along shoulder to shoulder.

Then a scream, shrill and high, rent the shuddering sky
   And they knew that some danger was near:
The Beaver turned pale to the tip of its tail,
   And even the Butcher felt queer.

He thought of his childhood, left far behind—
   That blissful and innocent state—
The sound so exactly recalled to his mind
   A pencil that squeaks on a slate!

" 'Tis the voice of the Jubjub!" he suddenly cried.
   (This man, that they used to call "Dunce".)
"As the Bellman would tell you," he added with pride,
   "I have uttered that sentiment once.

" 'Tis the note of the Jubjub! Keep count, I entreat.
   You will find I have told it you twice.
'Tis the song of the Jubjub! The proof is complete.
   If only I've stated it thrice."

The Beaver had counted with scrupulous care,
   Attending to every word:
But it fairly lost heart, and outgrabe in despair,
   When the third repetition occurred.

It felt that, in spite of all possible pains,
   It had somehow contrived to lose count,
And the only thing now was to rack its poor brains
   By reckoning up the amount.

"Two added to one—if that could but be done",
   It said, "with one's fingers and thumbs!"
Recollecting with tears how, in earlier years,
   It had taken no pains with its sums.

"The thing can be done," said the Butcher, "I think.
   The thing must be done, I am sure.
The thing shall be done! Bring me paper and ink,
   The best there is time to procure."

The Beaver brought paper, portfolio, pens,
    And ink in unfailing supplies:
While strange creepy creatures came out of their dens,
    And watched them with wondering eyes.

So engrossed was the Butcher, he heeded them not,
    As he wrote with a pen in each hand,
And explained all the while in a popular style
    Which the Beaver could well understand.

"Taking Three as the subject to reason about—
    A convenient number to state—
We add Seven, and Ten, and then multiply out
    By One Thousand diminished by Eight.

"The result we proceed to divide, as you see,
    By Nine Hundred and Ninety and Two:
Then subtract Seventeen, and the answer must be
    Exactly and perfectly true.

"The method employed I would gladly explain,
    While I have it so clear in my head,
If I had but the time and you had but the brain—
    But much yet remains to be said.

"In one moment I've seen what has hitherto been
    Enveloped in absolute mystery,
And without extra charge I will give you at large
    A Lesson in Natural History."

In his genial way he proceeded to say
    (Forgetting all laws of propriety,
And that giving instruction, without introduction,
    Would have caused quite a thrill in Society),

"As to temper the Jubjub's a desperate bird.
    Since it lives in perpetual passion:
Its taste in costume is entirely absurd—
    It is ages ahead of the fashion:

"But it knows any friend it has met once before:
    It never will look at a bribe:

"The Beaver brought paper, portfolio, pens"

And in charity-meetings it stands at the door,
    And collects—though it does not subscribe.

"Its flavour when cooked is more exquisite far
    Than mutton, or oysters, or eggs:
(Some think it keeps best in an ivory jar,
    And some, in mahogany kegs:)

"You boil it in sawdust: you salt it in glue:
    You condense it with locusts and tape:
Still keeping one principal object in view—
    To preserve its symmetrical shape."

The Butcher would gladly have talked till next day,
    But he felt that the Lesson must end,
And he wept with delight in attempting to say
    He considered the Beaver his friend:

While the Beaver confessed, with affectionate looks
    More eloquent even than tears,
It had learned in ten minutes far more than all books
    Would have taught it in seventy years.

They returned hand-in-hand, and the Bellman, unmanned
    (For a moment) with noble emotion,
Said "This amply repays all the wearisome days
    We have spent on the billowy ocean!"

Such friends, as the Beaver and Butcher became,
    Have seldom if ever been known;
In winter or summer, 'twas always the same—
    You could never meet either alone.

And when quarrels arose—as one frequently finds
    Quarrels will, spite of every endeavour—
The song of the Jubjub recurred to their minds,
    And cemented their friendship for ever!

FIT THE SIXTH

The Barrister's Dream

THEY sought it with thimbles, they sought it with care;
    They pursued it with forks and hope;
They threatened its life with a railway-share;
    They charmed it with smiles and soap.

But the Barrister, weary of proving in vain
    That the Beaver's lace-making was wrong,
Fell asleep, and in dreams saw the creature quite plain
    That his fancy had dwelt on so long.

He dreamed that he stood in a shadowy Court,
    Where the Snark, with a glass in its eye,
Dressed in gown, bands, and wig, was defending a pig
    On the charge of deserting its sty.

The Witnesses proved, without error or flaw,
    That the sty was deserted when found:
And the Judge kept explaining the state of the law
    In a soft under-current of sound.

The indictment had never been clearly expressed,
    And it seemed that the Snark had begun,
And had spoken three hours, before any one guessed
    What the pig was supposed to have done.

The Jury had each formed a different view
    (Long before the indictment was read),
And they all spoke at once, so that none of them knew
    One word that the others had said.

"You must know—' said the Judge: but the Snark exclaimed 'Fudge!'"

"You must know——" said the Judge: but the Snark
   exclaimed "Fudge!
  That statute is obsolete quite!
Let me tell you, my friends, the whole question depends
   On an ancient manorial right.

"In the matter of Treason the pig would appear
   To have aided, but scarcely abetted:
While the charge of Insolvency fails, it is clear,
   If you grant the plea 'never indebted'.

"The fact of Desertion I will not dispute:
   But its guilt, as I trust, is removed
(So far as relates to the costs of this suit)
   By the Alibi which has been proved.

"My poor client's fate now depends on your votes."
   Here the speaker sat down in his place,
And directed the Judge to refer to his notes
   And briefly to sum up the case.

But the Judge said he never had summed up before;
   So the Snark undertook it instead,
And summed it so well that it came to far more
   Than the Witnesses ever had said!

When the verdict was called for, the Jury declined,
   As the word was so puzzling to spell;
But they ventured to hope that the Snark wouldn't mind
   Undertaking that duty as well.

So the Snark found the verdict, although, as it owned,
   It was spent with the toils of the day:
When it said the word "GUILTY!" the Jury all groaned
   And some of them fainted away.

Then the Snark pronounced sentence, the Judge being quite
   Too nervous to utter a word:
When it rose to its feet, there was silence like night,
   And the fall of a pin might be heard.

"Transportation for life" was the sentence it gave,
   "And *then* to be fined forty pound."
The Jury all cheered, though the Judge said he feared
   That the phrase was not legally sound.

But their wild exultation was suddenly checked
   When the jailer informed them, with tears,
Such a sentence would have not the slightest effect,
   As the pig had been dead for some years.

The Judge left the Court, looking deeply disgusted
   But the Snark, though a little aghast,
As the lawyer to whom the defence was intrusted,
   Went bellowing on to the last.

Thus the Barrister dreamed, while the bellowing seemed
   To grow every moment more clear:
Till he woke to the knell of a furious bell,
   Which the Bellman rang close at his ear.

FIT THE SEVENTH

The Banker's Fate

THEY sought it with thimbles, they sought it with care;
  They pursued it with forks and hope;
They threatened its life with a railway-share;
  They charmed it with smiles and soap.

And the Banker, inspired with a courage so new
  It was matter for general remark,
Rushed madly ahead and was lost to their view
  In his zeal to discover the Snark.

But while he was seeking with thimbles and care,
  A Bandersnatch swiftly drew nigh
And grabbed at the Banker, who shrieked in despair,
  For he knew it was useless to fly.

He offered large discount—he offered a cheque
  (Drawn "to bearer") for seven-pounds-ten:
But the Bandersnatch merely extended its neck
  And grabbed at the Banker again.

Without rest or pause—while those frumious jaws
  Went savagely snapping around—
He skipped and he hopped, and he floundered and flopped,
  Till fainting he fell to the ground.

The Bandersnatch fled as the others appeared
  Led on by that fear-stricken yell:
And the Bellman remarked "It is just as I feared!"
  And solemnly tolled on his bell.

"So great was his fright that his waistcoat turned white."

He was black in the face, and they scarcely could trace
    The least likeness to what he had been:
While so great was his fright that his waistcoat turned white—
    A wonderful thing to be seen!

To the horror of all who were present that day,
    He uprose in full evening dress,
And with senseless grimaces endeavoured to say
    What his tongue could no longer express.

Down he sank in a chair—ran his hands through his hair—
    And chanted in mimsiest tones
Words whose utter inanity proved his insanity,
    While he rattled a couple of bones.

"Leave him here to his fate—it is getting so late!"
    The Bellman exclaimed in a fright.
"We have lost half the day. Any further delay,
    And we sha'n't catch a Snark before night!"

FIT THE EIGHTH

The Vanishing

They sought it with thimbles, they sought it with care;
    They pursued it with forks and hope;
They threatened its life with a railway-share;
    They charmed it with smiles and soap.

They shuddered to think that the chase might fail,
    And the Beaver, excited at last,
Went bounding along on the tip of its tail,
    For the daylight was nearly past.

"There is Thingumbob shouting!" the Bellman said.
    "He is shouting like mad, only hark!
He is waving his hands, he is wagging his head,
    He has certainly found a Snark!"

They gazed in delight, while the Butcher exclaimed
    "He was always a desperate wag!"
They beheld him—their Baker—their hero unnamed—
    On the top of a neighbouring crag,

Erect and sublime, for one moment of time,
    In the next, that wild figure they saw
(As if stung by a spasm) plunge into a chasm,
    While they waited and listened in awe.

"It's a Snark!" was the sound that first came to their ears,
    And seemed almost too good to be true.
Then followed a torrent of laughter and cheers:
    Then the ominous words "It's a Boo——"

Then, silence. Some fancied they heard in the air
    A weary and wandering sigh
That sounded like "—jum!" but the others declare
    It was only a breeze that went by.

"Then, silence."

They hunted till darkness came on, but they found
    Not a button, or feather, or mark,
By which they could tell that they stood on the ground
    Where the Baker had met with the Snark.

In the midst of the word he was trying to say,
    In the midst of his laughter and glee,
He had softly and suddenly vanished away—
    For the Snark *was* a Boojum, you see.

VII

Phantasmagoria
and other poems

with sixty-five illustrations by
Arthur B. Frost

"Upon a battlement"

Phantasmagoria

CANTO I

The Trystyng

ONE winter night, at half-past nine,
    Cold, tired, and cross, and muddy,
I had come home, too late to dine,
And supper, with cigars and wine,
    Was waiting in the study.

There was a strangeness in the room,
    And Something white and wavy
Was standing near me in the gloom—
I took it for the carpet-broom
    Left by that careless slavey.

But presently the Thing began
    To shiver and to sneeze:
On which I said "Come, come, my man!
That's a most inconsiderate plan,
    Less noise there, if you please!"

"I've caught a cold", the Thing replies,
    "Out there upon the landing."
I turned to look in some surprise,
And there, before my very eyes,
    A little Ghost was standing!

He trembled when he caught my eye,
    And got behind a chair.
"How came you here," I said, "and why?
I never saw a thing so shy.
    Come out! Don't shiver there!"

He said "I'd gladly tell you how,
    And also tell you why;
But" (here he gave a little bow)
"You're in so bad a temper now,
    You'd think it all a lie.

"And as to being in a fright,
    Allow me to remark
That Ghosts have just as good a right,
In every way, to fear the light,
    As Men to fear the dark."

"No plea", said I, "can well excuse
    Such cowardice in you:
For Ghosts can visit when they choose,
Whereas we Humans ca'n't refuse
    To grant the interview."

He said "A flutter of alarm
    Is not unnatural, is it?
I really feared you meant some harm:
But, now I see that you are calm,
    Let me explain my visit.

"Houses are classed, I beg to state,
    According to the number
Of Ghosts that they accommodate:
(The Tenant merely counts as *weight*,
    With Coals and other lumber).

"This is a 'one-ghost' house, and you,
    When you arrived last summer,
May have remarked a Spectre who
Was doing all that Ghosts can do
    To welcome the new-comer.

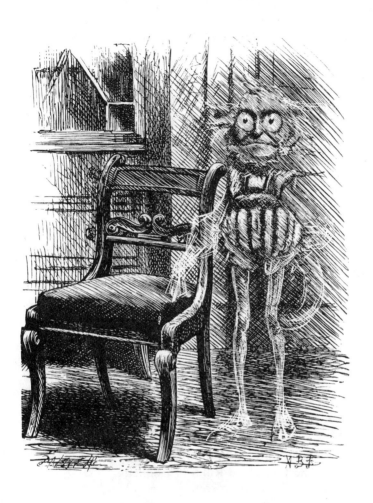

"In Villas this is always done—
        However cheaply rented:
For, though of course there's less of fun
When there is only room for one,
        Ghosts have to be contented.

"That Spectre left you on the Third—
        Since then you've not been haunted:
For, as he never sent us word,
'Twas quite by accident we heard
        That any one was wanted.

"A Spectre has first choice, by right,
 In filling up a vacancy;
Then Phantom, Goblin, Elf, and Sprite—
If all these fail them, they invite
 The nicest Ghoul that they can see.

"The Spectres said the place was low,
 And that you kept bad wine:
So, as a Phantom had to go,
And I was first, of course, you know,
 I couldn't well decline."

"No doubt", said I, "they settled who
 Was fittest to be sent:
Yet still to choose a brat like you,
To haunt a man of forty-two,
 Was no great compliment!"

"I'm not so young, Sir," he replied,
 "As you might think. The fact is,
In caverns by the water-side,
And other places that I've tried,
 I've had a lot of practice:

"But I have never taken yet
 A strict domestic part,
And in my flurry I forget
The Five Good Rules of Etiquette
 We have to know by heart."

My sympathies were warming fast
 Towards the little fellow:
He was so utterly aghast
At having found a Man at last,
 And looked so scared and yellow.

"At least", I said, "I'm glad to find
 A Ghost is not a *dumb* thing!
But pray sit down: you'll feel inclined
(If, like myself, you have not dined)
 To take a snack of something:

"In caverns by the water-side"

"Though, certainly, you don't appear
    A thing to offer *food* to!
And then I shall be glad to hear—
If you will say them loud and clear—
    The Rules that you allude to."

"Thanks! You shall hear them by and by.
    This *is* a piece of luck!"
"What may I offer you?" said I.
"Well, since you *are* so kind, I'll try
    A little bit of duck.

"*One* slice! And may I ask you for
    Another drop of gravy?"
I sat and looked at him in awe,
For certainly I never saw
    A thing so white and wavy.

And still he seemed to grow more white,
　　More vapoury, and wavier—
Seen in the dim and flickering light,
As he proceeded to recite
　　His "Maxims of Behaviour".

CANTO 2

Hys Fyve Rules

"MY First—but don't suppose," he said,
　　"I'm setting you a riddle—
Is—if your Victim be in bed,
Don't touch the curtains at his head,
　　But take them in the middle,

"And wave them slowly in and out,
　　While drawing them asunder;
And in a minute's time, no doubt,
He'll raise his head and look about
　　With eyes of wrath and wonder.

"And here you must on no pretence
　　Make the first observation.
Wait for the Victim to commence:
No Ghost of any common sense
　　Begins a conversation.

"If he should say '*How came you here?*'
　　(The way that *you* began, Sir),
In such a case your course is clear—
'*On the bat's back, my little dear!*'
　　Is the appropriate answer.

"If after this he says no more,
　　You'd best perhaps curtail your
Exertions—go and shake the door,
And then, if he begins to snore,
　　You'll know the thing's a failure.

"By day, if he should be alone—
　　At home or on a walk—
You merely give a hollow groan,
To indicate the kind of tone
　　In which you mean to talk.

"But if you find him with his friends,
　　The thing is rather harder.
In such a case success depends
On picking up some candle-ends,
　　Or butter, in the larder.

"With this you make a kind of slide
　　(It answers best with suet),
On which you must contrive to glide,
And swing yourself from side to side—
　　One soon learns how to do it.

"And swing yourself from side to side"

"The Second tells us what is right
   In ceremonious calls:—
'*First burn a blue or crimson light*'
(A thing I quite forgot to-night),
    '*Then scratch the door or walls.*' "

I said "You'll visit *here* no more,
   If you attempt the Guy.
I'll have no bonfires on *my* floor—
And, as for scratching at the door,
    I'd like to see you try!"

"The Third was written to protect
    The interests of the Victim,
And tells us, as I recollect,
To treat him with a grave respect,
    And not to contradict him."

"That's plain", said I, "as Tare and Tret,
    To any comprehension:
I only wish *some* Ghosts I've met
Would not so *constantly* forget
    The maxim that you mention!"

"Perhaps", he said, "*you* first transgressed
    The laws of hospitality:
All Ghosts instinctively detest
The Man that fails to treat his guest
    With proper cordiality.

"If you address a Ghost as 'Thing!'
    Or strike him with a hatchet,
He is permitted by the King
To drop all *formal* parleying—
    And then you're *sure* to catch it!

"The Fourth prohibits trespassing
    Where other Ghosts are quartered:
And those convicted of the thing
(Unless when pardoned by the King)
    Must instantly be slaughtered.

"That simply means 'be cut up small':
    Ghosts soon unite anew:
The process scarcely hurts at all—
Not more than when *you're* what you call
    'Cut up' by a Review.

"The Fifth is one you may prefer
    That I should quote entire:—
The King must be addressed as 'Sir'.
This, from a simple courtier,
    Is all the Laws require:

"But should you wish to do the thing
With out-and-out politeness,
Accost him as 'My Goblin King!'
And always use, in answering,
The phrase 'Your Royal Whiteness......!'

"I'm getting rather hoarse, I fear,
After so much reciting:
So, if you don't object, my dear,
We'll try a glass of bitter beer—
I think it looks inviting."

CANTO 3

Scarmoges

"AND did you really walk", said I,
    "On such a wretched night?
I always fancied Ghosts could fly—
If not exactly in the sky,
    Yet at a fairish height."

"And here it took the form of THIRST"

"It's very well", said he, "for Kings
    To soar above the earth:
But Phantoms often find that wings—
Like many other pleasant things—
    Cost more than they are worth.

"Spectres of course are rich, and so
    Can buy them from the Elves:
But *we* prefer to keep below—
They're stupid company, you know,
    For any but themselves:

"For, though they claim to be exempt
    From pride, they treat a Phantom
As something quite beneath contempt—
Just as no Turkey ever dreamt
    Of noticing a Bantam."

"They seem too proud", said I, "to go
    To houses such as mine.
Pray, how did they contrive to know
So quickly that 'the place was low',
    And that I 'kept bad wine'?"

"Inspector Kobold came to you——"
    The little Ghost began.
Here I broke in—"Inspector who?
Inspecting Ghosts is something new!
    Explain yourself, my man!"

"His name is Kobald," said my guest:
    "One of the Spectre order:
You'll very often see him dressed
In a yellow gown, a crimson vest,
    And a night-cap with a border.

"He tried the Brocken business first,
    But caught a sort of chill;
So came to England to be nursed,
And here it took the form of *thirst*,
    Which he complains of still.

"Port-wine, he says, when rich and sound,
     Warms his old bones like nectar:
And as the inns, where it is found,
Are his especial hunting-ground,
     We call him the *Inn-Spectre*."

I bore it—bore it like a man—
     This agonizing witticism!
And nothing could be sweeter than
My temper, till the Ghost began
     Some most provoking criticism.

"Cooks need not be indulged in waste;
     Yet still you'd better teach them
Dishes should have *some sort* of taste.
Pray, why are all the cruets placed
     Where nobody can reach them?

"That man of yours will never earn
     His living as a waiter!
Is that queer *thing* supposed to burn?
(It's far too dismal a concern
     To call a Moderator.)

"The duck was tender, but the peas
     Were very much too old:
And just remember, if you please,
The *next* time you have toasted cheese,
     Don't let them send it cold.

"You'll find the bread improved, I think,
     By getting better flour:
And have you anything to drink
That looks a *little* less like ink,
     And isn't *quite* so sour?"

Then peering round with curious eyes,
     He muttered "Goodness gracious!"
And so went on to criticize—
"Your room's an inconvenient size:
     It's neither snug nor spacious.

"That narrow window, I expect,
    Serves but to let the dusk in——"
"But please", said I, "to recollect
'Twas fashioned by an architect
    Who pinned his faith on Ruskin!"

"I don't care who he was, Sir, or
    On whom he pinned his faith!
Constructed by whatever law,
So poor a job I never saw,
    As I'm a living Wraith!

"What a re-markable cigar!
    How much are they a dozen?"
I growled "No matter what they are!
You're getting as familiar
    As if you were my cousin!

"Now that's a thing *I will not stand*,
    And so I tell you flat."
"Aha," said he, "we're getting grand!"
(Taking a bottle in his hand)
    "I'll soon arrange for *that*!"

And here he took a careful aim,
    And gaily cried "Here goes!"
I tried to dodge it as it came,
But somehow caught it, all the same,
    Exactly on my nose.

And I remember nothing more
    That I can clearly fix,
Till I was sitting on the floor,
Repeating "Two and five are four,
    But *five and two* are six."

What really passed I never learned,
    Nor guessed: I only know
That, when at last my sense returned,
The lamp, neglected, dimly burned—
    The fire was getting low—

Through driving mists I seemed to see
    A Thing that smirked and smiled:
And found that he was giving me
A lesson in Biography,
    As if I were a child.

CANTO 4

Hys Nouryture

"OH, when I was a little Ghost,
    A merry time had we!
Each seated on his favourite post,
We chumped and chawed the buttered toast
    They gave us for our tea."

"That story is in print!" I cried
    "Don't say it's not, because
It's known as well as Bradshaw's Guide!"
(The Ghost uneasily replied
    He hardly thought it was.)

"It's not in Nursery Rhymes? And yet
    I almost think it is—
'Three little Ghosteses' were set
'On posteses', you know, and ate
    Their 'buttered toasteses'.

"I have the book; so if you doubt it——"
    I turned to search the shelf.
"Don't stir!" he cried. "We'll do without it
I now remember all about it;
    I wrote the thing myself.

"It came out in a 'Monthly', or
    At least my agent said it did:
Some literary swell, who saw
It, thought it seemed adapted for
    The Magazine he edited.

"My father was a Brownie, Sir;
    My mother was a Fairy.
The notion had occurred to her,
The children would be happier,
    If they were taught to vary.

"The notion soon became a craze;
    And, when it once began, she
Brought us all out in different ways——
One was a Pixy, two were Fays,
    Another was a Banshee;

"The Fetch and Kelpie went to school
    And gave a lot of trouble;
Next came a Poltergeist and Ghoul,
And then two Trolls (which broke the rule),
    A Goblin, and a Double—

"(If that's a snuff-box on the shelf,"
    He added with a yawn,
"I'll take a pinch)—next came an Elf,
And then a Phantom (that's myself),
    And last, a Leprechaun.

"One day, some Spectres chanced to call,
  Dressed in the usual white:
I stood and watched them in the hall,
And couldn't make them out at all,
  They seemed so strange a sight.

"I wondered what on earth they were,
  That looked all head and sack;
But Mother told me not to stare,
And then she twitched me by the hair,
  And punched me in the back.

"Since then I've often wished that I
  Had been a Spectre born.
But what's the use?" (He heaved a sigh.)
"*They* are the ghost-nobility,
  And look on *us* with scorn.

"My phantom-life was soon begun:
  When I was barely six,
I went out with an older one—
And just at first I thought it fun,
  And learned a lot of tricks.

"I've haunted dungeons, castles, towers—
  Wherever I was sent:
I've often sat and howled for hours,
Drenched to the skin with driving showers,
  Upon a battlement.

"It's quite old-fashioned now to groan
  When you begin to speak:
This is the newest thing in tone——"
And here (it chilled me to the bone)
  He gave an *awful* squeak.

"Perhaps", he added, "to *your* ear
    That sounds an easy thing?
Try it yourself, my little dear!
It took *me* something like a year,
    With constant practising.

"And when you've learned to squeak, my man,
    And caught the double sob,
You're pretty much where you began:
Just try and gibber if you can!
    That's something *like* a job!

"*I've* tried it, and can only say
    I'm sure you couldn't do it, e-
ven if you practised night and day,
Unless you have a turn that way,
    And natural ingenuity.

"Shakespeare I think it is who treats
    Of Ghosts, in days of old,
Who 'gibbered in the Roman streets',
Dressed, if you recollect, in sheets—
    They must have found it cold.

"I've often spent ten pounds on stuff,
    In dressing as a Double;
But, though it answers as a puff,
It never has effect enough
    To make it worth the trouble.

"Long bills soon quenched the little thirst
    I had for being funny.
The setting-up is always worst:
Such heaps of things you want at first,
    One must be made of money!

"For instance, take a Haunted Tower,
    With skull, cross-bones, and sheet;
Blue lights to burn (say) two an hour,
Condensing lens of extra power,
    And set of chains complete:

"What with the things you have to hire—
    The fitting on the robe—
And testing all the coloured fire—
The outfit of itself would tire
    The patience of a Job!

"And then they're so fastidious,
    The Haunted-House Committee:
I've often known them make a fuss
Because a Ghost was French, or Russ,
    Or even from the City!

"Some dialects are objected to—
    For one, the *Irish* brogue is:
And then, for all you have to do,
One pound a week they offer you,
    And find yourself in Bogies!"

CANTO 5

Byckerment

"DON'T they consult the 'Victims', though?"
    I said. "They should, by rights,
Give them a chance—because, you know,
The tastes of people differ so,
        Especially in Sprites."

The Phantom shook his head and smiled.
        "Consult them? Not a bit!
'Twould be a job to drive one wild,
To satisfy one single child—
        There'd be no end to it!"

"Of course you ca'n't leave *children* free",
        Said I, "to pick and choose:
But, in the case of men like me,
I think 'Mine Host' might fairly be
        Allowed to state his views."

He said "It really wouldn't pay—
        Folk are so full of fancies.
We visit for a single day.
And whether then we go, or stay,
        Depends on circumstances.

"And, though we don't consult 'Mine Host'
        Before the thing's arranged,
Still, if he often quits his post,
Or is not a well-mannered Ghost,
        Then you can have him changed.

"But if the host's a man like you—
        I mean a man of sense;
And if the house is not too new——"
"Why, what has *that*", said I, "to do
        With Ghost's convenience?"

"A new house does not suit, you know—
　　It's such a job to trim it:
But, after twenty years or so,
The wainscotings begin to go,
　　So twenty is the limit."

"To trim" was not a phrase I could
　　Remember having heard:
"Perhaps", I said, "you'll be so good
As tell me what is understood
　　Exactly by that word?"

"It means the loosening all the doors,"
　　The Ghost replied, and laughed:
"It means the drilling holes by scores
In all the skirting-boards and floors,
　　To make a thorough draught.

"You'll sometimes find that one or two
  Are all you really need
To let the wind come whistling through—
But *here* there'll be a lot to do!"
  I faintly gasped "Indeed!

"If I'd been rather later, I'll
  Be bound," I added, trying
(Most unsuccessfully) to smile,
"You'd have been busy all this while,
  Trimming and beautifying?"

"Why, no," said he; "perhaps I should
  Have stayed another minute—
But still no Ghost, that's any good,
Without an introduction would
  Have ventured to begin it.

"The proper thing, as you were late,
  Was certainly to go:
But, with the roads in such a state,
I got the Knight-Mayor's leave to wait
  For half an hour or so."

"Who's the Knight-Mayor?" I cried. Instead
  Of answering my question,
"Well, if you don't know *that*, he said,
"Either you never go to bed,
  Or you've a grand digestion!

"He goes about and sits on folk
  That eat too much at night:
His duties are to pinch, and poke,
And squeeze them till they nearly choke."
  (I said "It serves them right!")

"And folk who sup on things like these—"
  He muttered, "eggs and bacon—
Lobster—and duck—and toasted cheese—
If they don't get an awful squeeze,
  I'm very much mistaken!

"He goes about and sits on folk"

"He is immensely fat, and so
    Well suits the occupation:
In point of fact, if you must know,
We used to call him years ago,
    The Mayor and Corporation!

"The day he was elected Mayor
    I *know* that every Sprite meant
To vote for *me*, but did not dare—
He was so frantic with despair
    And furious with excitement.

"When it was over, for a whim,
    He ran to tell the King;
And being the reverse of slim,
A two-mile trot was not for him
    A very easy thing.

"So, to reward him for his run
   (As it was baking hot,
And he was over twenty stone),
The King proceeded, half in fun,
   To knight him on the spot."

" 'Twas a great liberty to take!"
   (I fired up like a rocket.)
"He did it just for punning's sake:
'The man', says Johnson, 'that would make
   A pun, would pick a pocket!' "

"A man", said he, "is not a King."
   I argued for a while,
And did my best to prove the thing—
The Phantom merely listening
   With a contemptuous smile.

At last when, breath and patience spent,
   I had recourse to smoking—
"Your *aim*", he said, "is excellent:
But—when you call it *argument*—
   Of course you're only joking?"

Stung by his cold and snaky eye,
   I roused myself at length
To say, "At least I do defy
The veriest sceptic to deny
   That union is strength!"

"That's true enough," said he, "yet stay—"
   I listened in all meekness—
"*Union* is strength, I'm bound to say;
In fact, the thing's as clear as day;
   But *onions* are a weakness."

CANTO 6

Discomfyture

As one who strives a hill to climb,
    Who never climbed before:
Who finds it, in a little time,
Grow every moment less sublime,
    And votes the thing a bore:

Yet having once begun to try,
    Dares not desert his quest,
But, climbing, ever keeps his eye
On one small hut against the sky
    Wherein he hopes to rest:

Who climbs till nerve and force are spent,
    With many a puff and pant:
Who still, as rises the ascent,
In language grows more violent,
    Although in breath more scant:

Who, climbing, gains at length the place
    That crowns the upward track:
And, entering with unsteady pace,
Receives a buffet in the face
    That lands him on his back:

And feels himself, like one in sleep,
    Glide swiftly down again,
A helpless weight, from steep to steep,
Till, with a headlong giddy sweep,
    He drops upon the plain—

So I, that had resolved to bring
    Conviction to a ghost,
And found it quite a different thing
From any human arguing,
    Yet dared not quit my post.

But, keeping still the end in view
    To which I hoped to come,
I strove to prove the matter true
By putting everything I knew
    Into an axiom:

Commencing every single phrase
    With "therefore" or "because"
I blindly reeled, a hundred ways,
About the syllogistic maze,
    Unconscious where I was.

Quoth he "That's regular clap-trap:
    Don't bluster any more.
Now *do* be cool and take a nap!
Such a ridiculous old chap
    Was never seen before!

"You're like a man I used to meet,
    Who got one day so furious
In arguing, the simple heat
Scorched both his slippers off his feet!"
    I said *"That's very curious!"*

"Well, it *is* curious, I agree,
    And sounds perhaps like fibs:
But still it's true as true can be—
As sure as your name's Tibbs," said he.
    I said "My name's *not* Tibbs."

"*Not* Tibbs!" he cried—his tone became
    A shade or two less hearty—
"Why, no," said I. "My proper name
Is Tibbets—" "Tibbets?" "Aye, the same."
    "Why, then YOU'RE NOT THE PARTY!"

"Scorched both his slippers off his feet"

With that he struck the board a blow
    That shivered half the glasses.
"Why couldn't you have told me so
Three quarters of an hour ago,
    You prince of all the asses?

"To walk four miles through mud and rain,
    To spend the night in smoking,
And then to find that it's in vain—
And I've to do it all again—
    It's really *too* provoking!

"Don't talk!" he cried, as I began
    To mutter some excuse.
"Who can have patience with a man
That's got no more discretion than
    An idiotic goose?

"To keep me waiting here, instead
    Of telling me at once
That this was not the house!" he said.
"There, that'll do—be off to bed!
    Don't gape like that, you dunce!"

"It's very fine to throw the blame
    On *me* in such a fashion!
Why didn't you enquire my name
The very minute that you came?"
    I answered in a passion.

"Of course it worries you a bit
    To come so far on foot—
But how was *I* to blame for it?"
"Well, well!" said he. "I must admit
    That isn't badly put.

"And certainly you've given me
    The best of wine and victual—
Excuse my violence," said he,
"But accidents like this, you see,
    They put one out a little.

" 'Twas *my* fault after all, I find—
    Shake hands, old Turnip-top!"
The name was hardly to my mind,
But, as no doubt he meant it kind,
    I let the matter drop.

"Good-night, old Turnip-top, good-night!
    When I am gone, perhaps
They'll send you some inferior Sprite,
Who'll keep you in a constant fright
    And spoil your soundest naps.

"Tell him you'll stand no sort of trick;
     Then, if he leers and chuckles,
You just be handy with a stick
(Mind that it's pretty hard and thick)
     And rap him on the knuckles!

"Then carelessly remark 'Old coon!
     Perhaps you're not aware
That it you don't behave, you'll soon
Be chuckling to another tune—
     And so you'd best take care!'

"That's the right way to cure a Sprite
     Of such-like goings-on—
But gracious me! It's getting light!
Good-night, old Turnip-top, good-night!"
     A nod, and he was gone.

CANTO 7

Sad Souvenaunce

"WHAT'S this?" I pondered. "Have I slept?
    Or can I have been drinking?"
But soon a gentler feeling crept
Upon me, and I sat and wept
    An hour or so, like winking.

"No need for Bones to hurry so!"
    I sobbed. "In fact, I doubt
If it was worth his while to go—
And who is Tibbs, I'd like to know,
    To make such work about?

"If Tibbs is anything like me,
    It's *possible*", I said,
"He won't be over-pleased to be
Dropped in upon at half-past three,
    After he's snug in bed.

"And if Bones plagues him anyhow—
    Squeaking and all the rest of it,
As he was doing here just now—
I prophesy there'll be a row,
    And Tibbs will have the best of it!"

"And Tibbs will have the best of it"

Then, as my tears could never bring
    The friendly Phantom back,
It seemed to me the proper thing
To mix another glass, and sing
    The following Coronach.

And art thou gone, beloved Ghost?
    Best of Familiars!
Nay, then, farewell, my duckling roast,
Farewell, farewell, my tea and toast,
    My meerschaum and cigars!

The hues of life are dull and gray,
   The sweets of life insipid,
When thou, *my charmer, art away—*
Old Brick, or rather, let me say,
   Old Parallelepiped!"

Instead of singing Verse the Third,
   I ceased—abruptly, rather:
But, after such a splendid word
I felt that it would be absurd
   To try it any farther.

So with a yawn I went my way
   To seek the welcome downy,
And slept, and dreamed till break of day
Of Poltergeist and Fetch and Fay
   And Leprechaun and Brownie!

For years I've not been visited
   By any kind of Sprite;
Yet still they echo in my head,
Those parting words, so kindly said,
   "Old Turnip-top, good-night!"

Echoes

LADY Clara Vere de Vere
Was eight years old, she said:
Every ringlet, lightly shaken, ran itself in
    golden thread.

She took her little porringer:
Of me she shall not win renown:
For the baseness of its nature shall have
    strength to drag her down.

"Sisters and brother, little Maid?
There stands the Inspector at thy door:
Like a dog, he hunts for boys who know
    not two and two are four."

"Kind hearts are more than coronets,"
She said, and wondering looked at me:
"It is the dead unhappy night, and I must
    hurry home to tea."

A Sea Dirge

THERE are certain things—as, a spider, a ghost,
    The income-tax, gout, an umbrella for three—
That I hate, but the thing I hate the most
    Is a thing they call the Sea.

Pour some salt water over the floor—
    Ugly I'm sure you'll allow it to be:
Suppose it extended a mile or more,
    That's very like the Sea.

Beat a dog till it howls outright—
    Cruel, but all very well. for a spree:

Suppose that he did so day and night,
   That would be like the Sea.

I had a vision of nursery-maids;
   Tens of thousands passed by me—
All leading children with wooden spades,
   And this was by the Sea.

Who invented those spades of wood?
   Who was it cut them out of the tree?
None, I think, but an idiot could—
   Or one that loved the Sea.

It is pleasant and dreamy, no doubt, to float
   With "thoughts as boundless, and souls as free":
But suppose you are very unwell in the boat,
   How do you like the Sea?

There is an insect that people avoid
   (Whence is derived the verb "to flee").
Where have you been by it most annoyed?
   In lodgings by the Sea.

If you like your coffee with sand for dregs,
   A decided hint of salt in your tea,
And a fishy taste in the very eggs—
   By all means choose the Sea.

And if, with these dainties to drink and eat,
   You prefer not a vestige of grass or tree,
And a chronic state of wet in your feet,
   Then—I recommend the Sea.

For *I* have friends who dwell by the coast—
   Pleasants friends they are to me!
It is when I am with them I wonder most
   That anyone likes the Sea.

They take me a walk: though tired and stiff,
   To climb the heights I madly agree;
And, after a tumble or so from the cliff,
   They kindly suggest the Sea.

"And this was by the Sea"

I try the rocks, and I think it cool
    That they laugh with such an excess of glee,
As I heavily slip into every pool
    That skirts the cold cold Sea.

Ye Carpette Knyghte

I HAVE a horse—a ryghte goode horse—
    Ne doe I envye those
Who scoure ye playne yn headye course
    Tyll soddayne on theyre nose
They lyghte wyth unexpected force
    Yt ys—a horse of clothes.

"I have a horse"

I have a saddel—"Say'st thou soe?
    Wyth styrruppes, Knyghte, to boote?"
I sayde not that—I answere "Noe"—
    Yt lacketh such, I woote:
Yt ys a mutton-saddel, loe!
    Parte of ye fleecye brute.

I have a bytte—a ryghte good bytte—
    As shall bee seene yn tyme.
Ye jawe of horse yt wyll not fytte;
    Yts use ys more sublyme.
Fayre Syr, how deemest thou of yt?
    Yt ys—thys bytte of rhyme.

Hiawatha's Photographing

[In an age of imitation, I can claim no special merit for this slight attempt at doing what is known to be so easy. Any fairly practised writer, with the slightest ear for rhythm, could compose, for hours together, in the easy running metre of "The Song of Hiawatha". Having, then, distinctly stated that I challenge no attention in the following little poem to its merely verbal jingle, I must beg the candid reader to confine his criticism to its treatment of the subject.]

FROM his shoulder Hiawatha
Took the camera of rosewood,
Made of sliding, folding rosewood;
Neatly put it all together.
In its case it lay compactly,
Folded into nearly nothing;
But he opened out the hinges,
Pushed and pulled the joints and hinges,
Till it looked all squares and oblongs,

Like a complicated figure
In the Second Book of Euclid.

    This he perched upon a tripod—
Crouched beneath its dusky cover—
Stretched his hand, enforcing silence—
Said, "Be motionless, I beg you!"
Mystic, awful was the process.

    All the family in order
Sat before him for their pictures:
Each in turn as he was taken,
Volunteered his own suggestions,
His ingenious suggestions.

    First the Governor, the Father:
He suggested velvet curtains
Looped about a massy pillar;
And the corner of a table,
Of a rosewood dining-table.
He would hold a scroll of something,
Hold it firmly in his left-hand;
He would keep his right-hand buried
(Like Napoleon) in his waistcoat;
He would contemplate the distance
With a look of pensive meaning,
As of ducks that die in tempests.

Grand, heroic was the notion:
Yet the picture failed entirely:
Failed, because he moved a little,
Moved, because he couldn't help it.

Next, his better half took courage;
She would have her picture taken.
She came dressed beyond description,
Dressed in jewels and in satin
Far too gorgeous for an empress.
Gracefully she sat down sideways,
With a simper scarcely human,
Holding in her hand a bouquet
Rather larger than a cabbage.
All the while that she was sitting,
Still the lady chattered, chattered,
Like a monkey in the forest.
"Am I sitting still?" she asked him.
"Is my face enough in profile?
Shall I hold the bouquet higher?
Will it come into the picture?"
And the picture failed completely.

Next the Son, the Stunning-Cantab:
He suggested curves of beauty,
Curves pervading all his figure,
Which the eye might follow onward,
Till they centred in the breast-pin,
Centred in the golden breast-pin.
He had learnt it all from Ruskin
(Author of "The Stones of Venice",
"Seven Lamps of Architecture",
"Modern Painters", and some others);
And perhaps he had not fully
Understood his author's meaning;
But, whatever was the reason,
All was fruitless, as the picture
Ended in an utter failure.

Next to him the eldest daughter:
She suggested very little,
Only asked if he would take her
With her look of "passive beauty".

Her idea of passive beauty
Was a squinting of the left-eye,
Was a drooping of the right-eye,
Was a smile that went up sideways
To the corner of the nostrils.

"First the Governor, the Father"

A.B. FROST.

"Next the Son, the Stunning-Cantab"

"Next to him the eldest daughter"

"Last, the youngest son was taken"

Hiawatha, when she asked him,
Took no notice of the question,
Looked as if he hadn't heard it;
But, when pointedly appealed to,
Smiled in his peculiar manner,
Coughed and said it "didn't matter",
Bit his lip and changed the subject.

Nor in this was he mistaken
As the picture failed completely.

So in turn the other sisters.

Last, the youngest son was taken:
Very rough and thick his hair was,
Very round and red his face was
Very dusty was his jacket,
Very fidgety his manner.
And his overbearing sisters
Called him names he disapproved of:
Called him Johnny, "Daddy's Darling",
Called him Jacky, "Scrubby School-boy".
And so awful was the picture,
In comparison the others
Seemed, to one's bewildered fancy,
To have partially succeeded.

Finally my Hiawatha
Tumbled all the tribe together,
("Grouped" is not the right expression),
And, as happy chance would have it
Did at last obtain a picture
Where the faces all succeeded:
Each came out a perfect likeness.

Then they joined and all abused it,
Unrestrainedly abused it,
As the worst and ugliest picture
They could possibly have dreamed of.
"Giving one such strange expressions—
Sullen, stupid, pert expressions.
Really anyone would take us
(Anyone that did not know us)
For the most unpleasant people!"
(Hiawatha seemed to think so,
Seemed to think it not unlikely.)
All together rang their voices,
Angry, loud, discordant voices,
As of dogs that howl in concert,
As of cats that wail in chorus.

But my Hiawatha's patience,
His politeness and his patience,
Unaccountably had vanished,
And he left that happy party.
Neither did he leave them slowly,
With the calm deliberation,
The intense deliberation
Of a photographic artist:
But he left them in a hurry,
Left them in a mighty hurry,
Stating that he would not stand it,
Stating in emphatic language
What he'd be before he'd stand it.
Hurriedly he packed his boxes:
Hurriedly the porter trundled
On a barrow all his boxes:
Hurriedly he took his ticket:
Hurriedly the train received him:
Thus departed Hiawatha.

Melancholetta

WITH saddest music all day long
   She soothed her secret sorrow:
At night she sighed "I fear 'twas wrong
   Such cheerful words to borrow.
Dearest, a sweeter, sadder song
   I'll sing to thee to-morrow."

I thanked her, but I could not say
   That I was glad to hear it:
I left the house at break of day,
   And did not venture near it
Till time, I hoped, had worn away
   Her grief, for nought could cheer it!

My dismal sister! Couldst thou know
   The wretched home thou keepest!
Thy brother, drowned in daily woe,
   Is thankful when thou sleepest;
For if I laugh, however low,
   When thou'rt awake, thou weepest!

I took my sister t'other day
   (Excuse the slang expression)
To Sadler's Wells to see the play
   In hopes the new impression
Might in her thoughts, from grave to gay
   Effect some slight digression.

I asked three gay young dogs from town
   To join us in our folly,
Whose mirth, I thought, might serve to drown
   My sister's melancholy:

The lively Jones, the sportive Brown,
    And Robinson the jolly.

The maid announced the meal in tones
    That I myself had taught her,
Meant to allay my sister's moans
    Like oil on troubled water:
I rushed to Jones, the lively Jones,
    And begged him to escort her.

Vainly he strove, with ready wit,
    To joke about the weather—
To ventilate the last "*on dit*"—
    To quote the price of leather—
She groaned "Here I and Sorrow sit:
    Let us lament together!"

I urged "You're wasting time, you know:
    Delay will spoil the venison."
"My heart is wasted with my woe!
    There is no rest—in Venice, on
The Bridge of Sighs!" she quoted low
    From Byron and from Tennyson.

I need not tell of soup and fish
    In solemn silence swallowed,
The sobs that ushered in each dish,
    And its departure followed,
Nor yet my suicidal wish
    To *be* the cheese I hollowed.

Some desperate attempts were made
    To start a conversation;
"Madam," the sportive Brown essayed,
    "Which kind of recreation,
Hunting or fishing, have you made
    Your special occupation?"

Her lips curved downwards instantly,
    As if of india-rubber.
"Hounds *in full cry* I like," said she:
    (Oh, how I longed to snub her!)

"At night she sighed"

"Of fish, a whale's the one for me,
   It is so full of blubber! "

The night's performance was "King John"
   "It's dull", she wept, "and so-so!"
Awhile I let her tears flow on,
   She said they soothed her woe so!
At length the curtain rose upon
   "Bombastes Furioso".

In vain we roared; in vain we tried
   To rouse her into laughter:
Her pensive glances wandered wide
   From orchestra to rafter—
"*Tier upon tier!* " she said, and sighed;
   And silence followed after.

A Valentine

[Sent to a friend who had complained that I was glad enough to see him when he came, but didn't seem to miss him if he stayed away.]

AND cannot pleasures, while they last,
Be actual unless, when past,
They leave us shuddering and aghast,
    With anguish smarting?
And cannot friends be firm and fast,
    And yet bear parting?

And must I then, at Friendship's call
Calmly resign the little all
(Trifling, I grant, it is and small)
    I have of gladness,
And lend my being to the thrall
    Of gloom and sadness?

And think you that I should be dumb,
And full *dolorum omnium*,
Excepting when *you* choose to come
    And share my dinner?
At other times be sour and glum
    And daily thinner?

Must he then only live to weep,
Who'd prove his friendship true and deep,
By day a lonely shadow creep,
    At night-time languish,
Oft raising in his broken sleep
    The moan of anguish?

The lover, if for certain days
His fair one be denied his gaze,
Sinks not in grief and wild amaze,
  But wiser wooer,
He spends the time in writing lays,
  And posts them to her.

And if the verse flow free and fast,
Till even the poet is aghast,
A touching Valentine at last
  The post shall carry,
When thirteen days are gone and past
  Of February.

Farewell, dear friend, and when we meet,
In desert waste or crowded street,
Perhaps before this week shall fleet,
  Perhaps to-morrow,
I trust to find *your* heart the seat
  Of wasting sorrow.

The Three Voices

The First Voice

HE trilled a carol fresh and free,
He laughed aloud for very glee:
There came a breeze from off the sea:

It passed athwart the glooming flat—
It fanned his forehead as he sat—
It lightly bore away his hat,

All to the feet of one who stood
Like maid enchanted in a wood,
Frowning as darkly as she could.

With huge umbrella, lank and brown,
Unerringly she pinned it down,
Right through the centre of the crown.

Then, with an aspect cold and grim,
Regardless of its battered rim,
She took it up and gave it him.

A while like one in dreams he stood,
Then faltered forth his gratitude
In words just short of being rude:

For it had lost its shape and shine,
And it had cost him four-and-nine,
And he was going out to dine.

"To dine!" she sneered in acid tone
"To bend thy being to a bone
Clothed in a radiance not its own!"

The tear-drop trickled to his chin:
There was a meaning in her grin
That made him feel on fire within.

"Term it not 'radiance'," said he:
" 'Tis solid nutriment to me.
Dinner is Dinner: Tea is Tea."

And she, "Yea so? Yet wherefore cease?
Let thy scant knowledge find increase.
Say 'Men are Men, and Geese are Geese'."

He moaned: he knew not what to say.
The thought "That I could get away!"
Strove with the thought "But I must stay".

"To dine!" she shrieked in dragon-wrath.
"To swallow wines all foam and froth!
To simper at a table-cloth!

"Unerringly she pinned it down."

"He faltered 'Gifts may pass away.' "

"Say, can thy noble spirit stoop
To join the gormandizing troop
Who find a solace in the soup?

"Canst thou desire or pie or puff?
Thy well-bred manners were enough,
Without such gross material stuff."

"Yet well-bred men", he faintly said,
"Are not unwilling to be fed:
Nor are they well without the bread."

Her visage scorched him ere she spoke:
"There are", she said, "a kind of folk
Who have no horror of a joke.

"Such wretches live; they take their share
Of common earth and common air:
We come across them here and there:

"We grant them—there is no escape—
A sort of semi-human shape
Suggestive of the man-like Ape."

"In all such theories", said he,
"One fixed exception there must be
That is, the Present Company."

Baffled, she gave a wolfish bark:
He, aiming blindly in the dark,
With random shaft had pierced the mark.

She felt that her defeat was plain,
Yet madly strove with might and main
To get the upper hand again.

Fixing her eyes upon the beach,
As though unconscious of his speech,
She said "Each gives to more than each".

He could not answer yea or nay:
He faltered "Gifts may pass away".
Yet knew not what he meant to say.

"If that be so," she straight replied,
"Each heart with each doth coincide.
What boots it? For the world is wide."

"The world is but a Thought," said he:
"The vast unfathomable sea
Is but a Notion—unto me."

And darkly fell her answer dread
Upon his unresisting head,
Like half a hundredweight of lead.

"The Good and Great must ever shun
That reckless and abandoned one
Who stoops to perpetrate a pun.

"The man that smokes—that reads *The Times*—
That goes to Christmas Pantomimes—
Is capable of *any* crimes!"

He felt it was his turn to speak,
And, with a shamed and crimson cheek,
Moaned "This is harder than Bezique!"

But when she asked him "Wherefore so?"
He felt his very whiskers glow,
And frankly owned "I do not know".

While, like broad waves of golden grain,
Or sunlit hues on cloistered pane,
His colour came and went again.

Pitying his obvious distress,
Yet with a tinge of bitterness,
She said "The More exceeds the Less".

"A truth of such undoubted weight",
He urged, "and so extreme in date,
It were superfluous to state."

Roused into sudden passion, she
In tone of cold malignity:
"To others, yea: but not to thee."

"This is harder than Bezique!"

But when she saw him quail and quake,
And when he urged "For pity's sake!"
Once more in gentle tones she spake.

"Thought in the mind doth still abide
That is by Intellect supplied,
And within that Idea doth hide:

"And he, that yearns the truth to know
Still further inwardly may go,
And find Idea from Notion flow:

"And thus the chain, that sages sought,
Is to a glorious circle wrought,
For Notion hath its source in Thought."

So passed they on with even pace:
Yet gradually one might trace
A shadow growing on his face.

The Second Voice

THEY walked beside the wave-worn beach;
Her tongue was very apt to teach,
And now and then he did beseech

She would abate her dulcet tone,
Because the talk was all her own,
And he was dull as any drone.

She urged "No cheese is made of chalk":
And ceaseless flowed her dreary talk,
Tuned to the footfall of a walk.

Her voice was very full and rich,
And, when at length she asked him "Which?"
It mounted to its highest pitch.

He a bewildered answer gave,
Drowned in the sullen moaning wave,
Lost in the echoes of the cave.

He answered her he knew not what:
Like shaft from bow at random shot,
He spoke, but she regarded not.

She waited not for his reply,
But with a downward leaden eye
Went on as if he were not by—

Sound argument and grave defence,
Strange questions raised on "Why?" and "Whence?"
And wildly tangled evidence.

When he, with racked and whirling brain,
Feebly implored her to explain,
She simply said it all again.

Wrenched with an agony intense,
He spake, neglecting Sound and Sense,
And careless of all consequence:

"Mind—I believe—is Essence—Ent—
Abstract—that is—an Accident—
Which we—that is to say—I meant——"

When, with quick breath and cheeks all flushed,
At length his speech was somewhat hushed,
She looked at him, and he was crushed.

It needed not her calm reply:
She fixed him with a stony eye,
And he could neither fight nor fly.

While she dissected, word by word,
His speech, half-guessed at and half-heard,
As might a cat a little bird.

"He spake, neglecting Sound and Sense."

"Shall Man be Man?"

Then, having wholly overthrown
His views, and stripped them to the bone,
Proceeded to unfold her own.

"Shall Man be Man? And shall he miss
Of other thoughts no thought but this,
Harmonious dews of sober bliss?

"What boots it? Shall his fevered eye
Through towering nothingness descry
The grisly phantom hurry by?

"And hear dumb shrieks that fill the air:
See mouths that gape, and eyes that stare
And redden in the dusky glare?

"The meadows breathing amber light,
The darkness toppling from the height,
The feathery train of granite Night?

"Shall he, grown gray among his peers,
Through the thick curtain of his tears
Catch glimpses of his earlier years,

"And hear the sounds he knew of yore,
Old shufflings on the sanded floor,
Old knuckles tapping at the door?

"Yet still before him as he flies
One pallid form shall ever rise,
And, bodying forth in glassy eyes

"The vision of a vanished good,
Low peering through the tangled wood,
Shall freeze the current of his blood."

Still from each fact, with skill uncouth
And savage rapture, like a tooth
She wrenched some slow reluctant truth.

Till, like a silent water-mill,
When summer suns have dried the rill,
She reached a full stop, and was still.

Dead calm succeeded to the fuss,
As when the loaded omnibus
Has reached the railway terminus:

When, for the tumult of the street,
Is heard the engine's stifled beat,
The velvet tread of porters' feet.

With glance that ever sought the ground,
She moved her lips without a sound,
And every now and then she frowned.

He gazed upon the sleeping sea,
And joyed in its tranquillity,
And in that silence dead, but she

To muse a little space did seem,
Then, like the echo of a dream,
Harked back upon her threadbare theme.

Still an attentive ear he lent
But could not fathom what she meant:
She was not deep, nor eloquent.

He marked the ripple on the sand:
The even swaying of her hand
Was all that he could understand.

He saw in dreams a drawing-room,
Where thirteen wretches sat in gloom,
Waiting—he thought he knew for whom:

He saw them drooping here and there,
Each feebly huddled on a chair,
In attitudes of blank despair:

Oysters were not more mute than they,
For all their brains were pumped away,
And they had nothing more to say—

Save one, who groaned "Three hours are gone!"
Who shrieked "We'll wait no longer, John!
Tell them to set the dinner on!"

"He sat and watched the coming tide"

The vision passed: the ghosts were fled:
He saw once more that woman dread:
He heard once more the words she said.

He left her, and he turned aside:
He sat and watched the coming tide
Across the shores so newly dried.

He wondered at the waters clear,
The breeze that whispered in his ear,
The billows heaving far and near,

And why he had so long preferred
To hang upon her every word:
"In truth", he said, "it was absurd."

The Third Voice

Not long this transport held its place:
Within a little moment's space
Quick tears were raining down his face.

His heart stood still, aghast with fear;
A wordless voice, nor far nor near,
He seemed to hear and not to hear.

"Tears kindle not the doubtful spark.
If so, why not? Of this remark
The bearings are profoundly dark."

"He groaned aghast"

"Her speech", he said, "hath caused this pain.
Easier I count it to explain
The jargon of the howling main,

"Or, stretched beside some babbling brook,
To con, with inexpressive look,
An unintelligible book."

Low spake the voice within his head,
In words imagined more than said,
Soundless as ghost's intended tread:

"If thou art duller than before,
Why quittedst thou the voice of lore?
Why not endure, expecting more?"

"Rather than that", he groaned aghast,
"I'd writhe in depths of cavern vast,
Some loathly vampire's rich repast."

" 'Twere hard," it answered, "themes immense
To coop within the narrow fence
That rings *thy* scant intelligence."

"Not so," he urged, "nor once alone:
But there was something in her tone
That chilled me to the very bone.

"Her style was anything but clear,
And most unpleasantly severe;
Her epithets were very queer.

"And yet, so grand were her replies,
I could not choose but deem her wise;
I did not dare to criticise;

"Nor did I leave her, till she went
So deep in tangled argument
That all my powers of thought were spent."

A little whisper inly slid,
"Yet truth is truth: you know you did."
A little wink beneath the lid.

And, sickened with excess of dread,
Prone to the dust he bent his head,
And lay like one three-quarters dead.

The whisper left him—like a breeze
Lost in the depths of leafy trees—
Left him by no means at his ease.

Once more he weltered in despair,
With hands, through denser-matted hair,
More tightly clenched than then they were.

When, bathed in Dawn of living red,
Majestic frowned the mountain head,
"Tell me my fault," was all he said.

When, at high Noon, the blazing sky
Scorched in his head each haggard eye,
Then keenest rose his weary cry.

And when at Eve the unpitying sun
Smiled grimly on the solemn fun,
"Alack," he sighed, "what *have* I done?"

But saddest, darkest was the sight,
When the cold grasp of leaden Night
Dashed him to earth, and held him tight.

Tortured, unaided, and alone,
Thunders were silence to his groan,
Bagpipes sweet music to its tone:

"What? Ever thus, in dismal round,
Shall Pain and Mystery profound
Pursue me like a sleepless hound,

"Tortured, unaided, and alone"

"A scared dullard, gibbering low"

"With crimson-dashed and eager jaws,
Me, still in ignorance of the cause,
Unknowing what I broke of laws?"

The whisper to his ear did seem
Like echoed flow of silent stream,
Or shadow of forgotten dream,

The whisper trembling in the wind:
"Her fate with thine was intertwined,"
So spake it in his inner mind:

"Each orbed on each a baleful star:
Each proved the other's blight and bar:
Each unto each were best, most far:

"Yea, each to each was worse than foe:
Thou, a scared dullard, gibbering low,
AND SHE, AN AVALANCHE OF WOE!"

Tèma con Variazióni

[Why is it that Poetry has never yet been subjected to that process of Dilution which has proved so advantageous to her sister-art Music? The Diluter gives us first a few notes of some well-known Air, then a dozen bars of his own, then a few more notes of the Air, and so on alternately: thus saving the listener, if not from all risk of recognizing the melody at all, at least from the too-exciting transports which it might produce in a more concentrated form. The process is termed "setting" by Composers, and any one, that has ever experienced the emotion of being unexpectedly set down in a heap of mortar, will recognize the truthfulness of this happy phrase.

For truly, just as the genuine Epicure lingers lovingly over a morsel of supreme Venison—whose every fibre seems to murmur "Excelsior!"—yet swallows, ere returning to the toothsome dainty, great mouthfuls of oatmeal-porridge and winkles: and just as the perfect Connoisseur in Claret permits himself but one delicate sip, and then tosses off a pint or more of boarding-school beer: so also——]

I never loved a dear Gazelle—
  Nor anything that cost me much:
High prices profit those who sell,
  But why should I be fond of such?

To glad me with his soft black eye
  My son comes trotting home from school;
He's had a fight but can't tell why—
  He always was a little fool!

But, when he came to know me well,
  He kicked me out, her testy Sire:
And when I stained my hair, that Belle
  Might note the change, and thus admire

And love me, it was sure to dye
  A muddy green, or staring blue:
Whilst one might trace, with half an eye,
  The still triumphant carrot through.

A Game of Fives

FIVE little girls of Five, Four, Three, Two, One:
Rolling on the hearthrug, full of tricks and fun.

Five rosy girls, in years from Ten to Six:
Sitting down to lessons—no more time for tricks.

Five growing girls, from Fifteen to Eleven:
Music, Drawing, Languages, and food enough for seven!

Five winsome girls, from Twenty to Sixteen:
Each young man that calls, I say "Now tell
    me which you *mean*!"

Five dashing girls, the youngest Twenty-one:
But, if nobody proposes, what is there to be done?

"Now tell me which you mean!*"*

Five showy girls—but Thirty is an age
When girls may be *engaging*, but they somehow don't *engage*.

Five dressy girls, of Thirty-one or more:
So gracious to the shy young men they snubbed so much before!

        *   *   *   *   *   *

Five *passé* girls—Their age? Well, never mind!
We jog along together, like the rest of human kind:

But the quondam "careless bachelor" begins to think he knows
The answer to that ancient problem "how the money goes"!

Poeta Fit,
Non Nascitur

"How shall I be a poet?
    How shall I write in rhyme:
You told me once 'the very wish
    Partook of the sublime'.
Then tell me how! Don't put me off
    With your 'another time'!"

The old man smiled to see him,
    To hear his sudden sally;
He liked the lad to speak his mind
    Enthusiastically;
And thought "There's no hum-drum in him,
    Nor any shilly-shally."

"And would you be a poet
    Before you've been to school?
Ah, well! I hardly thought you
    So absolute a fool.
First learn to be spasmodic—
    A very simple rule.

"For first you write a sentence,
    And then you chop it small;
Then mix the bits, and sort them out
    Just as they chance to fall:
The order of the phrases makes
    No difference at all.

"Then, if you'd be impressive,
    Remember what I say,
That abstract qualities begin
    With capitals alway:
The True, the Good, the Beautiful—
    Those are the things that pay!

"Next, when you are describing
    A shape, or sound, or tint;
Don't state the matter plainly,
    But put it in a hint;
And learn to look at all things
    With a sort of mental squint."

"For instance, if I wished, Sir,
    Of mutton-pies to tell,
Should I say 'dreams of fleecy flocks
    Pent in a wheaten cell'?"
"Why, yes," the old man said: "that phrase
    Would answer very well.

"Then fourthly, there are epithets
    That suit with any word—
As well as Harvey's Reading Sauce
    With fish, or flesh, or bird—
Of these, 'wild', 'lonely', 'weary', 'strange',
    Are much to be preferred."

"And will it do, O will it do
   To take them in a lump—
As 'the wild man went his weary way
   To a strange and lonely pump'?"
"Nay, nay! You must not hastily
   To such conclusions jump.

"Such epithets, like pepper,
   Give zest to what you write;
And, if you strew them sparely,
   They whet the appetite:
But if you lay them on too thick,
   You spoil the matter quite!

"Last, as to the arrangement:
  Your reader, you should show him,
Must take what information he
  Can get, and look for no im-
mature disclosure of the drift
  And purpose of your poem.

"Therefore, to test his patience—
  How much he can endure—
Mention no places, names, or dates,
  And evermore be sure
Throughout the poem to be found
  Consistently obscure.

"First fix upon the limit
  To which it shall extend:
Then fill it up with 'Padding'
  (Beg some of any friend):
Your great SENSATION-STANZA
  You place towards the end."

"And what is a Sensation,
  Grandfather, tell me, pray?
I think I never heard the word
  So used before to-day:
Be kind enough to mention one
  'Exempli gratiâ'."

And the old man, looking sadly
  Across the garden-lawn,
Where here and there a dew-drop
  Yet glittered in the dawn,
Said "Go to the Adelphi,
  And see the 'Colleen Bawn'.

"The word is due to Boucicault—
  The theory is his,
Where life becomes a Spasm,
  And History a Whiz:
If that is not Sensation,
  I don't know what it is.

"The wild man went his weary way"

"Now try your hand, ere Fancy
   Have lost its present glow——"
"And then", his grandson added,
   "We'll publish it, you know:
Green cloth—gold-lettered at the back—
   In duodecimo!"

Then proudly smiled that old man
   To see the eager lad
Rush madly for his pen and ink
   And for his blotting-pad—
But, when he thought of *publishing*,
   His face grew stern and sad.

Size and Tears

WHEN on the sandy shore I sit,
   Beside the salt sea-wave,
And falling into a weeping fit
   Because I dare not shave—
A little whisper at my ear
Enquires the reason of my fear.

"He's thin and I am stout"

I answer "If that ruffian Jones
  Should recognise me here,
He'd bellow out my name in tones
  Offensive to the ear:
He chaffs me so on being stout
(A thing that always puts me out)."

Ah me! I see him on the cliff!
  Farewell, farewell to hope,
If he should look this way, and if
  He's got his telescope!
To whatsoever place I flee,
My odious rival follows me!

For every night, and everywhere,
  I meet him out at dinner;
And when I've found some charming fair,
  And vowed to die or win her,
The wretch (he's thin and I am stout)
Is sure to come and cut me out!

The girls (just like them!) all agree
  To praise J. Jones, Esquire:
I ask them what on earth they see
  About him to admire?
They cry "He is so sleek and slim,
It's quite a treat to look at him!"

They vanish in tobacco smoke,
  Those visionary maids—
I feel a sharp and sudden poke
  Between the shoulder-blades—
"Why, Brown, my boy! You're growing stout!"
(I told you he would find me out!)

"My growth is not *your* business, Sir!"
  "No more it is, my boy!
But if it's *yours*, as I infer,
  Why, Brown, I give you joy!
A man, whose business prospers so,
Is just the sort of man to know!

"It's hardly safe, though, talking here—
   I'd best get out of reach:
For such a weight as yours, I fear,
   Must shortly sink the beach!"—
Insult me thus because I'm stout!
I vow I'll go and call him out!

Atalanta in Camden-Town

AY, 'twas here, on this spot,
  In that summer of yore,
Atalanta did not
  Vote my presence a bore,
Nor reply to my tenderest talk "She had heard all that nonsense
  before".

She'd the brooch I had bought
  And the necklace and sash on,
And her heart, as I thought,
  Was alive to my passion;
And she'd done up her hair in the style that the Empress had
  brought into fashion.

I had been to the play
With my pearl of a Peri—
But, for all I could say,
She declared she was weary,
That "the place was so crowded and hot, and she couldn't
abide that Dundreary"

Then I thought "Lucky boy!
'Tis for *you* that she whimpe: "
And I noted with joy
Those sensational simpers:
And I said "This is scrumptious!"—a phrase I had learned
from the Devonshire shrimpers.

And I vowed " 'Twill be said
I'm a fortunate fellow,
When the breakfast is spread,
When the topers are mellow,
When the foam of the bride-cake is white, and the fierce
orange blossoms are yellow!"

O that languishing yawn!
Oh those eloquent eyes!
I was drunk with the dawn
Of a splendid surmise—
I was stung by a look, I was slain by a tear, by a tempest of sighs.

Then I whispered "I see
The sweet secret thou keepest.
And the yearning for *ME*
That thou wistfully weepest!
And the question is 'License or Banns?' though undoubtedly
Banns are the cheapest."

"Be my Hero," said I,
"And let *me* be Leander!"
But I lost her reply—
Something ending with "gander"—
For the omnibus rattled so loud that no mortal could quite
understand her.

The Lang Coortin'

THE ladye she stood at her lattice high,
  Wi' her doggie at her feet;
Thorough the lattice she can spy
  The passers in the street,

"There's one that standeth at the door,
  And tirleth at the pin:
Now speak and say, my popinjay,
  If I sall let him in."

Then up and spake the popinjay
  That flew abune her head:
"Gae let him in that tirls the pin:
  He cometh thee to wed."

O when he cam' the parlour in,
  A woeful man was he!
"And dinna ye ken your lover agen,
  Sae well that loveth thee?"

"And how wad I ken ye loved me, Sir,
  That have been sae lang away?
And how wad I ken ye loved me, Sir?
  Ye never telled me sae."

Said—"Ladye dear," and the salt, salt tear
  Cam' rinnin' doon his cheek,
"I have sent the tokens of my love
  This many and many a week.

"O didna ye get the rings, Ladye,
  The rings o' the gowd sae fine?
I wot that I have sent to thee
  Four score, four score and nine."

"They cam' to me," said that fair ladye.
  "Wow, they were flimsie things!"
Said—"that chain o' gowd, my doggie to howd,
  It is made o' thae self-same rings."

"And didna ye get the locks, the locks,
  The locks o' my ain black hair,
Whilk I sent by post, whilk I sent by box,
  Whilk I sent by the carrier?"

"They cam' to me," said that fair ladye;
  "And I prithee send nae mair!"
Said—"that cushion sae red, for my doggie's head,
  It is stuffed wi' thae locks o' hair."

"And didna ye get the letter, Ladye,
  Tied wi' a silken string,
Whilk I sent to thee frae the far countrie,
  A message of love to bring?"

"It cam' to me frae the far countrie
  Wi' its silken string and a';
But it wasna prepaid," said that high-born maid,
  "Sae I gar'd them tak' it awa'."

"O ever alack that ye sent it back,
  It was written sae clerkly and well!
Now the message it brought, and the boon that it sought.
  I must even say it mysel'."

Then up and spake the popinjay,
  Sae wisely counselled he.
"Now say it in the proper way:
  Gae doon upon thy knee!"

The lover he turned baith red and pale,
  Went doon upon his knee:
"O Ladye, hear the waesome tale
  That must be told to thee!

"For five lang years, and five lang years,
  I coorted thee by looks;
By nods and winks, by smiles and tears,
  As I had read in books.

"For ten lang years, O weary hours!
  I coorted thee by signs;
By sending game, by sending flowers,
  By sending Valentines.

"For five lang years, and five lang years,
  I have dwelt in the far countrie,
Till that thy mind should be inclined
  Mair tenderly to me.

"Now thirty years are gane and past,
  I am come frae a foreign land:
I am come to tell thee my love at last—
  O Ladye, gie me thy hand!"

"And out and laughed the popinjay"

The ladye she turned not pale nor red,
　But she smiled a pitiful smile:
"Sic' a coortin' as yours, my man," she said,
　"Takes a lang and a weary while!"

And out and laughed the popinjay,
　A laugh of bitter scorn:
"A coortin' done in sic' a way,
　It ought not to be borne!"

Wi' that the doggie barked aloud,
　And up and doon he ran,
And tugged and strained his chain o' gowd,
　All for to bite the man.

"O hush thee, gentle popinjay!
　O hush thee, doggie dear!
There is a word I fain wad say,
　It needeth he should hear!"

Aye louder screamed that ladye fair
　To drown her doggie's bark:
Ever the lover shouted mair
　To make that lady hark:

Shrill and more shrill the popinjay
　Upraised his angry squall:
I trow the doggie's voice that day
　Was louder than them all!

The serving-men and serving-maids
　Sat by the kitchen fire:
They heard sic' a din the parlour within
　As made them much admire.

Out spake the boy in buttons
　(I ween he wasna thin),
"Now wha will tae the parlour gae,
　And stay this deadlie din?"

And they have taen a kerchief,
  Casted their kevils in,
For wha will tae the parlour gae,
  And stay that deadlie din.

When on that boy the kevil fell
  To stay the fearsome noise,
"Gae in," they cried, "whate'er betide,
  Thou prince of button-boys!"

Syne, he has taen a supple cane
  To swinge that dog sae fat:
The doggie yowled, the doggie howled
  The louder aye for that.

Syne, he has taen a mutton-bane—
  The doggie ceased his noise,
And followed doon the kitchen stair
  That prince of button-boys!

Then sadly spake that ladye fair,
  Wi' a frown upon her brow:
"O dearer to me is my sma' doggie
  Than a dozen sic' as thou!

"Nae use, nae use for sighs and tears:
  Nae use at all to fret:
Sin' ye've bided sae well for thirty years,
  Ye may bide a wee langer yet!"

Sadly, sadly he crossed the floor
  And tirlëd at the pin:
Sadly went he through the door
  Where sadly he cam' in.

"O gin I had a popinjay
  To fly abune my head,
To tell me what I ought to say,
  I had by this been wed.

"Oh hush thee, gentle popinjay!"

"The doggie ceased his noise"

"O gin I find anither ladye,"
  He said wi' sighs and tears,
"I wot my coortin' sall not be
  Anither thirty years

"For gin I find a ladye gay,
  Exactly to my taste,
I'll pop the question, aye or nay
  In twenty years at maist."

Four Riddles

[These consist of two Double Acrostics and two Charades.

No. I. was written at the request of some young friends, who had gone to a ball at an Oxford Commemoration—and also as a specimen of what might be done by making the Double Acrostic *a connected poem* instead of what it has hitherto been, a string of disjointed stanzas, on every conceivable subject, and about as interesting to read straight through as a page of a Cyclopedia. The first two stanzas describe the two main words, and each subsequent stanza one of the cross "lights".

No. II. was written after seeing Miss Ellen Terry perform in the play of "Hamlet". In this case the first stanza describes the two main words.

No. III. was written after seeing Miss Marion Terry perform in Mr. Gilbert's play of "Pygmalion and Galatea". The three stanzas respectively describe "My First", "My Second", and "My Whole".]

1

THERE was an ancient City, stricken down
　　With a strange frenzy, and for many a day
They paced from morn to eve the crowded town,
　　And danced the night away.

I asked the cause: the aged man grew sad:
　　They pointed to a building gray and tall,
And hoarsely answered "Step inside, my lad,
　　And then you'll see it all."

———

Yet what are all such gaieties to me
　　Whose thoughts are full of indices and surds?
$$x^2 + 7x + 53$$
$$= \frac{11}{3}.$$

But something whispered "It will soon be done.
    Bands cannot always play, nor ladies smile:
Endure with patience the distasteful fun
    For just a little while!"

A change came o'er my Vision—it was night:
    We clove a pathway through a frantic throng:
The steeds, wild-plunging, filled us with affright:
    The chariots whirled along.

Within a marble hall a river ran—
    A living tide, half muslin and half cloth:
And here one mourned a broken wreath or fan,
    Yet swallowed down her wrath:

And here one offered to a thirsty fair
    (His words half-drowned amid those thunders tuneful)
Some frozen viand (there were many there),
    A tooth-ache in each spoonful.

There comes a happy pause, for human strength
    Will not endure to dance without cessation;
And every one must reach the point at length
    Of absolute prostration.

At such a moment ladies learn to give,
    To partners who would urge them overmuch,
A flat and yet decided negative—
    Photographers love such.

There comes a welcome summons—hope revives,
    And fading eyes grow bright, and pulses quicken:
Incessant pop the corks, and busy knives
    Dispense the tongue and chicken.

Flushed with new life, the crowd flows back again:
    And all is tangled talk and mazy motion—
Much like a waving field of golden grain,
    Or a tempestuous ocean.

And thus they give the time, that Nature meant
　　For peaceful sleep and meditative snores,
To ceaseless din and mindless merriment
　　And waste of shoes and floors.

And One (we name him not) that flies the flowers,
　　That dreads the dances, and that shuns the salads,
They doom to pass in solitude the hours,
　　Writing acrostic-ballads.

How late it grows! The hour is surely past
　　That should have warned us with its double knock?
The twilight wanes, and morning comes at last—
　　"Oh, Uncle, what's o'clock?"

The Uncle gravely nods, and wisely winks.
　　It *may* mean much, but how is one to know?
He opes his mouth—yet out of it, methinks,
　　No words of wisdom flow.

2

EMPRESS of Art, for thee I twine
　　This wreath with all too slender skill.
Forgive my Muse each halting line,
　　And for the deed accept the will!

———

O day of tears! Whence comes this spectre grim,
　　Parting, like Death's cold river, souls that love?
Is not he bound to thee, as thou to him,
　　By vows, unwhispered here, yet heard above?

And still it lives, that keen and heavenward flame,
　　Lives in his eye, and trembles in his tone:
And these wild words of fury but proclaim
　　A heart that beats for thee, for thee alone!

But all is lost: that mighty mind o'erthrown,
 Like sweet bells jangled, piteous sight to see!
"Doubt that the stars are fire," so runs his moan,
 "Doubt Truth herself, but not my love for thee!"

A sadder vision yet: thine aged sire
 Shaming his hoary locks with treacherous wile!
And dost thou now doubt Truth to be a liar?
 And wilt thou die, that has forgot to smile?

Nay, get thee hence! Leave all thy winsome ways
 And the faint fragrance of thy scattered flowers:
In holy silence wait the appointed days,
 And weep away the leaden-footed hours.

3

THE air is bright with hues of light
 And rich with laughter and with singing:
Young hearts beat high in ecstasy,
 And banners wave, and bells are ringing:
But silence falls with fading day,
And there's an end to mirth and play.
  Ah, well-a-day!

Rest your old bones, ye wrinkled crones!
 The kettle sings, the firelight dances.
Deep be it quaffed, the magic draught
 That fills the soul with golden fancies!
For Youth and Pleasance will not stay,
And ye are withered, worn, and gray.
  Ah, well-a-day!

O fair cold face! O form of grace,
 For human passion madly yearning!
O weary air of dumb despair,
 From marble won, to marble turning!
"Leave us not thus!" we fondly pray.
"We cannot let thee pass away!"
  Ah, well-a-day!

4

My First is singular at best:
    More plural is my Second:
My Third is far the pluralest—
So plural-plural, I protest
    It scarcely can be reckoned!

My First is followed by a bird:
    My Second by believers
In magic art: my simple Third
Follows, not often, hopes absurd
    And plausible deceivers.

My First to get at wisdom tries—
    A failure melancholy!
My Second men revered as wise:
My Third from heights of wisdom flies
    To depths of frantic folly.

My First is ageing day by day:
    My Second's age is ended:
My Third enjoys an age, they say,
That never seems to fade away,
    Through centuries extended.

My Whole? I need a poet's pen
    To paint her myriad phases:
The monarch, and the slave, of men—
A mountain-summit, and a den
    Of dark and deadly mazes—

A flashing light—a fleeting shade—
    Beginning, end, and middle
Of all that human art hath made
Or wit devised! Go, seek *her* aid,
    If you would read my riddle!

Fame's Penny-Trumpet

BLOW, blow your trumpets till they crack,
   Ye little men of little souls!
And bid them huddle at your back—
   Gold-sucking leeches, shoals on shoals!

Fill all the air with hungry wails—
   "Reward us, ere we think or write!
Without your Gold mere Knowledge fails
   To sate the swinish appetite!"

And, where great Plato paced serene,
   Or Newton paused with wistful eye,
Rush to the chace with hoofs unclean
   And Babel-clamour of the sty.

Be yours the pay: be their the praise:
   We will not rob them of their due,
Nor vex the ghosts of other days
   By naming them along with you.

They sought and found undying fame:
   They toiled not for reward nor thanks:
Their cheeks are hot with honest shame
   For you, the modern mountebanks!

"Go, throng each other's drawing-rooms"

Who preach of Justice—plead with tears
　　That Love and Mercy should abound—
While marking with complacent ears
　　The moaning of some tortured hound:

Who prate of Wisdom—nay, forbear,
　　Lest Wisdom turn on you in wrath,
Trampling, with heel that will not spare,
　　The vermin that beset her path!

Go, throng each other's drawing-rooms,
　　Ye idols of a petty clique:
Strut your brief hour in borrowed plumes
　　And make your penny-trumpets squeak:

Deck your dull talk with pilfered shreds
　　Of learning from a nobler time,
And oil each other's little heads
　　With mutual Flattery's golden slime:

And when the topmost height ye gain,
　　And stand in Glory's ether clear,
And grasp the prize of all your pain—
　　So many hundred pounds a year—

Then let Fame's banner be unfurled!
　　Sing Pæans for a victory won!
Ye tapers, that would light the world,
　　And cast a shadow on the Sun—

Who still shall pour His rays sublime,
　　One crystal flood, from East to West,
When *ye* have burned your little time
　　And feebly flickered into rest!

❧ VIII ❧

Three Sunsets
and other poems

with twelve illustrations by
E. Gertrude Thomson

Preface

NEARLY the whole of this volume is a reprint of the serious portion of *Phantasmagoria and other Poems*, which was first published in 1869 and has long been out of print. "The Path of Roses" was written soon after the Crimean War, when the name of Florence Nightingale had already become a household-word. "Only a Woman's Hair" was suggested by a circumstance mentioned in *The Life of Dean Swift*, viz., that, after his death, a small packet was found among his papers, containing a single lock of hair and inscribed with those words. "After Three Days" was written after seeing Holman Hunt's picture, *The Finding of Christ in the Temple*.

The two poems, "Far Away" and "A Song of Love", are reprinted from *Sylvie and Bruno* and *Sylvie and Bruno Concluded*, books whose high price (made necessary by the great cost of production) has, I fear, put them out of the reach of most of my readers. "A Lesson in Latin" is reprinted from *The Jabberwock*, a Magazine got up among the Members of "The Girls' Latin School, Boston, U.S.A." The only poems, here printed for the first time, are put together under the title of "Puck Lost and Found," having been inscribed in two books—*Fairies*, a poem by Allingham, illustrated by Miss E. Gertrude Thomson, and *Merry Elves*, a story-book, by whom written I do not know, illustrated by C. O. Murray—which were presented to a little girl and boy, as a sort of memento of a visit paid by them to the author one day, on which occasion he taught them the pastime—dear to the hearts of children—of folding paper-"pistols," which can be made to imitate, fairly well, the noise of a real one.

Jan. 1898.

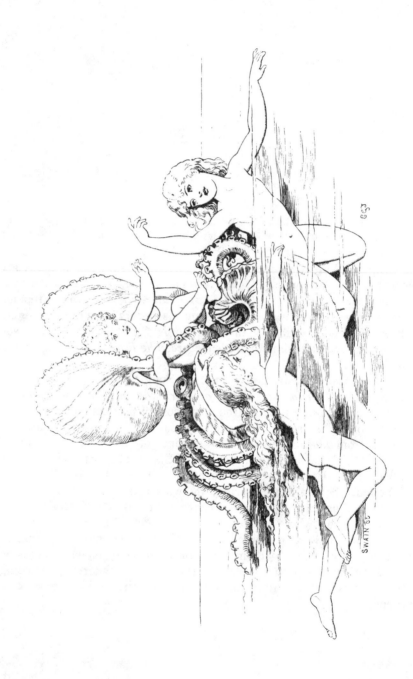

Three Sunsets

HE saw her once, and in the glance,
  A moment's glance of meeting eyes,
His heart stood still in sudden trance:
  He trembled with a sweet surprise—
All in the waning light she stood,
The star of perfect womanhood.

That summer-eve his heart was light:
  With lighter step he trod the ground:
And life was fairer in his sight,
  And music was in every sound:
He blessed the world where there could be
So beautiful a thing as she.

There once again, as evening fell
  And stars were peering overhead,
Two lovers met to bid farewell:
  The western sun gleamed faint and red,
Lost in a drift of purple cloud
That wrapped him like a funeral-shroud.

Long time the memory of that night—
  The hand that clasped, the lips that kissed,
The form that faded from his sight
  Slow sinking through the tearful mist—
In dreamy music seemed to roll
Through the dark chambers of his soul.

So after many years he came
　A wanderer from a distant shore:
The street, the house, were still the same,
　But those he sought were there no more:
His burning words, his hopes and fears,
Unheeded fell on alien ears.

Only the children from their play
　Would pause the mournful tale to hear,
Shrinking in half-alarm away,
　Or, step by step, would venture near
To touch with timid curious hands
That strange wild man from other lands.

He sat beside the busy street,
　There, where he last had seen her face;
And thronging memories, bitter-sweet,
　Seemed yet to haunt the ancient place:
Her footfall ever floated near:
Her voice was ever in his ear.

He sometimes, as the daylight waned
　And evening mists began to roll,
In half-soliloquy complained
　Of that black shadow on his soul,
And blindly fanned, with cruel care,
The ashes of a vain despair.

The summer fled: the lonely man
　Still lingered out the lessening days:
Still, as the night drew on, would scan
　Each passing face with closer gaze—
Till, sick at heart, he turned away,
And sighed "She will not come to-day."

So by degrees his spirit bent
　To mock its own despairing cry,
In stern self-torture to invent
　New luxuries of agony,
And people all the vacant space
With visions of her perfect face.

Then for a moment she was nigh,
  He heard no step, but she was there;
As if an angel suddenly
  Were bodied from the viewless air,
And all her fine ethereal frame
Should fade as swiftly as it came.

So, half in fancy's sunny trance,
  And half in misery's aching void,
With set and stony countenance
  His bitter being he enjoyed,
And thrust for ever from his mind
The happiness he could not find.

As when the wretch, in lonely room,
  To selfish death is madly hurled,
The glamour of that fatal fume
  Shuts out the wholesome living world—
So all his manhood's strength and pride
One sickly dream had swept aside.

Yea, brother, and we passed him there,
  But yesterday, in merry mood,
And marvelled at the lordly air
  That shamed his beggar's attitude,
Nor heeded that ourselves might be
Wretches as desperate as he;

Who let the thought of bliss denied
  Make havoc of our life and powers,
And pine, in solitary pride,
  For peace that never shall be ours,
Because we will not work and wait
In trustful patience for our fate.

And so it chanced once more that she
  Came by the old familiar spot:
The face he would have died to see
  Bent o'er him, and he knew it not;
Too rapt in selfish grief to hear,
Even when happiness was near.

And pity filled her gentle breast
  For him that would not stir nor speak,
The dying crimson of the west,
  That faintly tinged his haggard cheek,
Fell on her as she stood, and shed
A glory round the patient head.

Ah, let him wake! The moments fly:
  This awful tryst may be the last.
And see, the tear, that dimmed her eye,
  Had fallen on him ere she passed—
She passed: the crimson paled to gray:
And hope departed with the day.

The heavy hours of night went by,
  And silence quickened into sound,
And light slid up the eastern sky,
  And life began its daily round—
But light and life for him were fled:
His name was numbered with the dead.

Nov. 1861.

The Path of Roses

[Written soon after the Crimean War, when the name of Florence Nightingale had already become a household word, dear to all true British hearts.]

IN the dark silence of an ancient room,
Whose one tall window fronted to the West,
Where, through laced tendrils of a hanging vine,
The sunset-glow was fading into night,
Sat a pale Lady, resting weary hands
Upon a great clasped volume, and her face
Within her hands. Not as in rest she bowed,
But large hot tears were coursing down her cheek,
And her low-panted sobs broke awefully
Upon the sleeping echoes of the night.
  Soon she unclasp'd the volume once again,
And read the words in tone of agony,
As in self-torture, weeping as she read:

"He crowns the glory of his race:
He prayeth but in some fit place
To meet his foeman face to face:

"And, battling for the True, the Right,
From ruddy dawn to purple night,
To perish in the midmost fight:

"Where hearts are fierce and hands are strong,
Where peals the bugle loud and long,
Where blood is dropping in the throng:

"Still, with a dim and glazing eye,
To watch the tide of victory,
To hear in death the battle-cry:

"Then, gathered grandly to his grave,
To rest among the true and brave,
In holy ground, where yew-trees wave:

"Where, from church-windows sculptured fair,
Float out upon the evening air
The note of praise, the voice of prayer:

"Where no vain marble mockery
Insults with loud and boastful lie
The simple soldier's memory:

"Where sometimes little children go,
And read, in whisper'd accent slow,
The name of him who sleeps below."

Her voice died out: like one in dreams she sat.
"Alas!" she sighed. "For what can Woman do?
Her life is aimless, and her death unknown:
Hemmed in by social forms she pines in vain.
Man has his work, but what can Woman do?"
    And answer came there from the creeping gloom,
The creeping gloom that settled into night:
"Peace! For thy lot is other than a man's:
His is a path of thorns: he beats them down:
He faces death: he wrestles with despair.
Thine is of roses, to adorn and cheer
His lonely life, and hide the thorns in flowers."
    She spake again: in bitter tone she spake:
"Aye, as a toy, the puppet of an hour,
Or a fair posy, newly plucked at morn,
But flung aside and withered ere the night."
    And answer came there from the creeping gloom,
The creeping gloom that blackened into night:

"So shalt thou be the lamp to light his path,
What time the shades of sorrow close around."
    And, so it seemed to her, an awful light
Pierced slowly through the darkness, orbed, and grew,
Until all passed away—the ancient room—
The sunlight dying through the trellised vine—
The one tall window—all had passed away,
And she was standing on the mighty hills.
    Beneath, around, and far as eye could see,
Squadron on squadron, stretched opposing hosts,
Ranked as for battle, mute and motionless.
Anon a distant thunder shook the ground,
The tramp of horses, and a troop shot by—
Plunged headlong in that living sea of men—
Plunged to their death: back from that fatal field
A scattered handful, fighting hard for life,
Broke through the serried lines; but, as she gazed,
They shrank and melted, and their forms grew thin—
Grew pale as ghosts when the first morning ray
Dawns from the East—the trumpet's brazen blare
Died into silence—and the vision passed—
Passed to a room where sick and dying lay
In long, sad line—there brooded Fear and Pain—
Darkness was there, the shade of Azrael's wing.
But there was one that ever, to and fro,
Moved with light footfall: purely calm her face,
And those deep steadfast eyes that starred the gloom:
Still, as she went, she ministered to each
Comfort and counsel; cooled the fevered brow
With softest touch, and in the listening ear
Of the pale sufferer whispered words of peace.
That dying warrior, gazing as she passed,
Clasped his thin hands and blessed her. Bless her too,
Thou, who didst bless the merciful of old!
    So prayed the Lady, watching tearfully
Her gentle moving onward, till the night
Had veiled her wholly, and the vision passed.
    Then once again the solemn whisper came:
"So in the darkest path of man's despair,

Where War and Terror shake the troubled earth,
Lies woman's mission; with unblenching brow
To pass through scenes of horror and affright
Where men grow sick and tremble: unto her
All things are sanctified, for all are good.
Nothing so mean, but shall deserve her care:
Nothing so great, but she may bear her part.
No life is vain: each hath is place assigned:
Do thou thy task, and leave the rest to God."
And there was silence, but the Lady made
No answer, save one deeply-breathed "Amen".

   And she arose, and in that darkening room
Stood lonely as a spirit of the night—
Stood calm and fearless in the gathered night—
And raised her eyes to heaven. There were tears
Upon her face, but in her heart was peace,
Peace that the world nor gives nor takes away!

April 10, 1856.

The Valley of
the Shadow of Death

HARK, *said the dying man, and sighed,*
  To that complaining tone—
Like sprite condemned, each eventide,
  To walk the world alone.
At sunset, when the air is still,
I hear it creep from yonder hill:
It breathes upon me, dead and chill,
  A moment, and is gone.

My son, it minds me of a day
  Left half a life behind,
That I have prayed to put away
  For ever from my mind.
But bitter memory will not die:
It haunts my soul when none is nigh:
I hear its whisper in the sigh
  Of that complaining wind.

And now in death my soul is fain
  To tell the tale of fear
That hidden in my breast hath lain
  Through many a weary year:
Yet time would fail to utter all—
The evil spells that held me thrall,
And thrust my life from fall to fall,
  Thou needest not to hear.

The spells that bound me with a chain,
  Sin's stern behests to do,
Till Pleasure's self, invoked in vain,
  A heavy burden grew—
Till from my spirit's fevered eye,
A hunted thing, I seemed to fly
Through the dark woods that underlie
  Yon mountain-range of blue.

Deep in those woods I found a vale
  No sunlight visiteth,
Nor star, nor wandering moonbeam pale;
  Where never comes the breath
Of summer-breeze—there in mine ear,
Even as I lingered half in fear,
I heard a whisper, cold and clear,
  "That is the gate of Death.

"O bitter is it to abide
  In weariness alway:
At dawn to sigh for eventide,
  At eventide for day.
Thy noon hath fled: thy sun hath shone:
The brightness of thy day is gone:
What need to lag and linger on
  Till life be cold and gray?

"O well," it said, "beneath yon pool,
  In some still cavern deep,
The fevered brain might slumber cool,
  The eyes forget to weep:
Within that goblet's mystic rim
Are draughts of healing, stored for him
Whose heart is sick, whose sight is dim,
  Who prayeth but to sleep!"

The evening-breeze went moaning by,
    Like mourner for the dead,
And stirred, with shrill complaining sigh,
    The tree-tops overhead:
My guardian-angel seemed to stand
And mutely wave a warning hand—
With sudden terror all unmanned,
    I turned myself and fled!

A cottage-gate stood open wide:
    Soft fell the dying ray
On two fair children, side by side,
    That rested from their play—
Together bent the earnest head,
As ever and anon they read
From one dear Book: the words they said
    Come back to me to-day.

Like twin cascades on mountain-stair
    Together wandered down
The ripples of the golden hair,
    The ripples of the brown:
While, through the tangled silken haze,
Blue eyes looked forth in eager gaze,
More starlike than the gems that blaze
    About a monarch's crown.

My son, there comes to each an hour
    When sinks the spirit's pride—
When weary hands forget their power
    The strokes of death to guide:
In such a moment, warriors say,
A word the panic-rout may stay,
A sudden charge redeem the day
    And turn the living tide.

I could not see, for blinding tears,
   The glories of the west:
A heavenly music filled mine ears,
   A heavenly peace my breast.
"Come unto Me, come unto Me—
All ye that labour, unto Me—
Ye heavy-laden, come to Me—
   And I will give you rest."

The night drew onwards: thin and blue
   The evening mists arise
To bathe the thirsty land in dew,
   As erst in Paradise—
While, over silent field and town,
The deep blue vault of heaven looked down;
Not, as of old, in angry frown,
   But bright with angels' eyes.

Blest day! Then first I heard the voice
   That since hath oft beguiled
These eyes from tears, and bid rejoice
   This heart with anguish wild—
Thy mother, boy, thou hast not known;
So soon she left me here to moan—
Left me to weep and watch, alone,
   Our one beloved child.

Though, parted from my aching sight,
   Like homeward-speeding dove,
She passed into the perfect light
   That floods the world above;
Yet our twin spirits, well I know—
Though one abide in pain below—
Love, as in summers long ago,
   And evermore shall love.

So with a glad and patient heart
  I move toward mine end;
The streams, that flow awhile apart,
  Shall both in ocean blend.
I dare not weep: I can but bless
The Love that pitied my distress,
And lent me, in Life's wilderness,
  So sweet and true a friend.

But if there be—O if there be
  A truth in what they say,
That angel-forms we cannot see
  Go with us on our way;
Then surely she is with me here,
I dimly feel her spirit near—
The morning-mists grow thin and clear,
  And Death brings in the Day.

April 1868.

Solitude

I LOVE the stillness of the wood:
  I love the music of the rill:
I love to couch in pensive mood
  Upon some silent hill.

Scarce heard, beneath yon arching trees,
  The silver-crested ripples pass;
And, like a mimic brook, the breeze
  Whispers among the grass.

Here from the world I win release,
  Nor scorn of men, nor footstep rude,
Break in to mar the holy peace
  Of this great solitude.

Here may the silent tears I weep
  Lull the vexed spirit into rest,
As infants sob themselves to sleep
  Upon a mother's breast.

But when the bitter hour is gone,
  And the keen throbbing pangs are still,
Oh, sweetest then to couch alone
  Upon some silent hill!

To live in joys that once have been,
  To put the cold world out of sight,
And deck life's drear and barren scene
  With hues of rainbow-light.

For what to man the gift of breath,
　　If sorrow be his lot below;
If all the day that ends in death
　　Be dark with clouds of woe?

Shall the poor transport of an hour
　　Repay long years of sore distress—
The fragrance of a lonely flower
　　Make glad the wilderness?

Ye golden hours of Life's young spring,
　　Of innocence, of love and truth!
Bright, beyond all imagining,
　　Thou fairy-dream of youth!

I'd give all wealth that years have piled,
　　The slow result of Life's decay,
To be once more a little child
　　For one bright summer-day.

March 16, 1853.

Far Away

He stept so lightly to the land,
  All in his manly pride:
He kissed her cheek, he clasped her hand;
  Yet still she glanced aside.
"Too gay he seems," she darkly dreams,
  "Too gallant and too gay,
To think of me—poor simple me—
  When he is far away!"

"I bring my Love this goodly pearl
  Across the seas," he said:
"A gem to deck the dearest girl
  That ever sailor wed!"
She holds it tight: her eyes are bright:
  Her throbbing heart would say
"He thought of me—he thought of me—
  When he was far away!"

The ship has sailed into the West:
  Her ocean-bird is flown:
A dull dead pain is in her breast,
  And she is weak and lone:
But there's a smile upon her face,
  A smile that seems to say
"He'll think of me—he'll think of me—
  When he is far away!

"Though waters wide between us glide,
　　Our lives are warm and near:
No distance parts two faithful hearts—
　　Two hearts that love so dear:
And I will trust my sailor-lad,
　　For ever and a day,
To think of me—to think of me—
　　When he is far away!"

Beatrice

IN her eyes is the living light
  Of a wanderer to earth
From a far celestial height:
    Summers five are all the span—
    Summers five since Time began
To veil in mists of human night
    A shining angel-birth.

Does an angel look from her eyes?
    Will she suddenly spring away,
And soar to her home in the skies?
    Beatrice! Blessing and blessed to be!
    Beatrice! Still, as I gaze on thee,
Visions of two sweet maids arise,
    Whose life was of yesterday:

Of a Beatrice pale and stern,
    With the lips of a dumb despair,
With the innocent eyes that yearn—
    Yearn for the young sweet hours of life,
    Far from sorrow and far from strife,
For the happy summers, that never return,
    When the world seemed good and fair:

Of a Beatrice glorious, bright—
    Of a sainted, ethereal maid,
Whose blue eyes are deep fountains of light,
    Cheering the poet that broodeth apart,
    Filling with gladness his desolate heart,
Like the moon when she shines thro' a cloudless night
    On a world of silence and shade.

And the visions waver and faint,
  And the visions vanish away
That my fancy delighted to paint—
    She is here at my side, a living child,
    With the glowing cheek and the tresses wild,
Nor death-pale martyr, nor radiant saint,
    Yet stainless and bright as they.

For I think, if a grim wild beast
  Were to come from his charnel-cave,
From his jungle-home in the East—
    Stealthily creeping with bated breath,
    Stealthily creeping with eyes of death—
He would all forget his dream of the feast,
    And crouch at her feet a slave.

She would twine her hand in his mane:
  She would prattle in silvery tone,
Like the tinkle of summer-rain—
    Questioning him with her laughing eyes,
    Questioning him with a glad surprise.
Till she caught from those fierce eyes agáin
    The love that lit her own.

And be sure, if a savage heart,
  In a mask of human guise,
Were to come on her here apart—
    Bound for a dark and a deadly deed,
    Hurrying past with pitiless speed—
He would suddenly falter and guiltily start
    At the glance of her pure blue eyes.

Nay, be sure, if an angel fair,
  A bright seraph undefiled,
Were to stoop from the trackless air,
    Fain would she linger in glad amaze—
    Lovingly linger to ponder and gaze,
With a sister's love and a sister's care,
    On the happy, innocent child.

Dec. 4, 1862.

Stolen Waters

THE light was faint, and soft the air
   That breathed around the place;
And she was lithe, and tall, and fair,
   And with a wayward grace
Her queenly head she bare.

With glowing cheek, with gleaming eye,
   She met me on the way:
My spirit owned the witchery
   Within her smile that lay:
I followed her, I know not why.

The trees were thick with many a fruit,
   The grass with many a flower:
My soul was dead, my tongue was mute,
   In that accursëd hour.

And, in my dream, with silvery voice,
   She said, or seemed to say,
"Youth is the season to rejoice"—
   I could not choose but stay:
   I could not say her nay.

She plucked a branch above her head,
   With rarest fruitage laden:
"Drink of the juice, Sir Knight," she said:
   " 'Tis good for knight and maiden."

Oh, blind mine eye that would not trace—
   Oh, deaf mine ear that would not heed—
The mocking smile upon her face,
   The mocking voice of greed!

I drank the juice; and straightway felt
  A fire within my brain:
My soul within me seemed to melt
  In sweet delirious pain.

"Sweet is the stolen draught," she said:
  "Hath sweetness stint or measure?
Pleasant the secret hoard of bread:
  What bars us from our pleasure?"

"Yea, take we pleasure while we may,"
  I heard myself replying.
In the red sunset, far away,
  My happier life was dying:
My heart was sad, my voice was gay.

And unawares, I knew not how,
  I kissed her dainty finger-tips,
I kissed her on the lily brow,
  I kissed her on the false, false lips—
That burning kiss, I feel it now!

"True love gives true love of the best:
  Then take", I cried, "my heart to thee!"
The very heart from out my breast
  I plucked, I gave it willingly:
Her very heart she gave to me—
Then died the glory from the west.

In the gray light I saw her face,
  And it was withered, old, and gray;
The flowers were fading in their place,
  Were fading with the fading day.

Forth from her, like a hunted deer,
  Through all that ghastly night I fled,
And still behind me seemed to hear
  Her fierce unflagging tread;
And scarce drew breath for fear.

Yet marked I well how strangely seemed
  The heart within my breast to sleep:
Silent it lay, or so I dreamed,
  With never a throb or leap.

For hers was now my heart, she said,
  The heart that once had been mine own:
And in my breast I bore instead
  A cold, cold heart of stone.
So grew the morning overhead.

The sun shot downward through the trees
  His old familiar flame:
All ancient sounds upon the breeze
  From copse and meadow came—
  But I was not the same.

They call me mad: I smile, I weep,
  Uncaring how or why:
Yea, when one's heart is laid asleep,
  What better than to die?
So that the grave be dark and deep.

To die! To die? And yet, methinks,
  I drink of life, to-day,
Deep as the thirsty traveler drinks
  Of fountain by the way:
My voice is sad, my heart is gay.

When yestereve was on the wane,
  I heard a clear voice singing
So sweetly that, like summer-rain,
  My happy tears came springing:
My human heart returned again.

"A rosy child,
Sitting and singing, in a garden fair,
The joy of hearing, seeing,
The simple joy of being—
Or twining rosebuds in the golden hair
That ripples free and wild.

"A sweet pale child—
Wearily looking to the purple West—
Waiting the great For-ever
That suddenly shall sever
The cruel chains that hold her from her rest—
By earth-joys unbeguiled.

"An angel-child—
Gazing with living eyes on a dead face:
The mortal form forsaken,
That none may now awaken,
That lieth painless, moveless in her place,
As though in death she smiled!

"Be as a child—
So shalt thou sing for very joy of breath—
So shalt thou wait thy dying,
In holy transport lying—
So pass rejoicing through the gate of death,
In garment undefiled."

Then call me what they will, I know
   That now my soul is glad:
If this be madness, better so,
   Far better to be mad,
Weeping or smiling as I go.

For if I weep, it is that now
   I see how deep a loss is mine,
And feel how brightly round my brow
   The coronal might shine,
Had I but kept mine early vow:

And if I smile, it is that now
   I see the promise of the years—
The garland waiting for my brow,
   That must be won with tears,
With pain—with death—I care not how.

May 9, 1862.

Stanzas for Music

THE morn was bright, the steeds were light,
   The wedding guests were gay:
Young Ellen stood within the wood
   And watched them pass away.
She scarcely saw the gallant train:
   The tear-drop dimmed her e'e:
Unheard the maiden did complain
   Beneath the Willow-Tree.

"Oh, Robin, thou didst love me well,
   Till, on a bitter day,
She came, the Lady Isabel,
   And stole thy heart away.
My tears are vain: I live again
   In days that used to be,
When I could meet they welcome feet
   Beneath the Willow-Tree.

"Oh, Willow gray, I may not stay
    Till Spring renew thy leaf;
But I will hide myself away,
    And nurse a lonely grief.
It shall not dim Life's joy for him:
    My tears he shall not see:
While he is by, I'll come not nigh
    My weeping Willow-Tree.

"But when I die, oh, let me lie
    Beneath thy loving shade,
That he may loiter careless by,
    Where I am lowly laid.
And let the white white marble tell,
    If he should stoop to see,
'Here lies a maid that loved thee well,
    Beneath the Willow-tree.' "

1859.

Only a Woman's Hair

["After the death of Dean Swift, there was found among his papers a small packet containing a single lock of hair and inscribed with the above words."]

"ONLY a woman's hair!" Fling it aside!
   A bubble on Life's mighty stream:
Heed it not, man, but watch the broadening tide
   Bright with the western beam.

Nay! In those words there rings from other years
   The echo of a long low cry,
Where a proud spirit wrestles with its tears
   In loneliest agony.

And, as I touch that lock, strange visions throng
   Upon my soul with dreamy grace—
Of woman's hair, the theme of poet's song
   In every time and place.

A child's bright tresses, by the breezes kissed
   To sweet disorder as she flies,
Veiling, beneath a cloud of golden mist,
   Flushed cheek and laughing eyes—

Or fringing, like a shadow, raven-black,
   The glory of a queen-like face—
Or from a gipsy's sunny brow tossed back
   In wild and wanton grace—

Or crown-like on the hoary head of Age,
　　Whose tale of life is well-nigh told—
Or, last, in dreams I make my pilgrimage
　　To Bethany of old.

I see the feast—the purple and the gold;
　　The gathering crowd of Pharisees,
Whose scornful eyes are centred to behold
　　Yon woman on her knees.

The stifled sob rings strangely on mine ears,
　　Wrung from the depth of sin's despair:
And still she bathes the sacred feet with tears,
　　And wipes them with her hair.

He scorned not then the simple loving deed
　　Of her, the lowest and the last;
Then scorn not thou, but use with earnest heed
　　This relic of the past.

The eyes that loved it once no longer wake:
　　So lay it by with reverent care—
Touching it tenderly for sorrow's sake—
　　It is a woman's hair.

Feb. 17, 1862.

The Sailor's Wife

SEE! There are tears upon her face—
  Tears newly shed, and scarcely dried:
Close, in an agonized embrace,
  She clasps the infant at her side.

Peace dwells in those soft-lidded eyes,
  Those parted lips that faintly smile—
Peace, the foretaste of Paradise,
  In heart too young for care or guile.

No peace that mother's features wear;
  But quivering lip, and knotted brow,
And broken mutterings, all declare
  The fearful dream that haunts her now,

The storm-wind, rushing through the sky,
  Wails from the depths of cloudy space;
Shrill, piercing as the seaman's cry
  When death and he are face to face.

Familiar tones are in the gale:
  They ring upon her startled ear:
And quick and low she pants the tale
  That tells of agony and fear:

"Still that phantom-ship is nigh—
  With a vexed and life-like motion,
All beneath an angry sky,
  Rocking on an angry ocean.

"Round the straining mast and shrouds
    Throng the spirits of the storm:
Darkly seen through driving clouds,
    Bends each gaunt and ghastly form.

"See! The good ship yields at last!
    Dumbly yields, and fights no more;
Driving, in the frantic blast,
    Headlong on the fatal shore.

"Hark! I hear her battered side,
    With a low and sullen shock,
Dashed, amid the foaming tide,
    Full upon a sunken rock.

"His face shines out against the sky,
    Like a ghost, so cold and white;
With a dead despairing eye
    Gazing through the gathered night.

"Is he watching, through the dark,
    Where a mocking ghostly hand
Points a faint and feeble spark
    Glimmering from the distant land?

"Sees he, in this hour of dread,
    Hearth and home and wife and child?
Loved ones who, in summers fled,
    Clung to him and wept and smiled?

"Reeling sinks the fated bark
    To her tomb beneath the wave:
Must he perish in the dark—
    Not a hand stretched out to save?

"See the spirits, how they crowd!
    Watching death with eyes that burn!
Waves rush in——" she shrieks aloud,
    Ere her waking sense return.

The storm is gone; the skies are clear:
   Hush'd is that bitter cry of pain:
The only sound, that meets her ear,
   The heaving of the sullen main.

Though heaviness endure the night,
   Yet joy shall come with break of day:
She shudders with a strange delight—
   The fearful dream is pass'd away.

She wakes: the gray dawn streaks the dark:
   With early song the copses ring:
Far off she hears the watch-dog bark
   A joyful bark of welcoming!

Feb. 23, 1857.

After Three Days

["Written after seeing Holman Hunt's picture of *Christ in the Temple*."]

I STOOD within the gate
Of a great temple, 'mid the living stream
Of worshippers that thronged its regal state
   Fair-pictured in my dream.

Jewels and gold were there;
And floors of marble lent a crystal sheen
To body forth, as in a lower air,
   The wonders of the scene.

Such wild and lavish grace
Had whispers in it of a coming doom;
As richest flowers lie strown about the face
   Of her that waits the tomb.

The wisest of the land
Had gathered there, three solemn trysting-days,
For high debate: men stood on either hand
   To listen and to gaze.

The aged brows were bent,
Bent to a frown, half thought, and half annoy,
That all their stores of subtlest argument
   Were baffled by a boy.

In each averted face
I marked but scorn and loathing, till mine eyes
Fell upon one that stirred not in his place,
    Tranced in a dumb surprise.

Surely within his mind
Strange thoughts are born, until he doubts the lore
Of those old men, blind leaders of the blind,
    Whose kingdom is no more.

Surely he sees afar
A day of death the stormy future brings;
The crimson setting of the herald-star
    That led the Eastern kings.

Thus, as a sunless deep
Mirrors the shining heights that crown the bay,
So did my soul create anew in sleep
    The picture seen by day.

Gazers came and went—
A restless hum of voices marked the spot—
In varying shades of critic discontent
    Prating they knew not what.

"Where is the comely limb,
The form attuned in every perfect part,
The beauty that we should desire in him?"
    Ah! Fools and slow of heart!

Look into those deep eyes,
Deep as the grave, and strong with love divine;
Those tender, pure, and fathomless mysteries,
    That seem to pierce through thine.

Look into those deep eyes,
Stirred to unrest by breath of coming strife,
Until a longing in thy soul arise
    That this indeed were life:

That thou couldst find Him there,
Bend at His sacred feet thy willing knee,
And from they heart pour out the passionate prayer,
    "Lord, let me follow Thee!"

But see the crowd divide:
Mother and sire have found their low one now:
The gentle voice, that fain would seem to chide,
    Whispers, "Son, why hast thou"—

In tone of sad amaze—
"Thus dealt with us, that art our dearest thing?
Behold, thy sire and I, three weary days,
    Have sought thee sorrowing."

And I had stayed to hear
The loving words, "How is it that ye sought?"—
But that the sudden lark, with matins clear,
    Severed the links of thought.

Then over all there fell
Shadow and silence; and my dream was fled,
As fade the phantoms of a wizard's cell
    When the dark charm is said.

Yet, in the gathering light,
I lay with half-shut eyes that would not wake,
Lovingly clinging to the skirts of night
    For that sweet vision's sake.

Feb. 16, 1861.

Faces in the Fire

THE night creeps onward, sad and slow:
In these red embers' dying glow
The forms of Fancy come and go.

An island-farm—broad seas of corn
Stirred by the wandering breath of morn—
The happy spot where I was born.

The picture fadeth in its place:
Amid the glow I seem to trace
The shifting semblance of a face.

'Tis now a little childish form—
Red lips for kisses pouted warm—
And elf-locks tangled in the storm.

'Tis now a grave and gentle maid,
At her own beauty half afraid,
Shrinking, and willing to be stayed.

Oh, Time was young, and Life was warm,
When first I saw that fairy-form,
Her dark hair tossing in the storm.

And fast and free these pulses played,
When last I met that gentle maid—
When last her hand in mine was laid.

Those locks of jet are turned to gray,
And she is strange and far away
That might have been mine own to-day—

That might have been mine own, my dear,
Through many and many a happy year—
That might have sat beside me here.

Ay, changeless through the changing scene,
The ghostly whisper rings between,
The dark refrain of "might have been".

The race is o'er I might have run:
The deeds are past I might have done;
And sere the wreath I might have won.

Sunk is the last faint flickering blaze:
The vision of departed days
Is vanished even as I gaze.

The pictures, with their ruddy light,
Are changed to dust and ashes white,
And I am left alone with night.

Jan. 1860.

A Lesson in Latin

OUR Latin books, in motley row,
   Invite us to our task—
Gay Horace, stately Cicero:
Yet there's one verb, when once we know,
   No higher skill we ask:
This ranks all other lore above—
We've learned " '*Amare*' means '*to love*'!"

So, hour by hour, from flower to flower,
   We sip the sweets of Life:
Till, all too soon, the clouds arise,
And flaming cheeks and flashing eyes
   Proclaim the dawn of strife:
With half a smile and half a sigh,
"*Amare! Bitter One!*" we cry.

Last night we owned, with looks forlorn,
   "Too well the scholar knows
There is no rose without a thorn"—
But peace is made! We sing, this morn,
   "No thorn without a rose!"
Our Latin lesson is complete:
We've learned that Love is Bitter-Sweet!

May 1888.

Puck
Lost and Found

PUCK has fled the haunts of men:
  Ridicule has made him wary:
In the woods, and down the glen,
  No one meets a Fairy!

"Cream!" the greedy Goblin cries—
  Empties the deserted dairy—
Steals the spoons, and off he flies.
  Still we seek our Fairy!

Ah! What form is entering?
  Lovelit eyes and laughter airy!
Is not this a better thing,
Child, whose visit thus I sing,
  Even than a Fairy?

Nov. 22, 1891.

Puck has ventured back agen:
   Ridicule no more affrights him:
In the very haunts of men
   Newer sport delights him.

Capering lightly to and fro,
   Ever frolicking and funning—
"Crack!" the mimic pistols go!
   Hark! The noise is stunning!

All too soon will Childhood gay
   Realise Life's sober sadness.
Let's be merry while we may,
Innocent and happy Fay!
   Elves were made for gladness!

Nov. 25, 1891.

A Song of Love

Say, what is the spell, when her fledgelings are cheeping,
  That lures the bird home to her nest?
Or wakes the tired mother, whose infant is weeping,
  To cuddle and croon it to rest?
What the magic that charms the glad babe in her arms,
  Till it cooes with the voice of the dove?
'Tis a secret, and so let us whisper it low—
  And the name of the secret is Love!
    For I think it is Love,
    For I feel it is Love,
  For I'm sure it is nothing but Love!

Say, whence is the voice that, when anger is burning,
  Bids the whirl of the tempest to cease?
That stirs the vexed soul with an aching—a yearning
  For the brotherly hand-grip of peace?
Whence the music that fills all our being—that thrills
  Around us, beneath, and above?
'Tis a secret: none knows how it comes, how it goes—
  But the name of the secret is Love!
    For I think it is Love,
    For I feel it is Love,
  For I'm sure it is nothing but Love!

Say, whose is the skill that paints valley and hill,
　　Like a picture so fair to the sight?
That flecks the green meadow with sunshine and shadow,
　　Till the little lambs leap with delight?
'Tis a secret untold to hearts cruel and cold,
　　Though 'tis sung, by the angels above,
In notes that ring clear for the ears that can hear—
　　And the name of the secret is Love!
　　　For I think it is Love,
　　　For I feel it is Love,
　　For I'm sure it is nothing but Love!

　　Oct. 1886.